INTRODUCTION TO ADVANCED
INORGANIC CHEMISTRY

INTRODUCTION TO ADVANCED INORGANIC CHEMISTRY

PHILIP JOHN DURRANT, M.A., Ph.D.
Fellow and Lecturer in Chemistry, Selwyn College, Cambridge

AND

BERYL DURRANT, M.A.
*Sometime Yarrow Research Student of Girton College, Cambridge, and
Demonstrator in Physics at Bedford College, University of London*

JOHN WILEY & SONS INC
New York, N.Y.

PUBLISHED THROUGHOUT THE WORLD EXCEPT
THE UNITED STATES BY LONGMANS GREEN & CO LTD.

© PHILIP JOHN DURRANT AND BERYL DURRANT 1962

FIRST PUBLISHED 1962
SECOND IMPRESSION 1962

MADE AND PRINTED IN GREAT BRITAIN BY
WILLIAM CLOWES AND SONS, LIMITED, LONDON AND BECCLES

PREFACE

This book is a text-book of inorganic chemistry covering the whole range of the subject up to the point beyond which its study is best followed in monographs and reviews. The well-worn approach by which chemical substances are discussed largely in accordance with their accessibility and familiarity has been discarded in favour of a systematic treatment based on the principles of theoretical chemistry. As a foundation for this treatment the earlier chapters in the book are devoted to an exposition of the physics and mathematics which are used in discussing the chemical properties of matter. Theoretical work originally expressed in general and abstract terms has been translated into a form which may be understood by those who are debarred by lack of mathematical technique from following the full development of the theory. The discussion, though limited in range, is carried through from basic principles to its conclusion in such a way that each step is fully argued although in simple terms; in only one or two instances has it been found necessary to present unsupported mathematical statements or equations. For some purposes the authors have adopted a method of description which relies on the association of orbital and spin momentum with the real rotation of charge. A simple model based on this concept and on a reinterpretation of effective nuclear charge makes possible numerical predictions which are closely in accord with observation; bond lengths of many diatomic molecules may be calculated from experimental values of the bond energies, and estimates made of the dipole moments of simple molecules. It is shown that the recalculated effective nuclear charge accounts for the property of electronegativity, and also for the lanthanide contraction.

In order to bring together theoretical and descriptive chemistry it is desirable to select a rational classification for the compounds of each element, and for this purpose the authors have chosen for the normal elements modes of hybridisation developed in connection with the Valence Bond Theory, and for the transition elements the oxidation states of the element.

Both the Molecular Orbital and the Valence Bond Theories are discussed at some length in the chapters on valency, but the Valence Bond Theory is adopted for the most part as the more convenient method of expressing molecular structure in terms of the wave properties of the electron. One innovation emphasised in the book is the recognition of the ability of hybrid d orbitals to form πd bonds. This property of d orbitals makes it possible to account for the electronic structure of the ions of many oxyacids, and to assign structures to carbonyls and nitrosyls which are consonant with their chemical and magnetic properties.

Certain aspects of chemistry have been deliberately omitted; there is no discussion of thermodynamics or of chemical kinetics, and no mention is made of nuclear chemistry.

We desire to express our thanks to Dr. D. Harrison and to Dr. C. M. P. Johnson for reading the whole of the book in proof, to Dr. N. Sheppard for reading the chapters on spectroscopy, to Dr. W. Taylor for taking special photographs for the preparation of Figs. 12.7 and 12.8, and to Professor H. T. Flint for some valuable

v

comments. We also wish to place on record our appreciation of the courtesy, co-operation and skill shown by the officers and craftsmen of Longmans, Green and Co. Ltd., and of William Clowes and Sons, Ltd., during the making of this book.

P. J. DURRANT

B. DURRANT

Cambridge
1961

CONTENTS

PLATES

ACKNOWLEDGMENTS

For permission to redraw diagrams we are indebted to the following:

The American Institute of Physics for Fig. 8.9 from Begum & Fletcher, *J.chem.Phys.*, 29, 1958; Fig. 8.10 from Plyer, Tidwell & Benedict, *J.chem.Phys.*, 29, 1958; Fig. 9.1 from Emery & Taylor, *J.chem.Phys.*, 28, 1958; Fig. 9.2 from Bird, Baird & Williams, *J.chem.Phys.*, 28, 1958; Fig. 9.4 from Pake, *J.chem.Phys.*, 16, 1948; Fig. 10.8 (b), from Trefonas & Lipscombe, *J.chem.Phys.*, 28, 1958; Fig. 10.14 from Atoji & Rundle, *J.chem.Phys.*, 29, 1958; Fig. 7.13 from Bauer, Schott & Duff, *J.chem.Phys.*, 28, 1958; Fig. 3.7 from Siegbahn & Thoraeus, *J.opt.Soc.Amer.*, 13, 1926; Butterworths Scientific Publications for Fig. 10.11 from Pinsker, *Electron Diffraction*; The Institute of Metals for Fig. 6.16 from Raynor, *An Introduction to the Electron Theory of Metals*; Ejnar Munksgaard for Fig. 10.9 from Zachariesen, *Acta. cryst.* 7, 1954; The Editor and authors for Fig. 10.15 from Henshaw, Hurst & Pope, *Phys. Rev.*, 92, 1953; the Editor for Fig. 10.8(a) from *Rev. mod. Phys.*, 30, 1958; the authors and the Council of the Royal Society for Fig. 10.10 from Phillips & Powell, *Proc. roy. Soc. Lond.* A, 173, 1939; Friedr. Vieweg & Sohn for Fig. 3.5 from Sommerfeld, *Atombau und Spektrallinien*. Fig. 8.2 is redrawn from Gerhard Herzberg, *Infrared & Raman Spectra of Polyatomic Molecules*, copyright 1943, D. Van Nostrand Company, Inc., Princeton, New Jersey, U.S.A., and Fig. 7.11 from Gerhard Herzberg, *Spectra of Diatomic Molecules*, copyright 1950, D. Van Nostrand Company Inc., Princeton, New Jersey, U.S.A.

For permission to reproduce photographs we are indebted to the following:

The authors and the American Institute of Physics for Plates 10, 11, 13, 15, 17; the author and Messrs. Blackie & Son Ltd. for Plates 4, 8; Geest & Portig. K.-G. for Plate 22; the author and Ejnar Munksgaard for Plates 19, 21; Dr. Krishnan and Dr. Narayanan for Plate 12; the authors and the Editor, *Phys.Rev.* for Plates 1, 23, 24; the authors and the Physical Society for Plate 16; the author and Prentice-Hall Inc. U.S.A. for Plates 2, 3; the author and the Council of the Royal Society for Plate 18; the Council of the Royal Society for Plates 5, 7, 9, 20; Springer-Verlag for Plate 6 and Stichting Physica for Plate 14.

Other acknowledgments are made in the captions of diagrams. When a reference is made in a footnote to the contents of a Table, permission for the use of these contents has been obtained from the copyright holders.

NOTES

Temperatures (unless otherwise indicated) are expressed in degrees centigrade, and the "C" which designates the temperature scale is not printed after the numerical value of the temperature. Pressures are expressed as millimetres of mercury printed thus: 760 mm.

Interatomic distances are expressed in angstroms, but the symbol Å is normally omitted.

Formulae. An ionic formula is written with the superscripts indicating charge either inside or outside the brackets, for example $[Na]^+[Cl]^-$ or $[Ca^{2+}][Cl^-]_2$. The alternative presentations are used for the sake of clarity, and have no chemical significance. A double bond is indicated by printing "π" beside the σ bond. If necessary the nature of the atomic orbital contributed to the π bond by the central atom is also indicated by printing πp or πd, thus:

ethylene $H_2C\overset{\pi p}{=\!=}CH_2$, sulphate ion

$$
\begin{array}{ccc}
\overset{\text{O}}{} & & \text{O} \\
& \overset{\pi d}{\diagdown}\ \diagup & \\
& \text{S} & \\
& \diagup\ \underset{\pi d}{\diagdown} & \\
\overset{\text{O}}{} & & \text{O}
\end{array}
$$

Orbital diagrams. For explanation, see p. 163.

Oxidation state. For definition, see p. 487.

Certain physical constants, conversion factors, and equations.

VELOCITY OF LIGHT	c	$2 \cdot 997929 \times 10^{10}$ cm sec^{-1}
PLANCK'S CONSTANT	h	$6 \cdot 6252 \times 10^{-27}$ erg sec
AVOGADRO'S NUMBER	N	$6 \cdot 02474 \times 10^{23}$ molecules mole^{-1}
ELECTRONIC CHARGE	ϵ	$4 \cdot 8029 \times 10^{-10}$ e.s.u.
ELECTRONIC REST MASS	m_0	$9 \cdot 1085 \times 10^{-28}$ gm
1 ELECTRON MASS	$m_0 c^2$	$0 \cdot 510984 \times 10^6$ eV
COMPTON WAVE LENGTH (ELECTRON)	$\dfrac{h}{m_0 c}$	$2 \cdot 42625 \times 10^{-10}$ cm
PROTON/ELECTRON MASS RATIO	$\dfrac{M}{m_0}$	$1836 \cdot 3$
FIRST BOHR RADIUS	a_0	$0 \cdot 529171 \times 10^{-8}$ cm
RYDBERG'S CONSTANT	R	$109737 \cdot 309$ cm^{-1}
BOLTZMANN'S CONSTANT	k	$1 \cdot 38042 \times 10^{-16}$ erg deg^{-1}
1 ELECTRON VOLT	eV	$1 \cdot 60207 \times 10^{-12}$ erg $= 23 \cdot 053$ kcal mole^{-1}

1 ANGSTROM UNIT		Å	10^{-8} cm
1 RYDBERG		Rhc	13·54 eV = 312 kcal mole^{-1}
1 COULOMB		C	3×10^9 e.s.u.
BOHR MAGNETON:	(i)	$\dfrac{h\epsilon}{4\pi m_0 c}$	$3{\cdot}0932 \times 10^{-31}$ e.s.u.
	(ii)	$\dfrac{h\epsilon}{4\pi m_0}$	$9{\cdot}2732 \times 10^{-21}$ e.m.u.

GENERAL WAVE EQUATION: $\dfrac{\partial^2 u}{\partial x^2} + \dfrac{\partial^2 u}{\partial y^2} + \dfrac{\partial^2 u}{\partial z^2} = \dfrac{1}{v_\phi{}^2}\dfrac{\partial^2 u}{\partial t^2}$

SCHRÖDINGER'S EQUATION: $\dfrac{\partial^2 \psi}{\partial x^2} + \dfrac{\partial^2 \psi}{\partial y^2} + \dfrac{\partial^2 \psi}{\partial z^2} + \dfrac{8\pi^2 m}{h^2}(E - V)\psi = 0$

Element	Atomic Number	Atomic Weight	Element	Atomic Number	Atomic Weight
Actinium	89	227	Molybdenum	42	95·95
Aluminium	13	26·98	Neodymium	60	114·27
Americium	95	*243*	Neon	10	20·183
Antimony, stibium	51	121·76	Neptunium	93	*237*
Argon	18	39·944	Nickel	28	58·69
Arsenic	33	74·91	Niobium, columbium	41	92·91
Astatine	85	210	Nitrogen	7	14·008
Barium	56	137·36	Osmium	76	190·2
Berkelium	97	*245*	OXYGEN	8	16
Beryllium, glucinum	4	9·013	Palladium	46	106·7
Bismuth	83	209	Phosphorus	15	30·975
Boron	5	10·82	Platinum	78	195·23
Bromine	35	79·916	Plutonium	94	*242*
Cadmium	48	112·41	Polonium	84	210
Calcium	20	40·08	Potassium, kalium	19	39·1
Californium	98	*248*	Praseodymium	59	140·92
Carbon	6	12·011	Prometheum	61	*145*
Cerium	58	140·13	Protoactinium	91	231
Cesium	55	132·91	Radium	88	226·05
Chlorine	17	35·457	Radon, niton	86	222
Chromium	24	52·01	Rhenium	75	186·31
Cobalt	27	58·94	Rhodium	45	102·91
Copper	29	63·54	Rubidium	37	85·48
Curium	96	*245*	Ruthenium	44	101·1
Dysprosium	66	162·46	Samarium	62	150·43
Erbium	68	167·2	Scandium	21	44·96
Europium	63	152	Selenium	34	78·96
Fluorine	9	19	Silicon	14	28·09
Francium	87	*223*	Silver, argentum	47	107·880
Gadolinium	64	156·9	Sodium, natrium	11	22·991
Gallium	31	69·72	Strontium	38	87·63
Germanium	32	72·60	Sulphur†	16	32·066
Gold, aurum	79	197	Tantalum	73	180·95
Hafnium, celtium	72	178·6	Technetium	43	*99*
Helium	2	4·003	Tellurium	52	127·61
Holmium	67	164·94	Terbium	65	158·93
Hydrogen	1	1·008	Thallium	81	204·39
Indium	49	114·76	Thorium	90	232·05
Iodine	53	126·91	Thulium	69	168·94
Iridium	77	192·2	Tin, stannum	50	118·70
Iron, ferrum	26	55·85	Titanium	22	47·9
Krypton	36	83·8	Tungsten	74	183·92
Lanthanum	57	138·92	Uranium	92	238·07
Lead, plumbum	82	207·21	Vanadium	23	50·95
Lithium	3	6·94	Xenon	54	131·3
Lutetium, Cassiopeium	71	174·99	Ytterbium	70	173·04
Magnesium	12	24·32	Yttrium	39	88·92
Manganese	25	54·94	Zinc	30	65·38
Mercury, hydrargyrum	80	200·61	Zirconium	40	91·22

Italic figures indicate the mass of the most stable isotope.

† The atomic weight of this element has a range of ± 0·003.

Reproduced by permission of the proprietors, J. Whitaker & Sons Limited, from the 1960 Edition of *Whitaker's Almanack*.

CHAPTER ONE

WAVE MECHANICS AND THE QUANTUM THEORY

WAVE MOTION

A **wave** may be defined as *a disturbance which travels through a medium without change of form*. If the medium is distorted as the wave travels through it, but returns to its original condition when the wave has passed, the medium is said to be *elastic*. The distortion is caused by the displacement of the particles of which the medium is composed. When a succession or *train* of waves passes through the medium, the motion of any particle of the medium is periodic in time, there being no transference of the medium as a whole. The term "wave" is sometimes loosely applied either to a single wave or to a train of waves. In order to make a clear distinction between them, a single wave is often described as a *pulse*.

A **simple harmonic wave** may be produced in a medium by a body moving in the medium with simple harmonic motion. By considering this motion, it is possible to derive equations which describe a simple harmonic wave.

SIMPLE HARMONIC MOTION

If a body, moving in a straight line, is subject to a force acting along the line, and directed towards a fixed point in the line, and if this force is proportional to the distance of the body from the fixed point, the body is said to have **simple harmonic motion**. There are many examples of this type of motion, such as the vibrations of a spiral spring, the movement of the bob of a simple pendulum when it is oscillating over a small angle, and the motion of the particles of an elastic medium through which a simple harmonic wave is passing.

A somewhat academic example of simple harmonic motion is the motion of a body which is situated at the end of the projection of a rotating vector upon a fixed straight line (Fig. 1.1).

A point P is travelling with angular velocity ω in a circle of centre O and radius a, and OQ is the projection of OP upon

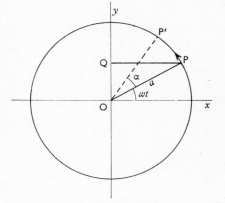

Fig. 1.1. As P moves round the circle with uniform velocity, Q moves with simple harmonic motion up and down the diameter.

the y axis. As P rotates, a body situated at Q moves forwards and backwards along the y axis.

If y is the displacement of Q after time t,

$$y = a \sin \omega t \tag{1.1}$$

$$\text{Velocity of } Q = \mathrm{d}y/\mathrm{d}t = a\omega \cos \omega t \tag{1.2}$$

$$\text{Acceleration of } Q = \mathrm{d}^2y/\mathrm{d}t^2 = -a\omega^2 \sin \omega t = -\omega^2 y. \tag{1.3}$$

Thus if the body at Q is of mass m, the force acting on it is $-m\omega^2 y$. The negative sign shows that this force is a "restoring" force, that is a force acting towards O, the undisplaced position. Since the restoring force is proportional to the displacement y, the motion is simple harmonic. As y increases the force increases, and the body gradually slows down till eventually the direction of motion is reversed.

Since the restoring force, F, may be expressed in two different ways,

$$F = m\,\mathrm{d}^2y/\mathrm{d}t^2, \quad \text{and} \quad F = -m\omega^2 y,$$

therefore

$$\frac{\mathrm{d}^2y}{\mathrm{d}t^2} + \omega^2 y = 0. \tag{1.4}$$

This equation is a linear differential equation of the second order, and is characteristic of simple harmonic motion; it shows that the motion is independent of the mass m of the body. The time T_v of one complete vibration is called the **periodic time**, thus

$$T_v = 2\pi/\omega. \tag{1.5}$$

If there is a second point P' also travelling round the circle with angular velocity ω (Fig. 1.1) and if the angle $POP' = \alpha$, then there is said to be a *phase difference* α between the motions of P and P'.

Energy of vibration. In order to start a body into motion, energy must be given to it by an external agency. If there is no loss through friction, etc. this energy is retained throughout the motion. If the body is vibrating with simple harmonic motion, the energy continually changes its form from kinetic energy to potential energy and back again. When the body passes through its undisplaced position (O in Fig. 1.1), the energy is all kinetic; when it is in the position of maximum displacement its velocity is zero momentarily, and the energy is all potential energy. At any intermediate position the energy is partly kinetic and partly potential. If E is the total energy or **energy of vibration**, T_V the kinetic energy, and V the potential energy,

$$E = T_V + V.$$

E may be expressed as the integral of the work done against the restoring force as the body moves from O to the position of maximum displacement. If a is the maximum displacement, known as the **amplitude**,

$$E = \int_0^a F\,\mathrm{d}y.$$

F, the restoring force may be written as $-ky$, where k is a constant known as the **force constant**, and

$$E = \int_0^a -ky\,\mathrm{d}y.$$

Therefore, for an amplitude a,

$$E = \frac{ka^2}{2}. \tag{1.6}$$

$$\text{The } \mathbf{frequency\ of\ vibration} \ \nu = \frac{1}{T_v} = \frac{\omega}{2\pi}$$

$$= \frac{1}{2\pi}\sqrt{\frac{k}{m}}. \tag{1.7}$$

PROGRESSIVE WAVES

If a body vibrates with simple harmonic motion in an elastic medium, the motion is transmitted to the particles of the medium which are in contact with the body. Since the medium is elastic, these particles, when displaced, are subject to a restoring force proportional to the displacement and will themselves move with simple harmonic motion. They in their turn transmit this motion to the next particles in contact with them, and so the vibration travels as a wave through the medium.

A wave can be transmitted in this manner if the particles of the medium are vibrating either transversely, that is at right angles to the direction of propagation of the wave, or longitudinally, that is along the direction of propagation of the wave. The properties of the particular elastic medium decide which type of wave is propagated. For instance, owing to surface tension, the ripples on the surface of water are transverse waves, whereas deeper in the water there can be a longitudinal vibration. Solids can transmit both transverse and longitudinal waves, while gases transmit longitudinal waves only.

Transverse and longitudinal waves have many properties in common, since they are both examples of simple harmonic motion, and wave equations which are based on the principles of simple harmonic motion apply to either equally. Moreover, it is possible to observe in nature certain phenomena which show the characteristic properties of simple harmonic waves, even though it is impossible to observe directly either any cause of wave motion or any medium through which it is transmitted. Such is the

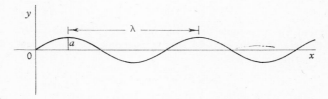

Fig. 1.2.   Simple harmonic wave.

case with light waves, X-rays, and wireless waves. They do not appear to need a tangible elastic medium since they can be propagated through a vacuum. Nevertheless their characteristic properties suggest that they are electromagnetic waves of a transverse simple harmonic type, and predictions made on this assumption may be verified by experiment. It will be shown later in this book that the wave concept is of great value in interpreting scientific observation, and indeed it appears to be fundamental to our understanding of the structure of matter.

The following sections of this chapter are concerned with the development of equations which relate to simple harmonic waves. The derivation of these equations is based on the properties of a tangible elastic medium, but in their final form they are independent of the properties of the medium, and so may be applied to any form of simple harmonic wave.

Progressive wave equation. Suppose that a simple harmonic vibration is repeated successively by a number of particles along the x axis. If the displacements of the particles at any moment are plotted along the y axis, this graphical representation will appear as a wave (Fig. 1.2). (An exactly similar picture would be obtained by plotting the displacements of a single particle against time t.) If the graph is repeated after a time $T/2$, where T is the periodic time, the crests of the wave will appear in the positions formerly occupied by troughs, and the wave will appear to have moved along. The distance from one crest of the wave to the next is the **wave length** and is denoted by

λ (Fig. 1.2). The distance travelled by one crest per second is the **velocity** of the wave and is denoted by v. The number of complete wave lengths that pass a given point in one second is the **frequency** of the wave and is denoted by ν.

These quantities are related by the equation

$$v = \nu\lambda$$

or

$$v = \frac{\lambda}{T}. \tag{1.8}$$

The **amplitude** of the wave is the maximum displacement, a, of a single particle.

If it were possible to send a single crest travelling along the x axis, the equation describing the displacement y inside the pulse (p. 1) would be of the form $y = f(x)$, since the displacement of any particle depends on its position in the pulse. If the pulse had velocity v, after a time t the origin must be moved a distance vt along the x axis in order to reach the pulse and to be able again to use the same equation $y = f(x)$. This is equivalent to writing the equation as $y = f(x - vt)$, which covers all positions of the pulse. The equation of a wave which travels with velocity v and shape unchanged must also be of this form, $y = f(x - vt)$.

Making use of equations (1.5) and (1.8), the equation of simple harmonic motion (1.1) may be written

$$y = a \sin \frac{2\pi}{\lambda} vt,$$

or

$$y = f(vt).$$

But the equation for the simple harmonic wave is of the form $y = f(x - vt)$, so with this slight difference, the equation for simple harmonic motion becomes the equation for the simple harmonic wave,

$$y = a \sin \frac{2\pi}{\lambda} (x - vt)$$

$$= a \sin 2\pi \left(\frac{x}{\lambda} - \frac{t}{T}\right). \tag{1.9}$$

This equation represents a plane wave travelling from left to right. For an equivalent wave travelling in the opposite direction, with velocity $-v$,

$$y = a \sin 2\pi \left(\frac{x}{\lambda} + \frac{t}{T}\right). \tag{1.10}$$

It may be shown that the equation $y = a \sin 2\pi \left(\frac{x}{\lambda} \pm \frac{t}{T}\right)$ is a solution of the differential equation of simple harmonic motion by differentiating it twice with respect to t and substituting in equation (1.4). It can also easily be verified by a similar process that the equation $y = a \cos 2\pi \left(\frac{x}{\lambda} \pm \frac{t}{T}\right)$ is a solution of equation (1.4), and is thus an alternative form of the equation for the simple harmonic progressive wave. It represents a wave of the same form as that of the first equation, but is a quarter of a wave length *out of phase* with it, that is, the wave picture is displaced by a distance $\lambda/4$ along the x axis.

Yet another possible form of the equation for the simple harmonic progressive wave may be obtained by the process known to mathematicians as *linear combination*. There is a very important mathematical theorem which states that if there is more than one solution of a linear differential equation, any linear combination (either by addition or subtraction) of the different solutions is also a solution of the differential equation. It is not necessary for the sine and cosine solutions to have the same amplitude. The most comprehensive form of the equation of the simple harmonic progressive wave is therefore,

$$y = A \sin 2\pi\left(\frac{x}{\lambda} - \frac{t}{T}\right) \pm B \cos 2\pi\left(\frac{x}{\lambda} - \frac{t}{T}\right). \tag{1.11}$$

The physical picture equivalent to this mathematical statement is that of a super-position of the sine and cosine waves of any amplitudes, resulting in a wave which itself shows the characteristics of simple harmonic motion. It is often convenient to describe y, or any symbol which takes the place of y, as a *wave function*.

Exponential form of progressive wave equation. The following expressions are also solutions of the differential equation of simple harmonic motion:

$$y = A e^{i\omega t}$$

$$y = A e^{-i\omega t}$$

$$y = A e^{i\omega t} \pm B e^{-i\omega t}. \tag{1.12}$$

This may be verified by differentiating each expression twice with respect to t. It will be noted that the constants A and B disappear; therefore they can take any value. As the same condition exists at a point $x = x$ at time t as existed at a point $x = 0$ at a time $(t - x/v)$, where v is the velocity of the wave, then the expression

$$y = A e^{\pm i\omega(t - x/v)}$$

or

$$y = A e^{\pm 2\pi i(x/\lambda - t/T)} \tag{1.13}$$

is yet another solution of equation (1.4).

The relation between the exponential, and the sine and cosine solutions may be seen by writing the sine and cosine solutions in their exponential forms. If

$$y = C \sin \omega t + D \cos \omega t,$$

$$y = C\left(\frac{e^{i\omega t} - e^{-i\omega t}}{2i}\right) + D\left(\frac{e^{i\omega t} + e^{-i\omega t}}{2}\right)$$

$$= \left(\frac{C}{2i} + \frac{D}{2}\right)e^{i\omega t} + \left(\frac{D}{2} - \frac{C}{2i}\right)e^{-i\omega t}$$

Let

$$\frac{C}{2i} + \frac{D}{2} = A, \quad \text{and} \quad \frac{D}{2} - \frac{C}{2i} = B,$$

then

$$y = A e^{i\omega t} + B e^{-i\omega t},$$

where A and B are partly real and partly imaginary. It is often convenient to use the exponential form of solution since it is easily differentiated.

The **intensity** of a wave is defined as the *energy per unit volume*. Equation (1.6) shows that the energy of a simple harmonic vibration is proportional to the square of the amplitude, and therefore the intensity of the wave at any point, at any moment, is proportional to the square of the amplitude at that point.

STATIONARY WAVES

If two exactly similar waves, travelling in opposite directions, are superposed (for example, a wave and its direct reflection), the displacement at any moment of a particle in the track of the combined wave is the algebraic sum of the displacements caused by the two waves separately. Fig. 1.3 shows a graphical representation of these displacements plotted at intervals of $T/4$. In each diagram one of the waves is represented by a broken line --------- and the other by ———. The resultant displacements of the particles in the track of the waves is in each case represented by a thick line. If the two waves are travelling in opposite directions, and if their displacements at any moment $t = 0$ are as in Fig. 1.3(i), after a time $T/4$ one wave will have moved a quarter of a wave length to the right and the other the same distance to the left, as is shown in Fig. 1.3(ii).

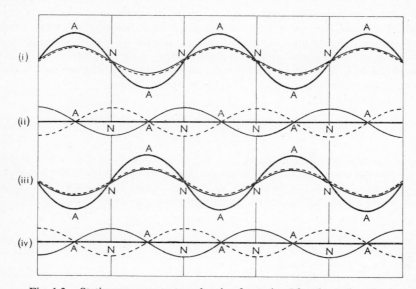

Fig. 1.3.   Stationary wave system showing formation of nodes and antinodes.

After another interval $T/4$ the waves will be in the position shown in Fig. 1.3(iii), and after another interval $T/4$ has elapsed, they will be as in Fig. 1.3(iv). The next interval $T/4$ brings them back again to the same relative positions as in Fig. 1.3(i), and the whole cycle will then be repeated. It is seen that there are certain points, N, in the path of the waves where the particles remain in their undisturbed position and the displace-

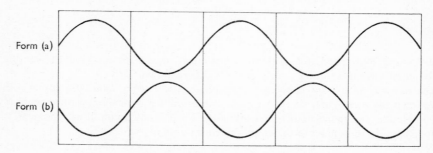

Fig. 1.4.   Stationary wave forms.

ment is zero throughout the whole period. These points of no motion are called *nodes*. At the points A in curves (i) and (iii) the displacements are double what they would have been in the presence of one wave only; the particles are in the undisplaced position in (ii) and (iv). The points labelled A are positions of maximum motion and are called *antinodes*.

The resultant wave is known as a stationary or standing wave as it appears to remain stationary, moving from form (a) to form (b) Fig. 1.4. The conventional way of representing a stationary wave gives both forms superposed as in Fig. 1.5, although the stationary wave really consists of a rapid alternation from one form to the other. It must be remembered that these two forms are not the two superposed waves, which are continually travelling, one from right to left and the other from left to right.

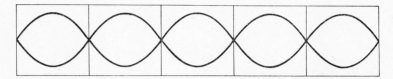

Fig. 1.5. Stationary wave forms superposed.

Stationary wave equation. The equation for the stationary wave is formed by adding the displacements, y and y' for the direct and reflected waves. If $u=$ resultant displacement at any moment,

$$u = y+y'$$

$$u = a \sin 2\pi\left(\frac{x}{\lambda}-\frac{t}{T}\right) + a \sin 2\pi\left(\frac{x}{\lambda}+\frac{t}{T}\right)$$

$$= 2a \sin 2\pi \frac{x}{\lambda} \cos 2\pi \frac{t}{T}. \qquad \text{(see note †)}$$

In general,

$$u = A \sin 2\pi \frac{x}{\lambda} \cos 2\pi \frac{t}{T} \quad \text{(where } A \text{ is a constant).} \qquad (1.14)$$

The equation for the reflected wave is sometimes written as

$$y' = a \sin 2\pi\left(-\frac{x}{\lambda}-\frac{t}{T}\right).$$

Then

$$u = y+y'$$

$$= A \cos 2\pi \frac{x}{\lambda} \sin 2\pi \frac{t}{T}.$$

This expression represents a wave of exactly similar form to that represented by (1.14).

Exponential form of stationary wave equation. The exponential form of the equation for a plane progressive wave is given on p. 5 (1.13):

$$y = A e^{\pm 2\pi i(x/\lambda - t/T)}.$$

$A e^{-2\pi i(x/\lambda - t/T)}$ represents a plane wave travelling from left to right, and $A e^{-2\pi i(-x/\lambda - t/T)}$ represents a plane wave travelling from right to left. If these two are superposed,

$$u = A(e^{-2\pi i(x/\lambda - t/T)} + e^{-2\pi i(-x/\lambda - t/T)})$$

$$= A e^{+2\pi i t/T}(e^{2\pi i x/\lambda} + e^{-2\pi i x/\lambda}).$$

The most general exponential expression for a stationary wave is

$$u = A e^{\pm 2\pi i t/T}(e^{2\pi i x/\lambda} + e^{-2\pi i x/\lambda}) \qquad (1.15)$$

† $\sin A + \sin B = 2 \sin \dfrac{A+B}{2} \cos \dfrac{A-B}{2}.$

It can readily be transformed back into the sine and cosine form if required, but in general the exponential form is more easily handled.

Wave packets. A wave packet is formed by the superposition of waves with slightly differing wave lengths and periodic times.

Let λ_1 and λ_2 be the slightly differing wave lengths, and T_1 and T_2 the slightly differing periodic times of two superposed progressive simple harmonic waves of identical amplitude a. Then,

$$y_1 = a \sin 2\pi\left(\frac{x}{\lambda_1} - \frac{t}{T_1}\right),$$

$$y_2 = a \sin 2\pi\left(\frac{x}{\lambda_2} - \frac{t}{T_2}\right).$$

Let u be the resultant amplitude. $u = y_1 + y_2$

$$u = 2a \sin 2\pi\left[\frac{x}{2}\left(\frac{1}{\lambda_1} + \frac{1}{\lambda_2}\right) - \frac{t}{2}\left(\frac{1}{T_1} + \frac{1}{T_2}\right)\right] \cos 2\pi\left[\frac{x}{2}\left(\frac{1}{\lambda_1} - \frac{1}{\lambda_2}\right) - \frac{t}{2}\left(\frac{1}{T_1} - \frac{1}{T_2}\right)\right].$$

If λ_1 and λ_2 are very little different, and λ and T are the mean wave length and mean periodic time,

$$u = 2a \sin 2\pi\left(\frac{x}{\lambda} - \frac{t}{T}\right) \cos 2\pi\left[\frac{x}{2} \mathrm{d}\left(\frac{1}{\lambda}\right) - \frac{t}{2} \mathrm{d}\left(\frac{1}{T}\right)\right] \qquad (1.16)$$

This equation may be regarded as that of a simple harmonic sine wave of amplitude $2a \cos 2\pi\left\{\frac{x}{2} \mathrm{d}\left(\frac{1}{\lambda}\right) - \frac{t}{2} \mathrm{d}\left(\frac{1}{T}\right)\right\}$, the velocity of the wave being λ/T.

Hence if A is the amplitude of the resultant wave,

$$A = 2a \cos 2\pi\left[\frac{x}{2} \mathrm{d}\left(\frac{1}{\lambda}\right) - \frac{t}{2} \mathrm{d}\left(\frac{1}{T}\right)\right]$$

$$= 2a \cos 2\pi\left[\frac{x}{2\left\{\dfrac{1}{\mathrm{d}(1/\lambda)}\right\}} - \frac{t}{2\left\{\dfrac{1}{\mathrm{d}(1/T)}\right\}}\right] \qquad (1.17)$$

By comparing this expression with that of the progressive wave it can be seen that the amplitude of the resultant wave due to superposition is not constant, but itself varies periodically in the manner of a simple harmonic wave with velocity v, where

$$v = \frac{\dfrac{1}{\mathrm{d}(1/\lambda)}}{\dfrac{1}{\mathrm{d}(1/T)}}$$

$$= \frac{\mathrm{d}(1/T)}{\mathrm{d}(1/\lambda)}. \qquad (1.18)$$

A familiar illustration of the superposition of two waves of slightly different frequency and wave length, is that of "beats" produced by sound waves. If two trains of waves of slightly different frequencies n_1 and n_2, reach the ear at the same time, the two tones are not heard separately, but a single tone of varying intensity is heard instead. This tone corresponds to the resultant wave of equation (1.16), which has a velocity λ/T. This velocity of the resultant wave train is known as the "phase velocity". The observer notices that the variation of intensity of the sound is regular, the number of maxima per second being the difference of frequency of the two sounds $n_2 - n_1$. Similar effects may be observed by superposing several trains of waves, each of a slightly different frequency. The nearer the frequencies are together and the larger the number of different wave trains, the sharper are the maxima or peaks of intensity. A peak produced in this way is sometimes known as a **wave packet**. It travels with the velocity of equation (1.18): this velocity is known as the **group velocity**.

GENERAL WAVE EQUATION

All simple harmonic waves are described by a differential equation known as the general wave equation. The equation of the stationary wave is a particular solution of the general wave equation, and may be used to derive the general form in a simple way. (The equation for a progressive wave may be used instead.)

For the stationary wave,

$$u = A \sin 2\pi \frac{x}{\lambda} \cos 2\pi \frac{t}{T},$$

$$\frac{\partial u}{\partial x} = \frac{2\pi A}{\lambda} \cos 2\pi \frac{x}{\lambda} \cos 2\pi \frac{t}{T}, \qquad \frac{\partial u}{\partial t} = -\frac{2\pi A}{T} \sin 2\pi \frac{x}{\lambda} \sin 2\pi \frac{t}{T},$$

$$\frac{\partial^2 u}{\partial x^2} = -\frac{4\pi^2 A}{\lambda^2} \sin 2\pi \frac{x}{\lambda} \cos 2\pi \frac{t}{T} \qquad \frac{\partial^2 u}{\partial t^2} = -\frac{4\pi^2 A}{T^2} \sin 2\pi \frac{x}{\lambda} \cos 2\pi \frac{t}{T}$$

$$= -\frac{4\pi^2}{\lambda^2} u. \qquad\qquad\qquad = -\frac{4\pi^2}{T^2} u.$$

Therefore,
$$\frac{\partial^2 u}{\partial x^2} = \frac{T^2}{\lambda^2} \frac{\partial^2 u}{\partial t^2} = \frac{1}{v_\phi{}^2} \frac{\partial^2 u}{\partial t^2},$$

where the phase velocity $v_\phi = \lambda/T$.

Hitherto equations have been expressed in one dimension only. The most general form of the wave equation is for a wave spreading out in all directions, and therefore it must be written in three dimensions. $\nabla^2 u$ is a short way of writing

$$\frac{\partial^2 u}{\partial x^2} + \frac{\partial^2 u}{\partial y^2} + \frac{\partial^2 u}{\partial z^2}.$$

The most general form of the wave equation is written as

$$\nabla^2 u = \frac{1}{v_\phi{}^2} \frac{\partial^2 u}{\partial t^2} \qquad (1.19)$$

For a spherical wave it is more convenient to use polar co-ordinates, and for a general wave in three dimensions, cylindrical co-ordinates are often used (p. 1141).

WAVE-PARTICLE DUALISM OF LIGHT AND MATTER

Photoelectric effect. Before the introduction of the quantum theory, it was a tenet of classical physics that waves were waves and particles were particles, and any observed motion was classified as the motion of either waves or particles. It proved impossible, however, on this basis, to find a satisfactory explanation of all the properties of light. Although experimental evidence suggested that light was a transverse wave motion, attempts to demonstrate the presence of an elastic medium in which light travelled (the so-called ether) were unsuccessful. In 1865 Maxwell put forward the theory that light was a form of electromagnetic radiation, and, by means of his famous equations, he produced expressions for the velocity and energy of the light wave in terms of the properties of the electric and magnetic fields in which the radiation took place. The fact that the observed value of the velocity of light was found to be almost identical with the calculated velocity of plane simple harmonic electromagnetic waves in empty space was considered to be conclusive evidence of the truth of his hypothesis. Subsequent investigation of the properties of radiation with wave lengths greater and

1*

less than those of visible light led to the conclusion that all observed radiation consists of electromagnetic waves.

In 1888 an important observation was made concerning ultraviolet light. It was noticed that when ultraviolet light falls on an electrically charged plate of zinc, the plate loses its charge if it is a negative one, but not if it is positive. The significance of this discovery was not understood until the end of the century when the phenomenon was explained in terms of the electron, the existence of which was first put forward as a hypothesis by Sir J. J. Thomson in 1897. It was then found that the effect was only one case of the liberation of electrons when light falls on matter, and the term "photoelectric effect" was given to the general action of light on matter. Experimental observations established beyond doubt the significant fact that the velocity of the liberated electrons depends on the frequency of the incident light and not on the intensity. This result is directly in conflict with the classical wave theory according to which the velocity of the liberated electrons should depend on the intensity of the incident light. This outstanding discrepancy was not resolved until it was explained by means of Planck's quantum theory.

Planck's quantum theory. The appearance of Planck's quantum theory in 1901 was a landmark in the history of physics. The theory was originally developed to explain the observed distribution of energy in the spectrum of the heat radiation from a hot black body. Planck made the revolutionary assumption that the interaction between matter and radiation can be explained only by assuming that radiation is emitted and absorbed, not as a continuous process, but as a series of individual "quanta" which may be described as small bundles of energy. These quanta of radiation are called *photons*, each of which has energy E where $E = h\nu$, where ν is the frequency of the radiation, and h is a constant, now known as Planck's constant. It has been found experimentally that $h = 6\cdot6252 \times 10^{-27}$ erg sec.

In 1905 Einstein applied the quantum theory to the results of experiments on the photoelectric effect, by introducing Planck's constant into the formula for the kinetic energy of an escaping electron. His formula is written as:

$$\tfrac{1}{2}mv^2 = h\nu - \phi$$

where m and v are the mass and velocity of the escaping electron, and ϕ is the "work function", that is the work done in liberating one electron from the metal to the surrounding atmosphere, and is characteristic for each metal.

Einstein's theory of mass equivalence. Einstein also put forward the theory that mass is equivalent to energy and *vice versa*. According to his "mass equivalence" relation, every energy E has an equivalent mass E/c^2, where c is the velocity of light. It appears then that every photon is associated with a mass $h\nu/c^2$, and a momentum $h\nu/c$ since it travels with velocity c. For instance, the mass associated with an X-ray photon is of the order of 10^{-27} gm, and it is interesting to compare this with the mass of an electron which is $0\cdot91085 \times 10^{-27}$ gm.

Compton effect. In 1922 an experiment on the scattering of short wave radiation was made by A. H. Compton. Graphite, or other suitable material, was placed in the path of monochromatic X-rays or γ-rays of known wave length. A spectroscopic examination was made of the radiation scattered laterally to the primary beam. Besides the line corresponding to the wave length of the original beam, another line corresponding to a longer wave length was observed. This could not be explained on the classical wave theory, but if it was assumed that the photon was behaving as a particle with momentum and that the usual mechanical laws of impact were observed when the particle collided with an electron, the difference in wave length, due to the loss of energy of the photon, could be calculated. This calculated value completely agreed with the spectroscopic results. It was therefore concluded that radiation can be observed either as an extended wave train or as a succession of particles, according to the circumstances under which the experimental observations are made.

The Compton effect may be simply illustrated by Fig. 1.6. Suppose that a photon of energy $h\nu$ collides with an electron of mass m situated at O. If, after the collision, the electron moves with velocity v in a direction making an angle θ with the incident radiation, and if, after the collision, the photon moves with energy $h\nu'$ in a direction making an angle α with the direction of the incident radiation, then by the conservation of momentum in the direction Ox,

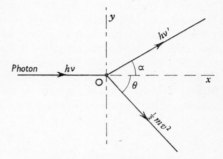

Fig. 1.6. Compton scattering.

$$\frac{h\nu}{c} = \frac{h\nu'}{c} \cos \alpha + mv \cos \theta,$$

and by the conservation of momentum in the direction Oy,

$$0 = \frac{h\nu'}{c} \sin \alpha - mv \sin \theta,$$

therefore

$$\sin^2 \theta = \frac{h^2\nu'^2 \sin^2 \alpha}{m^2 v^2 c^2},$$

$$\cos^2 \theta = \frac{h^2}{m^2 v^2 c^2} (\nu - \nu' \cos \alpha)^2,$$

and by addition

$$1 = \frac{h^2}{m^2 v^2 c^2} (\nu^2 - 2\nu\nu' \cos \alpha + \nu'^2).$$

If ν and ν' differ only by a small amount, this equation may be written,

$$1 = \frac{2h^2\nu^2}{m^2 v^2 c^2} (1 - \cos \alpha).$$

Since by the conservation of energy

$$h\nu - h\nu' = \tfrac{1}{2} mv^2,$$

$$\nu - \nu' = \frac{h\nu^2}{mc^2} (1 - \cos \alpha). \tag{1.20}$$

Since

$$\frac{\nu}{c} = \frac{1}{\lambda},$$

the quantity h/mc has the dimensions of length and is known as the *Compton wave length* of the electron.† A similar relation holds for the photon, for which (p. 10)

$$\text{momentum} = \frac{h\nu}{c}$$

$$= mc,$$

therefore

$$\frac{h}{mc} = \frac{c}{\nu} = \lambda.$$

† The full relativistic treatment yields a similar result.

De Broglie's wave theory of the electron. The quantity h/mv also has the dimensions of length. Since m and v represent the mass and velocity of the electron, de Broglie (1925) assumed that the expression h/mv represents the wave length associated with the electron, the wave length varying inversely with the velocity. This theoretical prediction was startlingly confirmed by G. P. Thomson, who obtained definite evidence of the diffraction of a beam of electrons by a thin metal foil. Almost simultaneously Davisson and Germer demonstrated the diffraction of electrons by reflexion from single crystals of metals. The diffraction patterns so obtained were very similar to those formed by the diffraction of X-rays by the same materials. It was assumed that the patterns were due to electron waves, the wave lengths of which could be accurately determined from the spacing of the diffraction rings (see Chapter 10).

Since a particle clearly resembles a wave packet more than an infinitely long train of monochromatic waves, it is reasonable to suppose that the velocity of the particle is a group velocity, while the velocity of the wave associated with the particle is a phase velocity. If this is so, for the group velocity (see p. 9)

$$v = \frac{d(1/T)}{d(1/\lambda)}$$

$$= \frac{d\nu}{d(1/\lambda)}$$

$$= \frac{d\nu}{d(mv/h)}$$

$$= \frac{h}{m}\frac{d\nu}{dv}.$$

Therefore

$$v = \frac{dE}{dp}, \tag{1.21}$$

where E and p are the energy and momentum respectively.

Since

$$mvdv = hd\nu,$$

by integrating,

$$\tfrac{1}{2}mv^2 = h\nu.$$

Hence the energy of the wave packet is equal to the energy of the de Broglie wave.

The expression for v given in equation (1.21) may also be obtained by considering the electron as a particle subject to the laws of classical relativity. According to the Einstein mass-equivalence relation, every energy is equivalent to a mass E/c^2 where c is the velocity of light. If m is the apparent mass of the electron when it is in motion, and m_0 its *rest mass* (mass of the electron at rest), and v the velocity of the electron, then according to the principles of classical relativity,

$$m = \frac{m_0}{\sqrt{(1-v^2/c^2)}}.$$

If p is the momentum of the electron,

$$p = mv$$

$$= \frac{m_0 v}{\sqrt{(1-v^2/c^2)}},$$

$$\frac{dp}{dv} = \frac{m_0}{(1-v^2/c^2)^{3/2}}.$$

If E is the energy equivalent to m,

$$E = mc^2$$

$$= \frac{m_0 c^2}{\sqrt{(1 - v^2/c^2)}}$$

$$\frac{\mathrm{d}E}{\mathrm{d}v} = \frac{m_0 v}{(1 - v^2/c^2)^{3/2}}.$$

Therefore

$$\frac{\mathrm{d}E}{\mathrm{d}p} = v.$$

This relation is identical with that obtained by considering the electron as a wave packet travelling with group velocity v. The associated electron wave travels with the phase velocity v_ϕ.

$$v_\phi = \lambda \nu$$

$$= \frac{h}{p} \frac{E}{h}$$

$$= \frac{c^2}{v}.$$

Therefore for all particles with velocity less than c, v_ϕ would be greater than c, a conclusion that is contrary to the theory of relativity, and which suggests that either the phase velocity of the electron wave has no physical meaning, or that both the particle and the phase wave travel with the velocity of light, an interpretation which meets with difficulties. Nevertheless it is found that the concept of a phase velocity is useful in calculation. By combining the relativistically corrected equations for the energy of a particle with the expression for the phase velocity, a solution may be found for the rest mass m_0.

$$m_0 = \frac{h}{c} \sqrt{\left\{ \left(\frac{v}{c} \right)^2 - \frac{1}{\lambda^2} \right\}}$$

$$= \frac{h}{c} \sqrt{\left\{ \left(\frac{v}{c} \right)^2 - \left(\frac{v}{v} \right)^2 \right\}}.$$

If the particle travels with the velocity of light, c,

$$v = c, \quad \text{and} \quad m_0 = 0.$$

The particle then has zero rest mass, and may be identified with the photon, which is thus seen to be the limiting case of the particle-wave concept.

From the above discussion it appears that a dual nature, that of wave and particle, is characteristic of both radiation and matter, but it is also evident that the equations of classical physics, although they can demonstrate this dualism, are not adequate to explain it. It has therefore been found necessary to examine more carefully the significance of the concepts "particle" and "wave", and to reassess the observational methods which give us the information from which these concepts have been derived.

Consideration of these methods shows that it is the type of experiment which determines whether the particle or wave aspect is predominant in the results. In fact, the mental attitude and wish of the experimenter is really the deciding factor. If he looks for a wave, always with the proviso that he looks where the known properties of the wave would allow the wave to be, he finds a wave. If he looks for a particle, using a "particle detecting" type of apparatus, placed in a position where it is possible for a particle to be, he finds a particle. The passage of electrons through a thin metal foil is a typical example. If the experimenter wishes to detect electrons as particles, he arranges a fluorescent screen on the side of the foil remote from the impinging electrons, and records scintillations on the screen. If he wishes to detect electrons as waves, he is careful to use a monochromatic electron beam, that is one in which all the electrons have the same velocity and therefore the same wave length. He also chooses a thickness of metal foil such that it will give diffraction rings of maximum clarity.

In the case of the scattering of light by small particles, experimental observation of the intensity of the scattered radiation is in good agreement with the classical theory of scattering based on the concept of light as a wave motion, whereas in order to explain the Compton effect (p. 10) it is necessary to adopt the concept of light as a series of photons.

Heisenberg's uncertainty principle. Heisenberg first pointed out the significant fact that there is no single experiment which gives us complete information as to the momentum, velocity, energy, and position of either particle or wave. In the case of an endless train of monochromatic light waves, the wave length may be accurately determined from a diffraction experiment, the frequency may be calculated from the formula $c = \nu\lambda$ and the energy from $E = h\nu$, but it is impossible to determine the position of the wave at any moment. The same is true of the de Broglie wave. If the wave length λ is determined from the diffraction experiment, since $\lambda = h/mv$, the momentum may be calculated, but again, the position of any part of the wave or, indeed, of the corresponding electron in the stream of electrons could not be observed.

If the electron is observed as a particle, it is possible to measure accurately its mass, momentum, and energy, but we cannot at the same time determine its position. The arrival of a single particle on a screen at a given moment could be recorded, but the act of recording would have changed its velocity, therefore its velocity, momentum, and energy would be uncertain. We thus see that it is impossible at any moment to gain complete information about either a wave or a particle.

It is helpful at this stage to return to the consideration of a small wave packet. This consists of a large number of superposed waves of slightly different wave lengths. Suppose these range from λ to $\lambda + \Delta\lambda$, then the velocities range from v to $v + \Delta v$, and the momentum from p to $p + \Delta p$. Δp is a measure of the uncertainty of the momentum. If the wave packet were infinitely thin, its position could be measured accurately, but if Δx is the extension of the wave packet, then Δx is a measure of the uncertainty of its position. The smaller the extension of the wave packet, the larger is the number of waves of which it is composed, and so the greater is the uncertainty of the momentum. For a monochromatic wave there is no uncertainty of momentum, but since the wave train is infinitely long, Δx is infinite. According to the uncertainty principle of Heisenberg the product of the uncertainty of the measurement of momentum and the uncertainty of the measurement of position is a constant, with minimum value $h/4\pi$. This relation applies to all so-called canonically conjugated variables. These are pairs of related quantities whose product has the dimensions of action, such as momentum × distance, or energy × time. We can therefore write the momentum equation $\Delta p \Delta x \geqslant h/4\pi$, and the energy equation $\Delta E \Delta t \geqslant h/4\pi$. If the momentum equation is written as

$$\Delta v \Delta x = \frac{h}{4\pi m}$$

it is seen that for large m, the product of $\Delta v \Delta x$ is very small; therefore in experiments with macroscopic bodies the uncertainties of momentum and position are very small, and so the laws of classical physics are adequate for problems on this scale.

It is customary to speak of those quantities which can be measured without uncertainty as "sharp" quantities. For instance, in the case of the monochromatic wave, the momentum p is sharp, but the position is not sharp. In the case of an electron in the act of hitting a screen, the position is sharp but the momentum is not.

The theories of atomic structure which are now to be discussed are all concerned only with the conditions of the atom where the energy is sharp.

BOHR THEORY OF ATOMIC STRUCTURE

Sir J. J. Thomson was the first to suggest that the atom had any internal structure at all. Before this, no advance had been made from the picture, accepted since the time of Dalton, of an atom of an element as an indivisible ball. Thomson's picture of the atom was a static one. He supposed that a positive charge distributed throughout the volume of the atom was neutralised by electrons arranged in the atom at fixed points. This concept was replaced by Rutherford's atomic model in which the positive charge was concentrated in a small nucleus which was surrounded by electrons. Nearly all the mass of the atom was assumed to be concentrated in the nucleus. His theory was supported by the results of experiments on the scattering of α particles.

These static models did not explain why under certain conditions an atom emitted radiation, while under other conditions it did not do so. A simple step forward was to assume that the electron in the Rutherford atom was not stationary but was moving in an orbit round the nucleus, the attraction between the electron and the nucleus being balanced by the centrifugal force due to the rotation. This assumption at once met with the difficulty that the rotating charge would, under all conditions, cause the emission of electromagnetic radiation, and according to classical principles the orbit would gradually contract, and the electron would slow down as it lost energy until it finally fell into the nucleus. This picture was clearly not in accordance with the facts.

Bohr was the first to introduce a dynamic model of the atom which was not subject to the limitations outlined above. His concept of the atom was governed by two postulates. The first postulate stated that the atom could exist in any one of a number of non-radiating "stationary states", each state corresponding to a possible value for the energy of the system. The different stationary states were characterised by the position of the electrons in different orbits or "energy levels". It was supposed that the electrons moved in these orbits round the nucleus, but did not emit radiation unless they "jumped" from one orbit to another. When this happened, the loss or gain of energy would not take place continuously, but would be emitted or absorbed in discrete amounts (quanta). According to Bohr's theory, the expression for the change of energy when an electron "jumps" from an orbit x of higher energy to an orbit y of lower energy is

$$E_x - E_y = h\nu,$$

where E_x is the energy of the electron in orbit x, and E_y is the energy of the electron in orbit y, ν is the frequency of the radiation emitted, and h is Planck's constant. The energy change is said to be *quantised*.

The second postulate of Bohr's theory (as formulated later by Sommerfeld) stated that the angular momentum of the electron in its orbit is equal to an integral number multiplied by $h/2\pi$, thus

$$mvr = \frac{nh}{2\pi} \qquad (1.22)$$

where mv is the linear momentum of the electron, r the radius of the orbit, and n, known as a *quantum number*, is any integer in the series $n = 1, 2, 3, 4 \ldots$. The angular momentum is therefore also quantised. The different values of n correspond to the different orbits.

At first it was assumed that the electron orbits were circular, and the theory in this form was able to account in a large measure for the spectrum of atomic hydrogen, but was not able to account for the spectra of heavier atoms. Some progress was made on the introduction by Sommerfeld of a second quantum number, but even so it was not possible to account for more than a very limited number of observed spectroscopic features. In the modern quantum mechanical description of the atom, the use of a second quantum number has been retained, but it has a different significance from the second quantum number of Bohr and Sommerfeld.

De Broglie later pointed out an interesting relation between equation (1.22) and the length of the de Broglie wave. If equation (1.22) is rearranged as

$$2\pi r = \frac{nh}{mv},$$

and if $\lambda =$ wave length of the de Broglie wave of the electron, since $\lambda = h/mv$, then

$$2\pi r = n\lambda,$$

a condition which would have to be observed if the concept of a particle electron in an orbit were to be replaced by that of a stationary wave. If the wave were not to be destroyed, it would obviously be necessary for the circumference of the orbit to be equal to a whole number of wave lengths.

Although Bohr's theory was inadequate for a full description of atomic structure, nevertheless he made the following two important contributions to the development of modern quantum theory: (1) the concept of states of the atom corresponding to definite values of the energy of the system; (2) the description of these states by quantum numbers.

WAVE MECHANICS

THE WAVE FUNCTION ψ

The experimental evidence furnished by the diffraction of electrons through a thin metal film establishes the fact that there is something with a wave character which is associated with the electron. The diffraction pattern obtained depends on the crystal structure of the metallic film, and may be a simple one of concentric rings or a symmetrical pattern of more complicated form. A reproduction of a typical electron diffraction pattern is shown in Plate 22. The interpretation of these patterns is of very great interest. Let the simplest case be considered, that in which the diffraction pattern consists of concentric rings. Not only must the electrons have uniform velocity if the rings are to be clearly defined, but there must be more than a certain minimum number of electrons in the beam for the rings to be complete; in fact the number of electrons in the beam must be very large for this to be so. The diffraction pattern might, therefore, be described either as the pattern formed by the diffraction of de Broglie waves, or the pattern formed by the unequal distribution of electrons received on the screen or photographic plate. The maxima of the rings may be regarded as regions of greatest concentration of electrons, and the minima as regions of least concentration of electrons. If a single electron could be isolated from the beam, it would not be possible to predict exactly where it would arrive on the screen, but it would be more likely to be found at a maximum than at a minimum. The position of the electron thus is not sharp; this is quite in accordance with the uncertainty principle as the velocity of the electron is sharp. (The velocity may be determined experimentally, since $\lambda = h/mv$, and λ may be calculated from measurements of the diameters of the rings.)

The important point is thus established that the intensity distribution of the pattern of rings can be used as a measure of the probabilities of the arrival of a single electron at different points on the screen.

If the pattern is now regarded as being formed by the superposition of a very large number of diffracted de Broglie waves, each wave being associated with one electron, it may be assumed that the intensity of the resultant wave at any point is a measure both of the number of electrons per unit volume, known as the *electron density* at that point, and of the probability of the arrival of a single electron at the point. It is in this connexion that the wave function ψ has significance. The simple case of the superposition of two waves of slightly differing frequency has been developed on p. 8; ψ plays the part of A, the variable amplitude in this simple example. Since the intensity of a wave is proportional to the square of the amplitude (p. 5) the assumption is made that the probability of an electron arriving at a point may be measured by the value of ψ^2 at that point, where ψ is the wave function of the resultant wave. If ψ is zero at a certain point, then the probability of finding an electron at this point is vanishingly small. If the units of ψ are chosen so that ψ^2 is numerically equal to the electron density at a point, then $|\psi|^2$ is the electron density, and the probability that an electron is in a small volume $(\mathrm{d}x\mathrm{d}y\mathrm{d}z)$ round the point is $|\psi|^2\mathrm{d}x\mathrm{d}y\mathrm{d}z$. This relation should hold whatever the number of electrons in the beam. Suppose that this number is gradually reduced until there is only one electron left; then it is logical to suppose that the probability of the arrival of this electron at a given point on the screen could be measured by the square of the wave function of its own de Broglie wave at that point, if such a measurement were possible.

In order to develop the theory further, a mathematical expression must be assigned to ψ, and for this purpose the electron diffraction experiment is a guide. Since the diffraction rings are similar to those produced by light, that is by simple harmonic electromagnetic waves, it is reasonable to suppose that the de Broglie wave also has a simple harmonic form although there is no evidence of any medium through which the wave is propagated. It has been shown that in certain respects the electron resembles a wave packet formed by the superposition of many waves of slightly differing frequency and wave length, and it is a plausible hypothesis that the de Broglie wave represents the monochromatic wave of phase velocity λ/T which accompanies the wave packet. The maximum value of ψ occurs in the wave packet itself. It is necessary to make the assumption that the wave packet is not dissipated by propagation in three dimensions; this may be so if there are suitable phase relations between its components.

If an infinite number of waves showing very slight variation of wave length and frequency were superposed, the amplitude ψ would show only a single peak located in the wave packet, and the probability of the electron's being in the volume occupied by the wave packet would be 100%. If there were a smaller number of superposed waves, ψ would show a number of subsidiary peaks besides the main wave packet, and in that case there would be some probability that the electron might be located in the subsidiary peaks, although it would still be more probable that it would be found in the main wave packet. The probability of the electron's being located in any peak would be $|\psi|^2\mathrm{d}x\mathrm{d}y\mathrm{d}z$, where $\mathrm{d}x\mathrm{d}y\mathrm{d}z$ is a very small volume round the peak, the value of ψ being that appropriate to the position of the particular peak.

The wave packet description of the electron as outlined above is a very useful concept, and forms an easily visualised link between the particle and wave aspects of the electron, but it must be emphasised that there is no experimental evidence of the existence of the superposed waves which form the wave packet, except the detection by means of electron diffraction of the supposed accompanying monochromatic de Broglie wave, analogous to the resultant sine wave of equation (1.16).

We are indebted to Born for the application of the concept of probability to electron distribution. He also made the assumption that every mass is associated with a wave, the "guiding wave", of which the de Broglie wave of the electron is but one example. Evidence of the existence of waves associated with material particles of greater mass than that of the electron has been obtained by the experiments of Stern on the diffraction of atoms and molecules with small velocities due to random thermal motion. He verified de Broglie's equation $\lambda = h/mv$ for the wave length associated with these heavier particles. These wave lengths are much shorter than those of electrons, which are of the order of $1 \cdot 0$ Å. No doubt there are waves associated with the larger bodies which are the concern of macrophysics, but they would be of such short wave length that it would be impossible to detect them. Table 1.1 shows the calculated wave lengths of various particles.

Table 1.1. *Wave Lengths of Certain Particles*

Particle	Mass gm	Velocity cm/sec	Wave length Å
1-volt electron	$9 \cdot 1 \times 10^{-28}$	$5 \cdot 9 \times 10^{7}$	$12 \cdot 0$
100-volt electron	$9 \cdot 1 \times 10^{-28}$	$5 \cdot 9 \times 10^{8}$	$1 \cdot 2$
10,000-volt electron	$9 \cdot 1 \times 10^{-28}$	$5 \cdot 9 \times 10^{9}$	$0 \cdot 12$
100-volt proton	$1 \cdot 67 \times 10^{-24}$	$1 \cdot 38 \times 10^{7}$	$0 \cdot 029$
100-volt α particle	$6 \cdot 6 \times 10^{-24}$	$6 \cdot 9 \times 10^{6}$	$0 \cdot 015$
H_2 molecule at 200°C	$3 \cdot 3 \times 10^{-24}$	$2 \cdot 4 \times 10^{5}$	$0 \cdot 82$
α particle from radium	$6 \cdot 6 \times 10^{-24}$	$1 \cdot 51 \times 10^{9}$	$6 \cdot 6 \times 10^{-5}$
22-rifle bullet	$1 \cdot 9$	$3 \cdot 2 \times 10^{4}$	$1 \cdot 1 \times 10^{-23}$
Golf ball	45	3×10^{3}	$4 \cdot 9 \times 10^{-24}$
Baseball	140	$2 \cdot 5 \times 10^{3}$	$1 \cdot 9 \times 10^{-24}$

After J. D. Stranathan, *The Particles of Modern Physics* (McGraw-Hill, 1942), Table, 1, p. 504.

SCHRÖDINGER'S EQUATION

A differential equation, developed by Schrödinger, forms the basis of the wave mechanical theory of the behaviour of the electron in the atom. In its simplest form the equation describes the space-dependency of ψ in terms of the energy state of the atom and the mass of the electron.

Viewed historically, the development of the equation for ψ was an act of mathematical faith and intuition rather than a process of logical reason. The justification for the equation is that it "works" as will be shown later in this book. The need for a physical picture was not felt, since the development of the theory was largely in the hands of mathematicians who have no use for models in the formulation of their equations.

The Schrödinger equation may be established as follows. Since ψ is a wave function which varies in a simple harmonic manner, the expression for ψ must obey the general wave equation (p. 9, equation (1.19)).

Therefore

$$\nabla^2 \psi = \frac{1}{v_\phi^2} \frac{\partial^2 \psi}{\partial t^2},$$

where v_ϕ is the phase velocity of the electron wave (p. 8).

Also,

$$\frac{d^2\psi}{dt^2} = -\omega^2\psi \quad \text{(equation (1.4), p. 2)}$$

$$= -4\pi^2\nu^2\psi.$$

But $\nu = v_\phi/\lambda$ and $\lambda = h/mv$ where v is the velocity of the electron as a particle (group velocity of wave packet), and therefore,

$$\nabla^2\psi = \frac{1}{v_\phi{}^2}\left(-\frac{4\pi^2 v_\phi{}^2}{\lambda^2}\right)\psi$$

$$= -\frac{4\pi^2 m^2 v^2}{h^2}\psi.$$

If the electron is free to move anywhere in space the only energy of the system (apart from the mass-equivalent energy) is the kinetic energy of the electron. If the electron is situated in the field of the positively charged nucleus, its potential energy V must also be considered. If E is the total energy of the system,

$$E = \tfrac{1}{2}mv^2 + V,$$

where V is a function of x, y, z.
Since

$$v^2 = \frac{2(E-V)}{m},$$

therefore

$$\nabla^2\psi = -4\pi^2\frac{m^2}{h^2}\frac{2(E-V)}{m}\psi$$

and

$$\nabla^2\psi + \frac{8\pi^2 m}{h^2}(E-V)\psi = 0. \tag{1.23}$$

Equation (1.23) is known as the **Schrödinger Equation**. It may also be expressed in a time dependent form, but the time factor is not significant if E has a sharp value. The equation is of a type which is familiar in physics, and is not peculiar to wave mechanics. It can be applied to a variety of mechanical problems, and may be derived from other considerations than that of the electron wave. All physical systems which can be described by equations of the type of the Schrödinger equation are characterised by the existence of **boundary conditions**. These conditions impose some limitation on the possible values which a quantity such as ψ can assume in a practical problem.

In applying the Schrödinger equation to the electron in the atom, the boundary conditions are introduced by the inclusion of the potential energy term. When $V=0$, the equation describes a progressive wave in a system with kinetic energy only (de Broglie wave of a free electron) and, with no boundary conditions, the equation has an infinite number of acceptable solutions. When the electron is bound to an atomic nucleus it cannot leave the atom except by receiving some additional energy. Thus an electron within the atom has a negative potential energy, and this imposes the boundary condition that ψ must be zero at infinity. It is therefore inferred that the electron wave in the atom is in the form of a stationary wave, since this is the only form of wave motion which can take place between boundaries without dissipation of energy. In fact it is impossible to set up a stationary wave at all without some limitation. For instance, where a stationary wave is formed by the reflection of a progressive wave (p. 5), it is necessary to have some object such as a wall from which the reflection can take place. Only those solutions of the Schrödinger equation are acceptable which "fit in" with the boundary conditions. It will be shown later in this chapter that if it is possible to solve the Schrödinger equation, and to obtain values for the energy of the system, it can easily be seen which solutions are acceptable.

In all vibration problems which are described by linear differential equations with boundary conditions, those values of the frequency or energy which correspond to possible stationary wave forms are known as **eigenvalues**, and the corresponding wave functions are known as **eigenfunctions**. This nomenclature was not introduced specially for wave mechanics. It is common to all vibration problems with boundary conditions.

APPLICATIONS OF SCHRÖDINGER'S EQUATION

Although Schrödinger's equation can be solved only in a limited number of cases, it may often be successfully used to determine the energy of a system without working out a solution for ψ. The procedure is as follows for simple systems with boundary conditions, in which the energy is all kinetic.

(1) The Schrödinger equation is written down.

(2) An expression for ψ is written down in the form of a simple harmonic wave equation, using the most general form for a stationary wave (p. 7, equation (1.15)) (omitting the time factor which here has no significance, p. 19)

$$\psi = A(e^{2\pi i x/\lambda} + e^{-2\pi i x/\lambda}).$$

(3) A value for λ is obtained by consideration of the boundary conditions, and this value is substituted in the expression for ψ.

(4) The expression is then differentiated twice and a value for $d^2\psi/dx^2$ is substituted in the Schrödinger equation which is then solved for E.

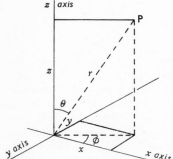

Fig. 1.7. Relation between polar and Cartesian co-ordinates.

Of the six following examples the first five illustrate this procedure. They all refer to simple atomic or molecular models of which the energy is wholly kinetic. The sixth example, that of the linear harmonic oscillator, includes the potential energy term which is a function of the variable x, and therefore the simple method used for the earlier examples cannot be applied.

It is often more convenient to use polar co-ordinates instead of Cartesian co-ordinates when the equation is applied to practical problems. Fig. 1.7 shows the connection between the two sets of co-ordinates. Further information on the method of transformation of equations from one set of co-ordinates to another will be found in the Appendix.

The angle ϕ is known as the "azimuthal angle". It lies in the xy plane, perpendicular to the plane of the paper.

If x, y, z, are the projections of r on the x, y, and z axes respectively

$$x = r \sin \theta \cos \phi$$
$$y = r \sin \theta \sin \phi$$
$$z = r \cos \theta.$$

Particle in a one-dimensional box (simple one-dimensional model of the electron between potential barriers). The "box" is a one-dimensional enclosure with "walls" formed by a potential barrier. It is supposed that the potential is zero inside the box, and that it rises to infinity at the boundaries.

If the wave aspect of the particle is considered, it is clear that the wave is reflected at the boundary, and a stationary wave is set up if the conditions are such that the distance between the barriers contains an integral number of half wave lengths. If it were not so the wave would die out (Fig. 1.8). If ψ is the wave function describing the particle as a stationary wave, then

$$\psi = A(e^{2\pi i x/\lambda} + e^{-2\pi i x/\lambda}).$$

If $p = 2\pi/\lambda$,

$$\frac{d\psi}{dx} = ip(Ae^{ipx} - Ae^{-ipx})$$

$$\frac{d^2\psi}{dx^2} = -p^2(Ae^{ipx} + Ae^{-ipx})$$

$$= -p^2\psi.$$

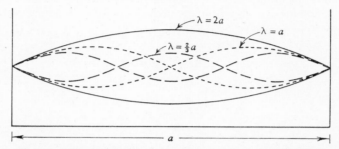

Fig. 1.8. Eigenfunctions of a particle in a one-dimensional box.

The Schrödinger equation is

$$\frac{d^2\psi}{dx^2} + \frac{8\pi^2 m}{h^2}[E - V]\psi = 0.$$

Since the energy of the particle is all kinetic, therefore

$$\frac{d^2\psi}{dx^2} = -\frac{8\pi^2 m E \psi}{h^2},$$

and

$$p^2 = \frac{8\pi^2 m E}{h^2}.$$

By the boundary condition, if a is the distance between the barriers, $a = n\lambda/2$, where n is an integer, hence

$$p = \frac{\pi n}{a},$$

$$\frac{\pi^2 n^2}{a^2} = \frac{8\pi^2 m E}{h^2},$$

and

$$E = \frac{h^2 n^2}{8ma^2}. \tag{1.24}$$

n can take one of the values 1, 2, 3, ..., and is a **quantum number**. Therefore the energy can take one of a series of eigenvalues.

It is interesting to note the effect of the dimensions of the box, or rather the distance between the potential barriers, on the permissible values of the energy of the system. When this distance is small, the energy is large and *vice versa*. If the particle is an electron which moves between potential barriers, the larger the space in which it can move about, the lower is the energy of the system.

Particle in a ring. Using polar co-ordinates, if the vibration takes place in the XY plane the Schrödinger equation becomes (see Appendix):

$$\frac{1}{r^2}\frac{d^2\psi}{d\phi^2} + \frac{8\pi^2 m}{h^2}[E - V]\psi = 0.$$

Since the energy is all kinetic

$$\frac{d^2\psi}{d\phi^2} + \frac{8\pi^2 m r^2 E}{h^2}\psi = 0.$$

In order to set up a stationary wave in the ring, the circumference must contain a whole number of wave lengths. Therefore, $2\pi r = n\lambda$ where n is an integer.

The solution is similar to that of the problem of a particle in a one-dimensional box.

If $p = 2\pi/\lambda$, and $a/r = \phi$, where a is the distance travelled along the circumference and ϕ is measured in radians

$$\psi = A(e^{2\pi i a/\lambda} + e^{-2\pi i a/\lambda})$$

$$= A(e^{ipr\phi} + e^{-ipr\phi}).$$

Hence

$$\frac{d^2\psi}{d\phi^2} = -r^2 p^2 \psi$$

$$= -\frac{4\pi^2 r^2}{\lambda^2}\psi.$$

Substituting in Schrödinger's equation

$$E = \frac{h^2}{2m\lambda^2}.$$

But

$$\lambda = \frac{2\pi r}{n},$$

and therefore

$$E = \frac{h^2 n^2}{8\pi^2 m r^2}, \tag{1.25}$$

where n has the values 1, 2, 3, ...

Therefore the energy can take one of a series of eigenvalues.

Particle in a three-dimensional box (model of an electron in a crystal). If the motion of the particle in three dimensions is considered, the Schrödinger equation becomes:

$$\frac{\partial^2\psi}{\partial x^2} + \frac{\partial^2\psi}{\partial y^2} + \frac{\partial^2\psi}{\partial z^2} + \frac{8\pi^2 m}{h^2}[E - V_x - V_y - V_z]\psi = 0.$$

$\psi_{(x,y,z,)}$ may be put equal to $X(x)Y(y)Z(z)$ where X, Y, and Z are each functions of one independent variable only (see Appendix). The equation may be split up into three separate differential equations each with one independent variable. Each equation is of the same form as that of the particle in the one-dimensional box.

$$\frac{d^2 X}{dx^2} + \frac{8\pi^2 m}{h^2}[E_x - V_x]X = 0, \quad \text{where} \quad X = A(e^{ipx} + e^{-ipx}).$$

$$\frac{d^2 Y}{dy^2} + \frac{8\pi^2 m}{h^2}[E_y - V_y]Y = 0, \quad \text{where} \quad Y = B(e^{ip'y} + e^{-ip'y}).$$

$$\frac{d^2 Z}{dz^2} + \frac{8\pi^2 m}{h^2}[E_z - V_z]Z = 0, \quad \text{where} \quad Z = C(e^{ip''z} + e^{-ip''z}).$$

Since the energy is all kinetic, $V_x = V_y = V_z = 0$, and since E is the sum of the energies in the x, y, z, directions, $E = E_x + E_y + E_z$. The expression for the total energy E of the system is

$$E = \frac{h^2}{8m}\left(\frac{n_x^2}{a^2} + \frac{n_y^2}{b^2} + \frac{n_z^2}{c^2}\right) \tag{1.26}$$

where n_x, n_y, n_z, are integers, and a, b, c, are the dimensions of the box. E is not continuous, but takes one of a series of eigenvalues as for the particle in the one-dimensional box.

Rotator with a rigid axis fixed in space (simplest model of a rotating diatomic molecule), Fig. 1.9. The boundary condition is that ψ must be single valued for each value of E, therefore ψ must have the same value after every revolution. The potential energy is zero, therefore $V = 0$. Suppose the rotator consists of two particles each of mass $M/2$, connected by a rigid weightless rod of length $2r$. Since the motion takes place in one plane only, and since polar co-ordinates must be used, the Schrödinger equation becomes

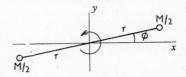

Fig. 1.9.   Rotator with a rigid axis.

$$\frac{1}{r^2}\frac{d^2\psi}{d\phi^2} + \frac{8\pi^2 ME}{h^2}\psi = 0,$$

or,

$$\frac{d^2\psi}{d\phi^2} + \frac{8\pi^2 IE}{h^2}\psi = 0 \tag{1.27}$$

where $I = Mr^2 = $ moment of inertia. A differential equation of this form has a solution

$$\psi = Ae^{iJ\phi}.$$

Since the position $\phi = 0$ may also be described as $\phi = 2\pi, 4\pi, 6\pi, \ldots$, in order that the function should be single valued, J must be a whole number, and the most general form of the equation must be written as

$$\psi = Ae^{iJ(2\pi n + \phi)}, \tag{1.28}$$

where n is a whole number.

(It may be verified that this expression is a solution of equation (1.27) by differentiating it twice with respect to ϕ.)

By an argument similar to that used on p. 22 for the particle in a ring

$$E = \frac{h^2 J^2}{8\pi^2 I} \tag{1.29}$$

and, as J must be a whole number, the values of E must be eigenvalues.

Rotator with a rigid axis free to move in space. The equation for the rigid rotator free to move in space must be expressed in polar co-ordinates. The model of such a rotator is identical with that employed on page 46 in the development of an expression for the angular momentum of the electron in the hydrogen atom. In this model the electron is regarded as a particle describing an orbit of constant radius a round the nucleus. The problem is treated in three dimensions and an expression for the energy is easily obtained by the use of the Schrödinger equation for the hydrogen atom. The expression for the kinetic energy of the rotating electron is (p. 46)

$$\tfrac{1}{2}I\omega^2 = \frac{h^2 l(l+1)}{8\pi^2 m_0 a^2}.$$

The expression for the kinetic energy of the rigid rotator free to move in space is exactly the same, but it is customary in this connection to use J as the rotation quantum number. Thus,

$$E = \frac{h^2 J(J+1)}{8\pi^2 I}. \tag{1.30}$$

The one-dimensional linear harmonic oscillator (simplest model of a vibrating molecule). In the problems which have so far been considered, the energy of the system has been wholly kinetic. In the problem now to be considered, the energy is partly kinetic and partly potential.

For a mass, m, moving with simple harmonic motion, it is characteristic of the motion that m moves under a restoring force proportional to the displacement. If m is moving along the x axis, and the frequency of oscillation is ν_0, then according to classical mechanics (equations (1.6) and (1.7), p. 2),

$$\text{potential energy} = \tfrac{1}{2}kx^2$$
$$= 2\pi^2\nu_0^2 mx^2.$$

The wave equation for one dimension is

$$\frac{d^2\psi}{dx^2} + \frac{8\pi^2 m}{h^2}(E - \tfrac{1}{2}kx^2)\psi = 0.$$

This equation cannot be solved in this form, nor can a value be found for E without further manipulation. Schrödinger employed the following method to solve the equation.

Let

$$\xi = 2\pi x\sqrt{\frac{m\nu_0}{h}}.$$

Then

$$x^2 = \frac{h\xi^2}{4\pi^2 m\nu_0}, \quad \text{and} \quad \frac{d\xi}{dx} = 2\pi\sqrt{\frac{m\nu_0}{h}}.$$

Since

$$\frac{d\psi}{d\xi} = \frac{d\psi}{dx}\frac{dx}{d\xi}, \quad \text{and} \quad \frac{d^2\psi}{d\xi^2} = \frac{d^2\psi}{dx^2}\left(\frac{dx}{d\xi}\right)^2$$

If $E = Ch\nu_0/2$, Schrödinger's equation becomes:

$$\left(\frac{d\xi}{dx}\right)^2\frac{d^2\psi}{d\xi^2} + \frac{8\pi^2 m}{h^2}\left[\frac{Ch\nu_0}{2} - \frac{k}{2}\frac{h\xi^2}{4\pi^2 m\nu_0}\right]\psi = 0$$

$$\frac{4\pi^2 m\nu_0}{h}\frac{d^2\psi}{d\xi^2} + \frac{8\pi^2 m}{h^2}\left[\frac{Ch\nu_0}{2} - \frac{4\pi^2\nu_0^2 mh\xi^2}{8\pi^2 m\nu_0}\right]\psi = 0,$$

which reduces to

$$\frac{d^2\psi}{d\xi^2} + [C - \xi^2]\psi = 0. \tag{1.31}$$

This seemingly simple equation still cannot be solved conveniently in this form.

Assume $\psi = e^{-\frac{1}{2}\xi^2}H$ where H is a function of ξ.

$$\frac{d\psi}{d\xi} = -\xi e^{-\frac{1}{2}\xi^2}H + e^{-\frac{1}{2}\xi^2}\frac{dH}{d\xi}$$

$$\frac{d^2\psi}{d\xi^2} = -e^{-\frac{1}{2}\xi^2}\frac{d}{d\xi}[H\xi] + H\xi^2 e^{-\frac{1}{2}\xi^2} + e^{-\frac{1}{2}\xi^2}\frac{d^2H}{d\xi^2} - \xi e^{-\frac{1}{2}\xi^2}\frac{dH}{d\xi}$$

$$= e^{-\frac{1}{2}\xi^2}\left[-\left(H + \xi\frac{dH}{d\xi}\right) + H\xi^2 + \frac{d^2H}{d\xi^2} - \xi\frac{dH}{d\xi}\right]$$

$$= e^{-\frac{1}{2}\xi^2}\left[\frac{d^2H}{d\xi^2} - 2\xi\frac{dH}{d\xi} + H(\xi^2 - 1)\right].$$

Substituting in equation (1.31),

$$\frac{d^2H}{d\xi^2} - 2\xi\frac{dH}{d\xi} + H(C-1) = 0. \tag{1.32}$$

The solution of this equation is a power series (see Appendix) which might be infinite or a polynomial. If it were an infinite power series, the value of H and therefore that of ψ would tend to infinity at infinity, but by the boundary condition, ψ (and so H) is zero at infinity, and therefore the solution must be a polynomial. (A polynomial is a power series that breaks off at a definite value.)

If H is expressed as a power series, let

$$H = a_0 + a_1\xi + a_2\xi^2 + a_3\xi^3 + \cdots$$

$$\frac{dH}{d\xi} = a_1 + 2a_2\xi + 3a_3\xi^2 + 4a_4\xi^3 + \cdots$$

$$\frac{d^2H}{d\xi^2} = 2a_2 + 6a_3\xi + 12a_4\xi^2 + \cdots.$$

Substituting in equation (1.32)

$$2a_2 + 6a_3\xi + 12a_4\xi^2 + \cdots = 2\xi[a_1 + 2a_2\xi + 3a_3\xi^2 + 4a_4\xi^3 + \cdots \\ - (C-1)[a_0 + a_1\xi + a_2\xi^2 + a_3\xi^3 + \cdots].$$

Equating coefficients of the same powers of ξ,

$$6a_3 = (2+1-C)a_1,$$
$$12a_4 = (4+1-C)a_2, \quad \text{etc.}$$

All these equations can be expressed in the form

$$(n+2)(n+1)a_{n+2} = (2n+1-C)a_n.$$

This is called a recursion or recurrence formula. It gives all the information required for the determination of the energy, so that it is not necessary to proceed further with the solution of the equation for ψ.

(1) If $(2n+1-C)$ does not vanish for any integral values of n, then H is given by a power series which is divergent, and H and ψ tend towards infinity.

(2) If $C = 2n+1$, the series comes to a definite end, and there is a numerical solution (in this particular case there are two solutions) for each value of ξ and at infinity H and ψ will be zero.† This can happen only when $C = 2n+1$ (n can have any integral value 0, 1, 2, 3, ...).

Therefore,

$$\frac{2E}{h\nu_0} = 2n+1$$

and

$$E = h\nu_0(n+\tfrac{1}{2}). \tag{1.33}$$

This equation gives the eigenvalues for the energy of the system.

For constant frequency ν_0, the energy required in the system to keep the oscillation going is determined by the amplitude of vibration. This principle is common to both classical and quantum theories, but with an important difference between them. In the classical theory the amplitude, and consequently the energy, can be varied continuously; in the quantum theory (p. 10) the energy can take each of a series of possible quantised values only. The quantum theory is further subdivided into the old (or

---

† Since $\psi = e^{-\frac{1}{2}\xi^2}H$, ψ will behave like the function $e^{-\frac{1}{2}\xi^2}\xi^n$. For large values of ξ the exponential part of the expression is dominating and the function dies away rapidly, and becoming zero at infinity in spite of the factor ξ^n.

classical) quantum theory, according to which the amplitude and energy of the vibration could be varied only within the limits of the relation $E = nh\nu_0$, and the wave mechanical quantum theory at present accepted, according to which the energy can be varied only within the limits of the relation $E = h\nu_0(n + \frac{1}{2})$.

This relation is illustrated by Fig. 1.10, which shows an energy curve for the harmonic oscillator. The horizontal lines show the different amplitudes of vibration corresponding to different values of n when the frequency is constant. It will be noticed that the different energy "levels" have the same energy difference between them, and that even

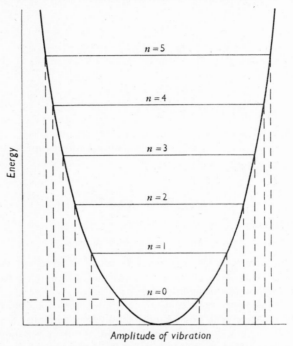

Fig. 1.10.   Energy of a harmonic oscillator.

in the state of lowest vibration energy, $n = 0$, the oscillator has a vibration energy $\frac{1}{2}h\nu_0$. This is known as the *zero point energy*. The energy curve for the harmonic oscillator according to the old quantum theory is identical with that of the wave mechanical theory, except that for $n = 0$, $E = 0$. The existence of zero point energy is in keeping with the uncertainty principle. If the energy of the oscillator were zero its position could be determined exactly, its momentum also would be zero, which is a definite value. This would be a violation of the uncertainty principle which demands that the product of the uncertainties of position and momentum shall not be less than $h/4\pi$.

APPLICATION OF SCHRÖDINGER'S EQUATION TO THE ELECTRON IN THE ATOM

Since the electron in the atom is subject to boundary conditions, the determination of the energy of the bound electron is an eigenvalue problem. Possible solutions of Schrödinger's equation correspond to certain eigenfrequencies, and as by Planck's fundamental relation the energy of the system is proportional to the frequency, there are certain possible eigenvalues of the energy. This is a most important conclusion, as it provides an explanation of Bohr's first quantum condition, which is that the electron can occupy only certain definite energy states in the atom. It was Schrödinger who first recognised that quantisation is an eigenvalue problem. In order to obtain values for the eigenfunctions ψ corresponding to the different energy states Schrödinger's equation must be solved, and to do this it is necessary to substitute appropriate values for V, the potential energy of the system. Although the negative charge on the electron is clearly bound by the positive charge on the nucleus, the laws which govern the force between them are not known. There is no reason to assume that those laws which are adequate to express electrostatic forces on a macroscopic scale are applicable on the microscopic scale of the atom's interior. However the best that can be done is to use the macroscopic law, Coulomb's Inverse Square Law, until it is possible to find out what laws do hold at such minute distances. As will be seen later, this proceeding is justified by a measure of agreement achieved between theory and observation.

In its application to the electron in the atom, the original interpretation given by Schrödinger to his equation was not entirely satisfactory. He identified ψ^2 with the electron density. Since it is possible to have more than one solution of the equation (more than one value of ψ for the same energy), and therefore different eigenfunctions for the description of an atomic or molecular system of given energy, this would lead to the interpretation that an electron could be in two places at once. This difficulty, and others of a similar nature, were overcome by Born's statistical interpretation which has already been mentioned (p. 18). He identified the expression $|\psi|^2 \, dx dy dz$ with the probability that the electron would be found in a definite small volume ($dx dy dz$). If a system containing many electrons were described by more than one eigenfunction, according to Born's interpretation the square of each wave function would be a measure of the number of electrons described by that wave function.

An alternative to Schödinger's method was first suggested by Bohr, and was developed by Heisenberg. He was determined to use only quantities which could be observed experimentally, and he made an attempt to calculate all the properties of any given atomic or molecular system from the intensities and frequencies corresponding to observed spectral lines. His mathematical system did not employ continuously variable co-ordinates, but he used instead series of discrete numbers in the form of matrices, the use of which had previously been developed for other purposes. This system is known as "matrix mechanics" and many mathematicians find it preferable to wave mechanics. The two methods yield the same quantitative results when applied to practical problems, and it can be proved rigorously that they are mathematically equivalent. This equivalence is sufficient justification for expressing the potential energy in Schrödinger's equation in the form of a Coulomb force. The methods of wave mechanics will be used in this book, as it is thought that many readers may be unfamiliar with matrix mechanics.

THE ELECTRON AS A STATIONARY WAVE

The fact that the Schrödinger equation is a stationary wave equation lends support to de Broglie's explanation of Bohr's second postulate (p. 15). For this explanation it is necessary to employ the concept of an electron as a stationary wave. On the basis of the assumption that a simple circular Bohr orbit of length $2\pi r$ would contain a whole number of wave lengths, the quantum condition that $mvr = nh/2\pi$ was deduced. It should be noted that the quantity v which is used in the calculation is the particle velocity, that is the group velocity of the wave packet, and not the phase velocity of the de Broglie wave.

It may well be asked whether it is possible to combine the picture of the electron as a wave packet with the picture of the electron as a stationary wave. Suppose that two de Broglie waves travel round a circular orbit in opposite directions. If they are not to cancel each other out, the condition will be one of a stationary wave whose wave length "fits in" to the circumference of the orbit, so that $n\lambda = 2\pi r$. If there is one marked amplitude peak in each wave, the peaks will travel (with velocity v) in opposite directions round the circle, and will continue to move round and round, provided the energy of the system is not dissipated by damping. If the concept is now extended to three dimensions, a thin spherical shell must be visualised, instead of a ring. Since there is no fixed orientation with regard to space, there is an equal probability of the peaks being found anywhere in the spherical shell. The electron therefore must be visualised as a cloud occupying the spherical shell. This cloud would have no resultant angular momentum. This supposition is reasonable because the electron in the non-radiating atom has sharp energy, and so by Heisenberg's uncertainty principle the position is not sharp. The position of the shell with regard to the nucleus would correspond to a particular value of the eigenfunction ψ, the density of the cloud being proportional to the probability of finding the electron in the cloud, and thus proportional to $|\psi|^2$. The units of ψ are usually chosen so that $|\psi|^2$ is numerically equal to the charge density. If there are other possible solutions of the appropriate Schrödinger equation, that is other values of ψ, there must be other spherical shells at different distances from the nucleus, and their charge density is to be measured by the appropriate $|\psi|^2$. The shells must be arranged like the coats of an onion, and the sum of the charges contained in the different shells must be the total charge on the electron. The charge cloud of the electron would be more diffuse in some cases than in others, and so the region of space occupied by the electron would be variable.

Use of complex quantities to express the intensity of the ψ wave. In discussing simple harmonic motion earlier in this chapter, it was mentioned that the equation of a wave, caused by the displacements of particles executing simple harmonic motion with a regular phase difference, can be expressed either in a sine or a cosine form. As there is no reason to suppose that either form is present to the exclusion of the other, it is assumed that in the most general expression for the harmonic wave function ψ both forms are present. This assumption is justified by experimental observation which suggests that the intensity of the ψ wave is independent of time, and is thus a constant for a particular value of the wave function. The time factor appears to have no effect on the electron when it is in a "stationary" energy state in the atom. It is thus necessary to assume that the intensity of the ψ wave is independent of time when the atom is not radiating. Since there is a 90° phase difference between the sine and cosine wave forms (p. 4) the superposition of the sine and cosine waves leads to an expression for the total intensity which is independent of time.

These ideas can be expressed mathematically thus[†],

$$|\psi|^2 = A^2(\cos^2 \omega t + \sin^2 \omega t) \tag{1.34}$$
$$= A^2$$

It is more convenient, however, to express ψ in exponential form. Equation (1.34) may be written

$$|\psi|^2 = A^2(\cos \omega t + \mathrm{i} \sin \omega t)(\cos \omega t - \mathrm{i} \sin \omega t)$$
$$= A^2(\mathrm{e}^{\mathrm{i}\omega t} \times \mathrm{e}^{-\mathrm{i}\omega t})$$
$$= A^2.$$

[†] $|\psi|$ represents the numerical value of ψ.

If $\psi = Ae^{-i\omega t}$, then the quantity $Ae^{+i\omega t}$ is known as its **complex conjugate** and is denoted by ψ^*. (The reader should not be disturbed by the fact that this nomenclature is reversed in some textbooks.)

Thus

$$|\psi|^2 = \psi\psi^*.$$

FURTHER MATHEMATICAL CONSIDERATIONS OF SCHRÖDINGER'S EQUATION

Normalisation. The Schrödinger equation is a homogeneous differential equation whose solution gives a value for ψ. But ψ multiplied by a constant factor would give the same differential equation. It is therefore necessary to find some condition which will indicate which constant factor is to be used.

Since the electron must be found somewhere, we can say that the probability of finding the electron in the whole of the space considered in a particular problem is unity. This is written mathematically as

$$\int |\psi|^2 \, d\tau = 1,$$

where τ is the volume of the whole space. This integral determines by what constant ψ must be multiplied for the solution of a particular problem. This constant is known as the **normalisation constant**.

An eigenfunction which has been completely evaluated in this way is said to have been "normalised".

Orthogonality. If there are two wave functions ψ_p and ψ_q which correspond to two values of the energy, E_p and E_q, and if these wave functions are separate solutions of Schrödinger's equation, then $\int \psi_p\psi_q d\tau = 0$, and the wave functions ψ_p and ψ_q are said to be *orthogonal*. This property will be proved for one dimension only. A proof extended to three dimensions will be found in many textbooks on quantum physics.

If the two Schrödinger equations are written in one dimension only (for the motion of a particle in a straight line),

$$\frac{d^2\psi_p}{dx^2} + \frac{8\pi^2 m}{h^2}(E_p - V_p)\psi_p = 0$$

$$\frac{d^2\psi_q}{dx^2} + \frac{8\pi^2 m}{h^2}(E_q - V_q)\psi_q = 0.$$

Multiply the first equation by ψ_q and the second by ψ_p and subtract.

$$\frac{d}{dx}\left(\psi_q\frac{d\psi_p}{dx} - \psi_p\frac{d\psi_q}{dx}\right) + \frac{8\pi^2 m}{h^2}(E_p - E_q - V_p + V_q)\psi_p\psi_q = 0.$$

Integrating with respect to x over the whole of space (from $-\infty$ to $+\infty$), since ψ and V are zero at infinity the first term vanishes, and

$$\frac{8\pi^2 m}{h^2}(E_p - E_q)\int_{-\infty}^{+\infty} \psi_p\psi_q \, dx = 0.$$

Since $E_p \neq E_q$ then

$$\int_{-\infty}^{+\infty} \psi_p\psi_q \, dx = 0 \tag{1.35}$$

It is possible to make a linear combination of orthogonal functions. Here, for the purpose of illustration, an analogy may be drawn with classical forces at right angles to each other. Although neither has a resolved part in the direction of the other force, it is possible to resolve them both in some direction intermediate between their lines of action. Any two linear combinations of orthogonal functions are themselves orthogonal. This property and others pertaining to orthogonal functions have long been known to mathematicians: they were not invented for wave mechanics.

Properties of ψ. Certain other postulates about the nature of wave functions must be made in order to develop a system of wave mechanics which can be applied successfully to practical problems. It has been stated by Pauling that "to be a satisfactory wave function, a solution of the Schrödinger wave equation must be continuous, single-valued, and finite throughout the configuration space of the system" These conditions usually hold for the mathematical functions which describe physical quantities; for instance, the displacement of an air particle in an organ pipe in which a stationary vibration is set up would be a wave function obeying these rules.

DEDUCTIONS CONCERNING THE WAVE MECHANICAL THEORY OF RADIATION

Non-radiating states of the atom. The units of ψ have been chosen so that $|\psi|^2$ shall be numerically equal to (but not identified with) the electron density. Therefore if N is the number of electrons per unit volume, ϵ the charge on the electron, and ρ the charge per unit volume,

$$\rho = \epsilon N = \epsilon|\psi|^2 = \epsilon\psi\psi^* \quad \text{numerically} \tag{1.36}$$

The product $\psi\psi^*$ is independent of time, and therefore the distribution of charge, due to the presence of the electron in the atom, does not vary with time. Hence the atom in a stationary state does not radiate.

Radiating states of the atom. The study of the vibrations of a stretched string show that it is possible for the string to execute a number of simultaneous vibrations of different frequencies and amplitudes, each of which obeys the boundary conditions due to the fixing of the two ends of the string. Similar phenomena are observed in other cases of stationary vibration, and thus by analogy it might be assumed that an electron would be able to vibrate simultaneously in two or more energy states corresponding to two or more eigenfunctions.

An attractive explanation due to Born,[†] of the radiation of energy from the atom, is provided by the assumption that during a transition from one state to another the two eigenfunctions are superposed, and the radiation emitted is a "beat phenomenon". If this is so, the charge density, ρ, at a point is given by:

$$\rho = \epsilon\psi_p\psi_q^*$$

where ψ_p is one eigenfunction and ψ_q^* is the complex conjugate of another eigenfunction, ψ_q. The eigenfunctions ψ_p and ψ_q describe two different energy states of the electron, corresponding to three dimensional stationary vibrations of different wave length, frequency, and amplitude. It is not easy to visualise such waves, so for the purpose of illustration let stationary waves along the x axis only be considered. These waves may be formed by the superposition of plane waves travelling from left to right and reflected waves travelling from right to left.

From the equation for a stationary wave ((1.15), p. 7):

$$\psi_p = Ae^{-2\pi it/T_p}(e^{+2\pi ix/\lambda_p} + e^{-2\pi ix/\lambda_p}),$$

and

$$\psi_q^* = Be^{+2\pi it/T_q}(e^{+2\pi ix/\lambda_q} + e^{-2\pi ix/\lambda_q}).$$

Writing the space dependent part of the wave function as ψ^0,

$$\psi_p = e^{-2\pi it/T_p}\psi_p^0$$

$$\psi_q^* = e^{+2\pi it/T_q}\psi_q^{*0}$$

[†] M. Born, *Atomic Physics*, Blackie and Co. Ltd., 6th Edition, 1957.

Hence,

$$\rho = \epsilon \psi_p^0 \psi_q^{*0} e^{-2\pi i t (1/T_p - 1/T_q)}$$

$$= \epsilon \psi_p^0 \psi_q^{*0} e^{-2\pi i t (\nu_p - \nu_q)}. \tag{1.37}$$

The value of the charge density shown here is not constant in time, it vibrates sinusoidally with a frequency $(\nu_p - \nu_q)$, analogous to the frequency of the beats produced by sounding together two musical notes of different frequency. According to equation (1.37), radiation of frequency $(\nu_p - \nu_q)$ would be emitted, and since by Planck's relation $\nu_p - \nu_q = (E_p - E_q)/h$ it appears that this radiation could be explained by an energy change $E_p - E_q$ inside the atom, due to the simultaneous execution of two vibrations by the electron. If we accept this interpretation, we must abandon Bohr's original idea that the emission of radiation corresponds to a "jump" of the electron from one location in the atom to another, as we should be required to picture the electron in two places at once. This visual conflict has obviously grown up through the constant use of the word "level". There is nothing inconsistent about a picture of an electron executing two simultaneous vibrations. A more serious difficulty arises because the theory does not explain how the radiation stops and the electron settles down to a state governed by one of the eigenfunctions only. The problem has however been solved satisfactorily by Dirac, who considered it in detail from another point of view, that of the interaction between the electric field binding the nucleus and electrons and the alternating electromagnetic field of the emitted radiation. He assumed this electromagnetic field also to be quantised. Dirac's electrodynamic theory is complicated, but by means of it he was able to account for the whole process of the emission of energy from the atom.

Forbidden transitions. Certain particular eigenfunctions when multiplied together give a zero product, $\psi_p \psi_q^* = 0$. (This must not be confused with orthogonality (p. 29).) In such a case the simultaneous execution of the two corresponding vibrations by the electron will not result in the emission of radiation. This accounts for what are known as "forbidden transitions", that is the absence of certain lines in spectral series. It is well known that in a strong electric or magnetic field these lines may actually appear (p. 87), and it is a plausible supposition that in these cases the eigenfunctions are distorted by the strong fields, and so the product $\psi_p \psi_q^*$ is no longer zero.

BOOKS FOR FURTHER READING

BORN, M., *Atomic Physics* (Blackie, Sixth Edition, 1957).

BOHM, D., *Causality and Chance in Modern Physics* (Routledge and Kegan Paul, 1957).

DE BROGLIE, L., *The Revolution in Physics* (Routledge and Kegan Paul, 1954).

DE BROGLIE, L., *Physics and Microphysics* (Hutchinson's Scientific and Technical Publications, 1955).

HUME ROTHERY, W., *Atomic Theory for Students of Metallurgy* (The Institute of Metals. 1952).

PAULING, L., and WILSON, E. B., *Introduction to Quantum Mechanics* (New York: McGraw Hill, 1935).

CHAPTER TWO

THE QUANTUM NUMBERS AND ATOMIC ORBITALS

DERIVATION OF THE QUANTUM NUMBERS

In writing down the Schrödinger equation for the hydrogen atom the potential energy is assumed to be that due to an attractive Coulomb force between a positively charged point nucleus and a single electron. This introduces boundary conditions, and therefore it is to be expected that quantum numbers will appear in the solution of the equation.

Schrödinger's equation for the hydrogen atom is

$$\nabla^2\psi + \frac{8\pi^2 m_0}{h^2}\left[E + \frac{\epsilon^2}{r}\right]\psi = 0,$$

where m_0 = mass of the electron,

ϵ = charge on the electron,

r = distance between electron and nucleus.

The problem must be treated in three dimensions; therefore the equation is expressed in polar co-ordinates (see Appendix).

Schrödinger's equation becomes

$$\frac{1}{r^2}\frac{\partial}{\partial r}\left(r^2\frac{\partial\psi}{\partial r}\right) + \frac{1}{r^2}\left[\frac{1}{\sin\theta}\frac{\partial}{\partial\theta}\left(\sin\theta\frac{\partial\psi}{\partial\theta}\right) + \frac{1}{\sin^2\theta}\frac{\partial^2\psi}{\partial\phi^2}\right] + \frac{8\pi^2 m_0}{h^2}\left[E + \frac{\epsilon^2}{r}\right]\psi = 0. \quad (2.1)$$

(The following method of solution is according to Pauling and Wilson†.) It is sometimes possible to solve an equation of this type by separating the variables. In order to do this, ψ is assumed to be a product of three functions, each of which is a function of one only of the co-ordinates r, θ, and ϕ. This assumption is justified if, by its means, it is possible to separate the original differential equation into three differential equations, each with a different independent variable.

Let $\psi(r, \theta, \phi) = R(r)\Theta(\theta)\Phi(\phi)$ (the brackets mean "function of").

Introducing this expression for ψ into equation (2.1), dividing by the product $R\Theta\Phi$ (see Appendix), and multiplying by $r^2\sin^2\theta$

$$\frac{\sin^2\theta}{R}\frac{d}{dr}\left(r^2\frac{dR}{dr}\right) + \frac{\sin\theta}{\Theta}\frac{d}{d\theta}\left(\sin\theta\frac{d\Theta}{d\theta}\right) + \frac{1}{\Phi}\frac{d^2\Phi}{d\phi^2} + \frac{8\pi^2 m_0 r^2\sin^2\theta}{h^2}\left[E + \frac{\epsilon^2}{r}\right] = 0. \quad (2.2)$$

By means of *separation constants* (see Appendix) this differential equation can be split up into three separate differential equations, each with a different independent variable.

The ϕ dependent equation. Since the sum of the terms which are independent of ϕ + the sum of the terms which are dependent on ϕ is equal to zero, each sum must be equal to a constant.

Therefore, let

$$\frac{1}{\Phi}\frac{d^2\Phi}{d\phi^2} = -m^2,$$

then

$$\frac{d^2\Phi}{d\phi^2} + m^2\Phi = 0. \quad (2.3)$$

† L. Pauling and E. B. Wilson, *Introduction to Quantum Mechanics* p. 113.

32

The θ dependent equation. Substituting the separation constant $-m^2$ for terms in ϕ in equation (2.2), and dividing by $\sin^2\theta$:

$$\frac{1}{R}\frac{d}{dr}\left(r^2\frac{dR}{dr}\right)+\frac{1}{\sin\theta}\frac{1}{\Theta}\frac{d}{d\theta}\left(\sin\theta\frac{d\Theta}{d\theta}\right)-\frac{m^2}{\sin^2\theta}+\frac{8\pi^2m_0r^2}{h^2}\left[E+\frac{\epsilon^2}{r}\right]=0.$$

The 2nd and 3rd terms are independent of r, and the 1st and 4th terms are independent of θ, therefore each set can be equated to a separation constant.

Let   the sum of the θ terms $=-\beta$
and   the sum of the r terms $=+\beta$.
Taking the θ terms and multiplying by Θ,

$$\frac{1}{\sin\theta}\frac{d}{d\theta}\left(\sin\theta\frac{d\Theta}{d\theta}\right)-\frac{m^2\Theta}{\sin^2\theta}+\beta\Theta=0. \tag{2.4}$$

The r dependent equation. Taking the r terms, multiplying by R and dividing by r^2,

$$\frac{1}{r^2}\frac{d}{dr}\left(r^2\frac{dR}{dr}\right)-\frac{\beta R}{r^2}+\frac{8\pi^2m_0}{h^2}\left[E+\frac{\epsilon^2}{r}\right]R=0. \tag{2.5}$$

The following procedure should now be observed for the solution of the three independent differential equations.

(1) Solve the ϕ dependent equation. Acceptable solutions will be found only for certain values of m.

(2) Introduce these values of m into the θ dependent equation. Acceptable solutions will only be found for certain values of β.

(3) Introduce these values of β into the r dependent equation. Acceptable solutions will be found only for certain values of E. These are the eigenvalues for the energy of the stationary states of the system.

Solution of the ϕ dependent equation,

$$\frac{d^2\Phi}{d\phi^2}=-m^2\Phi.$$

It may easily be verified that $\Phi=Ae^{-im\phi}$ and $\Phi^*=Ae^{im\phi}$ are solutions of this equation.

By the normalisation condition (p. 29)

$$\int_0^{2\pi}\Phi\Phi^*\,d\phi=1.$$

Therefore

$$\int_0^{2\pi}A^2\,d\phi=1,$$

$$A=\frac{1}{\sqrt{(2\pi)}},$$

and

$$\Phi=\frac{1}{\sqrt{(2\pi)}}\,e^{\pm im\phi}. \tag{2.6}$$

It is usually convenient to express Φ in terms of $\cos\phi$ or $\sin\phi$. Since $e^{im\phi}$ and $e^{-im\phi}$ are both solutions of the Φ equation, then a linear combination of them is also a solution. Therefore,

$$\Phi=B\left(\frac{e^{im\phi}+e^{-im\phi}}{2}\right)$$

and $\phi=B\cos m\phi$ are also solutions of the ϕ dependent equation.

2+A.T.I.C.

The normalisation constant, B, in this solution is different from that, A, in equation (2.6). The normalisation constant is found by integrating the expression for Φ, thus

$$B^2 \int_0^{2\pi} \cos^2 m\phi \, d\phi = 1$$

$$B^2 \int_0^{2\pi} \left(\frac{1 + \cos 2m\phi}{2} \right) d\phi = 1.$$

When $m = \pm 1$, since $\sin 2\phi$ vanishes in the limits of integration,

$$B = \frac{1}{\sqrt{\pi}}$$

and

$$\Phi = \frac{1}{\sqrt{\pi}} \cos m\phi.$$

Similarly it may be shown that for the linear combination $B\{(e^{im\phi} - e^{-im\phi})/2i\}$, when $m = \pm 1$,

$$\Phi = \frac{1}{\sqrt{\pi}} \sin m\phi.$$

It may easily be verified that when $m = 0$, $B = A = 1/\sqrt{2\pi}$.

Φ must be single valued, and therefore Φ must have the same value after any number of whole revolutions, and hence

$$e^{im\phi} = e^{im(\phi + 2\pi n)}$$
$$= e^{i(m\phi + 2\pi n m)}, \tag{2.7}$$

where n is a whole number, and therefore the product nm must be a whole number, and m must be a whole number. Possible values of m are $0, \pm 1, \pm 2, \pm 3, \ldots$. m is known as the **magnetic quantum number**. It will be shown later that it is concerned with the behaviour of the electrons in the atom when it is placed in a magnetic field.

Solution of θ dependent equation,

$$\frac{1}{\sin \theta} \frac{d}{d\theta} \left(\sin \theta \frac{d\Theta}{d\theta} \right) - \frac{m^2}{\sin^2 \theta} \Theta + \beta \Theta = 0.$$

Let $z = \cos \theta$, which varies between the limits $+1$ and -1. Replace Θ by P, where P is a function of z. The three following relationships may be written down:

(a) $$z^2 = 1 - \sin^2 \theta.$$

(b) $$\frac{d\Theta}{d\theta} = \frac{dP}{dz} \frac{dz}{d\theta} = -\frac{dP}{dz} \sin \theta.$$

(c) $$\frac{d^2\Theta}{d\theta^2} = \frac{dP}{dz} \frac{d^2z}{d\theta^2} + \left(\frac{dz}{d\theta} \right)^2 \frac{d^2P}{dz^2}.$$

Now,

$$\frac{1}{\sin \theta} \frac{d}{d\theta} \left(\sin \theta \frac{d\Theta}{d\theta} \right) = \frac{1}{\sin \theta} \sin \theta \frac{d^2\Theta}{d\theta^2} + \frac{\cos \theta}{\sin \theta} \frac{d\Theta}{d\theta}$$

$$= \frac{dP}{dz} \frac{d^2z}{d\theta^2} + \left(\frac{dz}{d\theta} \right)^2 \frac{d^2P}{dz^2} + \frac{\cos \theta}{\sin \theta} \frac{dP}{dz} \frac{dz}{d\theta}.$$

But

$$\frac{dz}{d\theta} = -\sin \theta \quad \text{and} \quad \frac{d^2z}{d\theta^2} = -\cos \theta = -z.$$

Hence

$$\frac{1}{\sin\theta}\frac{d}{d\theta}\left(\sin\theta\frac{d\Theta}{d\theta}\right) = -z\frac{dP}{dz}+(1-z^2)\frac{d^2P}{dz^2}-z\frac{dP}{dz}$$

$$= (1-z^2)\frac{d^2P}{dz^2}-2z\frac{dP}{dz}$$

$$= \frac{d}{dz}\left[(1-z^2)\frac{dP}{dz}\right].$$

Therefore

$$\frac{1}{\sin\theta}\frac{d}{d\theta}\left(\sin\theta\frac{d\Theta}{d\theta}\right)-\frac{m^2\Theta}{\sin^2\theta}+\beta\Theta = \frac{d}{dz}\left[(1-z^2)\frac{dP}{dz}\right]+\left[\beta-\frac{m^2}{1-z^2}\right]P,$$

and

$$\frac{d}{dz}\left[(1-z^2)\frac{dP}{dz}\right]+\left(\beta-\frac{m^2}{1-z^2}\right)P = 0. \tag{2.8}$$

Equation (2.8) has singular points (see Appendix) at $z=\pm 1$, both of which are regular. Therefore the solutions of the equation are in the form of a power series. It is convenient to put $x=1-z$ and $y=1+z$.

Let

$$R(x) = P(z),$$

then

$$\frac{d}{dx}\left[x(2-x)\frac{dR}{dx}\right]+\left(\beta-\frac{m^2}{x(2-x)}\right)R = 0. \tag{2.9}$$

Since the solution of this equation is a regular integral it can be expressed in the form of the series:

$$R_{(x)} = x^s(a_0+a_1x+a_2x^2+a_3x^3+\cdots).$$

If this value of R is substituted in the above differential equation (2.9), an *indicial equation*, giving a value of s is obtained. (See Appendix.)

The indicial equation shows that for the point $x=1-z$, $s=m/2$. Similarly for the point $y=1+z$, s $=m/2$. Therefore we may write

$$P(z) = x^{m/2}y^{m/2}G$$

$$= (1-z^2)^{m/2}G,$$

where G is a power series in terms of z.

Substituting for P in equation (2.8):

$$(1-z^2)\frac{d^2G}{dz^2}-2z(m+1)\frac{dG}{dz}+[\beta-m(m+1)]G = 0. \tag{2.10}$$

Let

$$G = a_0+a_1z+a_2z^2+a_3z^3+\cdots$$

$$\frac{dG}{dz} = a_1+2a_2z+3a_3z^2+4a_4z^3+\cdots$$

$$\frac{d^2G}{dz^2} = 2a_2+6a_3z+12a_4z^2+20a_5z^3+\cdots.$$

Then,

$$(1-z^2)(2a_2+6a_3z+12a_4z^2+\cdots)-2z(m+1)(a_1+2a_2z+3a_3z^2+\cdots)$$
$$+[\beta-m(m+1)](a_0+a_1z+a_2z^2+a_3z^3+\cdots) = 0.$$

This equation is an identity in z, and therefore coefficients of individual powers of z must vanish. Therefore,

$$2a_2 + [\beta - m(m+1)]a_0 = 0.$$
$$2 \times 3a_3 + [\beta - m(m+1)]a_1 - 2 \times 1(m+1)a_1 = 0.$$
$$3 \times 4a_4 + [\beta - m(m+1)]a_2 - 2 \times 2(m+1)a_2 - 2a_2 = 0.$$

Hence,

$$(\nu+1)(\nu+2)a_{\nu+2} + a_\nu[\beta - m(m+1) - \nu(\nu-1) - 2\nu(m+1)] = 0.$$

This gives the recurrence formula

$$a_{\nu+2} = \left[\frac{m(m+1) - \beta + 2\nu(m+1) + \nu(\nu-1)}{(\nu+1)(\nu+2)} \right] a_\nu.$$

This expression describes the relation between alternate coefficients, either between the evens or the odds.

If G were an infinite series it would converge for values of z between $+1$ and -1, but would diverge for $z = \pm 1$. Therefore it would not be acceptable as a wave function.

If the series is finite it can be broken off either for the odd or for the even series. (The other series can be made to vanish by equating a_0 or a_1 to zero.)

The series will break off at the term z^ν if

$$\beta = (\nu+m)(\nu+m+1)$$

where $\nu = 0, 1, 2, 3, \ldots$.

Let $\nu + m = l$, then

$$\beta = l(l+1), \tag{2.11}$$

where $l \geqslant m, (m+1), (m+2), (m+3), \ldots$.

l is known as the orbital quantum number. The actual solution of equation (2.10), written as

$$(1-z^2)\frac{d^2G}{dz^2} - 2z(m+1)\frac{dG}{dz} + [l(l+1) - m(m+1)]G = 0, \tag{2.12}$$

can be worked out by inserting the summed series for G, dG/dz, and d^2G/dz^2. An arbitrary constant a_0, or a_1 (according to whether the odd or even solution is taken) will appear in the solution. The value of this constant can be obtained by normalising the wave function Θ (p. 29).

The acceptable solutions of the Θ equation are

$$\Theta(\theta) = (1-z^2)^{m/2}G(z) = P(z). \tag{2.13}$$

The solutions may be written as $\Theta(\theta) = P_{m/l}(\cos\theta)$ where m is the order of the equation between P and G, and m and l are constants in equation (2.12). The solutions, a standard form known as *associated Legendre functions*, can be found directly in tables.

Solution of the r dependent equation,

$$\frac{1}{r^2}\frac{d}{dr}\left(r^2\frac{dR}{dr}\right) - \frac{\beta}{r^2}R + \frac{8\pi^2 m_0}{h^2}\left[E + \frac{\epsilon^2}{r}\right]R = 0.$$

E is negative since the total energy is insufficient to ionise the atom.

Let

$$\alpha^2 = -\frac{8\pi^2 m_0 E}{h^2}, \quad \text{and} \quad \lambda = \frac{4\pi^2 m_0 \epsilon^2}{h^2 \alpha},$$

and $\rho = 2\alpha r$ where ρ is a new independent variable lying between 0 and ∞.

Let $S(\rho) = R(r)$. Then since

$$\frac{dS}{d\rho} = \frac{dS}{dr}\frac{dr}{d\rho}, \quad \text{and} \quad \frac{d\rho}{dr} = 2\alpha,$$

putting $\beta = l(l+1)$ and making the appropriate substitutions, the r dependent equation becomes:

$$\frac{1}{\rho^2}\frac{d}{d\rho}\left(\rho^2\frac{dS}{d\rho}\right) + \left[-\frac{l(l+1)}{\rho^2} - \frac{1}{4} + \frac{\lambda}{\rho}\right]S = 0. \tag{2.14}$$

For large values of ρ equation (2.14) becomes approximately

$$\frac{d^2S}{d\rho^2} = \frac{S}{4}.$$

Solutions of this equation are $S = e^{\rho/2}$ and $S = e^{-\rho/2}$; only the second is suitable for wave functions. Assume that the solution of the complete equation is of the form:

$$S(\rho) = e^{-\rho/2}F(\rho); \quad 0 \leqslant \rho \leqslant \infty$$

then

$$\frac{dS}{d\rho} = e^{-\rho/2}\frac{dF}{d\rho} - \frac{1}{2}e^{-\rho/2}F,$$

and

$$\frac{d^2S}{d\rho^2} = e^{-\rho/2}\frac{d^2F}{d\rho^2} - \frac{e^{-\rho/2}}{2}\frac{dF}{d\rho} - \frac{e^{-\rho/2}}{2}\frac{dF}{d\rho} + \frac{e^{-\rho/2}}{4}F.$$

On making the appropriate substitutions, equation (2.14) becomes:

$$\frac{d^2F}{d\rho^2} + \frac{dF}{d\rho}\left(\frac{2}{\rho} - 1\right) + \left(\frac{\lambda}{\rho} - \frac{l(l+1)}{\rho^2} - \frac{1}{\rho}\right)F = 0. \tag{2.15}$$

Coefficients of $dF/d\rho$ and F possess singularities at the origin, which is a regular point (see Appendix). Therefore a power series can be substituted for F beginning with a non-vanishing constant term.

Let

$$F(\rho) = \rho^s L(\rho) \quad \text{where} \quad L(\rho) = a_0 + a_1\rho + a_2\rho^2 + a_3\rho^3 + \cdots.$$

Then

$$\frac{dF}{d\rho} = \rho^s\frac{dL}{d\rho} + s\rho^{s-1}L, \quad \text{and} \quad \frac{d^2F}{d\rho^2} = \rho^s\frac{d^2L}{d\rho^2} + 2s\rho^{s-1}\frac{dL}{d\rho} + s(s-1)\rho^{s-2}L.$$

Multiplying equation (2.15) by ρ^2:

$$\rho^2\frac{d^2F}{d\rho^2} + (2\rho - \rho^2)\frac{dF}{d\rho} + (\lambda - 1)\rho F - l(l+1)F = 0.$$

Substituting for $d^2F/d\rho^2$ and $dF/d\rho$:

$$\rho^{s+2}\frac{d^2L}{d\rho^2} + 2s\rho^{s+1}\frac{dL}{d\rho} + s(s-1)\rho^s L + 2\rho^{s+1}\frac{dL}{d\rho} + 2s\rho^s L - \rho^{s+2}\frac{dL}{d\rho}$$
$$- s\rho^{s+1}L + (\lambda - 1)\rho^{s+1}L - l(l+1)\rho^s L = 0. \tag{2.16}$$

This equation is an identity in ρ, and therefore coefficients of individual powers of ρ vanish. Taking the coefficients of ρ^s:

$$\{s(s-1) + 2s - l(l+1)\}a_0 = 0.$$

Since $a_0 \neq 0$, therefore $s(s-1) + 2s - l(l+1) = 0$.

Therefore either $s = l$ or $s = -(l+1)$, but the second value does not lead to an acceptable wave function.

Taking $s = l$,
$$F(\rho) = \rho^l L(\rho).$$

Substituting l for s and dividing by ρ^{l+1} in equation (2.16):

$$\rho\frac{d^2L}{d\rho^2} + \{2(l+1) - \rho\}\frac{dL}{d\rho} + (\lambda - 1 - l)L = 0. \tag{2.17}$$

Let
$$L = a_0 + a_1\rho + a_2\rho^2 + a_3\rho^3 + \cdots$$
$$\frac{dL}{d\rho} = a_1 + 2a_2\rho + 3a_3\rho^2 + \cdots$$

and
$$\frac{d^2L}{d\rho^2} = 2a_2 + 6a_3\rho + \cdots.$$

Substituting these values in equation (2.17):

$$2a_2\rho + 6a_3\rho^2 + 12a_4\rho^3 + \cdots + 2(l+1)(a_1 + 2a_2\rho + 3a_3\rho^2 + \cdots - a_1\rho$$
$$- 2a_2\rho^2 - 3a_3\rho^3 - \cdots + (\lambda - l - 1)(a_0 + a_1\rho + a_2\rho^2 + \cdots) = 0.$$

This equation is an identity in ρ, and therefore coefficients of powers of ρ must vanish individually. Hence

$$(\lambda - l - 1)a_0 + 2(l+1)a_1 = 0,$$
$$(\lambda - l - 1 - 1)a_1 + \{2 \times 2(l+1) + 1 \times 2\}a_2 = 0,$$
$$(\lambda - l - 1 - 2)a_2 + \{3 \times 2(l+1) + 2 \times 3\}a_3 = 0,$$
$$\text{etc.}$$

If ρ^ν is to vanish, the recurrence formula must be expressed as:

$$(\lambda - l - 1 - \nu)a_\nu + \{2(\nu+1)(l+1) + \nu(\nu+1)\}a_{\nu+1} = 0.$$

In order that the solution of the main equation may be acceptable as a wave function the series must break off after a finite number of terms (so that ψ approaches zero at infinity). If it breaks off after the term $\rho^{n'}$ then

$$\lambda - l - 1 - n' = 0,$$

where n' has an integral value, 0, 1, 2, ...

Let $\lambda = n$, then
$$n \geqslant l + 1. \tag{2.18}$$

Since l is an integer, n must be an integer of series 1, 2, 3, ... n is called the **principal quantum number.**

Thus the three quantum numbers defining the state of the hydrogen atom are:

Magnetic quantum number $m = 0, \pm 1, \pm 2, \pm 3, \ldots$
Orbital quantum number $l \geqslant m, (m+1), (m+2), (m+3), \ldots$
Principal quantum number $n \geqslant l + 1.$

It is more convenient for the interpretation of spectra to rewrite these numbers as

$$n = 1, 2, 3, \ldots$$
$$l = 0, 1, 2, \ldots, n-1$$
$$m = -l, -l+1, \ldots, -1, 0, +1, \ldots, +l-1, +l.$$

Table 2.5, p. 44, shows that for given values of n and l, there are $(2l+1)$ values of m. Since each value of m corresponds to an independent wave function, there are $2l+1$ possible wave functions for each given value of l.

The actual solution of equation (2.17) can be obtained by substituting for $d^2L/d\rho^2$, $dL/d\rho$, and L, and by using the recurrence formula to determine the coefficients a_1, a_2, a_3, ... in terms of a_0. The value of the constant a_0 can be obtained by normalising the wave function R.

The acceptable solutions for R are given by

$$R(r) = e^{-\rho/2}\rho^l L(\rho) \tag{2.19}$$

and are of a standard form known as *associated Laguerre functions*.

THE SPACE WAVE FUNCTION ψ FOR THE ELECTRON IN THE HYDROGEN ATOM

The possible values of ψ for the electron in the hydrogen atom are given by the product of the three solutions derived above:

$$\psi = e^{-\rho/2}\rho^l L(\rho) P_{ml}(\cos\theta) e^{\pm im\phi} \tag{2.20}$$

Equation (2.20) does not include the spin of the electron which is governed by a fourth quantum number (p. 55). The wave function which omits the spin of the electron will be referred to as the *space wave function*.

The product $\Theta\Phi$ describes the shape of a stationary wave in three dimensions; the value of R determines its overall size. An analogy might be drawn with the vibrations of a stretched string; the product $\Theta\Phi$ gives information analogous to the number of nodes and antinodes and amplitude of the stationary vibrations of the string; the value of R is analogous to the length of the string. The product $\Theta\Phi$ is known either as a *surface harmonic*, or as a *spherical harmonic*, or, if the functions $\sin\theta$, $\cos\theta$, etc. are expressed in exponential form, as a *tesseral harmonic*.

Computations of a large number of wave functions corresponding to different values of the quantum numbers n, l, m, have been made for the hydrogen atom. The results have been tabulated in detail by Pauling and others. For convenience of reference the separated functions $\Phi(\phi)$, $\Theta(\theta)$, and $R(r)$ of the hydrogen atom are first set out in Tables 2.1, 2.2, and 2.3. The space wave function for the hydrogen atom in any given state is obtained by multiplying together the appropriate separated functions (Table 2.4).

Table 2.1.   *Function Φ_m for the Hydrogen Atom*

Column 1 gives the value of m, column 2 gives the appropriate symbol for the function Φ, column 3 gives the expression for Φ (normalised to unity) in terms of ϕ; two alternative forms are given.

m	Φ symbol	Φ in terms of ϕ
0	Φ_0	$\dfrac{1}{\sqrt{(2\pi)}}$
1	Φ_1	$\dfrac{1}{\sqrt{(2\pi)}} e^{i\phi}$ or $\dfrac{1}{\sqrt{\pi}} \cos\phi$
-1	Φ_{-1}	$\dfrac{1}{\sqrt{(2\pi)}} e^{-i\phi}$ or $\dfrac{1}{\sqrt{\pi}} \sin\phi$
2	Φ_2	$\dfrac{1}{\sqrt{(2\pi)}} e^{2i\phi}$ or $\dfrac{1}{\sqrt{\pi}} \cos 2\phi$
-2	Φ_{-2}	$\dfrac{1}{\sqrt{(2\pi)}} e^{-2i\phi}$ or $\dfrac{1}{\sqrt{\pi}} \sin 2\phi$

Table 2.2.   *Function Θ_{ml} for the Hydrogen Atom*

Columns 1 and 2 give the values of l and m, column 3 gives the appropriate symbol for the function Θ, column 4 gives the expression for Θ (normalised to unity) in terms of θ.

l	m	Θ symbol	Θ in terms of θ
0	0	Θ_{00}	$\dfrac{\sqrt{2}}{2}$
1	0	Θ_{10}	$\dfrac{\sqrt{6}}{2}\cos\theta$
1	± 1	$\Theta_{1\pm1}$	$\dfrac{\sqrt{3}}{2}\sin\theta$
2	0	Θ_{20}	$\dfrac{\sqrt{10}}{4}(3\cos^2\theta-1)$
2	± 1	$\Theta_{2\pm1}$	$\dfrac{\sqrt{15}}{2}\sin\theta\cos\theta$
2	± 2	$\Theta_{2\pm2}$	$\dfrac{\sqrt{15}}{4}\sin^2\theta$

Table 2.3.   *Function $R(r)$ for the Hydrogen Atom*

Columns 1 and 2 give the values of n and l, column 3 gives the symbol for the orbital corresponding to the values of n and l, column 4 gives the appropriate symbol for the function R, column 5 gives the expression for R (normalised to unity) in terms of r and a constant a which is equal to $h^2/4\pi^2 m_0\epsilon^2$.

n	l	Orbital	R symbol	R in terms of r, and a
1	0	$1s$	R_{10}	$\dfrac{1}{a^{3/2}}\,2\,e^{-r/a}$
2	0	$2s$	R_{20}	$\dfrac{1}{2\sqrt{(2a^3)}}\left(2-\dfrac{r}{a}\right)e^{-r/2a}$
2	1	$2p$	R_{21}	$\dfrac{1}{2\sqrt{(6a^3)}}\dfrac{r}{a}e^{-r/2a}$
3	0	$3s$	R_{30}	$\dfrac{1}{9\sqrt{(3a^3)}}\left(6-4\dfrac{r}{a}+\dfrac{4}{9}\dfrac{r^2}{a^2}\right)e^{-r/3a}$
3	1	$3p$	R_{31}	$\dfrac{1}{9\sqrt{(6a^3)}}\left(4-\dfrac{2}{3}\dfrac{r}{a}\right)\dfrac{2}{3}\dfrac{r}{a}e^{-r/3a}$
3	2	$3d$	R_{32}	$\dfrac{1}{9\sqrt{(30a^3)}}\dfrac{4}{9}\dfrac{r^2}{a^2}e^{-r/3a}$

Table 2.4. *Space Wave Functions of the Hydrogen Atom*

n	l	m	Orbital		Wave Function
1	0	0	$1s$		$\psi_{100} = \dfrac{1}{\sqrt{(\pi a^3)}}\, e^{-r/a}$
2	0	0	$2s$		$\psi_{200} = \dfrac{1}{4\sqrt{(2\pi a^3)}}\left(2 - \dfrac{r}{a}\right) e^{-r/2a}$
2	1	0	$2p$	(p_z)	$\psi_{210} = \dfrac{1}{4\sqrt{(2\pi a^3)}}\dfrac{r}{a}\, e^{-r/2a} \cos\theta$
2	1	± 1	$2p$	(p_x)	$\psi_{211} = \dfrac{1}{4\sqrt{(2\pi a^3)}}\dfrac{r}{a}\, e^{-r/2a} \sin\theta \cos\phi$
				(p_y)	$\psi_{211} = \dfrac{1}{4\sqrt{(2\pi a^3)}}\dfrac{r}{a}\, e^{-r/2a} \sin\theta \sin\phi$
3	0	0	$3s$		$\psi_{300} = \dfrac{1}{81\sqrt{(3\pi a^3)}}\left(27 - \dfrac{18r}{a} + \dfrac{2r^2}{a^2}\right) e^{-r/3a}$
3	1	0	$3p$	(p_z)	$\psi_{310} = \dfrac{\sqrt{2}}{81\sqrt{(\pi a^3)}}\left(6 - \dfrac{r}{a}\right)\dfrac{r}{a}\, e^{-r/3a} \cos\theta$
3	1	± 1	$3p$	(p_x)	$\psi_{311} = \dfrac{\sqrt{2}}{81\sqrt{(\pi a^3)}}\left(6 - \dfrac{r}{a}\right)\dfrac{r}{a}\, e^{-r/3a} \sin\theta \cos\phi$
				(p_y)	$\psi_{311} = \dfrac{\sqrt{2}}{81\sqrt{(\pi a^3)}}\left(6 - \dfrac{r}{a}\right)\dfrac{r}{a}\, e^{-r/3a} \sin\theta \sin\phi$
3	2	0	$3d$	(d_{z^2})	$\psi_{320} = \dfrac{1}{81\sqrt{(6\pi a^3)}}\dfrac{r^2}{a^2}\, e^{-r/3a} (3\cos^2\theta - 1)$
3	2	± 1	$3d$	(d_{xz})	$\psi_{321} = \dfrac{\sqrt{2}}{81\sqrt{(\pi a^3)}}\dfrac{r^2}{a^2}\, e^{-r/3a} \sin\theta \cos\theta \cos\phi$
				(d_{yz})	$\psi_{321} = \dfrac{\sqrt{2}}{81\sqrt{(\pi a^3)}}\dfrac{r^3}{a^2}\, e^{-r/3a} \sin\theta \cos\theta \sin\phi$
3	2	± 2	$3d$	$(d_{x^2-y^2})$	$\psi_{322} = \dfrac{1}{81\sqrt{(2\pi a^3)}}\dfrac{r^2}{a^2}\, e^{-r/3a} \sin^2\theta \cos 2\phi$
				(d_{xy})	$\psi_{322} = \dfrac{1}{81\sqrt{(2\pi a^3)}}\dfrac{r^2}{a^2}\, e^{-r/3a} \sin^2\theta \sin 2\phi$

DIAGRAMMATIC REPRESENTATION OF SPACE WAVE FUNCTIONS

For convenience of presentation, the wave function is divided into two independent parts, (a) the r dependent part or radial function, which depends on the two quantum numbers n and l, and (b) the angular dependent part or polar function, which depends on the quantum numbers l and m.

2*

***r* dependent function.** The *r* dependent part of the wave function may be represented in one of three ways:

(1) the *r* dependent part of the wave function is plotted against different values of the variable *r* for given values of *n* and *l* (Fig. 2.1),

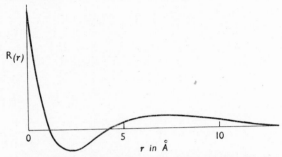

Fig. 2.1. $R(r)$, the *r* dependent part of the wave function ψ, plotted against *r*, for the hydrogen atom in the 3*s* state.

(2) the square of the *r* dependent part of the wave function is plotted for different values of the variable *r* for given values of *n* and *l*; this method gives a one-dimensional contour map of electron density at different distances from the nucleus (Fig. 2.2),

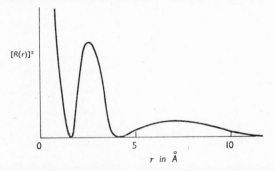

Fig. 2.2. $(R(r))^2$ plotted against *r*, for the hydrogen atom in the 3*s* state.

(3) the radial distribution function is plotted against different values of the variable *r* for given values of *n* and *l* (Fig. 2.3).

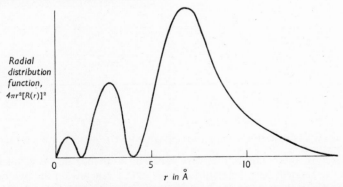

Fig. 2.3. Radial distribution function plotted against *r*, for the hydrogen atom in the 3*s* state.

The **radial distribution function** is the product $4\pi r^2(R(r))^2$. It represents the number of electrons which would be found on a spherical surface of area $4\pi r^2$, and therefore the graph shows the probabilities of finding the electron at different distances from the nucleus. The actual diagram does not present a three-dimensional picture, but it gives information about the three-dimensional distribution of charge density.

Angular dependent function. The polar function may be represented by (*a*) a two-dimensional graph in which the θ dependent part of the wave function only is concerned, or (*b*) by a three-dimensional picture of the θ and ϕ dependent functions simultaneously.

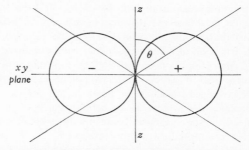

Fig. 2.4.   Graph of $\Theta(\theta)$, the θ dependent part of the wave function ψ, plotted against θ for $l=1$, $m=\pm 1$.

(*a*) There are two methods:

(1) A polar graph is drawn by plotting the θ dependent function against different values of θ for given values of l and m (Fig. 2.4).

(2) A polar graph is drawn by plotting the *square* of the θ dependent part of the wave function against different values of θ for given values of l and m. This type of graph gives a map of the angular distribution of electron density (Fig. 2.5).

The figures enclosed by the polar graphs of methods (1) and (2) are given an arbitrary size, since the angular distribution of electron density does not depend on the distance from the nucleus. It is usual to draw the polar graphs so that their boundaries are contour lines joining points where the charge density is 10% of the whole charge on the electron.

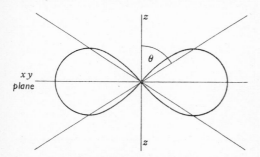

Fig. 2.5.   Graph of $[\Theta(\theta)^2]$ plotted against θ for $l=1$, $m=\pm 1$.

(*b*) The probability of finding the electron, and thus the charge density distribution, is independent of the ϕ dependent part of the wave function, which may be regarded as the superposition of a sine and a cosine wave travelling in a circular path. The square of the function would thus be a constant, and the polar graph of $|\Phi(\phi)|^2$ would be a circle. Therefore graphs of the ϕ dependent part of the wave function are not usually drawn. The pictorial representation of the θ and ϕ dependent parts of the wave function taken together is considered in the discussion on different types of orbitals later in this chapter (p. 49). Pictorial representations of certain of the hydrogen space wave functions are shown in Plate 1.

ORBITALS AND CHARGE CLOUDS

In any discussion on the spatial distribution of electrons in atoms and molecules firm distinction must always be made between the two expressions **orbital** and **charge cloud**. The **orbital** is a mathematical quantity which describes the energy state of an electron in an atom or molecule. The orbital is synonymous with the wave function

ψ, which is r, θ, and ϕ dependent, and can therefore be represented as extended in space. ψ may be $+$ or $-$, and the sign is of importance in considerations of symmetry which govern the overlap of the orbitals of different atoms in chemical combination. The **charge cloud**, which indicates the spatial distribution of electron density in an atom or molecule, is a function of ψ^2. ψ^2 is independent of the sign of ψ. The charge cloud is a convenient concept which makes it possible in some sort to envisage the actual structure of an atom or molecule as interpreted by wave mechanics.

To maintain the distinction between an orbital and a charge cloud the spatial distribution of an orbital ψ will be referred to as its **configuration**; the spatial distribution of a charge cloud ψ^2 will be referred to as its **shape**.†

The orbital concept is of great importance in quantum theory. Some investigators even treat it as of greater importance than the electron concept, and instead of describing an electron as being in, or not in, a certain energy state, they prefer to describe the system as an orbital which is either occupied or not occupied by an electron, the emphasis being on the orbital and not on the electron. This point of view is adopted throughout this book.

The possible orbitals which an electron can occupy are characterised by the quantum numbers n, l, m, and each orbital is described by a wave function. Table 2.5 shows the relation between the quantum numbers and the number of possible orbitals.

Table 2.5. *The Relation between the Quantum Numbers and the Numbers of Orbitals*

Quantum numbers			Number of orbitals for a given value of l	Total number of orbitals for a given value of n
n	l	m	$2l+1$	n^2
1	0	0	1	1
2	0	0	1	4
	1	$-1, 0, +1$	3	
3	0	0	1	9
	1	$-1, 0, +1$	3	
	2	$-2, -1, 0, +1, +2$	5	

All orbitals have the property of energy, and some orbitals have the property of angular momentum. These two properties will now be considered before discussing the special characteristics of the different types of orbitals.

EVALUATION OF THE TOTAL ENERGY E OF AN ORBITAL OF THE HYDROGEN ATOM

Since

$$\lambda = \frac{4\pi^2 m_0 \epsilon^2}{h^2 \alpha} \quad \text{(p. 36)},$$

and

$$\alpha^2 = -\frac{8\pi^2 m_0 E}{h^2},$$

---

† It is sometimes convenient to express the electron density in terms of complex quantities as $\psi\psi^*$ (p. 28).

therefore

$$\lambda^2 = -\frac{2\pi^2 m_0 \epsilon^4}{h^2 E}.$$

But

$$\lambda = n \quad \text{(p. 38)}.$$

Therefore

$$E = -\frac{2\pi^2 m_0 \epsilon^4}{h^2 n^2}. \tag{2.21}$$

This equation gives the eigenvalues for the energy of the system in terms of the quantum number n.

When the hydrogen atom is in the **ground state**, the electron occupies the $1s$ orbital ($n = 1$), and is as near to the nucleus as it can possibly be; it is subject to the maximum electrostatic attraction by the nucleus, and its binding energy is a maximum. In other words, the energy of the electron has its greatest negative value when the atom is in the ground state, since in this state the maximum amount of external energy is required to remove the electron from the atom. In general, the energy increases (becomes less negative) as the electron gets further away from the nucleus, until it becomes zero at infinity where the electron is supposed to be just outside the field of the nucleus. Hence within the atom, the energy of the electron is always negative. Equation (2.21) is identical with the expression formulated by Bohr and Sommerfeld for the energy of the electron with kinetic and potential energy in the Bohr orbit.†

Degeneracy. For the hydrogen atom the quantum number n is the only quantum number which occurs in the expression for the energy. It can be seen from Table 2.5 that for any values of n greater than one, there is more than one wave function which satisfies the ψ equation for a given value of the energy, which means that two or more different states of the atom have the same energy. A system which shows this characteristic is said to be **degenerate**. A system which corresponds to a single solution of the ψ equation is non-degenerate, a system which corresponds to two solutions is doubly degenerate or two-fold degenerate, a system with three solutions is three-fold degenerate, and so on. It is seen from Table 2.5 that for the hydrogen atom, any state with principal quantum number n is n^2 degenerate. (This applies to the hydrogen atom only and is not so for the atoms of other elements.)

It must be remembered that the various configurations corresponding to different values of l and m, are the resultant forms of vibration of the electron, due to the subjection of the de Broglie wave to an electric field with definite boundary conditions. It is most undesirable to picture the orbitals with different values of l as energy "levels" in the atom, although this term has been and still is used in spectroscopy. The principal quantum number n is the only quantum number to which the term "level" might be applied without objection, since a large value of n is equivalent to a large value of r, the distance between the nucleus and the region of greatest probability of finding the electron. A transition of the electron from one orbital of energy E_1 to another orbital of energy E_2 must be regarded as a transition from one form of vibration to another.

ANGULAR MOMENTUM

The theory of orbital and spin angular momentum is based largely on the study of spectra, especially the spectra of atoms subjected to an external magnetic field. In order to explain the observations recorded in these studies, it has been found necessary

---

† The reader should note the difference between equation (2.21) for the orbital energy of the hydrogen atom, and equation (1.25), p. 22, for the energy of the "particle in a ring". The difference arises because the electron in the atom has both kinetic and potential energy, whereas the particle in a ring has kinetic energy only.

to endow the orbital with angular momentum, and the electron with spin. It is possible to derive from the Schrödinger equation an expression for the orbital angular momentum which is satisfactory for the interpretation of spectra. The following simplified semi-classical calculation illustrates its derivation. The same expression may be obtained by means of a rigid wave mechanical proof which may be found in various textbooks on quantum mechanics. In order to calculate the moment of inertia of the electron it is here assumed to be a particle of mass m_0 at a constant distance from the nucleus. The same expression for the angular momentum is obtained by two alternative methods: (1) by using a θ dependent equation assuming r to be a constant, (2) by using the r dependent part of the equation for the hydrogen atom.

(1) The Schrödinger equation is expressed in polar co-ordinates:

$$\frac{1}{r^2}\frac{\partial}{\partial r}\left(r^2\frac{\partial\psi}{\partial r}\right)+\frac{1}{r^2}\left[\frac{1}{\sin\theta}\frac{\partial}{\partial\theta}\left(\sin\theta\frac{\partial\psi}{\partial\theta}\right)+\frac{1}{\sin^2\theta}\frac{\partial^2\psi}{\partial\phi^2}\right]+\frac{8\pi^2 m_0}{h^2}\left(E+\frac{\epsilon^2}{r}\right)\psi=0.$$

Let $r=a$ (constant); then the first term of the equation vanishes.
Let

$$\psi=\Theta(\theta)\Phi(\phi) \qquad \text{(see Appendix)}$$

Dividing the equation by the product $\Theta\Phi$ and multiplying by $a^2\sin^2\theta$

$$\frac{1}{\Theta}\sin\theta\frac{d}{d\theta}\left(\sin\theta\frac{d\Theta}{d\theta}\right)+\frac{1}{\Phi}\frac{d^2\Phi}{d\phi^2}+\frac{a^2\sin^2\theta\,8\pi^2 m_0}{h^2}\left(E+\frac{\epsilon^2}{a}\right)=0.$$

Putting the terms in ϕ equal to a constant $-m^2$, and the terms in θ equal to a constant $+m^2$ (the solution for ϕ is obtained as on p. 33) the equation for the terms in θ becomes:

$$\frac{\sin\theta}{\Theta}\frac{d}{d\theta}\left(\sin\theta\frac{d\Theta}{d\theta}\right)+\frac{a^2\sin^2\theta\,8\pi^2 m_0}{h^2}\left(E+\frac{\epsilon^2}{a}\right)=m^2.$$

Multiplying by Θ and dividing by $\sin^2\theta$:

$$\frac{1}{\sin\theta}\frac{d}{d\theta}\left(\sin\theta\frac{d\Theta}{d\theta}\right)-\frac{m^2\Theta}{\sin^2\theta}+\frac{8\pi^2 m_0 a^2}{h^2}\left(E+\frac{\epsilon^2}{a}\right)\Theta=0. \qquad (2.22)$$

This equation is in the form of an associated Legendre function, and is exactly similar in form to the θ dependent equation derived for the hydrogen atom (p. 33) except that the term $\dfrac{8\pi^2 m_0 a^2}{h^2}\left(E+\dfrac{\epsilon^2}{a}\right)$ takes the place of β. We may therefore put

$$\frac{8\pi^2 m_0 a^2}{h^2}\left(E+\frac{\epsilon^2}{a}\right)=l(l+1),$$

where l has the possible integral values, 0, 1, 2, 3, ...

Since the total energy = kinetic energy of rotation (K) + potential energy,

$$E=K-\frac{e^2}{a}.$$

Assuming that $K=\frac{1}{2}I\omega^2$, where I is the moment of inertia of the electron and ω its angular velocity $(I=m_0 a^2)$,

$$\frac{8\pi^2 m_0 a^2}{h^2}\tfrac{1}{2}I\omega^2=l(l+1).$$

Therefore

$$(I\omega)^2=\frac{l(l+1)h^2}{4\pi^2 m_0 a^2}\,m_0 a^2.$$

and the orbital angular momentum is given by

$$I\omega=\frac{h}{2\pi}\sqrt{(l(l+1))}. \qquad (2.23)$$

(2) A similar result may be obtained by considering the angular momentum of a particle moving in three dimensions in a radial field.

Take the r dependent equation for the hydrogen atom, separated as on page 33.

$$\frac{1}{r^2}\frac{d}{dr}\left(r^2\frac{dR}{dr}\right)+\frac{8\pi^2 m_0}{h^2}\left[E+\frac{\epsilon^2}{r}\right]R = \frac{\beta R}{r^2}.$$

Since $\beta = l(l+1)$ (p. 36),

$$\frac{1}{r^2}\frac{d}{dr}\left(r^2\frac{dR}{dr}\right)+\frac{8\pi^2 m_0}{h^2}\left[E+\frac{\epsilon^2}{r}-\frac{l(l+1)h^2}{8\pi^2 m_0 r^2}\right]R = 0.$$

Let $U(r)=rR(r)$, then

$$\frac{d^2 U}{dr^2}+\frac{8\pi^2 m_0}{h^2}\left[E+\frac{\epsilon^2}{r}-\frac{l(l+1)h^2}{8\pi^2 m_0 r^2}\right]U = 0. \tag{2.24}$$

This is very similar to the Schrödinger equation for one dimension, except for the term

$$l(l+1)\frac{h^2}{4\pi^2}\frac{1}{2m_0 r^2}.$$

According to classical theory the energy of a particle with motion in three dimensions exceeds that of a particle with motion in one dimension by an amount $\frac{1}{2}I\omega^2$, which is an expression for the kinetic energy of rotation. Therefore if it be assumed that the extra term in equation (2.24) represents the rotational energy,

$$\frac{1}{2}I\omega^2 = l(l+1)\frac{h^2}{4\pi^2}\frac{1}{2m_0 r^2}.$$

Since $I=m_0 r^2$, therefore

$$(I\omega)^2 = l(l+1)\frac{h^2}{4\pi^2},$$

and

$$I\omega = \frac{h}{2\pi}\sqrt{(l(l+1))},$$

which is the same expression as that derived from the θ equation. The orbital angular momentum is quantised in units of $h/2\pi$ and assumes the value $(h/2\pi)\sqrt{(l(l+1))}$ where $l=0, 1, 2, 3, \ldots$.

TYPES OF ORBITALS

The possible orbitals are characterised by the values of the quantum numbers n, l, m, as follows:

(1) The quantum number l determines the angular momentum of the orbital and the configuration of the orbital.

(2) The principal quantum number n determines the energy and overall size of the orbital, and the number of nodes in the orbital, which is equal to $n-1$. (For atoms other than hydrogen the energy of the orbital is slightly influenced by the value of l.)

(3) The quantum number m determines the orientation of the orbital relative to the direction of an external magnetic field, and it also indicates the component of angular momentum about an axis parallel to the direction of an external magnetic field.

The configuration of the orbital is further modified by the external surroundings of the atom. The following cases must be distinguished:

The free atom. The charge cloud of a free atom must be assumed to have spherical symmetry in the absence of an external electric or magnetic field. Each occupied orbital contains the whole charge of an electron, and if there is no external field to orientate the orbital there is equal probability of finding the electron at any point on a spherical surface whose centre is the nucleus of the atom.

The atom in an external magnetic field. In an external magnetic field, the configuration of a particular orbital depends on the values of the quantum numbers l and m. The behaviour of an orbital in a weak magnetic field is taken to be the distinguishing feature of different types of orbitals.

The atom in an external electric field. The configuration of a particular orbital is affected by an electric field, but although this has significance in spectra, it is not taken into consideration for the purpose of classification of orbitals, and so will not be further considered here.

The atom in chemical combination. In chemical combination the atomic orbitals of one atom overlap with the atomic orbitals of other atoms. The overlapping is a mathematical concept, and it depends not only on the configurations of the orbitals concerned, but also on their symmetry. In order to visualise how overlapping takes place it is convenient to picture a static non-rotating model of the orbital.

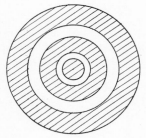

Fig. 2.6. Cross section through the centre of the spherically symmetrical charge cloud of the 3s orbital of the hydrogen atom. The shading indicates charge cloud with 10% contours as boundaries; the two unshaded rings are sections of the nodal spherical shells.

The electron density in an orbital is expressed by the shape of the corresponding charge cloud. The shape of a charge cloud is related to the configuration of the orbital (since, for example, when $\psi=0$, then $\psi^2=0$), but it is not coincident with it. The three types of orbitals of the most general interest in chemistry are the s, p, and d orbitals. The configurations of these orbitals and the shapes of the charge clouds are discussed in the following sections.

s orbitals. The s orbital is characterised by $l=0$. All s orbitals are spherically symmetrical under all circumstances. If $n=1$ there is no nodal surface; if $n=2$ there is one nodal surface which has the form of a spherical shell; if $n=3$ there are two concentric nodal shells, and so on (Fig. 2.6). Since $l=0$, there is no preferred direction of rotation of charge; thus s orbitals have no resultant angular momentum, and an s orbital has spherical symmetry. It is unaltered when the atom is in a magnetic field.

p orbitals. The p orbital is characterised by $l=1$. The static two-dimensional concept of the p orbital is derived from the polar diagrams. If the atom is supposed to lie in a weak magnetic field, for each value of the principal quantum number n (except $n=1$), the static configuration presents three possible orbitals denoted by the symbols p_x, p_y, p_z, corresponding to $m=\pm1$, 0. Each of these orbitals is represented (Fig. 2.4) as two contiguous circles; the equivalent p charge cloud is dumb-bell shaped (Fig. 2.5). It should be noted that there is a change in sign of the θ dependent wave function at a critical value of θ. This change is marked in Fig. 2.4 as a change from $+$ to $-$. The figure representing the charge cloud involves the square of the wave function and is positive throughout. It is the usual practice to take the z axis as the direction of the magnetic field; thus the p_z orbital, corresponding to $m=0$, lies with its axis in the direction of the field, and the p_x and p_y orbitals, corresponding to $m=\pm1$, have their axes lying along the x and y axes respectively.

For a three-dimensional representation, the ϕ dependent part of the wave function must be considered. Since

$$|\Phi|^2 = \Phi\Phi^*$$
$$= Ae^{im\phi} \times Ae^{-im\phi}$$
$$= A^2,$$

$|\Phi|^2$ is independent of ϕ, and the probability of finding the electron is the same for any value of ϕ.

It is customary to consider the Θ and Φ functions together, and to represent the charge clouds by imparting a solid three-dimensional look to the lobes depicted in Fig. 2.5. A better three-dimensional representation is that of Fig. 2.7(b), where the probability function (charge distribution) is shown to be constant for any value of ϕ. In this method of representation, the p_x and p_y charge clouds are superposed. A cross-section through this figure in the xz or yz plane gives the shape of the charge cloud depicted two-dimensionally in Fig. 2.5.

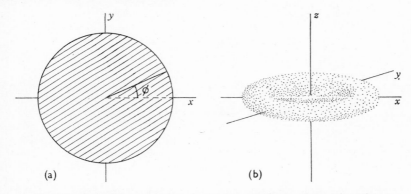

(a)   (b)

Fig. 2.7. Pictorial representation of a three-dimensional p_x and p_y charge cloud ($m = \pm 1$), showing that the charge distribution is independent of ϕ: (a) shows the circular section of the charge cloud viewed along the z axis; (b) shows the charge cloud concentrated in and near the xy plane.

d orbitals. The d orbital is characterised by $l = 2$; for each value of the principal quantum number n there are five d orbitals. In the absence of a magnetic field each orbital has four equal lobes and symmetry about four axes in one plane (Fig. 2.8(a)). The orbitals are distinguished according to their behaviour when the atom lies in a weak magnetic field, and are denoted by the symbols d_{z^2}, d_{xz}, d_{yz}, d_{xy}, $d_{x^2-y^2}$, corresponding to $m = 0$, ± 1, ± 2. Fig. 2.8(b) shows the usual representation of the charge clouds of the d orbitals when the atom is supposed to lie in a weak magnetic field. Such a field does not affect the shape of four of the d orbitals, but it does have a marked effect on the d orbital which lies with two lobes along the direction of the field. The part of the orbital lying along the field is enlarged, and the part transverse to the field is much contracted; in consequence, this orbital is known as the d_{z^2} orbital.

The $d_{x^2-y^2}$ orbital lies with its lobes along the cartesian axes x and y. The d_{xy} orbital lies in the same plane with its lobes along the diagonals between these axes; a corresponding position is occupied by the d_{xz} orbital in the xz plane, and by the d_{yz} orbital in the yz plane. The three orbitals d_{xy}, d_{yz}, and d_{xz} are mutually independent and are orthogonal.

It might be expected that there would be six d orbitals, including a $d_{z^2-x^2}$ orbital and a $d_{y^2-z^2}$ orbital, but there are only three independent cartesian axes, and it is not possible to form three mutually orthogonal wave functions whose lobes lie along these axes. Such wave functions are only orthogonal in pairs, and therefore it is concluded that there are only two independent wave functions of the type $d_{x^2-y^2}$, and thus only five independent d orbitals in all. In the presence of the weak magnetic field the wave

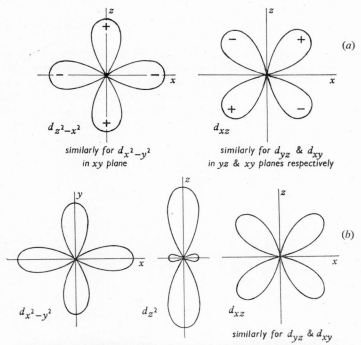

Fig. 2.8. (a) Static two-dimensional representation of d orbitals in the absence of a magnetic field.
(b) Static two-dimensional representation of d charge clouds in a magnetic field.

functions of the $d_{z^2-x^2}$ and the $d_{y^2-z^2}$ orbitals are identical, and either orbital becomes the d_{z^2} orbital. The forms of the wave functions also show that the sum of the wave functions of the three orbitals of the $d_{x^2-y^2}$ type is identically zero. The mutual independence of the d_{z^2} and $d_{x^2-y^2}$ functions may be visualised by considering the shapes of the charge clouds in the weak magnetic field (Fig. 2.8(b)). The large lobes of the d_{z^2}

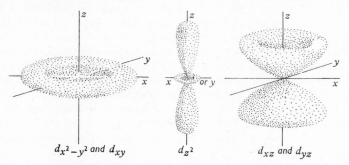

Fig. 2.9. Three-dimensional representation of d charge clouds in a magnetic field. (Precession is not shown.)

charge cloud are obviously independent of the lobes of the $d_{x^2-y^2}$ charge cloud, which is so distributed that there is an effective "hole" in its centre. This hole is just filled by the "collar" of the d_{z^2} charge cloud.

With d charge clouds as with the p charge clouds, the probability function is independent of the value of the angle ϕ, therefore a better representation of the d charge clouds is obtained by rotating the figures of the static charge clouds with the result shown in Fig. 2.9.

There are also orbitals and equivalent charge clouds corresponding to higher values of l, but these are of increasing complexity and energy and have not as much interest from the chemical point of view as the p and d orbitals and their charge clouds.

SPACE QUANTISATION

The whole development of the argument in this book is based on the concept of the actual rotation of charge. It has generally been assumed in recent years that this concept has been outmoded, since research in theoretical physics is now concentrated on the production of a unified field theory which shall be expressed solely in mathematical terms, and which shall be independent of other human concepts. It has not, however, been possible so far to produce a satisfactory mathematical theory of the universe, and even the partial success achieved has brought to light many difficulties Most theoretical chemistry is based on spectroscopic evidence, and in view of the fact that *all* observations of spectroscopists can be accounted for in terms of rotating charge, this concept may be taken as a satisfactory basis for an elementary study of the physics which forms the background to chemistry. It must, however, be emphasised that the explanation of many phenomena of great importance, such as the interaction of radiation and matter, is not within the scope of such a simple presentation.

In the days when the accepted model of atomic structure was that due to the Bohr theory, it seemed natural that angular momentum should be a property of an electron in an orbit. At first sight it is not easy to attach such a property to an electron occupying a three-dimensional wave-mechanical orbital. The picture is greatly simplified if the attention is concentrated on the orbital and not on the electron (p. 44). It should not be supposed that the electron has angular momentum in a stationary orbital, but that angular momentum is a property of the orbital, and that the electron acquires the property of angular momentum by virtue of its occupation of the orbital. Fig. 2.7(b) shows pictorially that the probability of finding the electron in the occupied p orbital is the same for all values of ϕ. This picture could be interpreted in one of two ways. Either it could represent a static charge cloud in the shape of a ring, or it could represent the track of a rotating charge cloud of shape shown in Fig. 2.5, p. 43. Either interpretation fulfills the condition that the charge density is independent of ϕ. Since an electron in an occupied orbital other than the s orbital has resultant angular momentum, and since the study of atomic spectra has led to the conclusion that a rotation of charge actually does take place, it is reasonable to conclude that the orbital is rotating, and that the electron has angular momentum by virtue of its occupation of the orbital.†

It is sometimes convenient to represent the rotation of charge as two opposite progressive waves $e^{im\phi}$ and $e^{-im\phi}$. This is equivalent to taking the p_x and p_y orbitals together, since

$$(\psi_{p_x})^2 + (\psi_{p_y})^2 = (\psi_{p_x} + i\psi_{p_y})(\psi_{p_x} - i\psi_{p_y})$$
$$= e^{im\phi} \times e^{-im\phi} \times F(\theta) \times F'(r),$$

† Compare J. L. Synge, *Geometrical Mechanics and de Broglie Waves* (Cambridge University Press), 1954, pp. 119, 12.

where $F(\theta)$ and $F'(r)$ are θ and r dependent factors. For this reason the rotating orbitals are often designated p_{+1} and p_{-1}. The kinematical concept of the rotating p_x and p_y orbitals is equivalent to this representation, and is retained throughout this book in order to present a vivid picture to the reader.

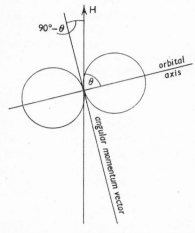

Fig. 2.10. *p* orbital in a magnetic field.

In the absence of an external magnetic field, the axis of rotation of an orbital is not orientated in any particular direction in space, and it must therefore be found as often in one direction as in another. It is thus not possible to detect the rotation unless some external condition is imposed which defines the orientation of the axis. The application to the atom of an external magnetic field imposes just such a restriction. The spherically symmetrical occupied *s* orbital has no resultant angular momentum and therefore no resultant magnetic moment, but the rotation of an orbital with directional properties, such as a *p* or a *d* orbital, gives it an orbital magnetic moment. This causes a definite orientation of the orbital with regard to the direction of the external field; it will now be shown that only certain orientations are possible.

Component of angular momentum in the direction of the field. Consider the case of a *p* orbital rotating in a magnetic field *H* (Fig. 2.10). If the axis of the orbital makes an angle θ with the direction of *H*, the angular momentum vector (axis of rotation) makes an angle $90° - \theta$ with the direction of *H*.

By equation (2.22), p. 46,

$$\frac{1}{\sin\theta}\frac{d}{d\theta}\left(\sin\theta\frac{d\Theta}{d\theta}\right) - \frac{m^2\Theta}{\sin^2\theta} + \frac{8\pi^2 m_0 a^2}{h^2}\left[E + \frac{\epsilon^2}{a}\right]\Theta = 0.$$

If θ is constant, the first term vanishes, and

$$\frac{8\pi^2 m_0 a^2}{h^2}\left(E + \frac{\epsilon^2}{a}\right)\Theta = \frac{m^2\Theta}{\sin^2\theta}.$$

But the term in brackets represents the kinetic energy, i.e. total energy − potentia energy.

If this kinetic energy is all energy of rotation, $\frac{1}{2}I\omega^2$, then

$$\frac{8\pi^2 m_0 a^2}{h^2}\tfrac{1}{2}I\omega^2 = \frac{m^2}{\sin^2\theta}.$$

Putting $I = m_0 a^2$,

$$\frac{4\pi^2}{h^2}(I\omega)^2 = \frac{m^2}{\sin^2\theta},$$

and

$$I\omega\cos(90° - \theta) = \frac{mh}{2\pi}. \tag{2.25}$$

m is the magnetic quantum number. It can take the integral values $-l, -l+1, \ldots, -1$ $0, +1, \cdots, +(l-1), +l$ (p. 38).

Hence the axis of orbital angular momentum can take up only those positions in which the component of orbital angular momentum in the direction of the field ($I\omega\cos(90° - \theta)$) is quantised. There is thus a limited number of definite positions, with different orientations to the direction of the field, in which the orbital can be found; the orbital is said to be **space quantised**.

Space quantisation of *p* orbitals in the presence of a weak magnetic field. In the case of the *p* orbitals, $l = 1$ and *m* can take the values $0, \pm 1$. Let the direction of the magnetic field be the *z* axis.

Before the field is applied, any orbital motion is free to take place about any axis through the nucleus. When the field is applied, the orbital motion may be resolved into two parts: (a) orbital angular motion about an axis at right angles to the field; and (b) orbital angular motion about an axis parallel to the field. These orbital motions may be represented as angular momentum vectors, one at right angles, the other parallel to the field. Alternatively, the system may be regarded as that of one resultant angular momentum vector **L** which makes an angle θ with the direction of the field.

Since for one electron (equation 2.23)

$$\mathbf{L} = \sqrt{(l(l+1))}\frac{h}{2\pi}$$

and the component of angular momentum in the direction of the field is $mh/2\pi$, therefore

$$\cos\theta = \frac{m}{\sqrt{(l(l+1))}}. \text{(Fig. 2.11.)}$$

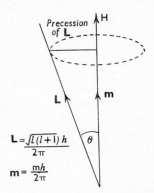

Fig. 2.11. Space quantisation of angular momentum in the presence of a weak magnetic field.

A resultant circulation of charge round the direction of **L** produces a resultant magnetic moment. This magnetic moment is subject to a couple due to the applied magnetic field and hence **L** precesses about the direction of the field. (Precession is discussed in detail in Chapter 3, p. 87.)

The resultant angular momentum **L** has a sharp value since it may be determined accurately from spectra, and therefore, by the uncertainty principle, the position of **L** cannot be sharp. The precession of **L** is a physical interpretation of this uncertainty; there is evidence from spectra that it really does take place, and although the angular velocity and frequency of precession can be determined (p. 102), there is no means of telling the exact position of **L** at any moment; all that is known is that it is somewhere on the cone of revolution and that it makes an angle θ with the direction of the field.

The magnitude of **L** can be expressed in terms of the three components of angular momentum which lie along the three axes *x*, *y*, *z*, respectively (Fig. 2.12).

$$\mathbf{L}^2 = \mathbf{L}_x^2 + \mathbf{L}_y^2 + \mathbf{L}_z^2$$
$$= \mathbf{L}_x^2 + \mathbf{L}_y^2 + \left(\frac{mh}{2\pi}\right)^2. \tag{2.26}$$

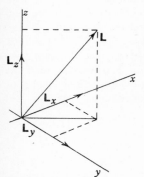

Fig. 2.12. Compounding of angular momenta.

$\mathbf{L}_z$ *component.* This component is sharp and has the value $mh/2\pi$. The values of m, ± 1, correspond to the rotation of the p_x and p_y orbitals in opposite directions. These orbitals have opposite magnetic polarity, a property which is confirmed by a study of the normal Zeeman effect (p. 99), which shows that the precession of the two orbitals is in opposite directions. The wave functions of the p_x and p_y orbitals need not be orthogonal, or rather cannot be proved to be orthogonal, but they should be regarded as two independent wave trains each containing a wave packet, which pass through each other and emerge unchanged.

L_x *and* L_y *components.* The components L_x and L_y correspond to the rotation of the p_z orbital. This rotation can be in any plane which contains the axis of the magnetic field. There is no preferred direction for the axis of rotation as long as it is always at right angles to the direction of the field. This is demonstrated by equation (2.26) which shows that the sum of the squares of the two components is constant, thus defining their resultant as a constant angular momentum, but no further information is provided except that the resultant vector of the p_z orbital angular momentum is always somewhere in the xy plane and has no component along the z axis ($m=0$). It can be shown that L_x and L_y cannot be measured separately and that their mean value is zero†.

Conservation of angular momentum. The p orbitals can have any orientation in the absence of a magnetic field, and thus the mean value of the angular momentum must be zero before the field is applied. When the field is applied, the mean value of L_x and L_y is zero, and the mean value of L_z is also zero, ($+mh-mh$). Thus the principle of the conservation of angular momentum is maintained.

Space quantisation may also be interpreted in terms of the probability charge distribution of the electron. It is clear that when $m=\pm l$, the component of angular momentum along the z axis, $mh/2\pi$, is nearly equal to the total angular momentum, particularly for large values of l. It would therefore be expected that the probability of finding the electron, $\psi\psi^*$, would be large in the xy plane, that is in the p_x and p_y orbitals. Analogous considerations apply to the d orbitals.

Space quantisation of d orbitals in the presence of a weak magnetic field. For the d orbitals, $l=2$ and $m=0$, ± 1, ± 2. The two orbitals d_{xy} and $d_{x^2-y^2}$ correspond to $m=\pm 2$. They rotate in opposite directions and, owing to the field, their angular momentum vectors precess in opposite directions about the z axis, the charge density being concentrated near the xy plane. The d_{xz} and d_{yz} orbitals correspond to $m=\pm 1$ and rotate in opposite directions. In the absence of the field the figure traced out would consist of two cones one on top of the other with their apices touching (Fig. 2.9); in the presence of the field the two angular momentum vectors precess in opposite directions round the z axis. The d_{z^2} orbital has no preferred direction of rotation, except that any rotation must always be about an axis at right angles to the z axis; therefore, on an average, the d_{z^2} orbital may be said to have effective spherical symmetry. As with the p orbitals, the resultant angular momentum vector L precesses round the direction of the field. The value of L may be derived from considerations analogous to those leading to equation (2.26) but they will not be developed here.

ELECTRON SPIN

One of the most important aspects of a theory of atomic structure is the amount of freedom which it allots to nature; a test of the acceptability of a theory is whether nature uses all the freedom which the theory provides. For instance, according to the classical theory of radiation, atoms of a given element could be of any size, and a rotating electron, while radiating, would take a spiral course into the nucleus. The fact that there was no evidence that this happened, or of the existence of different sizes of atoms of the same substance, was a clear pointer to the inadequacy of the

† This picture is consistent with Dirac's theory, according to which one of the p orbitals has effective spherical symmetry in a weak magnetic field.

theory. Nature's rule appears to be *what can happen will happen*. This postulate has been used frequently in this chapter in order to demonstrate the development of the quantum theory by a quasi-mathematical approach, and it has been shown that the principle serves as a guide to conclusions which in the first place were reached by mathematical reasoning alone.

One possible form of motion of the electron has not been discussed so far; it could have a rotation about its own axis, and such a motion has been postulated to explain certain experimental observations. Evidence, originally derived from the study of the spectra of atoms which have only one electron in the valency shell (such as the atoms of the alkali metals, silver, and hydrogen) shows that the number of possible energy states is twice as great as those predicted on the theory so far developed in this chapter. Uhlenbeck and Goudsmit showed that this doubling of the number of states would be expected if the electron were spinning about its own axis, and therefore had not only a magnetic moment due to orbital angular momentum, but angular momentum, and thus magnetic moment, due to spin as well.

Table 2.5 (p. 44) shows that for given n and l values there are $(2l+1)$ possible wave functions, corresponding to different values of m; in other words, there are $(2l+1)$ possible values of the component orbital angular momentum in the direction of the z axis for a given value of l. If s is the spin quantum number† it might be expected by analogy that there will be $(2s+1)$ possible energy states due to spin, as the result of different orientations of the spin angular momentum with regard to the orbital angular momentum. Since the splitting of the energy states into two occurs irrespective of the value of l (except for $l=0$), it can be concluded that s has a constant value.

Therefore if

$$2s+1 = 2$$
$$s = \tfrac{1}{2}. \tag{2.27}$$

This value for the spin quantum number is in accord with spectroscopic evidence (see Chapter 3 on Atomic Spectra).

MODEL OF SPINNING ELECTRON

Among theoretical physicists it is generally accepted that the mathematical quantity known as electron spin does not have its counterpart in the real rotation of charge.‡ Nevertheless, both theoretical and experimental physicists still find it convenient to describe the phenomena ascribed to spin in terms of the magnetic moment which would result from a rotating charge (p. 93). The reason for this state of affairs may be traced to the original introduction of spin into the mathematical theory by Dirac; this took place after the concept of spin as rotating charge had been used in spectroscopy by Uhlenbeck and Goudsmit to explain multiplicity (above). Dirac introduced into the Schrödinger equation an extra energy term, m_0c^2, representing the energy equivalent of the rest mass of the electron (p. 12). As a consequence of this introduction, by the formulation of the equation in a relativistically invariant form, the spin quantum number appeared in the solution.

It is possible to devise a simple and useful model of the spinning electron, based on

---

† The reader must be prepared to distinguish according to the context between *s* meaning the spin quantum number, and *s* meaning the electron state.

‡ It is the aim of mathematical physicists to formulate equations in such a manner that the universe may be described by them without any reference to the structure of matter. With this purpose in view the electron is represented as a point charge. So far this treatment has been partially successful but it has led to considerable mathematical difficulties which have not yet been overcome.

principles which are consonant with Dirac's theory and yet are formulated in terms of rotating charge. A satisfactory model must fulfil certain conditions:

(a) It must have the correct gyromagnetic ratio (p. 97).
(b) It must show the necessary invariant characteristics; in other words, it must satisfy the principles of relativity.
(c) It must account for the anomalous magnetic moment of the electron (p. 94).
(d) It must pass the most stringent of spectroscopic tests, that of accounting for the Lamb Retherford shift (p. 95).

An outline of the model is given below; it will be shown in the appropriate places in the text that it fulfils all the conditions tabulated above, and that it is useful for deducing certain properties of the electron and its electromagnetic field.

Since the electron with orbital momentum may be viewed either as a charged particle travelling round an orbit or as a stationary wave pattern, the length of a circular track must be nh/m_0v (p. 16) where m_0 is the mass of the electron and v its velocity. Two cases may be distinguished: (a) the non-relativistic case when v is not great enough to alter the mass appreciably; this case is exemplified by the orbital motion of the electron already discussed; (b) the relativistic case, where the mass observed experimentally is determined by a high value of v. It will be shown that in case (b) the length of the orbit is a Compton wave length (p. 11). This particular orbital motion is here used as a model to explain what is generally described as "spin"†. There is much experimental evidence to suggest that motions (a) and (b) take place simultaneously in the atom.

For orbital motion in a circle of radius r the quantisation of angular momentum leads to the relation,

$$2\pi r = \frac{nh}{m_0 v}.$$

The angular velocity ω is given by‡

$$\omega = \frac{nh}{2\pi m_0 r^2}.$$

For relativistic motion m_0 includes electromagnetic mass due to spin. If ω_s is the a gular velocity of spin,

$$\omega_s = \frac{nh\sqrt{(1-v^2/c^2)}}{2\pi m' r^2},$$

where m' is the mass of the electron without spin.

Therefore,

$$\omega_s^2 = \frac{n^2h^2}{4\pi^2 m'^2 r^4}\left(1 - \frac{r^2\omega_s^2}{c^2}\right)$$

$$\omega_s^2\left(1 + \frac{n^2h^2}{4\pi^2 m'^2 r^2 c^2}\right) = \frac{n^2h^2}{4\pi^2 m'^2 r^4}.$$

If r is taken to be the classical radius of the electron § and if the experimental

---

† The model here used is not that of a charge spinning about its own axis. Such a model would not be consonant with the principles of relativity.

‡ ω cannot be observed, but theoretical physics makes use of unobservables to facilitate calculation.

§ The "classical radius" of the electron, r, is the value obtained by equating the whole of the mass energy m_0c^2 to the potential energy ϵ^2/r due to its own charge.

value of m_0 is substituted for m', the second term in the bracket is of the order of 10^4.† However, m' must be less than m_0; therefore, to a close approximation,

$$\frac{\omega_s^2}{c^2} = \frac{1}{r^2} \quad \text{and} \quad v = \pm c.$$

Since

$$m_0 = \frac{m'}{\sqrt{(1 - v^2/c^2)}}$$

and m_0 is not zero, it must be concluded that $m' = 0$ and that the rest mass of the electron is electromagnetic in origin.‡

Energy of spin. It is generally accepted that an electron, located in space, may be represented by a wave packet, or stationary wave system. The simplest form is conventionally described as a half wave (single loop) which changes rapidly from A to B, B to A and so on (Fig. 2.13). In other words the system may be represented as a "particle in a box" (p. 21). The kinetic energy of the "particle" is given by equation (1.24),

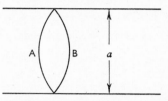

Fig. 2.13. Simple wave packet equivalent to particle in a box.

$$E = \frac{n^2 h^2}{8 m_0 a^2},$$

where n is the number of loops, a is the length of the box, and m_0 is the mass of the particle. This expression may be used for determining the energy of spin.

When $n = 1$,

$$a = \frac{\lambda}{2}.$$

Since the velocity of electron spin may be taken to be c, the wave representing the spin has a Compton wave length λ_e (p. 11), where

$$\lambda_e = \frac{h}{m_0 c}. \qquad \text{(see note §)}$$

Therefore for electron spin,

$$E = \frac{4 h^2}{8 m_0 \lambda_e^2}$$

$$= \tfrac{1}{2} m_0 c^2.$$

Thus the spin energy of the electron accounts for half its rest mass.

Radius of spin. Since the path traced out by the spin consists of one Compton wave length, the radius of spin, r, is given by the expression

$$r = \frac{h}{2\pi m_0 c}$$

$$= 3 \cdot 86 \times 10^{-11} \text{ cm.}$$

According to the uncertainty principle (p. 14) the product *uncertainty of position* × *uncertainty of momentum* is generally of the order h, with minimum value

† Even though the value of r used in the approximation is 100 times too small the approximation is well justified.

‡ Objections to this conclusion are discussed on page 58.

§ It should be noted that m_0 is a mass which already includes a relativistic correction.

$h/4\pi$. Since the circumference of spin is a measure of the uncertainty of position of the charged particle, then

$$\text{uncertainty of momentum} = h/2\pi r$$

$$= m_0 c.$$

Hence the spin momentum cannot be measured.

Alternatively, if it is assumed that the momentum is sharp and has the value $m_0 c$, the energy must be associated with a monochromatic wave train. The model thus illustrates the dual nature of the electron as particle and wave; it is not possible however, by this simple method, to throw any light on the fundamental nature of the electron.

Angular momentum of spin. For relativistic motion

$$\text{angular momentum} = (\text{energy}/c) \times r$$

$$= \frac{1}{2} \frac{m_0 c^2}{c} \frac{h}{2\pi m_0 c}$$

$$= \frac{h}{4\pi}.$$

Two-particle model of the electron. It is customary to apply the term "rest mass" to the mass of the electron without linear velocity.† If it refers to the mass of the electron without linear velocity and without spin, then according to the principles outlined above the rest mass is zero. Early theories of the spinning electron assumed that its mass was all electromagnetic in origin. This hypothesis was later rejected on relativistic grounds; it can be shown that the field created by a spinning charge has different transformation characteristics from those of the charge taken by itself. Nevertheless, if the field created by the spinning charge is represented as a particle spinning in the opposite sense, the two particles, taken together, form a single unit of zero spin. Such a two-particle unit has the correct transformation characteristics to satisfy the necessary invariant condition.

The existence of zero point energy in the electromagnetic field suggests that the unitary wave packet might be visualised classically as two loops side by side, or equally well by two identical charged particles with spin in opposite directions, each spin being orientated along the field of the other, with angular momentum $+h/4\pi$ and $-h/4\pi$. It is here necessary to make the somewhat bold assumption that the particle which represents the field of the electron is spinning backwards in time. This implies that it has negative velocity of spin and negative spin momentum. This assumption is not in contradiction to the quantum theory, which uses time-reversed angular momentum operators. Dirac has shown that negative energy states are to be expected on the theory of relativity according to which,

$$\frac{E}{c} = \pm \sqrt{(\text{momentum}^2)}.$$

Hence there are two solutions of the spin kinetic energy given by the expression

$$E = \pm \tfrac{1}{2} m_0 c^2.$$

The positive solution represents the kinetic energy of spin of the electron, the negative solution represents the kinetic energy of spin of the particle representing the field of the electron. Fig. 2.14 is a simple illustration of how two rotating charged particles

† See Katayama and Taketani, "On the origin of Electron mass", *Prog. Theoret. Phys.*, **21**, No. 6, 1959, 818.

with opposite angular momenta could provide a continuous oscillation of charge and thus account for the zero point energy of the field, even though the total angular momentum of the system is zero. It should be noted that this diagram is not intended to be a picture of the spinning electron. Although it is possible to use simple concepts of rotating charge as a method of description, and to a certain extent as a basis of calculation, it must be remembered that there is no reason to suppose that our macro-scopic concepts are adequate to describe what takes place within regions whose dimensions are of the order of a Compton wave length. The most that can be assumed is that the condition of maximum stability of the system is that of maximum interaction between the particles.

Static self-energy of the electron. The static self-energy of the electron is its potential energy due to its own charge; this is given by the expression ϵ^2/r_0, where r_0 measures the extension of the charge which is assumed to be spherical. The energy represented by this term cannot be distinguished from the energy due to inertial mass. Since the spin kinetic energy accounts for one half of the rest mass of the electron it is reasonable to suppose that the other half is expressed by the term ϵ^2/r_0.

On this assumption,

$$\frac{\epsilon^2}{r_0} = \tfrac{1}{2}m_0c^2$$

$$r_0 = 5 \cdot 6 \times 10^{-13} \text{ cm.}$$

This value is twice the "classical radius" of the electron which is derived by equating the whole mass energy to the static self-energy.

The two-dimensional picture of the spinning electron thus takes the form of a small spherical charge of radius $5 \cdot 6 \times 10^{-13}$ cm travelling with velocity c round a circular orbit of radius $3 \cdot 86 \times 10^{-11}$ cm. This conclusion is in keeping with Dirac's original equations according to

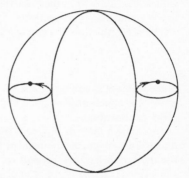

Fig. 2.14. Oscillation of charge caused by the coplanar circular motion of two identical charged particles with opposite angular momentum.

which the spinning electron always has a velocity c. This was considered to be a defect of the theory, but Schrödinger showed that this result is to be expected if an electron has a high-speed oscillatory motion superposed on its linear motion. The effect is known as the "Zitterbewegung"[†] in modern quantum theory; it is ascribed to a very rapid oscillation of charge which is manifested in a magnetic field, and is sometimes referred to as an orbital type of motion.

Since the "other particle" associated with the electron also has charge, it must have self-energy ϵ^2/r_0. Hence the picture of the companion particle[‡] to the electron is that of a particle without energy, since its total energy is given by

$$E = \frac{\epsilon^2}{r_0} - \tfrac{1}{2}m_0c^2$$

$$= 0.$$

Thus, from the point of view of an observer, this particle has no rest mass in the usual sense of the word, and no observable properties since it has zero energy. In fact its

[†] See H. Feshbach and F. Villars, "Elementary relativistic wave mechanics of spin 0 and spin $\tfrac{1}{2}$ particles", *Revs. Mod. Phys.*, **30**, 1958, 24.
[‡] T. Takabayasi (*Il Nuovo Cimento*, **12**, 1958, 119) shows that the Dirac field can be regarded as a continuous assembly of very small rotating particles.

presence could not be detected. Nevertheless, the particle pair forms a single unit in the field, and thus they both have the same potential energy in an external field. This point is of importance in connection with spectra (p. 96).

Spin wave function. The wave function of a particle with kinetic energy E may be written as

$$\psi_s = e^{\pm(2\pi i x/h)\sqrt{(2m_0E)}} \quad \text{(p. 183)}$$

Thus for the spin of the electron there must be an associated wave† described by the expression

$$\psi_s = e^{\pm(2\pi i x/h)\sqrt{(2m_0 \times \frac{1}{2}m_0c^2)}}$$

$$= e^{\pm 2\pi i x/\lambda_e} \quad \text{(see note ‡)}$$

$$= e^{\pm iCm_0x}$$

where λ_e is the Compton wave length of the electron and $C = 2\pi c/h$. The two possible values of ψ_s show that the electron can spin in one of two directions; these correspond to $s = \frac{1}{2}$ and $s = -\frac{1}{2}$ respectively.

The wave function of a particle with negative kinetic energy is given by the expression

$$\psi_s = e^{\pm(2\pi i x/h)\sqrt{(-2m_0 \times \frac{1}{2}m_0c^2)}}$$

$$= e^{\pm 2\pi x/\lambda_e}.$$

Since it is not possible for the wave to build up to an infinite amplitude, the solution $e^{+2\pi x/\lambda_e}$ is unacceptable; the acceptable solution, $e^{-2\pi x/\lambda_e}$, describes a wave which dies away exponentially.

It is shown later in this book that the two particle model is able to account for the anomalous magnetic moment of the electron (p. 94), and to give a theoretical value for the Lamb Retherford shift (p. 95) which is closely in accord with observation.

BOOKS FOR FURTHER READING

See Chapter 1, p. 31; also the following:

BOHM, D., *Quantum Theory* (Constable, 1951).

DIRAC, P. A. M., *The Principles of Quantum Mechanics* (4th Edition, Oxford University Press London, 1958).

HARNWELL, G. P., and STEPHENS, W. E., *Atomic Physics* (McGraw Hill, 1955).

HEITLER, W., *Elementary Wave Mechanics* (Oxford, Clarendon Press, 1945).

MOTT, N. F., and SNEDDON, I. N., *Wave Mechanics and Its Applications* (Oxford, Clarendon Press, 1948).

PITZER, K. S., *Quantum Chemistry* (Constable, 1953).

SLATER, J. C., *Quantum Theory of Matter* (McGraw Hill, 1953).

SLATER, J. C., *Quantum Theory of Atomic Structure*, Vols. I and II (McGraw Hill, 1960).

† See spin wave theory of ferromagnetism (p. 944).

‡ In field theory, "x" of the spin wave is generally written as x_5. It appears in the theory as a space-like fifth dimension and is the canonical conjugate (p. 14) of the particle mass. See, for instance S. Watanabe, *Il Nuovo Cimento*, **13**, 1959, 146, and N. Dallaporta, *Il Nuovo Cimento*, **13**, 1959, 593

CHAPTER THREE

ATOMIC SPECTRA AND THE PERIODIC TABLE

PERIODIC TABLE

ATOMIC NUMBER

The elements are classified in the periodic table of which a convenient form is given on the following pages.† The periodic table was originally constructed by writing down the elements in order of their ascending atomic weights in such a way that elements with similar characteristics fell into vertical columns. The table obtained by this procedure furnished a reasonable classification of the elements if the positions of argon and potassium, of nickel and cobalt, and of iodine and tellurium were interchanged.‡ This classification received its experimental justification from the X-ray experiments of Moseley which are discussed later in this chapter (p. 81). The order of the elements in the table is related to the structures of their atoms, and hence is of much significance. The order is marked by numbering the elements successively from hydrogen 1, helium 2, lithium 3, and so on. The number thus assigned to each element is called the **atomic number,** and is represented by Z. The atomic number of an element is shown later in this chapter to be the number of positive charges on the atomic nucleus, and hence the number of electrons in the neutral atom.

THE AUFBAU PRINCIPLE

Bohr first put forward the suggestion that the atom of each element can be notionally constructed by adding to the atom of the element which precedes it in the periodic table one unit of nuclear charge, and one electron. This is an example of the "aufbau" principle. The position in the atom taken up by the additional electron is decided by the nature of the available orbitals, and is such as to make the energy of the whole system a minimum. The properties of the orbitals are governed by the quantum numbers n, l, m, and s.

PAULI'S EXCLUSION PRINCIPLE

A governing principle of great importance was enunciated by Pauli.

It states that: *In no atomic system (atoms, molecules, or larger internally bound complexes) can there be two electrons which are described by identical sets of the four quantum numbers n, l, m, s.*

Since there can be two electrons with the same values of n, m, l if they have opposite spins, the principle can be alternatively stated: *No atomic or molecular orbital described by the three quantum numbers n, l, m can be occupied by more than two electrons.*

† It is not necessary to describe the form of the table in detail in this book. An elementary discussion of the periodic table is to be found in *General and Inorganic Chemistry* by P. J. Durrant Longmans, Green and Co. Ltd.), p. 115.

‡ The anomalous order of the two elements in each of the three pairs arises because the atomic weight of an element is the weighted mean of the atomic weights of its isotopes in their natural proportions. In general the variation in the proportions of light and heavy isotopes in the different elements are not great enough to invalidate the use of atomic weight instead of atomic number as a basis for the periodic classification. But in the case of argon and potassium, for example, the predominant isotopes are a heavy one of argon (40) and a light one of potassium (39). Hence the atomic weight order K,A is the opposite of the atomic number order A,K. The anomalous orders Ni, Co and I, Te are similarly explained.

The atomic number of the element is given above the symbol ; the ato
indicated by the headings N and T respecti

												Gr
PERIOD	SERIES	I		II		III		IV		V		
		N	N		T	N		T	N	T	N	T
1	1	1 H 1·008										
2	2	3 Li 6·94	4 Be 9·01			5 B 10·82			6 C 12·01		7 N 14·008	
3	3	11 Na 22·991	12 Mg 24·32			13 Al 26·98			14 Si 28·09		15 P 30·98	
4	4	19 K 39·096	20 Ca 40·08					21 Sc 44·46		22 Ti 47·90		23 V 50·95
	5				30 Zn 65·38	31 Ga 69·72			32 Ge 72·60		33 As 74·91	
5	6	37 Rb 85·48	38 Sr 87·63					39 Y 88·92		40 Zr 91·22		41 Nb 92·91
	7				48 Cd 112·41	49 In 114·76			50 Sn 118·7		51 Sb 121·76	
6	8	55 Cs 132·91	56 Ba 137·36					57 La 138·92 *Lanthanides* *58* *71* *Ce — Lu* *140·13 174·99*		72 Hf 178·6		73 Ta 180·95
	9				80 Hg 200·61	81 Tl 204·39			82 Pb 207·21		83 Bi 209·00	
7	10	87 Fr	88 Ra 226·05					89 Ac		90 Th 232·05		91 Pa 231

ments (after *Mendeléeff*)

ght is given below the symbol. The Normal and Transitional Sub-groups are
ments in transition series are printed in **bold type.**

VI N	VI T	VII N	VII T	VIII N	VIII T	IX T	X T	XI T
				2 He 4·003				
8 O 16·000		9 F 19·00		10 Ne 20·183				
16 S 32·066		17 Cl 35·457		18 A 39·944				
	24 **Cr** **52·01**		**25** **Mn** **54·94**		**26** **Fe** **55·85**	**27** **Co** **58·94**	**28** **Ni** **58·69**	**29** **Cu** **63·54**
34 Se 78·96		35 Br 79·916		36 Kr 83·8				
	42 **Mo** **95·95**		**43** **Tc**		**44** **Ru** **101·1**	**45** **Rh** **102·91**	**46** **Pd** **106·7**	**47** **Ag** **107·88**
52 Te 127·61		53 I 126·91		54 Xe 131·3				
	74 **W** **183·92**		**75** **Re** **186·31**		**76** **Os** **190·2**	**77** **Ir** **192·2**	**78** **Pt** **195·23**	**79** **Au** **197·0**
84 Po		85 At		86 Rn 222				
	92 **U** **238·07** *Uranides* 93 — 98 *Np* *Cf*							

Table 3.1. *Electron Configurations of the Elements*
Ground states of free neutral atoms

Element	K	L		M			N				O					Lowest state
	1s	2s	2p	3s	3p	3d	4s	4p	4d	4f	5s	5p	5d	5f	5g	
1. H	1															$^2S_{1/2}$
2. He	2															$^1S_0$
3. Li	2	1														$^2S_{1/2}$
4. Be	2	2														$^1S_0$
5. B	2	2	1													$^2P_{1/2}$
6. C	2	2	2													$^3P_0$
7. N	2	2	3													$^4S_{3/2}$
8. O	2	2	4													$^3P_2$
9. F	2	2	5													$^2P_{3/2}$
10. Ne	2	2	6													$^1S_0$
11. Na	2	2	6	1												$^2S_{1/2}$
12. Mg	2	2	6	2												$^1S_0$
13. Al	2	2	6	2	1											$^2P_{1/2}$
14. Si	2	2	6	2	2											$^3P_0$
15. P	2	2	6	2	3											$^4S_{3/2}$
16. S	2	2	6	2	4											$^3P_2$
17. Cl	2	2	6	2	5											$^2P_{3/2}$
18. A	2	2	6	2	6											$^1S_0$
19. K	2	2	6	2	6		1									$^2S_{1/2}$
20. Ca	2	2	6	2	6		2									$^1S_0$
21. Sc	2	2	6	2	6	1	2									$^2D_{3/2}$
22. Ti	2	2	6	2	6	2	2									$^3F_2$
23. V	2	2	6	2	6	3	2									$^4F_{3/2}$
24. Cr	2	2	6	2	6	5	1									$^7S_3$
25. Mn	2	2	6	2	6	5	2									$^6S_{5/2}$
26. Fe	2	2	6	2	6	6	2									$^5D_4$
27. Co	2	2	6	2	6	7	2									$^4F_{9/2}$
28. Ni	2	2	6	2	6	8	2									$^3F_4$
29. Cu	2	2	6	2	6	10	1									$^2S_{1/2}$
30. Zn	2	2	6	2	6	10	2									$^1S_0$
31. Ga	2	2	6	2	6	10	2	1								$^2P_{1/2}$
32. Ge	2	2	6	2	6	10	2	2								$^3P_0$
33. As	2	2	6	2	6	10	2	3								$^4S_{3/2}$
34. Se	2	2	6	2	6	10	2	4								$^3P_2$
35. Br	2	2	6	2	6	10	2	5								$^2P_{3/2}$
36. Kr	2	2	6	2	6	10	2	6								$^1S_0$
37. Rb	2	2	6	2	6	10	2	6			1					$^2S_{1/2}$
38. Sr	2	2	6	2	6	10	2	6			2					$^1S_0$
39. Y	2	2	6	2	6	10	2	6	1		2					$^2D_{3/2}$
40. Zr	2	2	6	2	6	10	2	6	2		2					$^3F_2$
41. Nb	2	2	6	2	6	10	2	6	4		1					$^6D_{1/2}$
42. Mo	2	2	6	2	6	10	2	6	5		1					$^7S_3$
43. Tc	2	2	6	2	6	10	2	6	6		1					$^6D_{9/2}$
44. Ru	2	2	6	2	6	10	2	6	7		1					$^5F_5$
45. Rh	2	2	6	2	6	10	2	6	8		1					$^4F_{9/2}$
46. Pd	2	2	6	2	6	10	2	6	10							$^1S_0$
47. Ag	2	2	6	2	6	10	2	6	10		1					$^2S_{1/2}$
48. Cd	2	2	6	2	6	10	2	6	10		2					$^1S_0$
49. In	2	2	6	2	6	10	2	6	10		2	1				$^2P_{1/2}$
50. Sn	2	2	6	2	6	10	2	6	10		2	2				$^3P_0$
51. Sb	2	2	6	2	6	10	2	6	10		2	3				$^4S_{3/2}$
52. Te	2	2	6	2	6	10	2	6	10		2	4				$^3P_2$
53. I	2	2	6	2	6	10	2	6	10		2	5				$^2P_{3/2}$
54. Xe	2	2	6	2	6	10	2	6	10		2	6				$^1S_0$
	2	8		18												

Table 3.1. (*contd.*). *Electron Configurations of the Elements*
Ground states of free neutral atoms

Element	K	L	M	N				O					P						Q
				4s	4p	4d	4f	5s	5p	5d	5f	5g	6s	6p	6d	6f	6g	6h	7s
54. Xe	2	8	18	2	6	10		2	6										
55. Cs	2	8	18	2	6	10		2	6				1						
56. Ba	2	8	18	2	6	10		2	6				2						
57. La	2	8	18	2	6	10		2	6	1			2						
58. Ce	2	8	18	2	6	10	2	2	6				2						
59. Pr	2	8	18	2	6	10	3	2	6				2						
60. Nd	2	8	18	2	6	10	4	2	6				2						
61. Pm	2	8	18	2	6	10	5	2	6				2						
62. Sm	2	8	18	2	6	10	6	2	6				2						
63. Eu	2	8	18	2	6	10	7	2	6				2						
64. Gd	2	8	18	2	6	10	7	2	6	1			2						
65. Tb	2	8	18	2	6	10	9	2	6				2						
66. Dy	2	8	18	2	6	10	10	2	6				2						
67. Ho	2	8	18	2	6	10	11	2	6				2						
68. Er	2	8	18	2	6	10	12	2	6				2						
69. Tm	2	8	18	2	6	10	13	2	6				2						
70. Yb	2	8	18	2	6	10	14	2	6				2						
71. Lu	2	8	18	2	6	10	14	2	6	1			2						
72. Hf	2	8	18	2	6	10	14	2	6	2			2						
73. Ta	2	8	18	2	6	10	14	2	6	3			2						
74. W	2	8	18	2	6	10	14	2	6	4			2						
75. Re	2	8	18	2	6	10	14	2	6	5			2						
76. Os	2	8	18	2	6	10	14	2	6	6			2						
77. Ir	2	8	18	2	6	10	14	2	6	9									
78. Pt	2	8	18	2	6	10	14	2	6	9			1						
79. Au	2	8	18	2	6	10	14	2	6	10			1						
80. Hg	2	8	18	2	6	10	14	2	6	10			2						
81. Tl	2	8	18	2	6	10	14	2	6	10			2	1					
82. Pb	2	8	18	2	6	10	14	2	6	10			2	2					
83. Bi	2	8	18	2	6	10	14	2	6	10			2	3					
84. Po	2	8	18	2	6	10	14	2	6	10			2	4					
85. At	2	8	18	2	6	10	14	2	6	10			2	5					
86. Em	2	8	18	2	6	10	14	2	6	10			2	6					
87. Fr	2	8	18	2	6	10	14	2	6	10			2	6					1
88. Ra	2	8	18	2	6	10	14	2	6	10			2	6					2
89. Ac	2	8	18	2	6	10	14	2	6	10			2	6	1				2
90. Th	2	8	18	2	6	10	14	2	6	10			2	6	2				2
91. Pa	2	8	18	2	6	10	14	2	6	10	2		2	6	1				2
92. U	2	8	18	2	6	10	14	2	6	10	3		2	6	1				2
93. Np	2	8	18	2	6	10	14	2	6	10	4		2	6	1				2
94. Pu	2	8	18	2	6	10	14	2	6	10	5		2	6	1				2
95. Am	2	8	18	2	6	10	14	2	6	10	7		2	6					2
96. Cm	2	8	18	2	6	10	14	2	6	10	7		2	6	1				2
97. Bk	2	8	18	2	6	10	14	2	6	10	8		2	6	1				2
98. Cf	2	8	18	2	6	10	14	2	6	10	10		2	6					2
99. E	2	8	18	2	6	10	14	2	6	10	11		2	6					2
100. Fm	2	8	18	2	6	10	14	2	6	10	12		2	6					2
101. Mv	2	8	18	2	6	10	14	2	6	10	13		2	6					2
102. No	2	8	18	2	6	10	14	2	6	10	14		2	6					2

ELECTRON SHELLS AND THE AUFBAU PRINCIPLE

The relations of the three quantum numbers n, l, and m are described on p. 38 where it is explained that for each value of n, l can take one of the values 0, 1, 2, ... up to $n-1$, and for each value of l, m can take one of the values $l, l-1, \ldots, 0, \ldots, -l+1, -l$. The maximum numbers of atomic orbitals which are possible for the first four values of n are set out in Table 3.2.

Table 3.2. *Numbers of Orbitals and Electrons in Electron Shells*

Shell	n	l	m	Number of orbitals	Nature of orbital	Maximum number of electrons in the orbitals	Maximum number of electrons in completed shell
K	1	0	0	1	s	2	2
L	2	0	0	1	s	2	8
		1	$-1, 0, 1$	3	p	6	
M	3	0	0	1	s	2	18
		1	$-1, 0, 1$	3	p	6	
		2	$-2, -1, 0, 1, 2$	5	d	10	
N	4	0	0	1	s	2	32
		1	$-1, 0, 1$	3	p	6	
		2	$-2, -1, 0, 1, 2$	5	d	10	
		3	$-3, -2, -1, 0, 1, 2, 3$	7	f	14	

It is sometimes convenient to speak of the electrons designated by a particular value of the principal quantum number n as an **electron shell**. A shell may be described either by the value of n, or by one of the letters, K, L, M, N, O, P, Q, where K corresponds to $n=1$, L to $n=2$, and so on. The maximum number of electrons in each shell is given in the final column of Table 3.2; it is clear that when each shell is filled it contains $2n^2$ electrons where n is the principal quantum number of the shell.

Examination of the periodic table (p. 62) shows that the numbers of elements in the first six periods are:

Period 1	Number of elements 2
2	8
3	8
4	18
5	18
6	32

The relation between the numbers of elements in the periods and the numbers of electrons in the atomic shells may be traced by an energy scheme with the aid of Bohr's aufbau principle. Fig. 3.1 shows a diagrammatic energy scheme. The energy values of the orbitals 1s, 2s, 3s, and so on, are shown by horizontal lines. Spectrum analysis shows that the differences between the energy values of s orbitals get less and less as the value of *n* increases, but for the sake of clarity the differences are indicated by equal vertical distances on the diagram. The energy values of the 2*p*, 3*p*, 4*p*, 5*p*, and 6*p* orbitals, and of the *d* and *f* orbitals of the higher values of *n*, are also indicated by horizontal lines. Energy values of the *s*, *p*, *d*, and *f* orbitals for each particular value of *n* are joined by inclined continuous lines. The dotted line indicates the route

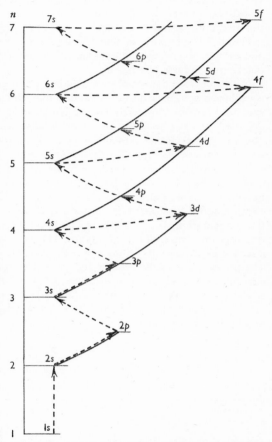

taken by a path leading in every case from a given orbital to the orbital of next higher energy value. It will be observed that the energy values increase in the order 1*s* < 2*s* < 2*p* < 3*s* < 3*p* < 4*s*. At this point there is a break in the sequence, and the orbital of next lowest energy is the 3*d*, so that, beginning at 4*s*, the sequence is 4*s* < 3*d* < 4*p*. This pattern is repeated: 5*s* < 4*d* < 5*p* < 6*s*. At this point another break occurs, and the orbital of next lowest energy is the 4*f*. The concluding sequence is 5*d* < 6*p* < 7*s* < 5*f*.

The diagram shows four patterns: (i) that corresponding to *n* = 1, (ii) that corresponding to *n* = 2 or 3, (iii) that corresponding to *n* = 4 or 5, (iv) that corresponding to *n* = 6. The following argument, based on the aufbau principle, shows that the increasing complexity of the patterns corresponds to increases in the numbers of elements in the appropriate periods in the periodic table.

The *K* shell (*n* = 1) is the only shell present in the hydrogen atom, in which it is occupied by one electron. In the helium atom there are two electrons in the *K* shell. This is the maximum

Fig. 3.1. Diagrammatic scheme of energy values of orbitals to be filled in applying the aufbau principle to the construction of the Periodic Table.

number for the *K* shell (Table 3.2). The *L* shell (*n* = 2) contains 8 electrons as the maximum; the development of the *L* shell corresponds to the building up of period 2. The *M* shell can contain 18 electrons, but period 3 contains only 8 elements. This is explained by reference to Fig. 3.1 from which it is seen that the 3*d* orbitals (which at the maximum could be occupied by 10 electrons) have a higher energy value than the 4*s* orbital. When the 3*s* and 3*p* orbitals have been filled, by the aufbau principle the next electron enters the 4*s* orbital, and the development of period 4 begins. But the pattern of period 3 is not repeated after the 4*s* orbital, because the next orbital of least energy is not the 4*p*, but the 3*d*. Hence period 4 begins with the two elements potassium and calcium with the two last added electrons in the 4*s* orbital, and continues with the transition elements, scandium to zinc, corresponding to the addition of 10 electrons to the 3*d* orbitals. At gallium, newly added electrons enter the 4*p* orbitals which are completely occupied at krypton. Period 5 is developed in a similar manner.

In period 6, the addition of the first electron to the 6*s* orbital produces the atom of caesium, and the addition of the second electron produces the atom of barium. The next electron to be added enters a 4*f* orbital, and the next 13 electrons also enter the 4*f* orbitals to yield the 14 lanthanides. Thereafter the pattern of periods 4 and 5 is repeated until period 6 is complete at radon.

Period 7 begins with the addition of 2 electrons to the 7*s* orbital to give francium and radium. It is uncertain whether the pattern of period 6 is repeated or not; the question is discussed on p. 1131.

In the previous paragraphs the building up of electron configurations in the atoms is explained with regard to the quantum numbers *n* and *l*. The part played by electron spin must now be considered. **Hund's law** states that: *The energy of a system of orbitals described by given values of the quantum numbers n and l is least if the spins of the electrons occupying the system are as far as possible parallel (unpaired)*. The state of lowest energy is the state of highest multiplicity.

For example, consider the application of the aufbau principle to period 2. The orbitals to be filled are the 2*s* ($l=0$) and the 2*p* ($l=1$). The 2*s* orbital is completed at beryllium. The next electron is placed in, say, the $2p_x$ orbital to give boron. The next electron added must be placed in the $2p_y$ or $2p_z$ orbital, so that the carbon atom has the configuration, $1s^2$, $2s^2$, $2p_x^1$, $2p_y^1$, or $1s^2$, $2s^2$, $2p_x^1$, $2p_z^1$. The nitrogen atom contains one electron in each of the 2*p* orbitals. The oxygen atom must be obtained by adding a second electron to one of the *p* orbitals, each of which already contains one electron. The procedure is made clear by the list of electronic configurations of atoms of the elements of period 2 shown in Table 3.3. It should be noted that the 2*s* orbital is completely occupied before the building up of the *p* orbitals begins; for a higher value of *n*, it is found that the *p* orbitals are completed before the building up of the *d* orbitals in the same shell.

Table 3.3. *Electron Configurations of Atoms of Elements in Period 2*
The arrows indicate the relative directions of spin.

Atom	Configuration				
	1*s*	2*s*	$2p_x$	$2p_y$	$2p_z$
Lithium	↓ ↑	↑			
Beryllium	↓ ↑	↑ ↓			
Boron	↓ ↑	↑ ↓	↑		
Carbon	↓ ↑	↑ ↓	↑	↑	
Nitrogen	↓ ↑	↑ ↓	↑	↑	↑
Oxygen	↓ ↑	↑ ↓	↑ ↓	↑	↑
Fluorine	↓ ↑	↑ ↓	↑ ↓	↑ ↓	↑
Neon	↓ ↑	↑ ↓	↑ ↓	↑ ↓	↑ ↓

Table 3.1 shows the electron configurations of all the elements.

ATOMIC SPECTRA

TYPES OF SPECTRA

The sorting out and correlation of the numerous lines and bands of the spectra of atoms and molecules is the result of the patient work of many spectroscopists. This work is of immense value, since the study of spectra is one of the most important sources of information concerning atomic structure. Its development has proceeded hand in hand with gradually advancing theory, so that historically it would be correct for any progressive account of atomic structure to be interspersed with supporting information from spectrum analysis. A continuous train of thought, however, has the advantage of clarity, and so in the opening chapters of this book, the current theory of atomic structure has first been presented, and is now to be followed by a description of spectrum analysis in so far as it throws light on, and confirms, this theory.

The passage of a beam of light through a glass prism or diffraction grating causes a deviation of the direction of the beam. The angle of deviation depends on the wave length of the incident light which also determines the colour. Therefore, if the beam consists of a mixture of coloured lights, it may be analysed into its constituent colours by passing it through a prism or grating. The image of a slit illuminated by the incident beam appears on the receiving screen as a series of coloured lines or bands. If light corresponding to a continuous series of wave lengths (white light) is present in the incident beam, a continuous band of colours is shown in the spectrum. Radiation corresponding to wave lengths longer or shorter than those of the visible spectrum can also be refracted or diffracted by means of suitable apparatus.

There are two main types of spectra, known as emission and absorption spectra. *Emission spectra* are produced from luminous and incandescent bodies, and consist, in the optical region, of bright coloured lines or coloured bands on a dark background. *Absorption spectra* are produced from white light which has passed through cool vapours or solutions. They consist of dark lines or bands on a brightly coloured background. Both types of spectra can be observed, by means of special techniques, in wave length regions outside that of the visible spectrum.

Continuous spectra. A continuous emission spectrum is observed, in the optical region, as a continuous, brightly coloured band. It includes radiation of every wave length in the region covered by the spectrum. Continuous spectra are emitted by bodies raised to such a high temperature that they become incandescent, as, for example, a piece of lime heated in the oxyhydrogen flame. A continuous absorption spectrum would of course be entirely black, therefore the term "continuous spectrum" is used in connection with emission spectra only.

Line spectra. Line spectra are characteristic of particular atoms. If a body emits light without being incandescent, the corresponding spectrum consists of a series of sharp, brightly coloured lines on a dark background. For instance, such a line spectrum is emitted by sodium vapour at the temperature of the Bunsen flame. If white light is passed through the same vapour when it is not luminous, the spectrum is reversed and consists of dark lines (corresponding to the same wave lengths as the bright lines in the previous emission spectrum) on a brightly coloured background. This reversed spectrum is an absorption line spectrum.

Band spectra. Just as line spectra are characteristic of atoms, so are band spectra characteristic of molecules. Band spectra are observed as absorption spectra only, because, with the exception of diatomic molecules and a few others, the temperature required to make a molecule emit light is sufficient, or more than sufficient, to break up the molecule into its constituent atoms. Like all absorption spectra, a band spectrum consists of dark lines on a bright background. These lines are grouped together in bands, in some cases the grouping is so close that the structure cannot be resolved even with instruments of very high resolving power. The bands are spaced regularly but not necessarily at equal distances apart. They each have one edge which is sharp and the other diffuse; the lines crowd closer and closer together at the sharp edge, and become spread out at the diffuse edge. Band spectra are discussed in detail in the chapters on molecular spectra.

Range of wave lengths. The wave lengths which can be observed spectroscopically extend from those of very short X-rays to those of long radio waves. Table 3.4 shows how the spectrum may be divided up into sections, each of which requires a special type of spectrograph for the recording of the spectra. Wave lengths in the visible and ultraviolet regions are usually measured in Angstrom units ($Å = 10^{-8}$ cm). In the infrared region the unit is the micron ($\mu = 10^{-4}$ cm) and in the X-ray region the unit is the X-unit ($XU = 10^{-3}$ $Å = 10^{-11}$ cm). The recording apparatus may be referred to as a "spectrograph", a "spectrometer", or a "spectroscope"; for details of the apparatus and experimental procedure the reader should consult a text book of spectroscopy.

Fine structure and hyperfine structure. Many spectral lines show **fine structure** when analysed by instruments of high resolving power. What appears to be a single line in a spectroscope of moderate resolving power is then shown to consist of a number of lines very close together. These are known as spectral multiplets and are due to the coupling of spin and orbital angular momenta (p. 90) (Plate 2).

Still greater resolving power such as that of microwave spectroscopy (p. 254) shows each fine structure line split into a number of lines exceedingly close together. This splitting is known as **hyperfine structure**. It is due to two effects: the isotope effect, and the effect due to angular momentum of the nucleus. The isotope effect is discussed on page 74 in connection with the Rydberg constant. The effect due to nuclear angular momentum is discussed on page 104 in connection with the coupling of the nuclear angular momentum to the angular momentum of the electrons.

EXCITATION OF SPECTRA

The emission of visible or ultraviolet radiation in the form of a photon is always associated with a reduction in the energy of an electron. The original energy may be the kinetic energy of a free electron, or the orbital energy of the electron in the atom.[†]

Table 3.4. *The Spectral Regions*

Wave length	Spectral region	Spectroscopic equipment
Below 100 Å	X-ray	Crystal or grating spectrograph
100–1800 Å	Vacuum ultraviolet	Vacuum concave grating
1800–4000 Å	Quartz ultraviolet	Quartz spectrograph or grating
4000–7000 Å	Visible region	Glass spectrograph or grating
7000–10,000 Å	Photographic (or near) infrared	Glass spectrograph or grating
1–20 μ	Infrared	Rock salt spectrograph or grating
20–400 μ	Far infrared	Echelette grating
Above 1000 μ	Microwave region	Radio wave guide techniques

W. Finkelnburg, *Atomic Physics* (McGraw-Hill), p. 68.

[†] The emission of infrared radiation is commonly due to changes of molecular rotational energy (p. 205).

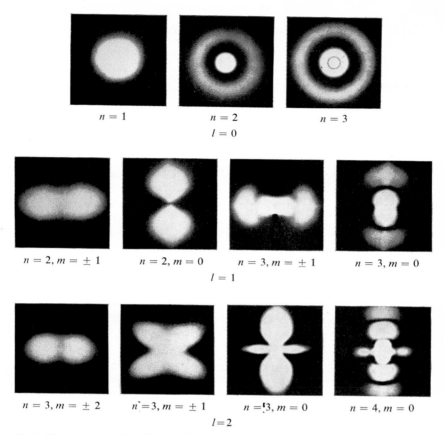

$$n = 1 \qquad n = 2 \qquad n = 3$$
$$l = 0$$

$$n = 2, m = \pm 1 \qquad n = 2, m = 0 \qquad n = 3, m = \pm 1 \qquad n = 3, m = 0$$
$$l = 1$$

$$n = 3, m = \pm 2 \qquad n = 3, m = \pm 1 \qquad n = 3, m = 0 \qquad n = 4, m = 0$$
$$l = 2$$

Pl. 1. Photographs, taken from models, showing the shape of the electron cloud for various states of the hydrogen atom: the probability density $\psi\psi^*$ is symmetrical about the magnetic axis (z), which is vertical. [White, *Phys. Rev.*, **37**. 1931.]

Pl. 2. Part of the Fe arc spectrum (showing multiplet structure). [Herzberg, *Atomic Spectra and Atomic Structure*.]

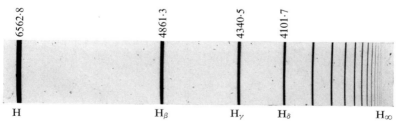

6562·8   4861·3   4340·5   4101·7

H H_β H_γ H_δ H_∞

Pl. 3. Spectrum of the hydrogen atom in the visible and near ultraviolet region (Balmer Series). [Herzberg, *Atomic Spectra and Atomic Structure*.]

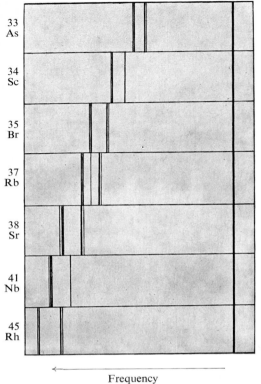

33
As

34
Sc

35
Br

37
Rb

38
Sr

41
Nb

45
Rh

← Frequency

Pl. 4. X-ray *K* series for elements between As (*Z*=33) and Rh (*Z*=45) showing increasing frequency with increasing atomic number. [Siegbahn and Thoraeous, *J. opt. Soc. Amer.* **13**, 1926.]

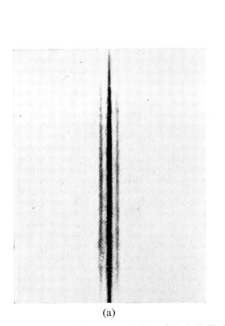

(a)

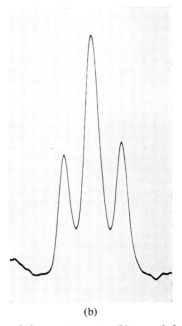

(b)

Pl. 5. Normal Zeeman splitting of Zn λ 6362, (a) recorded on spectrometer, (b) recorded on microphotometer. [McLennan and Durnford, *Proc. roy. Soc.* **A, 120,** 1928.]

Emission of radiation by a free electron. If a moving free electron collides with another particle, part of the original energy of the electron is transferred to the second particle, part is emitted as a photon, and part remains with the electron.

Energy of the photon = original energy of (electron + particle)
                        − final energy of (electron + particle).

The frequency of the photon ν is given by Planck's relation (p. 10)

Energy of photon = $h\nu$.

If such energy changes are undergone by a number of electrons moving with different speeds, photons are generated having a wide range of frequencies. The spectrum produced by the energy changes of all the electrons is therefore continuous, and has a short wave limit corresponding to the conversion of the whole of the kinetic energy of the fastest electron into radiation. Continuous spectra produced by the slowing down of electrons are known as *bremsstrahlung*. They are particularly prominent in X-ray spectra.

Emission of radiation by an electron in the atom. The energy of an electron in the atom is determined by the orbital occupied by the electron. The available orbitals in an atom may be classified in a sequence of increasing energy starting with the $1s$ orbital (Fig. 3.1). If the electrons in the atom occupy the orbitals in this sequence starting with the $1s$ orbital, the atom is then in a state of lowest possible energy, and is said to be in the **ground state.** When, by the gain of energy from some external source, an electron in such an atom is promoted to an orbital of higher energy, then the atom is said to be in an **excited state.** If the process by which the atom is brought to an excited state is a transient process, such as a collision with a fast moving electron, the excitation is at once followed by the return of the electron to the ground state orbital, with the simultaneous emission of a photon. The two-stage process may be represented thus:

(1) Atom in ground state + fast electron→atom in excited state + slow electron.

(2) Atom in excited state→atom in ground state + photon.

The energy and the frequency of the photon produced are related to the difference between the energy of the ground state orbital and that of the excited state orbital, thus:

Energy of excited orbital E_2 − energy of ground state orbital E_1 = energy of photon,
$$E_2 - E_1 = h\nu.$$

Since the energies of the orbitals are quantised, the value of ν is quantised, and the spectrum corresponding to the change of energy is a sharply defined bright line. If a number of atoms of the same element are excited so that electrons of different atoms are promoted to different orbitals (characterised by different energies), photons of different energy are emitted when the atoms return to the ground state. The energy of every photon is quantised, and therefore the spectrum of the element consists of a number of bright lines on a dark background; it is not continuous.

If the excitation of the atom results in the gain of so much energy that an electron is detached from it and given kinetic energy, the atom is changed to a positive ion, and is said to be **ionised.** An ionised atom may recapture a detached electron. The ionised atom may then either return directly to the ground state, or it may first adopt an excited state from which it may revert to the ground state.

If the atom returns directly to the ground state, an unquantised amount of energy is released. The energy is transformed into radiation and appears as part of a continuous spectrum, the continuity of which results from the variation in kinetic energy of the electrons recaptured by a large number of ionised atoms. If the ionised atom reverts first to an excited state, and then to the ground state, the first part of the process corresponds to the emission of unquantised energy, which as before, makes a contribution to the continuous spectrum, and the second part of the process which releases a quantised amount of energy corresponds to the emission of a particular line in a line spectrum which is characteristic of the recapturing atom. When a large number of atoms of the same element are present, all the possible excited states are represented, and the whole line spectrum is produced. This line spectrum extends beyond the short wave limit (corresponding to the greatest quantised energy change) into the continuous spectrum.

LINE SPECTRA

A line in a spectrum is characterised by its corresponding wave length, λ, but for spectroscopic purposes it is more convenient to designate the line by its "wave number" $\bar{\nu}$. $\bar{\nu}$ is the number of wave lengths per cm, or $1/\lambda$.

If c is the velocity of light,

$$\nu = \frac{c}{\lambda}$$

and

$$\bar{\nu} = \frac{\nu}{c}. \tag{3.1}$$

Balmer was the first to find any relationship between the wave lengths of spectral lines. In 1885 he discovered that four lines in the visible and near ultraviolet spectrum of hydrogen formed a "series". These lines are part of what is now known as the **Balmer series** (Plate 3). Rydberg found that the wave number of any line of this series could be represented as a difference of two terms where

$$\bar{\nu} = \frac{R}{2^2} - \frac{R}{n^2}. \tag{3.2}$$

R is a constant known as the **Rydberg constant** and n can take any of the integral values 3, 4, 5, 6, ...

The Lyman, Paschen, Brackett, and Pfund series were also subsequently found in the spectrum of atomic hydrogen, and were named after their discoverers. These series can also be described by formulae similar to that used to represent the Balmer series. In each case n can take one of a series of integral values, but the least possible value of n progressively changes by unity as we proceed from one series to the other if these are arranged in order, as in Table 3.5.

Table 3.5.　*Series observed in the Spectrum of Atomic Hydrogen*

(1)	$\bar{\nu} = R_H \left(1 - \dfrac{1}{n^2}\right)$	where n can have the values, 2, 3, 4, ... *Lyman Series*—ultraviolet
(2)	$\bar{\nu} = R_H \left(\dfrac{1}{2^2} - \dfrac{1}{n^2}\right)$	where n can have the values 3, 4, 5, ... *Balmer Series*—visible
(3)	$\bar{\nu} = R_H \left(\dfrac{1}{3^2} - \dfrac{1}{n^2}\right)$	where n can have the values 4, 5, 6, ... *Paschen Series*—infrared
(4)	$\bar{\nu} = R_H \left(\dfrac{1}{4^2} - \dfrac{1}{n^2}\right)$	where n can have the values 5, 6, 7, ... *Brackett Series*—far infrared
(5)	$\bar{\nu} = R_H \left(\dfrac{1}{5^2} - \dfrac{1}{n^2}\right)$	where n can have the values 6, 7, 8, ... *Pfund Series*—far infrared

(The Rydberg constant is here denoted by R_H since there is one constant for hydrogen, another for helium and so on.)

It can be seen from Table 3.5 that any wave number corresponding to a line in a series can be expressed as a difference of two terms. These terms all have the general form $R/(\text{integer})^2$, the integer being different for each term. A line series is formed by keeping one term constant and subtracting in turn a series of other terms. Table 3.5 shows clearly how the constant term differs from series to series.

The wave number corresponding to a spectral line can also be expressed in terms of the energies of the occupied orbitals, since by Planck's fundamental relation,

$$\nu = \frac{E_2}{h} - \frac{E_1}{h} \quad \text{and} \quad \bar{\nu} = \frac{E_2}{hc} - \frac{E_1}{hc}.$$

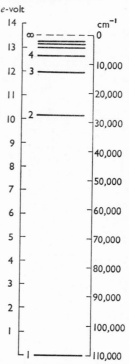

Fig. 3.2. Term diagram for the hydrogen atom. The energy value is on the left, and the wave number on the right. The value of n for the first four lines is stated against each line.

The term in a series formula can therefore be defined either by the energy of a particular orbital divided by hc, or by the expression R/n^2 where n is an integer different for each term.

It is convenient to represent a spectrum on a *term diagram*. Each term is represented by a horizontal line, and these lines are arranged in order of increasing value of the integer n, and become more crowded together as n increases. Different values of R/n^2 are plotted to obtain the spacing of the lines; the positions of the lines are alternatively marked with the corresponding energy values. Instead of using an *erg* as the unit of energy, the *electron volt* is often used instead. On the electron volt system an energy E is expressed as the difference of potential in volts through which an electron must fall in order to acquire an energy E.

Term systems. A number of spectroscopic terms form a **term system** if their subtraction from one another gives the wave numbers of lines in an observed spectral series. It is a general rule that two term systems do not combine with each other; that is, the subtraction of a term of one system from a term of another system does not give a wave number which corresponds to a line actually observed in the spectrum.

Fig. 3.2 shows an example of a term diagram marked on one side as electron volts, and on the other side as values of R/n^2. The value of n is shown for each level. Fig. 3.3 shows a similar diagram which represents the line series of the spectrum of atomic hydrogen. Arrows are drawn between terms whose difference corresponds to a spectral line.

Calculation of the Rydberg constant. It was shown on p. 45 that the energy of an electron occupying the orbital of a hydrogen atom may be expressed as

$$E = -\frac{2\pi^2 m_0 \epsilon^4}{h^2 n^2}.$$

E is a negative quantity as the electron is bound in the atom. Thus E_{n+1} is greater (less negative) than E_n and

$$\bar{\nu} = \frac{E_{n+1}}{hc} - \frac{E_n}{hc}$$
$$= -\frac{2\pi^2 m_0 \epsilon^4}{ch^3(n+1)^2} + \frac{2\pi^2 m_0 \epsilon^4}{ch^3 n^2}$$
$$= \frac{2\pi^2 m_0 \epsilon^4}{ch^3} \left[\frac{1}{n^2} - \frac{1}{(n+1)^2} \right].$$

From equation (3.2),

$$\bar{\nu} = R_H \left[\frac{1}{n^2} - \frac{1}{(n+1)^2} \right],$$

and therefore

$$R_H = \frac{2\pi^2 m_0 \epsilon^4}{ch^3}.$$

Hence the term number n is identical with the quantum number n, and

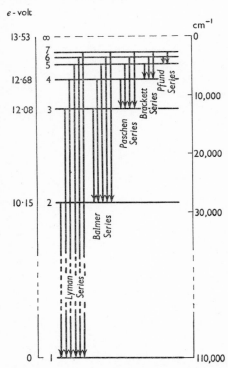

$$E = -\frac{hcR_H}{n^2}. \qquad (3.3)$$

The value of R_H calculated from this formula is in fairly good agreement with the value of R_H deduced from spectroscopic observation. The agreement is exact if both the electron and the nucleus are assumed to rotate about their common centre of gravity. Then

$$R_H = \frac{2\pi^2 m_0 \epsilon^4}{ch^3(1 + m_0/M)}, \qquad (3.4)$$

where m_0 = mass of the electron
        M = mass of the nucleus.

With this correction, the value of the Rydberg constant for hydrogen is given by

$$R_H = 109,677 \cdot 580 \pm 0 \cdot 004 \text{ cm}^{-1}.$$

The significance of R_H is evident from Planck's relation (p. 10). $-R_H hc$ is the energy of the electron in the hydrogen atom when $n=1$ (the ground state of the hydrogen atom). $R_H hc$ may be expressed either as the binding energy (p. 45) of the electron when the hydrogen atom is in the ground state, or the ionisation energy, that is the energy which must be supplied to remove the electron from that state out of the field of the nucleus.

Fig. 3.3. Term diagram for the hydrogen atom showing the relations of the spectral series to the atomic orbitals.

Hyperfine structure due to the isotope effect (see p. 70). Rydberg constants may be deduced for many atoms, and in each case the value of R is dependent on the mass of the atom in question. Since the spacing of the spectral lines of a series depends on R, a change of isotope causes a slight difference in the spacing of the lines of a given series. This is shown as a hyperfine structure when there is more than one isotope present. With heavy atoms an additional isotope effect is observed, because the nucleons (protons and neutrons in the nucleus) are differently arranged in different isotopes. The arrangement affects the energy of the atom, as with heavy atoms the nucleus no longer approximates to a point charge. By means of the measurement of the number, intensities, and separation of the lines, and by calculation of both isotopic effects, the nature, nuclear masses, and proportion of isotopes present can be estimated. This spectroscopic method is a valuable check on the atomic weights determined by means of the mass spectrograph.

Spectra of hydrogen-like ions. Ions with one electron only remaining in the field of the nucleus, such as an ionised helium atom He^+, are said to be hydrogen-like. The spectra of such ions show line series similar in structure to the Balmer series. The following line series have been ascribed to ionised helium.

$$\bar{\nu} = 4R_{He}\left(1 - \frac{1}{n^2}\right) \qquad n = 2, 3, 4, \ldots$$

$$\bar{\nu} = 4R_{He}\left(\frac{1}{2^2} - \frac{1}{n^2}\right) \qquad n = 3, 4, 5, \ldots$$

$$\bar{\nu} = 4R_{He}\left(\frac{1}{3^2} - \frac{1}{n^2}\right) \qquad n = 4, 5, 6, \ldots$$

$$\bar{\nu} = 4R_{He}\left(\frac{1}{4^2} - \frac{1}{n^2}\right) \qquad n = 5, 6, 7, \ldots$$

These series are similar to those of the hydrogen atom. All the lines of the helium series have wave lengths only one quarter of the wave lengths of the corresponding lines of the hydrogen atom, the whole set being shifted into the ultraviolet. In order to obtain an accurate value for R_{He}, correction must again be made for the revolution of the nucleus and electron about their centre of mass. By analogy with equation (3.3) the energy of an electron occupying an orbital in a helium ion, He^+, is given by the equation

$$E = -\frac{4hcR_{He}}{n^2} \qquad (3.5)$$

The lithium ion Li^{++} also has one electron in the field of the nucleus. The spectrum of this ion is still further displaced beyond the ultraviolet. Three lines have been observed in the extreme ultraviolet, but the other lines are calculated to lie in the region between the ultraviolet and X-rays where it is not possible to observe them. In general the energy of the electron of a hydrogen-like atom or ion can be expressed by the formula

$$E_n = -\frac{hcZ^2R}{n^2} \qquad n = 1, 2, 3, \ldots \qquad (3.6)$$

where Z is the nuclear charge.

Hydrogen-like ions can be formed only from atoms of low atomic number. Normally it is not possible to eject all but one of the electrons from an atom. By irradiation with visible light of short wave length, or with X-rays, or by thermal excitation, it is possible to promote an electron from an inner shell to an unoccupied orbital of higher energy value, or to eject it from the atom altogether. The vacancy in the orbital from which the electron was ejected is then filled by an electron from a higher level, and the energy change generates a spectral line. Since any electron in the atom can be excited by irradiation, and there are a number of ways in which its place can be filled by electrons from other orbitals, it is clear that the excitation of a large number of atoms gives rise to a spectrum containing many lines. These lines may be classified in series. The series are, however, more complicated than those of the hydrogen spectrum as the energy of orbitals in atoms other than those of hydrogen depends not only on n, but also, although to a lesser extent, on the quantum number l. This is an effect due to the presence of the unexcited electrons; the greater the number of electrons in the atom the greater the effect. Furthermore many of the lines may be resolved into doublets. This effect is due to electron spin, and is discussed more fully in a later part of this chapter (p. 91).

Spectra of the atoms of the alkali metals. The atom of an alkali metal consists of one ionisable valency electron and an atomic core consisting of the nucleus and the electrons in the closed shells. The core has a resultant positive charge of one unit. The valency electron should therefore show evidence of behaviour similar to the electron in the hydrogen atom.

There are four clearly discernible series in the spectra of the atoms of the alkali metals. These are known as the Principal, Sharp, Diffuse, and Fundamental series, and are characterised by the values 1, 2, 2, 3, respectively for the principal quantum number, n. For both the Sharp and Diffuse series $n = 2$. Fig. 3.4 shows the type of diagram which is drawn to demonstrate the interpretation of these series. The orbitals are indicated by horizontal lines drawn at the appropriate energy values. The oblique lines show transitions from higher to lower orbitals. These transitions occur after an electron originally present in the lower orbital has been promoted to a higher orbital, or ejected from the atom. The diagram shows that the Principal series is produced by transitions from p orbitals in various shells with different n values to the s orbital with $n = 1$, that is

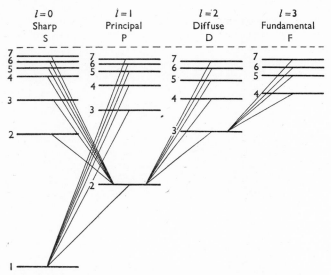

Fig. 3.4. Diagrammatic representation of the spectrum of the potassium atom. The figure shows the transitions which generate the four series, Sharp, Principal, Diffuse, and Fundamental.

to the K shell. In the Sharp series the transitions are from the s orbitals in various shells with differing n values (except $n = 1$) to p orbitals with $n = 2$ (the L shell). The Diffuse series consists of transitions from d orbitals with various n values, to p orbitals with $n = 2$. The Fundamental series corresponds to transitions from f orbitals with various n values to d orbitals with $n = 3$. It is to be noted that the characteristic quantum number of a series indicates the level at which a transition *finishes*. These transitions have been deduced from observed spectral lines, and as described above they correspond to an emission spectrum. For an absorption spectrum the transitions are reversed.

The diagram in Fig. 3.4 is drawn to illustrate the generation of the Principal, Sharp, Diffuse, and Fundamental series in the atomic spectra of the alkali metals. The diagram is incomplete, and many other transitions take place besides those shown, and give rise to corresponding spectral lines, not only in the optical spectrum, but over the whole range of detectable wave lengths. The complete diagram for transitions is shown in Fig. 3.5, below. A study of this diagram shows that there are a number of transitions which do not take place; for example, there is no transition from the *Ls* orbital to the *Ks* orbital. From the correlation of observed spectra *selection rules* have been drawn up which makes it possible to predict which lines will not be observed.

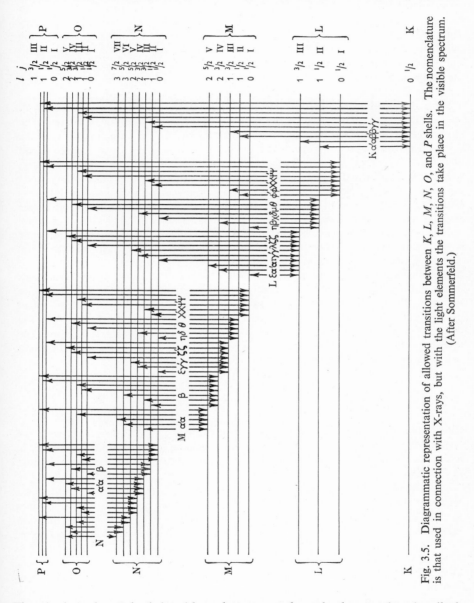

Fig. 3.5. Diagrammatic representation of allowed transitions between *K*, *L*, *M*, *N*, *O*, and *P* shells. The nomenclature is that used in connection with X-rays, but with the light elements the transitions take place in the visible spectrum. (After Sommerfeld.)

The selection rules can be deduced from the quantum theory by the procedure described on p. 83.

If the energy of excitation is low, the only electron to be affected in the atom of the alkali metal is the valency electron. It may be promoted to an orbital of higher energy value and may then fall back to the valency orbital of the atom in the ground state. The series produced are limited to those composed of transitions which end at the orbital which is that of the valency electron in the ground state.

All the series of the hydrogen atom are produced in this way, as there is only one electron and no completed inner shells. All the series of the lithium atom formed by the transitions of the valency electron end in energy states not lower than the L shell; with sodium, it is the M shell and so on. Other series whose transitions end in lower energy states are formed by the ejection of an electron from one of the inner shells, and the return to it of the excited valency electron or another electron from another shell. This process is the same as that responsible for the X-ray series (p. 81); for instance, the Principal Series of the alkali metals with transitions ending in the K shell ($n=1$) is really the X-ray K series.

Some deviation from hydrogen-like behaviour is shown by atoms of the alkali metals owing to the presence of the core instead of a point positive charge. The atom is also polarised to a greater or less extent because of the attraction between the valency electron and the nucleus, and the repulsion between the valency electron and the closed electron shells. Whereas for the hydrogen atom the term is given by R/n^2, where n is the principal quantum number, for an atom of an alkali metal the term is expressed as R/n_{eff}^2, where n_{eff} is the *effective principal quantum number*. If n_{eff} is evaluated from experimental evidence, the effective quantum numbers are no longer found to be integers, and the deviations from integral values can be used as a measure of the deviation from hydrogen-like behaviour. The greatest deviations are to be found when the electron is in an s or a p orbital. In general, for a highly excited atom, the disturbance due to the core is negligible.

Atoms with two electrons in the valence shell. The spectra of atoms with two electrons in the valence shell resemble the spectra of one electron systems in that they have Principal, Sharp, Diffuse, and Fundamental series. For example, these series are evident in the spectra of helium, the alkaline earth metals, and the metals Hg, Cd, Zn. The reason for this is to be found in the ionisation energies of the valence electrons. The ionisation energies, in electron volts, of the first and second electrons of the atoms of a few elements are given below

	H	Na	Ca	Zn
First electron	13·53	5·18	6·09	9·36
Second electron	—	47·10	11·82	17·90

Clearly the first valency electron of a divalent metal is ionised more easily than the second which may remain unionised as part of the core, and hence the conditions in which the spectra of divalent metals are generated are to this extent similar to those in the alkali metals.

The two electron system however shows other striking features, in particular two separate term systems. These systems have no intercombination lines, that is, no lines formed by transitions from one system to the other, Fig. 3.6, p. 79. One of the term systems is responsible for the series mentioned above, and is known as a *singlet* system, because there is no doubling of the lines as in the spectra of the alkali metals. The other term system is a *triplet* system, in which each term is replaced by three terms very close together; the term corresponding to the ground state is missing. In the case of helium it was at first thought that there were two types of helium which were named parahelium and orthohelium; these terms have been retained, but, as will be shown later, the explanation now given is derived from consideration of electron spin and the angular momentum of the occupied orbitals (p. 91). The separation into singlet and triplet systems is characteristic of the spectra of all atoms with two electrons in the outer shell. An element which has a term system in which the terms correspond to a number of atomic energy states which are very close together, is said to show *multiplicity* (p. 92). An alkali metal thus has a double multiplicity, and helium has both single and triple multiplicity.

Many electron atoms. The spectra of atoms with three electrons in the outer shell also show two term systems with no intercombination lines. One of these systems is a doublet system, the other a quartet system, the terms being double and four-fold respectively. A four electron atom has three non-combining term systems, a singlet, a triplet, and a quintet system. The five electron atom has a doublet, a quartet, and a

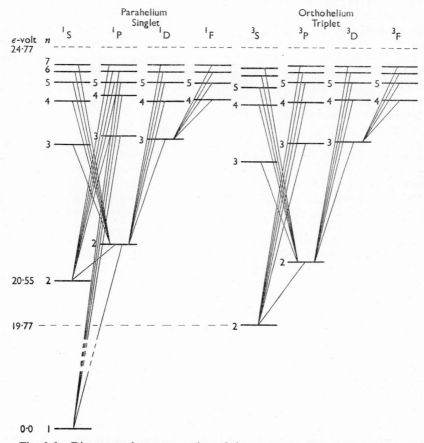

Fig. 3.6. Diagrammatic representation of the spectrum of the helium atom, omitting the fine structure of the triplet system.

sextet system. This progression can be stated in general terms as a rule. "In going from element to element in the periodic table, even and odd multiplicities of term systems alternate with each other in such a way that an atom with an even number of electrons in the outer shell has odd multiplicity, and an atom with an odd number of electrons in the outer shell has even multiplicity."

It is much more difficult to disentangle the spectra of heavy atoms than those of light ones, as the multiple energy states are much closer together for the atoms of the light elements than for those of the heavy ones. In the spectra of the light elements the multiple lines appear as a "fine structure" superposed on a clearly defined series;

in the spectra of the heavy elements the multiple lines are more separated, and the series are not clearly distinguished as there is considerable overlapping of term systems. There are also further complications due to the excitation of several electrons at once, and the simple Rydberg series are no longer observed.

Metastable states. It is evident from the study of multiple spectra, that there are some excited atomic states from which a transition to the ground state is forbidden. These are known as metastable states. The atom in one of these states can lose its energy only by collision and not by radiation, and conversely the atom in the ground state cannot get into the metastable state by absorption of radiation, but only by acquiring energy by collision.† The orbital of lowest energy of orthohelium is a metastable state (Fig. 3.6). If an atom in a metastable state is present in a gas, it is likely to lose energy to a gas molecule by collision, because a molecule has a large number of possible energy states, and the energy of excitation to one of them might correspond exactly to the energy difference between the metastable and stable states of the colliding atom. In some cases, the energy lost by the metastable atom is sufficient to ionise the gas molecule.

Intensity of spectral lines. The comparison of line intensities is a valuable source of information on the relative probabilities of various transitions in the processes of emission or absorption of radiation. The computation of line intensities in terms of probability and the quantum theory was first made by Einstein. For a complete analysis it is necessary to employ Dirac's electrodynamic theory, in which the interaction of radiation and matter plays an essential part.

Width of spectral lines. All spectral lines have a measurable width which is independent of the resolving power of the spectroscope. This width depends on the energy range or "width" of the two energy states concerned in producing the radiation corresponding to the line in question. If ΔE is the width of an energy state and t the mean life of the energy state, by the uncertainty principle the product $\Delta E \times t = h/2\pi$. Therefore any process which tends to diminish the mean life of the stationary state will have the corresponding effect of broadening the spectral lines.

There are many other causes of broadening, such as collisions between atoms, interaction of spins and so on, which will not be discussed here.

X-RAY SPECTRA

Mechanism of X-ray line emission. In an evacuated tube, X-rays are emitted from a metal plate (known as the *anticathode*) when it is in the path of high velocity electrons whose energy is of the order of 10,000–20,000 electron volts. Since optical spectra, which originate by the transition of electrons from one shell to another in the outer region of the atom, can be excited by the expenditure of considerably less energy, it has been concluded that X-rays are produced as the result of the ejection of electrons from the inner electron shells of the atoms of which the plate is composed. The characteristic X-ray spectra which are observed experimentally can be explained by the assumption that an electron in one of the inner shells, say the K or L shell, is given sufficient energy to leave the atom completely, and that its place is taken by an electron from one of the shells of higher quantum number. The wave number of the X-radiation emitted is determined by the energy difference between the shell of higher quantum number and that of the K or L shell from which an electron was originally ejected.

† The fact that the forbidden lines do sometimes appear faintly is ascribed to the existence of means other than that of the electric dipole (see p. 84) for producing radiation in certain atoms, for example a magnetic dipole, but the intensity of this radiation is small compared with that of the normal electric dipole. Also, as has been mentioned before, forbidden lines are sometimes apparent in heavy discharges.

In some cases the ejected electron does not leave the atom completely, but fills an unoccupied orbital in one of the outer shells. Even so, the energy required for this process is still practically the whole of the ionisation energy, as it is chiefly used in overcoming the strong field in the immediate vicinity of the nucleus. If the effect of the electrons in the outer shells and the screening effect of the other K electrons are neglected, the energy required to move an electron from the K shell is, to a first approximation, given by the expression, (equation (3.6) p. 75)

$$E = -\frac{hcZ^2R}{n^2},$$

where Z is the nuclear charge (atomic number). For instance, in the case of copper, atomic number 29, the energy required is of the order of 12,000 electron volts.

All transitions ending in the K shell give the K series; these transitions produce the most penetrating (hardest) X-rays. All transitions ending in the L shell give the L series, all transitions ending in the M shell give the M series, the softest X-rays. A transition from the L shell to the K shell causes a K line (K_α) to be emitted, a transition from the M shell to the K shell causes the line K_β to be emitted, a transition from the N shell to the K shell causes the line K_γ to be emitted. Transitions from shells of higher energy give lines closer together and the series appears to end in a continuous "tail". While it is not possible to excite the K series without at the same time exciting the L and M series, owing to the successive filling up of vacant orbitals in the electron shells, the softer series can be excited without the harder by using ionising electrons which have insufficient energy to remove an electron from an inner shell, but sufficient to remove one from, say, the L or M shell.

In 1913, from a study of X-ray spectra, Moseley deduced an empirical expression relating the frequency ν of X radiation to the square of a number, Z, which was a constant for each element:

$$\nu = \text{constant } (Z-b)^2.$$

This expression is sometimes known as **Moseley's law**. For K radiation, $b=1$, for L radiation, $b=2$. Moseley saw that Z was identical with the atomic number of the element which indicates its position in the periodic table (Fig. 3.7 and Plate 4).

E, the energy of an electron occupying an orbital of principal quantum number n in the hydrogen atom is given by equation (2.21) (p. 45).

$$E = -\frac{2\pi^2 m_0 \epsilon^4}{h^2 n^2}.$$

For a heavier atom, if the charge on the nucleus is Z, then it is approximately true that:

$$E = -\frac{2\pi^2 m_0 Z^2 \epsilon^4}{h^2 n^2}.$$

Hence,

$$E_{n+1} - E_n = \frac{2\pi^2 m_0 Z^2 \epsilon^4}{h^2} \left\{ \frac{1}{n^2} - \frac{1}{(n+1)^2} \right\}.$$

But $E_{n+1} - E_n = h\nu$, and hence $\nu = $ a constant $\times Z^2$ for a given value of n. This expression is similar to, but not identical with, that which Moseley derived from his experimental results.

A study of Moseley's formula shows clearly the connection between the optical spectra of the light elements and the X-ray spectra of the heavy ones. Since the frequency increases with the square of the atomic number, the K series, which is in the X-ray region for heavy atoms, is in a longer wavelength region for the light atoms. For most of the light elements the K series lies between the ultraviolet and the X-ray regions. For hydrogen, the lightest of all the elements, the K series is identical with the Lyman series, which is in the far ultraviolet.

X-ray line spectra are always observed on a background of continuous spectrum whatever the material of which the anti-cathode is made. This continuous background corresponds to the electron "bremsstrahlung" already mentioned in connection with optical spectra (p. 71). In the case of X-rays, some of the impinging electrons are retarded in the fields of the nuclei of the atoms of the anti-cathode, or sometimes completely stopped. The continuum on the short wave side has a definite limit corresponding to the stopping of an electron and the conversion of its entire kinetic energy into radiation; there is no limit on the long wave side. The continuous spectrum behind the K series is known as the K continuum; there are also L and M continua.

X-ray absorption spectra. It has been shown above that the lines of the K emission spectrum are produced when an electron from one of the outer atomic shells fills up

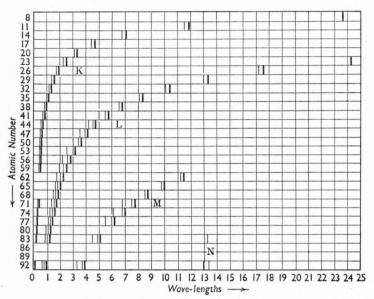

Fig. 3.7. Relation between the wave lengths of K, L, and M radiation and atomic number.

the orbital left unoccupied in the K shell by the removal of a K electron through ionisation or transition to the outer shell of the atom. The opposite process involves the orbital left unoccupied in the K shell by the removal of a K electron through absorption of energy. If a K electron of energy E_1 is to absorb radiation of frequency ν, it must be able to move into the state of energy E_2 where $E_2 - E_1 = h\nu$. This is not possible in the normal state of the atom when all the shells of low energy are filled. (The same argument applies to absorption in the case of the L or M shells.) There is, therefore, no absorption line spectrum in the usual sense of the term, but some line structure may appear due to the absorption by a K electron of sufficient energy to cause it to leave the atom, or to put it into an unoccupied orbital associated with the visible spectrum. The orbital which is left unoccupied in the K shell is refilled by another electron, and the K series is again emitted. In fact, the whole process is identical with that of the emission spectrum, the stimulus in one case being an impinging stream of fast electrons, and in the other case, radiation. A similar effect occurs with L and M electrons.

Close inspection of an X-ray line spectrum shows that lines such as K_α or K_β are made up of a number of lines close together. These lines appear because for a definite value of the principal quantum number n, there are $(2l+1)$ possible energy states for each value of l (p. 38). Transitions from these various energy states, all with the same n value, give a number of lines close together. Fig. 3.5, p. 77, gives a complete X-ray diagram for transitions from different energy states corresponding to different values of the quantum numbers n, l, m, s.

Moseley's work relating the frequencies of lines in the X-ray spectrum of an element with the position of the element in the periodic table established beyond doubt:

(1) that the periodic table furnished a rational classification of the elements,
(2) that the only missing elements were either those for which gaps had been left in the table, or those which might possess atomic numbers greater than that of uranium (92),
(3) that each rare earth element has a distinctive atomic number,
(4) that the positions in the table assigned to argon, potassium, tellurium, iodine, cobalt, and nickel are accurately determined by chemical analogies, and inaccurately by the chemical atomic weights of these elements.

The significance of position in the periodic table is emphasised by the **spectroscopic displacement law**, which may be stated thus: *The atomic spectrum of a given element is similar to that of the singly charged positive ion of the element which occupies the position in the periodic table next following that of the given element, and to that of the doubly charged positive ion of the element which occupies the position next but one following that of the given element.* The law requires modification if it is to be applied to spectra in which lines are doubled on account of electron spin.

Moseley's law and the spectroscopic displacement law are consistent with the pictorial representation of the atom as a positively charged nucleus surrounded by shells of electrons. Bohr's aufbau hypothesis, that each atom can be notionally constructed by adding to the atom which precedes it in the periodic table one additional unit of nuclear charge, and one additional outer electron, is, in turn, consistent with the atomic structures deduced from calculations based on wave mechanics and the quantum theory.

SELECTION RULES AND FORBIDDEN TRANSITIONS

It is mentioned on p. 31 that certain transitions do not take place; for example, the transition from the Ls orbital to the Ks orbital. From a study of Fig. 3.5, p. 77, it is evident that the selection rule that governs transitions demands that the quantum number l must change, and that the change must be by the values ± 1 only, whereas the quantum number m can change by $0, \pm 1$. The selection rules are determined by the interaction of radiation and the electric dipole in the atom. In order to explain these rules it is first necessary to discuss the polarisation of light.

Radiation and the polarisation of light. According to classical theory, radiation is caused by an oscillating electro-magnetic field, which is conveniently described in magnitude and direction by the electric and magnetic vectors which lie in the same plane and are at right angles to each other. The plane of the electric and magnetic vectors is at right angles to the direction of the propagation of the wave. The description of the wave may be given in terms of the electric vector alone. If the direction of the electric vector remains constant during one complete period, the light is said to be *linearly polarised*† in the direction of the electric vector. The direction of

† Linearly polarised light is sometimes called *plane polarised* light.

the electric vector in the vectorial plane may, however, vary with time. If the "tip" of the electric vector traces out a circle the light is said to be *circularly polarised*. If it traces out an ellipse the light is said to be *elliptically polarised*. If the direction of the electric vector is random, the light is said to be *unpolarised*; at any moment the electric field is uniform over the plane in which the electric vector lies. All of what has been said above about the electric vector applies *mutatis mutandis* to the magnetic vector.

According to the classical theory, linearly polarised radiation results from the oscillation of a constant electric charge about a mean position.

In the case of the hydrogen atom, the classical oscillating charge is provided by the vibration of the electron about its mean position, r from the nucleus. The radiation is emitted in a direction at right angles to the line of vibration. The vibration may be considered to be that of the electric dipole formed by the negatively charged electron, and the positively charged nucleus. The electric moment of the dipole may be measured classically by the product ϵr. In the case of an atom with several electrons, there is a total electric dipole moment of the form $\sum \epsilon r$.

According to wave mechanics, linearly polarised radiation corresponds to variations in the magnitude of charge at points along a straight line, these variations being governed by the laws of probability. The wave mechanical interpretation also ascribes the radiation to change of dipole moment, but this change is due to variation of charge and not to changes of r. On p. 30 the emission of radiation was described as the result of the simultaneous performance by the electron of two vibrations (of different frequencies) which are described by two eigenfunctions ψ_p and ψ_q. It was shown that if the probability function is composed of a contribution from each of these eigenfunctions,

$$|\psi|^2 = \psi_p \psi_q^*,$$

then the charge density ρ is given by

$$\rho = \epsilon \psi_p^0 \psi_q^{0*} \, e^{-2\pi i (\nu_p - \nu_q)t},$$

where ρ is not constant in time, but vibrates with a beat frequency.

The electric dipole moment μ of an atom may be written as

$$\mu = \int \rho r \, d\tau$$

where r is the radius vector from the nucleus to the position of greatest probability of finding the electron and $d\tau$ is a small element of volume. $d\tau = r^2 \sin \theta \, dr \, d\theta \, d\phi$. Polar co-ordinates for three dimensions are used since ρ is expressed in terms of r, ϕ, θ. (The wave functions are taken as a first approximation to be those of the hydrogen atom.) When the atom is not radiating, there is only one orbital to be considered, the probability function $\psi_p^0 \psi_q^{0*}$ is replaced by $\psi_p^0 \psi_p^{0*}$ and the frequency ν_q is replaced by ν_p. Therefore, if ψ is normalised, $\int \psi_p \psi_p^* \, d\tau = 1$, and the charge density distribution is constant. Therefore when there is no change of orbital there is no radiation.

If radiation does take place, the electric dipole moment due to a *transition*, or simultaneous vibration in two energy states, is given by the expression

$$\mu = \epsilon \int \psi_p^0 \psi_q^{0*} \, r \, d\tau.\dagger$$

μ may be "resolved" into components along the x, y, and z axes, where

$$\left. \begin{array}{l} x = r \sin \theta \cos \phi, \\ y = r \sin \theta \sin \phi, \\ z = r \cos \theta, \end{array} \right\} \quad \text{(p. 20)}$$

---

† The time dependent part of the expression is omitted because it is not relevant to the argument.

and the electric dipole moment of the atom may be considered as equivalent to three components in the x, y, and z directions respectively as follows:

$$\mu_x = \epsilon \iiint \psi_p^0 \psi_q^{0*} \sin \theta \cos \phi \; r^3 \sin \theta \; dr \; d\theta \; d\phi,$$
$$\mu_y = \epsilon \iiint \psi_p^0 \psi_q^{0*} \sin \theta \sin \phi \; r^3 \sin \theta \; dr \; d\theta \; d\phi,$$
$$\mu_z = \epsilon \iiint \psi_p^0 \psi_q^{0*} \cos \theta \; r^3 \sin \theta \; dr \; d\theta \; d\phi.$$

Owing to the fluctuations of charge density these three components of the electric dipole moment oscillate, causing the equivalent three components of the radiation. These components are linearly polarised along the x, y, and z axes respectively (the direction of propagation of the radiation being at right angles to each axis) and by considering them separately it is possible to deduce an explanation of the selection rules met with in the empirical recording of atomic spectra.

Selection rule for quantum number m. The magnetic quantum number m concerns the ϕ dependent part of the Schrödinger equation (p. 32). It has no meaning unless the atom is in the presence of a weak magnetic field. It is assumed in the following discussion that such a field is applied along the z axis.

Radiation linearly polarised along the z axis $(\theta = 0)$. The integral $\int \psi_p \psi_q^*$ with respect to ϕ (equation 2.6, p. 33) contains a term

$$\int_0^{2\pi} e^{i(m_p - m_q)\phi} \; d\phi.$$

This expression may be written as

$$\int_0^{2\pi} [\cos(m_p - m_q)\phi + i \sin (m_p - m_q)\phi] \; d\phi.$$

This integral vanishes because of the limits of integration unless $m_p = m_q$ $(\Delta m = 0)$. The quantum number m does not change during the emission of radiation, the cause of which may be represented either by a dipole oscillating along the z axis, or by a charge rotating with radius r about any axis at right angles to the z axis (see Zeeman effect, p. 99).

Radiation linearly polarised along the x axis or along the y axis. The expression for the radiation linearly polarised along the x axis can conveniently be considered with the expression for the radiation linearly polarised along the y axis.

(1) *Along the x axis*, the integral $\int \psi_p^0 \psi_q^{0*}$ with respect to ϕ contains a term

$$\int_0^{2\pi} \cos \phi \; e^{i(m_p - m_q)\phi} \; d\phi = \int_0^{2\pi} \frac{e^{i\phi} + e^{-i\phi}}{2} e^{i(m_p - m_q)\phi} \; d\phi$$
$$= \int_0^{2\pi} \frac{e^{i(m_p - m_q + 1)\phi} + e^{i(m_p - m_q - 1)\phi}}{2} \; d\phi.$$

(2) *Along the y axis*, the integral of $\psi_p^0 \psi_q^{0*}$ with respect to ϕ contains a term

$$\int_0^{2\pi} \sin \phi \; e^{i(m_p - m_q)\phi} \; d\phi = \int_0^{2\pi} \frac{e^{i\phi} - e^{-i\phi}}{2i} e^{i(m_p - m_q)\phi} \; d\phi$$
$$= \int_0^{2\pi} \frac{e^{i(m_p - m_q + 1)\phi} - e^{i(m_p - m_q - 1)\phi}}{2i} \; d\phi.$$

Because of the limits of integration, both integrals (1) and (2) vanish unless $m_p - m_q = \pm 1$. Therefore the selection rule for the quantum number m is $\Delta m = 0, \pm 1$. Further, since a simultaneously executed "cosine displacement" along the x axis and a "sine displacement" along the y axis represents the rotation of a radius vector (p. 1), the simultaneous oscillations of the dipole components along the x and y axes are equivalent to a rotating charge, or rather to two oppositely rotating charges since *m* changes either by $+1$ or by -1. There will therefore be two beams of radiation which will appear circularly polarised (p. 84) in opposite directions when viewed along the *z* axis, and as linearly polarised when viewed at right angles to the *z* axis. When it is remembered that the quantum number *m* does not change unless the atom is subjected to an external magnetic field, it is obvious that this conclusion is exactly the same as that derived from consideration of rotating orbitals (p. 100).

Selection rule for quantum number *l*. It is assumed that *m* has the same value for both ψ_p^0 and ψ_q^{0*}. Consider radiation linearly polarised along the *z* axis. The θ dependent part of the expression for μ_z is (p. 85)

$$\int_0^\pi \Theta_p \Theta_q^* \cos\theta \sin\theta \, d\theta.$$

The θ dependent differential equations for the two wave functions are (p. 33)

$$\frac{1}{\sin\theta} \frac{d}{d\theta}\left(\sin\theta \frac{d\Theta_p}{d\theta}\right) - \frac{m^2\Theta_p}{\sin^2\theta} + \beta_p\Theta_p = 0, \tag{3.7}$$

$$\frac{1}{\sin\theta} \frac{d}{d\theta}\left(\sin\theta \frac{d\Theta_q^*}{d\theta}\right) - \frac{m^2\Theta_q^*}{\sin^2\theta} + \beta_q\Theta_q^* = 0. \tag{3.8}$$

Putting

$$\beta_p = l_p(l_p+1) \quad \text{and} \quad \beta_q = l_q(l_q+1) \quad \text{(p. 36)},$$

multiplying (3.7) by Θ_q^* and (3.8) by Θ_p, and subtracting

$$\frac{1}{\sin\theta} \frac{d}{d\theta}\left[\sin\theta\left(\Theta_q^* \frac{d\Theta_p}{d\theta} - \Theta_p \frac{d\Theta_q^*}{d\theta}\right)\right] + \Theta_p\Theta_q^* [l_p(l_p+1) - l_q(l_q+1)] = 0.$$

On multiplying by $\sin\theta \, d\theta$ and integrating with respect to θ, the first term vanishes, on account of the vanishing of $\sin\theta$ at the limits, and

$$[l_p(l_p+1) - l_q(l_q+1)]\int_0^\pi \Theta_p\Theta^* \sin\theta \, d\theta = 0.$$

If l_p is not equal to l_q, then

$$\int_0^\pi \Theta_p\Theta_q^* \sin\theta \, d\theta = 0.$$

It is now necessary to use a proposition concerning associated Legendre functions which will not be proved here. It states that

$$\cos\theta \, \Theta_p = \Theta_{p+1} + \Theta_{p-1}.$$

Therefore

$$\int \cos\theta \, \Theta_p\Theta_q^* \sin\theta \, d\theta = \int \Theta_q^*(\Theta_{p+1} + \Theta_{p-1}) \sin\theta \, d\theta.$$

Since

$$\int \Theta_{p+1}\Theta_{p+1}^* \, d\theta = \int |\Theta_{p+1}|^2 \, d\theta \neq 0,$$

therefore

$$\int_0^\pi \Theta_{p+1}\Theta_q^* \sin\theta \, d\theta = 0 \text{ unless } q = p+1,$$

and

$$\int_0^\pi \Theta_{p-1}\Theta_q^* \sin\theta \, d\theta = 0 \text{ unless } q = p-1.$$

Therefore the integral $\int_0^\pi \cos\theta \, \Theta_p\Theta_q^* \sin\theta \, d\theta$ vanishes unless $q = p\pm 1$ and $l_q = l_p \pm 1$.

Therefore the quantum number *l* can change only by ± 1 if radiation is to take place. A similar conclusion can be reached by consideration of radiation linearly polarised along the x or y axes. In the case of an atom in the very strong electric field of a heavy discharge, the atomic wave function can be distorted and $\int \Theta_p \Theta_q^* \sin \theta \, d\theta$ will no longer be zero for values of q other than $p \pm 1$, and forbidden lines may appear in the spectrum.

ANGULAR MOMENTA AND SPECTRAL MULTIPLETS

The energy of an electron in an atomic orbital depends on the quantum numbers n and l,[†] and also on the spin quantum number s. The dependence of the energy on l and s indicates the dependence of the energy on orbital and spin angular momenta. The different ways of coupling the orbital and spin angular momenta in an atom produce a number of slightly different electron energy values, where without considering spin there would have been only a single energy value. Hence each line in the spectrum of the atom is split into a fine structure described as a *multiplet*.

It is therefore necessary to consider the behaviour of bodies which have angular momentum in order to understand the origin of spectral multiplets.

PRECESSION

Angular momenta are vector quantities, and may therefore be compounded by the well-known method exemplified by the parallelogram and triangle of forces. For instance, if a body has angular momentum about the x axis (Fig. 3.8) this may be represented in magnitude and direction by the vector OA. If a couple is now applied tending to give the system angular momentum about the y axis, and if OB represents the angular momentum so generated in a short time Δt, OA' represents the resultant of the two vectors OA and OB. The body's axis of rotation will therefore move from OA to OA', and if the angle between the axis of rotation and the axis of the applied couple remains constant, the axis of rotation continues to move, and itself rotates about the third axis OZ at right angles to OX and OY. This motion about the third axis is known as **precession**.

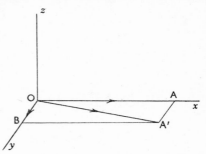

Fig. 3.8. Precession of angular momentum vector.

A simple experiment made with a gyrostat illustrates the precession of a system in which the *angle between the original axis of rotation and the axis of the applied couple is constant*.

The gyrostat (Fig. 3.9) consists of a heavy rotating wheel X on an axle AB. The wheel is supported on a frame made of two rigid circular wires PQ and CD which are fixed together at right angles to each other. This device enables the operator to set the wheel rotating with the axis AB in any direction. A string T is attached to the frame at O, and the frame is suspended from the string as in the diagram. If X is not rotating the frame drops until AB hangs vertically. If however, X is rotating, AB remains horizontal, or nearly so, and the whole frame rotates about the vertical axis OT. The wheel has angular momentum about the axis AB, it is given angular momentum about an axis at right angles to the plane of the paper by the gravitational couple due to the

---

[†]For the hydrogen atom for a given value of n, the energy values corresponding to different values of quantum number l are degenerate; hence the energy of an electron in an atomic orbital of hydrogen appears not to depend on l.

weight of the wheel, and so it precesses about the third axis *OT*. *AB* remains throughout at right angles to the axis of rotation due to the gravitational couple, and so the precessional revolution continues.

A similar condition applies to the spinning top. If the top is spinning in an upright position, a slight deflection of its axis of rotation causes the couple due to the weight of the top to be brought into play. This causes precession of the top about the vertical axis. The precession is also influenced by the friction between the top and the table. The full theory of the spinning top will not be given here since it is not relevant to the matter under discussion.

A slightly different precessional system is one in which the *axis of rotation due to the applied couple is fixed in space*, while the original axis of rotation is free to move.

Consideration of Fig. 3.8 shows that if *OB*, the axis of the applied couple, is fixed in space, *OA'* turns until it finally coincides with *OB*. The gyroscopic compass is an example of this type of system. If a gyrostat is supported in such a way that it experiences no gravitational couple, yet is free to turn in any direction (this may be accomplished by a somewhat elaborate system of gimbals), since it is subject to the earth's rotation, it turns until its axis of rotation lies along the earth's axis of spin.

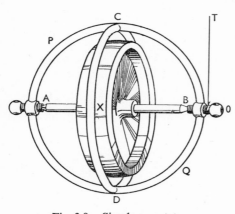

Fig. 3.9. Simple gyrostat.

Two rotating bodies, such as the earth and the gyroscope, which influence each other, are said to be "coupled", and their angular momenta may be compounded to give the total angular momentum of the rotating system.

Angular velocity of precession. In Fig. 3.8 if *p* is the angular momentum about *OA*, let *OA* represent *p* in magnitude and direction. In a short time Δt, *OA* moves to *OA'*. If Ω is the angular velocity of precession about *OZ*, $\angle AOA' = \Omega \Delta t$. If *OB* represents the angular momentum generated by the applied couple, *G*, in a short time Δt, if $\Omega \Delta t$ is small,

$$OB = AA' = OA\Omega \, \Delta t$$
$$= p\Omega \, \Delta t.$$

The applied couple *G*, which is equal to the time rate of change of angular momentum due to the couple, is given by:

$$G = \frac{p\Omega \, \Delta t}{\Delta t} = p\Omega.$$

Therefore the angular velocity of precession

$$= \frac{G}{p} = \frac{\text{applied couple}}{\text{angular momentum about } OA}.$$

THE COUPLING OF ANGULAR MOMENTA

Coupling of orbital angular momenta. Orbital angular momentum may be represented by a vector, and the angular momenta of all occupied orbitals in the atom may be combined vectorially to give a resultant orbital angular momentum. For instance, in a two electron atom, each orbital occupied by an electron has its own angular momentum, but it is also affected by the angular momentum of the other occupied orbital, since they are coupled together by electrostatic forces between the electrons, and between the electrons and the nucleus. Each angular momentum, therefore, acts on the other one, and causes precession round the direction of the resultant angular momentum which, by the principle of the conservation of angular momentum, remains constant in magnitude and direction (Fig. 3.10). The resultant angular momentum of the whole occupied orbital system is denoted by the vector **L**.† For a single electron the vector quantity l is given by the expression $l = \sqrt{(l(l+1))}h/2\pi$ and for many electrons, $\mathbf{L} = \sqrt{(L(L+1))}h/2\pi$ where L is the quantum number of the resultant orbital angular momentum. Each angular momentum vector l makes a constant angle with the direction of **L**; precession of each orbital angular momentum takes place about the direction of **L** in space. If one of the individual l's is already parallel to **L** it does not precess.

For an s orbital, $l = 0$; it can be shown empirically from the spectra of the inert gases that the resultant orbital angular momentum of a completed electron shell is zero. The resultant orbital angular momentum of an incomplete shell is determined by

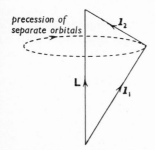

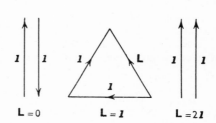

Fig. 3.10. Coupling of orbital angular momenta.

Fig. 3.11. Vectorial combination of orbital angular momenta, showing three possible values of **L**.

the relative orientation of the various orbitals of which it is composed. These can take up only those relative positions which cause **L** to be quantised. For instance (in the absence of an external magnetic field), the angular momenta of two p orbitals can combine vectorially in one of three ways, giving $\mathbf{L} = 0$, l, or $2 l$ (Fig. 3.11).

Orbital momenta are also coupled by their magnetic fields, but in the absence of an external magnetic field the magnetic coupling is masked by the stronger electrostatic coupling.

The atomic states and spectroscopic nomenclature. The resultant angular momentum of all the occupied orbitals in the atom is indicated by capital letters as follows, and these capital letters are used in indicating the *atomic state* (p. 92).‡

S indicates that $L = 0$ and the atom is in an S state
P indicates that $L = 1$ and the atom is in a P state
D indicates that $L = 2$ and the atom is in a D state
F indicates that $L = 3$ and the atom is in an F state

These capital letters are analogous to small letters s, p, d, f, used for denoting the type of a single occupied orbital, and the state of an electron which occupies the orbital.

† The use of vectors to represent angular momentum in wave mechanics can be justified by Group Theory.
‡ The reader must distinguish carefully between **L**, the resultant angular momentum which is *not* an integer and L, the orbital quantum number which takes one of the values 0, 1, 2, 3, ...

Coupling of spin momenta. Electron spin is of great importance in the interpretation of spectra. The coupling of occupied orbitals has been described above in terms of orbital angular momenta, and a description of the coupling of electron spins may be given in similar terms.

It has been deduced from the study of spectra that the spins of two electrons in the same orbital can take up two relative orientations only, that of spinning in the same direction, and that of spinning in opposite directions. The spins can be added vectorially and the resultant lies in the same straight line as the component vectors. In the many electron atom, the spins also combine vectorially. The resultant spin quantum number S takes an integral number when there is an even number of electrons, and a half integral value when there is an odd number of electrons. The resultant spin angular momentum vector $\mathbf{S}$ is related to the quantum number S by the expression

$$\mathbf{S} = \sqrt{(S(S+1))}\,\frac{h}{2\pi}.$$

Coupling of orbital and spin angular momenta. For a single electron it is clear that when orbital and spin angular momenta are coupled together it must be by means of their magnetic fields, since there is no electrostatic coupling between them. It has therefore been deduced that all coupling between orbital and spin angular momenta is magnetic.

The coupling of angular momenta in the atom may be described theoretically in one of two possible ways:

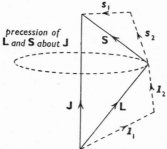

LS, or Russell Saunders coupling. The separate orbital angular momenta are coupled together *electrostatically* to give the resultant orbital angular momentum $\mathbf{L}$. The separate spin momenta are coupled together *electrostatically* to give the resultant spin angular momentum $\mathbf{S}$. $\mathbf{L}$ and $\mathbf{S}$ are coupled *magnetically*; combined vectorially, they give the resultant angular momentum of the atom $\mathbf{J}$ which is related to the quantum number J by the expression

Fig. 3.12.   Russell-Saunders (**LS**) coupling.

$$\mathbf{J} = \sqrt{(J(J+1))}\,\frac{h}{2\pi}.$$

J can take the values $L-S,\ L-S+1,\ \dots,\ L+S-1,\ L+S$. This form of coupling is known as the **LS** *coupling* or the *Russell Saunders* coupling. It has been deduced from the study of observed spectra, and in general applies to the lighter elements (Fig. 3.12).

jj coupling. The orbital and spin angular momenta are coupled together *magnetically* for each electron, to give the resultant angular momentum of the electron $\mathbf{j}$ (Fig. 3.13), related to the quantum number j by the expression

$$\mathbf{j} = \sqrt{(j(j+1))}\,\frac{h}{2\pi}.$$

All the $\mathbf{j}$'s are then combined *magnetically* to give the resultant angular momentum of the atom $\mathbf{J}$ where $\mathbf{J} = \sqrt{(J(J+1))}h/2\pi$. This method is known as the **jj** coupling, and is found to be applicable to the spectra of the heavy elements where evidently the electrostatic coupling between the electrons is small. Analysis of the spectra of the heavy elements is very difficult, but it appears from these spectra that the energy states of the heavy atom are not associated with definite values of L.

In the case of the Russell Saunders coupling, **L** and **S** precess round the direction of **J**. In the case of the **jj** coupling, the separate **j**'s precess round the direction of **J** (Fig. 3.14). In both cases the magnitude and direction of **J** remain constant.

The quantum numbers L and J have the same selection rule as that already deduced

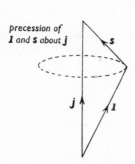

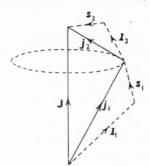

Fig. 3.13. Coupling of l and s for a single electron.

Fig. 3.14. jj coupling. j_1 and j_2 precess about **J**.

for the quantum number l on p. 86; they can only, and must, change by either of the values $+1$ or -1. In the heavy elements it sometimes occurs that two electrons change their momenta simultaneously without affecting L or J. In this case ΔL or ΔJ may be zero.

SPECTRAL MULTIPLETS

Spectra of atoms with one electron in the outer shell (doublet system). *Alkali metals.* Since these atoms have only one electron in the outer shell, there is only one orbital and one spin to be considered. j can take the values $l \pm \frac{1}{2}$, and therefore all the terms will be *double*, with the exception of the s terms. These s terms correspond to $l = 0$, the orbital momentum is zero, therefore there is no orbital magnetic field to orientate the spin.

For the p state j can take the values $1 \pm \frac{1}{2}$, that is $\frac{1}{2}, \frac{3}{2}$.

For the d state j can take the values $2 \pm \frac{1}{2}$, that is $\frac{3}{2}, \frac{5}{2}$.

Atomic hydrogen and He$^+$ *ion.* It would be expected that the spectra of the hydrogen atom and the He$^+$ ion would both show a double character. Spectroscopic methods have improved very greatly since the days of Balmer, and the detailed examination of certain lines in spectra of atomic hydrogen and He$^+$ has established the existence of a fine structure consisting of doublets, but it is hard to separate the lines as the energy values are so close together.

Spectra of atoms with two electrons in the outer shell (singlet and triplet systems). *Atoms such as helium and beryllium.* The LS coupling is used. The spins can be parallel or antiparallel. Thus S can have either the value 0 (antiparallel, $\frac{1}{2} - \frac{1}{2}$), or the value 1 (parallel, $\frac{1}{2} + \frac{1}{2}$).† For antiparallel spins, $S = 0$ and $J = L$, therefore the terms are *single*. For parallel spins, $S = 1$, and there are three possible values of **J** corresponding to the three possible ways of combining **L** and **S** vectorially (Fig. 3.15, p. 92). The terms therefore are *triple*.

There is no intercombining between the terms of the two systems since that would necessitate the reversal of spin of one of the electrons, and it seems that this is most unlikely to happen.

† $+S$ cannot be considered to give a different value from $-S$ since there is no external field to orientate the spin.

Spectra of atoms with three electrons in the outer shell (doublet and quartet systems). *Atoms such as boron.* The **LS** coupling is used. S can take the values $\frac{1}{2}$ or $\frac{3}{2}$. J can take all possible values between $|L-S|$ and $L+S$ (p. 90).

For instance, for a P state, $L=1$, $\begin{cases} \text{for } S=\frac{1}{2}, J=\frac{1}{2}, \frac{3}{2} \text{ and the terms are } \textit{double,} \\ \text{for } S=\frac{3}{2}, J=|-\frac{1}{2}|, \frac{1}{2}, \frac{3}{2}, \frac{5}{2} \text{ and the terms are } \textit{quadruple.} \dagger \end{cases}$

Spectra of atoms with four electrons in the outer shell (singlet, triplet, and quintuplet systems). *Atoms such as carbon.* The **LS** coupling is used. S can take the values 0, 1, 2.

For instance, for a P state, $L=1$, $\begin{cases} \text{for } S=0, J=1, \text{ and the terms are } \textit{single.} \\ \text{for } S=1, J=0, 1, 2, \text{ and the terms are } \textit{triple.} \\ \text{for } S=2, J=|-1|, 0, 1, 2, 3, \text{ and the terms are } \textit{quintuple.} \end{cases}$

Multiplicity and atomic states. The resultant angular momentum due to electron spin is indicated by the **multiplicity** which may be defined as *the number of lines in the atomic spectrum which are equivalent to a single line in the absence of spin.* Experimental observation leads to the empirical law:

$$\text{Multiplicity} = 2S+1$$

where S is the resultant spin quantum number. The law is consistent with the values of the multiplicity deduced from the above considerations of orbital and spin angular momentum.

For instance,

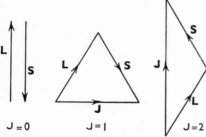

Fig. 3.15. Vectorial combination of **L** and **S** for a P state with $S=1$, giving three possible values of **J** corresponding to $J=$ 0, 1, 2.‡

multiplicity 1, $\quad S = 0$
2, $\quad S = \frac{1}{2}$
3, $\quad S = 1$
4, $\quad S = \frac{3}{2}$
5, $\quad S = 2.$

The multiplicity is written as a superscript in front of the capital letter indicating the resultant orbital angular momentum (p. 89), e.g. ^2P. Such a formula denotes the *atomic state* of the atom in question.

This type of formula is frequently used as a shorthand description of the electron configuration of an atom, but sometimes further information is included by

(a) putting the value of J as a subscript at the right-hand side of the symbol for the atomic state, e.g. $^2P_{3/2}$ $(J=\frac{3}{2})$,

(b) putting the principal quantum number of the outer shell as a full-size figure in front of the formula, e.g. $2^2P_{3/2}$ $(n=2)$,

(c) enumerating all the occupied orbitals in front of the symbol for the atomic state: a superscript on the right of the symbol for an orbital shows how many electrons are in this type of orbital, e.g.

$$1s^2\, 2s^2\, 2p^5\, {}^2P_{3/2}.$$

† **J** cannot have a negative value, and therefore, although the term scheme is technically a quartet, two of the terms $(J=\frac{1}{2}, J=|-\frac{1}{2}|)$ are superposed. Similar considerations apply to other multiplicities.

‡ The third case is often represented by drawing the vectors **S** and **L** in the same straight line. This arrangement was satisfactory for the simple vector model of the old quantum theory, but if $S=\frac{h}{2\pi}\sqrt{(S(S+1))}$, $L=\frac{h}{2\pi}\sqrt{(L(L+1))}$, and $J=\frac{h}{2\pi}\sqrt{(J(J+1))}$, the collinear model does not give J an integral value and hence for $J=2$, the third case must be represented as in Fig. 3.15.

ATOMIC MAGNETISM

ORBITAL MAGNETIC MOMENT

If an electron in an orbital has angular momentum, the rotating charge is associated with a magnetic moment. An expression for this moment may be developed very simply by considering the charge to be rotating orbitally at a fixed distance from the nucleus. If ω is the angular velocity, and T the periodic time and i the current,

$$i = \frac{\epsilon}{T} \quad \text{and} \quad T = \frac{2\pi}{\omega},$$

and therefore

$$i = \frac{\epsilon\omega}{2\pi}.$$

A current i flowing in a circle is equivalent to a magnetic shell of moment Ai/c where A is the area enclosed, and c is the velocity of light.

If, therefore, the radius of the path of the electron in the rotating orbital is r, the magnetic moment M_0 due to the orbital motion of the electron is given by

$$M_0 = \frac{\pi r^2}{c} \frac{\epsilon\omega}{2\pi}$$

$$= \frac{\epsilon\omega r^2}{2c}.$$

By equation (2.23), p. 46, the orbital angular momentum is given by:

$$I\omega = \sqrt{(l(l+1))} \frac{h}{2\pi}.$$

If m_0 is the mass of the electron

$$I\omega = m_0 r^2 \omega.$$

Therefore

$$M_0 = \frac{\epsilon r^2}{2c} \frac{\sqrt{(l(l+1))}}{m_0 r^2} \frac{h}{2\pi}$$

$$= \sqrt{(l(l+1))} \frac{h\epsilon}{4\pi m_0 c}. \tag{3.9}$$

SPIN MAGNETIC MOMENT OF THE ELECTRON

Spin is a phenomenon which must be treated relativistically, and therefore the spin magnetic moment may be simply derived from the radius of spin which was calculated relativistically (p. 57).

$$\text{Spin magnetic moment} = \frac{\epsilon\omega r^2}{2c}$$

$$= \frac{\epsilon r}{2}$$

$$= \frac{h\epsilon}{4\pi m_0 c}.$$

The quantity $h\epsilon/4\pi m_0 c$ is known as the **Bohr magneton**; it forms a convenient unit of atomic magnetism.†

---

† ϵ is measured in electrostatic units. The Bohr magneton expressed in electromagnetic units is

$$\frac{h\epsilon}{4\pi m_0}$$

Anomalous magnetic moment of the electron. For general purposes, the Bohr magneton may be taken as the magnetic moment of the electron; this value gives good agreement with spectroscopic observation. The most accurate measurements of the electron magnetic moment, however, show that it is very slightly (of the order of 0·1%) larger than the Bohr magneton. This apparent anomaly is due to the interaction between the electron and its own field. The correction may be conveniently expressed as the sum of the electrostatic and magnetic interactions of the electron with the particle which represents the field of the electron (p. 58). It is supposed that the centres of spin of the two particles are a Compton wave length apart. Considerable evidence from quantum theory points to this distance as the minimum distance which can be distinguished between two particles. It is generally accepted that the equations of electrodynamics cannot be applied within a region whose dimensions are less than a Compton wave length. The assumption is made that, viewed electrostatically, a spinning charge acts as if it were located at the centre of the spin orbit, and that each particle has potential energy due to the presence of the other.

The electrostatic field between the electron and the "other particle" acts as a drag on each spinning charge, and as a result the energy of spin is equivalent to the energy required to keep a charge $\epsilon + \epsilon'$ in spin orbital rotation. It is convenient to express the extra electrostatic energy in the form of a mass equivalent $m'c^2$ for each spinning particle.

Thus,

$$m'c^2 = \frac{\epsilon^2}{\lambda_e}$$

where λ_e is the Compton wave length.

Therefore

$$m' = \frac{m_0 \epsilon^2}{ch}$$

$$= \frac{\alpha}{2\pi} m_0,$$

where α is a constant known in spectroscopy as the *fine structure constant*.

If

$$\frac{\epsilon'}{m'} = \frac{\epsilon}{m_0}$$

then

$$\epsilon' = \frac{\alpha}{2\pi} \epsilon.$$

Hence the magnetic moment of the electron M', taking into account the electrostatic energy between electron and field, is given by the expression,

$$M' = \frac{(\epsilon + \epsilon')r}{2}$$

$$= \frac{h\epsilon}{4\pi m_0 c} \left(1 + \frac{\alpha}{2\pi}\right).$$

This expression is identical with that obtained as a first approximation from quantum electrodynamics.†

The magnetic interaction between the electron and its field accounts for the second order term of the anomalous electron magnetic moment. The effect is considerably smaller than that due to the electrostatic interaction and opposes it.

† J. Schwinger, *Phys. Rev.* **76**, 1950, 790.

The induction B in a magnetic field is commonly defined by the expression

$$B = \mu H$$

where μ is the permeability and H the magnetic field. The energy of a magnetic dipole of moment M placed in the field is the product of M and the induction.

If H is the field due to the " other dipole " (also of moment M), for the maximum magnetic interaction

$$H = \frac{2M}{R^3}$$

where R, the distance between the dipoles, is large compared with their dimensions.

Therefore, the maximum magnetic energy of one dipole due to the presence of the other dipole is given by,

$$\frac{2\mu M^2}{R^3}.$$

Substituting the expression for the Bohr magneton instead of M,

$$\text{Magnetic energy} = \frac{2\mu h^2 \epsilon^2}{16\pi^2 m_0^2 c^2 R^3}.$$

The electrostatic energy between two charges ϵ separated by a distance R is ϵ^2/kR, where k is the dielectric constant. For a gas or vacuum μ and k may be put equal to unity, and therefore, the ratio

$$\frac{\text{magnetic energy}}{\text{electrostatic energy}} = \frac{1}{8\pi^2}\left(\frac{\lambda_e}{R}\right)^2.$$

If the particles are at a distance λ_e apart,

$$\text{magnetic energy} = \frac{1}{8\pi^2} \times \text{electrostatic energy}.$$

If $m''c^2$ is the mass equivalent of the potential energy due to the magnetic interaction, and ϵ'' the equivalent charge, then by an argument similar to that used above,

$$\epsilon'' = \frac{1}{8\pi^2}\frac{\alpha}{2\pi}\epsilon,$$

and the magnetic moment of the electron, corrected for both electrostatic and magnetic interaction between the electron and its field, may be written as

$$\frac{h\epsilon}{4\pi m_0 c}\left(1 + \frac{\alpha}{2\pi} - \frac{\alpha}{16\pi^3}\right) = \frac{h\epsilon}{4\pi m_0 c}\left(1 + \frac{\alpha}{2\pi} - 2\cdot73\frac{\alpha^2}{\pi^2}\right)$$
$$= 1\cdot0011469 \text{ Bohr magnetons.}$$

A rigorous treatment by fourth order electrodynamics gives the result[†]

$$\frac{h\epsilon}{4\pi m_0 c}\left(1 + \frac{\alpha}{2\pi} - 2\cdot97\frac{\alpha^2}{\pi^2}\right) = 1\cdot0011454 \text{ Bohr magnetons.}$$

The experimental value for the magnetic moment of the electron is

$$1\cdot001146 \pm 0\cdot000012 \text{ Bohr magnetons.}$$

LAMB RETHERFORD SHIFT

The Lamb Retherford shift is an extremely small line displacement which can be observed in atomic spectra; it has been measured very accurately in the spectrum of atomic hydrogen. It is intimately connected with the anomalous magnetic moment of the electron, as the two effects may be attributed to a common cause. The interaction

[†] R. Karplus and N. Kroll, *Phys. Rev.*, 77, 1950, 536.

between the electron and the electromagnetic field described in the preceding paragraph alters, very slightly, the potential difference between the electron and the proton to which it is bound in the atom. It is shown below that this effect is very much smaller when the electron occupies a p orbital than when it occupies an s orbital; thus the $2s$ and $2p$ states are no longer degenerate; there is a difference in energy between them. This difference in energy, which may be expressed as $h\,d\nu$, has been measured very carefully for atomic hydrogen by causing a transition between the two states considered. The transition is accomplished by the absorption of radiation of the correct frequency; such radiation is found in the radiofrequency region. The effect is explained simply as follows.

Adopting the nomenclature of the preceding paragraph, the extra Coulomb energy between the electron in the s orbital and the proton† may be expressed as

$$\frac{(\epsilon'-\epsilon'')^2}{R},$$

where R is the distance between the electron and proton. This extra energy is shared between the electron and the particle representing the field. Thus,

$$2h\,d\nu_s = \frac{\epsilon^2(0\cdot0011469)^2}{R}.$$

The following values are inserted into the equation:

$$h = 6\cdot625 \times 10^{-27} \text{ erg sec}$$
$$\epsilon = 4\cdot803 \times 10^{-10} \text{ e.s.u.}$$
$$R = 2\cdot116 \times 10^{-8} \text{ cm} \quad \text{(radius of the second Bohr orbit)}$$

then
$$d\nu_s = 1\cdot080 \times 10^9 \text{ cycles per second}$$
$$= 1080 \text{ megacycles per second.}$$

In the s orbital the charge of the electron has spherical symmetry. The overall picture of an orbital charge density with spherical symmetry results from the equal probability that the electron may be found anywhere on the surface of a sphere with arbitrary radius, centred on the proton. In the p orbital the charge is divided into two parts, one in each lobe; therefore the energy of interaction between the electron and the field is only one-quarter of the energy of interaction when the electron is in the s orbital.

$$m'_{(p)}c^2 = \frac{\left(\dfrac{\epsilon}{2}\right)^2}{\lambda_e}$$
$$= \tfrac{1}{4}m'_{(s)}c^2.$$

This extra energy is divided between the two parts of the orbital, therefore

$$(\epsilon'-\epsilon'')_{(p)} = \tfrac{1}{8}(\epsilon'-\epsilon'')_{(s)},$$

and the extra Coulomb energy between the electron and the proton may be expressed as

$$\frac{(\epsilon'-\epsilon'')^2}{64R}.$$

Therefore
$$d\nu_p = 17 \text{ megacycles per second.}$$

The Lamb Retherford shift is given by

$$d\nu_s - d\nu_p = (1080 - 17) \text{ Mc/sec}$$
$$= 1063 \text{ Mc/sec.}$$

The experimental value is 1062 ± 5 Mc/sec.

† It may easily be shown that the charge on the proton is also raised by an amount $(\epsilon'-\epsilon'')$ due to the interaction between the proton and its field.

THE GYROMAGNETIC RATIO, AND THE LANDÉ SPLITTING FACTOR

Gyromagnetic ratio. The ratio of magnetic moment to angular momentum is known as the gyromagnetic ratio. This ratio is different for orbital motion and for spin. From equations (3.9) and (2.23),

$$\text{the orbital gyromagnetic ratio} = \frac{h\epsilon}{4\pi m_0 c} \sqrt{(l(l+1))} \times \frac{2\pi}{h\sqrt{(l(l+1))}}$$

$$= \frac{\epsilon}{2m_0 c}.$$

From pages 53 and 93,

$$\text{the spin gyromagnetic ratio} = \frac{h\epsilon}{4\pi m_0 c} \frac{4\pi}{h}$$

$$= \frac{\epsilon}{m_0 c}.$$

It was originally deduced from spectroscopic observation that the spin gyromagnetic ratio is twice the orbital gyromagnetic ratio. This deduction was subsequently confirmed by the full wave mechanical theory.

Landé g factor or splitting factor. In making certain calculations concerning the effect of the magnetic moment of the atom on spectra, as in the anomalous Zeeman effect (p. 101), it is convenient to make use of the Landé g factor. This factor is *not* the same as the gyromagnetic ratio but depends on it. When the resultant magnetic moment of the atom is due to orbital motion only, g has the value unity. When the resultant magnetic moment is due to spin only, g has the value 2.

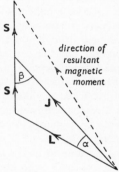

direction of resultant magnetic moment

The relation of g to the resultant magnetic moment is shown by the following calculation:

Fig. 3.16 represents the vectorial combination of orbital and spin angular momentum. Since the gyromagnetic ratio for spin is twice the gyromagnetic ratio for orbital motion, the resultant magnetic moment does not lie in the same direction as **J**, the resultant angular momentum formed by the vectorial combination of **L**, the resultant orbital

Fig. 3.16. Relation of direction of resultant magnetic moment to direction of **J**.

angular momentum, and **S** the resultant spin angular momentum. The scalar value of **J** is given by

$$|\mathbf{J}| = |\mathbf{S}| \cos \beta + |\mathbf{L}| \cos \alpha.$$

Let μ be the component of the magnetic moment along the direction of **J**,

$$\mu = \text{gyromagnetic ratio} \times \text{angular momentum}$$

$$= \frac{\epsilon}{m_0 c} \times |\mathbf{S}| \cos \beta + \frac{\epsilon}{2m_0 c} \times |\mathbf{L}| \cos \alpha$$

$$= \frac{\epsilon}{2m_0 c} (2|\mathbf{S}| \cos \beta + |\mathbf{L}| \cos \alpha)$$

$$= \frac{\epsilon}{2m_0 c} (|\mathbf{J}| + |\mathbf{S}| \cos \beta)$$

$$= \frac{\epsilon}{2m_0 c} |\mathbf{J}| g, \quad \text{where} \quad g = 1 + \frac{|\mathbf{S}| \cos \beta}{|\mathbf{J}|}.$$

Since

$$\cos \beta = \frac{|\mathbf{S}|^2 + |\mathbf{J}|^2 - |\mathbf{L}|^2}{2|\mathbf{S}|\,|\mathbf{J}|}$$

$$g = 1 + \frac{|\mathbf{S}|^2 + |\mathbf{J}|^2 - |\mathbf{L}|^2}{2|\mathbf{J}|^2}$$

therefore

$$g = 1 + \frac{S(S+1) + J(J+1) - L(L+1)}{2J(J+1)}.$$

When $S = 0$, $J = L$, and therefore $g = 1$. When $L = 0$, $J = S$, and therefore $g = 2$.

TYPES OF MAGNETISM

Diamagnetism. Diamagnetism is the induced magnetism, in opposition to the inducing field, which is shown by non-magnetic materials when they are placed in a magnetic field. An atom of a diamagnetic material has no permanent magnetic moment in the absence of the magnetic field, and so presumably the magnetic moments of the occupied orbitals cancel each other out and the electron spins are paired (each pair consisting of two spins, one in the opposite direction to the other). Hence there must be an even number of electrons in each atom, ion, or molecule of which the diamagnetic material is composed. When an external magnetic field is applied, the occupied orbitals are either speeded up or retarded according to their direction of rotation, and this causes a resultant magnetic moment in the atom. During the short time interval between the instant of application of the magnetic field and the instant when it reaches its maximum value, the field is changing and therefore an electromotive force is induced in the atom. The induced currents which flow in the atom as a result of this electromagnetic induction must be carried by the electrons. Since $i = \epsilon\omega/2\pi$, a change of i causes a change of ω, and hence a change of magnetic moment (p. 93).

According to Lenz's law, the induced magnetic field opposes the external magnetic field. As there is no electrical resistance in the atom, the extra current continues to flow and the induced magnetism persists as long as the external field is applied. When the field is cut off, the atom loses its magnetism as a result of the reverse process from that which came into operation when the external field was set up. All atoms show diamagnetism whether they have paired or unpaired electrons, but for those which have a permanent magnetism the diamagnetic effect is masked.

Paramagnetism. Paramagnetic materials have permanent magnetism in the absence as well as in the presence of an external magnetic field. Each atom has a resultant magnetic moment which tends to align itself so that it reinforces an external field. With increase of temperature, this alignment is hindered to a certain extent by the thermal motion of the atoms, and therefore paramagnetism diminishes with increase of temperature. This characteristic is shown by all paramagnetic substances. Atoms with closed electron shells would be expected to show no paramagnetism, since the resultant orbital momentum is zero and the spins are paired. This is found to be the case, and paramagnetism is found in substances with uncompleted shells, particularly those with unfilled shells in the inner part of the electron structure, such as certain compounds of the transition elements. Investigations of such paramagnetic substances are chiefly made by the method of paramagnetic resonance, a description of which is given in Chapter 9, p. 257.

Determination of the gyromagnetic ratio and the Landé factor leads to the conclusion that paramagnetism is due to the spin of an unpaired electron rather than to the angular momentum of its occupied orbital. Since most of the paramagnetic materials investigated have crystalline structures, it is supposed that the orientation of the orbitals is affected by the neighbouring ions in the lattice, and the orbitals are therefore unable to align themselves with the field. This effect is known as the "quenching of orbital momentum".

Ferromagnetism. Ferromagnetism is a large scale phenomenon due to aggregates of atoms, in contrast to paramagnetism and diamagnetism which are properties of individual atoms. The fact that single iron atoms and iron ions in solution show paramagnetism, and not ferromagnetism, is an indication that ferromagnetism is not a property of a single atom. It is significant that elements which are ferromagnetic have paramagnetic salts. Determination of the gyromagnetic ratio shows that ferromagnetism is due to spin. The theory depends on the properties of metallic crystals and is discussed in connection with the transition elements (p. 943).

THE EFFECT OF AN EXTERNAL MAGNETIC FIELD ON LINE SPECTRA

The following discussion is confined to atoms with LS coupling. In a strong magnetic field, the magnetic axes of atoms, whether paramagnetic or diamagnetic, lie as much as possible along the direction of the field, and the resultant magnetic moment of all the atoms is a maximum. In the presence of a weak magnetic field, each atom experiences a couple which directs its orientation with regard to the field direction, but which is not strong enough to bring the magnetic axes of all the atoms into line with the field. It is this case which is interesting to the spectroscopist, since the Zeeman effect, that is, the splitting of each single line into several lines, is observed in a weak magnetic field.

Under these conditions, the position taken up by the vector $\mathbf{J}$ is determined by the value of the quantum number M which is analogous to the quantum number m governing the behaviour of a single electron in an atom in an external magnetic field.

M can take all values from $+J$ to $-J$. For a given value of M, the direction of $\mathbf{J}$ makes a constant angle with the direction of the external field, and $\mathbf{J}$ precesses about this field direction. Where, in the absence of an external field, there was a single line in the spectrum corresponding to a transition to a state designated by a certain value of J, in the presence of the external field this line is split into a number of lines which correspond to the different energy values associated with change of values of M.

The number of lines into which the original line is split is governed by the selection rules for transitions. The rule is that J (and therefore M also) can change only by $0, \pm 1$ and the transition $0 \rightarrow 0$ is forbidden.

ZEEMAN EFFECT

Normal Zeeman effect (in weak external magnetic field). The so-called "normal" Zeeman effect was first observed experimentally by Zeeman in 1896. It is the splitting into three of each line in the series corresponding to transitions between singlet states. In these states the quantum number S governing the resultant spin angular momentum is zero, therefore $\mathbf{J} = \mathbf{L}$. $\mathbf{J}$ is space quantised in the direction of the field, and takes the value $Mh/2\pi$, where M is the magnetic quantum number. Since M can assume all possible integral values from $+J$ to $-J$, for a given value of J each term should split into $2J+1$ subsidiary terms. Where $J=1$ there are three subsidiary terms, where $J=2$ there are five subsidiary terms, where $J=3$ there are seven subsidiary terms, and so on. Whatever the number of subsidiary terms, however, the normal spectral line becomes a triplet. The reason for this is shown clearly in the diagram of Fig. 3.17. The triplet in each case corresponds to the three possible changes in M, (ΔM), which are

0, +1, −1. The difference in energy between the subsidiary terms of any atomic state is the same for all states, even though the number of subsidiary terms differs, and so, as is shown in the diagram, it is possible to obtain a transition, for instance where $\Delta M = 1$, in a number of different ways. The energy change in the transition is the same in each case, so that all possible transitions for $\Delta M = 1$ produce the same spectral line. A similar argument applies to the case where $\Delta M = 0$, or −1. It is therefore evident that each line which was single in the absence of an external magnetic field, splits into three lines when the external magnetic field is applied (Plate 5).

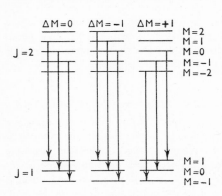

Fig. 3.17. Normal Zeeman effect. Term scheme for the singlet state showing transitions corresponding to $\Delta M = 0, \pm 1$. The difference in energy values for all transitions is constant for a given value of ΔM.

The normal Zeeman effect and the rotating orbital. Spectroscopic analysis shows that when an atom is radiating in a weak external magnetic field, if the light is received in any direction at right angles to the field, three lines are observed in place of one line seen in the absence of the field. Of the three lines, the middle one occupies the position of the original line, and is linearly polarised in the direction of the field. The other two are linearly polarised in a direction at right angles to the field. If the light is received in the direction of the field by means of a hole bored through the magnet, two lines only are observed. These are on either side of the position of the middle line which is missing. The radiation corresponding to the two lines is circularly polarised in opposite directions. The difference of frequency between the frequency of the original line and that of either of the displaced lines is exactly the Larmor frequency (p. 103).

The p_x and p_y orbitals are rotating in opposite directions, and the application of the external magnetic field imposes a couple tending to align them with the field. Since they have equal but opposite magnetic moments, the effect of the applied couple is to increase the speed of revolution of one of them and to decrease that of the other. The applied couple also makes them precess with the Larmor frequency round the direction of the field, but in opposite senses. The corresponding radiation which according to the wave mechanical theory is described as a fluctuation of charge density at a point, is circularly polarised in opposite directions. The circular movement of charge, when viewed at right angles to the field, appears as a linear displacement of charge in a direction at right angles to both the direction of the field and that along which the radiation is received.

The case of the p_z orbital is somewhat different. Space quantisation demands not that it should have no angular momentum, but that the component of angular momentum in the direction of the field should be zero. The only restriction on the rotation of the orbital is that the axis of rotation must be at right angles to the direction of the field; the rotation can be in any plane containing the z axis. The orbital thus shows spherical symmetry in accordance with Dirac's theory. There are two opposite directions in which it is equally probable that the rotation will take place; the simultaneous execution of the two possible rotations, half the charge rotating in each direction, would correspond to a linear fluctuation of charge up and down the z axis which is common to all possible planes of rotation. The corresponding radiation is unchanged in frequency from that of the original line, since the motion of the charge is along the lines of force. It is not visible in a direction parallel to the field because the linear fluctuations of charge will then be viewed "end on", but it is visible at right angles to the field, and is linearly polarised in the direction of the field.

Anomalous Zeeman effect. This title is misleading and is a relic of the old nomenclature of the empirical spectroscopist. It might well be renamed the "complex Zeeman effect". It refers to the action of an external magnetic field on the spectra of atoms which have both orbital and spin angular momenta. The spectra which result from energy changes of these atoms are very complicated. In the presence of an external magnetic field, lines which were originally single are split into many subsidiary lines. This complex splitting is due to the fact that the gyromagnetic ratio for spin is twice the gyromagnetic ratio for orbital motion, and the resultant magnetic moment of the atom is not in the same direction as the axis of **J**, but makes a constant angle with it (Fig. 3.16). The direction of the resultant magnetic moment precesses with **J** round the direction of the external magnetic field (Plate 6).

The reason for the complex splitting may be simply illustrated by considering the atom as equivalent to a small bar magnet (Fig. 3.18). If this magnet has a moment $\mathscr{M}$ and lies in a magnetic field of strength H, making an angle θ with the direction of the field, it has potential energy. This potential energy may be considered to be made up of two parts:

(a) potential energy $-\mathscr{M}H$ which the magnet has when it lies with its moment aligned with the field (this may be verified by considering the work done in bringing up unit positive pole from infinity to the magnet).

(b) potential energy $\mathscr{M}H(1-\cos\theta)$ acquired when work is done is twisting the magnet till it lies in a position making an angle θ with the direction of the field.

The resultant potential energy of the magnet lying at an angle θ with the direction of the field is therefore $-\mathscr{M}H\cos\theta$ or $-H\times$ component of magnetic moment in the direction

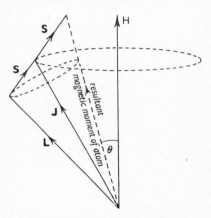

Fig. 3.18. Anomalous (or complex) Zeeman effect. Angular momentum vector diagram for atom with resultant spin in a magnetic field.

of H. Since the component of the magnetic moment in the direction of **J** is given by the expression $\epsilon Jg/2m_0c$ (p. 97), the component of the magnetic moment in the direction of the field is given by the expression $\epsilon \mathbf{M}g/2m_0c$ and the potential energy of the atom lying in the field is given by $-\epsilon H\mathbf{M}g/2m_0c$. This expression is dependent on g, and since (p. 98)

$$g = 1 + \frac{S(S+1)+J(J+1)-L(L+1)}{2J(J+1)}$$

the difference in energy for a change of **M** is different for different values of S, L, and J.†

The patient spectroscopist is able to sort out many of the spectral lines and, by measuring their separation, to determine their energy difference and so obtain a value for g. This is of importance in determining the quantum numbers J, I, and S for various states of the atom.

† In the case of the normal Zeeman effect, the difference of energy for a given change of M is the same whatever the values of L and J. S is zero and therefore $g=1$. Similarly when $L=0$, and $g=2$, the splitting is simple.

In cases where g can be both calculated theoretically and determined experimentally, there is close agreement.

PASCHEN-BACK EFFECT

If the normal and anomalous Zeeman effects are to be shown, the external magnetic field should not be a strong one. If the field is increased gradually until it becomes very strong, the spectra of atoms with both orbital and spin angular momenta at first show the anomalous Zeeman effect just described, then they pass through a stage of even greater complexity, until finally, when the field is very strong, the spectra show again only the normal Zeeman effect. The sequence of these changes follows the gradual uncoupling of the **LS** coupling, corresponding to the region of greatest complexity (this region is known as the Paschen-Back region), until the final stage is reached when instead of **L** and **S** precessing round **J**, and **J** precessing round the direction of the external field, **L** and **S** precess separately round the direction of the external field. (At this stage the Zeeman triplet does show a faint fine structure owing to a very slight **LS** coupling which still remains.) Plate 7 shows the Paschen–Back effect.

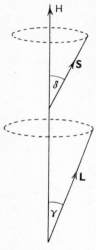

Fig. 3.19 shows the vector diagram for the completed Paschen-Back effect. **L** and **S** are quantised separately and there is no **J**. **L** precesses making an angle γ with the direction of the field; **S** precesses making an angle δ with the direction of the field. Hence,

$$\left.\begin{array}{r}\text{component of total magnetic moment}\\ \text{in the direction of the field}\end{array}\right\} = \frac{\epsilon}{2m_0c}(\mathbf{L}\cos\gamma + \mathbf{S}\cos\delta)$$

Fig. 3.19. Vector diagram for completed Paschen-Back effect.

$$= \frac{\epsilon}{2m_0c}(\mathbf{M}_L \pm \mathbf{M}_S),$$

where $\mathbf{M}_L$ and $\mathbf{M}_S$ are the quantised components of orbital and spin angular momenta in the direction of the field. The spin does not change during radiation, and the selection rules for changes of M_L are the same as for changes of M.

Therefore, since $\Delta M_L = 0, \pm 1$, the normal Zeeman effect is again shown.

ANGULAR VELOCITY, FREQUENCY, AND ENERGY OF ORBITAL PRECESSION

Fig. 3.20 shows the magnetic moment of the atom resolved into a component μ along the direction of **J** and a component at right angles to **J**. The component at right angles to **J** represents a magnetic moment which always lies in a plane at right angles to **J** but which may be orientated in any direction in this plane. The effective magnetic moment due to this component is nil, and the magnetic moment of the atom may be considered to be due to μ only. If **J** makes an angle θ with the field, the couple due to the field is $\mu H \sin\theta$.

The angular velocity of precession is equivalent to the angular velocity about the field H of the vector **J** $\sin\theta$. On page 88 it was shown that the angular velocity of precession ω is given by the expression

$$\omega = \frac{\text{applied couple}}{\text{angular momentum}},$$

therefore

$$\omega = \frac{\mu H \sin \theta}{\mathbf{J} \sin \theta}.$$

Since $\mu = \mathbf{J}g\epsilon/2m_0 c$ (p. 97),

$$\omega = \frac{\mathbf{J}g\epsilon}{2m_0 c} \times \frac{H \sin \theta}{\mathbf{J} \sin \theta}$$

$$= \frac{H\epsilon g}{2m_0 c}.$$

The frequency of precession,

$$\nu = \frac{1}{T} = \frac{\omega}{2\pi} = \frac{H\epsilon g}{4\pi m_0 c}.$$

It should be noted that ν is directly proportional to the strength of the field H, and is independent of μ, $\mathbf{J}$, and θ.

For the normal Zeeman effect, $S=0$ and $g=1$. Hence

$$\nu = \frac{H\epsilon}{4\pi m_0 c}.$$

This frequency is often referred to as the **Larmor frequency**. Since the energy of an atom in a field H is the product of the gyromagnetic ratio, the component of angular momentum in the direction of the field, and H, therefore

$$\text{energy} = -\frac{\epsilon H}{2m_0 c} \times \frac{Mh}{2\pi},$$

and since M can change only by ± 1, the energy change in a transition where M only changes is

$$\frac{H\epsilon h}{4m_0 \pi c} = h\nu,$$

where ν is the Larmor frequency.

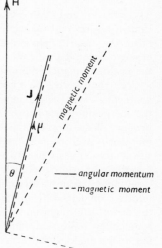

Therefore the difference in energy between successive space quantised orientations of the atom in the external magnetic field is equal to $h \times$ the frequency of precession about the direction of the field.

Fig. 3.20. Magnetic moment of the atom resolved into two components; one component lies along, the other at right angles to, the total angular momentum vector.

Experimental evidence has confirmed this conclusion. The frequency of precession of a paramagnetic atom in an external magnetic field of about 10,000 Gauss corresponds to radiation in the microwave region of the spectrum, and it has been shown that radiation of the right frequency is strongly absorbed by the atom.

The absorption is known as a "magnetic resonance" effect. By changing the strength of the field, it is possible to scan a range of Larmor frequencies; by observation of the absorption, the precession frequencies can be determined. The method is used extensively for the investigation of paramagnetic substances such as the transition elements, ferromagnetic substances, and organic free radicals; it is described in more detail in Chapter 9.

STERN-GERLACH EXPERIMENT

The existence of space quantisation has been brilliantly demonstrated by an experiment performed by the two workers Stern and Gerlach.[†] They deflected a beam of silver atoms in an *inhomogeneous* magnetic field and recorded the deviation of the silver atoms by means of a photograph. The silver atom has one electron only in the outer shell and the ground state is an S state ($L=0$), so the only possible values of J (and also of M) were $\pm\frac{1}{2}$. According to the classical theory, the passing of a beam of small magnets through an inhomogeneous magnetic field should produce a uniform broadening of the beam, since the small magnets might be orientated in any direction. According to the quantum theory, there are $2s+1$ possible directions only. Since $s=\pm\frac{1}{2}$ the beam should be split into two. This splitting was shown most clearly in the photograph (Plate 8), which forms a very striking demonstration of the validity of quantum principles.

STARK EFFECT

The effect of an external electric field on atomic spectra is in many ways similar to that of an external magnetic field, but there are significant differences. In the Stark effect the electric field produces an electric moment in the atom by displacing the electrons relative to the nucleus, thus polarising the atom. This causes a precession of the resultant angular momentum vector **J** about the direction of the electric field. In a very strong electric field **L** and **S** are uncoupled (as in the case of the strong magnetic field) with a result analogous to the Paschen-Back effect. The splitting of the lines and the energy difference between the subsidiary terms of the atomic states depends on the product of the dipole moment and the field strength. As the magnitude of the dipole moment is itself proportional to the field strength, the energy differences between the subsidiary terms are proportional to the square of the field strength, hence the effect of imposing an external electric field is sometimes called the *quadratic Stark effect*. The resulting spectrum is very complicated, and it will not be further discussed here. The information derived from the study of the spectra in the Stark effect cannot be used for the direct determination of atomic quantum numbers, and from this point of view it is much less important than the Zeeman effect. The real importance of the Stark effect lies in the analogy between the behaviour of atomic electrons in an external electric field, and the behaviour of molecular electrons in the axial electric field provided by the two nuclei in the diatomic molecule. The Stark effect is discussed more fully in connection with the determination of dipole moments (p. 308).

ANGULAR MOMENTUM OF THE NUCLEUS

One of the causes of hyperfine structure (p. 70) is the coupling of the angular momentum of the nucleus to the angular momentum of the rest of the atom. It is assumed that the nucleus has spin which is governed by the laws of quantum mechanics. According to this assumption, the total angular momentum of the nucleus is due to the effect of the combined spins of the nucleons. The total nuclear angular momentum is quantised in units of $h/2\pi$ and is governed by the quantum number I, which is integral where there is an even number of nucleons, and half integral where there is an uneven number of nucleons. The coupling of **I** with **J** gives the total angular momentum of the atom, which is governed by the quantum number F. Space quantisation takes place in the field of the electrons, and **J** and **I** precess about the direction

[†] O. Stern and W. Gerlach, *Z. Physik*, **41**, 1927, 563.

of F. In the presence of an external magnetic field, line splitting equivalent to the Zeeman and Paschen-Back effects can be observed. It is assumed that there is a nuclear magneton analogous to the Bohr magneton. If the mass of the proton is substituted for the mass of the electron, the magnetic moment of the nuclear magneton is approximately 1/1836 that of the Bohr magneton (p. 93)†.

For weak fields F is space quantised, and precesses round the direction of the field. The existence of this precession has been experimentally verified by experiments on the absorption of electromagnetic radiation. All radiation corresponding to a possible frequency of precession is found to be strongly absorbed.

BOOKS FOR FURTHER READING

See Chapter 1, p. 31, and Chapter 2, p. 60; also

CANDLER, A. C., *Atomic Spectra* (Cambridge University Press, 1937).

FINKELNBURG, W., *Atomic Physics* (McGraw-Hill, 1950).

HERZBERG, G., *Atomic Spectra and Atomic Structure* (Dover, 1946).

SYNGE, J. L., *Geometrical Mechanics and de Broglie Waves* (Cambridge Monographs on Physics, 1954).

WHITE, H. E., *Introduction to Atomic Spectra* (McGraw-Hill, 1934).

† The observed magnetic moment of the proton is 2·793 nuclear magnetons. The large anomalous magnetic moment is due to the interaction between the proton and its own field.

CHAPTER FOUR

VALENCY

The valency of an element may be defined in general terms as its combining power. An atom of a univalent element possesses one unit of valency which enables it to combine with another atom of the same kind, or with one atom of another univalent element. An atom of a bivalent element can combine with two atoms of a univalent element, and so on.

A study of valency reveals the principles:

(1) that the number expressing the valency of an atom is integral,
(2) that the valency of a given atom may have more than one value,
(3) that an atom in the univalent state can combine with not more than one atom of another univalent element; the atom then has no further combining power unless it changes its state of valency, and hence when an atom in a given state of valency is combined with the appropriate number of univalent atoms (or the equivalent number of polyvalent atoms) its combining power is saturated.

The valency forces exerted by an atom clearly differ from gravitational forces by which any given mass of matter attracts *all* other masses in the universe; it is observed that a given atom will combine with atoms of certain elements only.

A link between two atoms in a molecule which is established when they combine chemically is known as a valency bond, or shortly as a *bond*. An atom exerts one valency bond for each unit of valency employed. There are two principal kinds of bonds, ionic bonds and covalent bonds. A compound which contains an ionic bond in the molecule is known as an ionic compound, whether or not the molecule contains covalent bonds as well.

The ionic bond. The outstanding characteristic of an ionic compound is its power of conducting an electric current, either when it is itself in the liquid state, or when it is dissolved in some liquid of high dielectric constant, such as water, liquid ammonia, or liquid sulphur dioxide. The passage of the current is invariably accompanied by chemical reaction at the surfaces of the electrodes leading the current into and out of the melt or solution. It is accounted for by assuming that an ionic compound consists of ions of two kinds, the cations carrying positive charges, and the anions carrying negative charges, and that the ions are free to migrate independently of one another in the liquid phase. Experiments on electrolysis show that the charge on an ion depends on its nature, and that the smallest charges (whether positive or negative) carried by single ions are identical in magnitude.

Faraday showed that the quantity of electricity required to liberate 1 gram-equivalent of any product of the electrolysis of the aqueous solution of a salt is 96,500 coulombs. If it is assumed that 1 gram-equivalent of product is liberated by the discharge of 1 gram-ion at the electrode, then 96,500 coulombs of electricity is associated with

1 gram-ion. 1 gram-ion contains $6 \cdot 023 \times 10^{23}$ ions ($6 \cdot 023 \times 10^{23}$ is the Avogadro number). Hence the charge on the ion is

$$\frac{96,500}{6 \cdot 023 \times 10^{23}} = 1 \cdot 602 \times 10^{-19} \text{ coulombs.}$$

This value is identical with the charge on an electron determined by purely physical methods. Hence the ion in question in aqueous solution carries one electron more, or one electron less, than is required for electrical neutrality. It may be shown similarly that if one gram-ion on discharge during electrolysis liberates two gram-equivalents of product, the ion in question carries an excess or deficiency of two electrons, and so on.

Atoms judged on chemical grounds to be univalent are those which give rise to ions carrying a charge of one electron; atoms judged to be bivalent are those which give rise to ions carrying charges of two electrons. It is therefore accepted that the valency of an ion is determined by the number of charges it carries.

A univalent ion need not consist of a single charged atom; it may consist of a group of atoms such as (NH_4^+) or (ClO_4^-); the atoms within these groups are bonded by covalencies, the nature of which is discussed below. Simple ions carrying charges greater than 2 are rare, but complex ions frequently carry charges of 3 or 4.

The ionic bond in a molecule is assumed to consist solely of the mutual electrostatic interaction between the cation (positive) and the anion (negative). This assumption is consistent with the following behaviour of ionic compounds:

(1) Ionic compounds are crystalline solids which vaporise only at high temperatures. Sodium chloride, for example, boils at 1430°. The vapour consists of pairs of ions of opposite sign, but the high dipole moment of the ion pairs (about 8 debyes), and their behaviour on photodissociation, indicate that the force between the ions is electrostatic, and that there is no link other than this force.

(2) Crystals of ionic compounds consist of the ions arranged in close-packed structures. The ionic bond is therefore non-directional.

(3) When the crystals of a soluble ionic compound are dissolved in water, the component ions fall away from one another without being chemically decomposed. If an electric field is imposed on the solution, the ions of opposite sign move in opposite directions, and the solution conducts an electric current. The fused compound also conducts an electric current because the ions in the melt are free to move independently.

The covalent bond. The covalent bond is found in such molecules as those of the gases H_2, Cl_2, HCl, H_2O, and CH_4. These substances do not conduct an electric current, and it may be concluded that the bonds between the atoms differ from the ionic bond just described. Kekulé proposed that a unit of covalency be indicated by a stroke attached to the atomic symbol

$$\text{H--} \qquad \text{Cl--} \qquad \overset{|}{\underset{|}{-C-}} \qquad \text{--O--} \qquad \overset{|}{-N-}$$

and that the molecule of a compound should be represented by associating the strokes of component atoms thus

$$\text{H--Cl} \qquad \text{H--O--H} \qquad \text{H--}\overset{\overset{\text{H}}{|}}{\underset{\underset{\text{H}}{|}}{\text{C}}}\text{--H}$$

In practice a pair of strokes is drawn as one line, and each line then represents a covalent bond

$$\text{H--Cl} \qquad \text{H--O--H} \qquad \text{H--}\overset{\overset{\text{H}}{|}}{\underset{\underset{\text{H}}{|}}{\text{C}}}\text{--H}$$

Kekulé's convention successfully illustrates the limited combining power of a given atom. The combining power of the carbon atom is found to be saturated in the molecule of methane, CH_4, and the diagram above shows that in the molecule of methane all the Kekulé strokes of the carbon atom are used up. The chemical behaviour of such substances as acetaldehyde and ethyl cyanide, which in many instances react with other elements or compounds to form single products, can be represented by Kekulé's convention, if the assumption is made that it is possible for more than one covalent bond to terminate on a single atom, as, for example, in the formulae used in the equations:

$$H_2 + H_3C - C \begin{matrix} H \\ \diagup \\ \diagdown \\ O \end{matrix} = H_3C - \underset{H}{\overset{H}{C}} - OH, \qquad 2H_2 + H_3C - C \equiv N = H_3C - \underset{H}{\overset{H}{C}} - N \begin{matrix} H \\ \diagup \\ \diagdown \\ H \end{matrix}$$

The link represented by $C{=}O$ is known as a *double bond*, and the link $C{\equiv}N$ as a *triple bond*.

In organic chemistry this representation of the covalent bond has proved so satisfactory that for most purposes the study of carbon compounds can be carried on without using any more significant symbol. By its use it is possible to formulate homologous series, cyclic compounds, and unsaturated compounds. It enables interpretations to be made of the phenomena of both geometrical and optical isomerism. The study of optical isomerism has shown that directional properties may be assigned to bonds represented by Kekulé symbols. It has been deduced, for example, that the four bonds from a carbon atom are directed towards the four apices of a regular tetrahedron having the carbon atom at the centre, that the three bonds from a tricovalent nitrogen atom are not coplanar, and that the two bonds from a bicovalent oxygen atom are not collinear.

Kekulé's method of formulating covalent bonds, however, fails in certain cases to give an adequate representation of the properties of a compound. The concept of the multiple bond explains the chemistry of acetaldehyde and ethyl cyanide, but it gives the formula $H_2C{=}CH_2$ to ethylene, and implies that the molecule contains two carbon-to-carbon bonds. Carbon-to-carbon bonds are some of the least reactive in organic chemistry, but ethylene is a very reactive substance. To meet this difficulty Baeyer proposed his strain theory, which assumed that an increase of energy in the molecule was produced by the distortion of the tetrahedral bond angle, which would be necessary to produce the two parallel bonds between the two carbon atoms required by Kekulé's formula.

The formulae assigned by Kekulé to carbon monoxide $O{=}C\diagup^{\diagup}_{\diagdown}$ and methyl isocyanide $CH_3 - N{=}C\diagup^{\diagup}_{\diagdown}$ are not satisfactory. These formulae predict intense unsaturation of the carbon atom which is not found in experience. The alternative formulae, $O{\equiv}C$ and $CH_3 - N{\equiv}C$ are inadmissible, as they indicate a quadruple carbon link not found in any other compounds, and which on stereochemical grounds would be highly improbable.

Kekulé assigned to butadiene and benzene the formulae:

$$CH_2{=}\underset{H}{\overset{H}{C}} - \underset{H}{\overset{H}{C}}{=}CH_2$$

These formulae contain the unit C=C which is characteristic of the formula he assigned to ethylene. The ethylenic properties of butadiene are, in fact, less marked than would be predicted by this formula, and in benzene they are suppressed to a striking degree. Moreover the Kekulé formulation for benzene predicts two isomers of the type

but among the derivatives of benzene this type of isomerism has never been detected. In inorganic chemistry the covalent bond is less predominant than in organic chemistry, and the structures of the majority of inorganic compounds are not adequately described by formulae consisting solely of Kekulé symbols.

THE ELECTRONIC THEORY OF VALENCY

When the concept of the atom as a positively charged nucleus surrounded by electrons had become accepted, attempts were made to explain chemical combination by the grouping of electrons in the atoms concerned. The chemical inactivity of the inert gases suggested that their electronic configurations must be peculiarly stable. It was observed that atoms of all elements other than the inert gases are more stable in combination than in the isolated state, and so it was suggested that chemical combination of atoms results in the regrouping of their electrons into configurations similar to those of the inert gases. It was assumed that only the outer-most electrons in an atom would play a part in chemical combination; electrons near the nucleus would be undisturbed by the relatively small quantities of energy required for, or given out by, chemical change. These assumptions may be formulated thus:

In chemical combination an atom tends to gain or lose electrons so that the number of electrons in its outermost quantum shell may become either (i) *identical with the number of electrons in the outermost shell of the atom of the inert gas at the end of the Period of the periodic classification in which the element is found, or* (ii) *identical with the number of electrons in the outermost shell of the atom of the inert gas at the end of the previous Period.*

This formulation is referred to in the following discussion as the *inert gas rule*. This rule indicates that the hydrogen atom can enter into chemical combination only by increasing the number of electrons in its outermost shell to two, which is the number in the helium atom: this is completely in accord with experience. In conformity with the inert gas rule, the atoms of elements of Period 2 enter into chemical combination, either by increasing the number of electrons in their outermost shells to eight, the number in the outermost shell of the neon atom, or, by reducing the number to two, the number in the helium atom. It is found experimentally that the first two elements, lithium and beryllium, may either increase the number of electrons in their outermost shells to eight, or reduce the number to two; the remaining elements, boron, carbon, nitrogen, oxygen, and fluorine, always increase the number of electrons in their outermost shells when they enter into chemical combination. Nearly the whole of the chemical behaviour of the elements in Period 2 is described, fundamentally, by the inert gas rule. There are, however, a few cases of chemical combination to which it does not apply, of which the following compounds may serve as examples:

> lithium in lithium hydride LiH_2, and lithium dimethyl $Li(CH_3)_2$,
> beryllium in beryllium borohydride $Be(BH_4)_2$,
> boron in boron trimethyl $B(CH_3)_3$,
> carbon in triphenyl methyl $C(C_6H_5)_3$.

The inert gas rule applies, with some exceptions, to elements in the remaining Periods, particularly to elements in the normal sub-Groups. Elements beyond Period 2, however, can enter into very stable chemical combination by increasing the number of electrons in their outermost shells above eight; chemical experience shows that the maximum number of electrons held in the outermost shell of an atom is twelve for elements in Periods 3 and 4, and sixteen for elements in Periods 5 and 6. Elements of the transitional sub-Groups frequently enter into chemical combination by increasing the numbers of electrons in the penultimate, as well as in the outermost quantum shells.

Hence the inert gas rule is neither a complete nor a rigorous guide to the behaviour of atoms entering chemical combination, but it serves as a starting point for an account of ionic valency and covalency. It is shown later that the inert gas rule, in so far as it indicates that the number of electrons in the valency shell of a combined atom is adjusted to eight, is merely a statement of the prevalence of tetrahedral hybridisation.

IONIC VALENCY IN TERMS OF THE ELECTRONIC THEORY OF VALENCY

In terms of the electronic theory of valency an ionic bond (p. 106) between two atoms is formed by the complete transference of one or more electrons from one atom to the other. The inert gas rule (above) will serve, at the present stage of the discussion, as a guide to the number of electrons lost by the atom of the electropositive element and gained by the atom of the electronegative element. As an example, the formation of sodium chloride from an atom of sodium and an atom of chlorine may be considered. The configuration of the sodium atom may be represented as:

and that of the chlorine atom as:

If the outermost electron of the sodium atom is transferred to the chlorine atom, the ion pair Na^+Cl^- is obtained; the sodium ion has the electron configuration of the neon atom, and the chlorine ion has the configuration of the argon atom.

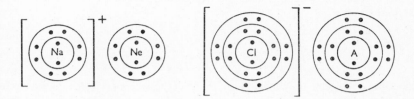

The transference of a single electron from one atom to another corresponds to a single ionic valency on the part of each atom.

Two electrons may be transferred from the atom of a metal which has two electrons more than are required for the configuration of the preceding inert gas; two electrons may be transferred to the atom of a non-metal which has two electrons fewer than the number in the atom of the following inert gas. The ions thus derived are bivalent.

In most cases the development of ionic bonds by single atoms confers an inert gas configuration on each ion, that is, it increases or decreases the number of electrons in the external shell of the ion to eight (or two in the cases of hydrogen and lithium). Other configurations of electrons, however, are sometimes present in stable monatomic ions.

COVALENCY IN TERMS OF THE ELECTRONIC THEORY OF VALENCY

The electronic theory of valency also explains covalency in terms of electronic configuration. A correlation between the electronic structure of an atom and its covalency was proposed by G. N. Lewis in 1916. He suggested that each covalent link be interpreted as a pair of electrons held in common by the two combined atoms. This is best shown diagrammatically. If the outermost shells of two chlorine atoms are drawn

$$\cdot \overset{\displaystyle \cdot \cdot}{\underset{\displaystyle \cdot \cdot}{Cl}} \cdot \qquad \cdot \overset{\displaystyle \cdot \cdot}{\underset{\displaystyle \cdot \cdot}{Cl}} \cdot$$

then the chlorine molecule is represented by

$$\cdot \overset{\displaystyle \cdot \cdot}{\underset{\displaystyle \cdot \cdot}{Cl}} \cdot \overset{\displaystyle \cdot \cdot}{\underset{\displaystyle \cdot \cdot}{Cl}} \cdot$$

The shared electrons are regarded as part of the electronic structure of each atom in the molecule, so that each chlorine atom has acquired the configuration of an atom of argon, and has increased the number of electrons in its outer shell by one.

In terms of the electronic theory of valency a double bond consists of 4 electrons (two pairs) held in common by the two doubly linked atoms. Consider, for example, the carbonyl group in the molecule of acetone

$$H_3C-\underset{\displaystyle \underset{O}{\|}}{C}-CH_3$$

The valency shells of isolated carbon and oxygen atoms have the respective electronic configurations

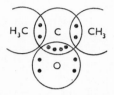

In the acetone molecule the carbon atom in the carbonyl group forms shared electron pairs with two other carbon atoms, and the remaining two electrons form two shared pairs with electrons of the oxygen atom:

Both the carbon atom and the oxygen atom thus acquire 8 electrons in their valency shells. The four electron pairs on the carbon atom are all shared, but the oxygen atom has four unshared electrons.

The numerical values of the ionic valency and the covalency of a given element must be equal, for if an element increases the number of its valency electrons by *one*, it either accepts wholly *one* electron from another atom (ionic valency), or, it accepts a share in *one* electron (covalency); if the element increases the number of its valency electrons by *two*, it either accepts wholly *two* electrons from another atom, or, it accepts a share in *two* electrons, and so on.

The total number of electrons present in an atom in chemical combination (including those gained by transference or by the process of sharing) is nearly always even. In the example of the molecule of chlorine just mentioned, each chlorine atom in a chlorine molecule possesses one shared *pair* of electrons and six unshared electrons. It is probable that the unshared electrons in an atom are grouped in pairs. In describing the structure of a covalent molecule, a distinction may be made between the *shared* electron pairs (those taking part in the formation of covalent bonds) and *unshared* electron pairs (those which take no part in the bonding). The concept of electron pairs is of great importance, and is carried on into the wave mechanical theory of valency.

In the account of covalency so far it has been assumed that a covalent bond is formed between two atoms without the disturbance of any electrons other than the pair which constitute the bond. It is possible, however, to envisage a redistribution of valency electrons between two atoms, which permits the sharing of one or more pairs of electrons in covalent bonds, and leaves a number of unshared pairs (but no single electrons) on each of the atoms. The molecule of carbon monoxide may be taken as an example. Carbon monoxide is similar in many respects to nitrogen. In terms of the electronic theory of valency, the nitrogen molecule may be considered as two nitrogen atoms linked by a triple covalent bond,

$$N\equiv N.$$

In the molecule there are ten valency electrons, six of which are shared. In the molecule of carbon monoxide there are also ten valency electrons, four originally on the carbon atom and six originally on the oxygen atom. If these are redistributed, so that there are five electrons on each atom, then a triple bond may be formed between the atoms leaving one unshared pair on each atom.

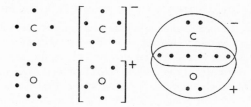

Since, however, the carbon atom has gained an electron and the oxygen atom has lost one, there is a formal redistribution of charge, and the molecule of carbon monoxide must be written $\bar{C}\!\equiv\!\overset{+}{O}$. The charges $-$ and $+$ written as superscripts are known as *formal charges* because they do not necessarily correspond to any real separation of charge. The separation of charge would be indicated by the dipole moment of the molecule, which is affected not only by the distribution of the valency electrons between the nuclei, but also by such factors as the magnitudes of the charges on the atomic nuclei, the screening power of the electrons, and the electronegativity of the atoms. The effect of the distribution of the electrons in the molecule of carbon monoxide is opposed by the other factors, with the result that the dipole moment found experimentally is close to zero.

A covalent bond which is dependent on the redistribution of electrons may be called a *co-ionic bond*, but there is no need to distinguish it from a covalent bond linking two neutral atoms.

An atom may attain a stable electronic configuration by the exertion of covalent bonds to a second atom after the transference of electrons to or from a third atom. If electrons are lost a cation is produced; if electrons are gained an anion is produced. For example, the nitrogen atom in ammonium chloride transfers an electron to a chlorine atom, producing the anion Cl$^-$, and then makes four covalent bonds with hydrogen atoms. The nitrogen atom thus becomes the central atom in the cation, and the ion pair which constitutes ammonium chloride is written:

$$\begin{bmatrix} H & & H \\ & N & \\ H & & H \end{bmatrix}^{+} \quad Cl^-$$

WAVE MECHANICAL INTERPRETATION OF VALENCY

The interpretation of valency in terms of wave mechanics has proceeded on the general principle that in a diatomic molecule A—B there is at least one orbital which extends over both the nuclei A and B. Such an orbital is referred to as a **molecular orbital**. Since the molecule A—B may be formed by bringing together the separate atoms A and B, and subsequently dissociated into separate atoms again, it is reasonable to suppose that the molecular orbital is formed by the association of atomic orbitals, and that it breaks down into atomic orbitals again when the nuclei are separated by a large distance. This line of approach makes use of certain general principles which will be explained before the theory of the formation of molecular orbitals is described in detail. These general principles may be grouped into two classes, (1) those concerning the energy of an orbital, the LCAO method† of combining atomic orbitals, and the identification of the most stable combined orbital, and (2) those which concern the symmetry of the combining atomic orbitals.

† LCAO is a contraction for Linear Combination of Atomic Orbitals.

ENERGY OF AN ORBITAL WITH WAVE FUNCTION ψ

The classical definition of electrostatic potential at a point is the *work done in bringing unit (notional)*† *positive charge from infinity to the point*; therefore the presence of an electric charge is associated with potential energy. The region surrounding the charge and influenced by it is known as the electric field. Potential energy is associated with the field as well as with the charge, since owing to the presence of the charge in the vicinity, work must be done in bringing unit (notional) positive charge to any point in the field. The classical picture of the field due to an electron is that due to a point charge. The wave mechanical theory supposes that the charge is distributed, though not uniformly, throughout the whole of the field. The energy of the field at any point is related to the quantity $|\psi|^2$ which is a measure of the probability of finding the electron at any point.

The energy at any point in the field may therefore be described in terms of the properties of the electron. If T_p is the kinetic energy and V_p the potential energy of the electron at a point in the field, T_p and V_p being functions of ψ, and E is the total energy of the electron,

$$\int E \times \text{probability of finding the electron at the point}$$
$$= \int (T_p + V_p) \times \text{electron density at the point.}$$

If the integration is carried out over τ, the whole volume of the field,‡

$$E \int \psi^2 d\tau = \int (T_p + V_p)\psi^2 d\tau, \tag{4.1}$$

and

$$E = \frac{\int (T_p + V_p)\psi^2 \, d\tau}{\int \psi^2 \, d\tau}. \tag{4.2}$$

Now the energy of the electron (other than that of the rest mass) is the energy of the orbital, therefore the energy of an occupied orbital described by a wave function ψ is given by equation (4.2). This equation has been derived by consideration of an orbital containing one electron. A similar expression may equally well be derived for an orbital containing two electrons bonding two atoms. V_p then describes the potential energy of the field at a certain point due to the presence of two charges, and ψ is the wave function describing a molecular orbital.

THE TWO-CENTRE MOLECULAR ORBITAL

LCAO method of combining atomic orbitals. The two-centre molecular orbital arises when an electron pair is shared by two atoms. It is formed by the combination of one atomic orbital from each of the two atoms. Let the wave functions of the original atomic orbitals be ψ_A and ψ_B. These wave functions may be combined by simple addition or subtraction to form another wave function, just as simple harmonic waves are combined when they are superposed. This process is described as a *linear combination* (p. 4). If ψ_A and ψ_B are solutions of a Schrödinger equation, then any linear combination of ψ_A and ψ_B is also a solution. Thus,

$$\psi = c_1\psi_A \pm c_2\psi_B$$

is a solution, where c_1 and c_2 are constants.

In other words, another orbital whose wave function is a solution of the Schrödinger equation may be constructed of the whole or parts of the two atomic orbitals.

---

† The term *notional* implies that the positive charge has no effect on the field round the point.

‡ It is customary to express the energy as a Hamiltonian, but this treatment is deliberately excluded from this book which is addressed to readers who do not possess advanced mathematical techniques.

Combined orbital of least energy. If the wave function ψ of a combined orbital is given by the expression

$$\psi = c_1\psi_A \pm c_2\psi_B,$$

then the expression for the energy of the orbital, from equation (4.2) is†

$$E = \frac{\int (T_p + V_p)(c_1\psi_A \pm c_2\psi_B)^2 \, d\tau}{\int (c_1\psi_A \pm c_2\psi_B)^2 \, d\tau}.$$

If ψ_A and ψ_B are the original atomic wave functions, the value of E varies with the values of c_1 and c_2. A stable molecule corresponds to a system with minimum energy; therefore c_1 and c_2 must be chosen so that E is a minimum.

Let $\psi_1 = c_1\psi_A + c_2\psi_B$ where ψ_A and ψ_B are normalised atomic wave functions. Then

$$E = \frac{\int (c_1{}^2\psi_A{}^2 + 2c_1c_2\psi_A\psi_B + c_2{}^2\psi_B{}^2)(T_p + V_p) \, d\tau}{\int (c^2{}_1\psi_A{}^2 + 2c_1c_2\psi_A\psi_B + c^2{}_2\psi_B{}^2) \, d\tau}.$$

Let

$$E_{AB} = \int \psi_A\psi_B(T_p + V_p) \, d\tau, \qquad E_{AA} = \int \psi_A{}^2(T_p + V_p) \, d\tau,$$

$$S_{AB} = \int \psi_A\psi_B \, d\tau, \qquad S_{AA} = \int \psi_A{}^2 \, d\tau.$$

Corresponding expressions are written for E_{BB}, E_{CC}, and so on.
Then

$$E = \frac{c_1{}^2 E_{AA} + 2c_1c_2 E_{AB} + c_2{}^2 E_{BB}}{c_1{}^2 S_{AA} + 2c_1c_2 S_{AB} + c_2{}^2 S_{BB}}. \tag{4.3}$$

The integral S_{AB} or $\int \psi_A\psi_B \, d\tau$ is known as the **overlap integral**. The reason for this name is shown by the diagram in Fig. 4.1 (after Coulson). The circles represent

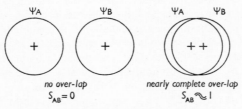

$\Psi_A \qquad \Psi_B \qquad\qquad \Psi_A \qquad \Psi_B$

$+ \qquad\qquad + \qquad\qquad\qquad + \, +$

no over-lap $\qquad\qquad\qquad$ nearly complete over-lap
$S_{AB} = 0 \qquad\qquad\qquad\qquad S_{AB} \approx 1$

Fig. 4.1. Overlapping of atomic orbitals.

boundaries outside which the effect of the wave functions is negligible. If the wave functions are normalised, and they overlap completely, then $S_{AB} = 1$. If they do not overlap at all, $S_{AB} = 0$.

Since the wave functions ψ_A and ψ_B are separately normalised, then

$$\int \psi_A{}^2 \, d\tau = 1 \quad \text{and} \quad \int \psi_B{}^2 \, d\tau = 1.$$

Therefore

$$S_{AA} = S_{BB} = 1.$$

If two graphs are drawn showing the change of E corresponding to changing values of c_1 and c_2, each curve shows a minimum value. At these points, $\partial E/\partial c_1 = 0$ and $\partial E/\partial c_2 = 0$ respectively. Differentiating equation (4.3) with respect to c_1, and writing $E = a/b$, where

$$a = c_1{}^2 E_{AA} + 2c_1c_2 E_{AB} + c_2{}^2 E_{BB},$$

and

$$b = c_1{}^2 S_{AA} + 2c_1c_2 S_{AB} + c_2{}^2 S_{BB},$$

† dτ refers to integration over all co-ordinates concerned.

then

$$b\frac{\partial E}{\partial c_1}+E\frac{\partial b}{\partial c_1} = \frac{\partial a}{\partial c_1}. \tag{4.4}$$

But

$$\frac{\partial E}{\partial c_1} = 0.$$

Therefore

$$E\frac{\partial b}{\partial c_1} = \frac{\partial a}{\partial c_1},$$

and

$$E(2c_1S_{AA}+2c_2S_{AB}) = 2c_1E_{AA}+2c_2E_{AB}.$$

Therefore

$$c_1(E_{AA}-ES_{AA})+c_2(E_{AB}-ES_{AB}) = 0. \tag{4.5}$$

Similarly it can be shown by differentiating equation (4.3) with respect to c_2 that

$$c_2(E_{BB}-ES_{BB})+c_1(E_{AB}-ES_{AB}) = 0. \tag{4.6}$$

Equations (4.5) and (4.6) may be used to find values for E and the ratio c_1/c_2.† Corresponding equations for the combination of more than two wave functions can be formed in a similar manner (p. 118); if there are n combining wave functions there are n equations. E_{AB} or $\int \psi_A\psi_B(T_p+V_p)\,d\tau$ is known as the **resonance integral**. It is often represented by the symbol β.

Meaning of the resonance integral. When two harmonic oscillators A and B, such as two pendula suspended from the same horizontal strip, are coupled together, there are two possible fundamental frequencies of vibration of the combined system, and thus two possible values of the energy. One of the frequencies associated with the combined system is greater than, and the other is less than, either of the natural frequencies of A and B. By suitable manipulation it is possible to make the combined system vibrate with either of the two possible frequencies. If the natural frequencies of A and B are the same or nearly the same, and if one of them only, say A, is set into vibration, B begins to vibrate with gradually increasing amplitude; the amplitude of A gradually diminishes until B is vibrating with maximum amplitude, and A is still. Immediately this state is reached, the energy begins to return to A. The whole process of handing the energy from A to B and back from B to A is continually repeated. The effect is most marked if A and B have the same natural frequency of vibration. In this case they are said to be in "resonance". The closeness of the coupling between A and B is indicated by a "coupling coefficient".

The resonance integral in the wave mechanical treatment of valency is so called because of the analogy between it and the term representing the energy handed from A to B and back from B to A in the example from classical mechanics discussed above. It is, however, important to realise that the appearance of the resonance integral is the direct mathematical result of the linear method of combining atomic orbitals. If ψ is the combined wave function at a point, and

$$\psi = \psi_A\pm\psi_B$$

then

$$\psi^2 = \psi_A{}^2\pm2\psi_A\psi_B+\psi_B{}^2.$$

Since ψ is an amplitude and the energy is proportional to the square of the amplitude, it is clear that in this simple illustration the term $2\psi_A\psi_B$ plays the part of the resonance integral.

† The wave function $\psi=c_1\psi_A-c_2\psi_B$ leads to analogous equations.

Energy conditions for the combination of atomic orbitals. Since

$$E_{AA} = \int \psi_A{}^2(T_p + V_p)\, d\tau \quad \text{and} \quad E_{BB} = \int \psi_B{}^2(T_p + V_p)\, d\tau$$

these expressions may be taken as representing the energy of each orbital separately when it is in the field of the other. This is not the same as the energy of the atomic orbital in isolation, but as an approximation in the evaluation of integrals, ψ_A and ψ_B are usually taken to be the wave functions of the isolated atoms.

Let E_{AA} be written as E_A and E_{BB} be written as E_B. Substituting in equations (4.5) and (4.6) and putting $S_{AA} = S_{BB} = 1$:

$$E_A - E + \frac{c_2}{c_1}(E_{AB} - ES_{AB}) = 0,$$

$$E_{AB} - ES_{AB} + \frac{c_2}{c_1}(E_B - E) = 0.$$

Eliminating c_2/c_1,

$$\frac{E - E_A}{ES_{AB} - E_{AB}} = \frac{E_{AB} - ES_{AB}}{E_B - E}.$$

Therefore

$$(E - E_A)(E_B - E) + (E_{AB} - ES_{AB})^2 = 0,$$

$$E^2 - E(E_B + E_A) + E_A E_B - (E_{AB} - ES_{AB})^2 = 0,$$

$$E = \frac{E_B + E_A \pm \sqrt{(E_B + E_A)^2 - 4E_A E_B + 4(E_{AB} - ES_{AB})^2}}{2}$$

$$= \frac{E_B + E_A \pm \sqrt{(E_B - E_A)^2 + 4(E_{AB} - ES_{AB})^2}}{2}. \tag{4.7}$$

Equation (4.7) shows that if effective combination is to take place the energies E_A and E_B must be of the same order. If this is not the case let E_B be much greater than E_A. Unless ψ_A and ψ_B completely overlap, S_{AB} is less than one; the value of the resonance integral E_{AB} is in general considerably smaller than either E_A or E_B. Therefore, when E_B is much greater than E_A, as a first approximation the term $4(E_{AB} - ES_{AB})^2$ may be neglected and the expression for E becomes approximately

$$E = E_B \quad \text{or} \quad E = E_A.$$

If there is very little overlap, E_{AB} and S_{AB} are very small and the expression again becomes approximately $E = E_A$ or $E = E_B$.

From the above discussion it may be concluded that the formation of a common orbital from two atomic orbitals requires:

(a) that the energies of the atomic orbitals should be of the same order, and

(b) there should be a considerable overlapping of the atomic orbitals.

Energy of homonuclear two-centre molecular orbital. If $E_A = E_B$ equation (4.7) reduces to

$$E = E_A \pm (E_{AB} - ES_{AB}),$$

or

$$E = \frac{1}{1 \pm S_{AB}}(E_A \pm E_{AB}), \tag{4.8}$$

where

$$E_A = \int \psi_A{}^2(T_p + V_p)\, d\tau,$$

$$E_{AB} = \int \psi_A \psi_B (T_p + V)\, d\tau,$$

$$S_{AB} = \int \psi_A \psi_B\, d\tau.$$

It is convenient to assume that S_{AB} is small compared with unity, but this assumption is not justified where there is a considerable overlap. However, it has been shown by Mulliken and Riecke that to a first approximation the neglect of S_{AB} in equation (4.8) compensates for the omission of the nuclear repulsion term which has not been included in the expression for the energy. Therefore, to a first approximation, writing E_{AB} as β (it should be noted that β is a *negative* quantity),

$$E = E_A \pm \beta. \tag{4.9}$$

Thus there are two possible combined orbitals. These have different energies. The orbital of lower energy $E = E_A + \beta$, is bonding. The orbital of higher energy $E = E_B - \beta$ is antibonding (p. 121).

If the overlap integral S_{AB} is taken into account, the expressions for the orbital energy become

$$E_+ = \frac{E_A + \beta}{1 + S_{AB}} \quad \text{for the bonding orbital,} \tag{4.10}$$

and

$$E_- = \frac{E_A - \beta}{1 - S_{AB}} \quad \text{for the antibonding orbital.} \tag{4.11}$$

These expressions show that $E_- - E_A > E_A - E_+$. The relations between the three energy values, E_A, E_-, and E_+, are shown diagrammatically below.

Diagrammatic illustration of the relation of E_- and E_+ to E_A.

THE THREE-CENTRE MOLECULAR ORBITAL

The three-centre molecular orbital is formed when an electron pair is shared by three atoms. The electron pair occupies one of the molecular orbitals formed by the combination of three atomic orbitals; each of the three atoms contributes one orbital to the three-centre system, and three molecular orbitals are formed. The three-centre bond is not often found in chemistry, but the concept is used to account for the structure of the boron hydrides (p. 511), and certain compounds of beryllium and aluminium.

In general, the concept of the three-centre molecular orbital gives a plausible explanation of the stability of electron deficient ions and compounds, where the system has more available orbitals than electrons to occupy them.†

If three atomic orbitals are combined by the method of linear combination, three equations may be developed, similar to the equations 4.5 and 4.6 derived from the linear combination of two atomic orbitals. The complete wave function ψ may be developed as follows:

Let the three atomic wave functions be ψ_A, ψ_B, ψ_C, then

$$\psi = c_1\psi_A + c_2\psi_B + c_3\psi_C.$$

† W. H. Eberhardt, E. Crawford, Jnr., and W. N. Lipscomb, *J. Chem. Phys.*, **22**, 1954, 989

Since, by equation (4.2),

$$E = \frac{\int \psi^2 (T_p + V_p)\, d\tau}{\int \psi^2\, d\tau}$$

therefore

$$E = \frac{\int (c_1\psi_A + c_2\psi_B + c_3\psi_C)^2 (T_p + V_p)\, d\tau}{\int (c_1\psi_A + c_2\psi_B + c_3\psi_C)^2\, d\tau}.$$

If

$$E_{AB} = \int \psi_A\psi_B (T_p + V_p)\, d\tau \quad \text{and} \quad S_{AB} = \int \psi_A\psi_B\, d\tau, \quad \text{etc.,}$$

then

$$E = \frac{c_1^2 E_{AA} + c_2^2 E_{BB} + c_3^2 E_{CC} + 2c_1c_2 E_{AB} + 2c_1c_3 E_{AC} + 2c_2c_3 E_{BC}}{c_1^2 S_{AA} + c_2^2 S_{BB} + c_3^2 S_{CC} + 2c_1c_2 S_{AB} + 2c_1c_3 S_{AC} + 2c_2c_3 S_{BC}}.$$

If E is the minimum energy,

$$\frac{\partial E}{\partial c_1} = 0, \qquad \frac{\partial E}{\partial c_2} = 0, \qquad \frac{\partial E}{\partial c_3} = 0.$$

Therefore,

$$E(2c_1 S_{AA} + 2c_2 S_{AB} + 2c_3 S_{AC}) = 2c_1 E_{AA} + 2c_2 E_{AB} + 2c_3 E_{AC},$$
$$E(2c_2 S_{BB} + 2c_1 S_{AB} + 2c_3 S_{BC}) = 2c_2 E_{BB} + 2c_1 E_{AB} + 2c_3 E_{BC},$$
$$E(2c_3 S_{CC} + 2c_1 S_{AC} + 2c_2 S_{BC}) = 2c_3 E_{CC} + 2c_1 E_{AC} + 2c_2 E_{BC},$$

and by rearrangement

$$c_1(E_{AA} - ES_{AA}) + c_2(E_{AB} - ES_{AB}) + c_3(E_{AC} - ES_{AC}) = 0$$
$$c_1(E_{AB} - ES_{AB}) + c_2(E_{BB} - ES_{BB}) + c_3(E_{BC} - ES_{BC}) = 0$$
$$c_1(E_{AC} - ES_{AC}) + c_2(E_{BC} - ES_{BC}) + c_3(E_{CC} - ES_{CC}) = 0.$$

There is reason to suppose that the formation of a three-centre bond takes place as the result of an interaction between a diatomic molecule and a single atom rather than a simultaneous collision between three atoms, which would be a rare event. It is therefore of interest to examine the case where two of the wave functions are identical and the third is different. It is assumed: (1) that the wave functions ψ_A and ψ_B are identical, and that $c_1 = c_2$, (2) that the resonance integrals E_{AC} and E_{BC} are identical, and different from the resonance integral E_{AB}, (3) that the wave functions are all normalised; $S_{AA} = S_{BB} = S_{CC} = 1$, (4) that the overlap integrals are constant and equal to zero; $S_{AB} = S_{AC} = S_{BC} = 0$, (5) that the Coulomb integrals are constant and equal; $E_{AA} = E_{BB} = E_{CC}$. Let the Coulomb integrals be written as E_A, the resonance integral E_{AB} be written as β (a constant), and the identical resonance integrals, E_{AC} and E_{BC} be written as γ (a constant).†

If the appropriate substitutions are made, the above equations become

$$c_1(\beta - E + E_A) + c_3\gamma = 0. \tag{4.12}$$

(The first and second equations are identical.)

$$2c_1\gamma + c_3(E_A - E) = 0. \tag{4.13}$$

Dividing (4.12) by (4.13)

$$(E_A - E)(\beta - E + E_A) = 2\gamma^2,$$

$$E^2 - 2E\left(E_A + \frac{\beta}{2}\right) + E_A^2 + E_A\beta = 2\gamma^2.$$

† The symbols β and γ are sometimes reversed.

Therefore

$$E_{\pm} = E_A + \frac{\beta}{2} \pm \sqrt{\left(E_A{}^2 + \beta E_A + \frac{\beta^2}{4} - E_A{}^2 - E_A\beta + 2\gamma^2 \right)}$$

$$= E_A + \frac{\beta}{2} \pm \sqrt{\left(\frac{\beta^2}{4} + 2\gamma^2 \right)}.$$

A more complete mathematical treatment shows that there is a third solution

$$E = E_A - \beta.$$

Two cases are of special interest.

(a) If three like atoms are collinear, or nearly so, then if C is the central atom and A and B are on either side of it,

$$\beta = 0$$

and

$$E_{\pm} = E_A \pm \gamma\sqrt{2}.$$

The third solution gives $E = E_A$, and represents a non-bonding orbital. This type three-centre bond is said to be *open*.

(b) If the three atoms are arranged in an equilateral triangle, $\beta = \gamma$,

$$E_+ = E_A + 2\beta$$

and

$$E_- = E_A - \beta.$$

There are two degenerate orbitals, each of energy $E_A - \beta$. This type of three-centre bond is said to be *closed*.

It is interesting to compare the expression for the energy of the three-centre bond with that of the two-centre bond, for which

$$E_+ = E_A + \beta.$$

The comparison provides an illustration of the principle that the *larger the number of wave functions combined by the LCAO method, the lower is the energy of the resulting E_+ combined orbital*. It is important, however, to notice the effect of the neglect of the overlap integrals. If an atom is surrounded by a large number of other atoms as in a crystal, the repulsive Coulomb forces due to the overlap of the charge clouds effectively cancel each other out. This is not so in the simple case of an isolated three-centre bond. It is probably for this reason that a calculation based on the foregoing method does not give the correct energy for the molecule H_3; the result suggests that the H_2 molecule is less, instead of more, stable than the H_3 molecule. It is also known from spectroscopic evidence that the linear form of H_3 is more stable than the triangular form. Since the potential energy of a molecule is largely due to Coulomb forces, it is reasonable to make a rough estimate of the relative stability of these structures by consideration of the Coulomb forces alone. The estimate, using a simple classical model, indicates that the order of increasing energy, and hence decreasing stability, is: H_2, the linear form of H_3, the triangular form of H_3; this order corresponds to the order found by experiment.

The simple treatment of the three-centre bond which has been outlined above is based on the assumption that all the atoms concerned are alike and that they are situated in identical environments. The concept of the three-centre bond can be applied to more complex cases in which only two atoms may be alike or all three may be different. The method may also be extended to more than three centres and in the limit it is found to be contained in the electron theory of metals as expounded in Chapter 6 (p. 179). The concept of the polycentred molecular orbital is of most value in the consideration of non-localised orbitals (p. 170), and the orbital structure of crystals. It has also proved to be helpful in the determination of the structure of compounds, such as the boron hydrides (p. 511); these have discrete molecules but nevertheless a structure which is intermediate between that of a metal and a covalent compound.

BONDING AND ANTIBONDING ORBITALS

Let $\psi_I = \psi_A + \psi_B$ and $\psi_{II} = \psi_A - \psi_B$ where ψ_I and ψ_{II} are the molecular orbitals formed by the combination of the atomic orbitals ψ_A and ψ_B of two similar atoms. At the mid-point between the atoms where $\psi_A = \psi_B$, $\psi_I^2 = 4\psi_A^2$, and $\psi_{II}^2 = 0$. Since ψ^2 is a measure of charge density, the wave function ψ_I corresponds to a piling up of charge between the nuclei, and the wave function ψ_{II} corresponds to a lack of charge between the nuclei.

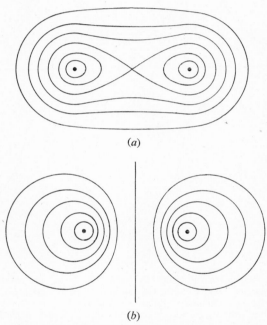

(a)

(b)

Fig. 4.2. Lines of constant charge density on a plane containing two identical nuclei (a) for a bonding orbital (b) for an antibonding orbital.

If a notional positive charge is brought up to a point at which there is a negative charge, the work done is negative (p. 114), and the point is said to have negative potential. The greater the concentration of negative charge between the two atomic nuclei discussed above, the more negative will be the potential energy of the system, and the greater the work which will have to be done on the system to separate the component parts. Hence the piling up of negative charge between the two nuclei results in an internuclear bond, and the molecular orbital ψ_I is said to be a *bonding orbital*. An absence of negative charge between the two nuclei results in internuclear repulsion, and hence the molecular orbital ψ_{II} is said to be an *antibonding orbital*.

Fig. 4.2 shows lines of equal charge density on a plane containing the two nuclei, (a) for the bonding orbital ψ_I (b) for the antibonding orbital ψ_{II}. It may be seen that for a given distance from the nucleus an electron in the bonding orbital ψ_I is most likely to be found on the internuclear axis in the region between the two nuclei. If the electron is in the antibonding orbital ψ_{II} it is least likely to be found between the nuclei. Fig. 4.3(a) and 4.3(b) show the charge density maps in elevation corresponding to Figs. 4.2(a) and (b). Although the form of the wave function demands that the maximum charge density be at the nucleus, the probability that the electron will be found at a very small distance, a, away from the nucleus is very small, since the electron would have to be contained within a very small spherical shell of volume $4\pi a^2 da$. Added to this consideration, the current theory of the nucleus suggests that, taking the nucleus as a centre, there is a definite radius within which other effects in addition to

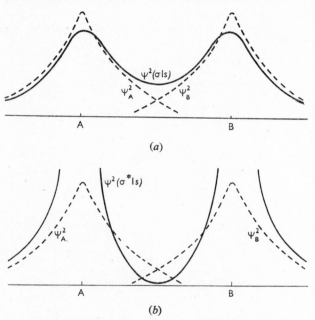

Fig. 4.3. The charge density (measured by ψ^2) plotted along the internuclear axis of the H_2^+ molecule (a) for a bonding orbital (b) for an antibonding orbital. $\psi_A{}^2$ and $\psi_B{}^2$ for the uncombined atomic orbitals are also shown; these are plotted on half the scale.

the Coulomb forces are significant. The diagrams of charge density are apt to be misleading unless these implications are understood.

Potential energy curves. The above discussion has been concerned with the distribution of charge and potential along the internuclear axis regardless of whether the length of the axis is such as to produce equilibrium conditions. The optimum length of the internuclear axis is such that the potential energy of the whole molecule is a minimum. As the nuclei approach one another, the attraction between the nuclei and electrons increases until the attraction is more than offset by the repulsions between the nuclei and between the electrons. There must obviously be some optimum position corresponding to greatest negative potential energy, that is maximum binding energy. The corresponding bond length depends on the number of electrons in the molecular orbitals. For instance, both the hydrogen molecule-ion and the hydrogen molecule have the same orbital system based on two hydrogen nuclei, but the bonding orbital contains only one electron in the hydrogen molecule-ion while it contains two electrons in the hydrogen molecule. The potential energy terms in the two Schrödinger equations are therefore different, the wave functions of the bonding orbitals are different, and the bond lengths are different.

It is of considerable interest to determine the relation between the length of the internuclear axis and the energy of the molecule. This energy is the quantity for which an expression was derived on page 118. The quantities E_A and β used in this expression are functions of the distance between the nuclei, for instance they include potential energy terms corresponding to the Coulomb attractions and repulsions in the molecule. Unfortunately the full computation of the energy involves the evaluation of complicated integrals and in general it is not possible to make the complete calculation. In the simplest of all cases, that of the hydrogen molecule-ion, the calculation can be made, and a potential energy curve (Fig. 4.4) drawn to show the variation of the

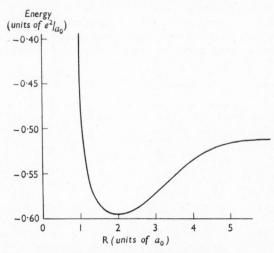

Fig. 4.4.   Variation of molecular energy with internuclear distance for diatomic molecule.

molecular energy with the internuclear distance. It is not possible to verify this curve experimentally since the hydrogen molecule-ion exists only transiently in the discharge tube. The potential energy curves for many other molecules can be drawn from data derived from the study of rotation vibration spectra (p. 218) and although these cannot be verified by calculation, their form is very similar to that of the potential energy curve calculated for the hydrogen molecule-ion. Potential energy curves are sometimes referred to as *energy curves* or as *Morse curves*. They are discussed in detail on p. 211, where it is explained how they may be plotted. The value of the energy of dissociation of the molecule (*D* in Fig. 7.2) taken from the curve is, for many molecules, in fair agreement with the value determined from thermochemical data.

SYMMETRY CONDITIONS FOR THE COMBINATION OF ATOMIC ORBITALS

Symmetric and antisymmetric wave functions. Consider two possible expressions for the wave function of a combined orbital:

$$\psi_I = \psi_A + \psi_B$$

and

$$\psi_{II} = \psi_A - \psi_B,$$

where ψ_A and ψ_B are the wave functions of s atomic orbitals. Let the signs of the wave functions ψ_A and ψ_B be interchanged (this is a symmetry operation through the centre of the molecule (p. 228)): ψ_I and ψ_{II} then become ψ_I' and ψ_{II}' where

$$\psi_I' = \psi_A + \psi_B$$

and

$$\psi_{II}' = \psi_B - \psi_A.$$

It will be observed that $\psi_I = \psi_I'$ and $\psi_{II} = -\psi_{II}'$. Hence the operation has no effect on the magnitude or sign of ψ_I; it has no effect on the magnitude of ψ_{II} but the sign of ψ_{II} is altered. Wave functions which are unaffected in magnitude and sign by a symmetry operation through the centre of the molecule (this is sometimes described as an interchange of electrons) are said to be **symmetric,** and wave functions which are unaffected in magnitude but which undergo a change of sign as the result of a symmetry operation through the centre of the molecule are said to be **antisymmetric.**†

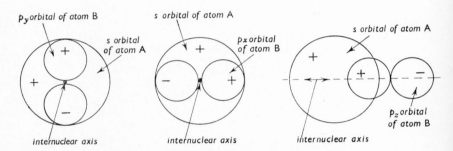

Fig. 4.5.   Overlapping of an s orbital of one atom A with a p orbital of another atom B. The p_z orbital of atom B approaches the s orbital of atom A end-on, but the p_x and p_y orbitals approach it broadside-on.

The symmetry of atomic orbitals is an important property. In certain cases it may decide whether or not two atomic orbitals can combine to form a molecular orbital. It is possible for two atomic orbitals to overlap without combining; in such a case the overlap integral is zero in all positions of the orbitals, that is $\int \psi_A \psi_B \, d\tau = 0$ and the wave functions are said to be orthogonal (p. 29). This effect may be seen when an s orbital of one atom overlaps with a p orbital of a second atom (Fig. 4.5). Since the internuclear axis is taken to be the z axis, the positive and negative parts of the p_x or p_y orbital (Fig. 2.4, p. 43) overlap equal amounts of the s orbital. This is true whether the r dependent values of the ψ_{B_p} wave function are greater or less than the corresponding r dependent values of the ψ_{A_s} wave function. Therefore,

$$\int \psi_{A_s} \psi_{B_{p_x}} \, d\tau = 0 \quad \text{and} \quad \int \psi_{A_s} \psi_{B_{p_y}} \, d\tau = 0.$$

For the same mutual orientation of the two atoms, the s orbital overlaps one lobe of the p_z orbital more than the other, but as there is an equal probability that this lobe will be either positive or negative in symmetry (p. 44), $\int \psi_{A_s} \psi_{B_{p_z}} \, d\tau$ is zero.

† The symmetric and antisymmetric functions are sometimes labelled "g" and "u" (gerade and ungerade) respectively.

CONFIGURATIONS OF MOLECULAR ORBITALS

The configurations of atomic orbitals are graphically determined by plotting polar diagrams of the angular dependent parts of the wave functions (p. 43). The configurations of molecular orbitals may also be determined by means of polar diagrams, and are discussed qualitatively below. The molecular orbitals formed (a) by the combination of two *s* orbitals, and (b) by the combination of two *p* orbitals will be considered.

The symmetry of an atomic orbital depends on the quantum number *l*. An *s* orbital ($l=0$) has spherical symmetry and is represented by ⊕. A *p* orbital is antisymmetric and is represented as ⊖⊕.

A molecular wave function is obtained by adding the appropriate overlapping atomic wave functions, or by subtracting one of the overlapping atomic wave functions from the other. This process may be represented geometrically by observing the following procedure. The atomic orbitals to be combined are assumed partially to overlap. If two *s* orbitals come together the overlap is represented as:

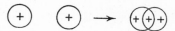

if two p_z orbitals come together the overlap is represented either as

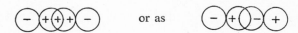

If the regions of the orbitals marked + overlap, the corresponding atomic wave functions are added, if the region + of one orbital overlaps with a region − of the other, the wave functions are subtracted from one another.

Configuration of σ molecular orbitals formed from atomic *s* orbitals. The bonding orbital is formed when the wave functions of two atomic *s* orbitals are added. The geometrical representation is:

where *AB* is the molecular axis. The orbital is symmetric about the midpoint of the molecule.

The antibonding orbital is formed by the subtraction of one *s* atomic orbital from another; this is equivalent to adding the two orbitals after the symmetry of one has been reversed. This is represented geometrically as:

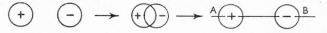

The resulting orbital is antisymmetric about the midpoint of the molecule, and the two regions are given the symmetry symbols + and −. Both the bonding orbital and the antibonding orbital possess cylindrical symmetry about the molecular axis *AB*. The bonding orbital consists of a single region of charge concentrated between the atomic nuclei; the antibonding orbital consists of two regions of charge, both chiefly on the sides of the nuclei remote from the centre of the molecule.†

The highest degree of symmetry attainable by an atomic orbital is spherical symmetry about the centre of the atom. The highest degree of symmetry attainable by a molecular

† The positive and negative signs in the diagram refer to symmetry and *not* to charge.

Valency

orbital is cylindrical symmetry about the molecular axis. The atomic orbital with spherical symmetry is called an *s* orbital; the molecular orbital with cylindrical symmetry is called a σ orbital. The bonding orbital is denoted σ, and the antibonding orbital σ^*.

Configuration of σ molecular orbitals formed from atomic *p* orbitals. An atomic *p* orbital may be represented:

It is antisymmetric about the midpoint of the atom. If the two atomic p_z orbitals approach one another along the *z* axis they overlap to produce two molecular orbitals. One is a bonding orbital of which the wave function is the sum of the atomic orbitals, and the other is an antibonding orbital whose wave function is the difference between the atomic wave functions. The formation of the bonding σ orbital may be represented geometrically:

The σ orbital is symmetric about the midpoint of the molecule. The formation of the σ^* antibonding orbital may be represented geometrically:

It is antisymmetric about the mid-point of the molecule. Since σ molecular orbitals can be produced either from *s* atomic orbitals or from p_z atomic orbitals, they must be distinguished by the symbol of the atomic orbital from which they have been formed. In the case just mentioned, if the principal quantum number of the atomic p_z orbital had been 2, the complete description of the molecular orbitals would be $\sigma 2p_z$ and $\sigma^* 2p_z$.

Configuration of π molecular orbitals formed from atomic *p* orbitals. When the $2p_z$ orbitals of the atoms have overlapped to form molecular $\sigma 2p_z$ and $\sigma^* 2p_z$ orbitals, the remaining $2p$ orbitals of the atoms may overlap to produce further molecular orbitals called π orbitals. In general, π orbitals can be formed only between atoms already bonded by a σ orbital; atoms are rarely bonded by π orbitals alone.

The $2p_y$ orbitals of two atoms already linked by a σ bond can be represented:

and the bonding $\pi 2p_y$ orbital formed by their overlapping has the configuration:

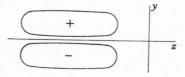

It may be described colloquially as two "sausages", one above the *z* axis and the other below it; the two sausages are parts of *one and the same orbital*. The $\pi 2p_y$ orbital is antisymmetric about the midpoint of the molecule.

The formation of the antibonding orbital may be represented geometrically:

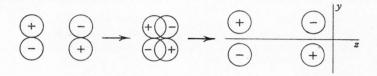

It is chiefly concentrated in the zy plane, but it is divided into four regions, and there is a deficiency of charge between the two nuclei; it is symmetric about the midpoint of the molecule. The antibonding orbital is designated π^*2p_y.

The $\pi2p_x$ (bonding) orbital and the π^*2p_x (antibonding) orbital are formed from the p_x atomic orbitals of the two combining atoms in a similar manner. The regions of charge concentration of both orbitals lie chiefly in the zx plane. A section through the mid-point of the molecule seen looking along the z axis would show the $\pi2p_y$ and $\pi2p_x$ bonding orbitals as:

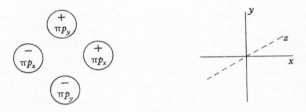

The symmetry of the bonding and antibonding π orbitals is thus opposite to that of the bonding and antibonding σ orbitals (p. 126).

Angular momenta of molecular orbitals. The above description of molecular orbitals assumes that the atomic orbitals from which they are formed have the static arrangement depicted in Fig. 2.4, p. 43. In fact however, the atomic orbitals possess angular momentum which is transferred to the molecular orbital derived from them. In the molecule, the molecular axis is defined without reference to an external magnetic field (p. 48); the angular momentum of a molecular orbital is characterised by the value of its component about the molecular axis. The component of angular momentum about the molecular axis is designated λ where $\lambda = \lambda h/2\pi$ (p. 207). λ may have one of the integral values $0, 1, 2, \ldots$. In the presence of an external magnetic field, the quantum number m_l shows the orientation by taking one of the values $\pm \lambda$.†

The symmetry of a molecular orbital is indicated by λ in the same way as that of an atomic orbital is indicated by l. The σs and $\sigma^* s$ orbitals have cylindrical symmetry about the molecular axis, and hence $\lambda = 0$. The σp_z and $\sigma^* p_z$ orbitals also have cylindrical symmetry about the molecular axis, and in these cases also $\lambda = 0$. The πp_x, πp_y, and $\pi^* p_x$, $\pi^* p_y$ orbitals have symmetry, but not cylindrical symmetry, about the molecular axis, and for these orbitals $\lambda = 1$. The "sausages" of the πp_x and πp_y orbitals rotate in opposite directions round the molecular axis, keeping their long axes always parallel to it. The $\pi^* p_x$ and $\pi^* p_y$ orbitals rotate in a similar manner; in this case the figures traced out are two rings with centres near the atomic nuclei. The nomenclatures of certain atomic and molecular orbitals are compared in Table 4.1.

---

† The magnetic quantum number m_l is concerned only with molecules which have a very short internuclear axis. More generally the quantum number M is introduced. M is related to the total angular momentum $\mathbf{J}$ of the molecule. The matter is discussed more fully in the chapter on molecular spectra (p. 224).

Table 4.1. *Comparison of the Nomenclature of Atomic and Molecular Orbitals*

Atomic Orbitals			Molecular Orbitals		
Quantum number l	Magnetic Quantum number m	Orbital symbol	Quantum number λ	Magnetic Quantum number for small internuclear distance m_l	Orbital symbols
0	0	$1s$	0	0	$\sigma 1s \quad \sigma^* 1s$
1	0 ± 1 $\left\{\vphantom{\begin{matrix}a\\b\\c\end{matrix}}\right.$	$2p_z$ $2p_x$ $2p_y$	0 1 1	0 ± 1	$\left\{\vphantom{\begin{matrix}a\\b\\c\end{matrix}}\right.$ $\sigma 2p_z \quad \sigma^* 2p_z$ $\pi 2p_x \quad \pi^* 2p_x$ $\pi 2p_y \quad \pi^* 2p_y$

THE ENERGY STATES OF MOLECULAR ORBITALS

The energy of an anti-bonding orbital is always greater than that of a bonding orbital formed from the same atomic orbitals. It is calculated that the energy of the $\sigma^* 2p_z$ orbital is very much greater than that of the corresponding $\sigma 2p_z$ orbital and exceeds the energy of each of the orbitals $\pi 2p_x$, $\pi 2p_y$, and $\pi^* 2p_x$, $\pi^* 2p_y$. These relationships are shown in Table 4.2. In the construction of the table it is assumed that two atoms of an element in the 2nd Period have interacted to form a molecule by the overlapping of the orbitals of the L shells; the interaction of the inner (K) shell is neglected because the overlap is very small. The energies of the molecular orbitals formed by the overlapping are shown in Table 4.2 in ascending order of magnitude (column 3).

Column 1 of Table 4.2 indicates the atomic orbitals (one orbital from each atom) which overlap to produce the molecular orbitals. Column 2 indicates the molecular orbitals so formed. The lines joining Column 1 and Column 2 indicate the particular

Table 4.2. *Molecular Orbitals Formed by the Overlapping of Orbitals in the L Shells of Two Similar Atoms*

1 Atomic Orbitals	2 Molecular Orbitals	3 Energy Levels	4 Value of Quantum Number λ	5 Value of Quantum Number m_l	6 Mulliken's Notation
	$\sigma^* 2p_z$	6th	0	0	u
$2p_x\ 2p_x$	$\pi^* 2p_x$ $\pi^* 2p_y$	5th	1 1	$\left.\vphantom{\begin{matrix}a\\b\end{matrix}}\right\} \pm 1$	v
$2p_y\ 2p_y$	$\pi 2p_x$ $\pi 2p_y$	4th	1 1	$\left.\vphantom{\begin{matrix}a\\b\end{matrix}}\right\} \pm 1$	w
$2p_z\ 2p_z$	$\sigma 2p_z$	3rd	0	0	x
$2s\ 2s$	$\sigma^* 2s$	2nd	0	0	y
	$\sigma 2s$	1st	0	0	z

(Increasing orbital energy — shown by vertical arrow alongside column 3)

molecular orbitals which are formed by the overlapping of two similar atomic orbitals. Starting from the bottom of the table it is observed that the two $2s$ atomic orbitals form a $\sigma 2s$ molecular orbital (bonding) and a σ^*2s molecular orbital (anti-bonding). The two $2p_z$ atomic orbitals form a $\sigma 2p_z$ molecular orbital (bonding) and a σ^*2p_z molecular orbital (anti-bonding). The two $2p_y$ atomic orbitals form $\pi 2p_y$ and π^*2p_y orbitals, and the two $2p_x$ orbitals the $\pi 2p_x$ and π^*2p_x orbitals. The order of the energies of the molecular orbitals is shown in Column 3. The Table shows that the highest energy state is that of the σ^*2p_z molecular orbital, and also that the energies of the bonding $\pi 2p_y$ and $\pi 2p_x$ orbitals are equal, and are lower than those of the antibonding π^*2p_y and π^*2p_x orbitals.

The notation in Column 6 was suggested by Mulliken. It indicates the energy levels of the molecular orbitals, the orbital of lowest energy being given the symbol z. This notation has the advantage that it does not consider the nature of the atomic orbitals from which the molecular orbitals were produced. It is therefore conveniently employed in discussing heteronuclear diatomic molecules in which molecular orbitals are formed from atomic orbitals of different denominations.

The molecular orbitals in Table 4.2 represent the total number of molecular orbitals that can be constructed by the appropriate combination of all the atomic orbitals in the L shells of two atoms. These molecular orbitals may be referred to as *possible molecular orbitals* because in any actual diatomic molecule formed by the union of two atoms, only some of the molecular orbitals are occupied by electrons.

The electrons which occupy the molecular orbitals are those which were originally present in the valency shells of the combining atoms. They are allotted to the molecular orbitals on the aufbau principle.

The strength of the bond represented by a system of molecular orbitals in a diatomic molecule is determined by the number of orbitals which are occupied by electrons. The $\sigma 2s$ orbital is bonding, and if this orbital only is occupied by an electron pair the atoms are strongly bound. The σ^*2s orbital is antibonding, and if this orbital is occupied as well as the $\sigma 2s$ orbital the atoms would fall apart, as the antibonding energy of the σ^*2s orbital is slightly greater than the bonding energy of the $\sigma 2s$ orbital. Introduction of electrons into the three orbitals of next lowest energy, $\sigma 2p_z$, $\pi 2p_y$, $\pi 2p_x$ produces an increasing bonding effect. All the orbitals of higher energy than these are antibonding, and their occupation by electrons weakens the inter-atomic bond. When the complete set of orbitals is occupied by 16 electrons the total antibonding effect exceeds the total bonding effect, and the atoms fall apart. This explains why the atoms of the inert gases with 8 electrons in the valency shell do not form diatomic molecules.

CELL DIAGRAMS

The application of the aufbau principle to determine the distribution of the available electrons among the possible molecular orbitals is best followed with the aid of a cell diagram. The cell diagram consists of two lateral sections and a central section. Each lateral section depicts the electronic configuration of one of the two atoms which come together to form the molecule; each orbital is indicated by a circle. The central section depicts the possible molecular orbitals in the molecule. An electron occupying a molecular orbital is represented by an arrow the direction of which indicates the spin; a possible molecular orbital without an electron contains no arrow. The energy states of the atomic and of the molecular orbitals are qualitatively indicated by the convention that the orbital of least energy is at the bottom of the diagram.

The hydrogen molecule, H_2

Atomic Orbitals	Molecular Orbitals		Atomic Orbitals
H	H_2		H
	σ^*1s $\bigcirc$		
$1s$ $(\uparrow)$			$(\downarrow)$ $1s$
	$\sigma1s$	$(\uparrow\downarrow)$	

The cell diagram shows that each hydrogen atom originally contains one electron in the $1s$ orbital. On combination the two electrons (which must have antiparallel spins) are described by the molecular $\sigma1s$ orbital. The possible antibonding σ^*1s orbital is unused.

The hydrogen molecule-ion, $H_2{}^+$

Atomic Orbitals	Molecular Orbitals		Atomic Orbitals
H	$H_2{}^+$		H^+
	σ^*1s $\bigcirc$		
$1s$ $(\uparrow)$			$\bigcirc$ $1s$
	$\sigma1s$	$(\uparrow)$	

The helium molecule-ion, $He_2{}^+$

Atomic Orbitals	Molecular Orbitals		Atomic Orbitals
He	$He_2{}^+$		He^+
	σ^*1s	$(\uparrow)$	
$1s$ $(\uparrow\downarrow)$			$(\uparrow)$ $1s$
	$\sigma1s$	$(\uparrow\downarrow)$	

The hypothetical helium molecule, He_2

Atomic Orbitals	Molecular Orbitals		Atomic Orbitals
	σ^*1s	$(\uparrow\downarrow)$	
$1s$ $(\uparrow\downarrow)$			$(\uparrow\downarrow)$ $1s$
	$\sigma1s$	$(\uparrow\downarrow)$	

It is seen from the above cell diagrams that in the hydrogen molecule-ion and in the helium molecule-ion (both of which have a definite although transient existence) the number of electrons occupying the bonding σ orbitals exceeds the number occupying the antibonding σ^* orbitals. In the hypothetical helium molecule the numbers of electrons in the bonding and in the antibonding orbital are equal. Hence there is no bonding effect, and the molecule He_2 does not exist.

The fluorine molecule, F_2. The orbital structure of the fluorine molecule is described below as an illustration of the use of the cell diagram. The meaning of the cell diagram is illustrated by reference to fluorine, but the diagram is common to all diatomic molecules formed by the overlapping of the L shells of two atoms. It is assumed that

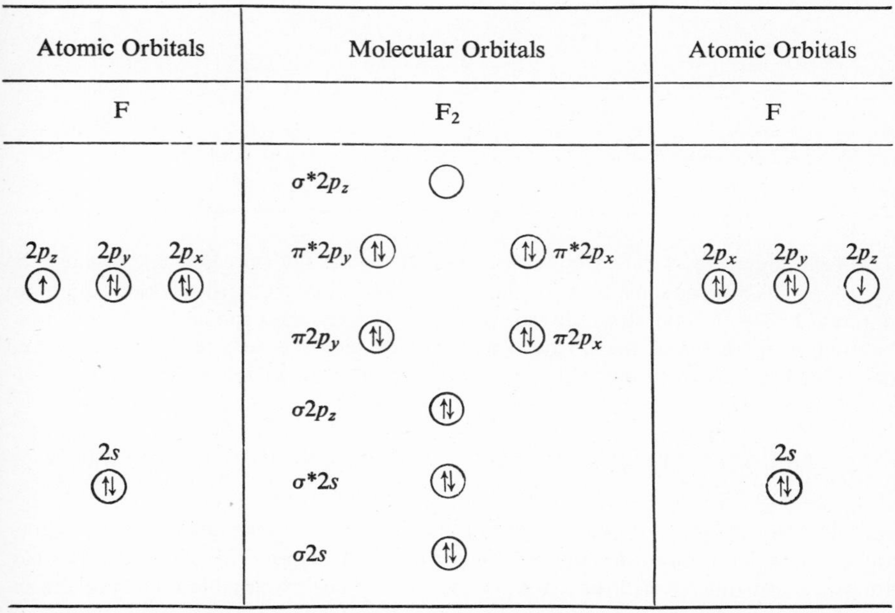

Atomic Orbitals	Molecular Orbitals		Atomic Orbitals
F	F_2		F
	σ^*2p_z ◯		
$2p_z$ $2p_y$ $2p_x$ ↑ ⇅ ⇅	π^*2p_y ⇅	⇅ π^*2p_x	$2p_x$ $2p_y$ $2p_z$ ⇅ ⇅ ↓
	$\pi2p_y$ ⇅	⇅ $\pi2p_x$	
	$\sigma2p_z$ ⇅		
$2s$ ⇅	σ^*2s ⇅		$2s$ ⇅
	$\sigma2s$ ⇅		

there is no overlap of the atomic orbitals in the K shells. The distribution among the molecular orbitals of the electrons originally present in the two fluorine atoms follows the procedure illustrated by Table 4.2, p. 128. The four electrons originally occupying the $2s$ atomic orbitals of the two fluorine atoms are transferred to the $\sigma2s$ and σ^*2s molecular orbitals. The two electrons originally occupying the two $2p_z$ atomic orbitals are transferred to the molecular orbital $\sigma2p_z$; the antibonding σ^*2p_z molecular orbital is unused. The eight electrons originally occupying the two sets of atomic orbitals $2p_y$ and $2p_x$ are transferred to the four molecular orbitals $\pi2p_y$, $\pi2p_x$, π^*2p_y, and π^*2p_x. The cell diagram shows that if the energy states of the bonding and antibonding orbitals of the same denomination are assumed to be nearly equal, then the resulting bonding effect is that of the $\sigma2p_z$ molecular orbital.†

Cell diagrams can be constructed for heteronuclear as for homonuclear diatomic molecules. As an example, the cell diagram for nitric oxide is given below.

---

† This conclusion is in accord with that derived from the application of the Heitler-London method (p. 132), to the structure of the fluorine molecule, that the two fluorine atoms in the molecule are linked by the bonding effect of one electron pair.

The nitric oxide molecule, NO

Atomic Orbitals	Molecular Orbitals	Atomic Orbitals
N	NO	O
	σ^*2p_z ○	
$2p_z$ (↓) $2p_y$ (↑) $2p_x$ (↓)	π^*2p_y (↑) ○ π^*2p_x	$2p_x$ (↑) $2p_y$ (↑) $2p_z$ (↑↓)
	$\pi 2p_y$ (↑↓) (↑↓) $\pi 2p_x$	
	$\sigma 2p_z$ (↑↓)	
$2s$ (↑↓)	σ^*2s (↑↓)	$2s$ (↑↓)
	$\sigma 2s$ (↑↓)	

This cell diagram is of the same pattern as that for the fluorine molecule because the valency shells of the atoms of nitrogen, oxygen, and fluorine, have principal quantum number 2. The orbital structure shown in the cell diagram indicates that the total bonding effect between the nitrogen and oxygen atoms is due to one σ bond and two π bonds, less the antibonding effect of one electron in the π^*2p_y orbital.

THE HEITLER-LONDON CONSTRUCTION OF HOMONUCLEAR INTERATOMIC ORBITALS

An alternative method of constructing interatomic orbitals was introduced by Heitler and London in connection with the valence bond theory (p. 173). Consider two like atoms, A and B, each with an unpaired electron of energy suitable for combination. These electrons, for the convenience of argument, may be labelled (1) and (2) although they are in principle indistinguishable. If A and B are far apart, the energy of the system is the sum of the energies of the separate atoms. If ψ_A and ψ_B are the atomic wave functions of A and B respectively, the probability that electron (1) may be found in a volume element $d\tau_1$ near A is $\psi_A{}^2(1)d\tau_1$ and the probability that electron (2) may be found in a volume element $d\tau_2$ near B is $\psi_B{}^2(2)d\tau_2$. The probability that in a volume $d\tau$ both of these statements are true at the same time is the product of the two probabilities concerning the separate atoms. Thus, if ψ_a is the wave function of the whole system,

$$\int \psi_a{}^2\, d\tau = \int \psi_A{}^2(1)\psi_B{}^2(2)\, d\tau_1\, d\tau_2$$

and

$$\psi_a = \psi_A(1)\psi_B(2).$$

If A and B approach each other sufficiently closely for the atomic orbitals to overlap, there is also a probability that electron (1) will be found near B and electron (2) near A. In that case, by similar reasoning to that used above,

$$\psi_b = \psi_A(2)\psi_B(1).$$

The most stable form of the system, that of the least energy, corresponds to a linear combination of the two possible combined wave functions. Therefore, for the molecule,

$$\psi = \psi_A(1)\psi_B(2) \pm \psi_A(2)\psi_B(1).$$

Then

$$\psi_{\mathrm{I}} = \psi_A(1)\psi_B(2) + \psi_A(2)\psi_B(1)$$

is the wave function for the bonding interatomic orbital. The wave function for the antibonding orbital is

$$\psi_{\mathrm{II}} = \psi_A(1)\psi_B(2) - \psi_A(2)\psi_B(1).$$

Now ψ^2 is a measure of the charge density, and

$$\psi^2 = (\psi_A(1)\psi_B(2))^2 \pm 2\psi_A(1)\psi_B(2)\psi_A(2)\psi_B(1) + (\psi_A(2)\psi_B(1))^2.$$

Thus it appears on this theory that the charge density distribution in a molecular system is dependent on the possibility of exchange of the two identical electrons.

In order to obtain an expression for the energy of a homonuclear diatomic molecule equations (4.5) and (4.6) (p. 116) are used; the energy is given by equations (4.10) and (4.11), p. 118. If the appropriate changes in notation are made

$$E_{\pm} = \frac{E_a \pm \beta}{1 \pm S_{ab}}.$$

Equations (4.5) and (4.6) were developed by use of a linear combination of wave functions of the form

$$c_1\psi_a \pm c_2\psi_b.$$

The Heitler-London theory puts

$$\psi_a = \psi_A(1)\psi_B(2) \quad \text{and} \quad \psi_b = \psi_A(2)\psi_B(1).$$

If these wave functions are substituted for ψ_A and ψ_B on p. 115, it is interesting to examine the meaning of the integrals which occur in equations 4.10 and 4.11.

Since the molecule considered is homonuclear, c_1 may be put equal to c_2.

$$S_{ab} = \iint \psi_A(1)\psi_B(2)\psi_A(2)\psi_B(1)\, d\tau_1\, d\tau_2$$

$$E_a = \iint (\psi_A(1)\psi_B(2))^2 (T_p + V_p)\, d\tau_1\, d\tau_2.$$

E_a represents the energy of the system when electron (1) is located in atom A, and electron (2) is located in atom B. The energy of the system under these conditions is approximately the sum of (i) the energy of two separate atoms in the ground state $(2E_0)$, and (ii) the "Coulomb" potential energy due to the electrostatic forces between the electrons, between the nuclei, and between the electrons and the nuclei. Therefore

$$E_a = \iint (\psi_A(1)\psi_B(2))^2 \left(2E_0 - \frac{\epsilon^2}{r_{b_1}} - \frac{\epsilon^2}{r_{a_2}} + \frac{\epsilon^2}{r_{12}} + \frac{\epsilon^2}{R} \right) d\tau_1\, d\tau_2$$

where r_{b_1} and r_{a_2} are the distances (respectively) of the two electrons from the "other" nucleus, r_{12} is the distance between the electrons and R is the distance between the nuclei. Since ψ_a is normalised,

$$E_a = 2E_0 + C$$

where

$$C = \iint (\psi_A(1)\psi_B(2))^2 \left(-\frac{\epsilon^2}{r_{b_1}} - \frac{\epsilon^2}{r_{a_2}} + \frac{\epsilon^2}{r_{12}} + \frac{\epsilon^2}{R} \right) d\tau_1\, d\tau_2.$$

The integral C is known as the *Coulombic integral*.

Similarly

$$\beta = \int\int \psi_A(1)\psi_B(2)\psi_A(2)\psi_B(1)\left(2E_0 - \frac{\epsilon^2}{r_{b_1}} - \frac{\epsilon^2}{r_{a_2}} + \frac{\epsilon^2}{r_{12}} + \frac{\epsilon^2}{R}\right)d\tau_1\,d\tau_2$$

$$= 2E_0 S_{ab} + A,$$

where

$$A = \int\int \psi_A(1)\psi_B(2)\psi_A(2)\psi_B(1)\left(-\frac{\epsilon^2}{r_{b_1}} - \frac{\epsilon^2}{r_{a_2}} + \frac{\epsilon^2}{r_{12}} + \frac{\epsilon^2}{R}\right)d\tau_1\,d\tau_2.$$

The integral A is known as the *exchange integral*, as it represents the energy associated with the interchange of the two electrons.

For the bonding orbital (p. 118)

$$E = \frac{E_a + \beta}{1 + S_{ab}}$$

$$= \frac{2E_0 + C + 2E_0 S_{ab} + A}{1 + S_{ab}}$$

$$= 2E_0 + \frac{C + A}{1 + S_{ab}}.$$

COMPLETE WAVE FUNCTION

The relation between symmetric and antisymmetric interatomic wave functions and Pauli's exclusion principle. The effect of Pauli's exclusion principle (p. 61) is seen at once if the two electrons in an interatomic orbital are given identical wave functions. Then,

$$\psi_A = \psi_B,$$

and

$$\psi_I = \psi_A(1)\psi_A(2) + \psi_A(2)\psi_A(1) \tag{4.14}$$

and

$$\psi_{II} = \psi_A(1)\psi_A(2) - \psi_A(2)\psi_A(1). \tag{4.15}$$

ψ_{II} vanishes and thus conforms to Pauli's exclusion principle, but ψ_I does not vanish and does not conform to Pauli's exclusion principle. Therefore the important conclusion is reached that *only antisymmetric wave functions are permitted by Pauli's exclusion principle*. The principle may be defined by this statement.

Spin function. At first sight it is somewhat disconcerting to note that although a σ interatomic bonding orbital corresponds to a symmetric wave function, Pauli's exclusion principle permits an antisymmetric wave function only. However, only the space dependent part of the wave function has been discussed so far. In order to obtain the *complete wave function* the space function must be multiplied by a wave function representing the spin, known as the *spin function*. It can readily be verified from equations (4.14) and (4.15) that the products $\psi_I \times \psi_I$ and $\psi_{II} \times \psi_{II}$ are symmetric, but the product $\psi_I \times \psi_{II}$ is antisymmetric. An antisymmetric function can therefore be obtained by multiplying a symmetric function by an antisymmetric function; thus the spin function must be either antisymmetric or symmetric according to whether the space function is symmetric or antisymmetric. The complete wave function may therefore be formed in one of two ways. (a) The space function used is the symmetric space function $\psi_A(1)\psi_B(2) + \psi_A(2)\psi_B(1)$. This function must be multiplied by an antisymmetric spin function in order that the complete wave function may obey Pauli's exclusion principle. (b) The space function used is the antisymmetric space function $\psi_A(1)\psi_B(2) - \psi_A(2)\psi_B(1)$. This function must be multiplied by a symmetric spin function if the complete wave function is to obey Pauli's exclusion principle.

Since an electron can spin in one of two opposite directions, the spin quantum number can take either of the values $\frac{1}{2}$, $-\frac{1}{2}$. Let α be the spin function when $s = \frac{1}{2}$ and β be the spin function when $s = -\frac{1}{2}$.

The following are possible spin combinations where (1) and (2) designate two electrons in the same interatomic orbital:

(i) $\alpha(1)\beta(2)$
(ii) $\alpha(2)\beta(1)$
(iii) $\alpha(1)\alpha(2)$
(iv) $\beta(1)\beta(2)$.

It should be noted that the functions (iii) and (iv) are complete in themselves, but it is necessary to take a linear combination of (i) and (ii) to provide for all possible combinations of the two electrons with opposite spin.

The possible spin functions may therefore be rearranged as follows:

$\alpha(1)\beta(2) + \alpha(2)\beta(1)$ symmetric S_1
$\alpha(1)\beta(2) - \alpha(2)\beta(1)$ antisymmetric   A
$\alpha(1)\alpha(2)$ symmetric S_2
$\beta(1)\beta(2)$ symmetric S_3

Complete wave function (a). There is only one antisymmetric spin function, and hence if the *space function* of the interatomic orbital is *symmetric*, there is only one complete wave function:

$$(\psi_A(1)\psi_B(2) + \psi_A(2)\psi_B(1))(\alpha(1)\beta(2) - \alpha(2)\beta(1)).$$

This wave function describes the ground state of the molecule.

Complete wave function (b). There are three symmetric spin functions and hence if the *space function* of the interatomic orbital is *antisymmetric*, there are three possible complete wave functions:

(1) $(\psi_A(1)\psi_B(2) - \psi_A(2)\psi_B(1))(\alpha(1)\beta(2) + \alpha(2)\beta(1))$
(2) $(\psi_A(1)\psi_B(2) - \psi_A(2)\psi_B(1))\alpha(1)\alpha(2)$
(3) $(\psi_A(1)\psi_B(2) - \psi_A(2)\psi_B(1))\beta(1)\beta(2).$

All three of these complete wave functions represent electrons with parallel spins. Hence each refers to an orbital which may be occupied by one electron only. It may be shown that if the spin-orbit coupling is considered, the energies of wave functions (1), (2), and (3) are not degenerate, but are slightly separated and correspond to a triplet state. The symmetry properties of the complete wave functions of the interatomic orbitals are summarised in Table 4.3.

Table 4.3. *Symmetry of Complete Wave Functions of Interatomic Orbitals*

Type of interatomic orbital	Complete wave function	Space function	Spin function	State
bonding	A	S	A	Singlet
antibonding	A	A	$\begin{cases} S_1 \\ S_2 \\ S_3 \end{cases}$	Triplet

A = antisymmetric S = symmetric

EFFECTIVE NUCLEAR CHARGE

Screening constants. An electron in an atomic orbital does not experience the full nuclear charge owing to the shielding effect of the other electrons in the atom. Slater† has shown that when there are several electrons in an atom, each one of them may be conveniently represented by the wave function of a single electron moving round a central positive charge which is less than the actual nuclear charge. The difference between the true nuclear charge and the charge actually experienced is known as the *screening constant*. The following rules have been developed for the evaluation of the screening constant in any particular case.

(1) There is no screening of a particular electron by other electrons in orbitals further from the nucleus.

(2) The screening constant for an s or p electron is made up of the following contributions:

    (a) 0·35 from each of the other electrons in the shell considered;

    (b) 0·85 from each of the other electrons in the next inner shell;

    (c) 1·0 from each of the other electrons still further in.

(3) The screening constant for a d or f electron is made up of the following contributions:

    (a) 0·35 from each other electron in the shell considered;

    (b) 1·0 from each other electron further in, including those in the next inner shell.

(4) The screening constant for a $1s$ electron is 0·30 from the other electron.

These rules may be usefully extended to the determination of the effective nuclear charge experienced by an electron in an interatomic bond. The justification of the empirical extension of the atomic screening rules to screening in a molecule is that by so doing it is possible, by means of a simple method, to calculate bond lengths in terms of bond energies and ionisation potentials (p. 327). The rules are used as for the atom, but with the modification that *all* the electrons which were in the original atomic orbitals contribute to the screening of another electron in the very near neighbourhood of the atom. Thus, in a single bond ($A—B$), it is assumed that the valence electron contributed by B to the bond is screened from nucleus A by all the A electrons, and vice versa. The effective nuclear charge thus computed to be exerted by a nucleus on an electron very close to the atom is referred to in the remainder of this book as $(Z_{eff})_{mol}$. For the purpose of calculating bond lengths the molecular bond envisaged is assumed to be strictly localised between the two atoms concerned.

EFFECTIVE NUCLEAR CHARGE AND THE PERIODIC TABLE

The relation between $(Z_{eff})_{mol}$ and the classification found in the periodic table may be shown by plotting $(Z_{eff})_{mol}$ against atomic number (Fig. 4.6). Elements of the same group are joined by dotted lines. Where the line is horizontal, those elements joined by it have the same effective nuclear charge. Elements of the short Periods lie on straight parallel lines of steep slope. Each long Period is represented by two straight lines which are parallel to each other and to those of the short Periods, but which are connected to each other by irregular lines of a less steep slope. These irregular lines link together the transition elements.

The values of $(Z_{eff})_{mol}$ for the elements of the first three Periods are given in Table 4.4. It should be noted that although the whole periodic table might be plotted on the same scheme as that of Fig. 4.6, the screening constants for atoms of high atomic number cannot be considered to be accurate.

† J. C. Slater, *Quantum Theory of Matter*, Chap. 6, (McGraw-Hill, 1953).

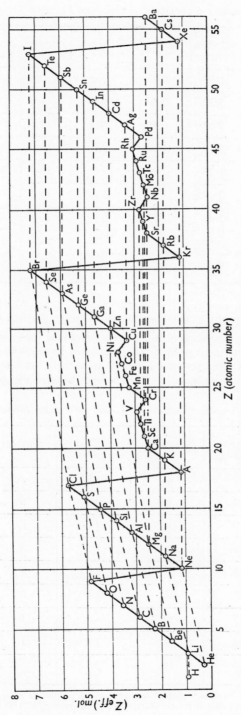

Fig. 4.6. Variation of $(Z_{eff})_{mol}$ with atomic number.

Table 4.4.　*Molecular Screening Constants and Effective Nuclear Charge*

Element	Atomic Number	Screening Constant	$(Z_{eff})_{mol}$	Element	Atomic Number	Screening Constant	$(Z_{eff})_{mol}$
H†	1	0·05	0·95	Ne	10	8·80	1·20
He	2	1·70	0·30	Na	11	9·15	1·85
Li	3	2·05	0·95	Mg	12	9·50	2·50
Be	4	2·40	1·60	Al	13	9·85	3·15
B	5	2·75	2·25	Si	14	10·20	3·80
C	6	3·10	2·90	P	15	10·55	4·45
N	7	3·45	3·55	S	16	10·90	5·10
O	8	3·80	4·20	Cl	17	11·25	5·75
F	9	4·15	4·85	A	18	16·8	1·20

EFFECTIVE NUCLEAR CHARGE AND ELECTRONEGATIVITY

Pauling has described the property of *electronegativity* as the power of an atom in a molecule to attract electrons to itself. He formulated an empirical scale (Table 4.5) in which a number of elements were assigned numerical electronegativity values in electron volts. This scale was based on the difference between the dissociation energy

Table 4.5.　*Electronegativity Values for certain Elements*

Element	Electro-negativity	Element	Electro-negativity	Element	Electro-negativity
H	2·1	Sr	1·0	As	2·0
Li	1·0	Ba	0·9	Sb	1·8
Na	0·9	B	2·0	O	3·5
K	0·8	Al	1·5	S	2·5
Rb	0·8	C	2·5	F	4·0
Cs	0·7	Si	1·8	Cl	3·0
Be	1·5	Sn	1·7	Br	2·8
Mg	1·2	N	3·0	I	2·4
Ca	1·0	P	2·1		

† It is assumed on general grounds that hydrogen has the same effective nuclear charge, $(Z_{eff})_{mol}$, as lithium; this value fits in well with the calculation of bond lengths (p. 327); the value deduced from the atomic screening constant for the 1s orbital is evidently too low (cf. R. F. Wallis, *Phys. Rev.*, **23**, 1955, 1256).

of a heteronuclear bond $D(A-B)$ and the geometric mean of the dissociation energies $D(A-A)$ and $D(B-B)$. The object of this scale was to establish an additive relation between the ionic energy in a heteropolar bond and the electronegativity differences between the atoms concerned.

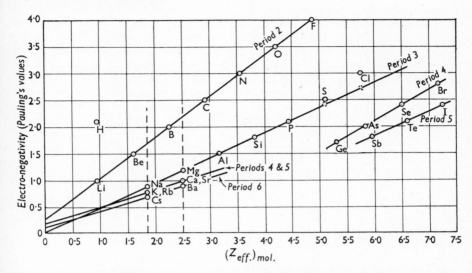

Fig. 4.7. Pauling's values for electronegativity plotted against $(Z_{eff})_{mol}$. (Pauling's values for S and Cl (Period 3) lie above the line. The electronegativity values S (2.4) and Cl (2.7) taken from the extrapolation of the line Na to P are used in Figs. 4.8 and 4.10.)

Fig. 4.7 shows that the relation between Pauling's electronegativity values and the values of $(Z_{eff})_{mol}$ is a linear one. For elements of low atomic number the relation is very accurate. Each Period is represented by a straight line, the slope of which, and the position on the graph, depends on the number of closed shells in the Period considered.

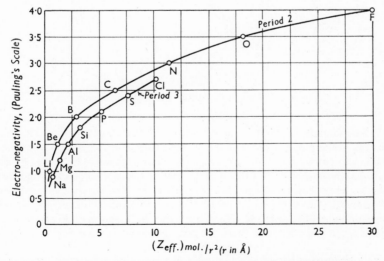

Fig. 4.8. Electronegativities on Pauling's scale plotted against values of $(Z_{eff})_{mol}/r^2$. (For electronegativity values of S and Cl see caption to Fig. 4.7.)

Although atomic screening constants are not considered to be accurate beyond the
M shell ($n=3$), some evidence is shown of a linear relation even among elements of
the higher Groups. Pauling's electronegativity values for sulphur and chlorine appear
too high. The adjusted values are shown on the graph; these are the values used in
subsequent graphical representations. The position at the head of each line is occupied
by a halogen atom, the most electronegative atom of its Period. Since the electronegativity of helium is zero on Pauling's scale, hydrogen is alone in Period 1.

The connection between the particularly high value of the electronegativity of
fluorine and the small size of the atom has long been recognised. Fig. 4.8 shows the
relation between electronegativity and $(Z_{eff})_{mol}/r^2$ for elements of Periods 2 and 3.
r represents the radius of the atom, and is taken to be the distance from the nucleus

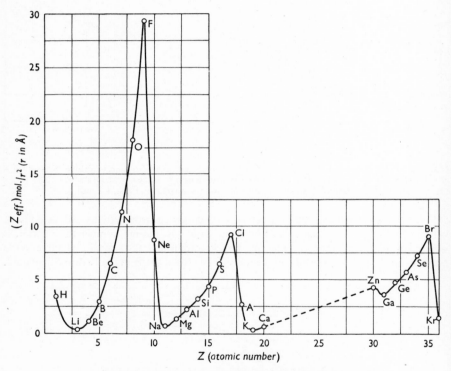

Fig. 4.9. $(Z_{eff})_{mol}/r^2$ plotted against atomic number.

at which the radial distribution function (Fig. 2.3, p. 42) is a maximum. This distance
corresponds to the modified Bohr radius of the Slater central field model of the atom
(p. 337). The quantity $(Z_{eff})_{mol}/r^2$ is thus a measure of what might be termed by analogy
the "surface charge density" of the atom as it would appear to an electron outside it.
The diagram emphasises the high electronegativity of fluorine, oxygen, and nitrogen.
Fig. 4.9 shows the function $(Z_{eff})_{mol}/r^2$ plotted against atomic number, Fig. 4.10 shows
electronegativity plotted against $(Z_{eff})_{mol}/Z$. Fig. 4.11 shows a linear relationship
between $(Z_{eff})_{mol}$ and $1/r$, the constants of proportionality being different for Periods 2
and 3.

The "r" determined by Slater's method is dependent on an effective nuclear charge
which is greater than $(Z_{eff})_{mol}$ by an amount $0·35$ equivalent to the shielding power of

the last electron in the valence shell. When the atom becomes a cation a still greater effective nuclear charge is operative, since the screening constant is reduced by the

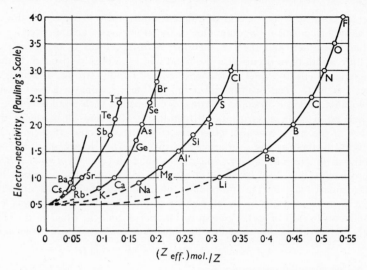

Fig. 4.10. Electronegativities on Pauling's scale plotted against values of $(Z_{eff})_{mol}/Z$. (For electronegativity values of S and Cl see caption to Fig. 4.7.)

removal of one or more electrons from the atom. This gives rise to a change in the value of r, so that r_{ion} is considerably smaller than r_{atom}. The effect is noticed clearly in the

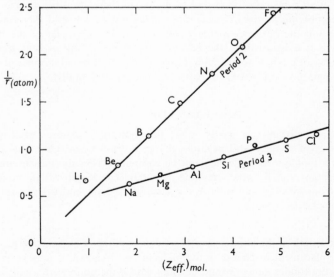

Fig. 4.11. $1/r$ (atom) plotted against values of $(Z_{eff})_{mol}$. The units of $1/r$ are $cms^{-1} \times 10^8$.

progressive contraction in the radii of ions of the transition metals, and in the "lanthanon contraction" (p. 1125).

APPLICATION OF THE HEITLER-LONDON PRINCIPLE TO
HETERONUCLEAR INTERATOMIC ORBITALS

If a molecule consists of two atoms of different kinds, there is some measure of ionic bonding as well as covalent bonding. One of the atoms has a greater effective nuclear charge than the other, and there is therefore a displacement of electrons from the position they would have occupied if the bond had been purely covalent. If there is a large difference in effective nuclear charge, the ionic bond is strong; if there is a small difference it is weak. The position taken up by the electrons in a part ionic, part covalent localised bond is discussed further in connection with bond lengths (p. 333).

The ionic bond is an electrostatic attraction (p. 107) and its existence must be allowed for in the wave function which describes the molecule. If there is a single covalent bond formed by the overlapping of two electron clouds, one from atom A and the other from atom B, and if $(Z_{eff})_{mol}$ has a different value for A and for B, there is a finite probability that both of the electrons will be found in the neighbourhood of one of the nuclei, say B. The probability of their interchange has already been considered in the wave function developed for the covalent bond, but it was assumed that one electron would be in the region of nucleus A, and the other in the region of nucleus B. The wave function including the ionic bond may therefore be written as:

$$\psi = \psi_A(1)\psi_B(2) + \psi_A(2)\psi_B(1) + \lambda\psi_B(1)\psi_B(2).$$

This expression is sometimes written as

$$\psi = \psi_{cov} + \lambda\psi_{ion}.$$

It should be noted that ψ_{cov} and ψ_{ion} are themselves molecular and not atomic wave functions. λ represents the relative contribution of ψ_{ion} to that of ψ_{cov} in the formation of the resultant orbital.

Although the problem as formulated concerns only the two electrons forming a single bond, in all cases other than that of hydrogen there are other electrons present in the two combining atoms. An accurate calculation of λ would therefore have to take into account the influence of these electrons on the character of the bond, and although there is evidence that the effect is not large, in the present state of our knowledge it is not possible to estimate it except in a very limited number of cases. An accurate estimation of λ is therefore best obtained experimentally.

DETERMINATION OF λ

If the bond in a molecule is partly ionic, the molecule possesses electric polarity and the centres of positive and negative charge are not coincident. This polarity is expressed as a dipole moment which can be computed from the measurement of the dielectric constant and by other methods (p. 300). The length of the bond may be determined from infrared and microwave spectra (p. 216), and the measured dipole moment μ may be expressed as

$$\mu = \alpha\epsilon r,$$

where r is the length of the bond and $\alpha\epsilon$ is a fraction of the electronic charge. Although the actual displacement of charge in the molecule is unknown, it may be argued that if the bond were totally ionic α would be unity, and if the bond were totally covalent α would be zero. Thus the product 100α gives the percentage ionic character of the bond. The percentage ionic character is related to λ as follows. Since the probability of an electron's being found at any position is proportional to ψ^2 at that point, the ratio of the probability of finding the bond in the covalent form to the probability of finding the bond in the ionic form is $1/\lambda^2$, and the percentage ionic character of the bond is expressed by the fraction $[\lambda^2/(1+\lambda^2)] \times 100$.

Pauling attempted to develop a satisfactory general correlation between λ and his scale of electronegativity. He was able to obtain an obvious parallel for certain classes of compounds, particularly the hydrogen halides, but inconsistent results were obtained with many other compounds. His calculations were carried out without consideration of the state of hybridisation of the atoms in the molecule, and it appears that this is an important factor in determination of the length of a bond, and therefore of its ionic character (p. 333). Attempts to develop a rigorous formula for λ in terms of wave mechanics have been no more successful owing to the extensive, and possibly erroneous, assumptions which must be made to confine the problem to manageable proportions. Therefore at present it is not possible to make any accurate comparison between λ and electronegativity.

BOOKS FOR FURTHER READING

See Chapter 5, p. 178.

CHAPTER FIVE

DIRECTED VALENCE

The theory of molecular orbitals can be extended to polyatomic molecules. The theory postulates, for instance, that the methane molecule consists of one carbon nucleus and four protons, with all the ten electrons occupying orbitals extending over the whole molecule. This method of regarding a polyatomic molecule is of value in interpreting spectral data in terms of electronic transitions in the molecule. For example, when considering the spectrum associated with the ionisation of methane to CH_4^+, it is more convenient to say that an electron has been removed from the molecular orbital of highest energy, than to attempt to discover which of the four covalent bonds has been disturbed. The theory of molecular orbitals however, cannot be used without further development to explain properties of bonds which involve direction and localisation. Chemical evidence has established beyond doubt that in polyatomic molecules such as those of water, ammonia, or methane, the angles between lines joining the centre of a given atom to the centres of other atoms have definite values, constant for the molecules of a particular compound, but differing for molecules of different compounds. The simple theory of covalency has always accepted without question the presence of strictly local bonds in polyatomic molecules. The numerical values of certain molecular properties, such as interatomic distances, heats of formation, refractivity, and magnetic susceptibility can frequently be predicted with fair accuracy by adding together standard values for each type of bond in the molecule.

There are two methods of calculating bond angles in molecules from the consideration of wave functions. One starts from atomic orbitals, from which it constructs new directed atomic orbitals; this procedure is known as *hybridisation*. The other starts from molecular orbitals from which it constructs a series of directed molecular orbitals known as *equivalent orbitals*.

HYBRIDISATION

Hybridisation consists in resolving into directed component parts the space wave functions of the whole or part of the atomic orbitals in the valence shell of an atom in its ground state, and recombining the component parts to yield a set of directed atomic orbitals called hybrid orbitals. The configuration of a hybrid orbital is indicated by the value of λ† (p. 127). A hybrid orbital which has cylindrical symmetry about the line joining the two nuclei which are to be linked, and which therefore has $\lambda = 0$, is called a σ hybrid. A hybrid orbital for which $\lambda = 1$ is called a π hybrid. The bond angles, at a given atom, are determined by the angles between its σ hybrids; the axis of a π bond always coincides with that of a σ bond.

An atom in which some or all of the atomic orbitals have been hybridised to give σ hybrids is said to be in a **valence state**. A valence state is entirely imaginary. It is to

† λ here indicates the angular momentum of an orbital about the internuclear axis. λ is also used to indicate the proportion of ionic character in a bond. This nomenclature has been adopted because it is in general use.

be regarded as called into being by the act of chemical combination; it is not an excited state of the atom which can be detected by spectroscopy. The valence state of an atom is determined solely by a particular set of σ hybrids and is not concerned with the presence or absence of π hybrids (p. 156). Table 5.1 shows some of the valence states of atoms which can be produced by the hybridisation of atomic orbitals. In the description of the mutual orientation of the σ hybrids, the atomic nucleus is assumed to be at the centre of a geometrical figure. The axes of the σ hybrids are directed from the atomic nucleus towards the corners or apices of the figure. If the figure is a triangle, the hybridisation is said to be trigonal, and the atom is said to be in the trigonal valence state; if an octahedron, it is said to be octahedral, and the atom is said to be in an octahedral valence state, and so on.

Table 5.1.   *Valence States of Atoms*

The nomenclature of the atomic orbitals assumes that the atom is in a weak magnetic field directed along the z axis.

Valence state of the atom	Geometrical figure defining the angular relation of the σ hybrid orbitals	Atomic orbitals used in hybridisation	Number of σ hybrid orbitals formed
Linear or digonal	Straight line	$s, p_z,$ or $s, \frac{1}{\sqrt{2}}p_x, \frac{1}{\sqrt{2}}p_y$	2
Trigonal	Triangle	s, p_x, p_y	3
Tetrahedral	Tetrahedron	s, p_x, p_y, p_z	4
Tetragonal plane	Square	$s, p_x, p_y, \frac{1}{\sqrt{2}}d_{xy}, \frac{1}{\sqrt{2}}d_{x^2-y^2}$	4
Trigonal bipyramidal	Trigonal bipyramid	$s, p_x, p_y, p_z, d_{z^2}$	5
Octahedral	Octahedron	$s, p_x, p_y, p_z, d_{z^2}, \frac{1}{\sqrt{2}}d_{xy}, \frac{1}{\sqrt{2}}d_{x^2-y^2}$	6

RULES FOR CONSTRUCTING HYBRID ORBITALS

(a) The whole of the *molecule* is taken to be in a weak magnetic field along the z axis.

(b) The hybrid functions must be normalised, and therefore for each hybrid function the sum of the squares of the coefficients of the component wave functions $= 1$.

(c) The sum of the squares of the coefficients of any one atomic wave function taken from all the hybrid functions in which it occurs is equal to 1 when the whole of the atomic wave function is used. If a fraction only of the atomic wave function is used, then the above sum is equal to the square of the fraction taken.

(d) The hybrid wave functions must be orthogonal to one another (p. 29).

(e) In the formation of σ hybrids, if p or d orbitals are included, it is necessary to take equal parts of wave functions of atomic orbitals with opposite angular momentum (such as p_x and p_y) so that the resultant orbital angular momentum about the z axis and about the bond axis is zero.

In the formation of π hybrids it is necessary either to take such parts of atomic wave functions that the angular momentum of a π hybrid is 1 unit about the axis of the σ bond on which it is superposed, or to take such parts of atomic wave functions that the resultant angular momentum is zero about the z axis.

(f) The hybrid wave functions are calculated from the usual atomic wave functions for hydrogen. In a weak magnetic field the maximum value of the polar hybrid functions will be less than those of equatorial hybrid functions. If, however, condition (e) is observed, the hybrid functions in the equatorial plane are independent of the magnetic field and where there is spherical symmetry, as in octahedral hybridisation, they may be taken as representing also the polar functions in the absence of the field.

(g) If a diagram is drawn of the superposed atomic orbitals, it is often possible to write down the hybrid functions by inspecting the symmetry of the diagram.

Table 5.2.   *Angular Dependent Parts of Wave Functions of the Hydrogen Atom*

Wave function	Maximum value of wave function
$\psi_s = 1$	1
$\psi_{p_x} = \sqrt{3} \sin \theta \cos \phi$	$\sqrt{3} = 1\cdot732$
$\psi_{p_y} = \sqrt{3} \sin \theta \sin \phi$	$\sqrt{3} = 1\cdot732$
$\psi_{p_z} = \sqrt{3} \cos \theta$	$\sqrt{3} = 1\cdot732$
$\psi_{d_{z^2}} = \dfrac{\sqrt{5}}{2} (3 \cos^2 \theta - 1)$	$\sqrt{5} = 2\cdot237$
$\psi_{d_{xz}} = \sqrt{15} \sin \theta \cos \theta \cos \phi$	$\dfrac{\sqrt{15}}{2} = 1\cdot937$
$\psi_{d_{yz}} = \sqrt{15} \sin \theta \cos \theta \sin \phi$	$\dfrac{\sqrt{15}}{2} = 1\cdot937$
$\psi_{d_{xy}} = \dfrac{\sqrt{15}}{2} \sin^2 \theta \sin 2\phi$	$\dfrac{\sqrt{15}}{2} = 1\cdot937$
$\psi_{d_{x^2-y^2}} = \dfrac{\sqrt{15}}{2} \sin^2 \theta \cos 2\phi$	$\dfrac{\sqrt{15}}{2} = 1\cdot937$

Throughout this chapter polar diagrams of atomic orbitals are elongated in order to keep the diagrams clear. The reader should note that the diagrams relate to orbitals, not charge clouds. It is assumed throughout the discussion that the principal quantum number n is constant; hence the r dependent part of the wave function is neglected.

Linear or digonal hybridisation (Figs. 5.1 and 5.2). Orbitals used: s, p_z, if the hybrids are to lie along the z axis; s, $(1/\sqrt{2})p_x$, $(1/\sqrt{2})p_y$ if the hybrids are to lie in the xy plane. For s, p_z hybrids, let ψ_1 and ψ_2 be the two hybrid wave functions and let

$$\psi_1 = a\psi_s + b\psi_{p_z} \tag{5.1}$$

then

$$\int \psi_1{}^2 \, d\tau = a^2 \int \psi_s{}^2 \, d\tau + b^2 \int \psi_{p_z}{}^2 \, d\tau + 2ab \int \psi_s \psi_{p_z} \, d\tau.$$

ψ_1, ψ_s and ψ_{p_z}, are normalised, and ψ_s and ψ_{p_z} are orthogonal, and therefore

$$1 = a^2 + b^2,$$

and equation (5.1) may be written:

$$\psi_1 = a\psi_s + \sqrt{(1-a^2)}\psi_{p_z}$$
$$= a + \sqrt{(1-a^2)} \sqrt{3} \cos \theta.$$

ψ_1 is a maximum when

$$\frac{d\psi}{d\theta} = 0$$

and hence $\theta = 0°$ or $180°$; the hybrid orbitals are co-linear and lie along the direction of

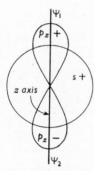

Fig. 5.1. Polar digonal σ hybridisation from s and p_z atomic orbitals.

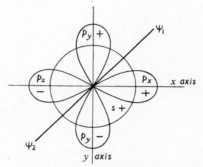

Fig. 5.2. Digonal σ hybridisation in the equatorial plane, from s and p atomic orbitals.

p_z. Since the charge density† in the two hybrids must be equal, ψ_s must be equally shared between them, therefore

$$a = \frac{1}{\sqrt{2}} \qquad b = \pm\frac{1}{\sqrt{2}},$$

and

$$\psi_1 = \frac{1}{\sqrt{2}}\psi_s + \frac{1}{\sqrt{2}}\psi_{p_z}$$

$$\psi_2 = \frac{1}{\sqrt{2}}\psi_s - \frac{1}{\sqrt{2}}\psi_{p_z}.$$

For digonal hybrids in the equatorial plane, there must be equal contributions from the p_x and p_y atomic orbitals; therefore the hybrid functions may be written as

$$\psi_1 = \frac{1}{\sqrt{2}}\psi_s + \frac{1}{2}\psi_{p_x} + \frac{1}{2}\psi_{p_y}$$

$$\psi_2 = \frac{1}{\sqrt{2}}\psi_s - \frac{1}{2}\psi_{p_x} - \frac{1}{2}\psi_{p_y}.$$

The reader may easily verify that these hybrid functions are orthogonal.

† The charge density is taken to be the square of the wave function.

Trigonal hybridisation (Fig. 5.3). Orbitals used: s, p_x, p_y.

Since the s orbital has spherical symmetry, each of the three hybrid orbitals contains one-third the equivalent charge density of the s orbital.

Let ψ_1, ψ_2, ψ_3, be the three hybrid wave functions, and suppose for convenience that one of the hybrid orbitals, corresponding to ψ_1, lies along the x axis.

If

$$\psi_1 = a_1\psi_s + b_1\psi_{p_x}$$

and

$$a_1{}^2 = \frac{1}{3},$$

and since all the wave functions are normalised and mutually orthogonal (Rules (b) and (d), p. 145)

$$\int \psi_1{}^2 \, d\tau = a_1{}^2 \int \psi_s{}^2 \, d\tau + b_1{}^2 \int \psi_{p_x}{}^2 \, d\tau$$

$$1 = a_1{}^2 + b_1{}^2$$

$$b_1{}^2 = \frac{2}{3}.$$

Therefore

$$\psi_1 = \frac{1}{\sqrt{3}}\psi_s + \sqrt{\frac{2}{3}}\psi_{p_x}.$$

ψ_2 must contain contributions from all three atomic wave functions, and may be written

$$\psi_2 = \frac{1}{\sqrt{3}}\psi_s + b_2\psi_{p_x} + c_2\psi_{p_y}.$$

Hence

$$1 = \frac{1}{3} + b_2{}^2 + c_2{}^2.$$

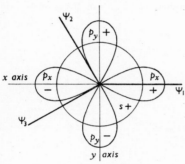

Fig. 5.3. Trigonal σ hybridisation in the equatorial plane, from s and p atomic orbitals.

Similarly for ψ_3,

$$1 = \frac{1}{3} + b_3{}^2 + c_3{}^2.$$

By Rule (d)

$$\int \left(\frac{1}{\sqrt{3}}\psi_s + \sqrt{\frac{2}{3}}\psi_{p_x}\right)\left(\frac{1}{\sqrt{3}}\psi_s + b_2\psi_{p_x} + c_2\psi_{p_y}\right) d\tau = 0,$$

and since ψ_s, ψ_{p_x}, and ψ_{p_y} are orthogonal, therefore

$$\frac{1}{3} + b_2\sqrt{\frac{2}{3}} = 0,$$

and similarly

$$\frac{1}{3} + b_3\sqrt{\frac{2}{3}} = 0.$$

Therefore

$$b_2 = b_3 = -\frac{1}{\sqrt{6}}$$

and

$$c_2 = c_3 = \pm\frac{1}{\sqrt{2}}.$$

Therefore the trigonal hybrid wave functions may be written as

$$\psi_1 = \frac{1}{\sqrt{3}}\psi_s + \sqrt{\frac{2}{3}}\psi_{Px}$$

$$\psi_2 = \frac{1}{\sqrt{3}}\psi_s - \frac{1}{\sqrt{6}}\psi_{Px} + \frac{1}{\sqrt{2}}\psi_{Py}$$

$$\psi_3 = \frac{1}{\sqrt{3}}\psi_s - \frac{1}{\sqrt{6}}\psi_{Px} - \frac{1}{\sqrt{2}}\psi_{Py}.$$

It may easily be verified that this set of wave functions conforms to the Rules (a), (b), (c), and (d) (p. 145).

In the xy plane, $\theta = 90°$, and since

$$\psi_{Px} = \sqrt{3}\cos\phi, \quad \text{and} \quad \psi_{Py} = \sqrt{3}\sin\phi,$$

$$\psi_2 = \frac{1}{\sqrt{3}} - \frac{1}{\sqrt{2}}\cos\phi + \sqrt{\frac{3}{2}}\sin\phi.$$

When ψ_2 is a maximum,

$$\frac{d\psi_2}{d\phi} = 0,$$

and therefore

$$\tan\phi = -\sqrt{3} \quad \text{and} \quad \phi = 120°.$$

Similarly it can be shown that for maximum value of ψ_3 the angle between ψ_2 and ψ_3 is 120°.

It is not necessary for ψ_1 to lie along the x axis. The system of charge clouds corresponding to the atomic orbitals s, p_x, p_y, is uniformly distributed in the plane xy, and therefore the set of three trigonal hybrids can be assumed to lie in any position in the plane; the angle between any two of them will always be 120°.

Tetrahedral σ hybridisation (Fig. 5.4). Orbitals used: s, p_x, p_y, p_z.

Let ψ_1, ψ_2, ψ_3, ψ_4, be the four hybrid wave functions, and let ψ_1 be directed along the z axis ($\theta = 0$), then

$$\psi_1 = a_1\psi_s + b_1\psi_{p_z}.$$

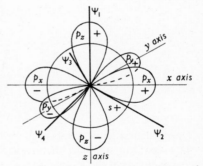

Fig. 5.4. Tetrahedral σ hybridisation from s and p atomic orbitals (I).

By reasoning similar to that of the preceding section,

$$1 = a_1^2 + b_1^2.$$

Since the system has spherical symmetry, the four bonds are of equal strength and it may be assumed that the s orbital charge cloud is shared equally between them; therefore $a^2_1 = a^2_2 = a^2_3 = a^2_4 = \frac{1}{4}$, and

$$\psi_1 = \frac{1}{2}\psi_s + \frac{\sqrt{3}}{2}\psi_{p_z}.$$

Let the second hybrid orbital lie in the xz plane, then

$$\psi_2 = \frac{1}{2}\psi_s + b_2\psi_{p_x} + c_2\psi_{p_z},$$

$$1 = \frac{1}{4} + b_2^2 + c_2^2,$$

and

$$\frac{1}{4} + \frac{\sqrt{3}}{2} c_2 = 0.$$

Therefore

$$c_2 = -\frac{1}{2\sqrt{3}}$$

$$b_2 = \sqrt{\frac{2}{3}},$$

and

$$\psi_2 = \frac{1}{2}\psi_s + \sqrt{\frac{2}{3}}\psi_{px} - \frac{1}{2\sqrt{3}}\psi_{p},$$

$$= \frac{1}{2} + \sqrt{\frac{2}{3}}\sqrt{3}\sin\theta - \frac{1}{2\sqrt{3}}\sqrt{3}\cos\theta.$$

When ψ_2 is a maximum,

$$\frac{d\psi_2}{d\theta} = 0$$

$$\tan\theta = -2\sqrt{2}$$
$$\theta = 109°28' \text{ which is the tetrahedral angle.}$$

The wave functions for the third and fourth hybrid orbitals can be found by inspection. Since ψ_3 and ψ_4 each contain fractions of all four atomic orbitals, it is only necessary to choose by trial and error the coefficient of each atomic orbital and its sign so that the system conforms to Rules (b), (c), and (d). The full set of tetrahedral wave functions thus obtained are

$$\psi_1 = \frac{1}{2}\psi_s + \frac{\sqrt{3}}{2}\psi_{pz}$$

$$\psi_2 = \frac{1}{2}\psi_s + \sqrt{\frac{2}{3}}\psi_{px} - \frac{1}{2\sqrt{3}}\psi_{pz}$$

$$\psi_3 = \frac{1}{2}\psi_s - \frac{1}{\sqrt{6}}\psi_{px} + \frac{1}{\sqrt{2}}\psi_{py} - \frac{1}{2\sqrt{3}}\psi_{pz}$$

$$\psi_4 = \frac{1}{2}\psi_s - \frac{1}{\sqrt{6}}\psi_{px} - \frac{1}{\sqrt{2}}\psi_{py} - \frac{1}{2\sqrt{3}}\psi_{pz}.$$

The particular set of tetrahedral σ hybrid orbitals just considered is symmetrical about the z axis; this simplifies the mathematical treatment, but since the distribution of the charge clouds of the atomic orbitals chosen for hybridisation, taken together, depends on r and not on θ or ϕ, it is possible to construct a set of tetrahedral σ hybrids orientated in any direction desired. A convenient set of tetrahedral σ hybrid functions may be written down by assuming that each hybrid orbital contains a quarter of the charge cloud of each component atomic orbital. The correct + and − signs, which represent the symmetry of the orbitals, may be determined by ascertaining that the set of orbitals obeys conditions (a), (b), (c), (d). By use of the diagram Fig. 5.5, the wave functions, with their appropriate signs, may be written down without further calculation:

$$\psi_1 = \frac{1}{2}\psi_s - \frac{1}{2}\psi_{px} - \frac{1}{2}\psi_{py} - \frac{1}{2}\psi_{pz}$$

$$\psi_2 = \frac{1}{2}\psi_s - \frac{1}{2}\psi_{px} + \frac{1}{2}\psi_{py} + \frac{1}{2}\psi_{pz}$$

$$\psi_3 = \frac{1}{2}\psi_s + \frac{1}{2}\psi_{px} - \frac{1}{2}\psi_{py} + \frac{1}{2}\psi_{pz}$$

$$\psi_4 = \frac{1}{2}\psi_s + \frac{1}{2}\psi_{px} + \frac{1}{2}\psi_{py} - \frac{1}{2}\psi_{pz}.$$

It may be shown that for maximum value of these hybrid wave functions, the angle between any two of the hybrids is the tetrahedral angle. This particular set of tetrahedral σ hybrid functions is convenient for use in connection with superposed πd hybrid orbitals (p. 159).

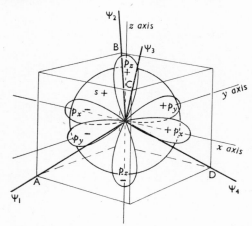

Fig. 5.5.   Tetrahedral σ hybridisation from s and
p atomic orbitals (II).

Tetragonal plane (square) σ **hybridisation** (Fig. 5.6). Orbitals used: s, p_x, p_y, $\frac{1}{\sqrt{2}} d_{xy}$, $\frac{1}{\sqrt{2}} d_{x^2-y^2}$.

In order that the total orbital angular momentum should be zero, half of the charge cloud of d_{xy} and half of the charge cloud of $d_{x^2-y^2}$ are used instead of the whole of

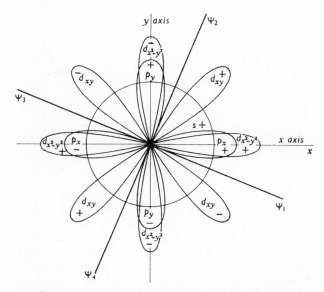

Fig. 5.6.   Tetragonal plane (square) σ hybridisation from s, p, and d atomic orbitals. (Fig. 5.9 shows alternative arrangement of equatorial hybridisation for use with superposed πd bonds.)

one of them. The axes of the hybrid orbitals lie as in the diagram. The wave functions†
may be written as:

$$\psi_1 = \frac{1}{2}\psi_s + \frac{a}{\sqrt{2}}\psi_{d_{x^2-y^2}} - \frac{a}{\sqrt{2}}\psi_{d_{xy}} + b\psi_{p_x} - c\psi_{p_y}$$

$$\psi_2 = \frac{1}{2}\psi_s - \frac{a}{\sqrt{2}}\psi_{d_{x^2-y^2}} + \frac{a}{\sqrt{2}}\psi_{d_{xy}} + c\psi_{p_x} + b\psi_{p_y}$$

$$\psi_3 = \frac{1}{2}\psi_s + \frac{a}{\sqrt{2}}\psi_{d_{x^2-y^2}} - \frac{a}{\sqrt{2}}\psi_{d_{xy}} - b\psi_{p_x} + c\psi_{p_y}$$

$$\psi_4 = \frac{1}{2}\psi_s - \frac{a}{\sqrt{2}}\psi_{d_{x^2-y^2}} + \frac{a}{\sqrt{2}}\psi_{d_{xy}} - c\psi_{p_x} - b\psi_{p_y}.$$

By Rule (c),

$$1 = \frac{1}{4} + a^2 + b^2 + c^2.$$

By Rule (d),

$$0 = \frac{1}{4} - a^2 + bc - bc,$$

and therefore

$$a = \frac{1}{2}, \quad \text{and} \quad b^2 + c^2 = \frac{1}{2}.$$

It is evident from the diagram (Fig. 5.6) that the ratio of the charge clouds contributed
by the p_x and p_y orbitals to, say ψ_1, is the ratio $\cos\phi/\sin\phi$.
  Since $\phi = 22\frac{1}{2}°$,

$$\frac{b^2}{c^2} = 2, \quad b = \frac{1}{\sqrt{3}}, \quad c = \frac{1}{\sqrt{6}},$$

and

$$\psi_1 = \frac{1}{2}\psi_s + \frac{1}{2\sqrt{2}}\psi_{d_{x^2-y^2}} - \frac{1}{2\sqrt{2}}\psi_{d_{xy}} + \frac{1}{\sqrt{3}}\psi_{p_x} - \frac{1}{\sqrt{6}}\psi_{p_y}$$

$$\psi_2 = \frac{1}{2}\psi_s - \frac{1}{2\sqrt{2}}\psi_{d_{x^2-y^2}} + \frac{1}{2\sqrt{2}}\psi_{d_{xy}} + \frac{1}{\sqrt{6}}\psi_{p_x} + \frac{1}{\sqrt{3}}\psi_{p_y}$$

$$\psi_3 = \frac{1}{2}\psi_s + \frac{1}{2\sqrt{2}}\psi_{d_{x^2-y^2}} - \frac{1}{2\sqrt{2}}\psi_{d_{xy}} - \frac{1}{\sqrt{3}}\psi_{p_x} + \frac{1}{\sqrt{6}}\psi_{p_y}$$

$$\psi_4 = \frac{1}{2}\psi_s - \frac{1}{2\sqrt{2}}\psi_{d_{x^2-y^2}} + \frac{1}{2\sqrt{2}}\psi_{d_{xy}} - \frac{1}{\sqrt{6}}\psi_{p_x} - \frac{1}{\sqrt{3}}\psi_{p_y}.$$

Trigonal bipyramidal σ hybridisation (Fig. 5.7). Orbitals used: s, p_x, p_y, p_z, d_{z^2}.
  For convenience, the diagram is separated into two parts: that showing the two
polar hybrid orbitals, and that showing the three equatorial hybrid orbitals.
  The equatorial hybrid wave functions are similar to those developed for the simple
trigonal hybridisation on p. 148. The component parts of the atomic orbitals used are
not quite the same; some of the s orbital is included in the polar functions, and this is
replaced by that part of the d_{z^2} orbital which lies in and near the equatorial plane.

  † An alternative set of wave functions for use with an equatorial πd bond is given on p. 155.

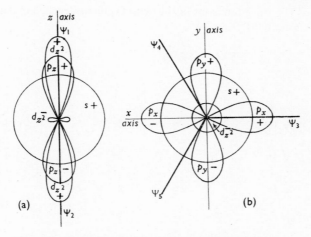

Fig. 5.7. Trigonal bipyramidal σ hybridisation from s, p, and d atomic orbitals. (a) polar hybridisation, (b) equatorial hybridisation.

The distribution of the total charge cloud of the atomic orbitals in this plane is independent of ϕ, and hence the trigonal orbitals may be imagined to be in any position relative to the x axis, as with the simple trigonal hybridisation.

This is convenient when consideration is given to π hybrids superposed on the σ hybrids (p. 161). The wave functions for the particular set of hybrid orbitals shown in the diagram are, by inspection (cf. p. 150):

$$\psi_1 = \frac{1}{\sqrt{8}} \psi_s + \frac{1}{\sqrt{2}} \psi_{p_z} + \sqrt{\frac{3}{8}} \psi_{d_{z^2}}$$

$$\psi_2 = \frac{1}{\sqrt{8}} \psi_s - \frac{1}{\sqrt{2}} \psi_{p_z} + \sqrt{\frac{3}{8}} \psi_{d_{z^2}}$$

$$\psi_3 = \frac{1}{2} \psi_s + \sqrt{\frac{2}{3}} \psi_{p_x} - \frac{1}{\sqrt{12}} \psi_{d_{z^2}}$$

$$\psi_4 = \frac{1}{2} \psi_s - \frac{1}{\sqrt{6}} \psi_{p_x} + \frac{1}{\sqrt{2}} \psi_{p_y} - \frac{1}{\sqrt{12}} \psi_{d_{z^2}}$$

$$\psi_5 = \frac{1}{2} \psi_s - \frac{1}{\sqrt{6}} \psi_{p_x} - \frac{1}{\sqrt{2}} \psi_{p_y} - \frac{1}{\sqrt{12}} \psi_{d_{z^2}}.$$

Octahedral σ hybridisation (Fig. 5.8). Orbitals used: s, p_x, p_y, p_z, d_{z^2}, $\frac{1}{\sqrt{2}} d_{xy}$. $\frac{1}{\sqrt{2}} d_{x^2-y^2}$.

For convenience, the diagram shows a set of orthogonal octahedral σ hybrids in two parts. The two polar orbitals are formed from part of s, part of d_{z^2}, and the whole of p_z. The four equatorial hybrids are formed in a similar manner as those of the tetragonal plane σ hybridisation (Fig. 5.6). There is a difference in the wave functions however; part of the s orbital is now used for the polar orbitals, the difference in the equatorial plane being made up by the portion of the d_{z^2} orbital with negative wave function. The wave functions of the hybrid orbitals depicted in the diagram may be written by inspection:

$$\psi_1 = \frac{1}{\sqrt{8}}\psi_s + \frac{1}{\sqrt{2}}\psi_{p_z} + \sqrt{\frac{3}{8}}\psi_{d_{z^2}}$$

$$\psi_2 = \frac{1}{\sqrt{8}}\psi_s - \frac{1}{\sqrt{2}}\psi_{p_z} + \sqrt{\frac{3}{8}}\psi_{d_{z^2}}$$

$$\psi_3 = \sqrt{\frac{3}{16}}\psi_s + \frac{1}{\sqrt{3}}\psi_{p_x} - \frac{1}{\sqrt{6}}\psi_{p_y} - \frac{1}{2\sqrt{2}}\psi_{d_{xy}} + \frac{1}{2\sqrt{2}}\psi_{d_{x^2-y^2}} - \frac{1}{4}\psi_{d_{z^2}}$$

$$\psi_4 = \sqrt{\frac{3}{16}}\psi_s + \frac{1}{\sqrt{6}}\psi_{p_x} + \frac{1}{\sqrt{3}}\psi_{p_y} + \frac{1}{2\sqrt{2}}\psi_{d_{xy}} - \frac{1}{2\sqrt{2}}\psi_{d_{x^2-y^2}} - \frac{1}{4}\psi_{d_{z^2}}$$

$$\psi_5 = \sqrt{\frac{3}{16}}\psi_s - \frac{1}{\sqrt{3}}\psi_{p_x} + \frac{1}{\sqrt{6}}\psi_{p_y} - \frac{1}{2\sqrt{2}}\psi_{d_{xy}} + \frac{1}{2\sqrt{2}}\psi_{d_{x^2-y^2}} - \frac{1}{4}\psi_{d_{z^2}}$$

$$\psi_6 = \sqrt{\frac{3}{16}}\psi_s - \frac{1}{\sqrt{6}}\psi_{p_x} - \frac{1}{\sqrt{3}}\psi_{p_y} + \frac{1}{2\sqrt{2}}\psi_{d_{xy}} - \frac{1}{2\sqrt{2}}\psi_{d_{x^2-y^2}} - \frac{1}{4}\psi_{d_{z^2}}.$$

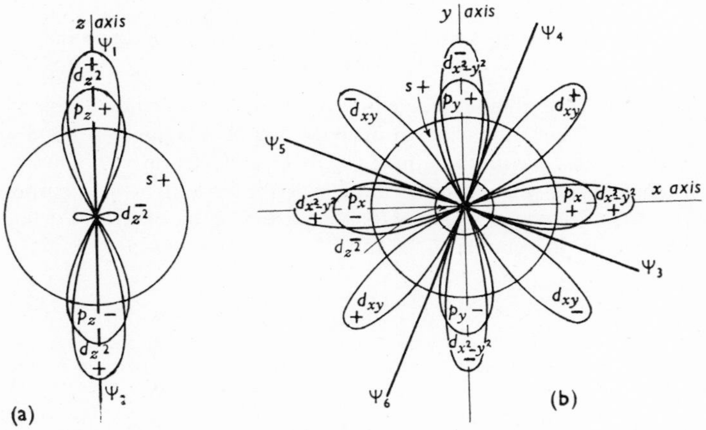

Fig. 5.8. Octahedral σ hybridisation from s, p, and d atomic orbitals. (a) Polar hybridisation, (b) equatorial hybridisation.

For σ octahedral hybrids in conjunction with one πd bond which lies over one of the σ bonds in the equatorial plane (p. 161), it is more convenient and simpler to describe a set of hybrid orbitals as follows. If the charge of the whole system is taken together, the orbitals concerned are s, p_x, p_y, p_z, d_{z^2}, d_{xy}, $d_{x^2-y^2}$; these have zero resultant angular momentum. The polar hybrids are formed as before from part of s, part of d_{z^2} and the whole of p_z. The equatorial hybrids are formed from part of s, part of d_{z^2}, and the whole of p_x, p_y, and d_{xy}. The equatorial wave functions are (Fig. 5.9):

$$\psi_3 = \sqrt{\frac{3}{16}}\psi_s + \frac{1}{2}\psi_{d_{xy}} + \frac{1}{2}\psi_{p_x} + \frac{1}{2}\psi_{p_y} - \frac{1}{4}\psi_{d_{z^2}}$$

$$\psi_4 = \sqrt{\frac{3}{16}}\psi_s - \frac{1}{2}\psi_{d_{xy}} - \frac{1}{2}\psi_{p_x} + \frac{1}{2}\psi_{p_y} - \frac{1}{4}\psi_{d_{z^2}}$$

$$\psi_5 = \sqrt{\frac{3}{16}}\psi_s + \frac{1}{2}\psi_{d_{xy}} - \frac{1}{2}\psi_{p_x} - \frac{1}{2}\psi_{p_y} - \frac{1}{4}\psi_{d_{z^2}}$$

$$\psi_6 = \sqrt{\frac{3}{16}}\psi_s - \frac{1}{2}\psi_{d_{xy}} + \frac{1}{2}\psi_{p_x} - \frac{1}{2}\psi_{p_y} - \frac{1}{4}\psi_{d_{z^2}}.$$

The $d_{x^2-y^2}$ supplies the πd bond in the equatorial plane (Fig. 5.12). The d_{xz} and d_{yz} orbitals are unused.

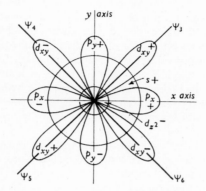

Fig. 5.9. Octahedral σ hybridisation.
Alternative description of equatorial
σ hybridisation for use with superposed
πd bonds.

The set of equatorial wave functions given above are suitable for tetragonal plane σ hybridisation in conjunction with a πd bond in the equatorial plane.

SIMPLE π BONDS

The preceding discussion on directed valence outlines a procedure for obtaining atomic hybrid orbitals with definite orientation. If all the hybrid orbitals of a given atom are each occupied by one electron, they can overlap with similarly occupied orbitals of other atoms to produce a molecule. The shape of the molecule is decided by the valence state of the central atom, thus

Boron trichloride   Methane   Sulphur hexafluoride
(Trigonal)   (Tetrahedral)   (Octahedral)

It does not follow, however, that every atomic orbital occupied by one electron is taken into the hybridised system of atomic orbitals. If a carbon atom were trigonally hybridised (sp_xp_z) the atomic orbitals available for bond formation would be the three trigonal σ hybrids and the unchanged p_y orbital. The structure of the ethylene molecule can be derived by assuming that two carbon atoms in this state are linked by the σ hybrids along the z axis, and by the other two σ hybrids to hydrogen atoms, thus and that the two p_y orbitals overlap to form a π bond which lies substantially in the zy plane (p. 126).

The presence of the π bond in the ethylene molecule explains its restricted "free rotation". Since the bond strength of a π bond is less than that of a σ bond, it also explains the readiness with which the molecule undergoes additive reactions in which each carbon atom becomes bonded to one additional univalent atom or group, and so changes to the tetrahedral valence state, in which it exerts four σ bonds.

In the acetylene molecule it is assumed (in terms of hybridisation) that the two carbon atoms are digonally hybridised (sp_z) and that the σ hybrids are used for binding the carbon atoms and two hydrogen atoms. The p_x and p_y orbitals on both atoms are not included in the hybridisation, and they are used for forming a double π bond (p. 127).

It must be emphasised that the shape of the skeleton of a molecule is fixed by the orientation of the σ hybrids; π bonds modify the dimensions of a molecule, but they do not alter the basic form. The π bond is rarely the only link between two atoms[†]; it is almost always superimposed on a σ bond.

SIMPLE πd BONDS

A π bond made by the overlapping of a d orbital from one atom and a p orbital from a second atom may be formed between atoms already linked by a σ bond. Such a bond may be called a πd bond. For the construction of a πd bond it is necessary that the symmetry of the combining orbitals be correct, and that the magnetic quantum number of the d orbital be the same as that of the overlapping p orbital. The second requirement precludes the use of the $d_{x^2-y^2}$ and the d_{xy} orbitals for the construction of simple πd bonds; hence simple πd bonds are always directed along the z axis. A list of orbital structures containing simple πd bonds for an atom in different valence states is shown in Table 5.3.

π HYBRIDS

The atomic orbitals left over after σ hybridisation may be hybridised among themselves to form π hybrids which are then available for the formation of π bonds superposed on σ bonds.[‡] According to the method used in this book, orbitals used for π hybrids are invariably d orbitals. A more general method, based on group theory, not given in this book, shows that there are other possibilities,[§] and that a complete set of σ and π hybrids can be constructed from s, p, and d atomic orbitals in one operation. There are important symmetry rules which limit the possible number of different combinations.

The π hybrids included in Table 5.4 are constructed by the linear combination of d orbitals. It is a condition of their construction that they shall be orthogonal, and that the angular momentum of a π hybrid shall be identical in magnitude (units of $h/2\pi$) and direction with that of the p orbital with which it will overlap. The bond formed by the overlapping of a π hybrid of one atom with a p orbital of another atom, the atoms being already linked by a σ bond, may be called a hybrid πd bond to distinguish it from a simple πd bond. A list of orbital structures containing hybrid πd bonds for an atom in difference valence states is shown in Table 5.4.

[†] An example is found in the tetrameric form of thallous ethoxide (p. 562).
[‡] The term σ hybrid is used to describe a hybrid atomic orbital which takes part in the formation of a σ interatomic orbital. Similarly, the term π hybrid is used to describe a hybrid atomic orbital which takes part in the formation of a π interatomic orbital.
[§] Giovanni Giacometti, *J. Chem. Phys.* **23**(2), 1955, 2070.

Table 5.3. *Simple πd Bonds which may be formed by an Atom*

σ valence state of atom	Orbitals used for σ hybridisation	Number of simple πd bonds	d Orbitals used in πd bonds	Resultant angular momentum of d orbitals used	Direction of πd bond
Tetrahedral (orientation I)	s, p_x, p_y, p_z	1 or 2	d_{xz} or d_{yz} d_{xz} and d_{yz}	± 1 $+1$ and -1	Along z axis Both bonds in the same direction along the z axis
Trigonal bipyramidal	$s, p_x, p_y, p_z, d_{z^2}$	1 or 2	d_{xz} or d_{yz} d_{xz} and d_{yz}	± 1 $+1$ and -1	Along z axis (polar) (a) Both bonds in the same direction along the z axis (b) Bonds in opposite directions along the z axis
Octahedral	$s, p_x, p_y, p_z, d_{z^2},$ $\frac{1}{\sqrt{2}} d_{xy}, \frac{1}{\sqrt{2}} d_{x^2-y^2}$	1 or 2	d_{xz} or d_{yz} d_{xz} and d_{yz}	± 1 $+1$ and -1	Along z axis (a) Both bonds in the same direction along the z axis (b) Bonds in opposite directions along the z axis

Table 5.4. *Hybrid πd Bonds which may be formed by an Atom in certain Valence States*

σ valence state of atom	Orbitals used for σ hybridisation	Number of hybrid πd bonds	d orbitals used in π hybridisation	Angular momentum in units of $h/2\pi$	Direction of hybrid πd bonds
Tetrahedral (orientation II)	s, p_x, p_y, p_z	2 3	$\frac{1}{\sqrt{2}}d_{xz}, \frac{1}{\sqrt{2}}d_{yz},$ $\frac{1}{\sqrt{2}}d_{xy}, \frac{1}{\sqrt{2}}d_{x^2-y^2}$ $d_{xz}, d_{yz}, d_{z^2},$ $\frac{1}{\sqrt{2}}d_{xy}, \frac{1}{\sqrt{2}}d_{x^2-y^2}$	1 about the axis of the σ bond for each πd bond	Along the axes of the tetrahedral σ bonds
Tetragonal plane (square)	$s, p_x, p_y,$ $\frac{1}{\sqrt{2}}d_{xy}, \frac{1}{\sqrt{2}}d_{x^2-y^2}$	1	$\frac{1}{\sqrt{2}}d_{xy}, \frac{1}{\sqrt{2}}d_{x^2-y^2}$	0 about the z axis	Along one of the σ bonds
Trigonal bipyramidal	$s, p_x, p_y, p_z, d_{z^2}$	1	$\frac{1}{\sqrt{2}}d_{xy}, \frac{1}{\sqrt{2}}d_{x^2-y^2}$	0 about the z axis	Along one of the equatorial σ bonds
Octahedral	$s, p_x, p_y, p_z, d_{z^2},$ $\frac{1}{\sqrt{2}}d_{xy}, \frac{1}{\sqrt{2}}d_{x^2-y^2}$	1	$\frac{1}{\sqrt{2}}d_{xy}, \frac{1}{\sqrt{2}}d_{x^2-y^2}$	0 about the z axis	Along one of the σ bonds in the xy plane

The procedure for the construction of π hybrids in which only d orbitals are used is described below.

Tetrahedral π hybrids (a). *When all five d orbitals of the atom are to be occupied by electrons* (Fig. 5.10). Orbitals used: d_{xz}, d_{xy}, d_{yz}, d_{z^2}.†

If each hybrid orbital contains one-quarter of the charge of each component atomic orbital, the wave functions may be written down from inspection of the diagram. The axes of the resultant hybrid orbitals lie exactly over those of the tetrahedral σ hybrids shown in Fig. 5.5. The wave functions are by inspection:

$$\psi_1 = +\tfrac{1}{2}\psi_{d_{xz}} + \tfrac{1}{2}\psi_{d_{yz}} + \tfrac{1}{2}\psi_{d_{z^2}} + \tfrac{1}{2}\psi_{d_{xy}}$$
$$\psi_2 = -\tfrac{1}{2}\psi_{d_{xz}} + \tfrac{1}{2}\psi_{d_{yz}} + \tfrac{1}{2}\psi_{d_{z^2}} - \tfrac{1}{2}\psi_{d_{xy}}$$
$$\psi_3 = +\tfrac{1}{2}\psi_{d_{xz}} - \tfrac{1}{2}\psi_{d_{yz}} + \tfrac{1}{2}\psi_{d_{z^2}} - \tfrac{1}{2}\psi_{d_{xy}}$$
$$\psi_4 = -\tfrac{1}{2}\psi_{d_{xz}} - \tfrac{1}{2}\psi_{d_{yz}} + \tfrac{1}{2}\psi_{d_{z^2}} + \tfrac{1}{2}\psi_{d_{xy}}$$

The wave functions ψ_2, ψ_3, ψ_4 have the correct symmetry for the formation of πd

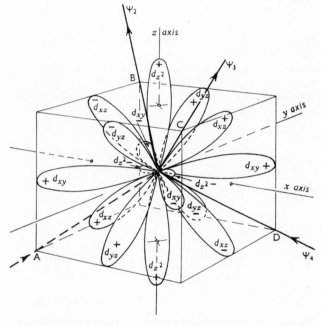

Fig. 5.10. Tetrahedral π hybridisation from d atomic orbitals (a). ψ_1 is shown by a broken line.

bonds with p orbitals from other atoms; the wave function ψ_1 is unsuitable in symmetry for the formation of a πd bond. The orbital may however, be occupied by an electron

†The four atomic orbitals d_{xz}, d_{xy}, d_{yz}, d_{z^2} are chosen for convenience of pictorial representation. The resulting hybrid orbitals have an orientation which coincides with that of the σ hybridisation of Fig. 5.5. To satisfy rule (e) however, the whole system would have to be moved through an angle of $22\tfrac{1}{2}°$ about the z axis. This is equivalent to selecting the orbitals $d_{xz}, d_{yz}, d_{z^2}, 1/\sqrt{2}\, d_{xy}, 1/\sqrt{2}\, d_{x^2-y^2}$ for the hybridisation. The d_{z^2} orbital plays the part of the s orbital which was essential for the tetrahedral σ hybridisation. The θ dependent part of the wave function of the d_{z^2} orbital is $\sqrt{5/2}(3\cos^2\theta - 1)$, and hence the wave function is positive for all values of θ for which $\cos\theta > 1/\sqrt{3}$; in and near the equatorial plane the d_{z^2} wave function is negative. The most satisfactory hybridisation procedure however, is to take the entire set of s, p, d, orbitals together, and from them to derive suitable orbitals of the correct symmetry for both σ and π bonding.

pair. The conclusion is therefore reached that four d orbitals hybridised in this way are capable of forming three tetrahedral πd bonds; the fourth hybrid orbital is non-bonding. The same conclusion is also reached by the application of group theory, and it is supported by chemical evidence.

Tetrahedral π hybridisation (b). *When two only of the d orbitals are to be occupied by electrons.* In this case, two only of the d orbitals are available for hybridisation.† Group theory shows that it is possible to hybridise two d orbitals so that they can be used in the formation of πd bonds superposed on two of the σ hybrids formed by tetrahedral (sp^3) hybridisation. The formation of two π hybrids may be visualised by the following simple geometrical procedure. If the orbitals used are the $d_{x^2-y^2}$ and d_{xz} orbitals, the construction of possible hybrids may be followed by reference to Fig. 5.11.

Suppose the wave functions of the hybrid orbitals are:

$$\psi_1 = \frac{1}{\sqrt{2}}\psi_{d_{x^2-y^2}} - \frac{1}{\sqrt{2}}\psi_{d_{xz}}$$

$$\psi_2 = \frac{1}{\sqrt{2}}\psi_{d_{x^2-y^2}} + \frac{1}{\sqrt{2}}\psi_{d_{xz}}.$$

ψ_1 may be visualised as being formed from the positive part of the $d_{x^2-y^2}$ orbital and the negative part of the d_{xz} orbital. ψ_2 may be visualised as being formed from half of the positive parts of the $d_{x^2-y^2}$ and d_{xz} orbitals and half of the negative parts of the same orbitals. ψ_2 then comes up from the plane of the paper over the quadrant marked A in Fig. 5.11. The angle between ψ_1 and ψ_2 is near the tetrahedral angle.

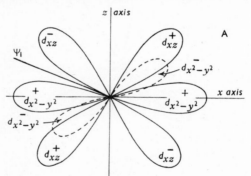

Fig. 5.11. Tetrahedral π hybridisation from d
atomic orbitals (b).

Tetragonal plane (square) π hybridisation.   Orbitals used: $\frac{1}{\sqrt{2}} d_{xy}$, $\frac{1}{\sqrt{2}} d_{x^2-y^2}$. The symmetry of the d_{z^2} orbital is unsuitable for this hybridisation.

One π hybrid orbital may be formed in the equatorial plane: this is represented by the wave function

$$\psi = \frac{1}{\sqrt{2}}\psi_{d_{xy}} - \frac{1}{\sqrt{2}}\psi_{d_{x^2-y^2}}.$$

The hybrid orbital has zero angular momentum about the z axis; on one side of the orbital axis there is a concentration of positive symmetry, on the other a concentration of negative symmetry. The hybrid π orbital is suitable therefore for overlapping with a p_z atomic orbital of another atom.

†G. E. Kimball, *J. Chem. Phys.*, **8** (1940), 188.

Since the distribution of the total charge clouds of the atomic orbitals used for the σ hybridisation (p. 151) is independent of ϕ, the σ hybrids can be imagined to be turned through any angle ϕ. Hence the πd bond may be formed over one of the σ bonds. A simpler equivalent description is that used on p. 154. If the whole set of orbitals are taken together, there is no resultant angular momentum of the charge, and the πd bond may be regarded simply as supplied by the $d_{x^2-y^2}$ atomic orbital (Fig. 5.12).

Trigonal bipyramidal π hybridisation. Orbitals used: d_{xz}, d_{yz}, $\dfrac{1}{\sqrt{2}} d_{xy}$, $\dfrac{1}{\sqrt{2}} d_{x^2-y^2}$.

The orbitals d_{xz} and d_{yz}, taken separately, are obviously suitable both in respect of symmetry and angular momentum for the formation of two polar πd bonds. One bond only can be formed in the equatorial plane; the wave function and position of the axis of the hybrid orbital are identical with those of the hybrid π orbital discussed

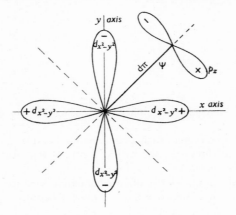

Fig. 5.12. $d_{x^2-y^2}$ atomic orbital forming πd bond with p_z orbital of another atom. This bond is superposed on one of the σ bonds corresponding to the hybridisation shown in Fig. 5.9.

at the beginning of the preceding paragraph for tetragonal plane π hybridisation. Since the trigonal bipyramidal σ hybrid orbitals are formed from atomic orbitals whose charge clouds taken together are independent of ϕ, the πd bond can be formed over any one of the σ bonds, and can overlap with the p_z orbital of another atom.

Octahedral π hybridisation. Orbitals used: d_{xz}, d_{yz}, $\dfrac{1}{\sqrt{2}} d_{xy}$, $\dfrac{1}{\sqrt{2}} d_{x^2-y^2}$.

Exactly the same bonds are formed as for the trigonal bypyramidal π hybridisation; two polar bonds, and one equatorial bond which can lie over any one of the σ hybrids, and which is suitable for overlapping with the p_z orbital or another atom. If the alternative set of σ orbitals (p. 154) is used, the πd bond is supplied by the $d_{x^2-y^2}$ orbital (Fig. 5.12).

π hybridisation from the linear combination of d_{xz} and d_{yz} orbitals. The linear combination of the d_{xz} and d_{yz} orbitals gives two hybrid π orbitals† of which the wave functions are:

$$\psi_1 = \frac{1}{\sqrt{2}} \psi_{d_{xz}} + \frac{1}{\sqrt{2}} \psi_{d_{yz}}$$

$$\psi_2 = \frac{1}{\sqrt{2}} \psi_{d_{xz}} - \frac{1}{\sqrt{2}} \psi_{d_{yz}}.$$

† Use is made of these hybrids in the discussion on the structure of the carbonyls (p. 1075).
6+A.T.I.C.

ψ_1 takes part in the formation of a πd bond along the z axis (Fig. 5.13(a)). Since the resultant angular momentum of the two original orbitals is zero, the bond must be made with a π orbital of another atom formed by the linear combination of a p_x and p_y orbital (Fig. 5.13(b)).

The hybrid orbital corresponding to ψ_2 can be visualised as a d orbital formed from the positive half of one of the combining atomic d orbitals and the negative half of

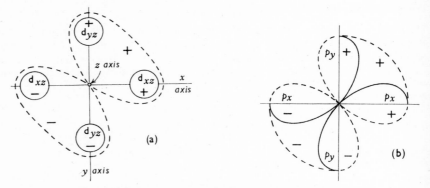

Fig. 5.13. Combination of orbitals: (a) d_{xz}, and d_{yz}, (b) p_x and p_y.

the other. It is difficult to represent such a combination in a two-dimensional diagram; the use of a model will show that the hybrid d orbital thus formed lies in a plane characterised by $\theta = 45°$ and $\phi = -45°$.

If ψ_1 is directed along an apical axis of an octahedron, then the direction of ψ_2 will be at right angles to a pair of opposite faces of the octahedron.

Table 5.5. *Total Number of πd Bonds (Simple and Hybrid) which may be formed by an Atom*

Valence state of atom	Number of πd bonds	Direction of πd bonds
Tetrahedral	1, or 2, or 3 2	Along different σ bonds Along the same σ bond
Tetragonal plane (square)	1	Along any σ bond
Trigonal bipyramidal	1	One along an equatorial σ bond or either of the polar σ bonds
	2	(i) Two along one polar σ bond, or (ii) one along each of the polar σ bonds, or (iii) one along a polar σ bond and one along an equatorial σ bond
	3	Any arrangement of three πd bonds except that not more than one can be along an equatorial σ bond, and not more than two can be along one polar σ bond
Octahedral	1, or 2, or 3	As for the trigonal bipyramidal valence state, the directions along the z axis being regarded as polar, and those in the xy plane as equatorial

NUMBER OF πd BONDS

The number of πd bonds which can be formed by an atom is important in discussing the structures of the oxyacid ions such as PO_4^{3-}, SO_4^{2-}, ClO_4^{-}, and of the carbonyls of the transition metals such as $Fe(CO)_5$. The number of πd bonds formed by an atom in different valence states, and their directions, are set out in Table 5.5. It should be noted that the geometry of a molecule is always decided by the σ hybridisation.

NON-BONDING ORBITALS

The orbital structures of the molecules of the hydrocarbons methane, ethylene, and acetylene are very simply described because the carbon atom has four atomic orbitals and four electrons in the valency shell. The atoms N, O, F, also have four atomic orbitals in the valency shell, but they have more than four valence electrons. In ammonia, for example, the nitrogen atom exerts three bonds and controls eight valence electrons, and hence one electron pair must occupy an orbital which is neither a bonding orbital nor an antibonding orbital. Such an orbital is known as a *non-bonding orbital*. By similar reasoning, the oxygen atom in water, and the fluorine atom in hydrogen fluoride, have respectively two pairs and three pairs of electrons in non-bonding orbitals. It may be stated generally that: *when an atom containing more than four electrons in its valency shell enters into combination, the atomic orbitals are hybridised, and at least one of the hybrid orbitals is occupied by a pair of electrons which plays no part in bond formation.* The pair of electrons occupying a non-bonding orbital is known as a *lone pair*.

A firm distinction must be drawn between a *lone pair* and an *inert pair*. Both terms refer to an electron pair in an atom which is combined with one or more other atoms. A lone pair occupies a non-bonding orbital which is one of a set of hybrid atomic orbitals. An inert pair is a pair of electrons which is in the valence shell of the atom, but occupies an orbital which has neither been selected for hybridisation, nor is forming π bonds. The inert pair remains in the original undisturbed atomic orbital. It takes no part in any reactions of the molecule except those which, by changing the valence state of the atom, bring its atomic orbital into hybridisation. Examples are found in the chemistry of tin and thallium (pp. 558, 629).

A lone pair of electrons, by contrast, is frequently a point of activity in a molecule. Compounds whose molecules contain a lone electron pair are powerful electron donors, and readily enter into complex formation. The properties of compounds containing hydrogen and hydroxyl bonds are elegantly explained (p. 372) on the assumption that the water molecule is effectively a spherical oxygen atom with the surface divided into four equal areas, two positively charged owing to the presence of protons, and two negatively charged owing to the presence of two lone pairs.

ORBITAL DIAGRAMS

A conventional orbital diagram is used to indicate the nature of the bonds in a molecule or ion which consists of a central atom surrounded by other atoms or groups. The orbital diagram shows which of the orbitals in the valence system of the central atom are hybridised, which are used to form σ bonds or π bonds, and which are occupied by lone pairs. As an example the orbital diagram for the iron atom in iron pentacarbonyl, $Fe(CO)_5$, is drawn in Fig. 5.14.

The headings $3d$, $4s$, and $4p$ indicate the orbitals of the valence group of the central atom, iron. The atomic orbitals of the central atom which are hybridised are enclosed in rectangles; inspection shows which form σ hybrids and which form π hybrids. The arrows in the top row represent electrons originally present in the central atom. An orbital of the central atom which is hybridised, but which before combination with the carbonyl group was not occupied by an electron, is indicated by a circle $_{\circ}$. The arrows in the bottom row represent electrons contributed by atoms making bonds with the central atom. An interatomic orbital corresponding to a bond is indicated by a pair of

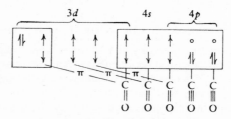

Fig. 5.14. Orbital diagram for $Fe(CO)_5$.

oppositely directed arrows, one above the other if the bond is covalent, and side by side if the bond is co-ionic.

A pair of oppositely directed arrows in the top line represents a lone electron pair. A π bond between the central atom (iron) and one of the atoms already linked to the iron atom by a σ bond is indicated by the symbol $-\pi-$.

Iron pentacarbonyl is a neutral complex. Many of the complexes usefully described by orbital diagrams are anions or cations. The orbital diagram for the sulphate anion is drawn in Fig. 5.15.

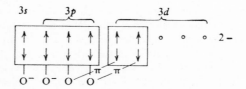

Fig. 5.15. Orbital diagram for the sulphate ion, SO_4^{2-}.

The symbols in the diagram have exactly the same meaning as those in Fig. 5.14. The superscript $^-$ against two of the oxygen atoms indicates that an electron has been transferred to each of these atoms from the metal forming the cation. As another example of an anion the diagram for $[Fe(CN)_6]^{3-}$ is drawn in Fig. 5.16.

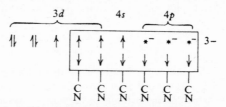

Fig. 5.16. Orbital diagram for the ferricyanide
ion, $[Fe(CN)_6]^{3-}$.

In this diagram the symbol $*^-$ represents an electron which has been transferred to the central atom (iron) from the metal forming the cation.

As an example of an orbital diagram of a cation that of $[Fe(NH_3)_6]^{2+}$ is drawn in Fig. 5.17. The iron atom has transferred two electrons to the atoms forming the anion, and six hybridised orbitals are used in forming co-ionic bonds with the nitrogen atoms of six ammonia molecules.

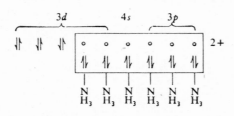

Fig. 5.17.   Orbital diagram for the complex cation $[Fe(NH_3)_6]^{2+}$

METHOD OF EQUIVALENT ORBITALS

In order to adapt the theory of molecular orbitals to the expression of directed valence, Lennard-Jones† showed that the molecular orbitals of the simple theory can be replaced by a set of *equivalent orbitals* directed in space. A molecule can be described equally well *either* by a set of molecular orbitals *or* by a set of equivalent orbitals; neither is more correct than the other. A simple illustration may be given by the superposition of a number of simple harmonic waves; the system may be described either as a number of separate wave forms, or by the resultant wave form, or by combining the separate waves in one or two groups of intermediate wave forms. Any one method of description of the system may obviously be converted to another.

It has been shown on p. 114 that simple molecular orbitals are obtained by the linear combination of atomic wave functions. It is possible to make a large number of these combinations, but from the practical standpoint not all of them have the same value. It is not possible from theoretical considerations only, to make the right selection of molecular orbitals suitable for transformation into a set of equivalent orbitals which will have directional properties corresponding to the direction of the bonds in a known molecule. It is necessary to consider the symmetry properties of the molecule deduced from experimental evidence before the selection is made. When the symmetry group of the molecule is established, those molecular orbitals are chosen whose symmetry is correct for this group. Even so, in some cases it is possible to develop more than one set of equivalent orbitals; the set chosen to represent the molecule consists of orbitals which are identical with each other except for their orientation. This cannot be determined unless the wave functions dealt with, whether atomic or molecular, are complete wave functions. The wave functions used in the LCAO method of forming simple molecular orbitals do not contain any spin function. Therefore in order to make the transformation from molecular to equivalent orbitals it is necessary to construct from molecular orbitals (obtained by LCAO) complete wave functions analogous to those used by Heitler and London for the combination of atomic orbitals. The complete wave functions must be expressed in the form of determinants. It has been shown that under such a transformation the total energy is invariant.

The method may be applied to determine an orbital structure for the nitrogen molecule, N_2. The electron configuration of each nitrogen atom in the ground state is $1s^2 2s^2 p_x p_y p_z$. The 1s electrons are not part of the valency shell and may be neglected. This leaves 10 electrons to be accommodated in molecular orbitals.

† *Proc. Roy. Soc.*, **A. 198**, 1949, 1, 14, and **A. 202**, 1950, 155, 166.

The molecular orbitals in a diatomic molecule are set out in Table 4.2, p. 128. The two lowest orbitals, $\sigma 2s$ and σ^*2s, are formed from the atomic $2s$ orbitals. They may be transformed into two equivalent orbitals, each accommodating one lone pair. The next three molecular orbitals are $\sigma 2p_z$, $\pi 2p_y$, $\pi 2p_x$. These orbitals may be linearly combined to give the wave functions:

$$\psi_1 = \frac{1}{\sqrt{3}}\psi_\sigma + \frac{\sqrt{2}}{\sqrt{3}}\psi_{\pi x}$$

$$\psi_2 = \frac{1}{\sqrt{3}}\psi_\sigma - \frac{1}{\sqrt{6}}\psi_{\pi x} + \frac{1}{\sqrt{2}}\psi_{\pi y}$$

$$\psi_3 = \frac{1}{\sqrt{3}}\psi_\sigma - \frac{1}{\sqrt{6}}\psi_{\pi x} - \frac{1}{\sqrt{2}}\psi_{\pi y}.$$

The coefficients in these equations are identical with those obtained for the trigonal hybridisation of atomic orbitals (p. 149). The shapes of the charge clouds of the equivalent orbitals, however, differ from those of the hybridised atomic orbitals, as the atomic orbitals radiate from one atomic nucleus, whereas the equivalent orbitals (like the molecular orbitals before transformation) embrace more than one nucleus. For instance, the atomic orbitals $2s$, $2p_x$, $2p_z$ of the boron *atom* can be hybridised to give three trigonal hybrids lying in the xz plane:

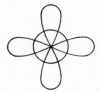

The $2s$, $2p_z$ and $2p_y$
orbitals of the
boron atom.

The three trigonal
hybrid atomic orbitals
of the boron atom.

The three molecular orbitals in the nitrogen *molecule*

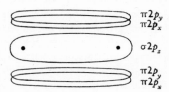

$\pi 2p_y$
$\pi 2p_x$

$\sigma 2p_z$

$\pi 2p_y$
$\pi 2p_x$

may be transformed into the equivalent orbitals

which have the property that they are turned into one another by rotation through 120° about the molecular axis.

By treatment closely similar to that applied to the nitrogen molecule the molecule of acetylene can be drawn

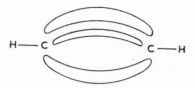

and the molecule of ethylene

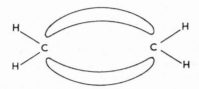

These bent equivalent orbitals are sometimes known as *banana bonds*. They suggest models for unsaturated carbon compounds which are reminiscent of the Baeyer strain theory (p. 108). The equivalent orbital method has been applied to the structures of many other molecules.†

When molecular orbitals are expressed as equivalent orbitals the electron potential energy divides into two parts; one part is the result of Coulomb forces, and the other, referred to as the exchange energy, depends on the distribution of electron spin as governed by Pauli's exclusion principle. The Coulomb distribution of charge is referred to as *charge correlation*, the distribution of spin as *electron correlation*.

Charge correlation. In simple terms, the system arranges itself so that the electron charges are as far away from each other as possible. If the molecules are described in terms of equivalent orbitals, then 90% of the forces between the charge clouds are described as Coulomb forces. For instance, it is inferred that the trigonal orientation of the equivalent orbitals in the nitrogen molecule is the result of the Coulomb forces between the electrons in the three orbitals, which take up positions as far away from each other as possible.

Electron correlation. The influence of Pauli's exclusion principle on valency is of great importance. The final position of a bond depends not only on charge correlation but also on the relative orientation of electron spins. The effect in a covalent bond can be simply described in terms of forces between the electrons by saying that opposite spins attract one another and parallel spins repel one another. In a covalent bond, the exchange integral is negative. The forces between electrons due to their spin are commonly known as *exchange forces*. In terms of the theory of equivalent orbitals they are responsible for about 10% of the bond energy.

To sum up, the methods of hybridisation and equivalent orbitals are two different ways of describing directed valence. *Hybridisation* is carried out notionally on atomic orbitals *before* they have overlapped with orbitals of another atom: the transformation to *equivalent orbitals* is carried out notionally *after* orbitals from different atoms have overlapped. The method of hybridisation is the easier to use in practice, and it is employed in this book.

† J. A. Pople, *Quarterly Reviews*, **11**, No. 3, 1957, 273.

RESONANCE

The space wave function of an interatomic orbital formed by the combination of orbitals of two different atoms may be written (p. 142)

$$\psi = \psi_{cov} \pm \lambda \psi_{ion}.$$

The wave function ψ_{cov} is that of the interatomic orbital when the link between the atoms is wholly covalent; the wave function ψ_{ion} is that of the interatomic orbital when the link is wholly ionic. The expression may also be regarded from the point of view of the molecule, in which case ψ is the correct wave function for the real molecule, ψ_{cov} is the wave function when the structure of the molecule is wholly covalent; the wave function ψ_{ion} is that of the molecule when the structure is ionic. This method of regarding molecular structure may be extended. If ψ_A, ψ_B, ψ_C, ψ_D, are the wave functions of the possible structures A, B, C, D of a molecule, then the correct wave function for the molecule is

$$\psi = a\psi_A + b\psi_B + c\psi_C + d\psi_D.$$

The structures A, B, C, D are called *canonical forms*. The molecule of which ψ is the correct wave function is said to be compounded of the *canonical forms in resonance*. It must be emphasised that ψ represents a wave motion which is the sum of the wave motions ψ_A, ψ_B, ψ_C, ψ_D. The four component wave motions are included in the resultant, but they are not individually recognisable. The structures A, B, C, D must similarly be regarded as included in the final molecular structure, but they themselves are not recognisable as real physical structures. They have no actual existence, and are postulated as a calculus for arriving at the correct molecular structure (see also p. 171).

This procedure for arriving at a correct molecular structure is known as the *method of resonance*. The principles of the method may be illustrated by one or two examples. If hydrogen chloride were under consideration the canonical forms would be H—Cl and H⁺Cl⁻. In terms of resonance the gas hydrogen chloride does not contain any molecules with these structures, but is made up of molecules described by a wave function compounded of wave functions corresponding to these two limiting structures.

In the case of hydrogen chloride, one canonical form is covalent and the other ionic. Very many systems in resonance, however, are built up of canonical forms, all of which are covalent, but differ in the arrangement of the covalencies. A good example is furnished by nitrogen dioxide (p. 658, Table 19.5), for which the five canonical forms are written:

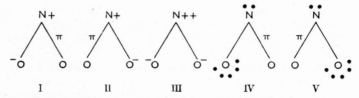

Forms I, II, and III contain co-ionic bonds and formal charges (p. 113) on the nitrogen and oxygen atoms. Form I differs from form II, and form IV from form V, only in the allocation of bonds to particular oxygen atoms. Other canonical forms for nitrogen dioxide could be invented, for example, the ionic form is a reasonable one, although the ion NO^{++} is not found as a cation. Any complete account of a molecule in terms of resonance would have to consider an exhaustive list of canonical forms. This would include not only all possible forms of the molecule in the ground state, but also forms in excited states. In practice, the treatment of structural problems by the method of resonance can consider only the most obvious canonical forms, and for this reason the method can be no more than approximate.

Resonance energy. If the correct wave function of a molecule is ψ, and if ψ_A and ψ_B are the wave functions corresponding to two possible canonical forms,

$$\psi = a\psi_A \pm b\psi_B.$$

The energy of the molecule is a function of ψ^2 where

$$\psi^2 = a^2\psi_A^2 + b^2\psi_B^2 \pm 2ab\psi_A\psi_B.$$

The term $2ab\psi_A\psi_B$ is a function of the resonance energy of the molecule, which is defined as the difference between the energy of the molecule with the correct compound wave function ψ, and the energy of one of the canonical forms. The definition of resonance energy is arbitrary, as its value depends on the canonical form selected as the standard. The greater the number of canonical terms combined, the lower is the energy corresponding to the resultant molecular wave function.

CONJUGATION

The molecules of many carbon compounds have been formulated in terms of the Kekulé notation as chains or rings of carbon atoms in which every other pair of carbon atoms is linked by a double bond. Such compounds are said to be *conjugated*. A list of a few conjugated compounds is given in Table 5.6.

Table 5.6. *Properties of Certain Conjugated Compounds*

Compounds	Bond lengths C—C	Difference between energy of molecule and calculated energy of the Kekulé structure, kcals per mole
Butadiene	1·35, 1·46	4·1
Hexatriene		24
Benzene	1·39	41
Naphthalene	1·35, 1·40, 1·42	77
Pyrene	1·37, 1·39, 1·45	152
Aniline	1·39	51
Pyridine	1·39	41

The average C—C is 1·54; the average C=C is 1·34.

It is found that the physical and chemical properties of conjugated compounds differ from those which would be predicted from a consideration of the simple Kekulé bond structures. The bond lengths between the carbon atoms concerned are intermediate between the average bond lengths (p. 317) for single and double bonds. The *heat of formation* of the compound from its elements is greater than the value calculated using the appropriate values for double and single bonds. The compound is less *chemically active* than its Kekulé formula would predict. In ring structures, such as that of the benzene molecule, the effect of a change at one carbon atom in the ring (such as the replacement of a hydrogen atom, by say, a chlorine atom) is felt at certain other carbon atoms in the ring. Such an effect can be explained only by a movement of electrons. Hence a conjugated molecule is assumed to be an isolated

6*

electrical conductor. On account of this property a very large conjugated molecule can play an important part in a biological structure, as it furnishes the means of transmitting an impulse from one part of the organism to another. The *diamagnetic effect*, particularly in ring structures, is large. Conjugated molecules show characteristic absorption spectra.

Conjugation is best discussed in terms of a real molecule, for example benzene. The benzene molecule consists of six carbon atoms at the apices of an equilateral hexagon. One hydrogen atom is attached to each carbon atom. The molecule is planar. The orbital structure may be regarded in one of three ways:

(1) As a completely non-localised structure of molecular orbitals. This structure is probably the most realistic, but the mathematical treatment would be so complex that it will not be considered.

(2) As a system of trigonally hybridised carbon atoms, each forming σ bonds with one hydrogen atom and two other carbon atoms. The remaining six p orbitals, one on each carbon atom, are combined to give six non-localised six-centre orbitals. This structure, which may be called the limited molecular orbital treatment is discussed in the following section.

(3) As a system of canonical forms in resonance. This structure is described on p. 171.

CONJUGATION IN TERMS OF A LIMITED MOLECULAR ORBITAL TREATMENT

The space wave function for the six-centre molecular orbital is given by:

$$\psi = c_1\psi_A + c_2\psi_B + c_3\psi_C + c_4\psi_D + c_5\psi_E + c_6\psi_F$$

where ψ_A, ψ_B, ψ_C, etc., are the space wave functions of the six atomic p orbitals. By following a procedure similar to that on p. 118 six equations may be written down. The first equation is

$$c_1(E_{AA} - ES_{AA}) + c_2(E_{AB} - ES_{AB}) + c_3(E_{AC} - ES_{AC}) + c_4(E_{AD} - ES_{AD})$$
$$+ c_5(E_{AE} - ES_{AE}) + c_6(E_{AF} - ES_{AF}) = 0.$$

The others follow the same pattern.

The solution may be simplified by making the assumption that:

(1) ψ is normalised so that

$$S_{AA} = S_{BB} = S_{CC} = S_{DD} = S_{EE} = S_{FF} = 1;$$

(2) to a first approximation the overlap integrals may be disregarded:

$$S_{AB} = S_{BC} = S_{CD} = S_{DE} = S_{EF} = S_{FA} = 0;$$

(3) only those resonance integrals referring to neighbouring atoms need be included, so that $E_{AC} = E_{AD} = E_{AE} = 0$, etc.;

(4) the resonance integrals between neighbouring atoms are equal, so that $E_{AB} = E_{BC} = E_{CD} = E_{DE} = E_{EF} = E_{FA}$, and each term may be written as β;

(5) $E_{AA} = E_{BB} = E_{CC} = E_{DD} = E_{EE} = E_{FF}$, and may be written as E_0;

(6) $E_0 - E$ may be written as A.

The six equations may then be written in a simplified form as

$$c_1 A + \beta(c_6 + c_2) = 0$$
$$c_2 A + \beta(c_1 + c_3) = 0$$
$$c_3 A + \beta(c_2 + c_4) = 0$$
$$c_4 A + \beta(c_3 + c_5) = 0$$
$$c_5 A + \beta(c_4 + c_6) = 0$$
$$c_6 A + \beta(c_5 + c_1) = 0.$$

These equations may be solved by the method of determinants (not given in this book); six values of E are obtained from the six roots. Of these six roots there are two pairs of identical values. In ascending order of magnitude, the possible values for the energy E are

$$E_0 + 2\beta, \quad E_0 + \beta, \quad E_0 + \beta, \quad E_0 - \beta, \quad E_0 - \beta, \quad E_0 - 2\beta.$$

The first three correspond to three bonding orbitals, and just accommodate the six electrons which remain to be disposed of after all the σ orbitals in the molecule are occupied. It is easily seen from the equations above, that for energy $E = E_0 + 2\beta$,

since $A = -2\beta$, $\qquad c_1 = c_2 = c_3 = c_4 = c_5 = c_6.$

There is only one molecular orbital of this energy.

For energy $E = E_0 + \beta$, since $A = -\beta$, it is evident that

$$c_1 = -c_4, \quad c_2 = -c_5, \quad c_3 = -c_6.$$

The total energy of the three occupied non-localised orbitals is given by:

$$E = 2(E_0 + 2\beta) + 4(E_0 + \beta)$$
$$= 6E_0 + 8\beta.$$

Six electrons in bonds localised between pairs of atoms would have the energy:

$$6(E_0 + \beta) = 6E_0 + 6\beta.$$

Hence the energy of delocalisation over the whole molecule is 2β.

The characteristic absorption spectrum of the molecule depends on transitions from the non-localised orbitals in the ground state (for which $E = E_0 + 2\beta$, or $E_0 + \beta$) to the excited antibonding non-localised orbitals.

CONJUGATION IN TERMS OF RESONANCE

On the assumption that all the bonds in the benzene molecule are localised σ bonds or localised π bonds, five canonical structures can be drawn:

The first two structures are known as the Kekulé structures; the double bonds consist of one σ and one π bond. The other three structures are known as the Dewar structures; the cross bonds in these structures are also π bonds. None of these structures has a real existence; the real benzene molecule is a combination of all these five forms in resonance. In the structure thus arrived at, each of the six carbon atoms has exactly the same function, and each of the six hydrogen atoms has exactly the same function.

COMPARISON OF THE MOLECULAR ORBITAL THEORY AND THE VALENCE BOND THEORY

It has not been found possible in the foregoing pages to present a wave mechanical theory of valency by following a single line of argument. Historically, there have been two methods of approach, the molecular orbital (M.O.) theory and the valence bond (V.B.) theory. The distinction between these theories has been greatly reduced by Lennard-Jones who used product wave functions (previously considered to be part of V.B. theory) in constructing molecular orbitals, by means of which he showed that directed valence could be deduced by M.O. theory. Many chemists prefer to maintain a distinction between the two theories, and therefore the claims of each are compared and contrasted in the following pages.

SUMMARY OF THE MOLECULAR ORBITAL THEORY

Non-directed orbitals.[†] All the atomic orbitals in the valence shells of the interacting atoms are combined in pairs. Each pair consists of one atomic orbital from each of the two combining atoms. It is immaterial whether the atomic orbitals were originally occupied by electrons or not. If ψ_A and ψ_B are the atomic wave functions, the form of the molecular orbital space function is:

$$\psi = c_1\psi_A \pm c_2\psi_B. \tag{5.2}$$

For combination of each pair of atomic orbitals the following conditions must apply:

(1) The combining orbitals must have approximately the same energy.
(2) The combining orbitals must overlap.
(3) The combining orbitals must have the same symmetry.

The number of molecular orbitals produced is equal to the number of atomic orbitals which combine; half the molecular orbitals are bonding and half antibonding. The molecular orbitals are arranged in ascending order of energy, and all the electrons originally present in the valence shells of the combining atoms are notionally placed in the molecular orbitals on the aufbau principle. Pauli's exclusion principle restricts the maximum number of electrons in each orbital to two.

The number of electrons in the system is always less than the number required completely to fill the molecular orbitals. As the bonding molecular orbitals have lower energies than the corresponding antibonding orbitals, the overall effect is bonding.

The energy of a molecular orbital is given by:

$$E_{\pm} = \frac{E_A \pm \beta}{1 \pm S_{AB}}$$

where E_A is

$$\int \psi_A{}^2(T_p + V_p)\,d\tau.$$

β, the resonance integral, is

$$\int \psi_A\psi_B(T_p + V_p)\,d\tau.$$

S, the overlap integral, is

$$\int \psi_A\psi_B\,d\tau.$$

The molecular orbital theory can be applied either to homonuclear or to heteronuclear diatomics without modification, because, if the combining atoms are different the effect of the difference in electronegativity is expressed by the relative values of the coefficients c_1 and c_2.

Directed orbitals. As explained on p. 165, it is possible to make a transformation from a set of non-directed molecular orbitals to a set of directed equivalent orbitals. The equivalent orbitals have definite orientation relative to one another, and correspond to the hybridised orbitals of the valence bond theory.

† Lennard-Jones, 1929; Hückel, 1930; Mulliken, 1932.

SUMMARY OF THE VALENCE BOND THEORY†

Homonuclear diatomics. The space wave functions of two *unpaired electrons* in the valence shells of the two interacting atoms are multiplied together, and an interatomic orbital is constructed of the form:

$$\psi = \psi_A(1)\psi_B(2) \pm \psi_A(2)\psi_B(1). \tag{5.3}$$

The conditions concerning energy, overlapping, and symmetry mentioned under "Summary of the molecular orbital theory" also apply. Pauli's exclusion principle is used to decide which spin functions are to be combined with space wave functions to give bonding orbitals; there is one antisymmetric complete wave function which is the bonding orbital, and three symmetric complete wave functions of higher energy which are antibonding.

The energy of the interatomic orbitals is given by:

$$E_\pm = 2E_0 + \frac{C+A}{1+S_{ab}}$$

where $E_0 =$ energy of original atom in the ground state. C, the Coulomb integral is

$$\iint (\psi_A(1)\psi_B(2))^2 \left(-\frac{\epsilon^2}{r_{b_1}} - \frac{\epsilon^2}{r_{a_2}} + \frac{\epsilon^2}{r_{12}} + \frac{\epsilon^2}{R} \right) d\tau_1\, d\tau_2.$$

A, the exchange integral is

$$\iint \psi_A(1)\psi_B(2)\psi_A(2)\psi_B(1) \left(-\frac{\epsilon^2}{r_{b_1}} - \frac{\epsilon^2}{r_{a_2}} + \frac{\epsilon^2}{r_{12}} + \frac{\epsilon^2}{R} \right) d\tau_1\, d\tau_2.$$

S_{ab} the overlap integral is

$$\iint \psi_A(1)\psi_B(2)\psi_A(2)\psi_B(1)\, d\tau_1\, d\tau_2.$$

Heteronuclear diatomics. The valence bond space wave function as given above takes no account of a difference of electronegativity between the combining atoms. Expression must be given to possible differences by an extra term in the space wave function:

$$\psi = \psi_A(1)\psi_B(2) \pm \psi_A(2)\psi_B(1) \pm \lambda\psi_B(1)\psi_B(2).$$

This equation is frequently written

$$\psi = \psi_{\text{cov}} + \lambda\psi_{\text{ion}}.$$

FEATURES COMMON TO BOTH THEORIES

(1) Both theories are approximations.

(2) Both interpret covalent bonds as orbitals embracing two atomic nuclei.

(3) Both require that combining atomic orbitals should be of nearly equal energy, that they should overlap, and that they should possess the same symmetry.

(4) Both make use of the same method (p. 115) for deciding the minimum energy of two overlapping atomic orbitals.

(5) Both predict a piling up of charge between the nuclei.

(6) Both account for directed valency.

FEATURES IN WHICH THE THEORIES DIFFER

(1) The M.O. theory forms molecular orbitals by LCAO of all atomic orbitals from the valence shells of each of the two atoms. The V.B. theory uses the Heitler-London

† Heitler and London, 1927; Pauling, 1931; Slater, 1931; W. Heitler, *Wave Mechanics*, Oxford University Press, 1945.

treatment, and thus produces an interatomic orbital by multiplying, exchanging, and combining the space wave functions of two unpaired electrons, one from each of the two atoms.

(2) Both theories predict the existence of bonding and antibonding orbitals. The M.O. theory, however, predicts antibonding orbitals which are capable of occupation by two electrons, while the V.B. theory predicts orbitals (usually referred to as repulsive states) which are capable of occupation by one electron only, since if a second electron could be introduced it would have a spin parallel to that of the first (p. 135).

(3) Without modification the M.O. theory provides for the presence of ionic character in a bond. The V.B. theory introduces a special term to express the presence of ionic character in a bond.

(4) Both use Pauli's exclusion principle, but in different ways. The M.O. theory uses it to decide how the electrons originally in the valence shells of the combining atoms are distributed among the molecular orbitals. The V.B. theory uses it to decide how to combine spin functions with space wave functions to produce bonding or antibonding orbitals.

(5) Both explain the existence of the singlet and triplet states of diatomic molecules, but in different ways. The M.O. theory assumes that in the singlet state all the occupied molecular orbitals contain electron pairs. Hence $S = 0$, and the multiplicity $(2S + 1) = 1$. In the triplet state the theory assumes that one electron pair is divided so that each electron occupies a separate orbital, and that the spins of these electrons are parallel. The spin is 1, and the multiplicity is 3.

The prediction of singlet and triplet states arises directly from the V.B. procedure for obtaining an interatomic orbital, without the introduction of any new postulates or assumptions (p. 135).

Both theories agree in predicting that the triplet state is an excited state.

(6) Both theories explain the non-existence of a helium molecule, but in different ays. According to the M.O. theory (p. 130) the numbers of electrons in the bonding and antibonding molecular orbitals of the hypothetical helium molecule are equal, and there is no bonding effect on the two atoms. According to the V.B. theory there is no opportunity for a helium atom to combine with any other atom, because in the isolated helium atom the only two electrons are already paired.

(7) The M.O. theory is used in constructing polycentric molecular orbitals, such as the three-centre bond in the boron hydrides (p. 511), and the polycentre orbitals in metallic crystals (p. 179).

(8) A very important difference between the two theories is their use of the term *resonance*.

The term *resonance integral* of M.O. theory is analogous to the coupling coefficient in a mechanical system in resonance. The M.O. theory, however, deals with stationary states described by ψ, from which the time-dependent parts have been deliberately excluded. The conclusion must be accepted that the term "resonance" in M.O. theory refers to the mathematical treatment only, and that this term does not describe physical events in the system. It is correct to use the term "resonance integral" in M.O. treatment; it is incorrect to use the term "resonance".

The expression for ψ in the V.B. theory contains terms which refer to different canonical forms. It must be emphasised that in V.B. theory the canonical forms have no real existence. The separate terms in the equation are not eigenfunctions of allowed stationary states; the only correct function is ψ which describes a stationary state. It is false to postulate that the molecule adopts each of the canonical forms in turn, and so resonates between them. Nevertheless, the V.B. concept of combining canonical forms to arrive at the correct value of ψ, is given the title of resonance by nearly all authors. The only alternative title is "mesomerism", but this is also unsatisfactory, because terms such as "polymerism", "isomerism", and even "dynamic isomerism" all refer to the structures of compounds which can be isolated and kept indefinitely. The title *resonance* will be used in this book for the combination of canonical forms to yield the structure of a molecule.

VALENCE STATES OF THE LIGHTER ELEMENTS

In the previous sections of this chapter it has been shown generally how an atom, by hybridisation of the atomic orbitals in its valency shell, can adopt various valence states. The question now arises: how is the adoption of particular valence states governed by the nature of a given atom? The answer must be given in terms of particular elements, and it is convenient to consider first the elements in Period 2. The valence shells of the atoms of these elements contain the atomic orbitals $2s$, $2p_x$, $2p_y$, $2p_z$.

The valence states of the neutral atoms will first be considered, and then the valence states of the atoms carrying formal charges. Table 5.7, constructed from "Types of Compounds" tables,† shows that the atoms of Li, Be, and B, which contain respectively one, two, and three valency electrons, exert one, two, or three σ bonds without forming π bonds or lone pairs. These atoms contain fewer than four electrons in the valence shell, and are therefore described as *electron deficient*. Lithium forms the homonuclear diatomic Li_2, produced by the overlapping of the $2s$ atomic orbital from each atom. Beryllium, of which the atom has two valency electrons, is in the digonal valence state in beryllium borohydride, $Be(BH_4)_2$. The boron atom, with three electrons in the valence shell, is in the trigonal valence state in a number of compounds (Table 17.1). In the compounds mentioned neither the beryllium atom nor the boron atom have attained the inert gas configuration. Both the boron atom and the beryllium atom, however, attain the tetrahedral valence state in other compounds by taking part in the formation of three-centre bonds.

Table 5.7. *Bonds formed by Neutral Atoms of Elements in Period 2 in different Valence States*

(lp = lone pair)

Atom	Valence states											
	s orbital bonding. Nos. of bonds formed			Digonal. Nos. of bonds formed			Trigonal. Nos. of bonds formed			Tetrahedral. Nos. of bonds formed		
	σ	π	lp	σ	π	lp	σ	π	lp	σ	π	lp
Li	1											
Be				2								
B							3					
C				2	2		3	1		4		
N				1	2	1	2	1	1	3		1
O							1	1	2	2		2
F										1		3

† Tables 15.1, 17.1, 18.1, 19.1, 20.1, 23.1

The carbon atom exerts four σ bonds in the tetrahedral valence state, but it also adopts the alternative arrangements of three σ and one π bond in the trigonal valence state, and two σ and two π bonds in the digonal valence state. The nitrogen atom adopts the tetrahedral, trigonal, and digonal valence states but with one lone pair present in each case. The oxygen atom adopts the tetrahedral and trigonal valence states, but with two lone pairs present, while the fluorine atom adopts the tetrahedral valence state only, and exerts one σ bond and three lone pairs.

The following rules emerge from Table 5.7.

(1) The total number of bonds exerted by an atom is the same whatever the valence state.

(2) Any occupied p orbital not taken into the hybridisation is used in forming a π bond.

(3) Atoms with less than five electrons in the valence shell do not form non-bonding orbitals on chemical combination with other atoms.

(4) The atoms of carbon, nitrogen, and oxygen exert one π bond when trigonally hybridised, and the atoms of carbon and nitrogen exert two π bonds when digonally hybridised.

The valence states of the elements in Period 2 given in Table 5.7 are deduced on the assumption that chemical combination is not accompanied by any formal redistribution of charge. It is explained, however, on p. 113 that the transfer of electrons from one atom to another is sometimes a preliminary stage in the union of atoms to form a molecule. Such a transfer will take place if it enables two atoms to adopt more stable valence states than they could assume in the neutral condition, for instance, the tetracovalent state is a very stable state for an atom of an element in Period 2. The carbon atom, which possesses four valency electrons, attains this state without gain or loss of formal charge. The atoms of all the other elements in Period 2 except fluorine can also attain this state, but only by gaining or losing electrons. (In terms of the electronic theory of valency, this is equivalent to the formation of co-ionic bonds, p. 113.) The number of electrons to be gained or lost is obtained by subtracting the

Table 5.8.   *Example of Compounds containing Elements of Period 2 in the Tetracovalent State*

Atom	Compound containing the atom in the tetracovalent state	Formal charge
Li	Lithium acetylacetonate	−3
Be	Beryllium acetylacetonate	−2
B	Boron trimethyl ammoniate, and compounds in Table 17.1	−1
C	Methane	0
N	The ion NH_4^+ in NH_4Cl	+1
O	Basic beryllium acetate	+2
F	None	

Periodic Group number of the element in question from the Periodic Group number of carbon, 4. Table 5.8 gives one example in each case of a compound in which the atom of the Period 2 element is in the tetracovalent state, and has a formal charge. In each case the atom is tetrahedrally hybridised.

It should be noted that the oxygen atom with two formal positive charges occurs only infrequently (Table 20.1), and that fluorine forms no compounds in which the atom has a formal positive charge. The strongly electronegative character of oxygen and fluorine clearly operates against the loss of electrons from the atoms.

According to rule (1), the number of bonds exerted by an atom of a given element is the same whatever the valence state, and it is interesting to see whether the atoms of the elements with the formal charge given in Table 5.8 can also adopt the trigonal or digonal valence state, and thus imitate the complete behaviour of the carbon atom shown in Table 5.7.

Table 5.9. *Valence States adopted by Atoms of Elements in Period 2, carrying Formal Charges*

Formal charge	Li	Be	B	C	N	O	F
−3	Tet.						
−2		Tet.					
−1			Tet.	Dig.			
0	(s bond)	Dig.	Trig.	Tet. Trig. Dig.	Tet. Trig. Dig.	Tet. Trig.	
+1				Trig.	Tet. Trig.		
+2						Tet.	
+3							

Table 5.9 shows that, with the exception of carbon and nitrogen, the atoms, when carrying formal charges, adopt the tetrahedral valence state only.

Atoms of elements in Period 3 are characterised by principal quantum number $n = 3$, and the maximum number of orbitals in the external shell of any atom in Period 3 is nine; the available orbitals of the isolated atom are

$$s \, p \, p \, p \, d \, d \, d \, d \, d.$$

The d orbitals differ from the p orbitals in the lack of readiness with which they enter into hybridisation to form σ hybrids. The elements in Period 3 which have sufficient number of electrons in the valence shell to exert more than four σ bonds in *simple* molecules are P, S, and Cl, but chlorine does not do so at all, and P and S do so only when in combination with fluorine.[†] Argon, the inert gas at the end of the Period, is completely non-reactive, its electron configuration makes no use of the d orbitals. Nevertheless, Na, Mg, Al, and Si all form *complex* compounds in which the atom is present in the octahedral valence state. This is in contrast to the behaviour of Li, Be, and C, which form no such compounds.

Since the atoms of the elements of Period 3 only rarely become octahedrally hybridised, they do, in fact, behave very much like the elements in corresponding Groups in Period 2. The processes of tetrahedral, trigonal, and digonal hybridisation

† The stability of the high polyvalent fluorides of phosphorus, PF_5, and sulphur, SF_6, is no doubt related to the low stability of the fluorine molecule.

of the *s* and *p* orbitals take place in the same way. This is also true for the elements of the N sub-Groups of later Periods.

The *d* orbitals of the valence shells of elements in Period 3 enable them to form π hybrids (p. 156), which are of importance in the orbital structures of certain compounds. Among these are the ions of oxyacids containing atoms of elements in Period 3 as the central atom (p. 789).

BOOKS FOR FURTHER READING

CARTMELL, E., and FOWLES, G. W. A., *Valency and Molecular Structure* (Butterworth's Scientific Publications, 1956).

COULSON, C. A., *Valence* (Oxford University Press, 1952).

HEITLER, W., *Elementary Wave Mechanics* (Oxford, 1945).

PALMER, W. G., *Valency, Classical and Modern* (Cambridge University Press, 2nd Edition, 1959).

PAULING, L., *Nature of the Chemical Bond* (Cornell University Press, 3rd Edition, 1960).

PITZER, K. S., *Quantum Chemistry* (Prentice-Hall, 1953).

SLATER, J. C., *Quantum Theory of Matter* (McGraw-Hill, 1953).

SYRKIN, Y. K., and DYATKINA, M. E., *Structure of Molecules* (Butterworth's Scientific Publications, 1950).

REVIEWS

DICKENS, P. G., and LINNETT, J. W., *Electron Correlation and Chemical Consequences* (*Quarterly Reviews*, **11**, No. 4, 1957, 291).

LONGUET-HIGGINS, H. C., *The Structures of Electron Deficient Molecules* (*Quarterly Reviews*, **11**, No. 2, 1957, 121).

POPLE, J. A., *The Molecular Orbital and Equivalent Orbital Approach to Molecular Structure* (*Quarterly Reviews*, **11**, No. 3, 1957, 273).

CHAPTER SIX

THE METALLIC BOND

ENERGY BANDS

Valency orbitals in metallic crystals. Metals in the solid state consist of close-packed crystalline structures characterised by high co-ordination numbers (p. 345), that is, each atom in the crystal is surrounded by a large number of neighbouring atoms which are approximately equidistant from it. The atoms of metals in the normal Groups of the periodic table have few valency electrons; metals of Group I have one valency electron, those of Group II have two, and those of Group III have three. The co-ordination number of each atom in the crystals of these metals exceeds the numbers of pairs of electrons available for covalent bond formation; only a fraction of a valency electron would be available for each bond. The problem of assigning an orbital structure to a metallic crystal is thus one of electron deficiency. A similar problem has already been encountered in connection with the three-centre bond (p. 118). Analogy suggests that if the metallic crystal is regarded as a giant molecule, each atom may be said to be bound, not only to its immediate neighbours, but to all other atoms in the crystal; if there are j atoms, the bond between each of them might be described as j centred.

It is shown (p. 118) that when two atomic orbitals, ψ_A and ψ_B, overlap, there are two solutions for the energy of a two-centre bond. Application of the LCAO treatment to two overlapping s orbitals, one from each of two atoms, produces two new orbitals, one corresponding to an energy lower than that of the two uncombined atomic orbitals, and the other corresponding to an energy higher than that of the two uncombined atomic orbitals. The electron in the bond might be found in either of the two states. Similar reasoning leads to three possible energy states for the three-centre bond (p. 120). By analogy, with j centres there are j possible energy states derived from all the possible linear combinations of j atomic wave functions.

In a metallic vapour at such a low pressure that there is no overlap of atomic orbitals, the possible energy states are few and are determined by the values of the quantum numbers n and l. If the atoms are forced sufficiently near together for the overlap of atomic orbitals to occur, a number of new combined orbitals are formed with slightly differing energies. The larger the number of overlapping orbitals the greater is the number of possible energy states. This number therefore depends on the number of atoms present. The system of atoms in the crystal is similar to that of the compressed metallic vapour. If there are j atoms in the crystal, each with one valency electron, there are j overlapping orbitals, and j possible energy states. The number of possible energy states depends on the number of atoms present, that is, on the size of the crystal.

Soft X-ray spectra. If a metal in the solid state is bombarded by high-speed electrons, an electron may be ejected from the K shell ($1s$ orbital) of the bombarded atom, and since the transition $2s$ to $1s$ is forbidden, an electron from the $2p$ orbital of the L shell may take its place with loss of energy equivalent to the emission of the $K\alpha$ line (p. 81). The position of this line in the spectrum is therefore an indication of the difference of energy between the L and K shells of an atom in the solid metal. Similarly the $K\beta$ line shows the difference of energy between the M and K shells ($3p$ to $1s$) of an atom in the solid metal. In general, the K spectrum consists of lines which correspond to the replacement of the K electrons by electrons from any of the available orbitals in the atom, including those of the valency electrons. The L and M series are produced in an analogous manner, the L series being formed by replacements of L ($2s$ or $2p$) electrons by electrons from orbitals of higher energy, and the M series by replacement of M ($3s$, $3p$ or $3d$) electrons by electrons from orbitals of higher energy. The complete diagram of transitions is given in Fig. 3.5, p. 77.

The study of X-ray spectra has been used to provide information about the energy of the valence electrons in metals.† Much useful information on this subject has been derived from experimental work on soft X-rays. It has been shown‡ that if the metal is present as a vapour at low pressure a line spectrum is observed. If the pressure is increased until the interatomic distance is of the order of 10^{-8} cm (which is roughly the length of unit cell in the crystal) the spectrum shows significant changes. While the lines due to certain transitions between the inner shells of the atoms remain unchanged, single lines due to transitions of electrons from the valency orbitals to the K and L shells split into bands of closely spaced lines. These bands are called **energy bands**;

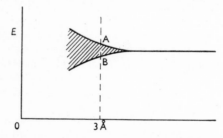

Fig. 6.1. Formation of an energy band as r, the interatomic distance in a metal vapour, is decreased. AB is the width of the band at the value of r equal to the interatomic distance in the *crystal*.

they are produced by transitions of valency electrons from orbitals which, as explained on p. 179, have slightly differing energies because they are formed from the overlapping of a large number of atomic orbitals. The range of energies covered by an energy band depends inversely on the distance between the atoms. It is of the order of 1–10 electron volts. Fig. 6.1 shows the broadening of a single energy level as the distance r between the atoms is decreased. Fig. 6.2, from the spectrum of metallic sodium, shows the formation and broadening of a number of adjacent energy bands with decreasing interatomic distance. It can also be seen from this diagram that the bands corresponding to the higher energy orbitals begin to broaden before the bands corresponding to the lower energy orbitals, and that as the atoms get closer and closer together, these broadened bands of higher energy orbitals are partly superposed. When superposition occurs, hybridisation takes place, and the orbital energies deduced from the spectra are those that would have been derived from hybrid wave functions.

$n(E)$ **and** $N(E)$ **curves.** The variation in intensity of soft X-ray spectra provides interesting information on the distribution of electrons in the various orbitals (energy states). From experimental observations of intensity the so-called "$n(E)$ curves" can

---

† These experiments should not be confused with those on X-ray diffraction, which are used for the determination of the positions of the atoms in the metallic crystal (see Chapter 9).
‡ H. W. B. Skinner, *Phil. Trans. Roy. Soc.* **A. 239**, 1940, 95.

be plotted (Fig. 6.3). $n(E)dE$ is the number of electrons per unit volume of metal with energies between E and $E + dE$. This quantity is plotted against values of E. The curve is of an irregular shape; it rises to a maximum and drops to zero, cutting the E axis at a certain value of E. As the temperature is decreased the fall of the $n(E)$ curve becomes steeper and steeper, and it has been deduced that at absolute zero it would intersect the E axis at right angles, Fig. 6.4. This observation may be explained as follows. Since by Pauli's exclusion principle each energy state can be occupied at the

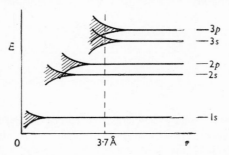

Fig. 6.2. The formation of energy bands by the reduction of the interatomic distance, r, in an assembly of sodium atoms. The energy states of an isolated sodium atom are shown diagrammatically on the right. The highest energy states, $3p$ and $3s$, are the first to broaden into bands, and at $r = 3.7$ Å, the interatomic distance in the crystal, the two bands overlap and a hybrid orbital is formed.

most only by two electrons, if there are N electrons present in unit volume of the metal, at absolute zero they occupy the $N/2$ lowest energy states. No electron is present in any state of energy higher than these, and hence the right hand boundary of the $n(E)$ curve at absolute zero is normal to the E axis. At temperatures above absolute zero, the thermal energy may be sufficient to raise some electrons into energy states higher than those of the $N/2$ lowest values, and if this is so the terminal slope

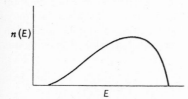

Fig. 6.3. $n(E)$ curve at normal temperature.

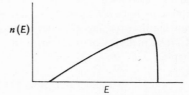

Fig. 6.4. $n(E)$ curve near absolute zero.

of the curve is no longer vertical. This effect naturally becomes more marked as the temperature rises. In the subsequent discussion it will be assumed that the energy states are those which correspond to a temperature of absolute zero.

The shape of the $n(E)$ curve is different for metals of different valency, but in all cases the area under the curve is proportional to the total number of electrons distributed over the particular energy range considered. If there are a number of broadened energy bands in the soft X-ray spectrum, which do not overlap, a complete $n(E)$ curve plotted over the whole range of energy shows that there are certain values of the energy for which there are no electrons (Fig. 6.5). The significance of these gaps is discussed later.

The knowledge of the number of energy states, N, available in a given crystal enables a further set of curves to be plotted, showing the relation between the energy and $N(E)dE$ (the number of energy states between E and $E+dE$). The shape of an $N(E)$ curve is the same as that of a complete $n(E)$ curve, but if the two curves are

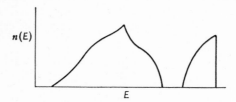

Fig. 6.5. $n(E)$ curve showing gap between energy states.

plotted on the same scale, since each energy state can be occupied by two electrons, the area under the $n(E)$ curve is twice that under the $N(E)$ curve. In many cases there are not enough electrons to fill the total number of energy states available. If that is so the $N(E)$ curve is complete but the $n(E)$ curve is incomplete. Fig. 6.6 shows the two

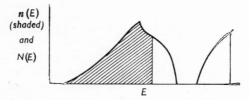

Fig. 6.6. $n(E)$ and $N(E)$ curves superposed showing incomplete filling of available energy states. ($n(E)$ is plotted on half the scale of $N(E)$).

curves superposed in a case of this kind. The scales are adjusted so that one diagram represents both $n(E)$ and $N(E)$, but the $n(E)$ curve extends over the shaded part only, showing that the energy states of higher energy are unoccupied. A simple calculation of $N(E)$ in terms of the energy and volume of the crystal is developed later in this chapter.

POTENTIAL BARRIERS IN A METALLIC CRYSTAL

The potential in a metallic crystal varies periodically throughout the crystal. It rises to positive values near the atomic nuclei and falls to negative values between the nuclei. The upper part of Fig. 6.7 represents a graph of the potential in the electric field of the metallic crystal plotted along a line passing through a succession of atomic nuclei in the x direction. For the purpose of this discussion a nucleus may be assumed to be a point charge; on this assumption the positive potential at the nucleus is infinite. Since the electron has a negative charge it would be expected to remain in the neighbourhood of a nucleus. It has been inferred however, from a study of electrical conductivity, that electrons are free to move throughout a crystal. Movement from the vicinity of one nucleus to that of the next requires the electron to pass through a region of negative potential which is a *barrier* to this movement, and it remains to be explained how this is possible. The lower part of Fig. 6.7 indicates diagrammatically the barriers which the electron has to surmount in moving along the chosen line. Even if the barriers are

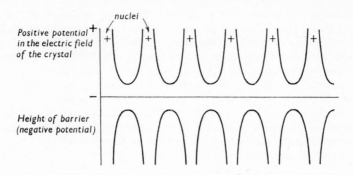

Fig. 6.7. (a) Potential in the electric field of a metallic crystal plotted along a line passing through a succession of atomic nuclei in the *x* direction. (b) Potential barriers which must be surmounted by an electron moving along the *x* direction.

"high" in comparison with the energy of the electron the movement is not entirely prohibited by reason of the so-called *tunnel effect*.

PASSAGE OF AN ELECTRON THROUGH A POTENTIAL BARRIER. THE TUNNEL EFFECT

In order to demonstrate how an electron may pass through a potential barrier it is necessary to discuss the wave mechanical properties of an electron under different limitations of potential and boundary conditions, and to deduce expressions for ψ in each case. The cases considered are (i) a free electron travelling in a field of zero potential, (ii) an electron leaving a field of potential V_1 and entering a field of potential V_2. In the discussion of the tunnel effect it is convenient to speak of fields of "high" and "low" potential. Since the electron is a negative charge, it must be kept in mind that *high potential* means *high negative potential* and that *low potential* means *low negative potential*.

Free electron in a field of zero potential. The Schrödinger equation for one dimension is:

$$\frac{d^2\psi}{dx^2} + \frac{8\pi^2 m_0}{h^2}(E-V)\psi = 0.$$

Writing

$$\psi = e^{-i2\pi x/\lambda},$$

it follows that

$$-\frac{4\pi^2}{\lambda^2} + \frac{8\pi^2 m_0}{h^2}(E-V) = 0.$$

Since $V=0$,

$$\frac{1}{\lambda^2} = \frac{2m_0 E}{h^2}.$$

Hence

$$\psi = e^{-(i2\pi x/h)\sqrt{(2m_0 E)}} \tag{6.1}$$

and, putting $k=2\pi/\lambda$,

$$E = \frac{k^2 h^2}{8\pi^2 m_0}. \tag{6.2}$$

This wave function and the energy are those of a free electron.

Electron moving from one field to another, the fields having fixed but different potentials. This problem is analogous to the optical one of a photon which passes from one medium of a certain refractive index to another medium of different refractive index. Under these circumstances, part of the wave is reflected and part is transmitted. (In terms of wave mechanics this does not mean that the photon is split up, but that there is a probability that some of the photons are reflected, and a probability that some of the photons are transmitted; these probabilities are generally not of the same value.) Analogy leads to the expectation that some electrons pass from the first field to the second, and some are reflected at the boundary between the fields; a confirmation of this expectation is obtained from the appropriate mathematical equations, which for simplicity are discussed in one dimension only.

Necessary condition for ψ and $\dfrac{d\psi}{dx}$ on crossing the boundary. Suppose the position of the boundary between the fields corresponds to $x=0$, the potential on the left of the boundary being V_1, and on the right of the boundary V_2. Let the electron approach the boundary from left to right. The Schrödinger equation describing the motion of the electron on the left of the boundary ($x<0$) is

$$\frac{d^2\psi}{dx^2} + \frac{8\pi^2 m_0}{h^2} (E-V_1)\psi = 0,$$

and the Schrödinger equation describing the motion of the electron on the right of the boundary ($x>0$) is

$$\frac{d^2\psi}{dx^2} + \frac{8\pi^2 m_0}{h^2} (E-V_2)\psi = 0.$$

At the boundary within a range Δx

$$\frac{d^2\psi}{dx^2} = \frac{8\pi^2 m_0}{h^2} (V-E)\psi,$$

where V is either V_1 or V_2. As Δx is reduced to zero the R.H.S. of the equation remains finite. At the boundary ($x=0$) $d^2\psi/dx^2$ changes discontinuously since V changes from V_1 to V_2.

Since

$$\frac{d\psi}{dx} = \int \frac{d^2\psi}{dx^2},$$

over the range Δx

$$\left(\frac{d\psi}{dx}\right)_{x+\Delta x} - \left(\frac{d\psi}{dx}\right)_x = \frac{8\pi^2 m_0}{h^2} \int_x^{x+\Delta x} (V-E)\psi \, dx.$$

As Δx goes to zero, the R.H.S. remains finite, but the limits of integration go to zero. Therefore the R.H.S. approaches zero. Hence in the limit, $d\psi/dx$ *is unchanged (continuous) on crossing the potential boundary*, and if the wave is transmitted, ψ *must also be continuous through the boundary*. In other words there is no kink in the wave as it passes through the boundary.

Necessary conditions for the propagation of a wave through the boundary. The Schrödinger equation for motion on the left of the boundary may be written as

$$\frac{d^2\psi}{dx^2} + p^2\psi = 0,$$

where

$$p^2 = \frac{8\pi^2 m_0}{h^2} (E-V_1).$$

On the left of the boundary ψ refers to a progressive wave, part of which may be reflected at the boundary. The wave function may be given the general expression:

$$\psi = Ae^{-ipx} + Be^{ipx},$$

where the quantity Ae^{-ipx} refers to the direct wave, and the quantity Be^{ipx} to the reflected wave.

The Schrödinger equation for ψ on the right-hand side of the boundary may be written:

$$\frac{d^2\psi}{dx^2} + q^2\psi = 0, \tag{6.3}$$

where

$$q^2 = \frac{8\pi^2 m_0}{h^2}(E - V_2). \tag{6.4}$$

On the right-hand side of the boundary the wave may continue to be propagated, or it may immediately die out. The most general expression for ψ in this region, which covers both the above cases, is

$$\psi = Ce^{-qx} + De^{qx}, \tag{6.5}$$

where q may be a real or imaginary quantity. If q is real, the wave dies out; if q is imaginary (that is, if the coefficient of x is written iq) the wave is propagated.

Since ψ is continuous through the boundary ($x=0$),

$$A + B = C + D.$$

Since $d\psi/dx$ is continuous through the boundary ($x=0$),

$$-ipA + ipB = -qC + qD.$$

From these equations,

$$A = C\left(\frac{ip+q}{2ip}\right) + D\left(\frac{ip-q}{2ip}\right) \tag{6.6}$$

$$B = C\left(\frac{ip-q}{2ip}\right) + D\left(\frac{ip+q}{2ip}\right). \tag{6.7}$$

Since there is no probability of the propagation of the wave from right to left on the right-hand side of the boundary, $D=0$, and

$$\frac{B}{A} = \frac{ip-q}{ip+q}.$$

The quantity B/A is the ratio of the number of electrons travelling to the left to the number travelling to the right on the left-hand side of the boundary, that is the ratio of the amplitudes of the reflected and direct waves. It is interesting to note that this ratio depends on conditions on the other side of the barrier, that is on the value of q. Therefore, in order to evaluate the ratio B/A there are two cases to be considered, (a) when E is greater than V_2, (b) when E is less than V_2.

E is greater than V_2. Equation (6.4) shows that when E is greater than V_2, q^2 is a positive quantity. Equation (6.3) therefore conforms to the requirements of the general wave equation, and the electron may appear in the field V_2 as a continuously propagated wave. Equation (6.3) is satisfied by a solution of the form:

$$\psi = Ce^{-iqx} + De^{iqx}.$$

Since ψ and $d\psi/dx$ are continuous across the boundary, and D must be zero

$$\frac{B}{A} = \frac{p-q}{p+q}$$

$$= \frac{\sqrt{(E-V_1)} - \sqrt{(E-V_2)}}{\sqrt{(E-V_1)} + \sqrt{(E-V_2)}}.$$

Since $V_1 \neq V_2$, B is not zero, and some of the electrons are reflected at the boundary into the field of potential V_1, even though they have enough energy to enter the field of potential V_2. These equations hold only if the change of potential is built up in a distance which is short compared with the wave length of the electron.

E is less than V_2. Equation (6.4) shows that when E is less than V_2, q^2 is a negative quantity. Equation (6.3) then becomes:

$$\frac{d^2\psi}{dx^2} - q^2\psi = 0,$$

where q is real. This equation describes a disturbance which either builds up exponentially to infinity, or else dies out; it does not describe a propagated wave. The motion of the electron in the field V_2 is therefore described by equation (6.5) with the condition that q is real. As the disturbance cannot build up exponentially, D must be zero. From equation (6.6)

$$C = A\,\frac{2ip}{ip+q}.$$

Now

$$|C|^2 = \frac{4p^2}{p^2+q^2}\,|A|^2.$$

Hence C is not zero, and a disturbance which rapidly dies out is created in the field of potential, V_2. (It may be shown that B/A is again not zero; thus, again, part of the direct wave is reflected.)

The above discussion shows that there is a probability that an electron may enter a potential field even though, according to classical principles, it has insufficient energy to do so. The electron enters the region of high negative potential as a disturbance which rapidly dies away. If the region of high negative potential is in contact on its right-hand side with a region of lower negative potential, it is known as a **potential barrier**. If the barrier is "thin", that is, of small extension spatially, it is possible that the disturbance, although dying away exponentially, may not be extinguished by the time it reaches the second region of lower negative potential. By further development of the mathematical argument it may be shown that the disturbance in the barrier produced by an electron entering from the left-hand side may generate a new train of waves which travels from left to right in the second region of lower negative potential. The amplitude of such a wave is less than the amplitude of the original wave. This does not mean that part of an electron is propagated through the barrier, but that there is a smaller probability that it will be found on the right-hand side of the barrier than on the left-hand side. The barriers are thin enough (of the order of 10^{-8} cm) to allow low energy electrons to pass through them by the tunnel effect, and therefore both low and high energy electrons are able to move through the crystal.

The tunnel effect may be explained also in terms of the wave packet theory of the electron. If the electron "particle" is supposed to be formed by the superposition of a large number of waves of slightly differing wave lengths, which at a given moment reinforce each other inside a certain potential enclosure, after a lapse of time, owing to phase differences, they may cancel each other out inside the potential enclosure and reinforce each other in the region outside it. The conditions inside the barrier have a limiting effect on the formation of wave packets beyond it, and these will only appear under certain special conditions depending on the height and thickness of the potential barrier.

The mobility of electrons in a metallic crystal may be explained as an exchange interaction coupled with the tunnel effect. Certain energy considerations restrict the mobility of the electrons in some of the possible energy states, but as the electrons are considered in principle to be interchangeable, they must all be regarded as having the same mobility. Since electrons are not continually entering and leaving the crystal, it is obvious that there are certain boundary conditions which must be observed if the crystal is to retain its form. These boundary conditions are that the wave functions of all the electrons must be zero at the boundaries of the crystal. This condition limits the number of possible energy states which the electrons may occupy.

THE ELECTRON IN A PERIODIC POTENTIAL

A crystal may be regarded as a series of potential enclosures separated by barriers, and consequently the potential in a crystal may be represented as a potential which varies periodically; it is known as a *periodic potential*. In the description of simple harmonic motion (p. 2) the word *periodic* was associated with the *time* of one complete vibration. In the following discussion, the word period refers to distance. The length of unit cell is referred to as the *period of the crystal*. The distance in the crystal over which the potential makes one complete cycle of variation is referred to as the *period of the potential*.

The energies corresponding to the possible energy states of an electron in a metallic crystal may be calculated using Schrödinger's equation. The following conditions must be observed:

(1) The wave function ψ and its first derivative $d\psi/dx$ must be continuous at the boundary of a potential discontinuity.
(2) The wave function ψ must be zero at the beginning and end of the crystal.
(3) The periodic potential must "fit" into the unit cell of the crystal, that is the period of the potential must be equal or a multiple or sub-multiple of the period of the crystal.

BLOCH'S THEOREM. THE WAVE FUNCTION OF AN ELECTRON IN A PERIODIC POTENTIAL

Bloch has shown how to develop an expression for the wave function of an electron in a periodic potential which satisfies the above conditions.

The one-dimensional Schrödinger equation is

$$\frac{d^2\psi}{dx^2} + \frac{8\pi^2 m_0}{h^2}(E - V)\psi = 0.$$

If ψ_x is a solution of this equation, and a is the length of unit cell in the direction x, then ψ_{x+a} is also a solution, since V is periodic with a period which is equal to a, or is a multiple or sub-multiple of a.

Let $f_{(x)}$ and $g_{(x)}$ be two independent real solutions such that $f_{(x+a)}$ and $g_{(x+a)}$ are also real solutions, and let

$$f_{(x+a)} = \alpha_1 f_{(x)} + \alpha_2 g_{(x)}$$

and

$$g_{(x+a)} = \beta_1 f_{(x)} + \beta_2 g_{(x)}$$

where $\alpha_1, \alpha_2, \beta_1, \beta_2$, are real functions of E. If

$$\psi_{(x)} = A f_{(x)} + B g_{(x)}$$

where A and B are constants but are not necessarily real, then

$$\psi_{(x+a)} = A f_{(x+a)} + B g_{(x+a)}$$
$$= (A\alpha_1 + B\beta_1)f_{(x)} + (A\alpha_2 + B\beta_2)g_{(x)}.$$

It is possible to choose a quantity λ such that

$$A\alpha_1 + B\beta_1 = \lambda A$$
$$A\alpha_2 + B\beta_2 = \lambda B.$$

Then

$$\psi_{(x+a)} = \lambda A f_{(x)} + \lambda B g_{(x)}.$$

Therefore

$$\psi_{(x+a)} = \lambda \psi_{(x)}. \tag{6.8}$$

But

$$A(\alpha_1 - \lambda) = -B\beta_1$$
$$A\alpha_2 = B(\lambda - \beta_2),$$

therefore

$$\frac{\alpha_1 - \lambda}{\alpha_2} = \frac{-\beta_1}{\lambda - \beta_2}$$
$$(\beta_2 - \lambda)(\alpha_1 - \lambda) = \beta_1 \alpha_2.$$

This is a quadratic equation which has two roots λ_1 and λ_2. Therefore there are two solutions of the Schrödinger equation:

$$\psi_{1(x+a)} = \lambda_1 \psi_{1(x)} \tag{6.9}$$

and

$$\psi_{2(x+a)} = \lambda_2 \psi_{2(x)}.$$

In the crystal $V_x = V_{(-x)}$. Therefore $\psi_{(-x)}$ is a solution, also $\psi_{(x-a)}$ is a solution. Replace x by $x - a$ in equation (6.9).

$$\psi_{1(x-a+a)} = \lambda_1 \psi_{1(x-a)}.$$

Therefore

$$\psi_{1(x-a)} = \frac{1}{\lambda_1} \psi_{1(x)}.$$

Replace x by $-x$

$$\psi_{1-(x+a)} = \frac{1}{\lambda_1} \psi_{1(-x)}.$$

This equation has the property of equation (6.8). But there are only two independent functions which have the property of equation (6.8). Therefore

$$\frac{\psi_{1-(x+a)}}{\psi_{1-(x)}} = \frac{\psi_{2(x+a)}}{\psi_{2(x)}}.$$

Therefore

$$\lambda_2 = \frac{1}{\lambda_1}$$

and

$$\lambda_2 \lambda_1 = 1. \tag{6.10}$$

This is true for real roots for some ranges of E, and for complex roots for other ranges of E.

Therefore λ_1 and λ_2 may be expressed as

$$\left.\begin{array}{l} \lambda_1 = e^{\mu a} \\ \lambda_2 = e^{-\mu a} \end{array}\right\} \quad \text{where } \mu \text{ is a real number and } a \text{ is the length of unit cell;}$$

or

$$\left.\begin{array}{l} \lambda_1 = e^{ika} \\ \lambda_2 = e^{-ika} \end{array}\right\} \quad \text{where } k \text{ is a real number, and } a \text{ is the length of unit cell.}$$

Both the above pairs of expressions satisfy the equation $\lambda_1 \lambda_2 = 1$.

The expression $\lambda_1 = e^{\mu a}$ corresponds to a disturbance which builds up increasingly, and the expression $\lambda_2 = e^{-\mu a}$ corresponds to a disturbance which dies away exponentially, so both of these values are rejected.

Both the expressions $\lambda_1 = e^{ika}$ and $\lambda_2 = e^{-ika}$ are wave functions with the period of the lattice (a = length of unit cell). Therefore, since

$$\psi_{(x+a)} = \lambda \psi_{(x)}$$

the correct wave function in the crystal is the original wave function for the free electron multiplied by a wave function with the period of the lattice.

A more convenient way to represent λ is as follows:

$$
\begin{aligned}
e^{-ika} &= \cos ka - i \sin ka \\
&= \cos (ka + 2\pi n) - i \sin (ka + 2\pi n) \\
&= e^{-i(ka + 2\pi n)} \qquad\qquad \text{where } n \text{ is an integer} \\
&= e^{-i(k + 2\pi n/a)a}. \qquad\qquad\qquad\qquad\qquad (6.11)
\end{aligned}
$$

Equation (6.11) describes the wave function λ in terms of the period of the lattice, and shows that it has the same value at points distance a apart on the x axis, which is taken to be the axis of propagation of the wave. The wave function λ may equally well be described in terms of the disturbance as it appears at any point x on this axis, and would then be written as $e^{-i(k + 2\pi n/a)x}$. This description would be true for any value of k and so it is usually used in the simplest form, that in which $k = 0$.

If the original wave function of the free electron is written as e^{-iKx}, the wave function of the electron in the crystal is expressed as

$$\psi_{(x+a)} = e^{-(2\pi n i/a)x} e^{-iKx}.$$

Therefore

$$\psi_{(x+a)} = e^{-i(K + 2\pi n/a)x}.$$

This expression describes a wave travelling through the crystal from left to right. For a wave travelling in the opposite direction,

$$\psi_{-(x+a)} = e^{+i(K + 2\pi n/a)x}.$$

The effect of the periodic potential in the crystal is to "modulate" the frequency of the original wave which is proportional to K, by subjecting it to a periodic fluctuation. One complete fluctuation takes place between two adjacent potential barriers, that is in each unit cell. For instance, if the wave function at one potential barrier is $\psi_{(x)}$ and the wave function at the next potential barrier is $\psi_{(x+a)}$, and if

$$\psi_x = e^{-iKx}$$

and

$$\psi_{(x+a)} = e^{-iK'x}$$

then

$$e^{-iK'x} = e^{-i(K + 2\pi n/a)x}$$

and

$$K' - K = \frac{2\pi n}{a}. \qquad\qquad (6.12)$$

Equation (6.11) may also be written

$$e^{-ika} = e^{-i(k - 2\pi n/a)a},$$

in which case

$$K - K' = \frac{2\pi n}{a}.$$

The most general statement of the relation between K, K', and a is

$$K - K' = \pm \frac{2\pi n}{a}. \qquad\qquad (6.13)$$

The relation between K and K' may also be obtained from energy considerations.

ENERGY OF AN ELECTRON IN A PERIODIC POTENTIAL

The dimensions of energy are those of charge multiplied by potential. The potentia energy at a point x in the crystal may therefore be expressed as

$$CV_{(x)}|\psi|^2$$

where C is a constant and $V_{(x)}$ is the potential at x. As it is likely that there will be a contribution to the charge from both the direct wave ψ_K and a wave $\psi_{K'}$ (not necessarily of the same period) reflected from the potential barrier, $|\psi|^2$ may be written as the product $\psi_K \psi_{K'}^*$.

The potential $V_{(x)}$ at any point x between the potential barriers is periodic and so may be written as a Fourier series. (A Fourier series consists of a fundamental vibration together with all its possible harmonics, that is a series of simple harmonic vibrations whose frequencies bear a simple numerical relation to each other.) Then

$$V_{(x)} = \sum V_{(n)} e^{2\pi n i x/a}$$

for all values of n from $-\infty$ to $+\infty$ (n is an integer). Therefore the potential energy at x due to the negative charge is given by the expression

$$E_{(x)} = C \sum V_{(n)} e^{i(K'-K+2\pi n/a)x}$$

for all values of n from $-\infty$ to $+\infty$.

Therefore the potential energy over the whole crystal length L ($L=qa$ where q is an integer) is given by the expression

$$E = C \sum V_{(n)} \int_0^L e^{i(K'-K+2\pi n/a)x} \, \mathrm{d}x. \tag{6.14}$$

The integral of any sinusoidal function taken over a large region such as the length of the whole crystal is zero, therefore the energy is zero unless

$$K - K' = \frac{2\pi n}{a}.$$

The above discussion shows also that the potential energy is periodic with the period of the crystal since the expression

$$E_{(x)} = C \sum V_{(n)} e^{2\pi n i x/a} |\psi|^2$$

contains the periodic term $e^{2\pi n i x/a}$. This periodicity implies that a whole number of complete energy fluctuations takes place as the electron travels between opposite boundaries of a unit cell. The value for the total energy may be determined from the Schrödinger equation by inserting appropriate values for ψ and its derivatives. This process is described for one dimension on p. 192.

Maximum values of K. If the approximation is made that the energy of the electron is that of a free electron, E is proportional to K^2 (Equation (6.2), p. 183) and so K is greatest when E is greatest, that is when all the energy of the direct wave is reflected at the potential barrier between unit cells. In this case,

$$K = -K'$$

and

$$K = \frac{n\pi}{a}.$$

Under this condition of total reflection a standing wave is set up in the unit cell. When E is *not a maximum*, K can still be expressed as a multiple of π/a and may be written $K=n'\pi/a$, where n' is *not an integer* but takes some value between integral values of n. (The convention is here adopted of reserving the letter n for integers only.)

Energy bands. The range of energy between two integral values of n is the range of energy covered by an energy band (p. 179). Fig. 6.8 shows the energy plotted against phase for various integral values of n between which are the appropriate values of n'. It will be noted that the width of an energy band is small for low values of n, the width increasing as n increases. Each energy band contains j possible energy states where j is the number of valency electrons in the crystal. For low values of n the energy states are close together, and the energy band is narrow, with higher values of n the energy states are further apart and the bands are wider. For large values of n the band becomes very broad and the possible energy states become those of the free electron. For the purpose of illustration, the bands in Fig. 6.8 have been drawn with the energy states continuous. This corresponds theoretically to a crystal of infinite size, containing an infinite number of atoms with an infinite number of overlapping wave functions. For a large crystal the energy states are effectively continuous since

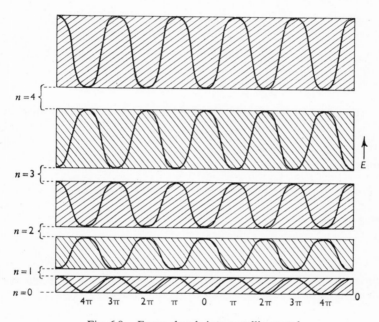

Fig. 6.8. Energy bands in a metallic crystal.

they are "broadened" by a number of factors such as the considerable reflection of waves which have n' very nearly equal to n.

Energy gaps. It will be noted in Fig. 6.8 that there are gaps between the energy bands. These gaps arise because there are two values of the energy for each integral value of n. The origin of the two energy values may be explained qualitatively as follows.

Integral values of n correspond to complete reflection of the incident wave. When this occurs a standing wave is set up. This wave must "fit in" to the length of unit cell and there are two ways in which this may be done; either there is a node at the centre of the cell and antinodes at the boundaries, or there is an antinode at the centre, and nodes at the boundaries. It is easiest to visualise this in terms of the overlapping of two space wave functions. In the first case the wave functions of the direct and reflected waves are combined antisymmetrically, and in the second case the wave functions of the direct and reflected waves are combined symmetrically. It was shown in the discussion on σ covalent bonding (pp. 121, 135) that the antisymmetric combination has a higher energy than the symmetric combination. Similar conditions apply to the three-dimensional standing wave, and therefore for a given integral value of n there are two solutions for the energy in the crystal. This problem will now be considered mathematically.

ENERGY STATES IN A CRYSTAL

ENERGY STATES IN A ONE-DIMENSIONAL CRYSTAL†

Let two wave functions ψ_K and $\psi_{K'}$ of amplitude A and A', and energy E_K and $E_{K'}$ respectively, be superposed in the crystal.

Writing $\psi_K = e^{iKx}$ and $\psi_{K'} = e^{iK'x}$ where $K - K' = 2\pi n/a$ the resultant wave function becomes

$$\psi = Ae^{iKx} + A'e^{iK'x}$$

and

$$\frac{d\psi}{dx} = iKAe^{iKx} + iK'Ae^{iK'x},$$

$$\frac{d^2\psi}{dx^2} = -K^2Ae^{iKx} - K'^2A'e^{iK'x}$$

Let $V_{(x)}$ be the potential at a point x. The Schrödinger one-dimensional equation is,

$$\frac{d^2\psi}{dx^2} + \frac{8\pi^2 m_0}{h^2}(E - V_{(x)})\psi = 0.$$

Substituting for ψ and $d^2\psi/dx^2$

$$Ae^{iKx}\left(-K^2 + \frac{8\pi^2 m_0}{h^2}(E - V_{(x)})\right) + A'e^{iK'x}\left(-K'^2 + \frac{8\pi^2 m_0}{h^2}(E - V_{(x)})\right) = 0. \quad (6.15)$$

Multiplying by $\frac{h^2}{8\pi^2 m_0}e^{-iKx}$,

$$A\left(-\frac{K^2 h^2}{8\pi^2 m_0} + E - V_{(x)}\right) + A'e^{-2\pi nix/a}\left(-\frac{K'^2 h^2}{8\pi^2 m_0} + E - V_{(x)}\right) = 0.$$

As an approximation the energies E_K and $E_{K'}$ may be taken as those of free electrons and from equation (6.2), p. 183,

$$E_K = \frac{h^2 K^2}{8\pi^2 m_0}.$$

Therefore

$$A(E - E_K - V_{(x)}) + A'e^{-2\pi nix/a}(E - E_{K'} - V_{(x)}) = 0.$$

Integrating from 0 to a, and taking the zero of energy to be such that $\int_0^a V_{(x)}\,dx = 0$

$$Aa(E - E_K) + A'(E - E_{K'})\int_0^a e^{-2\pi nix/a}dx - A'\int_0^a V_{(x)}e^{-2\pi nix/a}dx = 0.$$

Divide by a and let

$$V = \frac{1}{a}\int_0^a V_{(x)}e^{-2\pi nix/a}\,dx,$$

where V is the periodic potential. Since

$$\int_0^a e^{-2\pi nix/a}\,dx = 0,$$

† N. F. Mott and H. Jones, *The Theory of the Properties of Metals and Alloys*, Oxford 1936, p. 60.

therefore

$$A(E-E_K)-A'V^* = 0.$$

where V^* is the complex conjugate of V.

If equation (6.15) is multiplied by $(h^2/8\pi^2 m_0)e^{-iK'x}$ and developed by a similar process to that above, it may be shown that

$$-AV+A'(E-E_{K'}) = 0.$$

Eliminating A and A',

$$(E-E_K)(E-E_{K'}) = VV^*$$
$$E^2 - EE_{K'} - EE_K + E_K E_{K'} - VV^* = 0.$$

Hence
$$E = \tfrac{1}{2}[E_K+E_{K'} \pm \sqrt{\{(E_K+E_{K'})^2 - 4E_K E_{K'} + 4VV^*\}}]$$
$$= \tfrac{1}{2}[E_K+E_{K'} \pm \sqrt{\{(E_K-E_{K'})^2 + 4VV^*\}}]. \tag{6.16}$$

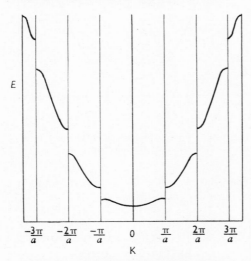

Fig. 6.9. Energy plotted against values of K for the electron in a metallic crystal of unit cell length a.

If $E_K - E_{K'}$ is not small, equation (6.16) may be written approximately (by making use of the binomial theorem)

$$E = \frac{1}{2}\left[(E_K+E_{K'}) \pm \left(E_K-E_{K'} + \frac{2VV^*}{E_K-E_{K'}}\right)\right].$$

From equation (6.13), p. 189, if K is just less than $n\pi/a$, $-K'$ must be just greater than $n\pi/a$; since E is proportional to K^2, $E_K < E_{K'}$ and since E is greater than either E_K or $E_{K'}$ the negative value of the square root must be taken. If K is just greater than $n\pi/a$, $E_K > E_{K'}$ and therefore the positive value of the square root must be taken.

If $K=n\pi/a$, then $E_K=E_{K'}$, $A=A'$, and $K=-K'$, and since $|V|^2=VV^*$, equation (6.16) may be written $E=E_K \pm V$; there is thus a jump in the energy, $\Delta E=2V$, giving two values of the energy for the one K value $n\pi/a$. It may be shown that in between these two values of the energy K is imaginary.

Fig. 6.9 is a graph of energy plotted against K. It shows gaps in the curve at each value of $n\pi/a$ (n is an integer). On referring back to Fig. 6.8 it can be seen that these gaps correspond to the gaps between the energy bands. For comparison Fig. 6.10 shows the energy of a free electron plotted against values of K.

7+A.T.I.C.

In Fig. 6.9, the two values of the energy for the one value of K, $n\pi/a$, correspond to the symmetric and antisymmetric forms of the resultant wave function. The anti-symmetric solution has the higher energy and thus corresponds to the lowest energy

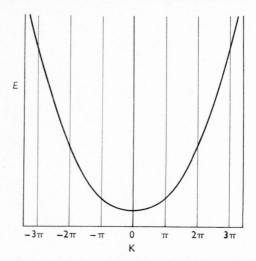

Fig. 6.10.   Energy plotted against values of K
for the free electron.

value of the higher energy band, while the symmetric solution corresponds to the highest energy value of the lower energy band.

ENERGY STATES IN A THREE-DIMENSIONAL CRYSTAL: BRILLOUIN ZONES

The three-dimensional problem, though naturally more complicated than the one-dimensional, gives an analogous picture of energy gaps. The three-dimensional energy ranges between the gaps are known as **Brillouin zones**, since L. Brillouin was the first to do extensive work in this field. These zones are manifested as energy bands in the X-ray spectrum.

The interior of a Brillouin zone corresponds to values of n which are not integral, and the boundaries, which are surfaces of constant energy, correspond to integral values of n. The reader should note that Fig. 6.9 is plotted in units of K, which has the dimensions of 1/length. Diagrams purporting to show three-dimensional Brillouin zones are also drawn proportional to values of K, and are thus said to be diagrams in "K space", "reciprocal space" or "momentum space". The reader will also find in the literature frequent references to the "reciprocal lattice" of a crystal, that is to a crystal structure represented in K space. The diagrams in K space are apt to present difficulties to the beginner and it must be strongly emphasised that Brillouin zones are regions of energy values, and not regions in the crystal. For the specialist the diagrams are a very convenient method of representation of the possible energy values in a crystal, especially as their "shape" depends on the properties of the crystal in different directions.

As in the one-dimensional problem, the energy gaps correspond to total reflection of the direct wave, which is characterised by the relation $K = n\pi/a$ (n is an integer).

The wave is unable to travel through the lattice, and a standing wave is set up in the crystal. If a wave with $K = n\pi/a$ is incident on the outside of the crystal, it is reflected from the surface. It should be remembered, however, that even with "total" reflection there is always a small probability that the electron will penetrate the potential barrier owing to the tunnel effect (p. 183). This penetration is represented mathematically by an attenuated wave which dies away very quickly.

In the preliminary discussion of $N(E)$ curves (p. 182) energy gaps were shown diagrammatically and mentioned in the text but no reason was given for their appearance. These gaps may now be identified as the gaps between the Brillouin zones, or alternatively, gaps between the energy bands. The size of the gap shows considerable

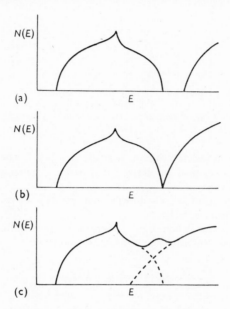

Fig. 6.11.   Shapes of $N(E)$ curves, showing: (a) well marked energy gaps between Brillouin zones; (b) no energy gap, with Brillouin zones contiguous; (c) overlapping Brillouin zones.

variation with different crystalline substances. Some specimen $N(E)$ curves of different types are shown in Fig. 6.11. In some cases such as (a) the energy gaps are clearly marked with the Brillouin zones well separated from each other. In a few others such as Fig. 6.11(b) the zones do not overlap but are adjacent to each other with no energy gap. Frequently the zones actually overlap as in Fig. 6.11(c). Here the lower energy states of the upper Brillouin zone have lower energies than those of the upper states of the lower zone, and the simple theory requires modification. With heavy atoms and many valence electrons there is considerable overlapping of many zones which become indistinguishable and the $N(E)$ curves are very complicated.

NUMBER OF ENERGY STATES

One-dimensional crystal. By regarding the bonds between atoms in crystals as many-centre bonds it was concluded (p. 179) that the number of energy states in a metallic crystal depends on the number of atoms present. If there is one atom per unit cell the number of atoms present is equal to the number of unit cells present, which is L/a. This number gives the number of overlapping wave functions and so also the number of possible energy states. The same conclusion can be obtained independently from energy considerations as follows:

The simplest case for which the number of possible energy states of an electron subject to boundary conditions may be calculated is that of an electron with kinetic energy only, the electron wave being completely reflected at opposite boundaries. A standing wave is set up and since $\psi=0$ at the boundaries, these must be the location of nodes in the standing wave. The problem has been discussed for the one-dimensional

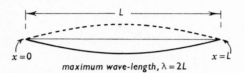

maximum wave-length, $\lambda = 2L$

Fig. 6.12. Condition for maximum wave length of the stationary wave of an electron in a one-dimensional crystal, for lowest energy state.

case (Chapter 1, p. 20) under the title of "particle in a box". The system may also be regarded as the limiting case of an electron in a periodic potential which varies from zero to some negative value.

For the free electron in a one-dimensional crystal, there are two boundary conditions governing total reflection:

(1) $\psi=0$ when $x=0$ and when $x=L$, where L is the length of the crystal. The maximum wave length of the standing wave is $2L$, and $K=\pi/L$.

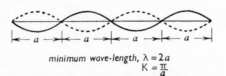

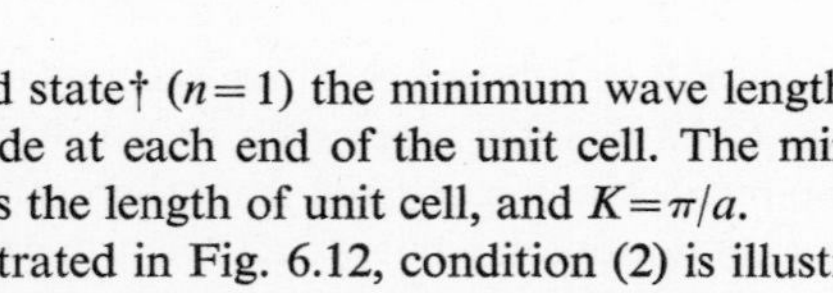

minimum wave-length, $\lambda = 2a$
$K = \dfrac{\pi}{a}$

Fig. 6.13. Minimum wave length of the stationary wave of an electron in a one-dimensional crystal, for lowest energy state.

(2) For a non-excited state† ($n=1$) the minimum wave length of the standing wave is that which has a node at each end of the unit cell. The minimum wave length is therefore, $2a$, where a is the length of unit cell, and $K=\pi/a$.

Condition (1) is illustrated in Fig. 6.12, condition (2) is illustrated in Fig. 6.13.

The energy of the free electron is given by the expression

$$E = \frac{h^2 K^2}{8\pi^2 m_0} \quad \text{(equation (6.2))}.$$

E is large when K is large and small when K is small, therefore the minimum value of K, π/L, corresponds to the lowest energy state, the wave length of the standing wave

---

† It is necessary to consider only the case of $n=1$ in condition (2). Higher values of n correspond to excited states of the electron, but there is still only one wave function to each unit cell, therefore the number of possible energy states is the same as for $n=1$, although the actual values of the corresponding energies will be different.

being a maximum, $2L$. The maximum value of K, π/a, corresponds to the highest energy state, the wave length of the standing wave being a minimum, $2a$.

Now the maximum energy may be written as

$$E(\text{max}) = \frac{C}{(\lambda_{\text{min}})^2}, \text{ where } C \text{ is a constant,}$$

and the minimum energy may be written as

$$E(\text{min}) = \frac{C}{(\lambda_{\text{max}})^2}.$$

In order that both boundary conditions may be observed simultaneously the wave length corresponding to a given energy state must at the same time be a multiple of λ_{min} and a sub-multiple of λ_{max}. Fig. 6.14 shows the wave lengths for the possible energy states for the hypothetical case in which

$$\lambda_{\text{max}} = 6\lambda_{\text{min}}.$$

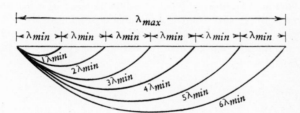

Fig. 6.14. Relation between maximum and minimum wave lengths in a one-dimensional crystal, showing hypothetical case where $\lambda_{\text{max}} = 6\lambda_{\text{min}}$.

It is easily seen from the diagram that

$$\text{number of energy states} = \frac{\lambda_{\text{max}}}{\lambda_{\text{min}}}.$$

But

$$\frac{\lambda_{\text{max}}}{\lambda_{\text{min}}} = \sqrt{\frac{E_{\text{max}}}{E_{\text{min}}}},$$

and since

$$E_{\text{max}} = \frac{h^2}{8m_0 a^2},$$

and

$$E_{\text{min}} = \frac{h^2}{8m_0 L^2},$$

therefore the number of possible energy states $= L/a$.

Three-dimensional crystal. In general the properties of the crystal are different along the three axes x, y, z.

Let

$$\frac{L_x}{a_x} = q_x, \qquad \frac{L_y}{a_y} = q_y, \qquad \frac{L_z}{a_z} = q_z$$

and let $q_x^2 + q_y^2 + q_z^2 = r^2$ in the three-dimensional space. This equation is satisfied by a number of values of q_x, q_y, q_z, for each set of which there is the same value of r. The possible energy states may therefore be represented as lying within a sphere of which r is the radius. Let $r = L/a$ where $L = (\text{Volume of crystal})^{1/3}$, and a is the "effective length" of unit cell.

The metallic bond

Now if a sphere contains a number of points unit distance apart, the number of points is numerically equal to the volume of the sphere. A similar relation exists in one- and two-dimensional systems. For the one-dimensional case the number of unit cells in a straight line is equal to the length of the line when the centres of adjacent cells are unit distance apart.

$$N = \frac{L}{a}$$

$$= L, \quad \text{when } a = 1.$$

Similarly, if a square is composed of points unit distance apart, the number of points in the square is numerically equal to the area.

For the sphere, number of unit cells is given by

$$N = \frac{4}{3} \pi r^3.$$

The energy states are real only for positive values of q_x, q_y, q_z which are contained in $\frac{1}{8}$th of the volume of the sphere. Therefore $r/2$ must be used instead of r.

Since the energy of the free electron $= h^2 K^2 / 8\pi^2 m_0$, and for the state of greatest energy $K = \pi/a$, and since $r = L/a$, number of possible energy states N with energy equal to or less than E is given by

$$N(E) = \frac{4}{3} \pi \frac{r^3}{8}$$

$$= \frac{4}{3} \pi \frac{L^3 K^3}{8\pi^3}$$

$$= \frac{4}{3} \pi V \frac{(2m_0 E)^{3/2}}{h^3}, \tag{6.17}$$

where V is the volume of the crystal.

Number of energy states $N(E)$ with energy between E and $E + dE$ is found by differentiating equation (6.17)

$$\frac{dN}{dE} dE = N(E) \, dE = \frac{2\pi V}{h^3} (2m_0)^{3/2} E^{1/2} \, dE. \tag{6.18}$$

If the possible energy states are all occupied, the number of electrons with energy between E and $E + dE$ is $2N(E)dE$.

THE SHAPE OF $N(E)$ CURVES

The free electron distribution of energy states is often referred to as the **Fermi distribution**. It can be used as a rough picture of the energy states of an electron in a metal crystal. If an electron travelling through a crystal has low energy, it will most probably be found in positions equidistant from neighbouring nuclei since, by analogy with the case of the covalent molecule, this is the position of minimum energy. In a univalent metal such as sodium the conditions approximate to those of the free electron, and it is found that for these metals the $N(E)$ curve, plotted empirically from the data obtained from experiments on soft X-rays, approximates to a parabola at low energies (Fig. 6.15). This would be expected from consideration of equation (6.18), since $N(E) \, dE$ is proportional to $E^{1/2}$.

Energy contours. A three-dimensional graphical representation of the variation of E with r would show points of equal energy lying on the surface of a sphere for each value of r. Such a surface is known as an **energy contour**. Since r is proportional to

K, energy contours may be plotted either from r or from K values. The representation is usually in the form of a two-dimensional diagram. The reason for the characteristic shapes of $N(E)$ curves may be most easily understood by the study of the corresponding energy contour diagrams. Fig. 6.16† shows the energy contours for the first Brillouin zone of a two-dimensional square lattice. The lines of low energy are in the centre of the diagram and these are approximately circles. As the energy is increased, the surfaces of equal energy approach the boundary of the first Brillouin zone, and the energy contours become distorted from the spherical form. In the diagram, the discontinuous lines show the zone boundary.

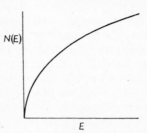

Fig. 6.15. Relation between $N(E)$ and E for the free electron model.

The corresponding $N(E)$ curve (Fig. 6.11, p. 195) is parabolic in form over the low energy range; this part of the curve is equivalent to the region of circular contours in Fig. 6.16. The beginning of the distortion of these contours is marked by a steep rise in the $N(E)$ curve; in this region a small change in the value of K covers a large range of energy. After the steep rise, the curve shows an almost equally steep decline and there is increasing distortion of the energy contours; the exact shape of both the curve and the contours depends on the particular metal investigated. The continual decline of the curve indicates that there are fewer and fewer energy states available in the upper energy region, and for the most general case, the curve comes right down to zero with $N(E)=0$. This corresponds to the boundary of the Brillouin zone in the contour diagram. After the energy gap the curve starts up again for the second Brillouin zone.

The fall of the $N(E)$ curve to zero may be explained in terms of the wave packet theory of the electron. The velocity of the electron is a group velocity (p. 8) and is given by the expression

$$v = \frac{dv}{d(1/\lambda)}.$$

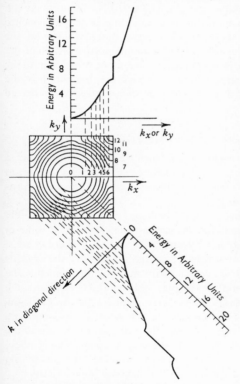

Fig. 6.16. Energy contours for the first Brillouin zone of a two-dimensional square lattice.

Since $E = hv$ and $K = 2\pi/\lambda$, the velocity is proportional to dE/dK, and as E does not change along the energy contour, the direction of motion of the wave packet and therefore of the electron, must be perpendicular to the energy contours which are surfaces when plotted in three dimensions. If these are spherical the

† Raynor's "Introduction to the Electron Theory of Metals", G. V. Raynor, *Inst. Metals Monograph and Rep.* series No. 4, 1949.

direction of the wave is the same as that of the wave packet, but when the contours become distorted the direction of the wave packet is not the same as that of the electron wave. Under these conditions the simple relation $K = n\pi/a$ does not hold. The number of possible energy states available for an electron travelling in the direction of the wave is severely limited as the boundary of the Brillouin zone is approached, and sinks to zero when the boundary is reached. Fig. 6.11(a) shows that at the edge of the zone $dK/dE = 0$, therefore $v = \infty$ or 0, and so it may be concluded that the electron has no velocity at the zone boundary.

Many factors which were neglected in the simple theory must be taken into consideration for the complete theory of Brillouin zones, and for the calculation of $N(E)$ curves for metals of higher valency than one. For instance, the wave functions must be modified as far as possible to be in accord with the known shape of the crystal lattice, allowance must be made for the electrostatic effect of the valency electrons on each other and of the inner shells of electrons. The original atomic states (s, p, or d) of the valency electrons must be taken into account, and consideration given to the directional effect of the p and d electrons. The time during which the electron is close to the field of the nucleus is also of importance. Calculations of $N(E)$ curves for the simpler forms of metallic crystal suggest that correlation between theory and experiment is closest for the monovalent metals. Spectroscopic evidence from the determination of gyromagnetic ratios (p. 97) suggests that the effect of the strong electric field in the crystal is to "quench" the orbital angular momentum of the valency electrons. In this connection the word "quench" does not mean annihilate. It appears that the electric field is sufficiently strong to prevent the orientation of the orbital magnetic moment in an applied magnetic field. The spin moment is unaffected by the electric field of the crystal.

CONDUCTORS, INSULATORS, AND SEMI-CONDUCTORS

Owing to the tunnel effect, there is a constant movement of electrons throughout a crystal. This takes place in both insulators and conductors, but there is a significant difference between crystals belonging to these two classes. This difference concerns the number of electrons in the Brillouin zones.†

Conductors. In conductors, the outermost occupied Brillouin zone is not completely filled, so that when an electric field is applied to the crystal, the electrons in some of the lower energy states of the unfilled zone are transferred to higher energy states, and there is a resultant unidirectional movement of charge throughout the crystal; this is shown by the passage of an electric current. With most common metals the $N(E)$ curves show overlapping of Brillouin zones (Fig. 6.11(c)) which facilitates the movement of the electrons. The lower energy states of the second zone can be below the higher energy states of the first zone, and even if the first zone is not completely filled, application of an electric field may cause some of the electrons to move into the second zone. If the first zone is completely filled, and the second zone partially filled, the electrons of the first zone do not take part in conduction. An increase of the number of valency electrons does not necessarily mean an increase in conductivity.

Insulators. When an electric field is applied to an insulator, there is no uni-directional movement of electrons since there are no unfilled energy states in the zones which they occupy, and there is a large energy gap between the zones. If the applied field is very large, the electrons may be given sufficient energy to bridge the gap and to transfer

† Although theoretically there may be any number of Brillouin zones waiting for electrons to fill them, in practice the small number of valency electrons available, especially in metals, ensures that the occupied zones are in general only the first and sometimes the second, and even these may not be completely filled.

them to energy states in a higher zone which has hitherto been entirely unoccupied. Under these circumstances the insulator is said to *break down*. The $N(E)$ curve of Fig. 6.11(a) is typical of insulators.

Semi-conductors. These are substances with crystalline structures which are insulators under normal conditions, but which may be made conducting by rise of temperature or by the presence of impurities. They are divided into two classes: (a) intrinsic semi-conductors and (b) n and p semi-conductors.

Intrinsic semi-conductors. These are characterised by $N(E)$ curves of the type shown in Fig. 6.11(b). The Brillouin zones do not overlap but are contiguous, and there are no partially filled zones. A small amount of energy, such as that acquired by thermal excitation, is sufficient to raise some of the electrons from the higher energy states of the filled zone to the lower energy states of the next zone, which has hitherto been empty. There are then two partially filled zones, and when an external electric field is applied some of the electrons can move into the unoccupied energy states. The heated substance therefore behaves as a conductor. Graphite is a well known example of an intrinsic semi-conductor, but there are not many such substances which have their Brillouin zones exactly or very nearly contiguous without overlapping.

n and p semi-conductors. These are substances which are not conductors in the pure state, but which may be made conducting by the introduction of impurities. Their $N(E)$ curves show small energy gaps, which contain energy levels due to the impurity.

n type. The application of heat causes some of the electrons from the impurity energy levels to be transferred to the lower energy states of the upper zone, which then, by reason of being partially filled, endow the crystal with conducting properties. If there are only small traces of the impurity present, continued application of heat uses up all the electrons available from the impurity energy levels between the Brillouin zones, and at higher temperatures conductivity may diminish owing to the increased thermal vibration of the lattice.

p type. In substances of this type, the application of heat causes some of the electrons from the first zone to be transferred to some of the energy levels of the impurity. The first zone remains only partially filled, and so the crystal shows conducting properties. A greater increase of temperature may result in a diminution of conductivity as with the n type.

BINDING ENERGY OF METALS

The mathematical difficulties associated with the calculation of the binding energy of a metal are very considerable, even in the case of the simplest monovalent metals. As with many of the calculations of wave mechanics the theory contains much approximation, but by introducing as many refinements as possible, calculation of the binding energies of crystals of the monovalent metals sodium and lithium has given fairly good results.

The binding energy of a crystal is equal to the work required to dissociate the crystal into free neutral atoms. It may be measured in practice by the heat of sublimation. Theoretically, the energy of the crystal is considered as being made up of the kinetic and potential energy of the electrons. For the computation of the binding energy to be as exact as possible the following terms should be included in the expression for the potential energy:

(a) The *Coulomb* term, that is the electrostatic energy due to the forces between the nuclei, the forces between the electrons, and the forces between the electrons and the nuclei.

(b) The *exchange* term, analogous to the exchange integrals which appear in the expression for the energy of the molecular covalent bond.

7*

(c) The *correlation* term which is concerned with the relative positions of the electrons. The usual probability considerations as applied to the position of the electron with regard to the nuclei must also be taken into account.

Different workers have used different approximations with varying success. The following brief account indicates some of the ways in which a solution of the problem has been attempted.

(1) Bloch attempted to calculate the energy of crystal orbitals (analogous to molecular orbitals) from the linear combination of atomic orbitals. He took into account only those atoms which were very near each other, and neglected all overlap integrals. His calculations were not in close agreement with experimental results.

(2) Pauling and Slater made a mostly qualitative investigation using the Heitler-London resonance method.

(3) The most successful pioneer work was done by Wigner and Seitz. Their method is sometimes known as the *cellular* method since they considered the energy of a single electron in an *atomic cell*, and summed such energy terms for all the electrons throughout the crystal. A simplified account of their method is as follows:

The crystal lattice is considered to be divided up into atomic cells by planes midway between the atoms and perpendicular to the line joining them. If a body-centred lattice of the alkali metals is considered, each nucleus occupies the centre of a cube with eight neighbours at the corners, and the bisecting planes form an octahedron round the central nucleus. Six other neighbouring nuclei are slightly further away, and planes separating them from the central nucleus have the effect of cutting off the corners of the octahedron. To a first approximation, the resulting polyhedron may be replaced by a sphere of the same volume. It is also assumed that on an average each sphere contains one atom consisting of a nucleus, with an electron core (of small radius in the case of the sodium) and one valency electron. The interelectronic reactions between one atomic sphere and the others are neglected, and the energy of one electron in its sphere is assumed to be unaffected by its neighbours. The total energy of the crystal is approximately taken to be the sum of the energies of all the electrons.

The energy of the single electron is considered to be composed of the following two terms:

(a) Energy of the electron due to its position in the atom, subject to the boundary condition that $d\psi/dr=0$ at the surface of the sphere (radius r).

(b) Energy of the electron in the periodic field of the crystal.

The Bloch wave function is used (p. 189):

$$\psi = e^{i(K+2\pi n/a)x}.$$

This function may be inserted into the Schrödinger equation and a solution obtained for the case where $K=0$. The potential energy term V is computed for the electron in the field of the nucleus and the core. A value for the corresponding energy E_0 may be calculated. It is more difficult to solve the Schrödinger equation for values of K other than 0, but as a rough approximation the energy E_K may be written as

$$E_K = E_0 + \frac{h^2 K^2}{8\pi^2 m_0}. \tag{6.19}$$

The quantity $E_K - E_0$ is known as the *Fermi energy*, and the energy of the electron in the crystal is expressed in terms of this quantity. Equation (6.19) shows that to a first approximation the Fermi energy is equal to the energy of the free electron. In the case of the sodium atom this is a fairly good approximation. For metals generally the expression becomes

$$E_K - E_0 = \frac{h^2 K^2}{8\pi^2 m^*}.$$

Here m^* is called the *effective electronic mass*, which for free electrons becomes the mass of the electron. The ratio m^*/m is different for different metals; for lithium it is 1·53 and for sodium it is very nearly unity, 0·94. That is why a pretty good approximation may be obtained for sodium using the equation for the free electron, but it is not really significant as m^* is a sum of integrals.

For any energy band, the Fermi energy is a maximum at the edge of the Brillouin zone. This is a clear cut energy state only at absolute zero, since a rise of temperature causes a blurring of the energy states. It is therefore always assumed in the simple theory that the discussion relates to conditions at absolute zero.

The mean Fermi energy in an energy band may be calculated as follows. Since each crystalline orbital can be occupied by two electrons, the maximum number of electrons in the available energy states is twice the number of possible energy states.

Therefore $n = 2N(E)$, and by equation (6.17), p. 198,

$$2N(E) = \frac{8}{3}\frac{\pi V}{h^3}(2m_0 E)^{3/2}.$$

Therefore

$$E_{max}^{3/2} = \frac{3}{8}\frac{nh^3}{\pi V(2m_0)^{3/2}}.$$

$$\text{Total energy\dag of electrons} = 2\int_0^{E_{max}} E N(E)\, dE$$

$$= 2\int_0^{E_{max}} \frac{2\pi V}{h^3}(2m_0)^{3/2}E^{3/2}\, dE$$

$$= 2\left[\frac{2}{5} \times \frac{2\pi V}{h^3}(2m_0)^{3/2}E^{5/2}\right]_0^{E_{max}}$$

$$= \frac{8}{5}\frac{\pi V}{h^3}(2m_0)^{3/2}E_{max}^{5/2}$$

$$= \frac{3}{5}nE_{max}.$$

Therefore the mean Fermi energy E_F (Fermi energy per electron) is given by:

$$E_F = \frac{3}{5}E_{max}$$

$$= \frac{3}{5}\frac{h^2(K_{max})^2}{8\pi^2 m^*}. \qquad (6.20)$$

The energy per atom of a crystal may be expressed in terms of E_F, since

$$E_K = E_F + E_0.$$

Therefore total binding energy per atom in the crystal

$$= E_I + E_F + E_0,$$

where E_I is the ionisation energy. E_0 is a negative quantity and is obtained from the Schrödinger equation for $K = 0$, E_F is obtained from the above calculation, and E_I may be obtained experimentally. Hence a computation of the binding energy per atom in the crystal may be made. Table 6.1 shows the stages in the calculation for the binding energy of lithium and sodium. It can be seen that the last three terms almost cancel each other out.

\dag This is the Fermi energy as it is expressed in terms of the energy of free electrons (p. 183). Any contribution from the periodic field (E_0) must therefore be contained in the left-hand side of the equation.

Table 6.1. *Binding Energy of* Li *and* Na (*kcals per mole*)

Energy term	Li	Na
Ionisation of atom E_I	123·4	118·7
Lowest crystal orbital E_0	−206·0	−185·9
Mean Fermi energy E_F	43·6	42·9
Sub-total ($E_I + E_0 + E_F$)	− 39·0	− 24·3
Coulomb term E_C	114·8	89·6
Exchange term E_{ex}	− 90·2	− 69·2
Correlation term E_{cor}	− 21·7	− 19·6
Total calculated	− 36·1	− 23·5
Experimental	− 37·3	− 26·0

K. S. Pitzer, *Quantum Chemistry* (Prentice-Hall, 1953), p. 298.

Calculations of the binding energies of other metals have also been made by this method but there is considerable discrepancy between the theoretical and experimental results. The increased size of the electron core, particularly in potassium, may have a disturbing effect on the binding energy. Löwdin,† has made a very careful calculation of the binding energy of sodium using the LCAO method of combining Bloch wave functions. By an ingenious mathematical device which he names "combined atomic orbitals", he is able to make calculations of the energy of a many-centre bond, which obviously must be nearer to the true energy condition in a crystal than the energy of a number of single cellular atoms each unaffected by its neighbours. Löwdin claims that the overlap integrals which are neglected in the simple Wigner and Seitz theory are of fundamental importance. His method has been criticised on the grounds that it neglects the electron correlation effects, but he obtained extremely good agreement between theoretical and experimental results in the case of sodium. Löwdin has shown that the lowest wave functions on the cellular method have the same characteristics as the lowest wave functions calculated by his method.

BOOKS FOR FURTHER READING

DEKKER, A. J., *Solid State Physics* (Macmillan, 1958).
HUME ROTHERY, W., *Atomic Theory for Students of Metallurgy* (The Institute of Metals, 1952).
MOTT, N. F., and JONES, H., *The Theory of the Properties of Metals and Alloys* (Oxford University Press, 1936).
PITZER, K. S., *Quantum Chemistry* (Prentice-Hall, 1953).
SLATER, J. C., *The Quantum Theory of Matter* (McGraw-Hill, 1953).

REVIEWS

RAYNOR, G. V., *The Band Structure of Metals* (Reps. Prog. Phys., **15**, 1952, 173).

† P.-O. Löwdin, *J. Chem. Phys.*, **19**, 1951, 1570, 1579.

CHAPTER SEVEN

MOLECULAR SPECTRA (1)

Much evidence concerning the structure and properties of molecules has been derived from the study of molecular spectra. Information on internuclear distances, the geometrical arrangements of the atoms in molecules, moments of inertia, the vibration and rotation of molecules, and the types and stability of bonds, can be obtained from spectrum analysis.

The energy of a molecule may be considered under four headings:

(1) The potential energy due to the arrangement of the electrons in orbitals.

(2) The quantised energy of vibration of the component atoms with respect to each other. The vibration is conveniently referred to as *molecular vibration*.

(3) The quantised energy of rotation of the molecule about the three mutually perpendicular axes of least, greatest, and intermediate moment of inertia. The rotation is conveniently referred to as *molecular rotation*.

(4) The unquantised kinetic energy of translation of the molecule in space. This is neglected in the present discussion since it has no bearing on spectra.

Molecular spectra are much more complicated than atomic spectra. Whereas the atomic spectrum is due solely to changes of energy arising from electron transitions from one orbital to another, the molecular spectrum is the result of changes of molecular rotational and vibrational energy, as well as changes of energy due to transitions of electrons from one molecular orbital to another. If an electron transition takes place in the molecule it must do so in the presence of an electric field along the molecular axis due to the charges on the two nuclei. When the atoms are strongly bound the internuclear distance is small, and the electric field strong. The spectrum of such a molecule therefore shows marked similarities to the spectrum of the atomic Stark effect (p. 104). When the atoms are weakly bound the internuclear distance is large and the electric field weak. In this case the pattern of the spectrum bears some resemblance to that which would be obtained by superposing two atomic spectra.

SPECTRA OF DIATOMIC MOLECULES

CLASSIFICATION

Molecular spectra are due to three types of energy change. These are concerned with:

(a) molecular rotation,
(b) molecular vibration,
(c) electron transition.

The spectra of diatomic molecules may accordingly be classified as follows.

Pure rotation spectra. Pure rotation spectra are the simplest molecular spectra. They occur in the far infrared and microwave regions, and are derived from quantised changes in rotational energy only. For diatomic molecules the spectra consist of equidistant lines; for many polyatomic molecules the line sequences are also relatively simple.

Rotation vibration spectra. Rotation vibration spectra occur in the near infrared and infrared regions; their wave lengths lie in the range 2–50 μ. They are due to simultaneous changes of quantised vibrational and rotational energy. A rotation vibration spectrum consists of a single *band system*, that is, a group of bands, each band consisting of a number of lines.

Band spectra. Band spectra lie mainly in the infrared, visible, and ultraviolet parts of the spectrum. They are derived from simultaneous energy changes of all three types (a), (b), (c). The change of greatest magnitude is that due to electron transition; the change of least magnitude is that due to molecular rotation. A band spectrum may be analysed into three superposed structures corresponding to the three types of energy change. These are:

A number of clearly separated groups of bands. Each group is a band system. The position of a band system in the spectrum depends on an electron transition. All bands of the same band system correspond to the same electron transition.

The bands in each band system. The position of an individual band is determined by a change of quantised vibrational energy.

The lines in each band. The position of an individual line in a band is determined by a change of quantised rotational energy.

In addition to these three types of spectra, continuous spectra are sometimes present. A true continuous spectrum is due to non-quantised energy changes.

It should be noted that although there are many emission spectra of diatomic molecules, observed spectra of polyatomic molecules are, almost without exception, absorption spectra. The temperature required for the emission of characteristic molecular radiation is nearly always sufficient to dissociate a large molecule. However, by using special low current discharges it is possible to produce emission spectra from certain large polyatomic molecules although they are easily dissociated. For the sake of maintaining a comprehensive view of molecular spectra reference will be made throughout to emission as well as absorption spectra.

RADIATION AND ELECTRIC DIPOLE MOMENT

Both the classical and wave-mechanical theories of radiation postulate that the production of radiation is dependent on a change of electric dipole moment in the atom or molecule. If an electron changes its energy state in any atom or molecule (change of orbital), there is, except in a few cases, a change of dipole moment owing to the redistribution of charge and, as a result, radiation is emitted (p. 84).

When vibrational and rotational changes only are considered, a distinction must be made between homonuclear and heteronuclear molecules. In a heteronuclear diatomic molecule there is an asymmetric distribution of charge (permanent dipole moment) because of the differing electronegativities of the combined atoms. A change of vibration or rotation state produces a change in magnitude or angular velocity of the dipole moment, and corresponding spectra are produced. In a homonuclear diatomic molecule the charge is distributed symmetrically about the centre of the molecule, there is no permanent dipole moment, and therefore lines and bands due to rotation and vibration are absent from the spectra of homonuclear molecules. It is possible, however, by means of the Raman effect (p. 249), to show that homonuclear molecules do rotate and vibrate.

TERM SYMBOLS FOR DIATOMIC MOLECULES

An atomic orbital is described by three quantum numbers, n, l, m (p. 38). An analogous but not so precise description can be given to a molecular orbital. In the chapter on valency (p. 127) the importance of the quantum number λ was stressed. λ determines the component of angular momentum about the molecular axis, this quantity being measured by the vector $\boldsymbol{\lambda}$ where $\boldsymbol{\lambda} = \lambda h/2\pi$; λ can take integral values $0, 1, 2, 3, \ldots$. These values also indicate the symmetry of the molecular orbital with regard to the molecular axis. A molecular orbital is described by a letter σ, π, δ, ϕ, etc., according to the λ values 0, 1, 2, 3, etc. The total orbital angular momentum of all the molecular orbitals about the molecular axis, Λ, $(\Lambda = \Lambda h/2\pi)$, is obtained by adding vectorially the λ values of the separate orbitals. The possible states of the molecule corresponding to $\Lambda = 0, 1, 2, 3, \ldots$, are designated by the symbols Σ, Π, Δ, Φ. $\mathbf{K}$ is the total angular momentum of the molecule apart from spin.

The electron spins, which are coupled more strongly together than individually with the field, are combined vectorially to give the quantised resultant spin $\mathbf{S}$, which precesses about the molecular axis. The component of $\mathbf{S}$ along this direction is designated by $\boldsymbol{\Sigma}$.†

The component spin quantum number Σ can take values differing by unity, from $+S$ to $-S$. $\boldsymbol{\Lambda}$ and $\boldsymbol{\Sigma}$ combine vectorially owing to their magnetic coupling to give the component of total angular momentum about the molecular axis, Ω. For each value of Λ there are $2S+1$ values of Ω. As in the case of the atom, the value of $2S+1$ indicates the multiplicity (p. 92).

So far the quantum number n which plays such an important part in the description of atomic structure has not been mentioned at all in connection with the molecule. The reason for this is that n is not independent of the internuclear distance r_0 as is λ. When the two atoms in the molecule are very close together (r_0 small) conditions approximate to that of an atom, and the number of possible energy states is approximately that of a "united atom" formed by merging the two nuclei. The energy is related to the size of the united atomic orbital in terms of a quantum number n as for a single atom. As r_0 increases, there is a change in the relation between the size of the orbital and the corresponding energy, until the nuclei are so far apart that the system becomes one of two isolated atoms instead of one molecule. The simple relation of n to the energy then returns. However, although the quantum number n must be dispensed with in the molecule, the number of possible energy states for a given molecule remains the same even if the internuclear distance varies.

As with the atom, the angular momentum of the molecule is represented by the vector quantity $\mathbf{J}$. It is obtained by the vectorial combination of orbital and spin angular momenta with the angular momentum of the molecule about an axis at right angles to the internuclear axis.‡

† The Greek capital letter sigma is used:

  (i) in the style $\boldsymbol{\Sigma}$ to indicate the quantised component of the total electron spin about the molecular axis,
  (ii) in the style Σ to indicate the quantum number associated with the total electron spin about the molecular axis,
  (iii) also in the style Σ to indicate the state of the molecule when $\Lambda = 0$.

‡ The angular momentum due to the rotation of the molecule about an axis at right angles to the internuclear axis is denoted by $\mathbf{N}$. The resultant orbital angular momentum of the electrons (neglecting spin) is quantised, and is most often strongly coupled to the internuclear axis, thus maintaining a constant angle of 90° with $\mathbf{N}$. $\mathbf{J}$, the total angular momentum is also quantised, and therefore in these circumstances $\mathbf{N}$ will not in general have an integral quantum number. Fig. 7.15, illustrating Hund's cases (a) and (b), shows two usual couplings of this kind. There are some less usual cases where the orbital coupling to the internuclear axis is weak, and $\mathbf{N}$ may then have an integral quantum number.

Molecular states. The arrangement of the term symbols designating molecular states is similar to that of the symbols for the atomic states. The multiplicity $(2S+1)$ is written as a superscript on the left of the term symbol. A subscript on the right-hand side shows the value of Ω for the particular energy state described.[†] For instance, the term symbols of the four possible energy states of a three-electron molecule with total spin 3/2 and $\Lambda = 2$ are,

$$^{4}\Pi_{7/2}, \; ^{4}\Pi_{5/2}, \; ^{4}\Pi_{3/2}, \; ^{4}\Pi_{1/2}.$$

For a complete description of the molecule, the symbol for the molecular orbital is written before the term symbol. For instance, the ground state for the hydrogen molecule formed from two $1s$ atomic electrons is written as $(\sigma 1s)^{2}\Sigma_{0}$.

The multiplicity rule is the same as for the atom. Molecules with an even number of electrons have an odd multiplicity, and molecules with an odd number of electrons have an even multiplicity. This rule is useful for distinguishing between the spectra of molecules and those of their ions.

Selection rules for diatomic molecules.[‡]

(1) Λ can change by 0 or ± 1.

(2) There can be no electron transition from an energy state which belongs to one term system (see Chapter 3, pp. 78 and 92) to an energy state belonging to another term system, as this would involve reversal of electron spin.

VIBRATION OF DIATOMIC MOLECULES

The analysis of spectra shows that molecular vibration in gases (though not in liquids and solids) is always accompanied by molecular rotation. In the later sections of this chapter the different types of spectra are discussed in detail, but for the purpose of exposition it is desirable first to discuss the vibration of diatomic molecules independently of their rotation. Evidence from the study of spectra suggests that the vibration of a diatomic molecule may be assumed to be that of the two nuclei about an equilibrium position, the vibration being along the molecular axis. Since the mass of an electron is so much smaller than that of an atomic nucleus, the contribution of the electrons to the molecular vibration may be neglected.

POTENTIAL ENERGY CURVES

In the discussion on the energy of the simplest diatomic molecule, the hydrogen molecule-ion, it was shown (Fig. 4.4, p. 123) that if the total energy of the molecule is plotted as a function of the internuclear distance, the curve shows a minimum corresponding to an equilibrium position of greatest stability. Since it is possible to solve the Schrödinger equation explicitly for the hydrogen molecule-ion and thus to calculate the potential energy function with accuracy, the potential energy curve can be obtained theoretically. It is not possible to solve the Schrödinger equations (and thus to calculate the potential energy functions) for most diatomic molecules, but potential energy curves of certain diatomic molecules can be plotted from information derived from the study of molecular spectra (p. 218). Such experimental evidence is not available for the unstable hydrogen molecule-ion. It may be assumed, however, that the principles operating in the case of the hydrogen molecule-ion are also responsible for the behaviour of more complicated diatomic molecules, and the interpretation of their potential energy curves may be based on this assumption.

[†] The word "component" is sometimes used to describe one of a number $(2S+1)$ of multiple energy states. As far as possible, its use in this context will be avoided in this book.

[‡] Selection rules are not always obeyed in heavy discharges.

If r_0 is the internuclear distance for minimum energy, at any instant the potential energy of a vibrating diatomic molecule, assuming it to be a harmonic oscillator, is given by the expression (p. 2)

$$E_p = \tfrac{1}{2}k(r-r_0)^2$$

where r is the distance between the nuclei, and k is the force constant.

If the molecule is supposed not to be rotating, the total energy E of the molecule is the sum of the energy of vibration E_{vib} and the potential energy due to the distribution of the electrons in the orbitals E_{el}:

$$E = E_{\text{vib}}+E_{\text{el}}.$$

Therefore, at any instant during the vibration,

$$\text{kinetic energy of vibration} = E-E_{\text{el}}-E_p.$$

It is convenient to write

$$\rho = \frac{r-r_0}{r_0} \quad \text{and} \quad \beta = \frac{kr_0^2}{2}.$$

Then

$$\text{kinetic energy of vibration} = E-E_{\text{el}}-\beta\rho^2.$$

The one dimensional Schrödinger equation is

$$\frac{\mathrm{d}^2\psi}{\mathrm{d}r^2}+\frac{8\pi^2 m_0}{h^2}(E-V)\psi = 0.$$

For the vibration problem m_0 must be replaced by the *reduced mass* of the molecule μ, where $\mu=\dfrac{m_1 m_2}{m_1+m_2}$; m_1 and m_2 are the masses of the two atoms in the molecule (see Appendix).

$$\frac{\mathrm{d}\psi}{\mathrm{d}\rho} = \frac{\mathrm{d}\psi}{\mathrm{d}r}\times\frac{\mathrm{d}r}{\mathrm{d}\rho} = r_0\frac{\mathrm{d}\psi}{\mathrm{d}r}$$

$$\frac{\mathrm{d}^2\psi}{\mathrm{d}\rho^2} = \frac{\mathrm{d}}{\mathrm{d}r}\left(r_0\frac{\mathrm{d}\psi}{\mathrm{d}r}\right)\times\frac{\mathrm{d}r}{\mathrm{d}\rho} = r_0^2\frac{\mathrm{d}^2\psi}{\mathrm{d}r^2}.$$

Therefore

$$\frac{\mathrm{d}^2\psi}{\mathrm{d}\rho^2}+\frac{8\pi^2 r_0^2\mu}{h^2}(E-V)\psi = 0.$$

If μr_0^2, the moment of inertia of the molecule with the nuclei in the mean position is written as I, then

$$\frac{\mathrm{d}^2\psi}{\mathrm{d}\rho^2}+\frac{8\pi^2 I}{h^2}(E_{\text{vib}}-\beta\rho^2)\psi = 0.$$

This is the equation of a linear harmonic oscillator (p. 24). The solution (equation (1.33)), gives quantised values of the energy of the form $E=h\nu_0(n+\tfrac{1}{2})$ where ν_0 has the dimensions of frequency, and n can take one of the values 0, 1, 2, 3, 4, ...

Fig. 7.1 shows the potential energy curve of a linear harmonic oscillator. This curve is identical with that in Fig. 1.10 (p. 26). It is reproduced here for comparison with Fig. 7.2 which represents the experimentally determined potential energy curve of a diatomic molecule. The experimental curve also shows a minimum, but it is not symmetrical. This result is not surprising since there are certain conditions in the molecule which cause the molecular vibration to be anharmonic. For instance, the atomic nuclei cannot come closer together than a certain minimum distance because of Coulomb repulsion. As the atomic nuclei move apart, they are each subject to a restoring force due to the attraction of the electron shells of the other atom. This force, unlike the restoring force characteristic of simple harmonic motion, diminishes with

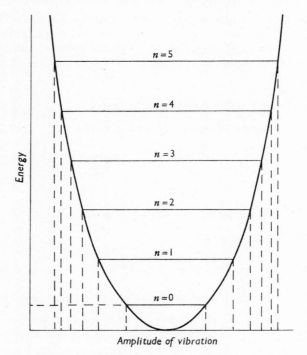

Fig. 7.1. Potential energy curve of a linear harmonic oscillator.

increasing displacement. If the vibration has a large amplitude, a point is reached where the atoms become independent of each other and the molecule is disrupted. With a smaller amplitude of vibration, the restoring force is sufficient to bring the

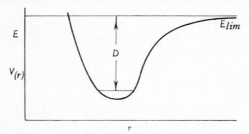

Fig. 7.2. Experimentally determined potential energy curve of a diatomic molecule.

atoms together again. The molecule thus behaves as an anharmonic oscillator. The displacement curve of such an oscillator can be analysed into the superposed displacements (of varying amplitude) of oscillators whose frequencies form a harmonic or Fourier series.

Each energy state of the molecule has its own corresponding potential energy curve. The lowest curve in Fig. 7.3 represents that of the molecule in the ground state; the energy curves of the molecule in excited states lie above it. In all experimentally determined curves, as r increases, the energy increases asymptotically to a value which is constant for each state, and which is indicated in Fig. 7.3 by E_{lim}. The difference between the minimum energy for a particular state, and the value of E_{lim} for that state is the dissociation energy, D, of the molecule in that state. The energy curves plotted from observed spectra show (i) that the equilibrium distance between the nuclei is usually greater for a molecule in an excited state than for a molecule in the ground state, and (ii) that, as a general rule, the more excited the state, the smaller the value of D. In Fig. 7.3 the minima of the three curves lie on the same vertical line. This condition is not generally necessary (p. 214).

Morse potential function. A pseudo-theoretical potential energy curve may be plotted by a method of trial and error. This involves the choice of a potential function which,

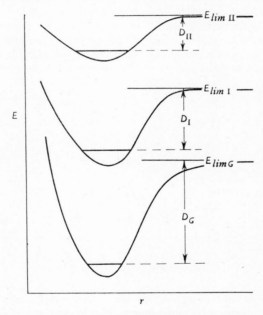

Fig. 7.3. Potential energy curves of a diatomic molecule in the ground state and in excited states.

when plotted, reproduces as nearly as possible the experimental curve. The function chosen must obviously be different from that of a harmonic oscillator. Various expressions for the potential energy have been suggested. One of the first to be put forward was that of Morse. He expressed the potential energy $V(r)$ by the relation

$$V(r) = D_e[1 - e^{-a(r-r_0)}]^2 \qquad (7.1)$$

where $a = 2\pi\nu_0 \sqrt{\dfrac{\mu}{2D_e}}$, $\mu = \dfrac{m_1 m_2}{m_1 + m_2}$, and m_1 and m_2 are the masses of the vibrating particles. ν_0 is the zero point frequency, and $D_e = D + \frac{1}{2}h\nu_0$

Energy of anharmonic oscillator. If, instead of the simple harmonic function, the Morse potential function is substituted for the potential energy in the Schrödinger equation, it is possible, as for the harmonic oscillator, to obtain an expression for the total energy E without solving the equation for ψ.

If D is the dissociation energy of the non-excited molecule, and $\sqrt{(\beta/2\pi^2 I)}$ is written as ν_0, the calculations, which will not be made here, lead to the following expression for the energy of the anharmonic oscillator,[†]

$$E = -D + h\nu_0(v+\tfrac{1}{2}) - \frac{h^2\nu_0^2}{4D}(v+\tfrac{1}{2})^2. \qquad (7.2)$$

Since

$$\beta = \frac{kr_0^2}{2} \quad \text{and} \quad I = \mu r_0^2, \quad (\text{p. 209})$$

$$\nu_0 = \frac{1}{2\pi}\sqrt{\frac{k}{\mu}}. \qquad (7.3)$$

The vibration quantum number v (equation 7.2) takes one of the values 0, 1, 2, 3, ... Since $h\nu_0$ is a constant, by using the Morse function it is possible to construct potential energy curves for different values of v. The energy levels are shown in Fig. 7.4; they become closer and closer together with increasing value of v, and as they approach E_{lim} they become so close together as to be indistinguishable. The curve so obtained approximates closely to those derived from experimental values.

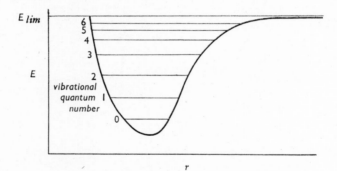

Fig. 7.4.   Morse potential energy curve.

Calculation of dissociation energy. A vibration spectrum can be constructed artificially by taking all the frequencies corresponding to $J=0$ in the rotation vibration spectrum (p. 216). Such a series may be plotted as a line spectrum corresponding to purely vibrational energy changes. It is useful for the following calculation:

If E' is the energy of vibration when the vibration quantum number is v', and E'' is the energy of vibration when the vibration quantum number is v'', and if ν is the frequency of a line in the spectrum equivalent to a change of energy $E' - E''$, then from equation (7.2),

$$\nu = \nu_0(v'-v'') - \frac{h\nu_0^2}{4}\left(\frac{(v'+\tfrac{1}{2})^2}{D'} - \frac{(v''+\tfrac{1}{2})^2}{D''}\right). \qquad (7.4)$$

By observing the frequencies of a number of neighbouring lines, equation (7.4) and others similar to it can be used for the determination of D' and D'', the dissociation energies of the two vibrational states.

[†] ν_0 is sometimes called the natural frequency of the molecular vibration. It should be noted that ν_0 is not the frequency ν of a line in the spectrum.

Selection rule for vibrating diatomic molecule. For the harmonic oscillator the vibration quantum number v can change only by ± 1. For the anharmonic oscillator which resembles the molecule more closely, v can change by ± 1, ± 2, ± 3, ..., but with decreasing probability.

SIMULTANEOUS ELECTRON TRANSITION AND VIBRATION

Franck-Condon Principle. The transition of an electron in a vibrating molecule may be described as a transition from one potential energy curve of wave function ψ_p to another of wave function ψ_q, with a simultaneous change of vibrational quantum number v.

There are no hard and fast vibrational selection rules known to operate when there is simultaneous electron transition and change of vibration. Observation of the spectra produced, and particularly measurement of line intensity, shows that some vibrational changes are preferred to others. Franck and Condon interpreted these relative line intensities in terms of the probability of various transitions. They supposed that the electron transition takes place very rapidly compared with the internuclear vibration, and that transitions are most likely to take place between states for which the nuclei have the same velocity. On p. 30 it was shown that the emission of radiation from an atom can be described as a simultaneous execution of two standing vibrations by the electron in the atom. The expression for the fluctuating charge density is:

$$\rho = \epsilon \psi_p^0 \psi_q^0 {}^* e^{-2\pi i t (v_p - v_q)}.$$

A similar expression can be developed for molecular radiation. This also contains the product of the contributions of the two eigenfunctions involved, $\psi_p^0 \psi_q^0{}^*$, and is a measure of the probability of the transition from state p to state q. Franck and Condon supposed that the most probable transition of an electron from one molecular state to another is a transition from the maximum value of one wave function to the maximum value of the other. The maximum values of the wave functions correspond to positions where there is the greatest probability of finding the atom during a molecular vibration. Such positions will be those in which the atom remains the longest. According to classical mechanics, both for the harmonic and the anharmonic oscillator, an oscillating particle remains longest at the turning point of the oscillation, that is, at the position of greatest displacement. This is also approximately true according to the wave mechanical theory. On the potential energy curve, the different vibrational energy states are marked as energy levels (Fig. 7.4). A molecular vibration may be visualised as taking place from one end of a vibrational energy "level" to the other, within the bounds of the potential energy curve. Therefore, for a given vibrational energy level corresponding to ψ_p^0, the positions where ψ_p^0 has a maximum value are the two points where the vibrational energy level cuts the potential energy curve. Vertical lines drawn between end points of vibrational energy levels on the diagram correspond to most probable transitions. According to wave mechanical theory the end points are not completely sharp, but there is a finite region round each of them where a transition is very likely to take place. An important difference between classical and wave mechanical theory is shown at the lower energy levels. According to the classical view, ψ_{max} occurs at the ends of all the vibration levels, but according to the wave mechanical view, as the energy is reduced, the position for ψ_{max} moves towards the centre of the vibration range, and for the lowest energy level it is located at the centre.

Since the electron transition takes place much more rapidly than the internuclear vibration, it is most probable that the transition occurs while the internuclear distance r_0 remains constant. Spectrum analysis shows, however, that transitions corresponding to a change of internuclear distance can take place, but with less probability.

Fig. 7.5 represents most probable electron transitions from one vibrational level to another in three possible cases:

(a) when the internuclear distance is unchanged,
(b) when excitation loosens the molecular bond,
(c) when excitation tightens the molecular bond.

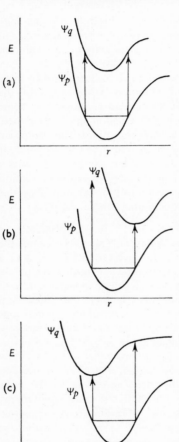

Fig. 7.5. Most probable transitions according to the Franck-Condon principle, (a) when the internuclear distance is unchanged, (b) when excitation loosens the molecular bond, (c) when excitation tightens the molecular bond.

In each case the transitions expected on the Franck-Condon principle are indicated by vertical lines.

By the use of potential energy curves it is possible to estimate the effect of excitation on the dissociation energy. The intensity distribution in the band spectrum is observed, and by means of the Franck-Condon principle the potential energy curves for the ground and excited states are plotted in their correct relative positions on the same diagram. Any change in the form of the curve, in the internuclear distance, and in dissociation energy can be observed on the diagram. Fig. 7.6(a) shows the internuclear distance increased by excitation. Fig. 7.6(b) shows a case where excitation changes the molecule from a stable to an unstable form; the potential energy curve for the excited state here shows no minimum.

The relative positions of the two potential energy curves have an important effect on the type of spectrum observed. There are two extreme cases: (a) When the potential energy curves have minima almost vertically above each other (Fig. 7.5(a)). The most probable transitions from round about the turning points of the vibrations have nearly the same change of energy, and both the emission and absorption spectra consist of groups of narrow bands close together; the spectrum is known as a *group spectrum*. (b) When the potential energy curves are in very different positions and are not "opposite" each other. The emission spectrum is a band sequence corresponding to transitions from the same upper state to different lower states; the absorption spectrum is a band sequence consisting of transitions from the same lower state to different upper states. The spectrum is known as a *band sequence spectrum*; in both emission and absorption the bands are much further spaced apart than in case (a).

The *Franck-Condon Principle* can be summarised as follows:

(1) The most probable transitions occur between vibrational energy states whose wave functions have simultaneous maximum values.

(2) The most probable transitions occur without a change in the nuclear velocity.

(3) The most probable transitions occur without a change of internuclear distance.

When the above conditions cannot be fulfilled other less probable transitions may occur. The probability of a given transition between two vibrational energy states

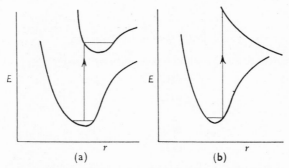

Fig. 7.6. Change in potential energy curve (a) when the internuclear distance is increased by excitation, (b) when excitation causes a change from a stable to an unstable state.

thus depends on the relative positions of the corresponding potential energy curves on the diagram, and the relative range of vibration of the two states considered.

The different types of spectra mentioned on p. 205 will now be discussed for diatomic molecules in order of increasing complexity.

ROTATION SPECTRA OF DIATOMIC MOLECULES

PURE ROTATION SPECTRA

It is possible to observe in the far infrared region an absorption line spectrum which is due to quantised changes of molecular energy of rotation only, without accompanying vibration and electron transition. This spectrum consists of equidistant lines. It is very difficult to observe except by means of microwave spectroscopy (p. 254). For reasons explained on page 206, there is no rotation spectrum for a homonuclear diatomic molecule although such molecules do give rotation lines in the Raman spectrum (p. 252). The following discussion is therefore applicable to the quantised changes of rotation energy of heteronuclear diatomic molecules only.

The diatomic molecule may be assumed to be a rotator with a rigid axis free to move in three dimensions; thus it has the following possible energy values (p. 24):

$$E(\text{rotation}) = hBJ(J+1),$$

where $J = 0, 1, 2, 3, \ldots$, and $B = h/8\pi^2 I$. I is the moment of inertia, μr_0^2, where μ is the reduced mass.

The total angular momentum is represented by the vector quantity **J** compounded from orbital and electron spin momenta and the angular momentum of the molecule about an axis at right angles to the internuclear axis. As in the atom $\mathbf{J} = \sqrt{(J(J+1))}h/2\pi$ where J is the rotation quantum number.

If absorption of energy causes a quantised change in the rotational energy, J changes by $+1$, and if a quantum of energy is emitted, J changes by -1. The selection rule is thus $\Delta J = \pm 1$, and transitions can take place only between neighbouring rotational energy states. The absorption spectrum only is observed for pure rotation. This spectrum corresponds to positive values of J. The relation of the changes in J

to the frequencies corresponding to the lines in the spectrum, and the distance apart of the lines, may be shown in the following manner:
Since

$$J(J+1) = (J+\tfrac{1}{2})^2 - \tfrac{1}{4},$$

and

$$(J+1)(J+2) = (J+\tfrac{3}{2})^2 - \tfrac{1}{4}, \text{ etc.,}$$

therefore, if J changes to $J+1$, radiation is absorbed of frequency ν_1, where,

$$\nu_1 = B((J+\tfrac{3}{2})^2 - (J+\tfrac{1}{2})^2)$$
$$= B(2J+2).$$

Similarly

$$\nu_2 = B((J+\tfrac{5}{2})^2 - (J+\tfrac{3}{2})^2)$$
$$= B(2J+4),$$

and

$$\nu_2 - \nu_1 = 2B. \tag{7.5}$$

Therefore the difference in frequency between the lines is a constant, and the lines appear equally spaced in the spectrum. The spacing is independent of the actual value of J, but the frequencies of the lines depend on J.

By analysis of rotation spectra the possible values of the rotational energy of the molecule may be determined, and the moment of inertia calculated. Since the masses of the component atoms are known this leads to an estimate of the internuclear distance. For the homonuclear molecule these values may be obtained from the rotational Raman spectra, or from the analysis of band spectra caused by simultaneous electron transition, vibration, and rotation, although such spectra are not so easy to analyse as the simple rotation spectrum of a heteronuclear molecule. The effect of an external magnetic field on the rotation spectrum of a diatomic molecule is considered (p. 224) in conjunction with a similar effect on the rotation spectra of linear polyatomic molecules.

ROTATION VIBRATION SPECTRA

The next type of spectrum to be considered in order of increasing complexity is that due to simultaneous changes in the vibrational and rotational energy of the molecule. The rotation vibration spectrum is found in the infrared and may be observed by means of the older spectroscopic methods without recourse to microwave spectroscopy. The spectrum consists of a number of bands composed of approximately equidistant lines. Each band position is determined by the vibration quantum number v, and the position of each line in the band is determined by the quantum number J. In this spectrum, each band consists of two branches corresponding to a pure rotation spectrum. One, the positive or R branch is due to positive changes ($\Delta J = +1$) in positive values of J; the other, the negative or P branch, is due to negative changes ($\Delta J = -1$) in negative values of J. The centre line corresponding to $J=0$ is missing. At first sight it seems odd that lines belonging to an emission spectrum (negative branch) should appear in an absorption spectrum. The reason for this is that both rotational and vibrational changes take place together, and so long as the vibrational energy change is greater than the rotational energy change, the net result will be an absorption of energy because a decrease of rotational energy will be more than offset by the increase in vibrational energy. The rotational changes in the rotation vibration spectrum when v changes to $v+1$ are shown in Fig. 7.7. The R and P branches also appear in an emission rotation vibration spectrum when this can be excited without dissociating the molecule.

If the moment of inertia of the molecule were the same in all rotational states, the bands of the rotation vibration spectrum would consist of lines spaced a distance $2B$ apart as in the pure rotation spectrum. It is found, however, that the distance apart of the lines depends on the vibrational state of the molecule, and it has been concluded that the vibrational and rotational states of the molecule are not completely independent of each other. The energy of the system cannot, therefore, be computed simply by adding the vibrational and rotational energies together. There must also be added a term which contains both v and J. An expression of this type has been developed which predicts a spectrum closely in agreement with that observed experimentally.

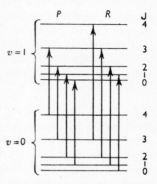

Fig. 7.7. Rotational changes in rotation vibration spectrum when v changes from 0 to 1.

The intensity distribution in each band of the rotation vibration spectrum shows that the intensity in each branch rises to a maximum and then falls (Fig. 7.8). The maximum intensity of the band as a whole corresponds to a maximum change of dipole moment with a small change of r. The absolute value of the dipole moment must obviously vary with the distance between the atoms in the molecule. If the atoms were pushed closer and closer together they would eventually coincide and form a single atom with no dipole moment. If they were moved further and further apart, they would eventually become separate atoms, and there would be no molecule and no

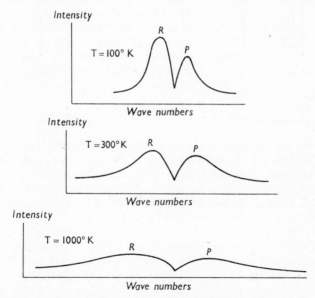

Fig. 7.8. Intensity distribution in P and R branches of rotation vibration bands at 100°K, 300°K, and 1000°K (after Herzberg).

dipole moment. Therefore, if a curve is plotted of dipole moment against internuclear distance, there is a certain position of the atoms which corresponds to a maximum dipole moment. At internuclear distances where the dipole moments are large, a change of vibration or rotation state gives a greater value of $d\mu/dr$ than that produced at internuclear distances where the dipole moments are small.

Experimental determination of potential energy curves. Potential energy curves may be plotted from information derived from the rotation vibration spectrum. The moment of inertia, and thus the internuclear distance, can be calculated from the rotation structure of each band corresponding to a vibration state. The corresponding energies can be calculated from equations (7.2) and (7.4) (p. 212) by observation of a number of neighbouring bands. With the help of microwave technique, it is now customary first to derive all information possible from the analysis of the far infrared pure rotation spectrum.

BAND SPECTRA

Band spectra are due to electron transitions accompanied by changes of vibration and rotation. They are more easily observed than the pure rotation and rotation vibration spectra since they occur in the photographic infrared, visible, and ultraviolet regions. They are, however, more complicated and therefore more difficult to analyse. These spectra consist of a number of clearly separated *band systems* (p. 206). The position of a line in a band is determined by a change of rotation quantum number; the position of the band in the band system is determined by a simultaneous change of vibration quantum number, the position of the band system in the whole spectrum is determined by an electron transition. The absolute position of any line in the spectrum is therefore due to the superposition of three simultaneous energy changes. In the analysis of band spectra it is convenient to designate the position of a line by its wave number $\bar{\nu}$ which is simply related to the energy by equation (3.1), p. 72:

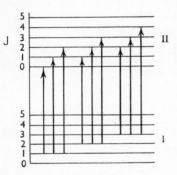

Fig. 7.9. Different rotational sequences belonging to two different molecular states I and II.

$$\bar{\nu} = \frac{E}{hc}.$$

It is seen from the potential energy curves in Fig. 7.3 (p. 211) that the internuclear distance, and therefore the moment of inertia of the molecule, is considerably altered by electron transition. That the binding forces are also changed is shown by the different depths of the potential minima in the curves belonging to the different molecular states. Different molecular states have different sequences of both rotational and vibrational states which causes considerable complication in the actual band analysis and identification of the lines. Fig. 7.9 shows diagrammatically the two different rotational sequences belonging to two different molecular states, *I* and *II*. Assuming that there is no vibrational change, if electron transition and rotational change take place together, a change of rotational quantum number is a change from a rotational level in state *I* to a different rotational level in state *II*. The selection rule for such a change is $\Delta J = 0, \pm 1$. The ± 1 changes give rise to P and R branches in the spectrum similar to those of the rotation vibration spectra. In addition there may be a Q branch which corresponds to $\Delta J = 0$. The reason for the appearance of this branch is that in general an electron transition always causes a change of dipole moment in a molecule; this is an essential condition for the emission of radiation. It is therefore possible to obtain a change of dipole moment even if there is no change of rotational quantum number. With the pure rotation and rotation vibration spectra, unless J changes, there is no emission of radiation, since, with a few exceptions, a change of vibration quantum number does not alter the dipole moment. Band spectra in the visible and ultraviolet regions are therefore shown by all diatomic molecules, even by homonuclear ones such as H_2, O_2, N_2, which do not give rotation vibration or pure rotation spectra owing to the symmetrical distribution of charge in the molecule (p. 206). Plates 9 and 10 show parts of the band spectra of hydrogen and the helium molecule ion He_2^+.

An electron transition accompanied by a simultaneous change of vibration and rotation quantum numbers can be represented by a diagram such as Fig. 7.10. The diagram represents two orbital states of the molecule, ψ_p and ψ_q, each of which is subdivided into vibration states, and the vibration states are again subdivided into rotation states. The transition depicted is from state ψ_p to state ψ_q. It is accompanied by a change of vibrational quantum number from $v_p = 2$ to $v_q = 3$, and of rotational quantum number from $J_p = 6$ to $J_q = 5$. There would of course be other possible changes of vibration quantum number, each of which would be associated with rotational changes such as are shown diagrammatically in Fig. 7.10.

Fortrat diagram. From the expression for the energy of the rigid rotator (p. 215)

$$E = hBJ(J+1). \qquad (7.6)$$

If it is assumed that the total energy change from a state of energy E' (with vibration and rotation quantum numbers v' and J') to a state of energy E'' (with vibration and rotation quantum numbers v'' and J'') is the sum of the energy changes due to electron transition, change of

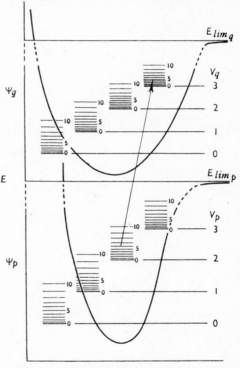

Fig. 7.10. Simultaneous change of electron state, vibration and rotation.

vibration quantum number, and change of rotation quantum number, neglecting any variation of the moment of inertia of the molecule, then

$$\bar{\nu} = \bar{\nu}^* + \frac{B_{v'}}{c}J'(J'+1) - \frac{B_{v''}}{c}J''(J''+1), \qquad (7.7)$$

where $\bar{\nu}$ is the wave number of the line emitted, and where $\bar{\nu}^*$ is the wave number corresponding to the energy changes due to electron transition and change of vibration quantum number only.

Using this approximation, Fortrat devised an ingenious method for sorting out the observed lines in the spectrum of a diatomic molecule. A graph is plotted, with the wave numbers of observed lines as abscissae, and values of J' as ordinates (Fig. 7.11(a)). Three parabolas are obtained, which correspond to the P, Q, and R branches. The value of $\bar{\nu}^*$ can be obtained from the point where the Q branch cuts the horizontal axis. The point $J=0$ is missing from the P and R branches. In certain cases such as singlet molecular states with angular momentum about the internuclear axis, the minimum value of J is not 0 but Λ. The value of $\bar{\nu}^*$ can then be found by extrapolation of the Q branch.

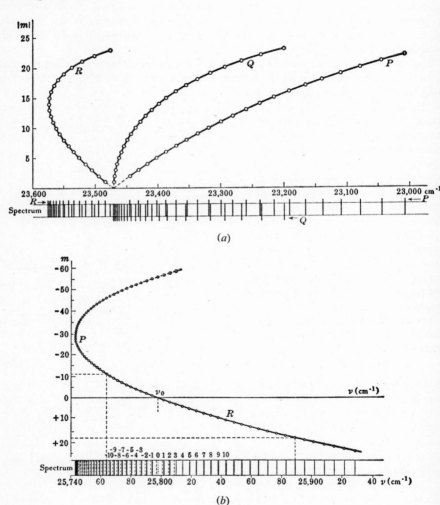

Fig. 7.11. (a) Fortrat diagram of the AlH band 4241 Å (after Herzberg). The schematic spectrum below is drawn to the same scale as the parabolas above; the lines of the P and R branches (with the exception of the lines of the returning limb of the R branch) are shown extended above, and those of the Q branch below the schematic spectrum. For the R branch, $m=J+1$; for the P branch $m=-J$ (see G. Herzberg, Spectra of Diatomic Molecules, p. 112) (b) Fortrat parabola of the CN band 3883 Å (after Herzberg). Here, positive values of m are plotted below and negative values above the zero line. (The relation between curve and spectrum is indicated by broken lines for two points ($m=-11$ and $m=+18$.) No line is observed at $m=0$, and there is no Q branch.)

In cases where there is no change of electronic state as in a Σ to Σ change, there is no Q branch, as there is no change of dipole moment unless J changes. The value of $\bar{\nu}^*$ can then be calculated from the rotation vibration spectrum.

Much information may be obtained from Fortrat diagrams. The "shading" (head) of the band is first easily determined by inspection. The position of the apparent head of the band is seen to depend on the orientation of the parabolas. This orientation depends on the relative values of B_v' and B_v'', that is on whether the moment of inertia is greater in the one or the other vibration state. Fig. 7.11(b) shows the band "shaded" towards the violet, the P parabola forming the edge, $(B_v' > B_v'')$, and Fig. 7.11(a) shows the band "shaded" towards the red,† the R parabola forming the edge $(B_v' < B_v'')$. In cases where the moment of inertia is identical in the two vibration states the parabolas open out and become practically straight lines with no apparent band head, the Q branch being almost vertical. Such a simplified diagram would be obtained by applying the same procedure to a rotation vibration spectrum.

An inspection of the Fortrat diagram is sufficient to determine whether the moment of inertia and the internuclear distance are greater in the upper or lower vibration state. An appropriate Fortrat diagram can be drawn for each band in each band system. Complete analysis of each band gives all information as to the moment of inertia and internuclear distance in the different vibration and rotation states.

EFFECTS WHICH MODIFY SIMPLE RELATIONS IN BAND SYSTEMS

Band spectra are complicated for several reasons of which the following are important:

Magnetic field due to rotation of the molecule as a whole. The frequency of a line in the band has been shown to depend on the quantum number J (p. 216) which describes the quantised total angular momentum of the molecule. The total angular momentum is derived as a result of the vectorial combination of angular momentum due to orbital and electron spin motion and angular momentum of the molecule about an axis at right angles to the internuclear axis. Not only does a change of molecular state cause a change of electron orbital motion, but the rotation of the whole molecule causes a magnetic field which varies with increasing rotation, and couples with the spin. Hund has shown that this effect accounts for various distortions of the Fortrat diagrams and for some missing lines.

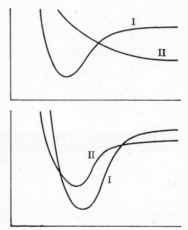

Fig. 7.12. Crossing of potential energy curves.

Effects due to isotopes. The presence of more than one isotope causes a multiplication or splitting of the parabolas of the Fortrat diagram. Even if two isotopes are in the same molecular state and have the same vibration quantum numbers, their parabolas will not be superposed, as their moments of inertia will be different owing to the difference of their masses.

Predissociation. In the spectrum of some diatomic molecules, diffuse bands are observed in a normal band sequence. These have been ascribed to *predissociation*, that is to the dissociation of the molecule by a transition which is not accompanied by radiation. It is possible for this process to take place when there is crossing of the two potential energy curves corresponding to two different electronic states (Fig. 7.12). In the region of the crossing, an electron in state *I* can change to state *II* without emission

---

† The expression "degraded to the red" is frequently used. This means that the tail and not the head of the band is in the red direction.

or absorption of energy. In so doing it leaves the region of quantised energy changes belonging to state *I* and enters the region above the curve of state *II*, that is into the region of continuous energy changes which are shown as a continuous spectrum. The effect is enhanced by the extreme rapidity of a non-radiative change of state. Owing to the uncertainty principle if the molecule changes very rapidly from one state to the other and possibly back again there will be a resulting "blurring" of the sharpness of the energy associated with each state.

Since

$$\Delta E \, \Delta t \sim h$$

$$h \, \Delta \nu \, \Delta t \sim h$$

$$\Delta \nu \, \Delta t \sim 1$$

Δt may be termed the "lifetime" of the given state. If Δt is very small, $\Delta \nu$ is large.

If the energy of a bonding state is very near that of an antibonding state (p. 118), it

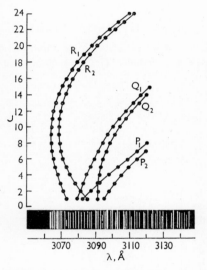

Fig. 7.13. Portion of the OH spectrum emitted by a discharge lamp. The Fortrat diagram shows doublet splitting due to spin. (After Bauer, Schott, and Duff.)

may be possible for the molecule to change from one state to the other without emission or absorption of radiation. If the molecule passes from the bonding to the antibonding state, it may be that the latter, although a higher energy state, has a lower energy E_{lim}, above which dissociation occurs, and the molecule will therefore dissociate on passing to the antibonding state. This theory is supported by the fact that dissociation does take place when the molecule is irradiated by radiation whose wave length is that of the diffuse band. Predissociation is commonly shown only in absorption, not in emission.

Formation of multiplets. In addition to the isotope effect, the *P*, *Q*, and *R* branches can all show multiplet structure. The law is the same as for atomic multiplets (p. 92): Multiplicity $= 2S + 1$. A multiplicity of 2 is shown in the Fortrat diagram (Fig. 7.13). The origin of the singlet and triplet term systems has been discussed (p. 174) with reference to diatomic molecules. Two explanations were put forward, that of the valence bond theory and that of the molecular orbital theory. The valence bond explanation appears to be the more satisfactory in application to the theory of multiplets. According to this explanation, in the triplet system each term consists of three energy states close together, all of which have the same space function but each of which has a different spin function. Transitions to or from multiple energy states lead to multiplicity of what would otherwise be single lines in the spectrum.

Hyperfine structure and nuclear spin. For the purpose of simplicity in exposition, nuclear spin has so far been omitted from the discussion on the angular momentum of the molecule. For a complete description of the molecule the angular momentum of the nucleus must be included in the vectorial addition from which the total angular momentum of the molecule is derived. The presence of nuclear spin does not affect the position of the lines and bands hitherto discussed, but shows itself as a very fine splitting of the lines. This hyperfine splitting is due to the alternative ways in which the spins of the two nuclei can be coupled. The spin of a nucleus depends on the structure of the nucleus. The nuclear spin of the hydrogen atom (of which the nucleus is a single proton) is $\pm\frac{1}{2}$, therefore the total nuclear spin for the hydrogen molecule is either 0, or 1. Since there are three different ways in which spin 1 can be combined vectorially with J (cf. p. 92), it might be expected that two forms of molecule would be found in hydrogen gas, one form of which would occur statistically three times as often as the other; this expectation has been fulfilled. It can further be shown that molecules with parallel nuclear spins (orthohydrogen) have rotational energy states corresponding only to odd numbers of J,† while those with antiparallel nuclear spins (parahydrogen) have rotational energy states corresponding only to even numbers of J. It can be seen from analysis of the spectrum that transitions to states with odd numbers of J show a triple energy splitting owing to the three ways of coupling the nuclear spin 1 with J. The multiplicity rule holds for nuclear spin

$$\text{Multiplicity} = 2S + 1.$$

As with electron spin, there are three possible symmetric nuclear spin functions and one antisymmetric nuclear spin function. A further discussion on the chemical and physical properties of ortho- and para-hydrogen will be found on p. 368.

Owing to the small moment of inertia of hydrogen, the hyperfine structure is not resolved in the spectrum but shows itself by the variation of intensity of alternate lines, every other line is approximately three times as intense as those on either side of it. As there is no pure rotation spectrum for homonuclear diatomic molecules, the hyperfine structure of their molecular spectra must be studied in connection with the Raman effect (p. 249), or with band spectra due to simultaneous electron transition, vibration, and rotation.

A further hyperfine splitting has been observed due to the asymmetric distribution of charge in the nucleus. This asymmetry is described as the *electric quadrupole moment* of the nucleus; the coupling between the nuclear quadrupole moment and the electric field due to the nuclei and electrons shows itself both as the splitting of a rotation structure for heteronuclear diatomic molecules, and as a faint pure quadrupole spectrum in the radio frequency region for homonuclear and heteronuclear diatomic molecules. Its study provides much useful information about the structure of the nucleus (p. 268).

Intensity of band spectra. The intensity of band spectra may be interpreted in terms of the Franck-Condon principle. The intensity distribution shows the preferred transitions, a study of which gives information about the vibration states of the molecule. This information, combined with that derived from the rotation spectrum, is sufficient to determine the degree of anharmonicity of the molecular vibration and so it is possible to evaluate the force constants (p. 2) of any two combining molecular states. It should, however, be noted that the intensity distribution is dependent on the temperature, and for an accurate determination of molecular constants it is necessary to have thermal equilibrium. On the other hand, if the molecular constants are known, the intensity distribution in the spectrum may be used as a sensitive method of measuring high temperatures such as those of electric arc discharges.

---

† The spatial symmetry of the molecule is influenced by the nuclear spin, and this is reflected in the absence of alternate values of J for a particular value of resultant spin. A complete explanation of the relation between spin and hyperfine structure can be given in terms of group theory which is beyond the scope of this book.

EFFECT OF AN EXTERNAL MAGNETIC FIELD ON THE MOLECULAR ROTATION SPECTRA OF DIATOMIC MOLECULES

The molecule has so far been discussed without reference to its orientation in space. If it has a resulting magnetic moment, and is subject to a directing agent such as a

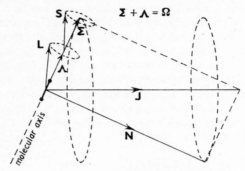

No external magnetic field

Fig. 7.14.   Hund's case (a).

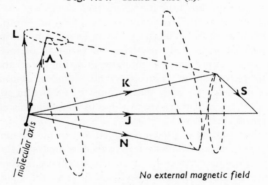

No external magnetic field

Fig. 7.15.   Hund's case (b).

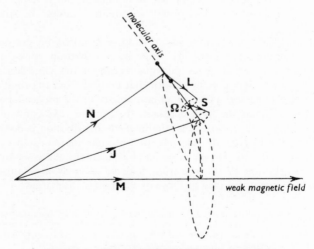

Fig. 7.16.   Zeeman effect for Hund's case (a).

weak external magnetic field, the component of total angular momentum is quantised in the direction of the field and the lines are split. The effect will be discussed only for two relatively simple couplings; these couplings are found in both diatomic and linear polyatomic molecules. They are known as Hund's cases (a) and (b). There are other

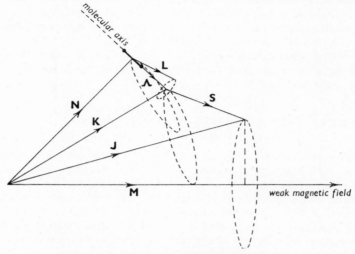

Fig. 7.17. Zeeman effect for Hund's case (b).

couplings but these are the most usual. Even these represent extreme cases and various intermediate couplings are found in practice. All couplings described are magnetic.

Absence of external magnetic field. (a) The molecular axis is associated with a sufficiently strong magnetic field to couple the orbital and spin momenta to it. The

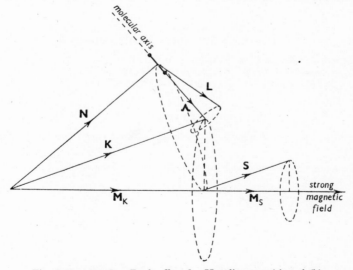

Fig. 7.18. Paschen-Back effect for Hund's cases (a) and (b).

total electronic angular momentum Ω about the molecular axis is the sum of the components of orbital and spin angular momenta $\Omega = \Lambda + \Sigma$ (Fig. 7.14).

8 + A.T.I.C.

(b) The field associated with the molecular axis is not strong enough to couple the spin. Λ (p. 207) combines vectorially with N† to give K, the resultant angular momentum apart from spin. S combines vectorially with K to give J, the total angular momentum (Fig. 7.15).

Presence of external magnetic field. *Zeeman effect* (weak magnetic field). (a) Ω and N precess round J, and J precesses round the direction of the field (Fig. 7.16). M is the quantised component of J. (b) Λ and N precess round K, K and S precess round J, J precesses round the direction of the field (Fig. 7.17).

Paschen-Back effect (strong magnetic field). (a) and (b) K and S are not coupled together but are coupled directly to the field. K and S precess separately round the direction of the field (Fig. 7.18).

EFFECT OF EXTERNAL ELECTRIC FIELD ON THE ROTATION SPECTRA OF LINEAR MOLECULES. STARK EFFECT

The rotation of a diatomic or linear polyatomic molecule can take place only about an axis at right angles to the molecular axis. Since the axis of the electric dipole moment, if any, is the molecular axis, there is no component of the dipole moment in the direction of the angular momentum vector, and therefore the application of an external electric field has no effect on the direction of the angular momentum vector. Since the molecular axis containing the permanent dipole moment is rotating in a plane containing a component of the field, any effect of the field on the permanent dipole moment averages to zero.

Linear molecules therefore show no *first order Stark effect*. The applied electric field, however, induces a small dipole moment which has a component in the direction of the resultant angular momentum vector, and a small splitting results. This is known as the *second order Stark effect*; it cannot be detected except in the absence of the first order effect. The Stark effect is conveniently observed by means of microwave spectra, and is of great importance in the determination of molecular dipole moments (p. 308).

BOOKS FOR FURTHER READING

FINKELNBURG, W., *Atomic Physics* (McGraw Hill, 1950).
HERZBERG, G., *Spectra of Diatomic Molecules* (Van Nostrand, 1950).
JOHNSON, R. C., *Introduction to Molecular Spectra* (Methuen, 1949).

REVIEWS

CONDON, E. U., *The Franck-Condon Principle and Related Topics* (*Am. J. Phys.*, **15**, 1947, 365–74).

† The interaction between rotational and orbital angular momentum gives rise to what is known as Λ doubling when $\Lambda \neq 0$.

CHAPTER EIGHT

MOLECULAR SPECTRA (2)

THE SPECTRA OF POLYATOMIC MOLECULES

The analysis of the spectra of polyatomic molecules is a stupendous task, and requires a rather different method of approach from that adopted in the case of diatomic spectra. Nevertheless, the principles governing the production of spectra remain the same, and the spectra of polyatomic molecules may therefore be regarded as elaborate variations on the diatomic theme. The assumption that the spectrum of a polyatomic molecule, in common with that of the diatomic molecule, is due to changes of vibration, rotation, and electron transition, occurring separately or together, seems to be well justified. It is also reasonable to suppose that the vibration of a polyatomic molecule could be analysed into a number of superposed harmonic oscillations of its component parts.

For the determination of the structure of a polyatomic molecule it is necessary to know something of the geometrical and spatial arrangement of the atoms with regard to each other. With this purpose in view, one of the chief aims of the spectroscopist has been to use the observed spectrum to determine what is known as the "symmetry" of the molecule. The complexity of the molecular spectrum is such, however, that it would be impossible by sheer codification of the line positions to argue back to a possible geometrical shape for the molecule. A much more fruitful line of attack has been the approach from the other end of the problem. The method consists of the following three stages:

(1) A theoretical consideration of all the possible configurations which a given molecule might assume.

(2) A calculation of the number of possible vibrations and rotations associated with each possible configuration.

(3) The selection of the correct configuration by correlation with the actual vibrations and rotations of the molecule deduced from observed spectra. This is not an easy operation, since allowance must be made for many disturbing factors, but in most cases, with the aid of chemical evidence, a good guess can be made as to the most likely molecular configuration, and confirmation of this assumption may be obtained by observation of the actual spectrum.

These three stages in the analysis of molecular spectra will now be considered in further detail.

THE SYMMETRY OF MOLECULES

The possible groupings of atoms in a molecule may be considered as abstract geometrical arrangements. Such arrangements can be distinguished from each other by their so-called *symmetry properties*. It is not really necessary to imagine the geometrical arrangement as containing anything but points and lines, but the significance of the symmetry properties of a figure as applied to molecular configuration cannot be appreciated until the points are replaced by the atoms of which the molecule is composed. Group theory is used extensively as a short cut to the determination of the symmetry properties of any given molecular configuration. The theory deals with the purely abstract manipulation of imaginary figures and the effect on their symmetry properties of all possible manoeuvres. It is of great assistance to have all these worked out and tabulated, so that the results may be directly applied to the choice of a possible molecular configuration. To appreciate the significance of this method it is first necessary to give a brief summary of the meaning of some of the terms commonly encountered in a discussion of this nature.

Symmetry elements. It is possible for a molecule to have one or more of the following:

(a) A plane of symmetry.
(b) An axis of symmetry.
(c) A symmetry point or centre of symmetry.

Such properties are known as *symmetry elements*; there are others, but the three listed above are the most important.

Plane of symmetry. If a molecule has a plane of symmetry, the half of the molecule on one side of the plane is the mirror image of the other half, and a complete interchange of pairs of atoms from one half to the other results in a configuration which cannot be distinguished from the original.

Axis of symmetry. If a molecule has an axis of symmetry, such an axis may be 2-fold, 3-fold, 4-fold, etc. For instance, if it is 2-fold, a rotation of $2\pi/2$ brings it into a configuration which cannot be distinguished from the original. The same result is achieved by a rotation of $2\pi/3$ in the case of a 3-fold axis, and a rotation of $2\pi/4$ in the case of a 4-fold axis.

Symmetry point. If a molecule has a symmetry point, a straight line drawn from any atom in the molecule and passing through the symmetry point will subsequently pass through an identical atom at an equal distance on the other side of the molecule.

It is convenient to divide molecules into groups which have certain symmetry elements in common. Not all combinations of symmetry elements are possible; for instance, a single 3-fold axis and a single 4-fold axis are incompatible; no molecule could have both. This kind of consideration imposes some limits on the number and constitution of the possible symmetry groups. The presence of some symmetry elements inevitably implies the presence of others; for instance, the intersection of two planes of symmetry is an axis of symmetry.

Symmetry operations and groups. An operation, such as a rotation about an axis or a reflection at a plane, which produces a configuration indistinguishable from the original is said to be a *symmetry operation*; a whole set of such operations would be recognised by a mathematician as a *group*. It should be noted that a symmetry operation is a purely imaginary process analogous to the manipulation of the figures of pure geometry. The symmetry groups are also entirely abstract concepts. They are distinguished from each other by a special nomenclature which will not be explained here. Tables of groups with their nomenclature and particular symmetry properties can be found in textbooks on group theory.

The relative positions of the atoms in a given molecule determine the number of symmetry operations which may be notionally carried out on it. The number and type of these operations may be determined from the spectrum of the molecule, and thus the positions of the atoms may be deduced with the aid of group theory. The groups into which different molecules may be divided according to their symmetry properties are known as point groups.

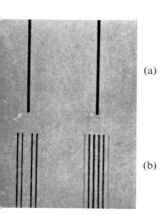

(a)

(b)

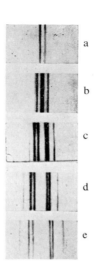

a

b

c

d

e

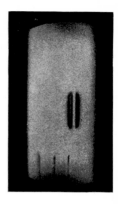

6. Anomalous Zeeman splitting of Na D-lines: without magnetic field, with magnetic field. [Back d Landé, *Zeemaneffekt und ultiplettstruktur der Spektrallinien*, 1925.]

Pl. 7. Paschen-Back effect for the beryllium doublet ^{2}S-^{2}P, showing splitting of the doublet in increasing fields. [Kapitza, Shelkov and Laurman, *Proc. roy. Soc.* **A, 167,** 1938.]

Pl. 8. Stern Gerlach effect: splitting of a beam of lithium atoms in a non-homogeneous magnetic field. [After Taylor.]

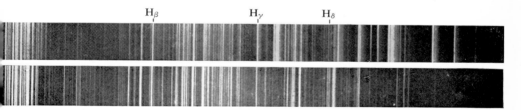

H_β H_γ H_δ

9. Part of the hydrogen band spectrum at 300° (above) and at 85° (below). [McLennan, Smith and Lea, *Proc. roy. Soc.* **A, 113,** 1926.]

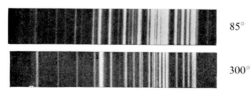

85°

300°

Pl. 10. Helium band 3680 Å showing fine structure. [McLennan, Smith and Lea, *Proc. roy. Soc.* **A, 113,** 1926]

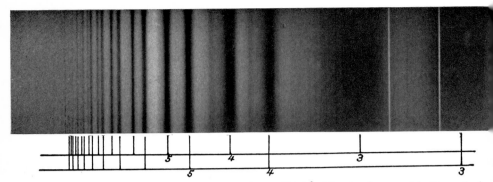

Pl. 11. Rydberg absorption series of CS_2 converging to 856·5 Å. [Tanaka, Jursa and LeBlanc, *J. che Phys.*, **28**, 1958.]

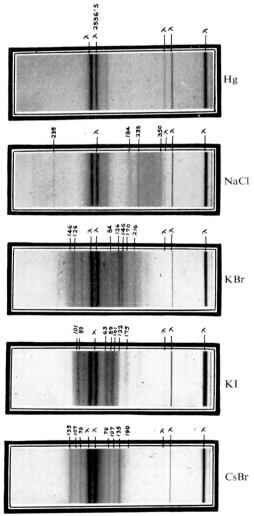

Pl. 12. Raman spectra of alkali halides. Figures indicate frequency shifts in cm.$^{-1}$ Exciting Radiation Hg λ 2536·5 Å. Other mercury lines are marked λ. [Krishnan and Narayanan.]

VIBRATIONS OF POLYATOMIC MOLECULES

Normal vibrations. The molecular vibration of a polyatomic molecule is the resultant of the vibrations of all the atoms of which the molecule is composed. The motion of an atom is considered to be that of the nucleus, and it is assumed that the nuclei move in straight lines with simple harmonic motion. The molecular vibration may be simple, or it may be complex with continually changing form. A molecule is said to have a *normal mode of vibration* when all its component atoms oscillate harmonically with the same frequency and in the same phase. The oscillations of different atoms may, however, differ in amplitude, but since the frequencies of vibration are the same, and they are in the same phase, the atoms reach their position of maximum displacement at the same moment, and also pass through their undisplaced

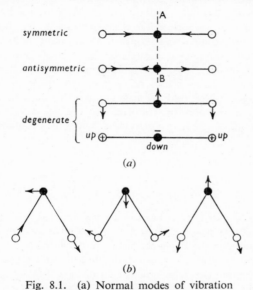

Fig. 8.1. (a) Normal modes of vibration of a linear triatomic molecule XY_2. The number of vibrational degrees of freedom
  $= 3N-5$
  $= 4$, where N is the number of particles.
(b) Normal modes of vibration of a bent triatomic molecule XY_2. The number of vibrational degrees of freedom $= 3N-6$
  $= 3$.

positions simultaneously. There may be several normal vibrations of different frequencies characteristic of a given molecule. If two or more normal vibrations are superposed, the result is not in general a normal vibration. If, as happens in some cases, several normal vibrations have the same frequency, they are said to be *degenerate normal vibrations*. For instance, if two normal vibrations have the same frequency, they are said to be *doubly degenerate*. The number of normal vibrations, degenerate and non-degenerate, has been calculated in detail for different symmetry groups. Fig. 8.1 shows the normal modes of vibration of linear and bent triatomic molecules XY_2.

Degrees of freedom. A degree of freedom may be defined as the motion of a smooth particle which may be stopped mechanically. For instance, a smooth sphere has three translational degrees of freedom but no degrees of rotational freedom since, if it is perfectly smooth, there is no means of telling whether it is rotating or not. A smooth circular plate has three translational and two rotational degrees of freedom.

It is necessary to have 3 co-ordinates to describe the position of a single particle at any moment, and so if it is in motion, 3 co-ordinates are necessary to describe this motion. The particle has three degrees of freedom, and its motion may be resolved into three components. If there are N particles, $3N$ co-ordinates are necessary to describe their motion, and the whole system has $3N$ degrees of freedom. Therefore a molecule with N atoms in it has $3N$ degrees of freedom. Of these, 3 are concerned with the translation of the molecule as a whole, and 3 with the rotation of the molecule as a whole. The number of vibrational degrees of freedom is therefore $3N-6$. For a linear molecule, the number of vibrational degrees of freedom is $3N-5$ since the linear molecule has only two rotational degrees of freedom.†

Frequency of normal vibration. A body moving with simple harmonic motion is subject to a restoring force proportional to the displacement. This force may be written $-ky$ where y is the displacement and k is the force constant (p. 2).

In the molecule, the displacement of any atom due to the vibration can be described in terms of the co-ordinates x_1, y_1, z_1. The restoring force which causes the atom to return to its undisplaced position may be resolved into three parts along the x, y, z axes. In the most general case, each of these components must be described in terms of the three displacements, since the restoring force in one direction may be affected by the displacements in the other two directions. The three components may therefore be written

$$F_x{}^1 = -k_{xx}{}^{11}x_1 - k_{xy}{}^{11}y_1 - k_{xz}{}^{11}z_1$$
$$F_y{}^1 = -k_{yx}{}^{11}x_1 - k_{yy}{}^{11}y_1 - k_{yz}{}^{11}z_1$$
$$F_z{}^1 = -k_{zx}{}^{11}x_1 - k_{zy}{}^{11}y_1 - k_{zz}{}^{11}z_1$$

where the k's are force constants. It has so far been assumed that the atom considered is the only one which is moving. In fact they are all moving, and terms must be introduced to account for the dependence of the displacement of one atom on the displacements of the others. It is assumed throughout that the displacements are small, and so all the equations can take a linear form. The full set of equations‡ may therefore be written

$$F_x{}^1 = -k_{xx}{}^{11}x_1 - k_{xy}{}^{11}y_1 - k_{xz}{}^{11}z_1 - k_{xx}{}^{12}x_2 - k_{xy}{}^{12}y_2 - k_{xz}{}^{12}z_2 - \cdots - k_{xz}{}^{1N}z_N$$
$$F_y{}^1 = -k_{yx}{}^{11}x_1 - k_{yy}{}^{11}y_1 - k_{yz}{}^{11}z_1 - k_{yx}{}^{12}x_2 - k_{yy}{}^{12}y_2 - k_{yz}{}^{12}z_2 - \cdots - k_{yz}{}^{1N}z_N$$
$$F_z{}^1 = -k_{zx}{}^{11}x_1 - k_{zy}{}^{11}y_1 - k_{zz}{}^{11}z_1 - k_{zx}{}^{12}x_2 - k_{zy}{}^{12}y_2 - k_{zz}{}^{12}z_2 - \cdots - k_{zz}{}^{1N}z_N$$

$$\cdots\cdots\cdots\cdots\cdots\cdots\cdots\cdots\cdots\cdots\cdots\cdots\cdots\cdots\cdots\cdots\cdots\cdots\cdots\cdots\cdots$$

$$F_z{}^N = -k_{zx}{}^{N1}x_1 - k_{zy}{}^{N1}y_1 - k_{zz}{}^{N1}z_1 - k_{zx}{}^{N2}x_2 - k_{zy}{}^{N2}y_2 - k_{zz}{}^{N2}z_2 - \cdots - k_{zz}{}^{NN}z_N$$

$$\text{(8.1)}$$

Since there are N particles, there are $3N$ equations, with $3N$ unknown quantities (the displacements). If the equations are combined, an equation of the $3N$th order will be obtained. If this equation is solved for ν the common frequency, $3N$ possible values for ν will be found.§ The molecule, therefore, has $3N$ possible normal vibrations.

---

† The term *degree of freedom* has two other meanings which have no connection with that defined in the above paragraph:
  (i) it is used to indicate the total number of parameters (or "square terms") upon which the energy of a single particle depends,
  (ii) it is used to indicate the number of variables which can be changed without destroying the nature of a system in equilibrium described by the phase rule.
It is an unfortunate accident that the title "degree of freedom" describes three unrelated quantities.
‡ E. Teller, *Hand-und Jahr. d. Chem. Phys.*, **9**, II, 1934, 43.
§ ($F_x{}^1 = 4\pi^2\nu^2 m_1 x_1$, etc.)

A closer examination of the equations by more rigorous mathematical methods shows that six of the possible roots are equal to zero (five for a linear molecule). These correspond to the translational and rotational motions of the molecule and are called *non-genuine vibrations*. It is therefore concluded that (i) the number of genuine normal vibrations is equal to the number of degrees of freedom of vibration, and (ii) since these normal vibrations correspond to all the possible values of v, that any vibrational motion of the molecule can be analysed into a number of superposed normal vibrations.

Co-ordinates of vibration. The displacement of a particle executing a normal vibration is commonly described in terms of the so-called *normal co-ordinates* x, y, z. These represent periodic variations of the Cartesian co-ordinates x_0, y_0, z_0, where

$$x = x_0 \cos 2\pi v_x t$$
$$y = y_0 \cos 2\pi v_y t$$
$$z = z_0 \cos 2\pi v_z t.$$

If the equations containing the force constants are expressed in terms of Cartesian co-ordinates, they are considerably complicated because the displacements of the particles are not all measured from a common point of origin, the displacement of each particle being referred to its equilibrium position. In order to rectify this trouble, both Cartesian and normal co-ordinates are referred to points and angles in the molecule itself, the translational and rotational motions of the molecule as a whole being thus neglected. The co-ordinates of such a system are known as *internal co-ordinates*.

Symmetric and antisymmetric vibrations. Suppose a symmetry operation to be performed on a molecule while it is vibrating. If the vibration remains unchanged by the operation it is said to be *symmetric* to this symmetry operation. A normal vibration which is symmetric to all possible symmetry operations is said to be a *totally symmetric normal vibration*.

If the symmetry operation changes the normal vibration to one in the opposite position with regard to the plane, axis, or point of symmetry about which the operation takes place (in effect this means changing the sign of the displacements of the vibration), the normal vibration is said to be *antisymmetric* to the symmetry operation. If AB is a plane of symmetry, Fig. 8.1(a) shows a normal vibration which is symmetric to the symmetry operation of reflection at AB, and a normal vibration which is antisymmetric to the symmetry operation of reflection at AB.

Effect of a symmetry operation on normal vibrations. A symmetry operation in the molecule may theoretically have one of the following results:

(a) The normal vibration may remain unchanged.

(b) The displacements of the normal vibration may change their sign.

(c) The normal vibration may be changed into another vibration.

If a normal vibration is *non-degenerate*, a symmetry operation results only in a symmetric or antisymmetric change of co-ordinates, but *degenerate vibrations* can also combine linearly in various proportions, resulting in a new vibration. Thus condition (c) applies to degenerate vibrations only. The number of degenerate vibrations depends on the symmetry elements of the particular molecule. For instance, doubly degenerate vibrations are always present if the molecule has a 3-fold axis of symmetry.

The possible normal vibrations which are associated with particular molecular groups (each group representing a special combination of symmetry elements) are classified according to their symmetry properties into different *symmetry types* or *symmetry species* which are denoted by certain letters and numerals. For instance, every molecule has some totally symmetric normal vibrations. These are labelled A, or A_1, or A^1.

Effect of symmetry operations on the vibrational wave function. The vibrational wave function is a function of the potential energy and can be expressed in terms of normal co-ordinates. The potential energy of the system obviously remains the same during a symmetry operation, and so is said to be *invariant to symmetry operations*. The wave function therefore responds to symmetry operations in the way that the normal co-ordinates do; its magnitude does not change during a symmetry operation and it also is said to be invariant to symmetry operations. If the wave function represents a non-degenerate vibration it can only be symmetric or antisymmetric to a symmetry operation. If it represents a degenerate state it can be symmetric or antisymmetric to a symmetry operation, but there is a further possibility that the symmetry operation may transform it to another wave function formed by the linear combination of degenerate wave functions. This is also true of the rotational and electronic wave functions which are discussed later in the chapter.

Franck-Condon principle. The Franck-Condon principle as formulated for diatomic molecules applies also to polyatomic molecules. The three assumptions of the principle are set out on p. 214. The assumption that in an electron transition there is no change of internuclear distance, implies that the three co-ordinates defining the position of an atom in a polyatomic molecule are unchanged during a change of vibration quantum number. The vibration selection rule is $\Delta v = \pm 1$ when there is no electron transition.

If it is assumed that the symmetry of the initial and final electronic states is the same, only those vibrations tend to be excited which preserve that symmetry. This means that totally symmetric vibrations are preferred. It is possible, however, to have vibrational transitions when the vibrations are non-totally symmetric. This occurs in the case when the initial and final electronic states have not the same symmetry, but have certain symmetry elements in common. The transitions which then take place tend to be those which preserve the symmetry elements common to both states.

Energy of vibration. The total energy of vibration of the molecule is the sum of the energies of all the vibrating atoms, that is, the sum of the energies of all the harmonic oscillators, and so may be written, using equation (1.33), p. 25:

$$E = h \sum \nu_0 (v + \tfrac{1}{2})$$

where v is the vibrational quantum number with possible values 0, 1, 2, ...

If the amplitude of oscillation is large, the motion of the particles is anharmonic, and terms containing higher powers of $(v + \tfrac{1}{2})$ must be added (p. 212). The full expression for the energy of the anharmonic oscillator is not only the sum of the energies of all the normal vibrations, but includes cross terms containing the vibration quantum numbers of more than one normal vibration.

Potential energy of vibration states. The potential energy of a vibration state in a polyatomic molecule is best represented by a potential energy surface. The variation of the potential energy in one direction may be represented by a two-dimensional potential energy curve which is a section of the surface. All molecules which are not planar, and some linear molecules, whatever the nature of the atoms or groups of atoms of which they are composed, show two minima in their potential energy curves.†
This phenomenon is known as *inversion doubling*. It results from an exchange of all the nuclei through the centre of mass of the molecule; the two configurations before and after inversion cannot be changed into each other simply by rotating the molecule. Owing to the tunnel effect (p. 183), there is a certain probability that this exchange will occur, and this is shown by a splitting of the energy levels. If the exchanging atoms are different, optical isomers are produced which, in some cases, may be separated.

---

† In some cases there are more than two potential minima; the number of split components of the energy is equal to the number of potential minima.

Both forms of the molecule have the same rotational states. Fig. 8.2 shows the variation in potential of a pyramidal molecule XY_3 with the distance of the X atom from the Y_3 plane.

The two potential minima show that there are two positions of equilibrium for the atoms in the molecule. Each of these configurations has its corresponding wave function, and the fact that there are two possible linear combinations of these wave functions is responsible for the two values of the energy. If ψ_{+x} is one wave function

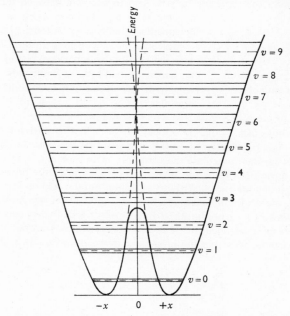

Fig. 8.2. Potential energy curve for pyramidal molecule XY_3. The energy is plotted against the distance of the X atom from the Y plane. The diagram shows two potential minima and splitting of the vibrational energy levels; the splitting of the lower vibrational states is greatly exaggerated. (After Herzberg.)

and ψ_{-x} is the other wave function, the complete molecular wave function is given by:

$$\psi = \psi_{+x} + \psi_{-x}$$

or

$$\psi = \psi_{+x} - \psi_{-x}.$$

Since the energy depends on the square of the wave function, the difference between the two energy values depends on the product

$$\psi_{+x}\psi_{-x}.$$

Since the energy of an anharmonic oscillator increases with increasing value of the quantum number v, the value of the wave function also increases with v, and the difference in energy between the two split values also increases with v (Fig. 8.2). The *inversion spectrum* due to the splitting of the energy levels is very sensitive to the height of the potential barrier through which the nuclei must pass. This height depends on the position of the atoms in the molecule and is thus very sensitive to the slight centrifugal distortion due to the rotation of the molecule. As a result the inversion

8*

spectrum shows considerable complication. In many cases the separation is either very slight or unresolved.

The inversion spectrum of ammonia has been investigated in more detail than any other. The splitting of the energy levels is marked since the potential barrier is low. It is supposed that the three hydrogen atoms lie in one plane with the nitrogen atom to one side (Fig. 8.3). As a result of inversion the nitrogen atom passes through the potential barrier in the plane of the hydrogen atoms to a stable position on the other side of the plane; the molecule may be said to oscillate between the two forms. The movement of the nitrogen atom is compensated by movement of the hydrogen atoms so that the system as a whole has no linear momentum. The two types of molecule cannot be separated chemically, in fact they can hardly be said to exist independently of each other. If the hydrogen atoms in the molecule were replaced by dissimilar atoms or groups as in Fig. 8.4, then the inversion would produce a molecule which would be the mirror image of the original, and the two molecules would be optical isomers. In this particular instance optical isomerism has not been detected, and it appears that the potential barrier is not high enough to prevent the immediate racemisation of the isomers.

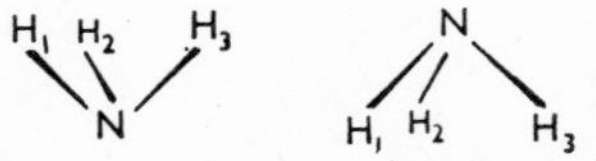

Fig. 8.3. Inversion of the molecule of ammonia.

For the purpose of considering inversion, each atom in the molecule is notionally treated as an individual, even if there are other similar atoms in the molecule. For instance, the molecule of methane has an unresolved inversion spectrum. The molecule consists of a carbon atom at the centre of four hydrogen atoms arranged at the four points of a tetrahedron. If these hydrogen atoms are labelled 1, 2, 3, 4, as in Fig. 8.5, it can be seen that the process of inversion produces a figure which could

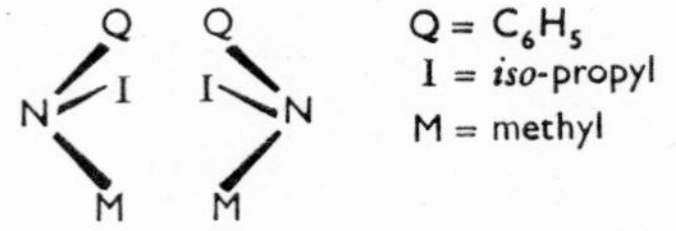

$Q = C_6H_5$
$1 = iso\text{-propyl}$
$M = \text{methyl}$

Fig. 8.4.

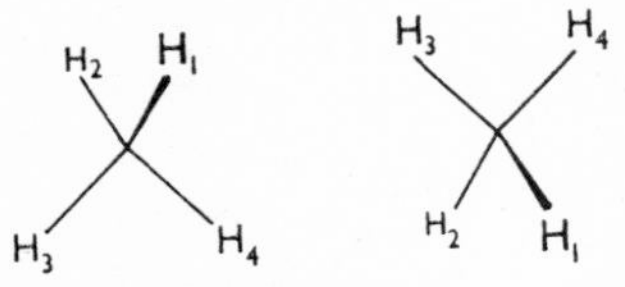

Fig. 8.5. Inversion of the molecule of methane.

not be obtained by the simple rotation of the whole molecule. In the case of a tetrahedral molecule, the potential barrier is high. If each of the four hydrogen atoms in the molecule of methane is replaced by a different atom or group, the two forms related by inversion may be recognised as a pair of optical isomers. Each form can be isolated and preserved indefinitely at room temperature, but racemisation may take place if the temperature is raised.

APPLICATION OF THE THEORY OF NORMAL VIBRATIONS
TO THE DETERMINATION OF MOLECULAR STRUCTURE

Except in the case of a molecule which has only totally symmetric vibrations, the complete determination of molecular structure cannot be made by the study of molecular vibration alone. It is necessary to consider vibration in conjunction with rotation (infrared rotation vibration spectra) and to correlate the results with observations on the microwave (pure rotation spectra) and Raman spectra (p.249). It is, however, helpful at this stage to consider the practical value of the connection between symmetry operations and normal vibrations.

The first step in the determination of molecular structure is to make a guess from chemical evidence as to the shape of the molecule and the number of symmetry elements which it contains. The molecule can then be assigned tentatively to a symmetry group, and since the symmetry of the molecule imposes certain restrictions (according to the group) on the possible normal vibrations and wave functions, it remains to be seen whether the observed rotations and vibrations are consistent with the chosen group.

The second step is to ascertain from tables the number of normal vibrations common to members of the chosen group. Certain very helpful simplifications are found to be applicable in special cases. For instance, some polyatomic molecules, particularly the larger ones, can be divided up into sets of identical nuclei which may exchange positions as a result of a symmetry operation. Also, if a nucleus is situated on a plane or axis of symmetry, for a non-degenerate vibration it can move along the plane or axis of vibration only if the vibration is symmetric to the plane or axis, and it can move at right angles to the plane or axis only if the vibration is antisymmetric to the plane or axis. A certain simplification can be achieved by the assumption† that the vibrations take place either (i) along the direction of the valence forces, causing stretching of the bonds, or (ii) at right angles to these bonds, causing deformation of the valence angles, or (iii) by a torsional movement around the direction of the valence bond. This assumption, which neglects all interatomic forces except those along or at right angles to the valence bonds, works quite well as a first approximation for many polyatomic molecules, and the results give a reasonably good agreement with those obtained directly from spectra. Whatever the actual nature of the displacement, the simplified one discussed above leads to the correct classification of vibrations into the different symmetry classes.

A vibration which takes place along the direction of a molecular bond is known as a *valence vibration* or *bond stretching vibration*; a vibration at right angles to the bond is known as a *deformation vibration* or more usually as a *bond bending vibration*. Other forms of vibration are *rocking*, when the atoms or groups of atoms at the end of a bond oscillate or "rock" about a fixed point in the bond; *breathing* when the oscillation is three dimensional, involving several identical bonds such as in methane. It appears that there is a smaller restoring force and therefore a smaller force constant if the vibration is at right angles to the bond with the bond length constant, than if it is along the direction of the bond and is stretching it. Mecke has observed that the frequency of the bond stretching vibration is always greater than the frequency of the bond bending vibration. The bond stretching rather than the bond bending vibration is characteristic of a given bond. In general, the best results are obtained by assuming that the vibration takes place along the direction of the valence forces which are assumed to be the restoring forces. An alternative concept is that of *central forces*. This theory supposes that the restoring force on the atom considered is the resultant effect of the attractions and repulsions of all the other atoms in the molecule. There is evidence that there are attractive forces between some pairs of atoms and repulsion between some other pairs. This is consistent with the theory of symmetric and antisymmetric molecular orbitals. In some cases a combination of the two theories seems to be required in order to give the best agreement with experimental results, but in general the *valence force* theory is the more successful of the two.

When the probable number and type of normal vibrations of the molecule have been determined theoretically, the third stage in the determination of the molecular structure should be to develop equations analogous to those on p. 230 and to solve them for the frequencies of the normal vibrations. These theoretically determined

† Mecke, Z. *J. Phys. Chem.*, B. **16**, 1932, 409, 421.

frequencies should then be compared with the frequencies of observed spectral lines. The theoretical calculations are, however, very difficult. It has been possible to carry them through only for a few molecules with a high degree of symmetry and few component atoms, but in most cases it is not possible. If it is assumed that only "valence" forces are acting it reduces the number of constants in the final equation for the frequency, and so it may then be possible to solve the equation. For a general solution, however, the number of unknown constants is usually greater than the number of values of ν, and in that case the equations cannot be solved. In certain cases it is possible to calculate the force constants from experimental data, but in practice a qualitative "trial and error" method is adopted for the identification of molecular symmetry. The spectrum of the molecule in question is inspected, together with spectra of isotopic molecules, with the object of picking out sets of fundamental frequencies which correspond to well known symmetry classes. These frequencies are then compared with the frequencies predicted from the symmetry of a possible model of the molecule. By this method it is usually possible to establish the correct molecular symmetry for the molecule concerned without the necessity of making calculations. Useful information concerning the frequencies of normal vibrations of a molecule can sometimes be obtained by subjecting it to radiation of different wave lengths. Resonance takes place with strong absorption if the frequency of the radiation is the same as that of one of the normal vibrations. Absorption of polarised infrared radiation is often used to assign vibrations to their symmetry classes. Information may also be obtained from the study of the pattern of the fine structure lines of vibration rotation bands, and from observation on the polarisation of the Raman lines (p. 251).

The rôle played by certain atoms in molecular vibration may be determined by the use of isotopes of one or more of the constituent atoms. The degree of alteration of the vibration spectrum is a measure of the degree of participation in the vibration of the atom concerned.

Frequencies which are characteristic of a certain group of atoms may be observed in different molecules each of which contains this group. Table 8.1 gives examples of groups of atoms which possess characteristic frequencies. It is seen from the Table that the characteristic frequency changes to a significant extent when the environment

Table 8.1. *Characteristic frequencies* (cm^{-1})

(R represents an alkyl group)

Atom group	Molecule containing the group	Characteristic frequency
S—H	RSH	2573
C≡N	RCN	2444
NH_2	RNH_2	3372
C=O	$RCOCH_3$	1710
	RCHO	1720
	$RCOOCH_3$	1735
	RCOCl	1780
C=C	$RHC=CH_2$	1642
C≡C	HC≡CH	1960
	RC≡CH	2100
	RC≡CR	2230

of the group of atoms in the molecule is changed. If the aliphatic group R in the molecule $RHC{=}CH_2$ is replaced by an aromatic group with which the $C{=}C$ group can enter into resonance, the characteristic frequency falls to about 1600 cm^{-1}.

The constancy of the characteristic frequency is related to the constancy of the force constant of the bond. Different atoms of about the same atomic weight may replace one another in a given type of group without greatly changing the characteristic frequency. For example, for single bonded homo- or hetero-nuclear diatomic groups composed of carbon, nitrogen, or oxygen atoms, the characteristic frequency is about 1000 cm^{-1}, for double bonded diatomic groups about 1650 cm^{-1}, and for triple bonded groups about 2150 cm^{-1}. The constancy of the characteristic frequency of a given atom group is most marked when either the masses vibrating or the force constants are very different from those in the rest of the molecule. If a group consists of a heavy atom attached to a light one, such as a hydrogen atom, the vibration may be taken to be approximately that of the hydrogen atom alone.

ROTATION SPECTRA OF POLYATOMIC MOLECULES

PURE ROTATION SPECTRA

Polyatomic molecules, like diatomic molecules, have a pure rotation line spectrum in the far infrared.

A rotating molecule may, in a limited sense, be regarded as a spinning top, and on this analogy a polyatomic molecule may be placed in one of the four following classes:

- (a) Symmetric tops.
- (b) Spherical tops.
- (c) Linear molecules.
- (d) Asymmetric tops.

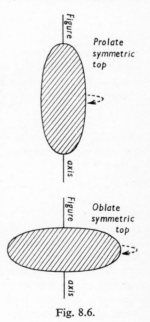

Fig. 8.6.

The differentiation of these classes depends on the relation between the moments of inertia of the molecule about the three principal axes; these are denoted by the symbols I_x, I_y, I_z (often I_A, I_B, I_C).

The principal axes are related to the symmetry of the molecule. For instance, where there is an axis of symmetry, this is a principal axis of inertia. If there is a plane of symmetry at right angles to the axis of symmetry the other two principal axes lie in it. There is no pure rotation spectrum unless the molecule has a permanent electric dipole moment. If there is a single molecular axis of symmetry in a molecule with a dipole moment, this moment acts along the axis. Since the molecule cannot have two dipole moments, if it has more than one axis of symmetry the dipole moment must be zero. For a rotating molecule with an axis of symmetry and permanent dipole moment, the axis of symmetry is generally taken to be the z axis.

Symmetric tops. For a symmetric top, two of the moments of inertia are equal, and the third about the axis of symmetry is different.

If I_y is greater than I_z the top is said to be *prolate*; if I_z is greater than I_y the top is said to be *oblate* (Fig. 8.6). For instance, CH_3Cl is a prolate symmetric top, BCl_3 is an oblate symmetric top. The axis of symmetry (z axis) is often known as the *figure axis* and it is also the axis of the dipole moment. The total angular momentum **J** is quantised.

If there is no gain or loss of energy by the system as a whole, the magnitude of J is constant and its direction, which does not in general lie along the figure axis, is fixed in space. The axis of the dipole moment rotates with angular momentum N about a direction at right angles to its own axis. Such a rotation causes precession of the figure axis about the direction of the total angular momentum vector (Fig. 8.7).

Spherical tops. In this case $I_z = I_x = I_y$. There is an infinite number of axes of symmetry and therefore there is no dipole moment. Thus there is no pure rotation spectrum, even though the molecule may be rotating, but a spherical top molecule does give a rotation vibration spectrum as it vibrates sufficiently to cause a fluctuating dipole moment (p. 245). CH_4, CCl_4, and SF_6 are examples of spherical top molecules.

Linear molecules. The behaviour of a linear molecule is similar to that of a diatomic molecule. There is one moment of inertia only to be considered (with reference to internal co-ordinates) since $I_x = I_y$ and $I_z = 0$. CO_2, C_2H_2, C_2N_2 are linear molecules.

Asymmetric tops. For an asymmetric top $I_z \neq I_x \neq I_y$. There is no general guide to the direction of the principal axes; each molecule must be considered on its own merits. A large number of polyatomic molecules belong to this class; for example H_2O, H_2CO, NO_2, CH_2Cl_2 are asymmetric tops.

It must be noted that a molecule, although really an asymmetric top, might accidentally conform to the requirements of the spherical or symmetric tops owing to the coincidence that the distribution of the masses of the atoms present might cause the moments of inertia about the principal axes to be equal. This possibility does not usually arise, and it will be ignored in the following discussion.

ENERGY OF ROTATING MOLECULE

Symmetric top. An expression for the energy of the rotating symmetric top molecule may be derived by the following semi-classical method. The same result may also be obtained from a rigid wave mechanical proof.

The kinetic energy of a rotating body may be written as

$$E = \tfrac{1}{2}I_x\omega_x^2 + \tfrac{1}{2}I_y\omega_y^2 + \tfrac{1}{2}I_z\omega_z^2$$

where ω_x, ω_y, ω_z, are the components of the angular velocity in the x, y, z directions. If P is the angular momentum then $P = I\omega$, and since P is a vector quantity E may be written,

$$E = \frac{P_x^2}{2I_x} + \frac{P_y^2}{2I_y} + \frac{P_z^2}{2I_z}. \tag{8.2}$$

The vector K is the component of total angular momentum about the axis of symmetry (z axis) and plays the same part as the vector Λ, which is the component of total angular momentum about the molecular axis (p. 207) in the diatomic molecule. K can take the values $+J, J-1, J-2, \ldots, -J$. Thus for a given value of J there are $2J+1$ possible energy states. Unfortunately the letter K is used also for the total angular momentum, apart from spin, of the electrons in a linear or diatomic molecule. A freer use of the alphabet would cause less confusion, but the practice has now been established and the nomenclature in common use must be accepted.

For the symmetric top,

$$P_z = K = \frac{Kh}{2\pi}.$$

Fig. 8.7 shows the vector diagram where

$$N^2 = P_x^2 + P_y^2.$$

If **J** is the total angular momentum,

$$|\mathbf{J}|^2 = |\mathbf{K}|^2 + |\mathbf{N}|^2.$$

Therefore, since $I_x = I_y$,

$$E = \frac{|\mathbf{N}|^2}{2I_x} + \frac{|\mathbf{K}|^2}{2I_z}.$$

But

$$\mathbf{J} = \sqrt{(J(J+1))}\,\frac{h}{2\pi}, \quad \text{and} \quad \mathbf{K} = \frac{Kh}{2\pi}.$$

Therefore,

$$E = \frac{h^2}{8\pi^2 I_x}(J(J+1)) + \frac{h^2 K^2}{8\pi^2}\left(\frac{1}{I_z} - \frac{1}{I_x}\right). \tag{8.3}$$

The first term of this expression for the energy is similar to that developed for the energy of the rotating diatomic molecule (p. 23). In the special case of a spherical top, the expression for the energy of the molecule would be the same as that of a diatomic molecule since $I_x = I_y = I_z$.

Since the axis of the dipole moment of a symmetric top molecule is the axis of symmetry (z axis), a change of angular momentum about this axis does not affect the dipole moment. Therefore one of the selection rules governing the changes necessary for the production of a pure rotation spectrum by a symmetric top molecule is $\Delta K = 0$. The other selection rule is that $\Delta J = 0$, ± 1. For absorption, the selection rule is $\Delta J = +1$. Where it is possible to produce an emission spectrum, the selection rule is $\Delta J = -1$, but most polyatomic molecules break up if the temperature is raised sufficiently high for an emission spectrum to be produced. Some molecular emission

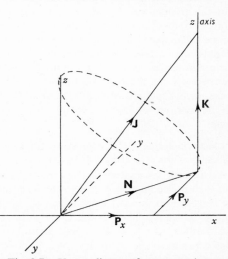

Fig. 8.7.   Vector diagram for symmetric top.

spectra have been produced by means of microwave techniques, using the molecular beam method.

The frequency of a line in the pure rotation spectrum may be calculated from the change of energy corresponding to a change of J to $J+1$.

$$\nu = \frac{E' - E''}{h} = \frac{h}{8\pi^2 I_x}((J+1)(J+2) - J(J+1)) \quad \text{(cf. p. 216)}$$

$$= \frac{h}{8\pi^2 I_x}(2J+2)$$

$$= 2B(J+1) \quad \text{where} \quad B = \frac{h}{8\pi^2 I_x}.$$

The frequency is independent of the quantum number K, and the spectrum is similar to the pure rotation spectrum of the diatomic molecule. Theoretically the spectrum should consist of a series of lines spaced equidistantly, the distance between them being $2B$ as for the rotation spectrum of the diatomic molecule. In actual practice, both for diatomic and polyatomic molecules, allowance has to be made for centrifugal stretching of bonds during the rotation. In both cases the stretching increases with the frequency of rotation, but there is an important difference between the linear and non-linear polyatomic molecules. The linear molecule has a centrifugal distortion term which is independent of K; the inclusion of this term in the expression for the energy causes a small displacement of the absorption lines. With the non-linear polyatomic molecule, in addition to this term, other terms dependent on K must be included in the expression for the energy. I_x and I_y become functions of the energy, and all main transitions are split into $2J+1$ components due to the $2J+1$ possible values of K. For instance, if $J=2$, K can take the values 0, 1, 2. In the far infrared spectrum, which is very difficult to observe except by microwave techniques, the splitting, if not sufficient to be well resolved, is revealed by the intensities of the unresolved lines, the intensity increasing with increasing value of J. If microwave recording can be used, the resolution is much greater, and the components due to splitting appear separated. There is no splitting for linear molecules, since the rotation is independent of K. The pure rotation spectrum may therefore be used as a simple indication of the shape of a molecule.

If the frequencies of sufficient lines in the infrared spectrum are recorded, the moment of inertia of the molecule about an axis perpendicular to the axis of symmetry can be calculated. Using the expression for the energy (equation (8.3), p. 239), I_x may be obtained in terms of the frequencies and the value of I_z calculated. The internuclear distances may then be estimated. This is most accurately done by recording the spectra when the atoms in the molecule are replaced by different isotopes.

The wave functions of symmetric top molecules depend on certain angles related to the inclinations of the top to the x, y, and z axes. These are known as *Eulerian angles*.

Linear molecules. The expression for the energy of a rotating linear molecule is the same as for a rotating diatomic molecule (p. 215).

Asymmetric top molecules. The spectra of these molecules are extremely complicated and each molecule must be treated as a special case. Different methods for calculating the wave numbers seem to be suited to different molecules; sometimes with a single kind of molecule one method is suitable for energy states with high quantum numbers, and another for those with low quantum numbers. As will be shown below, the consideration of the symmetry of each molecule is very important. Some success has been obtained by treating the asymmetric top as a symmetric top which is precessing round a fixed direction with a nutation, that is the angle which the axis of the top makes with the fixed direction varies periodically. The selection rule $\Delta K=0$ is removed; K can take all values from $+J$ to $-J$; $\Delta J=0$, ± 1, even for absorption only. The interested reader should pursue the subject in some specialised text book, and in the very many original papers which have been published in recent years.

Hyperfine structure due to nuclear spin. In addition to the complications already mentioned, microwave technique reveals a further hyperfine splitting of the absorption lines in the pure rotation spectra of polyatomic molecules. The splitting is ascribed either to magnetic coupling between the nuclear magnetic moment and the magnetic field produced by molecular rotation, or in some cases to the coupling between the nuclear quadrupole moment (p. 268) and the electric field in the rest of the molecule. A description of this effect is beyond the scope of this book, but it is of great interest in providing information about the nucleus. Where there are several nuclei, there are several molecular forms which are distinguished by their different resultant nuclear spin (analogous to ortho- and para-hydrogen, p. 223). Each form has its own set of rotational energy states.

ROTATIONAL LEVELS OF POLYATOMIC MOLECULES AND SYMMETRY CONSIDERATIONS

In describing the spectra of polyatomic molecules it is customary to refer to energy states as *levels*, and although this nomenclature has been purposely omitted from the earlier chapters of this book, it will be adopted in the following résumé of some important selection rules pertaining to rotational energy changes. The reader will find in the literature references to *even* and *odd rotational levels*. These correspond to even and odd values of the rotational quantum number *J*. The complete derivation of the selection rules is based on group theory which will not be developed here.

Positive and negative rotational levels. A rotational level is said to be *positive* if the molecular rotational wave function remains unchanged in sign when there is an imaginary reflection at the centre of symmetry of all the *particles* (nuclei and electrons) of which the molecule is composed. A rotational level is said to be *negative* if the molecular rotational wave function changes its sign when there is an imaginary reflection of all the particles at the centre of symmetry. A rotational level is thus either positive or negative, and as is shown later in this chapter, certain selection rules depend on this distinction.

The notional reflection described above is applied to the wave functions of both diatomic and polyatomic molecules, in order to decide whether an energy level is positive or negative. It is essentially a symmetry operation, but in all non-planar molecules the inversion actually occurs with the production of two forms of molecule (p. 234).

Rotational levels "symmetric or antisymmetric in the nuclei". Rotation levels are further qualified by the effect on the molecular rotational wave function of another symmetry operation. This symmetry operation is the exchange of all the *nuclei* on one side of the centre of symmetry with all the nuclei on the other side. If the wave function remains unchanged by this notional operation, it is said to be *symmetric in the nuclei*; if it changes in sign, it is said to be *antisymmetric in the nuclei*. This property is determined by the number and directions of the nuclear spins. The symmetry operation is applied to diatomic and polyatomic molecules, except for asymmetric tops which have no centre of symmetry. Positive and negative levels have opposite symmetry; if the positive level is symmetric the negative level is antisymmetric; if the positive level is antisymmetric the negative level is symmetric.

SYMMETRY SELECTION RULES (NOT FOR RAMAN SPECTRA)

The following shorthand symbols are used for allowed and forbidden changes: $\longleftrightarrow$ (allowed), $\longleftarrow\!\!|\!\!\longrightarrow$ (forbidden). These symbols, when used in conjunction with the signs $+$ and $-$, refer to changes between positive and negative levels; when used in conjunction with the words "symmetric" and "antisymmetric" they describe changes between states with symmetric and antisymmetric properties.

Example $+\longleftarrow\!\!|\!\!\longrightarrow+$ $-\longleftarrow\!\!|\!\!\longrightarrow-$ $+\longleftrightarrow-$

The energy changes described by these symbols are:

Forbidden, positive to positive, and negative to negative.

Allowed, positive to negative, and negative to positive.

The selection rules for linear, symmetric, and spherical top molecules differ from those for asymmetric top molecules.

Selection rules for linear, symmetric top, and spherical top molecules.

(1) Changes can take place only between positive and negative levels.

$+\longleftrightarrow-$ $+\longleftarrow\!\!|\!\!\longrightarrow+$ $-\longleftarrow\!\!|\!\!\longrightarrow-$

(2) Changes between symmetric and antisymmetric levels are forbidden.

$$\text{antisymmetric} \longleftarrow\!\mid\!\longrightarrow \text{symmetric}$$

A homonuclear molecule with a centre of symmetry cannot obey both these rules simultaneously, which is another way of saying that such molecules have no dipole moment and no rotation spectrum.

Each linear and symmetric top molecule has, in addition to the rules mentioned above, its own selection rules appropriate to its particular type of symmetry.

Selection rules for asymmetric top molecules. A slightly different classification is adopted here. The single symmetry operation, necessary to decide whether a rotational level in a linear or symmetric top molecule is positive or negative, is superseded by two symmetry operations, and the energy level is labelled in accordance with the behaviour of the wave function when these two operations are carried out successively. The possible levels are designated briefly

$$+\,+, \qquad +\,-, \qquad -\,+, \qquad -\,-.$$

There are two sets of selection rules. One applies when an axis of symmetry is present; the other when it is absent.

If an axis of symmetry is present.

(1) If the axis of the dipole moment is the axis of least moment of inertia, $+\,+\longleftarrow\!\!\longrightarrow-\,+$ and $+\,-\longleftarrow\!\!\longrightarrow-\,-$ are the only changes possible.

(2) If the axis of the dipole moment is the axis of intermediate moment of inertia, $+\,+\longleftarrow\!\!\longrightarrow-\,-$ and $+\,-\longleftarrow\!\!\longrightarrow-\,+$ are the only changes possible.

(3) If the axis of the dipole moment is the axis of greatest moment of inertia, $+\,+\longleftarrow\!\!\longrightarrow+\,-$ and $-\,+\longleftarrow\!\!\longrightarrow-\,-$ are the only changes possible.

If there is no axis of symmetry. Levels of the same symmetry cannot combine.

$$+\,+\longleftarrow\!\mid\!\longrightarrow+\,+ \qquad +\,-\longleftarrow\!\mid\!\longrightarrow+\,-$$
$$-\,+\longleftarrow\!\mid\!\longrightarrow-\,+ \qquad -\,-\longleftarrow\!\mid\!\longrightarrow-\,-$$

HINDERED ROTATION

If a molecule contains one or more groups of atoms which are free to rotate in relation to the rest of the molecule and do so without change of dipole moment, the rotation spectrum is unaffected. If there is a potential barrier opposing the internal rotation, and if the height of the barrier is great compared with the internal torsional energy of the molecule, slow torsional vibrations may take place without affecting the spectrum. If the energy of the internal rotation is large compared with the height of the potential barrier, a complete rotation may take place. The potential energy curve of a planar molecule of the form shown in Fig. 8.8 shows two potential minima; the exchange of Y_1 and Y_2 cannot be brought about except by an internal rotation of part of the molecule. This rotation is hindered by the potential barrier; the phenomenon is known as *hindered rotation*. If one complete revolution passes through x positions of equilibrium, separated by x potential barriers, there are x potential minima in the energy curve. The rotation of part of the molecule in relation to the remainder may be visualised as proceeding with a series of "clicks" corresponding to the surmounting of each potential barrier in turn. For instance, ethane shows hindered rotation of this type. If the rotating atoms and the stationary atoms are of different kinds and if the

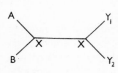

Fig. 8.8. Form of planar molecule which may show hindered rotation.

potential barriers are high enough to give stability to the positions of equilibrium, geometrical isomers are produced by the exchange. If the rotating atoms or groups of atoms are of the same kind, a splitting of the levels analogous to inversion doubling (p. 234) takes place, due to the linear combination of wave functions. The splitting is usually unresolved but may be detected by measurements of intensity. The spectrum is very complicated.

The particular significance of hindered rotation lies in the field of organic chemistry. The effect was first noticed for methyl alcohol, and has since been observed in other compounds. Its analysis has been used to determine the heights of the potential barriers between groups of atoms in the molecule.

ROTATION VIBRATION SPECTRA OF POLYATOMIC MOLECULES

When the molecule is rotating, the co-ordinates which describe the configuration of the molecule are rotating with it. For instance, in a linear molecule, the molecular axis continues to be the z axis regardless of the fact that its direction in space is continually changing. The result of this rotation of both the molecule and the co-ordinates is that the rotating nuclei appear to be subject to two additional forces. The first is the familiar *centrifugal force*. This necessitates the introduction of the stretching constant already mentioned on p. 240. The second additional force is called the *Coriolis force* after its discoverer.

The effect of a Coriolis force is felt by a man seated near the periphery of a rotating room when he attempts to move. If he is at a distance x from the centre of rotation, and then leans backwards so that his head is at a distance y from the centre of rotation $(x < y)$, he feels as if he has been dealt a blow on the side of the head. Since his angular velocity is constant, his linear velocity must increase with increasing distance from the centre of rotation, and thus a change from a distance x to a distance y involves an acceleration with its accompanying sensation of force. If a molecule is rotating and vibrating at the same time, Coriolis forces are brought into play since the vibration is along the "radius" of the angular motion. If the co-ordinates of the rotating molecule are referred to rotating axes, in order to translate these co-ordinates into the usual stationary Cartesian system, it is necessary to postulate an additional force which acts at right angles to the direction of vibration, and at right angles to the axis of rotation. If this compensatory force is introduced, the co-ordinates of the molecule referred to the rotating axes may be used in the equations as if the molecule were not rotating. When a diatomic molecule is considered, it is not necessary to introduce a Coriolis force, as such a force would merely rotate the molecule as a whole. With a linear polyatomic molecule, the Coriolis force distorts the centre relative to the rest of the molecule. When the rotation of the co-ordinates has been compensated by the introduction of the Coriolis force, it is found that the nuclei move in ellipses during a vibration instead of in straight lines. There is therefore a definite *vibrational angular momentum* associated with vibration; this is designated by the letter l and has appropriate selection rules. The effect of the coupling of the overall rotation with the Coriolis rotation is to produce a splitting of the lines which increases with increasing value of J since the Coriolis force increases with the speed of rotation. This effect is known as *l-type doubling*. During simultaneous vibration and rotation both centrifugal and Coriolis forces act on linear, symmetric, spherical, and asymmetric top molecules.

The actual spectrum observed depends on the symmetry of the particular molecule considered, and all spectra show the usual hyperfine structure due to nuclear spin.

Linear polyatomic molecules. The spectra consist of numbers of bands in the photographic infrared. The rotation vibration spectra of linear polyatomic molecules are

similar to those of diatomic molecules, but they contain additional lines because the
linear polyatomic molecule has additional possibilities of vibration. The atoms not
only vibrate along the internuclear axis, but also at right angles to it, and this vibration
can cause a change of dipole moment. Such a vibration is sometimes called a *perpen-*

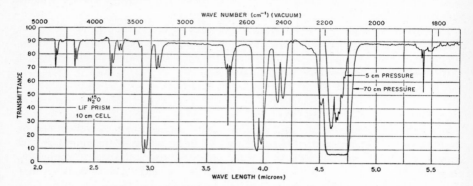

Fig. 8.9.   Infrared spectrum of $N^{15}N^{15}O$. (After Begum and Fletcher.)

dicular vibration. The transition with $\Delta J = 0$ is allowed as well as $\Delta J = \pm 1$, and in addition to the P and R branches of the spectrum, a Q branch corresponding to $\Delta J = 0$ is
shown between them. The Q branch appears in the spectrum as a strong central line
between the P and R branches as the lines for $\Delta J = 0$ for different J values fall very
nearly on top of each other. Fig. 8.9 shows part of the rotation vibration spectrum of
the linear non-symmetrical molecule N_2O.

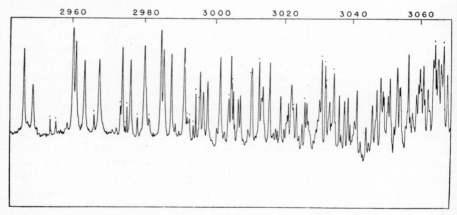

Fig. 8.10.   Vibration-rotation bands of ammonia between 2940 and 3070 cm^{-1}. (After
Tidwell and Benedict.)

Symmetric top molecules have degenerate vibrational states on account of their
symmetry; the Coriolis splitting of these states is very large. Interaction between the
vibrational angular momentum and the angular momentum of rotation is also shown.
The actual spectrum produced is determined by the symmetry properties of symmetric
tops in general, and those of the particular molecule under consideration; inversion
doubling is shown by molecules such as ammonia. To a first approximation the
selection rules are the same as for the linear polyatomic molecule, $\Delta v = \pm 1$, $\Delta J = 0, \pm 1$,

but the rotation selection rule is somewhat modified according to whether the change of dipole moment occurs in a direction parallel ($\Delta K = 0$) or at right angles to the axis of the top ($\Delta K = \pm 1$). Fig. 8.10 shows some rotation vibration bands of NH_3.

Spherical top molecules. These are also affected by centrifugal distortion and Coriolis forces. Some of the degenerate vibrational states are split, and there is a marked Coriolis splitting of the rotational levels for each value of J. The selection rules are ($\Delta v = \pm 1$) and ($\Delta J = 0, \pm 1$). The molecules investigated have been chiefly the tetra-hedral group for which it has been possible in many cases to determine the rotational constants, moments of inertia, and internuclear distances.†

Asymmetric top molecules. As always, the spectra of these molecules are very complicated. The action of centrifugal and Coriolis forces is evident but no general rules applying to the whole class can be made. The symmetry of the molecule is all important even if it is a complete lack of symmetry. The selection rules depend on whether the dipole moment lies along the axis of greatest, intermediate, or least moment of inertia. A detailed study has been made of many of these spectra and the reader should consult original publications on the subject.

BAND SPECTRA OF POLYATOMIC MOLECULES

These spectra appear in the visible and ultraviolet regions. They are due to simultaneous changes of electron state, vibration, and rotation. Their analysis is not easily carried out. Some of the major difficulties are:

(a) The number of possible vibrational and rotational frequencies which may be associated with electron transitions is very large.

(b) The vibrations show strong anharmonicity effects due to the simultaneous excitation of a large number of normal vibrations.

(c) There is strong interaction between vibration and rotation; in some cases torsional vibration goes over into rotation.

(d) There are often many possible ways in which a polyatomic molecule can dissociate, and therefore many of its excited states are unstable and the band spectra become diffuse or continuous.

(e) For large molecules, the lines are often very close together, and the band spectra frequently appear to be continuous. For instance, the lines due to rotation become closer and closer together as the size of the molecule increases.

(f) Predissociation (p. 221) is frequently observed.

However, much painstaking and useful work has been done on the band spectra of a number of polyatomic molecules. In many cases the analysis has been a very valuable contribution to the determination of the structure of a particular molecule. The selection rules are in all cases governed by the symmetry of the molecule under investigation. The vibration symmetry considerations have already been discussed and it has been shown that the vibration selection rules depend on the symmetry elements which the initial and final states have in common (p. 232). The selection rules for simul-taneous changes of electron state, vibration and rotation assume the symmetry of the initial and final states to be the same, as according to the Franck-Condon principle, a change of electron state is most likely to take place without any change of the positions of the nuclei. If the molecule remains in the lowest vibration state during the transition, the symmetry is not affected, since the lowest vibration state is totally symmetric. If the molecule changes to an excited vibration state at the same time as the electron transition, the symmetry and therefore the energy of the final electronic state is affected. Besides

† All tetrahedral molecules should show inversion doubling, but the potential barrier is very high and so the splitting is not resolved.

anharmonic vibrations, other disturbing factors such as collisions between molecules or the interaction of electron transition with rotation (although this is usually small) may upset the electron transition selection rules, and forbidden transitions may appear. The intensity of these forbidden transitions is often increased by a rise in temperature.

The multiplicity rules are similar to those which concern atomic spectra and the notation adopted is the same. Although it is not possible to obtain exact mathematical expressions for the wave functions of the different electron states, it is possible in many cases to obtain exact information on the symmetry properties of a given state. The states are classified according to their symmetry and are distinguished by the use of symmetry nomenclature.

It might be thought that the advent of microwave spectroscopy with its powerful methods of determining moments of inertia and internuclear distances would make the study of band spectra redundant, but microwave spectra cannot be obtained unless there is a molecular dipole moment. The study of band spectra is the only spectroscopic means of gaining information on excited states of the molecule, and its analysis shows that the moment of inertia, rotational constant, and internuclear distance all change their value when the molecule is excited. In gaseous microwave spectroscopy, the molecules are generally in a 1Σ state. Paramagnetic resonance experiments are chiefly performed on ions in crystals, and thus cannot give information about molecular shapes and sizes.

Isotope effect. Since the energy of an electronic state depends on the distance between the nuclei and not on their masses, a change of isotope does not affect transitions which are due solely to change of electron state. Both vibrational and rotational transitions are dependent on nuclear mass, and therefore a change of isotope is helpful in distinguishing between the effects of vibration, rotation, and electronic transition.

ELECTRON TRANSITIONS WITHOUT ROTATIONAL AND VIBRATIONAL CHANGES

Certain electron transitions in the molecule produce spectra independent of the rotation and vibration states. These spectra may be divided into two classes:

Rydberg series. The molecular Rydberg † series are line spectra analogous to the atomic Rydberg series (p. 72). They are difficult to observe, even in absorption, as they occur in the vacuum ultraviolet. The lines correspond to the removal of electrons from the valence shell to near ionisation energy states and their subsequent return to the valence shell. In the excited state, the electron is still within the field of the molecule but far enough away for the field to approximate to that of a point charge. The excited states may therefore be approximately described by atomic orbitals. Where it is possible to observe such a spectrum, useful information may be obtained concerning the ionisation potentials of the molecule and the distribution of charge. Plate 11 shows part of the Rydberg absorption series of CS_2.

Charge transfer spectra. The transition corresponds to a change from a neutral molecular (covalent) state which may be denoted by AB, to an ionic state $A+$, $B-$, with accompanying transfer of one electron from one atom to the other. Where there are many bonds there may be many such transfers. The spectra caused by such transitions are called *charge transfer spectra*.

Chromophoric groups and charge transfer spectra. In polyatomic molecules it is possible for radiation to be absorbed by the transition of an electron which is strongly

---

† Vibrational changes are sometimes observed in conjunction with Rydberg transitions in polyatomic molecules.

localised in a group of atoms, the resulting spectrum being independent of the rest of the molecule to which the group is attached. Such a spectrum is usually found in the visible or near ultraviolet region and shows strong localised absorption bands, the exact colour absorbed depending on the particular group attached. These groups are therefore called *chromophoric groups*. Detailed analysis of the spectrum gives important information about the electronic binding within the group.

In general, highly coloured compounds, including those which contain chromophoric groups, are characterised by intense absorption in a very localised region of the spectrum. It is thought that such absorption is due to charge transfer. The radiating molecules often show high polarisability (p. 250) which would tend to encourage such a transfer. It has been suggested that intense colour is associated with resonance between various possible molecular structures, the change from one to the other being effected by a transference of an electron between atoms of the same element existing in different valency states. Many photochemical reactions are thought to be initiated by charge transfer, and it has been suggested that the formation of various molecular complexes is brought about by resonance between alternative structures by means of charge transfer.

ZEEMAN AND STARK EFFECTS

All spectra of polyatomic molecules show Zeeman and Stark effects which are exceedingly complicated and which will not be further discussed here. The effects in the spectra of linear polyatomic molecules are identical with those of diatomic molecules (p. 224). Symmetric tops have a component of their dipole moment in the direction of the total angular momentum vector, and therefore they show a large first order Stark effect. This is of considerable assistance in the determination of dipole moments (p. 308).

SUMMARY OF TOPICS RELATED TO MOLECULAR PROPERTIES ON WHICH INFORMATION MAY BE OBTAINED FROM THE STUDY OF MOLECULAR SPECTRA

I. PURE ROTATION SPECTRA

(a) Rotational energy states
(b) Moments of inertia
(c) Bond lengths and angles
(d) Mass ratios
(e) Inversion
(f) Hindered rotation
(g) Zeeman effect
(h) Stark effect
(i) Dipole moments

II. ROTATION VIBRATION SPECTRA

(a) Frequencies of normal vibrations
(b) Force constants
(c) Symmetry of molecules
(d) Energy of dissociation
(e) Potential energy of molecules

III. BAND SPECTRA

(a) Excited states of the atom

(b) Change of bond lengths, bond angles, and potential energy curves with change of electron state

(c) Heats of dissociation

(d) Identification of isotopes

(e) Polarisability

(f) Molecular refractivity

(g) Symmetry of molecules

(h) Equilibrium constants of chemical reactions

IV. RAMAN SPECTRA

(a) Fundamental frequencies of vibration and rotation

(b) Polarisability

(c) Force constants

(d) Symmetry of molecules

(e) Hindered rotation

BOOKS FOR FURTHER READING

BRODE, W. R., *Chemical Spectroscopy* (John Wiley, 1943).

HERZBERG, G., *Infrared and Raman Spectra* (Van Nostrand, 1945).

JOHNSON, R. C., *Introduction to Molecular Spectra* (Methuen, 1949).

REVIEWS AND DISCUSSIONS

Applications of Infrared Spectra to Chemical Problems (*Trans. Faraday Soc.*, **279**, 1945, 171).

Technique of Organic Chemistry, Vol. IX, *Chemical Applications of Spectroscopy* (N.Y. Interscience Publications, 1956).

ORGEL, L. E., *Charge Transfer Spectra and some Related Phenomena* (*Quarterly Reviews*, **8**, No. 4, 1954, 422).

SHEPPARD, N., and SIMPSON, D. M., *The Infrared and Raman Spectra of Hydrocarbons* (*Quarterly Reviews*, **6**, No. 1, 1952, 1).

Spectroscopy and Molecular Structure (*Dis. Far. Soc.*, **9**, 1950, 1).

SPONER, H., and TELLER, E. *Electronic Spectra of Polyatomic Molecules* (*Rev. Mod. Phys.*, **13** 1941, 76).

WHIFFEN, D. H., *Rotation Spectra* (*Quarterly Reviews*, **4**, No. 2, 1950, 131).

CHAPTER NINE

RAMAN SPECTRA, MICROWAVE SPECTRA, AND MAGNETIC RESONANCE SPECTRA

RAMAN SPECTRA

Observation of the scattering of light by matter shows either

(a) that the scattered light has the same frequency as that of the incident light, and there is no loss or gain of energy by the scattering molecule, or

(b) that the scattered light has a different frequency from that of the incident light, and energy is gained or lost by the scattering molecule. The change of energy is small.

The first type of scattering is known as *Rayleigh scattering*, the second type as *Raman scattering*. The Raman effect may be observed as follows.

If a gas, or a transparent liquid or solid, is illuminated by a source of light giving a line spectrum, some of the light is scattered. If the scattered light, observed at right angles to the incident beam, is analysed spectroscopically, it is found that the original lines are present, but that each line of frequency ν is accompanied by either one or two faint additional lines corresponding to the frequencies $\nu \pm \nu_0$ where ν_0 is the frequency of some molecular vibration or rotation of the scattering molecule. If energy $h\nu_0$ is lost *to* the molecule during the scattering process, the spectrum shows a line of frequency $\nu - \nu_0$. If energy $h\nu_0$ is lost *by* the molecule during the scattering process, the spectrum shows a line of frequency $\nu + \nu_0$. The line of frequency $\nu - \nu_0$ is known as a *Stokes line*; the line of frequency $\nu + \nu_0$ is known as an *anti-Stokes line*. The effect is most easily observed with monochromatic light. If the spectrograph has high resolution, a single Rayleigh scattered line is seen with a faint spectrum of equidistant lines on either side of it. It is found that the difference in frequency between the Rayleigh line and a given Raman line is characteristic for the scattering substance and proportional to one quantum of energy of rotation or vibration of the scattering molecule.† Although it is theoretically possible to produce Raman lines in any part of the spectrum the choice is limited to some extent by the wave lengths of easily obtained sources of monochromatic radiation. Plate 12 shows the Raman specta of certain alkali halides.

POLARISATION

Before discussing Raman spectra in detail the relation must be established between the terms "polarisation" and "dipole moment" as applied to a molecule. *Polarisation* here means the separation of positive and negative charge in the molecule so that it has

---

† It is important that the Raman effect should not be confused with fluorescence, which occurs only if a molecule absorbs radiation of a critical frequency ν_c. As a result of the absorption, the molecule is raised to a higher energy state, from which it returns to the ground state, probably in more than one stage, at the same time emitting its own fluorescent spectrum of frequencies less than ν_c. In the case of fluorescence, not only must the incident light have a special frequency, but it is almost all absorbed by the molecule. Rayleigh and Raman scattering are examples of true scattering, while fluorescence is a normal emission spectrum generated by molecules which have previously been excited by radiation of the critical wave length.

positive and negative electric poles.† The *dipole moment* is the electric moment possessed by the molecule as a consequence of polarisation. A molecule may have a permanent dipole moment, or it may acquire an induced dipole moment as the result of being polarised by an external electric field which causes the centres of positive and negative charge to be separated (p. 300). Even a molecule with a permanent dipole moment suffers further polarisation when placed in the external field. If M is the electric moment acquired by a molecule when it is placed in the external field E,

$$M = \alpha E.$$

α is a characteristic constant for the molecule, and is known as the *polarisability*; it may be defined as the *electric moment per unit field*.

Polarisability and the appearance of the Raman lines. The connection between polarisability and the frequencies of the observed Raman lines may be shown classically as follows:

When light is incident on a molecule, polarisation of the molecule is caused by the electric field E of the incident radiation. Since this field is alternating,

$$E = E_0 \cos 2\pi\nu t$$

where ν is the frequency of the incident light. If α is the polarisability of the molecule,

$$M = \alpha E_0 \cos 2\pi\nu t.$$

It is here assumed that the molecule is simple and spherical with no permanent dipole moment, and that there is no vibration and rotation to be considered. The scattered radiation from such a molecule would therefore have frequency ν, the scattering would be elastic, and the polarisability of the molecule, α, would be constant.

It is evident, however, that in the molecule the polarisability is periodically influenced by rotation and vibration.

If

$$\alpha = \alpha_0(1 + \gamma \cos 2\pi\nu_0 t) \quad \text{where } \gamma \text{ is constant,}$$

then

$$\begin{aligned} M &= \alpha_0(1 + \gamma \cos 2\pi\nu_0 t)E_0 \cos 2\pi\nu t \\ &= \alpha_0 E_0 \cos 2\pi\nu t + \alpha_0\gamma E_0 \cos 2\pi\nu t \cos 2\pi\nu_0 t \\ &= \alpha_0 E_0 \cos 2\pi\nu t + \frac{\alpha_0\gamma}{2} E_0\{\cos 2\pi(\nu+\nu_0)t + \cos 2\pi(\nu-\nu_0)t\}. \end{aligned}$$

The expression for M shows the presence of both Rayleigh and Raman scattering. The first term describes the Rayleigh scattering; the second term describes the Raman scattering. The constant γ is characteristic of a given Raman transition and is of the order $1/10$–$1/100$. The quantity $\alpha_0 E_0$ plays the part of an amplitude, and since intensity is proportional to (amplitude)^2, the intensity of the Rayleigh scattered line is proportional to α_0^2, but the intensity of the Raman scattered lines is proportional to $\gamma^2\alpha_0^2/4$ and they are therefore much fainter than the Rayleigh scattered line. According to the simple classical theory, the intensities of the Stokes and anti-Stokes lines should be the same, but it has been observed that the Stokes lines are much stronger than the anti-Stokes lines for high values of ν_0. This is because there is a greater probability that the molecule will be in the ground state than in an excited state and the anti-Stokes lines originate in an excited state.

It has so far been assumed that α is constant and that the polarisability of the molecule is the same in all directions. This is true for molecules with spherical symmetry, but for all others the polarisability is different in different directions, and the resultant

† The reader should note that the word *polarisation* is used in two senses, (a) polarisation of the incident and scattered radiation, and (b) the separation of positive and negative charge in the scattering molecule.

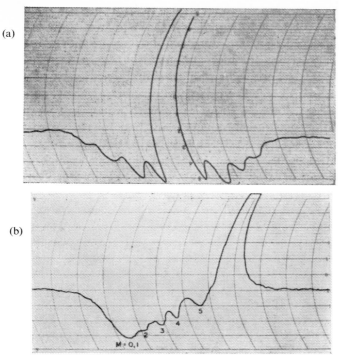

Pl. 13. Microwave spectrum of (a) $C^{12}D_3O^{16}H$, (b) $C^{12}H_3O^{16}D$. (a) Shows 1st order Stark components at 50 volts. (b) Shows 2nd order Stark components at 600 volts. [Venkateswauli, Edwards and Gordy, *J. chem. Phys.*, **23**, 1955]

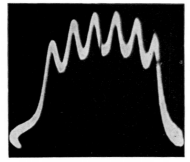

Pl. 14. Hyperfine structure in part of the paramagnetic resonance spectrum of $MnSO_4$ ($I = 5/2$, giving 6 split levels). [Schneider and England, *Physica*, **17**, 1951.]

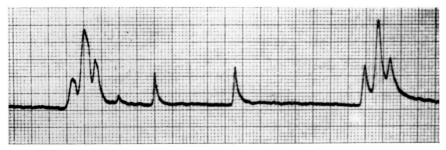

Pl. 15. Nuclear magnetic resonance spectrum of SF_4 (the lines between the triplets are due to impurities). [Cotton and George, *J. chem. Phys.*, **28**, 1958.]

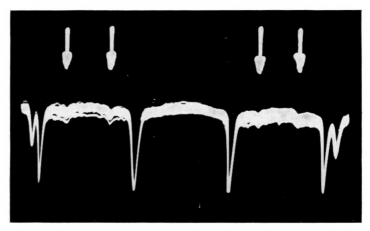

Pl. 16. Hyperfine structure in the paramagnetic resonance spectrum of copper due to electric quadrupole interaction. [Bleaney, Powers and Ingram, *Proc. phys. Soc. Lond.*, **64A**, 1951.]

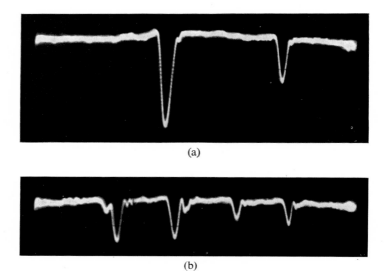

(a)

(b)

Pl. 17. Cl^{35} pure quadrupole resonance spectrum of cyanuric chloride (a) without Zeeman splitting, (b) with Zeeman splitting. [Adrian, *J. chem. Phys.*, **29**, 1958.]

electric moment does not in general lie along the direction of the electric vector of the incident radiation. It is convenient to describe the molecule in terms of an *ellipsoid of polarisability*. This is an imaginary figure of which the semi-axes are given by the three values of $1/\sqrt{\alpha}$ in the directions of the three principal axes x, y, z. A change of polarisability, such as that due to vibration of the molecule, can then be described as a deformation of this ellipsoid. In the special case of a diatomic molecule whose molecular axis lies along the direction of the polarising field of the incident radiation, the polarisation of the molecule is entirely along the molecular axis, and is zero at right angles to this axis. In this special case the ellipsoid of polarisability has no width; for all other orientations of the molecule α has a value both along and at right angles to the field; these values are in general different from each other.

INTENSITY OF RAMAN SPECTRA

Although many factors, such as symmetry, nuclear spin, degeneracy of energy states, etc., modify the intensities of the Raman lines, the results of analysis of intensities indicate that the process of transference of energy in the Raman effect takes place in two stages, A to B and B to C. Although the energy transference corresponds to the difference of energy of the two states A and C, the probability of the transference, and hence the intensity of the corresponding line, depends on the product of the probability A to B and B to C. The process A to B is one of absorption of energy, and the process B to C is one of emission of energy.

Degree of depolarisation. In the simplest case of a spherical molecule, the Rayleigh scattered radiation observed at right angles to the incident beam is always polarised completely in the plane at right angles to the incident beam, since the vector **E** lies in this plane whether the incident beam is polarised or not (p. 83). This is true only for a spherical molecule for which α is a constant and for which the ellipsoid of polarisability is a sphere. When it is a true ellipsoid, the scattered light is *depolarised* to a greater or lesser extent for both Rayleigh and Raman scattering.

If the z axis is the direction of propagation of the incident light, the *degree of depolarisation*, ρ, is defined as the ratio of the intensity of the scattered light polarised perpendicularly to the xy plane, $I_\perp$, to the intensity of the scattered light polarised parallel to this plane, $I_\parallel$. The degree of depolarisation depends on whether the incident light was polarised or not, and therefore for a standard it is convenient to take completely unpolarised light. It has been shown by Born and others that for completely unpolarised light

$$\rho = \frac{6\beta^2}{45\alpha^2 + 7\beta^2}$$

where α and β are functions of the polarisability of the scattering molecule. ρ is dependent on the symmetry of the molecule†; it is a maximum when $\alpha = 0$, and therefore for the greatest possible degree of depolarisation $\rho = 6/7$. The minimum value of the degree of depolarisation is zero, when $\beta = 0$. This corresponds to Rayleigh scattering.

VIBRATIONAL RAMAN EFFECT

It is assumed in the following discussion that the molecule remains in the electronic ground state.

If the vibrational Raman effect is to appear at all, it is essential that the vibration should change the shape or size, or orientation of the ellipsoid of polarisability, so

† The constant α is not the same as α used on p. 250.

that the induced dipole moment of the molecule varies periodically. The theory, which will not be discussed in detail here, is based on symmetry considerations. It gives the important result that with totally symmetric vibrations (p. 231), ρ can take any value between 0 and 6/7, with the exception of the cubic point group for which $\rho = 0$ for such vibrations. For all non-totally symmetric vibrations, if the Raman lines are present at all, they show the maximum depolarisation. The treatment accounts, on the grounds of probability consideration, for the weakness of the anti-Stokes lines compared with the Stokes lines. Except in the special case of spherical molecules (see below), the vibrational Raman effect does not appear without a simultaneous rotation effect, but it will be found that it is customary in textbooks on the subject to consider the vibration separately and to superpose the rotation theoretically afterwards. Raman spectra are very valuable in helping to identify molecular vibrations; the theory is complicated by the necessity of allowing for the presence of overtones and combination frequencies although these are usually weak. Fig. 9.1 shows the B—H stretching region in the Raman spectrum of $[^{11}BH_4]^-$.

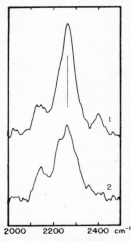

Fig. 9.1. The B—H stretching region in the Raman spetrum of $[^{11}BH_4]^-$; (1) perpendicularly polarised incident light, (2) parallel polarised incident light. (After Emery and Taylor.)

ROTATIONAL RAMAN SPECTRA

The pure rotation spectra are not so easily resolved as the vibration Raman spectra.

Linear molecules. If the Raman spectrum is to appear, the rotation must cause a change of molecular polarisability with respect to some fixed direction, that is a change of orientation of the ellipsoid of polarisability. If the rotation takes place about the molecular axis, there is no change of orientation of the ellipsoid of polarisability and no Raman spectrum. If the rotation is about an axis at right angles to the molecular axis, there is a change of orientation of the ellipsoid of polarisability and thus there is a Raman spectrum for both homonuclear and heteronuclear diatomic molecules.

Any change in rotational energy of the molecule must be such that **J**, the total angular momentum of the molecule excluding nuclear spin, changes from one quantised value to another. Thus the possible values of the angular momentum of the ellipsoid of polarisability, though quantised, have no integral quantum number (p. 207). The selection rule for the rotational Raman spectrum of linear molecules is $\Delta J = 0, \pm 2$. The ellipsoid of polarisability returns to its original position twice in one molecular revolution, therefore the changes of polarisability occur with a frequency which is twice the frequency of molecular rotation. The symmetry selection rules $+ \longleftrightarrow +$, $- \longleftrightarrow -$, $+ \longleftrightarrow -$ are the exact opposite of the selection rules for the infrared spectra (p. 241). The lines of the spectrum are equally spaced and are twice as far apart as those of the infrared pure rotation spectrum.

Symmetric top molecules. The axis of symmetry must be one of the semi axes of the ellipsoid of polarisability, hence a rotation about this axis does not distort the ellipsoid and does not affect the induced dipole moment. The Raman spectrum is therefore unaffected by a change in the value of K. The selection rules are:

$$\Delta K = 0; \quad \Delta J = 0, \pm 1, \pm 2 \quad (\Delta J = \pm 1 \text{ is missing for } K = 0).$$

For the pure rotation absorption spectrum, as with the infrared pure rotation spectrum, the process must start with an absorption of energy and so only the positive values of ΔJ have any meaning. The symmetry selection rule is the same as for linear molecules.

Spherical top molecules. The polarisability ellipsoid becomes a sphere; all molecules placed in the polarising field acquire an induced dipole moment, but since the direction of the field remains constant, the direction of the induced dipole also remains constant however much the molecule rotates. As the molecule has spherical symmetry it has no permanent dipole moment, thus the orientation of the ellipsoid of polarisability is unchanged on rotation, and the molecule has no Raman rotation spectrum.

Asymmetric top molecules. If there is an axis of symmetry it coincides with one of the axes of the polarisability ellipsoid, but there may be no axis of symmetry. The Raman spectra are likely to be very complicated and only in very few cases have they been recorded and analysed.

To sum up, wherever there is an ellipsoid of polarisability which is not a sphere, and wherever there is a change of orientation of the ellipsoid on rotation, there is a Raman rotation spectrum.

ROTATION VIBRATION RAMAN SPECTRA

The interaction of rotation and vibration is similar to that of the infrared spectrum. The rotational effect should appear as the fine structure of bands due to vibrational changes, but for most Raman spectra the rotational structure is not resolved. The vibration bands are narrow and appear more like lines than bands. The selection rules developed for pure vibrational and pure rotational changes remain approximately the same. If the vibrational Raman spectrum is to appear, the shape of the polarisability ellipsoid must change periodically during the vibration. The effect on the spectrum of the change of shape depends on the symmetry of the molecule under consideration. For instance, the symmetric top molecule shows a strong sharp Q branch in the Raman spectrum of totally symmetric vibrations, while the Raman spectrum of non-totally symmetric vibrations is diffuse. Degenerate vibrational states are always non-totally symmetric and therefore give broad maxima. Useful information may thus be derived from a preliminary inspection of the Raman vibration spectrum. With a spherical molecule, a pure vibration spectrum without rotation is obtained when the vibration is totally symmetric, such as the breathing vibration of methane. The ellipsoid of polarisability, which in this case is a sphere, retains its shape but alters its size during the vibration. The spectrum consists of Stokes and anti-Stokes lines $(\nu \pm \nu_0)$ with no rotational fine structure. If the sphere were distorted in shape during the vibration, rotational structure would be shown.

The P, Q, R branches introduced in connection with the Fortrat diagram (pp. 216, 219) are also evident in Raman spectra. Two additional branches O and S are added to correspond with the change $\Delta J = \pm 2$. Table 9.1 shows the change of J corresponding to the different branches.

Table 9.1.

Branch	O	P	Q	R	S
ΔJ	-2	-1	0	$+1$	$+2$

The P and R branches are missing for the linear molecule.

The analysis of the rotation vibration spectra is very difficult. It is further complicated by the presence of overtones and combination frequencies, though these are usually weak. The selection rules will not be discussed here. Raman spectra corresponding to electron transitions accompanied by simultaneous vibration and rotation changes have been observed, but they are too complicated to be of much use for determination of molecular structure.

INFORMATION DERIVED FROM THE STUDY OF RAMAN SPECTRA

A summary of information derived from different types of spectra is given on p. 247. That obtained from Raman spectra is of most value when it is considered in conjunction with that obtained from infrared spectra. The selection rules show that certain transitions which are allowed in the infrared spectra are forbidden in Raman spectra and *vice versa*. For molecules with a centre of symmetry, the Raman and infrared transitions are mutually exclusive; what is allowed in one is forbidden in the other. For example, carbon dioxide shows three strong absorption bands corresponding to three fundamental vibrations; two of these occur in the infrared and a different one in the Raman spectrum. Theoretical considerations show that a planar triatomic molecule has three fundamental vibrations only; it has therefore been deduced that the molecule of carbon dioxide is planar and has a centre of symmetry. This simple type of argument cannot be applied in every case since the spectrum is governed by the symmetry properties of the molecule concerned, and these alone may limit the number of possible transitions. However, conclusions such as those deduced for carbon dioxide may be confirmed in a number of ways, for instance by further spectrum analysis, X-ray and electron diffraction, and by chemical evidence. The degree of depolarisation (p. 251) is also a direct guide to the symmetry properties of the molecule. In many cases, knowledge of the fundamental frequencies leads to calculation of the force constants. The calculations are somewhat complicated; they are at the best approximations, but the force constants for different types of binding can be roughly estimated. A comparison of the force constants gives some idea of the relative strengths of different types of bonds. The force constants of a complex molecule can sometimes be estimated from those of a number of related simpler molecules; this method, though not accurate, is helpful in calculating possible vibration frequencies for the complex molecule.

Some Raman frequencies are characteristic of special groups of atoms in the molecule. Although the frequency characteristic of a certain group depends to some extent on the rest of the molecule with which it is associated, it is nevertheless possible through the observation of the Raman spectra of a series of related compounds to assign certain fundamental frequencies of vibration of a molecule to the presence in it of certain groups of atoms. Much useful information may be derived by replacing a particular group of atoms in a molecule by other groups or by isotopes, and observing the corresponding modifications of the Raman spectrum. The Raman effect has been a useful tool for the investigation of hindered rotation (p. 242). This application will not be further discussed, as it chiefly concerns organic chemistry.

MICROWAVE SPECTROSCOPY

The study of pure rotation spectra has been greatly facilitated by the introduction of microwave technique. This was highly developed for use in connection with radar in the 1939–1945 war, and it has since been adapted for spectroscopic purposes. Most pure rotation spectra lie in the far infrared region where the radiation may be regarded either as very long wave length red waves, or as very short radio waves, according to the method used for their generation and detection. They are now almost exclusively studied by means of radio techniques and are therefore referred to as *microwaves*, since from the point of view of a radio operator they are of very short wave length; the range of wave length is about 1 mm to 30 cm. If microwave methods are used, the resolution of the lines in the spectrum is very much greater than that obtained by the older methods of infrared analysis.

Microwave experiments may be divided into two classes; *gaseous microwave spectroscopy* and *paramagnetic resonance*. Gaseous microwave spectroscopy is concerned with changes of rotational energy of the molecules of a gas which is subjected to radiation of critical frequency. Paramagnetic resonance spectra are obtained when substances whose molecules contain one or more unpaired electrons are placed in a magnetic field and subjected to radiation of microwave frequency. The spin magnetic moments of the unpaired electrons are coupled to the applied magnetic field and the absorption of microwave energy of just the right frequency causes transitions between the Zeeman levels. The substance investigated may be in the solid, liquid, or gaseous state. In microwave spectroscopy, the spectra observed are nearly always absorption spectra; a quantum of energy in the microwave region is very small and it is therefore not easy to produce satisfactory emission spectra.

Microwaves are easily generated by means of a *klystron valve*. The circuit must be designed with great care in order that the frequency of the emitted radiation may be kept constant by automatic tuning, and also that, when required, it may easily be changed to another value which in its turn may be kept constant. In practice the frequency can be varied very rapidly over a small range by what is known as a *klystron sweep*.

When very short waves with wave lengths of the order of a few millimetres are required, the output from a klystron is multiplied in frequency by a crystal harmonic generator. The frequency of the microwaves can be measured to an accuracy of 1 in 10^7, so the absorption spectrum can be plotted with a very high degree of resolution. The reader should consult specialist textbooks for details of the production and detection of microwaves. The whole apparatus of production and detection is often known as a *microwave spectrometer*. The design of a particular spectrometer depends on the purpose for which the microwaves are to be used.

GASEOUS MICROWAVE SPECTROSCOPY

The gas is subject to radiation which is as nearly monochromatic as possible; the frequency of the radiation can be varied by the klystron sweep. The radiation is passed through the gas and received by a sensitive detector. A "spectrum" may be recorded by plotting the response of the detector against the frequency of the incident microwaves. When this frequency is the same as that of some natural frequency of rotation in the molecule which is irradiated, absorption of energy by the molecule takes place and the detector records a diminished response. Not only amplitude changes but also phase changes can be recorded. It is possible to make the whole apparatus automatic, and to record the absorption spectrum on a cathode ray oscillograph. Owing to the high resolution, even the hyperfine structure due to the interaction of the electric field in the molecule with the quadrupole moment of the nucleus (p. 257) is clearly marked.

The theory of the energy changes in the microwave region is the same as that developed for the infrared pure rotation spectra (pp. 215, 238). As there is such a high resolution in the microwave spectrum it should be possible to measure the moments of inertia of a molecule very accurately, and thus, given data from a number of isotopic molecules, to calculate bond lengths and angles with very considerable precision. It is just that high resolution, however, which reveals the need for correction of the simple theory of rotation spectra. Allowance must be made for centrifugal, and in some cases Coriolis, distortion of the molecule during its rotation if a formula is to be devised which will allocate each line to the position in which it is actually observed. Unless these corrections can be accurately made, the bond lengths and angles cannot be calculated with a precision comparable to that of the data obtained from measurements made with the microwave spectrometer.

There are also certain practical difficulties to be overcome. For accurate measurement of resonance frequencies not only must the resolution of the spectrometer be high, but also the lines must be sharp and narrow. Various effects are found to contribute to line broadening and these must be minimised as far as possible. For high resolution the following conditions must be observed:

(1) The pressure of the gas must be low (< 1 mm Hg).
(2) The gas must be at a low temperature.
(3) The power generated by the klystron must be low.
(4) The rate of variation of the frequency must be neither too high nor too low; an optimum value causing least broadening may be found by experiment.

RESULTS OF GASEOUS MICROWAVE SPECTROSCOPY

The rotation spectra of very light diatomic and linear molecules with small moments of inertia lie outside the range of microwave spectroscopy, but the method is generally applicable to those molecules which contain more than one fairly heavy atom.

Diatomic molecules. There is a fairly good agreement between the observed and calculated centrifugal distortion correction. Since the distortion increases with the angular momentum, moments of inertia may be most easily determined by using lines corresponding to transitions involving small values of J.

Linear polyatomic molecules. The agreement between observation and theory of the centrifugal distortion is not very good. The lines frequently show l type doubling due to the bending vibrations set up by Coriolis forces (p. 243). By isotopic substitution and recording of the corresponding spectra, an accurate comparison of isotopic masses can be made. Alternatively, bond lengths may be determined and the linear nature of the molecule confirmed by substitution of isotopes of known mass; if the masses are not very different it may be assumed that the centrifugal distortion is the same after each substitution and thus it may be eliminated from the calculations. It is desirable to make several experiments with different isotopes.

There can be no primary *Stark effect* with linear molecules (p. 226). The secondary (quadratic) Stark effect, due to the dipole induced by applied electric field, is present in all molecules except those whose internuclear axes happen to lie along the direction of the field. These cannot have an induced dipole component along the axis of rotation if the field is at right angles to it.

Symmetric tops. The distortion theory is again not in very good agreement with observation, and l type doubling is present in the spectrum. To obtain values for the distances between the nuclei of the component atoms, a number of measurements with different isotopes must be made. It is not possible to obtain from the spectrum a value for the moment of inertia I_z about the axis of symmetry since the permanent dipole lies along this axis, but a value may be deduced for I_y, the moment of inertia about an axis at right angles to the axis of symmetry. The ratio I_z/I_y may be obtained from the infrared spectrum, and hence I_z can be calculated, and also bond lengths and angles. Gaseous halogen compounds have been studied extensively by this method. Both primary and secondary *Stark effects* are shown by symmetric tops. The dipole moment may be calculated from the primary Stark effect (p. 308).

The inversion spectrum of ammonia has been investigated thoroughly, and a formula devised for the centrifugal distortion which fits the observed lines well.

Ammonia is, strictly speaking, a symmetric top, but it holds a special place owing to the inversion effect which is due to oscillation between the two forms of the molecule corresponding to the two possible positions of the nitrogen atom relative to the hydrogen atoms (see p. 233). Not only is there doubling of the absorption spectrum, but there is also absorption due to transitions between the energy levels corresponding to the two forms. This should theoretically give one *inversion frequency* which is the same at all levels, but actually it is spread out into a spectrum because the inversion frequency depends on the centrifugal distortion as it is very sensitive to change of distance between the nuclei. The centrifugal distortion increases with the rotational quantum number.

Asymmetric tops. As usual, the asymmetric tops present the most difficult cases, and each one must be treated on its own merits. The magnitude and direction of dipole moments can sometimes be estimated from the Stark splitting.

Zeeman effect. Before absorption of microwave radiation takes place, most of the molecules of the gas are in a 1Σ state and thus they possess no resultant magnetic moment. The Zeeman effect is therefore small in gaseous microwave spectroscopy, since it is due only to the coupling of the applied magnetic field to the nuclear magnetic moment and to the magnetic field due to the rotation of the molecule as a whole. Even for a few substances, such as oxygen, which have one or more unpaired electrons in the molecule, the Zeeman effect, though larger, is still small compared with the Stark effect.

Hyperfine splitting. All microwave spectra show hyperfine splitting even in the absence of applied electric and magnetic fields. Two effects may be distinguished; a Zeeman effect due to the coupling of nuclear magnetic moment with the magnetic field of the rotating molecule, and a larger effect due to the interaction of the nuclear electric quadrupole moment with the molecular electric field surrounding the nucleus. An electric quadrupole moment is a measure of lack of uniformity in the distribution of nuclear charge. The determination of such moments from pure quadrupole resonance spectra is discussed on p. 268. Analysis of the hyperfine structure of microwave spectra suggests that in some nuclei there is an even more complicated distribution of charge, ascribed to an octupole moment.

Plate 13 shows Stark components and the effect of the interchange of isotopes in a microwave spectrum.

INFORMATION DERIVED FROM GASEOUS MICROWAVE SPECTROSCOPY

Experiments on gaseous microwave spectroscopy provide information on:

(1) Moments of inertia, and hence bond lengths and bond angles.
(2) Dipole moments.
(3) Molecular energy levels.
(4) Inversion.
(5) Energy barriers and hindered rotation.
(6) Centrifugal distortion.
(7) Electric quadrupole interaction and, in a few cases, octupole interaction.

PARAMAGNETIC RESONANCE

When a *diamagnetic substance* (p. 98) is subjected to an external magnetic field (of the order of 10,000 gauss), the Zeeman effect is small since the external field is coupled only to the small magnetic field due to the nuclear spin and to the rotation of the molecule as a whole. There is only a small splitting of the energy levels by an amount which is of the order of a quantum of radiation of *radio frequency* (10^{-7} e.v.).

When a *paramagnetic substance* is submitted to an external magnetic field of the same order, the Zeeman effect is much larger, as the external field is coupled to a considerable permanent magnetic moment. The splitting of the energy levels is therefore much greater than in the case of a diamagnetic substance, and the energy difference between the split levels is of the order of a quantum of radiation of *microwave frequency* (10^{-3}–10^{-5} e.v.). If a paramagnetic substance is placed in an external magnetic field, and at the same time it is subjected to microwave radiation of varying frequency, absorption is shown at each frequency whose corresponding quantum of energy is sufficient to cause a transition to take place from a lower energy to a higher energy Zeeman component. If a magnet of moment M is placed in a field of strength H the energy stored in the field is proportional to the product MH, the constant of proportionality depending on the angle which the magnet makes with the external field. If the magnetic moment of the magnet could be increased, the system would gain energy, and if the magnetic moment could be diminished the system would lose energy.

When a paramagnetic substance is placed in a field of strength H and radiation of frequency ν is absorbed, the gain of energy may be expressed as gain of magnetic moment × field strength.

$$h\nu = g\beta H \tag{9.1}$$

where β is the Bohr magneton (p. 93) and g is a number which may be determined from this relation.

Equation (9.1) describes the change of energy during a transition from one Zeeman component to another; g is the *spectroscopic splitting factor*. This g is very nearly, but not exactly, the same as the Landé splitting factor described on p. 97. The Landé factor refers to the electron in a free atom, and the paramagnetic g refers to an electron in an atom, ion, or molecule, whose energy states are modified by an external electric field provided by neighbouring atoms, ions, or molecules in the liquid or solid state. Only in the few cases of paramagnetic resonance in gases at low pressure does g have the same significance as the Landé factor. However, in all cases the value of g may be regarded as the number of Bohr magnetons which correspond to the change of energy which takes place during the transition, and in all cases a value of 2 for g indicates that paramagnetic resonance is due to the spin moment only. A value for g less than 2 indicates that there is some coupling of spin with orbital angular momentum. It is therefore of great interest that the value of g should be determined accurately in order that it may give information about binding forces in the solid and liquid states.

If the paramagnetic body is a monatomic ion in a crystal, the energy levels are already disturbed by the effect of the electric field inside the crystal. This field interacts with the charge on the electron, and alters the LS coupling (p. 90). As a result, the absorption frequencies corresponding to the difference in energy between two Zeeman levels are altered from the values they would have if the ion were free. If the electric field of the crystal is very strong, it may separate originally degenerate levels by so much that when the external magnetic field is applied, the splitting due to the combined effect of the electric and magnetic fields is so great that a quantum of microwave energy is not sufficient to cause a transition from one Zeeman level to another. However, if there is an odd number of unpaired electrons in the ion, no electric field can completely remove the degeneracy, as the odd electron has always two possible spins and so there are some Zeeman energy states sufficiently close together for paramagnetic resonance to take place. Since monatomic ions have no dipole moment, there is no first order Stark splitting in an external electric field.

The recording of a paramagnetic resonance spectrum can provide information concerning any atom, molecule, or group which is characterised by the presence of one or more unpaired electron spins. The method is chiefly suitable for the investigations of crystals and free radicals since there are very few stable gases which have resultant electronic angular momentum in the ground state. For instance, NO is the only stable diatomic molecule which has resultant orbital angular momentum; a few molecules, notably O_2, NO_2, and ClO_2, have resultant spin angular momentum only. There are, however, many unstable radicals such as OH, CH, etc., which have a transient existence in solids subjected to ionising radiation, and whose lifetime is long enough to show paramagnetic resonance. In some cases the free radicals can be detected in liquid solution. The method of paramagnetic resonance is particularly suitable for the investigation of such problems as (a) the electronic configurations of the transition elements, rare earths, actinides, and certain metallic complexes; (b) the determination of the g values (spectroscopic splitting factors) for free radicals, and the estimation of the degree of delocalisation of the unpaired electron in the radical; (c) the structure of ferromagnetic and antiferromagnetic substances.

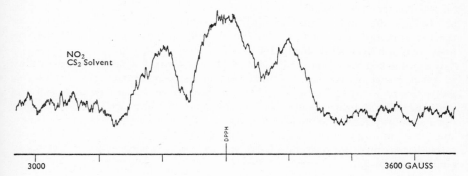

Fig. 9.2. Paramagnetic resonance spectrum of NO_2 showing fine structure. (After Bird, Baird, and Williams.)

The paramagnetic resonance spectrum is usually obtained by plotting the intensity, shape and width of the absorption line against the strength of the applied magnetic field while the frequency of the impinging radiation is kept constant. A similar spectrum may be produced by keeping the field constant and varying the frequency, but the method of the variable field is usually preferred. All measurements are repeated at different temperatures.

In practice it is convenient to perform a number of experiments in each of which the crystal has a different orientation. There are considerable practical difficulties to be overcome, particularly in the matter of making the absorption lines narrow and sharp. This does not mean that the experimenter wishes to suppress the fine structure of the lines. On the contrary, the greatest interest lies in the analysis of the fine structure and the hyperfine structure, and for this to be feasible it is of the first importance that any spurious line broadening or blurring should be eliminated. With this end in view it is desirable to have a low power source of microwave radiation as with gaseous microwave spectroscopy; the design of the apparatus must also be such that the field is as uniform as possible. Fig. 9.2 shows the paramagnetic resonance spectrum of NO_2 with fine structure, and Plate 14 shows the hyperfine structure in part of the paramagnetic resonance spectrum of a solution of $MnSO_4$.

Important causes of line broadening are:

(1) *Spin-lattice relaxation.* This effect is due to an interchange of energy between the thermal motion of the lattice and the spins of the electrons in the paramagnetic ion. The time taken for the exchange of energy between the spin system and the crystal lattice is known as the *spin-lattice relaxation time.* When microwave radiation is absorbed, the time spent in the excited energy state ("lifetime" of the energy state) may be reduced by spin-lattice relaxation with consequent broadening of the energy level. Also the lattice vibrations may be sufficiently strong at ordinary temperatures to cause transitions between the Zeeman levels without absorption of microwave radiation. Both these effects are greatly diminished by lowering the temperature.

(2) *Spin-spin relaxation.* This effect is sometimes described as "dipole-dipole" interaction. It is due to the magnetic coupling of the spins of adjacent ions. It is not removed by change of temperature, but can be greatly diminished by dilution of the paramagnetic ions with diamagnetic ions from some salt which enters into solid solution with the given salt.

(3) *Exchange interaction.* This effect depends on the exchange forces between the ions; its magnitude depends on whether the ions are close together or far apart, and on whether they are similar or dissimilar. The line may be sharpened or broadened according to the nature of the exchange forces in the particular case considered. The effect may be distinguished from spin-spin broadening; in some cases the exchange forces may greatly diminish the spin-spin effect.

It is of the first importance that the strength of the magnetic field should be known to a high degree of accuracy. This may be done by an ingenious method employing *proton resonance.* If a hydrogen nucleus (for instance in a molecule of water) in a magnetic field absorbs radiation of just the right frequency its spin axis changes orientation with respect to the field. The particular frequency required depends on the strength of the magnetic field. Since the gyromagnetic ratio for the proton has been very carefully measured, the strength of the field can be calculated with an accuracy of 1 in 10^5.

RESULTS OF PARAMAGNETIC RESONANCE SPECTROSCOPY

Paramagnetic resonance in ionic crystals. The value of g varies considerably with the angle between the direction of the external magnetic field H and the crystal axis. It is customary for two values of g to be determined, $g_{\parallel}$ when H is parallel to the crystal axis, and $g_{\perp}$ when H is at right angles to the crystal axis. In order to correlate the calculated value of g with the value determined experimentally, the simple theory must be extended to take account of the following effects:

(1) The spin-orbit magnetic coupling of the electron.

(2) The spin-spin magnetic coupling and exchange forces between electrons in the ion.

(3) The magnetic coupling of electron spin to the nuclear magnetic moment.

(4) The influence of the strong electric field of the crystal on the nuclear quadrupole moment (p. 268) and so, on the orientation of the nucleus, thus affecting the magnetic coupling of nucleus and electron.

(5) The influence of the strong electric field of the crystal on the LS coupling in the ion.

Each allowed orientation of the nucleus in the electric field of the crystal is accounted for in the hyperfine structure which is very well resolved.

In general, information may be obtained on:

(1) Energy levels in crystals (their determination is assisted by measurements of intensity).

(2) The nature of the electric fields in crystals.

(3) The number of unpaired electrons associated with an ion. In some cases it is possible to ascertain their distribution throughout the molecule of a complex.

(4) The valence state of an ion. This may often be deduced by estimating the orbital and spin coupling. If the total spin is S and there is little or no orbital-spin coupling, the Zeeman levels are equally spaced with $(2S+1)$ components in all. If there is a considerable orbital-spin coupling the spacings are not equal, and each of the $2S$ transitions between the $2S+1$ energy states is different. A similar alteration of the Zeeman levels from equal spacing is caused by crystal fields with less than cubic symmetry. It has been found possible to identify certain valence electrons in members of the actinon group as $5f$ rather than $6d$.

(5) Bond strengths. The magnetic coupling of electron spin to the nuclear magnetic moment causes a hyperfine splitting of each absorption line into $(2I+1)$ components. The separation of these components depends on the probability of finding the electron in a given orbital, and on the shape of the orbital, and is thus a measure of charge transfer in the bond, and of its ionic character. It has been shown that for certain types of complex, the electron transfer away from the nucleus and the bond strength increase as the valence electron in successive compounds moves from the $3d$ to the $4d$ to the $5d$ orbital. A similar effect has been shown for a change from a $4f$ to a $5f$ orbital. Such an increase in charge transfer and bond strength would be expected as the result of the increase in orbital radius. It is also possible, for a given type of complex, to compare the strengths of bonds to different ligands.

(6) Nuclear spin and nuclear quadrupole moment.

(7) The exchange forces between neighbouring ions. It has been found that two paramagnetic ions can interact to form a combined system of energy states, the distance between the spectroscopic lines (or breadth of line when they are just not resolved) is a measure of the exchange forces.

(8) The symmetry and structure of a paramagnetic complex. This can be investigated by following the changes in the absorption spectrum as the crystal is rotated.

Paramagnetic resonance from free radicals. The resonance (often known as *electron spin resonance*) is from the spin of one or more unpaired electrons in a chemical group. The experiments are most easily performed with large and comparatively stable organic radicals but it has been found that some lighter radicals are sufficiently stable at low temperatures to give electron spin resonance. The experiments are best carried out in very dilute solid or liquid solutions in order to eliminate exchange interaction as far as possible. The value of g is found to be approximately 2, that of an electron without orbital angular momentum, and the analysis of the hyperfine structure shows the influence of more than one nucleus. In concentrated solutions, the hyperfine structure is missing and the resonances are sharp. These results have led to the conclusion that the electron with unpaired spin is delocalised and is not located on any definite atom of the group. Resonance may be obtained, not only from groups with an odd number of electrons, but also from groups containing an even number of electrons with two unpaired spins.

Paramagnetic resonance from conductors and semi-conductors. The absorption of microwave radiation by metals is largely prevented by a "skin effect", but resonance experiments can be carried out on metals if the specimen irradiated is first ground up into very small particles. Plate 16 shows hyperfine structure in the paramagnetic resonance spectrum of copper due to electric quadrupole interaction. The value of g is found to be nearly 2 which suggests that the spin-orbit interaction is very small, a result to be expected on the Bloch theory (p. 187) which supposes that the conducting electrons are delocalised. The line width, however, is not in good agreement with that expected from the theory, and it has been suggested that the movement of the conduction electrons modifies the field of the microwave radiation.

Resonance experiments on semi-conductors (p. 201) confirm the theory that it is the electrons in the impurities (donor atoms) which are responsible for the conducting properties of semi-conductors. It would not otherwise be possible to obtain a paramagnetic resonance from substances which are diamagnetic.

Paramagnetic resonance from ferro- and antiferro-magnetic substances. In both ferromagnetic and antiferromagnetic substances the exchange forces are very strong. In ferromagnetic substances the exchange integral is positive and neighbouring electron spins are aligned parallel to each other (p. 945); in antiferromagnetic substances the exchange integral is negative and adjacent electron spins are antiparallel (p. 946). The strong internal fields may be investigated by means of paramagnetic resonance; the theory is complicated and not entirely in agreement with experiment. Discrepancies between calculated and observed values of g are ascribed to very strong exchange forces between neighbouring electrons.

Cyclotron or diamagnetic resonance. If resonance experiments are carried out in diamagnetic solids by means of the steady field method (p. 259), Larmor precession of the electron spins (cf. p. 103) may be detected. In the formula for the frequency

$$\nu = \frac{H\epsilon}{2\pi m^* c} \qquad \text{(see note †)}$$

m^* is the "effective" mass of the electron, and its determination from resonance experiments on semi-conductors is of interest in providing information about the conducting electrons.‡ Experiments have been carried out with germanium.

Paramagnetic resonance from F and V centres and other irradiated systems. The irradiation of crystalline substances by X-rays, γ-rays, and neutrons leads to irregularities in the crystal structure. By means of paramagnetic resonance it is possible to detect such anomalies as F and V centres. F centres are vacancies in the crystal lattice which contain an electron instead of a negative ion; V centres are atoms trapped in the lattice. In crystals of the alkali halides, the trapped atoms are halogen ions which have lost their valence electron.

INFORMATION DERIVED FROM EXPERIMENTS ON PARAMAGNETIC RESONANCE

Paramagnetic resonance gives information on:

(1) Binding forces in the solid state.
(2) Energy bands in metals.
(3) Conduction electrons in metals and semi-conductors.
(4) Magnetic moments and electric quadrupole moments.
(5) Transition elements and some metallic complexes.
(6) Free radicals.
(7) g factors in spectroscopy.
(8) Ferromagnetism and antiferromagnetism.

† The frequency is twice that of orbital precession since the gyromagnetic ratio is $e/m_0 c$ for spin.
‡ In general, m^* is not equal to m_0 in solids; cf. spin defect in ferromagnetism, p. 944.

NUCLEAR MAGNETIC RESONANCE

Nuclear magnetic resonance is concerned with the absorption of energy by a nucleus when it lies in a magnetic field and is at the same time subject to radiation of varying frequency. Marked absorption takes place when the quantum of energy absorbed is equal to the energy required for a transition from one nuclear Zeeman level to another. For a field of 10,000 gauss this energy is of the order of a quantum of radiofrequency (10^{-7} eV). Nuclear magnetic resonance is shown by all substances which have a resultant nuclear magnetic moment, whether they are paramagnetic or not, but it is not easy to observe in the presence of paramagnetism, and the resonances are broadened when the absorbing atom has a nuclear electric quadrupole moment.

The properties of spin and magnetic moment are associated with the nucleus, and for the purpose of this discussion the nucleus is regarded as a small magnet which possesses angular momentum. The angular momentum is quantised so that

$$\text{angular momentum } \mathbf{I} = \frac{h}{2\pi} \sqrt{(I(I+1))},$$

where I is the nuclear spin quantum number (not to be confused with the moment of inertia).

In an external magnetic field the component of the nuclear angular momentum in the direction of the field is quantised. It takes the value $mh/2\pi$ where m is the magnetic quantum number: m can take one of the values $I, I-1, I-2, \ldots, -I$. There are $(2I+1)$ possible orientations to the field of the small nuclear magnet, therefore there are $(2I+1)$ possible energy states, which are equally spaced (cf. p. 55).

It is found that the gyromagnetic ratio of a nucleus may be represented by a quantity $g\epsilon/2Mc$ where g is a number appropriate to the particular nucleus considered. g is analogous to, but not the same as, the Landé splitting factor used in connection with electron spin (p. 97). M is the mass of the proton.

If the nucleus is subjected to an external magnetic field H, since its angular momentum component in the direction of the field is quantised, and

$$\text{magnetic moment} = \text{gyromagnetic ratio} \times \text{angular momentum},$$

$$\text{therefore, potential energy of the nucleus} = -H \times \frac{g\epsilon}{2Mc} \times \frac{mh}{2\pi}$$

$$= -Hmg\mu,$$

where μ is a unit of magnetism known as the nuclear magneton ($\mu = h\epsilon/4\pi Mc$) analogous to the Bohr magneton (p. 93). Transitions between the $(2I+1)$ possible Zeeman states give rise to the nuclear magnetic resonance spectrum. The selection rule is $\Delta m = \pm 1$.

It was shown on p. 103 that if a magnetic field is applied to a small rotating magnet, the couple exerted by the field on the magnet causes it to precess round the direction of the field, and that an electron thus precesses round an applied magnetic field with the Larmor frequency. In a similar manner it may be shown that a rotating nucleus precesses round an applied magnetic field with the appropriate Larmor frequency $Hg\epsilon/4\pi Mc$. If a quantum of energy $h\nu_0$, corresponding to the difference of energy of two neighbouring Zeeman states, is absorbed by the nucleus, it is just sufficient to provide the extra energy required to keep the precession of the nucleus going with the Larmor frequency when the nucleus takes up a new allowed position with regard to the magnetic field.

$$h\nu_0 = \text{potential energy in state } (m) - \text{potential energy in state } (m+1)$$
$$= -Hg\mu m + Hg\mu(m+1)$$
$$= Hg\mu,$$

and

$$\nu_0 = \frac{Hg\epsilon}{4\pi Mc}.$$

The nucleus precesses round the direction of the field with constant angular velocity independent of the quantised energy changes.

Although the quantum number m can change by either $+1$ or -1, absorption is slightly more probable than emission. If it were not so there would statistically be no nuclear magnetic resonance spectrum. By Boltzmann's law, the number of nuclei in the upper energy state N_1 is related to the number of nuclei in the lower energy state N_0 by the expression

$$\frac{N_1}{N_0} = e^{-h\nu_0/kT}$$

where k is the Boltzmann constant and T the absolute temperature. The number of nuclei in the lower energy state is slightly greater than the number of nuclei in the upper energy state, therefore there are a few more absorption energy changes than emission energy changes. This condition would not be maintained if the nuclei raised to the upper state did not lose their excess energy rapidly by the coupling of the nuclear precession to the thermal vibrations of the surrounding medium. The interaction between the nuclear spin and the surrounding lattice of a crystal is known as *nuclear spin-lattice relaxation* and the time taken for an interchange of energy between them is known as *nuclear spin-lattice relaxation time*.

For experimental purposes it is convenient to use radiation of radio frequency and magnetic fields of the order of 10,000 gauss. One of two methods may be used. Either the field is kept constant and the frequency altered until absorption takes place, or the frequency is kept constant and the field strength altered until absorption takes place. The intensity of the absorption is plotted either against the frequency or against the field strength according to the method employed. It is important that there should be no paramagnetic atoms present. The lines in the resonance spectrum are equivalent to the energies required to "flip" the nucleus from one allowed orientation to another. Since the energy levels are in theory equally spaced, it would be expected that the lines would all be superposed and appear as one line. There is a fine structure, however, since the nucleus lies not only in the external magnetic field but in the magnetic field of its neighbours.

NUCLEAR MAGNETIC RESONANCE IN CRYSTALS

Nuclei with spin $\frac{1}{2}$ have no quadrupole moment (p. 268).

Early experiments were concerned only with simple cases where there are pairs of like nuclei, each with resultant spin $\frac{1}{2}$, close together in unit cell of a crystal in which no other atom has a resultant spin. For instance, in a crystal of gypsum ($CaSO_4,2H_2O$) the water molecules are so arranged that the protons are found in pairs, and a given pair is not much influenced by the fields of other pairs.†

Consider the potential energy of one of the protons in a field composed of the external magnetic field together with the magnetic field due to the spin of the other proton. There are two possible values for the energy; one for the case when the external field reinforces the field of the other proton, the other when the external field opposes the field of the other proton. Both protons have magnetic moments; therefore they both precess around the direction of the external field. On p. 102 it was shown that precessional motion about a fixed axis may be resolved into two parts; a "static" part, which is a steady angular motion about the direction of the field, and a rotating angular momentum vector at right angles to the direction of the field. The precession of a charged body therefore corresponds to a static magnetic field which lies along the direction of the external field, and another magnetic field

† Pake, G. E., *J. Chem. Phys.*, **16**, 1948, 327.

which lies at right angles to the first and rotates about it; the average value of the rotating field is zero (Fig. 9.3). The static field of the second electron may either reinforce the external field or may oppose it. Thus there are two values for the potential energy of the first electron. For two like nuclei, such as protons, the absorption line is therefore a doublet, the separation of which depends on how near each proton is to the

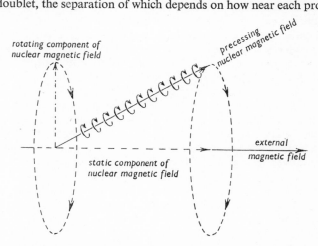

Fig. 9.3. Precession of magnetic field due to nuclear spin.

other, and also on the angle between the inter-proton axis and the direction of the external field. From the separation of the doublet it is possible to calculate the distance between the protons. Fig. 9.4 shows the proton magnetic resonance spectrum of powdered gypsum.

Various factors contribute to line broadening. According to the uncertainty principle, an energy state occupied by a nucleus for a very short time cannot be

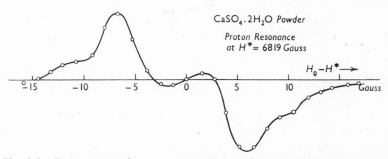

Fig. 9.4. Proton magnetic resonance spectrum of powdered gypsum. (After Pake.)

clearly defined; the width of the absorption line is largely dependent on how long the absorbing nucleus remains in each energy state concerned in the transition. If a precessing nucleus is near another nucleus precessing at the same rate, there is an exchange of energy between the neighbouring spins. As a result there is a slight diminution of the time spent by any one nucleus in any one energy state. The width of the line is very sensitive to the distance between the precessing nuclei. This inter-action is known as a *nuclear spin-spin relaxation*; the time taken for the exchange of

9*

energy between the nuclei is known as the *nuclear spin-spin relaxation time*. The spin-spin relaxation time is very much shorter than the spin-lattice relaxation time in crystals, and is much the more important in determining line widths.

Absorption spectra have been recorded for groups of more than two nuclei; the shape of the absorption curve obtained is in each case characteristic of the number of nuclei in the group. For instance, where three nuclei are arranged in a triangle, the curve shows three peaks; a tetrahedral arrangement gives a curve with a flat top. Where the grouping is complicated, the absorption lines coalesce with no well-defined structure. Van Vleck, however, has shown that measurements of line width in these cases can lead to an estimation of the distances apart of the nuclei.† The quantity measured experimentally is the mean square width of the line and is known as the *second moment*. It is possible to use Van Vleck's method to locate hydrogen atoms in crystals when the positions of the other atoms have been established by X-ray or electron diffraction.

Absorption curves may be directly recorded on a cathode ray oscillograph; the characteristic curves for different crystals are sometimes described as *line shapes*. Theoretical line shapes may be calculated for different groupings of atoms in the particular crystal investigated; theoretical and experimental curves may then be compared and the correct crystal structure identified.

Nuclei with spin greater than $\frac{1}{2}$ may have nuclear quadrupole moments, owing to a distribution of charge which is not spherically symmetrical (p. 268). The quadrupole moment is coupled to the electric field of the crystal; this coupling depends on the field gradient. The coupling constant is not the same for all the $(2I+1)$ allowed positions of the nucleus in the external magnetic field, since the potential energy of the charged nucleus depends on its orientation in the electric field. The effect is shown as a hyperfine structure of the absorption line. For instance, suppose a proton is in the field of a nucleus with spin $\frac{3}{2}$. The simple proton resonance line is split into four because of the four allowed positions of its neighbour in the external magnetic field ($m = \frac{3}{2}, \frac{1}{2}, -\frac{1}{2}, -\frac{3}{2}$); these are the *fine structure* lines. Each of the fine structure lines shows a hyperfine structure, usually shown as a broadening of the absorption line, since the energy levels are raised due to the quadrupole interaction. For spin $\pm\frac{1}{2}$ the energy levels are raised slightly, for spin $\pm\frac{3}{2}$ the energy levels are raised considerably. If the coupling constants are known, the positions of the nuclei can be estimated to a high degree of accuracy.

Line shapes may be calculated for groups of resonating nuclei, but in cases where the line shape is not easily identified, the second moment may still be calculated from the line width, and the relative positions of the hydrogen atoms located even if the complete pattern of the structure is not revealed. In crystals where the molecules are close together some line broadening occurs as the result of intermolecular exchange of energy. This may be distinguished from the intramolecular broadening by observation of absorption by groups containing one or more substituted nuclei, such as the deuteron for the proton.

Analysis of the fine structure can provide information on such topics as the mobility of ions in the solid state, hindered rotation, and the rate of exchange reactions. The width of the lines decreases as the temperature is raised owing to the increased thermal motion which tends to average out the effect of the magnetic fields of the molecules and ions on each other. In order that the fine structure should be resolved, it is necessary for the nucleus to remain in one position for a time which is greater than $1/\Delta\nu$ where $\Delta\nu$ is the frequency difference between the lines which are to be resolved. The mobility of protons in hydrogen compounds has been estimated by means of a

† Van Vleck, *Phys. Rev.*, **74**, 1948, 1168.

method which is based on this fact. There is evidence that with some crystalline substances a reorientation of an ion in the crystal takes place at a critical temperature.

NUCLEAR MAGNETIC RESONANCE IN LIQUIDS

Molecular motion in liquids is very vigorous compared with that in solids, therefore the resonance lines from liquids are much narrower than those from solids. The absorption may be considered to be that of a single molecule unaffected by the magnetic fields of its neighbours, since the thermal motion averages out their fields to zero. Nevertheless, in each molecule, the magnetic field experienced at a nucleus is not the same as the applied field. It varies by a factor which depends on the chemical environment of the nucleus; therefore if there are several like nuclei such as protons in the molecule, they give different resonance lines if they are associated with different groups of atoms within the molecule. The change of position of a resonance line due to a change of chemical environment is often referred to as a *chemical shift*. If H is the applied field, and H' is the field experienced by the nucleus, $H' = H(1 - \sigma)$, where σ is characteristic of a particular compound. σ contains two terms. The first is due to the induced diamagnetism in the electron cloud surrounding the nucleus, and is nearly constant for each type of complex. The second term is due to a change of paramagnetism in the electron cloud consequent on the promotion by the applied field of some electrons to excited states.[†] The temperature dependence of the energy changes has also been investigated.

The absorption lines have a hyperfine structure caused by the interaction of a nucleus and its electrons with the nuclear magnetic fields of the neighbouring nuclei in its own group of atoms within the molecule. This is known as *electron coupled nuclear spin-spin interaction*. Each nucleus has $(2I + 1)$ allowed positions in the applied field, and this causes the resonance lines of its neighbours to be split into $(2I + 1)$ lines since each possible value of the field occurs if a large number of molecules are present. The analysis of the hyperfine structure can lead to an estimation of the distance apart of the atoms in a molecule or group within a molecule, and gives valuable information on chemical bonding.

The width of the line depends on the relaxation processes, that is on the exchange of energy of the nucleus with its immediate surroundings. If the nucleus has a quadrupole moment the time of relaxation is often very short, and as a result the line is broad. If there is a very strong interaction of the field gradient at the nucleus with the quadrupole moment, there is a possibility that the turning over of the molecule due to the thermal motion in the liquid will pull the nucleus out of one allowed orientation into another. Such a process is shown as a change of width of the line.[‡]

A typical nuclear magnetic resonance spectrum, that of SF_4 in the liquid state, is shown in Plate 15.

INFORMATION DERIVED FROM EXPERIMENTS ON NUCLEAR MAGNETIC RESONANCE

Nuclear magnetic resonance gives information on:

(1) The grouping of atoms in a molecule; the method has particular value in the case of hydrogen atoms.

(2) Internuclear distances and bond lengths in crystals, leading to the calculation of bond angles.

[†] R. E. Richards, *J. Inorg. Nuclear Chem.*, 1958, 7–8, 423.

[‡] If the experiment is conducted on a diamagnetic liquid, the addition of a small number of paramagnetic ions reduces the relaxation time and causes consequent line broadening; this is the basis of a method for estimating the amount of spin-orbital coupling in a paramagnetic ion or complex.

(3) Nuclear magnetic moments and gyromagnetic ratios.
(4) Exchange of energy between nuclei.
(5) Relaxation processes.
(6) Energy barriers.
(7) Hindered rotation.
(8) Solid state forces.

NUCLEAR QUADRUPOLE MOMENTS

If a nucleus has a resultant spin greater than $\frac{1}{2}$ it is generally found that the distribution of nuclear charge is not spherically symmetrical. Such a nucleus is said to have a *quadrupole moment*; this is usually denoted by Q. If there is a pronounced electric field gradient close to the nucleus, the coupling of the quadrupole moment to the field gradient is shown by the splitting of nuclear energy levels (p. 266). The analysis of the quadrupole splitting is therefore a very useful tool for the investigation of the electric field near a particular nucleus, and in general for the investigation of the nature and properties of chemical bonds.

QUADRUPOLE COUPLING CONSTANTS

The potential energy of the nucleus in the electric field surrounding it is proportional to the product $\epsilon Q q$, where ϵ is the charge on the nucleus, Q the nuclear quadrupole moment, and q the field gradient. If the field is uniform there is no coupling. The product $\epsilon Q q$ is known as the *quadrupole coupling constant*. In most cases it is not possible to obtain a separate value of Q, but the coupling constant can be determined from observations on spectra in the microwave or radiofrequency regions according to the nature of the specimen investigated. A considerable amount of interest is attached to the determination of the coupling constant, since its value is an indication of the properties of a chemical bond which exists in a certain molecular environment. If the environment is altered, the coupling constant is altered. Q may be either positive or negative; in a few cases an actual value can be assigned to Q by means of atomic beam techniques which are not discussed here. When Q is positive, it appears that the distribution of positive charge is prolate with regard to the spin axis; if Q is negative, the distribution of positive charge is oblate with regard to the spin axis (Fig. 9.5).

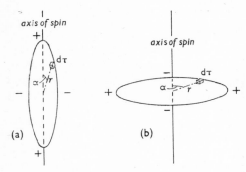

Fig. 9.5. Distribution of nuclear charge relative to the axis of spin. (a) Q positive; distribution prolate. (b) Q negative; distribution oblate. The centre of gravity of the charge need not be on the axis of spin.

Q is related to the charge density by the expression

$$Q = \int \rho r^2 (3 \cos^2 \alpha - 1)\, d\tau$$

where ρ = nuclear charge density at a point in the volume element $d\tau$,

r = distance of centre of gravity of the charge from the volume element $d\tau$.

α = angle between r and the spin axis.

The origin of the term quadrupole moment is evident from the pictorial representation of the charge distribution shown in Fig. 9.5.

Quadrupole coupling in solids. The quadrupole moment of the nucleus is coupled to the field gradient of the crystal, and the nucleus can take up one of $(2I+1)$ allowed orientations. The difference of energy between the different possible nuclear positions is of the order of a quantum of radiofrequency. Resonance absorption spectra are obtained by subjecting the crystal to radiation of varying radiofrequency in the *absence* of an external magnetic or electric field. If a quantum of energy of the right frequency is absorbed, the nucleus "flips" from one allowed position to another. The spectrum obtained is known as a *pure quadrupole resonance spectrum* (Plate 17); its analysis gives information on coupling constants and on the nature of electric fields in crystals.

Quadrupole coupling in liquids. Owing to the thermal motion in liquids, at any molecule the average value of the field gradient due to the other molecules is zero. There is therefore no pure quadrupole resonance spectrum. The presence of a quadrupole moment in a nucleus shows itself, however, by its interaction with the field gradient due to the other nuclei and electrons in its own molecule. The result is shown as a hyperfine structure in the nuclear magnetic resonance spectrum, and has already been mentioned on p. 267.

Quadrupole coupling in gases. As with liquids, the field gradient at the nucleus due to other molecules varies very rapidly and so averages to zero and there is no pure quadrupole resonance spectrum. The presence of a nuclear quadrupole moment is shown by its interaction with the field gradient due to the electrons and other nuclei in its own molecule. This is observed as the hyperfine structure of the pure rotation gaseous microwave spectrum (p. 257).

RESULTS OBTAINED FROM THE STUDY OF COUPLING CONSTANTS

Experimental evidence suggests that the spherically symmetrical s orbitals and completed shells do not contribute much to the field gradient. It appears that the charge in the d and f orbitals is too far from the nucleus to have a significant effect. It has therefore been deduced that the field gradient near the nucleus is largely due to the occupied p orbitals of the valence shell. If the chemical bond investigated is ionic in character the value of the coupling constant is small; this fact may be used as the basis of a method of determining the percentage ionic character of a bond (p. 142).

If the coupling constants in a gaseous molecule can be determined by some other method, a study of the hyperfine structure of the pure rotation (microwave) spectrum of a gas is a method of investigating centrifugal distortion.

Although the difficulty of interpretation of the experimental results increases with the size of the molecule investigated, it is possible in some cases to make an estimate of the percentage of double bond character and the nature of hybridisation in a polyatomic molecule. Information on the direction of covalent bonds in a crystal lattice may sometimes be obtained. In all these calculations allowance must be made for the various factors which distort the field.

INFORMATION DERIVED FROM THE STUDY OF QUADRUPOLE MOMENTS

Observations on pure quadrupole resonance spectra, and the determination of coupling constants give information on:

(1) The ratios of the quadrupole moments of different isotopes.

(2) Absolute values of quadrupole moments in a few cases.

(3) The field gradient just outside the nucleus, and hence the type of chemical binding.

(4) Solid state forces.

(5) The structure of liquids.

BOOKS FOR FURTHER READING

HERZBERG, G., *Infrared and Raman Spectra* (Van Nostrand, 1945).

INGRAM, D. J. E., *Spectroscopy at Radio and Microwave Frequencies* (Butterworth's Scientific Publications, 1955).

LOW, W. *Paramagnetic Resonance in Solids* (Academic Press, New York and London, 1960).

POPLE, J. A., SCHNEIDER, W. G. and BERNSTEIN, H. J., *High Resolution Nuclear Magnetic Resonance* (McGraw-Hill, 1959).

TOWNES, C. H. and SCHAWLOW, A. L., *Microwave spectroscopy* (McGraw-Hill, 1955).

REVIEWS

BLEANEY, B., *The radiofrequency spectroscopy of gases* (*Rep. Prog. Phys.*, 11, 1946, 178).

BLEANEY, B. and STEVENS, K. W. H., *Paramagnetic Resonance* (*Rep. Prog. Phys.*, 16, 1953, 108).

BOWERS, K. D. and OWEN, J., *Paramagnetic Resonance* (*Rep. Prog. Phys.*, 18, 1955, 304).

GLOCKLER, G., *The Raman Effect* (*Revs. Mod. Phys.*, 15, 1943, 112).

GORDY, W., *Microwave Spectroscopy* (*Handbuch der Physik*, edited by S. Flügge, Vol. XXVIII).

MENZIES, A. C., *Raman Effect in Solids* (*Rep. Prog. Phys.*, 16, 1953, 83).

Technique of Organic Chemistry, Vol. IX, *Chemical Applications of Spectroscopy*, Chap. 2, (N.Y. Interscience Publications, 1956).

Microwave and Radiofrequency Spectroscopy (*Discuss. Faraday Soc.*, 19, 1955, 9).

NYHOLM, R. S., *Magnetism and Inorganic Chemistry* (*Quarterly Reviews*, 7, No. 4, 1953, 377).

ORVILLE-THOMAS, W. J., *Nuclear Quadrupole Coupling and Chemical Bonding* (*Quarterly Reviews*, 11, No. 2, 1957, 162).

RICHARDS, R. E., *The Location of Hydrogen Atoms in Crystals* (*Quarterly Reviews*, 10, No. 4, 1956, 480).

SHERIDAN, J., *Review of Microwave Spectroscopy of Gases* (*Research*, 8, 1955, 88).

SMITH, J. A. S., *Nuclear Magnetic Resonance Absorption* (*Quarterly Reviews*, 8, No. 3, 1953, 279).

WHIFFEN, D. H., *Electron Resonance Spectroscopy of Free Radicals* (*Quarterly Reviews*, 12, No. 3, 1958, 250).

WOODWARD, L. A., *Raman Spectra of Inorganic Compounds* (*Quarterly Reviews*, 10, No. 2, 1956, 185).

CHAPTER TEN

THE DETERMINATION OF INTERNUCLEAR DISTANCES BY THE DIFFRACTION OF X-RAYS, ELECTRONS, AND NEUTRONS

Much information concerning the structure of molecules and crystals has been derived from the study of the diffraction of X-rays, electrons, and neutrons.

X-rays are photons of high penetrating power, with wave lengths of the order of 1 Å; they have no rest mass. When X-rays impinge on an atom some of the radiation is scattered by the outer electrons. During the process of scattering, the electrons absorb energy from the periodic electric field of the X-radiation, and re-emit most of it as radiation of the original wave length.

Experiments on X-ray scattering, more usually described as *diffraction*, yield information on the distribution of electron density in the molecule or crystal and hence on the positions of the atoms. The high penetrating power of X-rays makes them very suitable for diffraction experiments on crystals.

Electron waves are de Broglie waves which accompany the passage of electrons. The wave length depends on the velocity (v) of the electron (p. 12); it is of the order of the wave length of hard X-rays. Since electron waves are accompanied by a charged particle they can be deflected by electric and magnetic fields. Electron waves are diffracted by the electrons of an atom; the effect is enhanced because of their strong interaction with the electric field in the atom, and consequently they do not penetrate far into solid substances. Their diffraction is chiefly used for investigating the structure of gaseous molecules, and the surface structure of crystals.

Neutron waves are similar to electron waves, but the particles with which they are associated are 1838 times as heavy as the electron, and consequently the wave length of the neutron wave is 1838 times shorter than the wave length of the electron wave with the same group velocity. Since neutrons are uncharged, they are unaffected by the field of the electrons in the outer part of the atom, but they are scattered by the nucleus, the diameter of which is comparable with the wave length of the neutron, and thus the observation of neutron diffraction is of great value in helping to locate the nuclei in a molecule or crystal. The diffraction of X-rays, electrons, and neutrons is discussed separately and in further detail in this chapter. In the discussion it is assumed that the scattering is *coherent*. This means that the scattering occurs without change of wave length. In many experiments there is a more or less marked background of continuous radiation due to *incoherent* scattering, the wave length of the radiation having been changed during the scattering process. The intensity of this background is small compared with that of the coherent scattering.

X-ray diffraction phenomena were originally explained in terms of classical optical theory and for many purposes this theory is sufficient; for the interpretation of X-ray diffraction spectra there is no need to consider the quantum mechanical theory of the interaction of the X-radiation with the electron. A simple classical explanation of the phenomenon of diffraction may be given as follows.

Diffraction of light. The mechanism of diffraction is easily visualised in terms of the wave theory of light. When radiation impinges on an obstacle in its path, a geometrical shadow is formed. Under certain circumstances some of the radiation may be observed within the boundary of the shadow, and this phenomenon is known as *diffraction*. Huyghens explained this effect by supposing that each point of contact of the incident wave with the obstacle becomes a source of secondary wavelets, and that the wavelets from different sources interfere with each other, sometimes reinforcing and sometimes cancelling each other out, and so form a pattern of light and dark known as a *diffraction pattern*. The secondary wavelets are usually described as scattered radiation.

A simple example of diffraction is shown in Fig. 10.1. Suppose a plane mono-

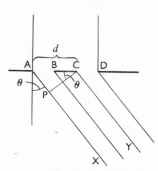

chromatic wave impinges on two parallel slits *AB*, *CD*, where $AB=BC=CD$, and $AC=d$. On passing through the slits the radiation is scattered in all directions. Consider a direction *AX* making an angle θ with the direction of the incident beam. Some radiation is scattered from *A* in the direction *AX*, and some radiation is scattered from *C* in a parallel direction *CY*. These scattered waves overlap, and whether they reinforce or cut out each other depends on the relation of their path difference, *AP*, to the wave length λ of the radiation (λ is assumed to be the same before and after scattering). If *AP* contains

Fig. 10.1.   Diffraction from two parallel slits.

an even number of half wave lengths, the overlapping waves reinforce each other giving maximum brightness; if it contains an odd number of half wave lengths the overlapping waves cancel each other out. If the scattered radiation is received on a screen, the image appears as a series of alternate bright and dark lines.

For a bright line,

$$AP = n\lambda = d \sin \theta,$$

where *n* is an integer $< d/\lambda$.

Hence

$$\sin \theta = \frac{n\lambda}{d}.$$

θ is known as the *angle of diffraction*.

For a constant wave length the image shows a series of bright lines corresponding to values of $\sin \theta$ determined by the value of *n*. For a slit of constant width *d*, the difference between values of $\sin \theta$ corresponding to a change of unity in the value of *n* increases with increasing wave length. For shorter wave lengths the bright lines, or *diffraction maxima*, are closer together. For good resolution of the diffraction pattern the slits must be narrow, but *d* must always be greater than λ. A lens may be arranged so that the diffracted images from a number of slits close together reinforce each other on a screen. A succession of slits is obtained by ruling a number of very fine lines extremely close together on a transparent surface; the distance between the slits must be of the order of a wave length of the radiation diffracted; the arrangement is known as a *diffraction grating*. The image received from the grating consists, for monochromatic light, of alternate bright and dark lines becoming fainter as the distance from the central image increases; for white light each image is a continuous spectrum since the diffraction maxima are located at positions which depend on the wave length of the radiation. When the lines are very close together the central image occupies the whole field.

The complete theory of the diffraction grating takes into account many factors neglected in the above simple description.

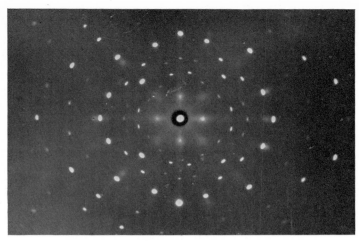

Pl. 18. Laue photograph of NaCl at room temperature. [Preston, *Proc. roy. Soc.* **A, 172**, 1939.]

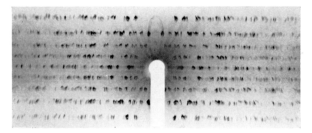

Pl. 19. Rotation photograph of a single crystal of $CuSO_4 5H_2O$ using Cu K_α radiation. [Roof, *Acta. cryst.*, **8**, 1955.]

Pl. 20. Powder photograph of alloy FeAl (using Fe K_α and K_β radiation). [Bradley and Jay, *Proc. roy. Soc.* **A, 136**, 1932.]

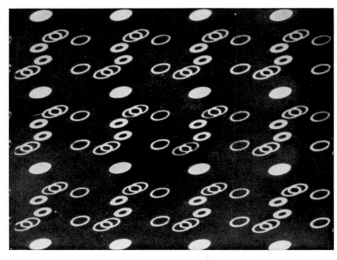

Pl. 21. Enlargement of a small part of the "fly's eye" diopside grating. [de Vos, *Acta. cryst.*, **1**, 1948.]

Pl. 22. Electron diffraction pattern of $Ni(OH)_2$ (normal incidence). [Germer, *Z. Kristallog.*, **100**, 1938–9.]

Pl. 23. Composite photograph of the domain configuration in a surface of a nickel iron film 5000 Å thick. [Fowler and Fryer, *Phys. Rev.*, **100**, 1955.]

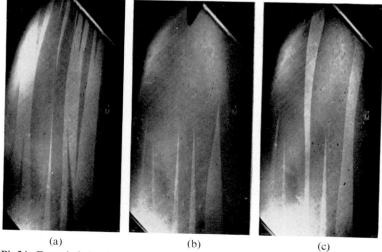

(a)   (b)   (c)

Pl. 24. Domain behaviour in a small portion of the film as the S pole of a small compass needle is brought up to the film edge and then removed. [Fowler and Fryer, *Phys. Rev.*, **100**, 1955.]

X-RAY DIFFRACTION

DIFFRACTION OF X-RAYS BY GRATINGS

Owing to the small wave length of X-rays it is not possible to rule a grating finely enough to obtain a well-resolved X-ray diffraction spectrum by transmission. Theoretical considerations show that when X-rays pass from a less dense to a more dense medium they are refracted away from the normal. It is therefore to be expected that if X-rays impinge on a finely ruled grating at grazing incidence the scattering will take place by reflection. The effect of grazing incidence would be to make the path difference

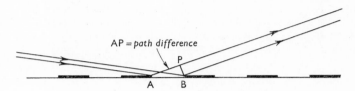

Fig. 10.2. Diffraction of X-rays by reflection at a grating.

between adjacent scattered waves greater than if the angle of incidence were small (Fig. 10.2). A. H. Compton succeeded in producing a reflected diffraction spectrum of X-rays by scattering at grazing incidence from a very finely ruled grating. This experiment was of considerable importance since it provided a standard means of measuring the wave length of X-radiation.

DIFFRACTION OF X-RAYS BY CRYSTALS

Laue equations. The diffraction of X-rays by a row of atoms in one plane of a crystal is similar to the scattering of X-rays by the lines of a ruled grating, but it is

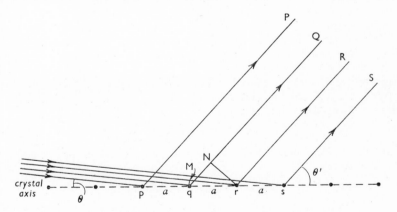

Fig. 10.3. Diffraction of X-rays by a row of atoms in a crystal.

possible to obtain diffraction patterns from a crystal by transmission as well as by reflection since the atoms of a crystal are much closer together than are the lines of the finest grating.

Let p, q, r, s (Fig. 10.3), represent a number of atoms of the same kind, distance a apart, in a row parallel to a given axis in the crystal. Let the incident beam of monochromatic X-rays make an angle θ with the axis of the crystal. The radiation is scattered in all directions of which one, represented by pP, qQ, rR, makes an angle θ' with the crystal axis. The path difference between radiation scattered in this direction from neighbouring atoms such as q and r is $Mr - qN$. For a diffraction maximum, $Mr - qN = n\lambda$ where n is a whole number, and

$$a(\cos \theta - \cos \theta') = n\lambda.$$

For complete cancellation, n is equal to an odd number of half wave lengths, and for the diffraction image to be sharp there must be complete cancellation for an angle very little different from θ'. Such cancellation cannot occur by the interference of scattered radiation from two adjacent atoms because the path difference is too small; it appears only as a result of interference of scattered radiation from atoms some distance apart. If the crystal is not large enough to include atoms separated by the required distance, the boundary of the diffraction maxima are not sharp. Absorption,

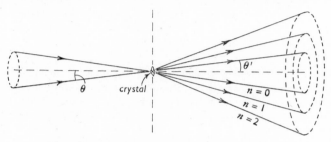

Fig. 10.4.   Three-dimensional scattering in a crystal.

thermal effects, Compton scattering, and the emission of secondary X-rays also reduce the sharpness of the maxima.

It is not necessary for the incident beam, scattered beam, and crystal axis to be in the same plane. In general, for a diffraction maximum, an incident beam in a given direction gives rise to a cone of scattered rays, all of which make the same angle θ' with the crystal axis. The incident beam itself may also be in the form of a cone of rays all making the same angle θ with the crystal axis. Since n can take any integral value, the whole process of diffraction by the crystal may be represented as a cone of incident rays and a series of coaxial cones of scattered rays (Fig. 10.4), each of which corresponds to a different integral value of n. For each diffraction maximum the scattered ray lies on the surface of a cone and

$$a(\cos \theta - \cos \theta') = n\lambda.$$

If two other crystallographic axes are considered, similar relations may be developed, giving a set of three equations:

$$\left.\begin{aligned} a(\cos \theta - \cos \theta') &= n\lambda \\ b(\cos \phi - \cos \phi') &= m\lambda \\ c(\cos \xi - \cos \xi') &= l\lambda. \end{aligned}\right\} \tag{10.1}$$

These equations are known as the *Laue equations*. They are concerned with the distance between the atoms located along given crystal axes.

Bragg's law. If a monochromatic beam of X-rays penetrates a series of identical parallel planes in a crystal, as the beam meets each plane of atoms some of the radiation is scattered and some is transmitted. A case of special interest is that of radiation scattered in such a direction that the angle of incidence is equal to the angle between the scattered beam and the normal. This is called a *Bragg reflection* (Fig. 10.5). From the figure it can be seen that the path difference between a ray scattered at X and a ray scattered at Q is $PQ + QX - RX$.

But

$$RX = SX,$$

and therefore,

$$\text{path difference} = PQ + QS.$$

If d is the distance apart of two successive planes of atoms in the crystal, and if the incident and scattered beams both make an angle θ with the crystal plane, the scattered beams from the two successive planes reinforce each other if the path difference contains a whole number of wave lengths.

If this is so,

$$
\begin{aligned}
n\lambda &= PQ + QS \\
&= 2d \sin \theta. \quad (10.2)
\end{aligned}
$$

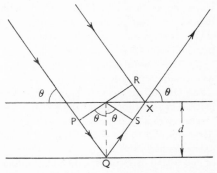

This relation is known as *Bragg's law*. If the crystal contains a series of atomic planes, distance d apart, the minute portions of radiation reflected at each successive plane reinforce each other and a strong reflected beam results, the angle θ being such that Bragg's law is obeyed.

Fig. 10.5. Bragg reflection in a crystal.

The simple relation given by Bragg's law is true only to a first approximation, but for many purposes it is accurate enough. Where high precision is required a small correction must be introduced into the equation to allow for the slight refraction of X-rays away from the normal when they pass from a less dense to a more dense medium.

CRYSTAL ANALYSIS

The diffraction of X-rays by crystals obviously provides a very convenient instrument for the investigation of crystal structure, since the d of Bragg's law and the a of the Laue equation can be determined experimentally provided the wave length is known. At first it was not possible to obtain an accurate value for the wave length, and so the investigation of the structure of an unknown crystal had to be carried out by comparing its diffraction pattern with that of a standard simple crystal whose structure had been inferred from symmetry considerations and chemical evidence. When it was found that X-rays could be diffracted by reflection from a ruled grating it was possible to make an independent and accurate determination of the wave length.

There are several methods which are used for the investigation of crystal structure by X-ray diffraction, the choice of which depends on the problem to be investigated. The main methods are here described in outline only; for experimental details the reader is referred to the many technical books on the subject.

Laue method. This method was the first, and is the only one to employ continuous radiation. The incident beam, usually produced from a tungsten target, passes through a slit and impinges on a small specimen of the crystal which is to be investigated. The diffracted radiation produces spots on a film in regular patterns which are determined by the spacing of the atoms. Several photographs are taken with the incident beam parallel to well defined crystallographic directions such as the main crystal axes. The diffraction photographs are easily obtained but difficult to interpret, and the method in its original form is no longer in use although it is the basis from which some modern methods have been developed. Plate 18 shows a Laue photograph of NaCl.

Bragg spectrometer method. In the early days of X-ray diffraction much pioneer work was done by W. H. and W. L. Bragg, using an X-ray spectrometer, which in its simple form is similar to the equivalent optical instrument. Although this method has been of great value it is now superseded by other methods.

Rotation and oscillation method. This is essentially a development of the Laue method but with the following differences:

(a) The radiation is effectively monochromatic. It is commonly the K radiation from copper or molybdenum; it may contain both K_α and K_β radiation, but the spots due to the latter are easily identified by their low intensity.

(b) The crystal, which is very much smaller than that used in the Laue method, is usually less than a millimetre in diameter.

(c) The crystal undergoes complete rotation, or oscillation about a small angle, whereas in the Laue method it is fixed.

(d) One of the principal crystallographic axes corresponds with the axis of rotation instead of the direction of the incident beam as with the Laue method.

The diffraction pattern, although it may be recorded on a flat plate behind the crystal perpendicular to the incident beam, is most usually received on a cylindrical film whose axis coincides with the axis of rotation of the crystal. The pattern so recorded consists of successive *layer lines*. These are circular lines of spots, the plane of each circle being perpendicular to the axis of rotation. If the cylindrical film is opened out the lines are straight. The positions of the spots may be interpreted in a simple way as follows:

Suppose that a beam of X-rays is incident normally on a row of atoms in a stationary crystal; A, B are two successive atoms in this row, separated by a distance a. (Fig. 10.6(i)). If θ' is the angle between the diffracted beam and the row of atoms, for a diffraction maximum,

$$a \cos \theta' = n\lambda \quad \text{(Laue equation, p. 274)}$$

where n is an integer. The scattered rays from other atoms in the row contribute to the diffracted beam. Other diffracted beams are also formed corresponding to different integral values of n (Fig. 10.6(ii)). Theoretically it should be possible to receive on a screen or film these beams corresponding to diffraction maxima, but the diffraction from a single row of atoms is not sufficiently strong unless it is reinforced by Bragg reflections from planes of atoms further in the crystal. If the crystal is rotated about the axis which contains the row of atoms (one of the principal axes of the crystal) until it is in such a position that the diffraction from the row of atoms along the axis is reinforced by a Bragg reflection, the diffraction maxima are then shown strongly as spots on the screen or film. Further rotation of the crystal brings successive planes of atoms in the crystal into the right position for reinforcement of the diffracted beam (Fig. 10.6(iii)). The different positions of the diffraction maxima thus appear as *layer lines* consisting of horizontal lines of bright spots (Fig. 10.6(iv)). The same Bragg reflection for different values of n in the Laue diffraction is represented by a row of spots which lie on a curve cutting across the layer lines. This is known as a *row line*. The distance between the row lines may be used to determine the distance between the crystal planes (d of the Bragg reflection), and the distance between the layer lines to determine the distance between neighbouring atoms a.

By taking a number of photographs corresponding to the rotation of the crystal about each of its principal axes in turn, it is possible to calculate the lattice parameters and the shape and volume of unit cell. The complete analysis of the rotation photographs can be most easily performed in terms of the reciprocal lattice (p. 194). The analysis provides information on the type of crystal and its space group, the dimensions and shape of unit cell, and the number of atoms or molecules per unit cell. Three rotation photographs about the three principal axes of the crystal are usually sufficient to provide complete information about the position of the atomic planes and the size of unit cell. Plate 19 shows a rotation photograph of a single crystal of $CuSO_4,5H_2O$.

The method may be varied by oscillating the crystal through a small angle instead of using complete rotation. This helps to correlate certain spots with reflections at certain planes. In order to assist still further the analysis of complicated diffraction

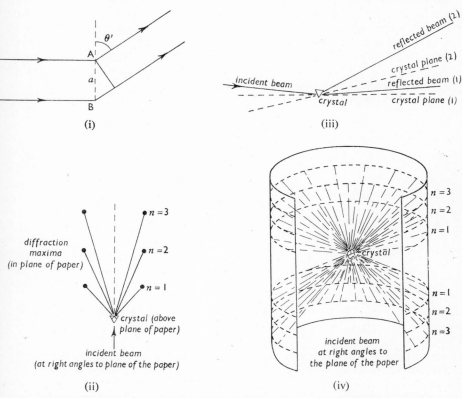

Fig. 10.6. Diffraction of X-rays by rotation (oscillation) method: (i) diffraction of beam by two neighbouring atoms; (ii) formation of a number of diffraction maxima; (iii) reinforcement of diffraction maxima by Bragg reflection; (iv) formation of layer lines on a cylindrical film.

patterns, moving film methods have been employed. Different workers have adopted various modifications of camera design. The two systems most generally used are (a) the *Weissenberg goniometer*, in which the film is displaced parallel to the axis of rotation of the crystal, and (b) the *Buerger precession method* by means of which a single layer line can be spread out into a magnified undistorted two-dimensional diffraction pattern which is the image of the reciprocal lattice. This leads directly to a determination of the equivalent crystal lattice under investigation.

Powder method. The methods so far described are applicable to the investigation of single crystals only. The value of X-ray diffraction as an investigator's tool in chemical analysis was greatly extended by the introduction of the powder method by means of which X-ray diffraction photographs can be obtained not only of powdered crystals, but also of polycrystalline aggregates and of polycrystalline surfaces such as those of metals.

It may be assumed that in any chaotic and random arrangement of a collection of very fine particles of a crystalline substance, every possible position of the crystal is represented. If such a system is irradiated by monochromatic X-rays the diffraction photograph shows spots corresponding to Bragg reflection from each set of parallel planes. Since the crystals are orientated in all directions, the diffracted rays form a series of concentric cones, and the diffraction pattern received on a flat plate is a number of concentric rings. If the receiving film is cylindrical, when the film is opened out the intersections of the cones with the film appear as a series of nearly parallel lines. A further advantage of the cylindrical film is that photographs may be taken both behind, and in front of, the specimen to be examined. For instance, transmission photographs may be taken with very thin films of metal, and reflection photographs may be taken from the surfaces of metal blocks. As the diffraction photographs are usually very complicated, the incident radiation must be as nearly monochromatic as possible. There have been many advances in experimental technique since the powder method was first introduced. Unfortunately the method can be applied only to substances with a high degree of symmetry, since the photographs obtained from solids of low symmetry are too complicated for analysis. Crystalline structures of a high degree of symmetry may often be identified by simple inspection of their diffraction photographs. Plate 20 shows a powder photograph of the alloy FeAl.

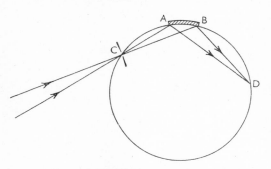

Fig. 10.7.   Seemann-Bohlin focusing device.

One disadvantage of the original powder method is that it needs more energy to obtain a good photograph from a crystalline powder than from a single crystal. Early experimenters had to make very long exposures to attain the requisite intensity; this was particularly the case with heavy metals. The trouble was eliminated by the invention of the *Seemann-Bohlin camera*. This camera employs a divergent beam and contains a focusing device. In the original model, the collimating slit, the specimen, and the film were all located on the circumference of the same circle (Fig. 10.7). Since the angles subtended by the same chord on the same arc of a circle are equal, it can be seen from the diagram that there is a focusing action, and that the image at D consists of the superposition of all the diffracted beams with the same angle of diffraction. Where a focusing device is used, a good photograph may be obtained very rapidly. The specimen AB must be made to conform to the shape of the circumference of the circle either by the grinding of a solid specimen, or by sticking a powder on to a curved surface. Various modifications and improvements to the camera have been introduced. The incident radiation is "monochromatised" by some form of crystal cut-off, that is, by some device which allows the passage of radiation of a single wave length only.

Another method of recording which is widely used is that of the *Geiger diffractometer*. Geiger counters have long been used for the detection of the ionisation produced by X-rays. The simple counter consists of a small cylindrical metal chamber containing gas; an insulated wire runs down the centre of the chamber. The wire and chamber walls act as electrodes and a high potential is put on between them. If X-rays pass through the walls, both primary and secondary ions are produced in the gas, and a current flows between the two electrodes. The current may be amplified, and its presence demonstrated in a variety of ways, and its magnitude may be automatically recorded on a revolving drum of ruled paper. This method is employed in the Geiger diffractometer; the recording shows a series of peaks which may be used as a direct measure of the intensity of the diffracted beams. The method is very sensitive, and therefore only short exposures are necessary.

Space group of the crystal. In order to describe the symmetry of a crystal it is necessary to know not only the spatial relation of a single atom to the other atoms in the unit cell but also the spatial relation of the contents of one unit cell to the contents of another. In discussing the symmetry of isolated molecules and its effect on molecular spectra (p. 228) it is sufficient to consider the point groups only, since there is no particular space relation of one molecule to another to be considered. The arrangement of atoms in an isolated molecule is therefore classified by the notional symmetry operations of the point groups, as the result of which the molecule in its final position is indistinguishable from the molecule in its initial position. Such symmetry operations are sufficient to classify crystals if they are considered merely from the point of view of external form, but a further refinement must be introduced in order to assign a particular position to an atom in a unit cell of a crystal. If a correct position has been assigned to the atom in the unit cell, it must be possible to carry out a symmetry operation appropriate to the point group of the macroscopic crystal, and at the same time to carry out a translational motion which leaves the atom in a neighbouring cell in the same position which it occupied in the original cell. For this type of symmetry operation the crystal is assigned to one of 230 possible *space groups*. The symmetry operations then considered are those of the point groups combined with translation in space. For instance, an axis of rotation may become a *screw axis*, that is, one which gives a rotation through an angle of $2\pi/n$ with a simultaneous translation parallel to the axis. A simple reflection plane may become a *glide plane*, that is, one which gives a reflection across the plane with a simultaneous translation parallel to the plane. This advanced classification embraces not only the external geometrical forms of the crystal but also the concepts of a crystal as an infinite series of unit cells. It is very important to distinguish clearly between the point group characteristic of the external geometrical properties of the crystal and the space group characteristic of the atoms in the unit cell. The translation appropriate to a space group is of atomic dimensions and is negligible when the crystal is considered as a macroscopic structure. In many cases it is possible to identify the crystal space group from the diffraction pattern, but unfortunately it is not usually possible to show the asymmetry of a structure in this way as nearly all crystals diffract as though they had a centre of symmetry. As a consequence, the interpretation of diffraction spectra may be ambiguous in some cases, and where any doubt arises, the space group must be confirmed by information from other sources.

ANALYSIS OF DIFFRACTION PATTERNS

Position of diffracted beams. The identification of the crystal space group depends on the absence of certain features of the diffraction pattern. The positions of the atoms may be such that there is interference between the waves scattered by one atom and the waves scattered by another, resulting in a modification of the diffraction pattern and the absence of certain maxima. Hull and Davey have prepared useful charts for assisting the identification of crystals of the hexagonal, tetragonal, and rhombohedral classes, each class having its own charts.† To identify the crystal class it is first necessary to measure the distance d between neighbouring atomic planes. From Bragg's Law (p. 275), d is inversely proportional to sin θ; θ may be measured from the diffraction pattern, either from the diameter of the rings for a flat plate film, or from the distance apart on the cylindrical film of two layer lines equidistant from the centre and on either side of it. The distance of the film from the specimen must be known; this may be deduced by calibrating the instrument with a crystal of known structure. By means of strips of paper calibrated according to the values of d and applied in a special manner to the Hull charts, the crystal class can be identified, provided it is one for which a chart has been made. Identification without the chart can nevertheless be made by means of somewhat tedious calculations.

If the values of d are known for three directions parallel to the crystal axes, and if the class of crystal is known, the lengths of the edges of unit cell and so the volume of unit cell can be calculated. The lengths are usually denoted by a, b, c; they are known as *lattice parameters*. The three-dimensional wave in the crystal is described as three component waves travelling parallel to the three crystal axes. If the edges of unit cell are parallel to the crystal axes, there is a diffracted beam when a, b, and c each contain a whole number of wave lengths. The nomenclature usually adopted is that of h wave lengths in a, k wave lengths in b, and l wave lengths in c where h, k, l are integers. A strong diffracted beam is formed when the scattered beams from all the unit cells are in phase and reinforce one another by Bragg reflection.

It is found that owing to errors due to the absorption of X-rays by the specimen, and because it is almost impossible to place the specimen exactly in the centre of the X-ray beam, the experimentally determined values of the lattice parameters are not the same for different values of θ. The errors due to these two causes are proportional to $\cos^2 \theta$; therefore they should diminish as the value of θ approaches 90°. To obtain the true value of a lattice parameter, a graph is plotted of the parameter against $\cos^2 \theta$ and extrapolated to $\theta = 90°$. The density ρ of the specimen must be measured and if the average atomic weight of the atoms in the cell is known, the number of atoms in unit cell, N, may be calculated as follows:

Let the volume of unit cell be V c.c., then

$$\rho = \frac{\text{total mass of atoms in unit cell}}{V}.$$

Total mass of atoms in unit cell

$$= N \times \text{average atomic weight } (A)$$
$$\times \text{mass of an atom of unit atomic weight } (1 \cdot 660 \times 10^{-24} \text{ gm}),$$

therefore

$$N = \frac{\rho V}{1 \cdot 660 \times 10^{-24} A}. \tag{10.3}$$

SUMMARY OF THE INFORMATION DERIVED FROM THE CONSIDERATION OF THE POSITION OF DIFFRACTED BEAMS, THE RESULTS OF CHEMICAL ANALYSIS, AND THE EXPERIMENTAL DETERMINATION OF DENSITY

(1) Type of lattice.
(2) Class of crystal.
(3) Size of unit cell.
(4) Space group of crystal.
(5) Number of each kind of atom in unit cell.

† Hull, A. W. and Davey, W. P., *Phys. Rev.*, **17**, 1921, 549.

If the structural units of the crystals are single atoms the above information is sufficient to determine completely the structure of the specimen. If the units are polyatomic ions or molecules, for the complete elucidation of structure it is necessary to consider also the observed intensities of the diffraction pattern.

INTENSITY OF DIFFRACTED BEAMS

According to simple wave theory (p. 2) intensity of the disturbance at a point over which a wave is passing is proportional to (amplitude)². In X-ray diffraction, this relation is expressed as

$$I \propto F^2(hkl)$$

where I is the intensity, and F is the amplitude of the composite wave made up by the superposition of all the scattered waves which are "Bragg reflected" in a certain direction from three sets of parallel planes in the crystal. The integers h, k, l define the planes belonging to the sets. The scattering centres are assumed to be the outer electrons of the atoms in the unit cell, the number and kind of which have already been determined. If these scattering centres were points distributed uniformly and exactly on the atomic planes of the crystal, each diffracted beam would show the same intensity. The electron, however, must be regarded as having a distribution in space since it may be represented by a probability function, and the effect of the spreading of charge is to cause some interference even at the diffraction maxima. There are other disturbing factors, such as thermal motion, which also have the effect of diminishing the intensity.

Atomic scattering factors. When an atom scatters radiation it is the outer electrons of the atom which are responsible for the scattering. The amplitude of a scattered wave is usually written as

$$f e^{2\pi i \left(\frac{x}{\lambda_x} + \frac{y}{\lambda_y} + \frac{z}{\lambda_z} \right)}$$

where f is characteristic of a single atomic scattering centre and is called an *atomic scattering factor*. It is defined as the ratio of the amplitude of the wave scattered by the atom to the amplitude of the wave scattered by a free electron.[†]

The atomic scattering factor is a function of the atomic number and thus of the number of electrons in the atom. The scattering power of a heavy atom is therefore very much greater than that of a light atom. The atomic scattering factor also depends on the distrubution of electrons in the atom. This distribution has been calculated for various atoms, and with this information a general expression for f has been developed. Since the scattering is affected by thermal motion, the expression must have a temperature correction. Tables of calculated atomic scattering factors have been compiled from the collected results of the work of many investigators.

The resultant amplitude of each diffracted beam is formed by the summation of amplitudes of all the scattered waves in the beam. It is therefore customary to write for n atoms

$$F(hkl) = \sum_{0}^{n} f_j e^{2\pi i \left(\frac{hx_j}{a} + \frac{ky_j}{b} + \frac{lz_j}{c} \right)} \tag{10.4}$$

where the subscript j indicates quantities appropriate to the jth atom.

[†] The amount of scattering, and thus the atomic scattering factor, is found to be a function of the angle of scattering; it is proportional to $(\sin \theta)/\lambda$. It is not feasible, therefore, in practice to use very small scattering angles.

a, b, c, are the lengths of the sides of unit cell measured parallel to the crystal axes, and *x, y, z,* are the usual Cartesian co-ordinates. The diffracted beam is thus represented as a Fourier synthesis, that is, as the resultant of the superposition of simple harmonic waves. $F(hkl)$ is known as the *structure factor*.

Tables giving the general expression for the structure factor in terms of atomic scattering factors have been compiled for the Bragg reflections of each of the 230 space groups.

Electron density expressed as a Fourier series. Since the atomic scattering centres are composed of electrons, and the electrons of the atoms in a unit cell are not at definite points, their distribution is decided by probability functions, and the unit cell must therefore be regarded as a cloud of scattering matter whose density varies throughout the cell.

The number of electrons in a small volume $dx\,dy\,dz$ round a point with co-ordinates x, y, z, is $\rho\,dx\,dy\,dz$ where ρ is the electron density at the point, measured in electrons per c.c. The resultant wave scattered from the atoms in unit cell may therefore be regarded either as the superposition of a number of discrete waves each corresponding to a different atomic scattering factor, or as the integration over the unit cell of the wave scattered from a small volume of electron density.

According to the second interpretation the amplitude $F(hkl)$ of the resultant wave scattered from unit cell may be written

$$F(hkl) = \int_0^a \int_0^b \int_0^c \rho e^{2\pi i\left(\frac{hx}{a}+\frac{ky}{b}+\frac{lz}{c}\right)} dx\,dy\,dz.$$

For the most general case when *a, b, c,* are not inclined at right angles to each other, the right-hand side of the equation contains a term *abc* which has the dimensions of a volume but is not the same as V the volume of unit cell. Since the quantity $F(hkl)$ applies to unit cell, the right-hand side of the equation must therefore be divided by the product *abc* and multiplied by V in order that it may apply to the same volume as the left-hand side. The equation for the most general case is therefore written as

$$F(hkl) = \frac{V}{abc} \int_0^a \int_0^b \int_0^c \rho e^{2\pi i\left(\frac{hx}{a}+\frac{ky}{b}+\frac{lz}{c}\right)} dx\,dy\,dz. \tag{10.5}$$

The scalar value of $F(hkl)$ is known as the *structure amplitude*. Now the electron itself may be regarded as a wave, so that the electron density may reasonably be expressed as a Fourier series (see Appendix). Thus,

$$\rho(xyz) = \sum_{-\infty}^{+\infty}\sum\sum A(pqr)e^{2\pi i\left(\frac{px}{a}+\frac{qy}{b}+\frac{rz}{c}\right)}.$$

Where $A(pqr)$ is the coefficient of the general term characteristic of the integers p, q, r This general form represents a superposition of an infinite number of waves.

Substituting this expression for ρ in the expression for $F(hkl)$ in equation (10.5)

$$F(hkl) = \frac{V}{abc} \int_0^a \int_0^b \int_0^c \left[\sum_{-\infty}^{+\infty}\sum\sum A(pqr)e^{2\pi i\left(\frac{px}{a}+\frac{qy}{b}+\frac{rz}{c}\right)}\right] e^{2\pi i\left(\frac{hx}{a}+\frac{ky}{b}+\frac{lz}{c}\right)} dx\,dy\,dz.$$

The expression becomes zero except when $p=-h, q=-k, r=-l$. In this case,

$$F(hkl) = \frac{V}{abc} \int_0^a \int_0^b \int_0^c A(\bar{h}\bar{k}\bar{l})\,dx\,dy\,dz$$
$$= VA(\bar{h}\bar{k}\bar{l}).$$

The expression for the electron density may therefore be written

$$\rho(xyz) = \sum_{-\infty}^{+\infty}\sum\sum \frac{|F(hkl)|}{V} e^{-2\pi i\left(\frac{hx}{a}+\frac{ky}{b}+\frac{lz}{c}\right)}$$

The expression $e^{-2\pi i\left(\frac{hx}{a}+\frac{ky}{b}+\frac{lz}{c}\right)}$ is a general form for a simple harmonic wave in three dimensions. It contains both cosine and sine forms, the addition of which, by a linear combination, produces a resultant wave which is not in the same position (or phase) as either of the two constituent waves. The position or phase of this resultant wave depends on the phase difference between the cosine and sine forms. The wave may therefore be alternatively expressed as a cosine form with a phase difference from the origin. The description of the wave (amplitude, frequency, wave length, etc.), is incomplete unless the phase is also stated. The expression for the electron density may thus be written

$$\rho(xyz) = \sum_{-\infty}^{+\infty}\sum\sum \frac{|F(hkl)|}{V} \cos 2\pi \left(\frac{hx}{a}+\frac{ky}{b}+\frac{lz}{c}-\alpha)hkl\right), \tag{10.6}$$

where $\alpha(hkl)$ is the phase constant associated with the amplitude $|F(hkl)|$, each structure factor having its own phase constant.

The electron density may thus be expressed as a three-dimensional Fourier series in terms of the structure amplitudes; the electron density is proportional to the sum of all the structure amplitudes and the intensity is proportional to the square of this sum (this is only exactly true for very small crystals). The electron density therefore depends on the phase differences of the scattered waves which are reflected from the various planes of atoms in the crystal. It would, however, be possible to arrive at the same value for the intensity by a number of different combinations of the component waves by varying their phase relations. A knowledge of the phase differences is essential for a unique solution for the electron density, which, if this knowledge is available, can then be computed for a large number of points and a contour map drawn showing the distribution of the electron density in the crystal under consideration, and hence the positions of the atoms in unit cell (Fig. 10.8). Any map of electron density so obtained is in three dimensions, but a two-dimensional projection can be constructed.

Unfortunately the positions of light atoms, particularly of hydrogen, do not show up clearly in the electron density map since their atomic scattering factors are very small (p. 281). In order to show up the hydrogen atoms a difference method is adopted. An electron density map is drawn from the calculated results of scattering from the heavy atoms only. This map is compared with the map derived from the experimental results, and the difference between the two maps used to deduce the positions of the hydrogen atoms. It is desirable to obtain confirmation of this deduction from the results derived by means of other methods such as those of neutron diffraction (p. 295) and nuclear magnetic resonance (p. 263).

Computation of electron density. The first step towards obtaining values for the electron density distribution is to make rough evaluations of $F(hkl)$. This may be done by means of equation (10.4), p. 281, which utilises the concept of atomic scattering factors. Consideration of chemical evidence usually enables a guess to be made of the positions of atoms in the unit cell. Using these estimated positions to determine the phase constants and by use of calculated atomic scattering factors, values of the structure factor for reflection from a given crystal plane may be obtained. A check is provided by intensity measurements of beams diffracted by very small crystals (p. 276); in this case the intensity may be assumed to be directly proportional to the square of the structure factor. A further check may be obtained by measuring the intensity of beams diffracted by larger crystals, using an empirical formula derived to correlate intensity with structure factor. If the agreement between theory and experiment is not good, a correction is made in the estimated position of the atoms in the unit cell, and the whole recalculated, the process being repeated until a structure is found which gives reasonably good agreement between experiment and theory. The process is one of successive approximation often referred to as *refinement*. A test of the success of a

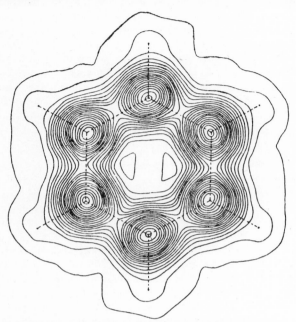

Fig. 10.8.   (a) Electron density map of crystalline benzene.
(After Cox.)

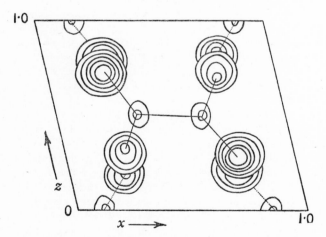

Fig. 10.8.   (b) Composite electron density map of B_2F_4 made from three-dimensional sections of electron density through the atomic centres. The diagram shows the relation of the complete molecule at the centre of the cell to its neighbours.
(After Trefonas and Lipscomb.)

trial structure is whether it "refines" satisfactorily. After each refinement the shape of the contours of the map of electron density near the centres of the atoms should become more nearly circular.

The phase problem. For a final computation of electron density the triple Fourier series in equation (10.6) must be evaluated. This cannot be done without the phase constants. As there is no method for their determination, they must either be guessed or some means devised for the interpretation of the electron density in terms of quantities which do not require a knowledge of the phase constants. The computations required to evaluate the triple Fourier series are formidable even if the phase constants have been estimated.

A large number of crystals have centres of symmetry, and in these cases the structure wave must be symmetrical about this point, and thus only a trough or a maximum can coincide with it. The two possible forms of the wave are those which are identical with each other but are exactly opposite in phase. They are represented by identical formulae, one of which has a positive sign, the other a negative sign. Crystals which have a centre of symmetry are said to be "centrosymmetrical", and for these the electron density may be written (equation (10.6), p. 283)

$$\rho(xyz) = \sum_{-\infty}^{+\infty}\sum\sum \pm \frac{|F(hkl)|}{V} \cos 2\pi\left(\frac{hx}{a}+\frac{ky}{b}+\frac{lz}{c}\right).$$

The problem is therefore capable of solution for crystals of this type, although the computation is very formidable indeed if anything like a detailed map of electron distribution is to be obtained. A certain measure of simplification can be achieved by the adoption of Bragg's method of projection. With this method the three-dimensional map is imagined to be projected on to a plane, and a two-dimensional map plotted. This requires the computation of a two-dimensional Fourier series only. The method has certain disadvantages, particularly that due to the overlapping of images, but it has proved to be of great value in obtaining actual electron density maps.

By a refinement method the results of the calculated distribution of electron density may be used to correct the original estimated positions of the atoms in unit cell, and the whole then recalculated until a constant distribution is achieved. Whether the three- or two-dimensional Fourier series is employed, it is desirable that a large number of terms should be included in the calculation, since with an insufficient number spurious features appear in the maps.

Improvements of Fourier technique and the use of computers now enable corrections to be made for errors due to the premature termination of the Fourier series with insufficient terms and for the overlapping of peaks due to thermal motion. A great many ingenious methods, both mathematical and electronic, have been devised to assist the tremendous labour of computation, for details of which specialist textbooks should be consulted.

The following methods have been used to circumvent the phase problem.

The "Patterson F^2 series". Many mathematical devices have been employed in attempts to interpret the intensity distribution of X-ray diffraction spectra in terms of electron density without a knowledge of the phase constants of the Fourier series components. Of these purely mathematical methods the best known and the most useful is that of the "F^2 series" due to A. L. Patterson.[†] The method is not an easy one to visualise, but the idea lying behind it is simple. Since in any wave motion the intensity of the disturbance is proportional to the square of the amplitude and is thus independent of phase, it should be possible to interpret the observed intensities of X-ray spectra independently of the phase constants by expressing the intensity as a function of the (structure amplitude)^2.

Patterson considers two points in the unit cell (for instance the positions of two atoms), one with co-ordinates x, y, z, and the other with co-ordinates $x+x'$, $y+y'$,

[†] A. L. Patterson, *Phys. Rev.*, **46**, 1934, 372; *Z. Krist.*, **90**, 1935, 517.

$z+z'$. In order to obtain an expression containing F^2 he has to multiply two electron density expressions together. He therefore multiplies the electron density at the point x, y, z, by the electron density at the point $x+x'$, $y+y'$, $z+z'$, and integrates the product over the whole unit cell. He takes a function, $A(x'y'z')$, such that when it is multiplied by the volume of unit cell, it is equal to the integral.

Thus,

$$A(x'y'z') = \frac{1}{V}\int_0^a\int_0^b\int_0^c \rho(xyz)\rho(x+x', y+y', z+z')\,dx\,dy\,dz.$$

If the expressions for the electron density at the two points are now replaced by the corresponding Fourier series,

$$A(x'y'z') = \frac{1}{V}\int_0^a\int_0^b\int_0^c \sum\sum_{-\infty}^{+\infty}\sum \frac{|F(hkl)|^2}{V^2}\,e^{-2\pi i\left(\frac{h}{a}(x+x'-x)+\frac{k}{b}(y+y'-y)+\frac{l}{c}(z+z'-z)\right)}\,dx\,dy\,dz.$$

$F(hkl)$, V, x', y', and z' are constant, therefore,

$$A(x'y'z') = \frac{1}{V^2}\sum\sum_{-\infty}^{+\infty}\sum |F(hkl)|^2\,e^{-2\pi i\left(\frac{hx'}{a}+\frac{ky'}{b}+\frac{lz'}{c}\right)} \tag{10.7}$$

Since (structure amplitude)^2 can be expressed in terms of the measured intensity, the function A can be calculated directly in terms of the intensity at points corresponding to different values of x', y', z'. Since x', y', z', are vector quantities, a "Patterson vector map" can be drawn, showing the value of A for different values of x', y', z'. At first sight it is difficult to see what this map describes, but it is nevertheless a guide to the electron density distribution, because where the electron density is high so also will the Patterson function have a high value. It should be noted that the vectors x', y', z', measure the *difference* between the co-ordinates of points with regard to which the electron density is considered.

The supreme value of the method is that it gives a guide to electron density distribution in terms of vector quantities which are independent of phase, but there are considerable difficulties in the interpretation of the Patterson vector maps. Particularly where there are many atoms in the unit cell (since the function A is derived from the overlapping of the electron density due to all the atoms) there are a large number of vectors concerned. The student should consult a specialist textbook for the detailed methods of interpretation.

A further development of the method has shown that it is often possible to make several arrangements of points giving the same vector distances, so that the method does not give a unique solution of the positions of the atoms in the unit cell. With simple compounds, chemical evidence often decides which arrangement is the correct physical solution. If the phase relations are correct, the electron density map plotted from the Fourier synthesis should not show any negative values for the density at positions away from the nuclei. Fig. 10.9 shows a Patterson vector map.

Practical methods of phase determination.

(a) *Substitution of a heavy atom.* A heavy atom has a much greater scattering power than a light one. It is therefore sometimes possible to determine phase constants by attaching a heavy atom to a molecular complex, and observing whether it reinforces or diminishes the intensity of the diffraction maxima. If there are several heavy atoms in the unit cell, it is often possible to estimate their relative positions by a Patterson vector map, and thus to calculate what their contribution would be to the structure factors of various diffraction maxima. From the observed intensity of these maxima it is sometimes possible to calculate their phase relation to each other, and to the rest of the atoms in unit cell. The matter is greatly simplified if a heavy atom is situated at some point or plane of symmetry of the crystal. Each case must be considered individually; it is not possible to make general rules which apply to all cases. The positions of the atoms are often revealed if a method of successive approximation is used.

(b) *Isomorphous substitution.* This is an extension of the heavy atom method, and consists of the replacement of one heavy atom by another, such as chlorine by bromine, the two crystalline structures being as little different as possible. The advantage of this method over the previous one is that the rest of the atom need not consist of light atoms only, since the phase relations are determined by a difference effect. Bijvoet made an important advance by using an atom which can be excited by radiation of a certain wave length. The change of structure amplitude when this particular wave length is used reveals the part played by this special atom. In all experiments with heavy atoms very small crystals are used where possible, to diminish the absorption effects. The absorption effect of a heavy atom is greater than that of a light atom.

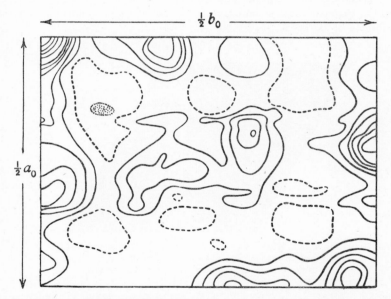

Fig. 10.9. Part of the Patterson projection on (001) of a crystal of di-n-propylmonocyanogold. The two lowest contours are shown by broken lines and one very low region is shaded. (After Phillips and Powell.)

Experimental techniques have also been developed by means of which a two-dimensional map of electron distribution may be projected directly on to a receiving surface without any preliminary computation. Of these methods the following two are particularly well known.

Bragg's "fly's eye" camera. This method employs the principle of the pin-hole camera. The apparatus consists of a screen which is perforated by a large number of pin-holes. These are arranged in a network so that the holes represent the corners of a large number of unit cells. Since each hole is shared by four unit cells, the number of holes is equal to the number of unit cells. The screen is illuminated, and black discs representing the atoms are arranged between the source of illumination and the screen in such relative positions as the atoms are thought to occupy in the unit cell. A photographic plate is placed close behind the screen, a photograph is taken and the image is received on the plate. This image, consisting of light and dark areas, shows the repeated pattern of the two-dimensional projection of the discs, and so resembles the projection of the pattern formed by the atoms in the unit cells of the crystal. The accuracy of this representation can be tested by using the pattern received on the screen as a diffraction grating, illuminating it with monochromatic light from a point source, and so obtaining an optical diffraction spectrum. The different maxima should show relative intensities similar to those of the maxima of the X-ray diffraction spectrum of the real crystal. By means of trial and error methods, the apparatus can be so adjusted that a picture may be obtained which can be taken as a good diagrammatic representation of the projection of the crystal structure which is being investigated. The "fly's eye" camera cannot give a very precise measurement of the position of the atoms in the crystal, but it is a very useful guide to the general "lay-out" of a crystal. If an accurate computation is to be made, the "fly's eye" camera can carry out much of the preliminary trial and error work before the real computation begins. Plate 21 shows a picture of the diopside grating obtained by the "fly's eye" camera. The method has been considerably improved by the use of a large number of tiny perspex lenses instead of pin-holes.

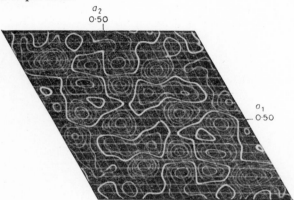

Fig. 10.10. XRAC synthesis of orthoboric acid (zero contour lines appear heavier than the rest; both positive and negative contour lines are included). (After Zachariasen.)

Pepinsky's XRAC.† This machine is an electronic analogue computer, and can perform a Fourier synthesis in two dimensions, using at least 400 terms. The method depends on the following principles: When an alternating electric potential is generated, it does not alter instantaneously from maximum positive to maximum negative value, but passes through a succession of values which, when plotted against time, form a sine, or simple harmonic, curve. The terms of a Fourier series can therefore be represented by alternating potentials, whose amplitudes and phases can be easily adjusted to any required value. The experiment consists of feeding into the machine a number of alternating potentials which form the terms of a "trial" Fourier series. The resultant complex electrical wave is fed into a cathode ray oscillograph. By means of a television scan an image of the electronic distribution contours is received on a screen, or traced on a photographic plate. Fig. 10.10 shows electron density contours obtained by this machine. The great advantage of XRAC is that the syntheses may be made with extreme rapidity; the effect of altering the number of terms, their amplitude, and phase, can be observed very easily. It should be noted that the machine does *not*

† R. Pepinsky, *J. Applied Physics*, **18**, 1947, 601.

determine the phases and amplitudes of the component waves; it can deal only with such phases and amplitudes as are supplied to it by the operator, and indeed it is possible to obtain the same pattern of electron density contours by an infinite number of different phase combinations. The question therefore arises as to whether there is any unique physical solution of the phase problem, since without further information there is no unique mathematical solution.

ELECTRON DIFFRACTION

The diffraction of electron waves was first observed by investigators who were seeking to establish the wave nature of the electron. Davisson and Germer, and at the same time G. P. Thomson, obtained diffraction rings by the interaction of electrons with metals, p. 12. Subsequent experiments on electron diffraction have been used to make accurate determinations of the wave lengths of electron waves and to examine the structure of molecules in crystal surfaces and in gases. These experiments have provided a satisfactory confirmation of the wave character of the electron and a verification of de Broglie's formula. It has also been possible to demonstrate the polarisation of electrons. Plate 22 shows the electron diffraction pattern of $Ni(OH)_2$.

Although the theory of the diffraction of electron waves by crystals is similar to that of the diffraction of X-rays, there are several important differences because the electron wave is associated with a charged particle, and the X-ray photon is not charged. There is a considerable interaction between the impinging electron wave and the scattering centre, which leads to loss of energy of the incident wave, particularly if it accompanies a slow electron. It may be shown that the ratio of the intensity of the scattered electron wave to the intensity of the incident electron wave is of the order of a million times greater than the same ratio for scattered X-rays. The presence of light atoms with few scattering centres is more clearly shown by electron diffraction than by X-ray diffraction.

Both X-rays and electrons are diffracted by gases, but owing to the strong inter-action of electrons with the diffracting atoms it is possible to use a much smaller quantity of gas or vapour when electron waves are used than when X-rays are used. Electron diffraction is therefore the most favoured method employed for the investigation of the molecular structure of gases and vapours. The electron diffraction method is also very suitable for the investigation of the structure of thin crystalline and amorphous films, crystallisation processes such as the growth of crystals, sub-microscopic crystallography, and the structure of polished surfaces and lubricant films. Electron diffraction patterns are often useful in supplementing X-ray diffraction patterns in the determination of some special molecular structure. In general fast electrons are used, for although slow electrons were used in the original experiments on electron diffraction, their use involves considerable experimental and theoretical difficulty and it is easier to interpret the patterns obtained from fast rather than from slow electrons. It has been found possible to apply the methods of Fourier analysis to electron diffraction in crystals and to show the positions of light atoms such as hydrogen, which are not revealed by X-ray diffraction. Contour maps may be constructed showing the variation of electrostatic potential in the crystals. These maps do not give a faithful picture of electron density in the scattering atoms since any bonds of ionic character in the molecule investigated produce strong local fields which have a pronounced effect on the electron scattering. The presence of such fields nevertheless gives a sharply defined map. X-ray electron density maps become less clear in the presence of a strong internal crystalline field and it is desirable wherever possible to use electron diffraction rather than X-ray diffraction to investigate crystals containing bonds of ionic character. Fig. 10.11 shows an electron diffraction map.

10+A.T.I.C.

Since the electron wave is deflected by magnetic fields, it is possible to focus the electron beam by passing it through a system of magnetic lenses. It is highly desirable to obtain a monochromatic incident beam, and for this purpose magnetic deflection

Fig. 10.11. Electron diffraction map of potential distribution in BaF_2 (projection of a cubic face-centred lattice on the cube face). (After Pinsker.)

can also be used to sort out electrons of uniform velocity from a polychromatic beam, but this method of obtaining monochromatic waves is not very satisfactory because the final selected beam is of low intensity.

INFORMATION ON STRUCTURE DERIVED FROM ELECTRON DIFFRACTION

Gaseous molecules. The information derived from the diffraction by gases of the waves of fast electrons has provided a most useful contribution to the solution of the problems of molecular structure, since it is possible to calculate approximate bond lengths and angles from a study of the diffraction patterns.

Earlier in this chapter the discussion on the scattering of waves by crystals was confined to coherent scattering only (p. 271), that is, to scattering without change of wave length, the scattered radiation being totally reflected according to the Bragg relation. This coherent scattering is usually accompanied by a background of incoherent scattered radiation which has suffered a change of wave length during the scattering process.† When X-rays and fast electrons are diffracted by crystals, the coherent scattered radiation is so strong that measurements of its position and intensity may be made independently of the incoherent background.

When the diffracting material is gaseous, for accurate work both coherent and incoherent scattering should be taken into account, but the incoherent effect is usually small compared with the coherent scattering, and for practical work it is often sufficient to use the formula for coherent scattering only; the derivation of the formula is shown in the following discussion.

† Examples of incoherent scattering are the Raman effect (p. 249) and the Compton effect (p. 10).

Coherent scattering; Wierl equation. It is assumed that the diffracting gaseous molecules are orientated at random in all possible directions and that the incident electron beam is scattered by each molecule independently of the others. It is also assumed that the atoms in the molecule are identical, that they have spherical symmetry, and that they are equidistant from each other. The theory calculates the scattering for a single molecule in some arbitrary fixed position, and averages the results over all possible orientations.

Suppose that the ith and jth atom in the scattering molecule are situated at O and Q respectively (Fig. 10.12). O is in the plane of the paper, XY, and Q is above it. The axis OZ is at right angles to the XY plane and stands out from the plane of the paper.

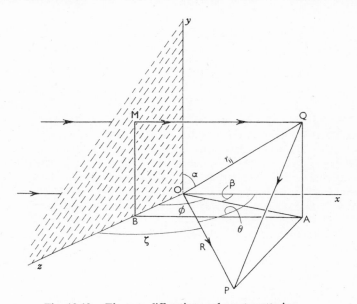

Fig. 10.12. Electron diffraction; coherent scattering.

Let A be the foot of the perpendicular from Q on to the XZ plane. It is supposed that an incident beam of monochromatic planar electron waves is incident perpendicularly on the YZ plane (emerging from it at O and M) and is scattered by O and Q. The scattered radiation is received at P. P lies in the XZ plane. If δ is the path difference between rays scattered from Q and O,

$$\delta = MQ + QP - OP = AB + QP - OP.$$

It should be remembered that the angles ZOX, OBA, QAO, and QAB are right angles although they do not appear to be so owing to the difficulty of representing a three-dimensional model in a two dimensional diagram.
Therefore

$$QP^2 = QA^2 + AP^2$$
$$AP^2 = OA^2 + OP^2 - 2OP.OA \sin(\xi + \beta).$$

Therefore

$$QP^2 = OA^2 + QA^2 + OP^2 - 2OP.OA \sin(\xi + \beta)$$
$$= r_{ij}^2 + R^2 - 2Rr_{ij} \sin \alpha \sin(\xi + \beta).$$

In practice, although not in the diagram, r_{ij} is very small compared with R, therefore terms in $r_{ij}{}^2$ may be neglected. To a first approximation

$$QP = \sqrt{(R^2 - 2Rr_{ij} \sin \alpha \sin (\xi + \beta))}.$$

If the square root is expanded by the binomial theorem, using the first two terms only

$$QP = R - r_{ij} \sin \alpha \sin (\xi + \beta).$$

Therefore

$$\delta = AB - r_i \, \sin \alpha \sin (\xi + \beta)$$

$$= r_{ij} \sin \alpha \sin \phi - r_{ij} \sin \alpha \sin (\xi + \beta).$$

Since

$$\phi + \beta = \theta + \xi = 90°,$$

therefore

$$\delta = r_{ij} \sin \alpha \sin \phi - r_{ij} \sin \alpha \sin (\theta + \phi)$$

$$= r_{ij} \sin \alpha \left(2 \cos \frac{\theta + 2\phi}{2} \sin \frac{\theta}{2} \right).$$

The amplitude of an electron wave travelling along the x axis may be expressed as $A_0 e^{ikx}$ where $k = 2\pi/\lambda$. This plane wave impinges on atoms i and j, the scattered waves from both being spherical. The amplitude of the wave received at a given point depends on the scattering factors f_i and f_j of the ith and jth atoms respectively, and the distance r of the point from the scattering centre.† The amplitude ψ_i of the wave scattered from the ith atom is $A_0 f_i e^{ikr}/r$; the amplitude ψ_j of the wave scattered from the jth atom is $A_0 f_j e^{ik(r+\delta)}/r$.

The resultant amplitude at P is the sum of ψ_i and ψ_j, and since $OP = R$,

$$\psi = \psi_i + \psi_j$$

$$= \frac{A_0}{R} e^{ikR}(f_i + f_j e^{ik\delta}).$$

Since the intensity of an electron wave is measured by the square of the amplitude ψ multiplied by its complex conjugate ψ^* gives an expression for the intensity at P.

$$\psi \psi^* = \frac{A_0{}^2}{R^2} e^{ikR}(f_i + f_j e^{ik\delta}) e^{-ikR}(f_i + f_j e^{-ik\delta})$$

$$= \frac{A_0{}^2}{R^2} \left\{ f_i{}^2 + f_j{}^2 + 2f_i f_j \left(\frac{e^{ik\delta} + e^{-ik\delta}}{2} \right) \right\}$$

$$= \frac{A_0{}^2}{R^2} (f_i{}^2 + f_j{}^2 + 2f_i f_j \cos k\delta)$$

$$= \frac{A_0{}^2}{R^2} \left\{ f_i{}^2 + f_j{}^2 + 2f_i f_j \left(2 \cos^2 \frac{k\delta}{2} - 1 \right) \right\}$$

$$= \frac{A_0{}^2}{R^2} \left[(f_i - f_j)^2 + 4 f_i f_j \cos^2 \frac{k\delta}{2} \right].$$

Since the distance between the atoms is very small compared with R, θ may be taken as the scattering angle for both atoms, and if for simplicity it is assumed that f_i and f_j

---

† The intensity of a three-dimensional wave varies as $1/r^2$ where r is the distance from the scattering source, therefore the amplitude varies as $1/r$.

are not very different, the first term may be neglected,† then

$$\psi\psi^* = \frac{4A_0^2}{R^2} f_i f_j \cos^2 \frac{k\delta}{2}.$$

The intensity I at P due to scattering from all the atoms in the molecule is given by the expression

$$I = \frac{4A_0^2}{R^2} \sum_i \sum_j f_i f_j \cos^2 \frac{k\delta}{2}.$$

This expression gives the intensity at P due to scattering from a single molecule in a fixed orientation. To obtain the mean value of the intensity at P, it is necessary to integrate the expression over the volume of a unit sphere and to divide it by 4π, which is the solid angle at the centre of the sphere. The result gives the average intensity due to molecules with random orientation. Therefore for the mean value of the intensity:

$$I_{AV} = \frac{4A_0^2}{R^2} \sum_i \sum_j f_i f_j \frac{1}{4\pi} \int_0^{2\pi} \int_0^{\pi} \cos^2 \frac{k\delta}{2} \sin \alpha \, d\phi \, d\alpha. \qquad \text{(see note ‡)}$$

$$= \frac{4A_0^2}{R^2} \sum_i \sum_j f_i f_j \frac{1}{4\pi} \int_0^{2\pi} \int_0^{\pi} \cos^2 \left\{ kr_{ij} \sin \alpha \sin \frac{\theta}{2} \cos \left(\phi + \frac{\theta}{2} \right) \right\} \sin \alpha \, d\phi \, d\alpha.$$

(It is necessary to have a knowledge of Bessel functions to evaluate this integral.)
On integration,

$$I_{AV} = \frac{4A_0^2}{R^2} \sum_i \sum_j f_i f_j \frac{\sin sr_{ij}}{sr_{ij}}, \qquad (10.8)$$

where

$$s = 2k \sin \frac{\theta}{2}$$

$$= \frac{4\pi}{\lambda} \sin \frac{\theta}{2}.$$

This equation was first derived for the molecular scattering of X-rays; it was used by Wierl in connection with electron diffraction, and is known as the *Wierl equation*.

Practical application of the Wierl equation. Although it is possible to obtain very elegant electron diffraction patterns, the interpretation of the patterns is extremely difficult. The method employed is essentially one of trial and error. A possible structure, based on chemical evidence, is assumed for the molecule under consideration. The various values for r_{ij} are then calculated, based on this assumed model, and a theoretical intensity curve is plotted for the different values of θ. An experimental intensity curve is then plotted, the positions of the maxima being obtained from observation of the diameters of the diffraction rings. Intensities can be estimated from the diffraction patterns, either by a microphotometer or visually.

To evaluate the intensity theoretically it is necessary to know the atomic scattering

† The term is anyway not important for the determination of bond lengths, since it is constant for a given value of R. It is shown later in this chapter that the interest lies in the variation of intensity with r_{ij} and θ.

‡
$$\text{Solid angle} = \frac{\text{area of base of cone}}{\text{radius}^2}$$

$$d\Omega = \frac{r \sin \alpha \cdot d\phi \cdot r d\alpha}{r^2}$$

$$= \sin \alpha \cdot d\phi \cdot d\alpha$$

If this expression is integrated from 0 to 2π for ϕ, and from 0 to π for α, the whole surface of the sphere will have been covered.

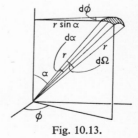

Fig. 10.13.

factors. These are complicated functions and depend on the atomic number, the angle of scattering, and the wave length of the incident electron. For practical purposes it is often sufficient to use the atomic number instead of the scattering factor since it is only necessary to produce discontinuities in the theoretical intensity curve in order to compare it with the observed intensity curve. As it is impossible to make accurate experimental measurements of intensity, only the *positions* of the maxima are used, and a curve is plotted from these to see whether they correspond with the positions of the theoretical maxima.

Crystalline structures. As these structures are in most cases more easily investigated by X-ray rather than by electron diffraction, they will be considered only very briefly here. Since slow electrons lose considerably more energy in the surface layers than do fast electrons, quite different diffraction patterns are obtained for slow and fast electrons, and for thick and thin diffracting films. It is necessary to have two different theories to explain the experimental results for films thicker or thinner than about 10^{-5} cm. The kinematic theory, applicable to films of thickness less than 10^{-5} cm is analogous to the theory of X-ray diffraction, while the dynamic theory applicable to films of thickness greater than 10^{-5} cm, is concerned with the distribution of potential inside the crystal lattice. Quite different results are obtained according to whether the electrons emerge from the surface on which they fall (Bragg case), or from a different surface (Laue case).

The simple Bragg Law, $n\lambda = 2d \sin \theta$, does not hold experimentally unless it is assumed that the electron has a different wave length in the crystal from that *in vacuo*, that is, that the crystal has a refractive index for the electron wave. This refractive index is greater than one, while that for X-rays (p. 273) is very slightly less than one. The refraction of electron waves is a much more marked effect than that of X-rays, which for a long time was undetected.

In the case of crystals, the method adopted is often that of comparison with the diffraction pattern of a standard crystal of known structure, but errors may be introduced by any deformation or irregularity in either crystal. However, if appropriate corrections are made, calculations of the size of unit cell are frequently in close agreement with similar calculations from X-ray diffraction.

There are many technical difficulties to be overcome in the application of electron diffraction to the study of crystals and gases; for instance, it is not easy to measure accurately the velocity of the electron. Correction must be made for temperature, the relativistic change of mass of the electron with change of speed, and the distribution of charge in the scattering atom. In addition, molecular scattering cannot be recorded

Table 10.1.   *Comparison of Electron Diffraction and Spectroscopic Determinations of Interatomic Distances* (in Å) †

Molecule	From band spectra	From electron diffraction
F_2	1·28 ‡	1·45 ± 0·05
S_2	1·88	1·92 ± 0·03
Cl_2	1·983	2·00 ± 0·02
Se_2	2·15	2·19 ± 0·02
Br_2	2·28	2·28 ± 0·02
ICl	2·315	2·30 ± 0·03
Te_2	2·61	2·59 ± 0·02
I_2	2·660	2·66 ± 0·01

† Z. G. Pinsker, *Electron Diffraction* (Butterworth, 1953), p. 309.
‡ This value probably refers to an excited state of the F_2 molecule.

independently of atomic scattering; in actual practice there is always a background of atomic scattering, both coherent and incoherent, which is stronger than the molecular scattering. This makes it very difficult to detect the scattered radiation from the light atoms, and various practical devices have been adopted to cut out waves which have been scattered atomically rather than by the molecule as a whole. None of these devices has been entirely successful, but it is possible to cut out a large part of the atomic scattering; results for bond lengths have been obtained, even for some molecules containing hydrogen, which have been in quite good agreement with those derived from the study of molecular spectra and X-ray diffraction data.

The nature of the methods described above shows that electron diffraction experiments are best used in conjunction with other methods of determining molecular structure. Table 10.1 gives a comparison of the values of certain bond lengths in some diatomic molecules calculated from band spectra and from electron diffraction.

NEUTRON DIFFRACTION

The wave length of a neutron is about two thousand times shorter than the wave length of an electron of the same speed ($\lambda = h/mv$). Neutrons at a temperature of between 0° and 100° can easily be obtained from an atomic pile, and these have wave lengths of about 1 Å, which is very suitable for atomic and molecular diffraction. The neutron is uncharged; it is therefore unaffected by the outer electrons of the atom except for a very small magnetic coupling; thus the penetrating power of neutron waves is considerably greater than that of electron waves. The scattering centre is the nucleus of the diffracting atom, unless the whole atom has a residual magnetic moment in which case scattering by electrons also takes place. The diffracting atom may be part of a molecule in a gas or in a crystal.

Neutron diffraction by crystals. In comparison with the diffraction of X-rays, neutron diffraction shows poor resolution and low intensity. These disadvantages are, however, offset by certain advantages. The scattering factors of different atoms for neutron diffraction, although distinct from each other, are all of the same order, and hence the scattering power of hydrogen for neutrons is not much less than the scattering power of any other atom. The results obtained from neutron diffraction are therefore particularly useful in locating the positions of hydrogen atoms in crystals. Owing to the poor resolution of neutron diffraction spectra they are best used to supplement the information derived from X-ray diffraction. Neutron diffraction is said to "fill in the details" of X-ray diffraction.

Another important advantage of neutron over X-ray and electron diffraction is that the scattering factor does not depend on the angle of scattering[†]; the scattering factor of X-rays is a function of $(\sin \theta)/\lambda$ and the scattering factor for electrons is a function of $(\sin \frac{1}{2}\theta)/\lambda$. Although the intensity of neutron scattering is small, it can be measured much more easily than that of X-rays. The absolute intensity may be measured by comparison with the intensity of scattering by a standard substance. As the experimental difficulties are gradually overcome, so the method comes more and more into general use, and its range is likely to be greatly extended in the future.

The Fourier analysis method may be applied to neutron diffraction by crystals, but the electron density maps show false detail in the shape of diffraction rings round individual atoms when only a finite number of terms is taken in the Fourier series, which should be summed to infinity. The problem of the phase differences between neutron waves scattered from centres in a crystal is analogous to the phase problem discussed in connection with the scattering of X-rays (p. 285). Some approach to a

† This is not true for magnetic scattering.

direct solution of the problem has been made by considering the scattering of neutrons by hydrogen atoms. Fig. 10.14 shows an electron density map derived from neutron scattering.

Although the scattering factor of hydrogen is of roughly the same magnitude as that of oxygen and carbon, it is said to be of opposite sign, as the scattering from hydrogen does not show the phase change which is observed when neutron waves are scattered by most elements. The presence of hydrogen on the contour map of electron density as plotted by the method of Fourier analysis is therefore shown by the absence of contour lines, equivalent to a trough in the intensity curve. Deuterium on the other hand shows positive scattering, so that if it is possible to replace hydrogen atoms in a compound by deuterium, and to obtain electron density maps of both substances by means of neutron diffraction, the difference between the two maps will be due not only to the different scattering power of the two atoms, but also to the change of phase. It has been suggested that there is a basis here for a method of phase determination.

Magnetic scattering of neutrons. Magnetic scattering is due to the interaction of the magnetic moment of the neutron with the magnetic moment of an atom which has

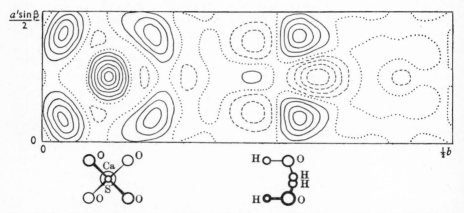

Fig. 10.14. Neutron scattering density projection on (101) of a crystal of $CaSO_4.2H_2O$. (After Atoji and Rundle.) The key diagrams below indicate the positions of the atoms.

resultant magnetism. The method is useful for the investigation of the magnetic moments of atoms.

In magnetic scattering the scattering centres are electrons. Experiments have been performed on various crystalline substances, and it is found that in certain cases, notably among the transition elements, the observed magnetic moment is not in good agreement with the value calculated from the Landé splitting factor (p. 97) unless it is assumed that the magnetism is largely due to the spin and not to the orbital motion of the electrons of the scattering atom; it is supposed that the orbital motion is "quenched" by the crystalline field (p. 99). Since closed shells do not have a resultant magnetic moment, it is the d electrons in the transition elements which are responsible for the effect (p. 945). In the rare earths, the resultant magnetism is due to the f electrons which are not so much affected by the surrounding field since they are further inside the atom and protected by other electrons. With all cases of magnetic scattering there is a large incoherent effect due to spin interaction.

Much work has been done on the scattering of neutrons by ferromagnetic and antiferromagnetic materials, and the method has been found to be useful for the investigation of magnetic alloys. As the scattering agent is an electron cloud of considerable dimensions compared with the approximate point source of the nucleus, there is considerable overlapping of diffracted waves from different parts of the electron cloud. There is, however, less false detail in the electron density maps, because, with magnetic scattering, there is a considerable falling off of intensity with increasing values

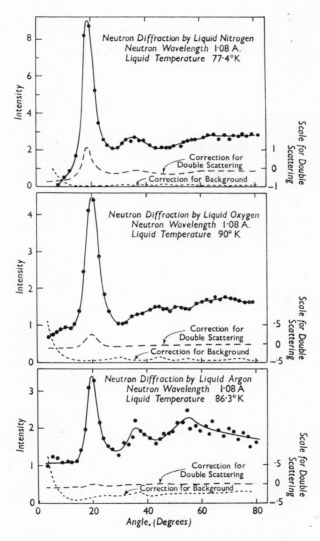

Fig. 10.15. Neutron diffraction scattering curves for liquid nitrogen at 77·4°K, liquid oxygen at 90°K, and liquid argon at 86·3°K. Corrected intensities in arbitrary units are plotted against the scattering angle. (After Henshaw, Hurst and Pope.)

of θ, and so a short Fourier series does not have such a marked effect in introducing spurious features. It is possible to distinguish between the two types of scattering, nuclear and magnetic, by the fact that the neutron waves are polarised by magnetic scattering and not by nuclear scattering.

10*

Table 10.2. *Comparison of X-ray and Neutron Diffraction†*

Wave length	X-rays	Neutrons
	Order of 1·5 Å	Order of 1 Å
Energy for $\lambda = 1$ Å	$10^{18} h$.	$10^{13} h$, same order as energy quantum of crystal vibration.
Atomic scattering	Electronic.	Nuclear.
	Scattering factor depends on $(\sin \theta)/\lambda$.	Isotropic, no angular dependent factor.
	Angular dependent polarisation factor.	
	Regular increase of scattering power with atomic number, calculable from known electronic configurations.	Irregular variation with atomic number, dependent on nuclear structure, and only determined empirically.
	No difference among isotopes.	Amplitude is different for different isotopes, and is dependent also on nuclear spin.
	Phase change is 180° on scattering.	Phase change is 180° for most nuclei, but H, Li, Ti, V, Mn, and Ni^{62} give zero phase change.‡
Magnetic scattering	No additional scattering.	Additional scattering by atoms with magnetic moments. (1) Diffuse scattering by paramagnetic materials. (2) Coherent diffraction peaks for ferromagnetic and antiferromagnetic materials. Amplitude of scattering falls off with $(\sin \theta)/\lambda$. Amplitude is calculable from moment and is different for ions with different spin quantum numbers.
Absorption coefficient	Very large, true absorption, being much greater than scattering, increasing with atomic number.	Absorption usually very small, and less than scattering, with some exceptions. Varies with isotopes.
Absolute intensity measurement	Difficult. Interpretation depends on precise knowledge of atomic scattering factors.	Straightforward, particularly by powder methods.

† G. E. Bacon, *Neutron Diffraction* (Clarendon Press, Oxford, 1955), p. 160.

‡ The scattering amplitude is composed of two terms, one positive and the other negative. In the case of hydrogen and a few other elements there is no phase change of the wave, but the negative term in the scattering amplitude predominates, and the scattering is said to be negative. The reader should note that it is sometimes stated that there is a phase change on scattering by hydrogen; this statement refers to the change of sign of the scattering amplitude, and not to an actual change of phase in the wave.

Neutron diffraction by gases and liquids. Neutron scattering by gases is of very low intensity, and the experimental technique required is difficult. Theoretically the intensity curve shows marked diffraction peaks over the whole range because of the non-dependence of the scattering on the scattering angle θ. This is in marked contrast to the similar curve for X-rays, for which the intensity falls off very rapidly with the function $(\sin \theta)/\lambda$. It is not possible to apply the method of Fourier analysis either to electron or to neutron diffraction in gases because of the random orientation of the molecules. Certain useful information about the outer electrons in the scattering atom may, however, be obtained from experiments on neutron diffraction by gases because it is possible to observe the scattering over small as well as large angles. Neutron scattering may also be detected in certain liquids and amorphous solids (Fig. 10.15).

BOOKS FOR FURTHER READING

BACON, G. E., *Neutron Diffraction* (Oxford University Press, 1955).

BOOTH, A. D., *Fourier Technique in Organic Structure Analysis* (Cambridge Series of Physical Chemistry, Cambridge University Press, 1948).

BRAGG, W. L., *Recent Advances in X-ray Analysis* (Postgraduate Lectures: Heffer, Cambridge, 1950).

BUNN, C. W., *Chemical Crystallography* (Oxford University Press, 1945).

CLARK, G. L., *Applied X-Rays* (McGraw-Hill, 1955).

KLUG, H. P., and ALEXANDER, L. E., *X-ray Diffraction Procedures* (Chapman and Hall, 1954).

PINSKER, Z. G., *Electron Diffraction* (Butterworth's Scientific Publications, 1953).

PIRENNE, M. H., *Diffraction of X-Rays and Electrons by Molecules* (Cambridge Series of Physical Chemistry, Cambridge University Press, 1948).

ROBERTSON, J. M., *Organic Crystals and Molecules* (Cornell University Press, 1953).

REVIEWS

BACON, G. E., and LONSDALE, K., *Neutron Diffraction* (*Rep. Prog. Phys.*, **16**, 1953, 1).

GUIGRICH, N. S., *Diffraction of X-rays by Liquid Elements* (*Rev. Mod. Phys.*, **15**, 1943, 90).

JEFFERY, G. A., and CRUICKSHANK, D. W. J., *Molecular Structure Determination by X-ray Crystal Analysis* (*Quarterly Reviews*, 7, No. 4, 1953, 335).

RINGO, G. R., *Neutron Diffraction and Interference* (Handbuch der Physik, S. Flügge, Springer).

THEWLIS, J., *Neutron Diffraction* (*Ann. Reports of Chem. Soc.*, **47**, 1950, 420).

CHAPTER ELEVEN

DIPOLE MOMENTS, BOND LENGTHS, AND BOND ENERGIES

DIPOLE MOMENTS

Information on dipole moments may be of considerable help in the deduction of molecular structure. If a charge $+e$ is separated from another charge $-e$ by a distance d, the system is said to be an *electric dipole* and to have an electric *dipole moment*, measured by the product ed, which is a vector quantity. The unit of dipole moment is a debye; 1 debye $= 10^{-18}$ e.s.u. cm. An electric dipole exists where two atoms of different electronegativity come together to form a molecule. If a molecule contains more than two atoms there may be several dipoles, the vector combination of whose moments gives the resultant dipole moment of the molecule. A material which consists of molecules possessing dipole moments is said to be *polar*. In the theoretical consideration of molecular dipoles, the quantity discussed is usually the *dipole moment per unit volume*, known as the *polarisation*. There are several methods of measuring the polarisation; in all of them the material is placed in an electric field. The resulting polarisation is made up of two parts: the *induced polarisation*, due to the displacement of the positive and negative charges from their natural positions in the atom or molecule, and the *orientation polarisation* due to the orientation by the field of any already existing permanent dipoles. The *total polarisation* P of the dielectric is the sum of the induced polarisation P_I and the orientation polarisation P_O,

$$P = P_I + P_O.$$

P, P_I, and P_O are all measured in a direction parallel to the field.†

INDUCED POLARISATION P_I

It should first be noted that as polarisation is the dipole moment per unit volume it has the dimensions of $\dfrac{\text{charge}}{\text{area}}$. These dimensions are the same as those of an electric field.‡ Suppose that a plate AB in a vacuum is given a positive charge of $+\sigma$ per unit area. If another plate CD is placed parallel to it, a negative charge $-\sigma$ per unit area is induced on one side of CD and a positive charge $+\sigma$ per unit area is induced on the

---

† P_I may be further subdivided into P_E due to the movement of electrons relative to the nuclei, and P_A, known as the *atom polarisation* due to the relative movement of the nuclei. Both these effects are included in the quantity P_I, which appears in the simple theory given in this chapter. The material which is placed in the electric field is known as the *dielectric*.

‡ The reader is reminded that the terms "electric field", "field strength", "intensity of the field" and "intensity" are synonymous. The term "field" will be adopted here. It should also be noted that the definition of field at a point is "the force on unit notional positive charge placed at that point". By the inverse square law, the force F between two charges q_1 and q_2 at a distance r apart in a vacuum is given by the expression:

$$F = \frac{q_1 q_2}{r^2}.$$

If q_1 is a unit charge, force on q_1 is q_2/r^2, therefore field may be written as charge per unit area.

other side (Fig. 11.1(i)). If the plate *CD* is then earthed, the induced positive charge on *CD* runs to earth, while the other charges remain in the system opposite each other (Fig. 11.1(ii)). If a dielectric is introduced between the plates, the field due to the charge on *AB* aligns the molecules of the dielectric so that the effect of their induced dipole moments opposes the field (Fig. 11.1(ii)). To find the relation between the field between the plates without the dielectric and σ, the charge per unit area introduced into the system, another system, that of a field at a distance r from a point charge q, may first be considered.

$$\text{Field} = \frac{q}{r^2}.$$

Hence the field is constant over a spherical shell of radius r.
  Field may be written as

$$\frac{q}{r^2} \times \frac{\text{surface area of sphere}}{\text{surface area of sphere}},$$

or

$$\text{Field} = \frac{\text{charge}}{\text{surface area of sphere}} \times \frac{\text{surface area of sphere}}{r^2}.$$

If the spherical shell is a closed conductor, the charge is located on the surface, therefore

$$\text{Field} = \text{charge per unit area} \times \text{solid angle subtended by}$$
$$\text{the surface of the sphere at its centre}$$
$$= 4\pi\sigma.$$

Hence the field is independent of the radius of the sphere.
  The plate *AB* may be considered to be part of a sphere with infinite radius. If a dielectric is placed between the plates, let the field in the dielectric between the plates be *E*. Then, since the effect of the polarisation is to reduce the field between the plates, and since P_I has the dimensions of charge per unit area,

$$E = 4\pi(\sigma - P_I).$$

A quantity k known as the *dielectric constant* is defined as the ratio of the field between the charged plates when there is a vacuum between them, to the field between the charged plates when they have the dielectric between them.

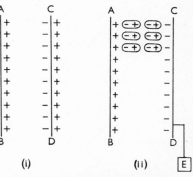

Fig. 11.1. Induced polarisation.

$$k = \frac{4\pi\sigma}{4\pi(\sigma - P_I)}. \tag{11.1}$$

Therefore,

$$E(k-1) = 4\pi P_I. \tag{11.2}$$

Equation (11.1) is sometimes written as $kE = D$ where *D* is known as the *displacement*.
  Suppose that the plate *AB* has been charged by means of an applied field *X*. It is now necessary to relate the applied field to the field *E* inside the dielectric. In order to do so consideration is given to the resultant force acting on a notional unit positive charge imagined to be placed in the dielectric. P_I is the *average* dipole moment per unit volume, thus *E* is the *average* field in the dielectric and is not the resultant force on a single particle with unit charge. This resultant force may be divided into two parts:
  (a) the force equal to $4\pi\sigma$ due to the charge σ per unit area on the plates,

(b) the force due to the induced polarisation around the unit charge. The latter force is usually calculated by assuming that the unit charge is situated inside a spherical cavity in the dielectric. Consider the charge on the surface of the cavity. It can be seen from Fig. 11.2 that the area of the annular ring depicted is $2\pi r\,RS\sin\beta$ or $2\pi r^2\sin\beta\,d\beta$.

P_I is defined as the charge per unit area due to polarisation on a surface parallel to the plates. Therefore the charge per unit area on the surface of the ring is $P_I\cos\beta$, and the charge on the whole surface of the ring is $2\pi r^2 P_I\sin\beta\cos\beta\,d\beta$. This charge produces a force on the unit charge at the centre of the cavity, the force making an angle β with the direction of the field. Therefore the force on unit charge at the centre in the direction of the field is:

$$\frac{2\pi r^2 P_I\sin\beta\cos\beta\,d\beta\cos\beta}{r^2} = 2\pi P_I\sin\beta\cos^2\beta\,d\beta,$$

and the force on unit charge at the centre due to the whole surface of the cavity is

$$2\pi P_I\int_0^\pi\sin\beta\cos^2\beta\,d\beta = \frac{4\pi}{3}P_I.$$

No account has been taken of the force due to the induced polarisation inside the cavity. Lorentz has shown that this is zero if the molecular distribution is completely random, or if the crystal has a cubic lattice. For non-associated liquids and gases it is approximately zero.

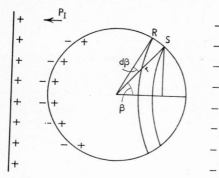

Fig. 11.2.

The total force on unit positive charge is equal to the applied field X. This is made up of the field inside the dielectric, E, and the force due to polarisation:

$$X = E+\frac{4}{3}\pi P_I \qquad (11.3)$$

If n is the number of molecules per unit volume, and $\bar{m}_I$ their average induced dipole moment, it may be assumed that $\bar{m}_I$ is proportional to the applied field X.

Let

$$\bar{m}_I = \alpha X,$$

then

$$P_I = n\bar{m}_I$$
$$= n\alpha X.$$

From equation (11.3)

$$P_I = n\alpha\left(E+\frac{4}{3}\pi P_I\right),$$

and from equation (11.2)

$$P_I = n\alpha\left(\frac{4\pi P_I}{k-1}+\frac{4\pi P_I}{3}\right).$$

Therefore

$$\frac{k-1}{k+2} = \frac{4\pi n\alpha}{3}. \qquad (11.4)$$

This equation is known as the **Clausius-Mossotti equation**. If both sides of the equation are multiplied by the molecular weight M and divided by the density ρ,

$$\frac{k-1}{k+2} \cdot \frac{M}{\rho} = \frac{4}{3}\pi N\alpha$$
$$= P_M \tag{11.5}$$

where N is Avogadro's number and P_M is known as the *molar polarisation*.† The molar polarisation may be measured by determining the dielectric constant and α may be calculated.

The classical theory outlined above can be applied to the induced polarisation caused by the relative displacement of the electrons and the nucleus in the atom, and also to induced polarisation in ionic compounds due to the relative displacement of the positive and negative ions. Electronic polarisation should properly be treated by quantum mechanics, and such a theory has been developed. It has been found, however, that the classical theory gives very nearly the same results as the quantum theory, and is sufficiently accurate for practical purposes.

ORIENTATION POLARISATION P_O

If a gas of which each molecule possesses a permanent dipole moment is placed in an external magnetic field, the molecules tend to arrange themselves in line with the direction of the field. This tendency is opposed by thermal motion. The total energy of the system depends on the absolute temperature T, and is the sum of the kinetic energy of the molecules and the potential energy of the dipoles in the electric field.

Suppose a dipole of moment μ makes an angle θ with the field X (Fig. 11.3). Its potential energy (which is exactly analogous to that of a small magnet in a magnetic field (p. 101) is given by the expression

$$-\mu X \cos \theta.$$

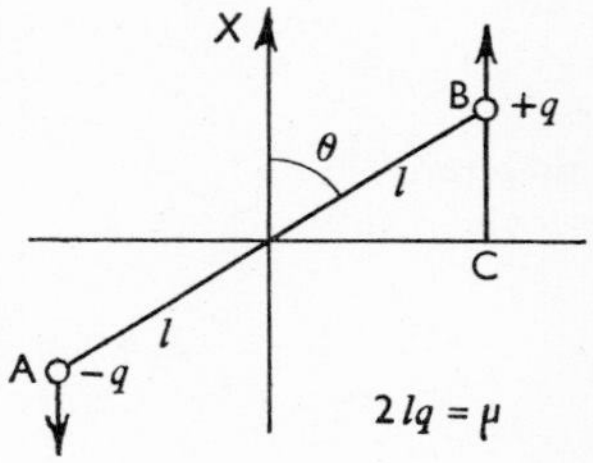

Fig. 11.3.

If it is assumed that out of all the molecules there are n' molecules per unit volume making an angle θ with the field, and that μ is the average dipole moment of the molecules, then

$$-n'\mu X \cos \theta = W$$

where W is the potential energy of the system of n' molecules. Assuming that the distribution of molecules in different energy states follows Boltzmann's law‡ the number of molecules n_1 orientated at an angle θ at a temperature T is given by the expression

$$n_1 = n_0 e^{W/n'k_bT}$$
$$= n_0 e^{\mu X \cos \theta / k_b T},$$

where n_0 is a constant, and k_b is the Boltzmann constant.

If n_1 is the number of molecules orientated at an angle θ in unit solid angle, then the number of molecules so orientated in a small element of solid angle $d\omega$ is given by the expression:

$$n_1 = n_0 e^{\mu X \cos \theta / k_b T} d\omega. \tag{11.6}$$

† The molar polarisation here refers to induced polarisation only; the Clausius-Mosotti relation cannot be applied where there are permanent dipoles. It holds only for molecules present in gases and in dilute solution in non-polar solvents.

‡ The proof that electric dipoles in an electric field conform to Boltzmann's law is given in textbooks of physics, for example, Georg Joos, *Theoretical Physics* (Blackie and Son, Ltd., London, 1947), p. 435.

The average value of the dipole moment per molecule parallel to the field may be expressed as:

$$\bar{m}_0 = \frac{\int n_0 e^{\mu X \cos\theta / k_b T} \mu \cos\theta \, d\omega}{\int n_0 e^{\mu X \cos\theta / k_b T} \, d\omega}.$$

Let

$$\frac{\mu X}{k_b T} = x, \quad \cos\theta = y.$$

Since

$$d\omega = 2\pi \sin\theta \, d\theta \qquad \text{(See note †)}$$
$$= -2\pi \, dy,$$

then

$$\frac{\bar{m}_0}{\mu} = \frac{\int_{-1}^{+1} e^{xy} y \, dy}{\int_{-1}^{+1} e^{xy} \, dy}.$$

Since

$$\int_{-1}^{+1} e^{xy} \, dy = \frac{e^x - e^{-x}}{x}$$

and

$$\int_{-1}^{+1} e^{xy} y \, dy = \frac{e^x}{x} - \frac{e^x}{x^2} + \frac{e^{-x}}{x} + \frac{e^{-x}}{x^2},$$

therefore

$$\frac{\bar{m}_0}{\mu} = \frac{e^x + e^{-x}}{e^x - e^{-x}} - \frac{1}{x}$$

$$= \coth x - \frac{1}{x}. \tag{11.7}$$

The expression, $\coth x - 1/x$, is known as the **Langevin function** and is often denoted by $L(x)$. It was first developed by Langevin in calculating the mean magnetic moment of a gas whose molecules have a permanent magnetic moment.

TOTAL MOLAR POLARISATION

The Langevin function was applied by Debye to the calculation of molecular polarisation due to the orientation of molecules which have a permanent electric dipole moment. The function $L(x)$ may be expanded as a power series, $L(x) = x/3 - x^3/45 + \dots$,

† An annular solid angle is considered

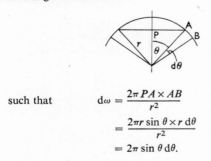

such that

$$d\omega = \frac{2\pi PA \times AB}{r^2}$$

$$= \frac{2\pi r \sin\theta \times r \, d\theta}{r^2}$$

$$= 2\pi \sin\theta \, d\theta.$$

and since x is of the order 10^{-3}, it is sufficiently accurate to put $L(x) = x/3$, and

$$\bar{m}_0 = \frac{\mu x}{3}$$

$$= \frac{\mu^2 X}{3k_b T}.$$

P_O, the orientation polarisation, is defined as the dipole moment per unit volume parallel to the field, therefore

$$P_O = n\bar{m}_0$$

$$= \frac{n\mu^2 X}{3k_b T}.$$

The total dipole moment per unit volume parallel to the field is given by:

$$P = P_I + P_O$$

$$= nX\left(\alpha + \frac{\mu^2}{3k_b T}\right).$$

An expression for the *total molar polarisation* may be developed analogous to the expression given on page 303 for the molar polarisation due to induced polarisation only. The quantity α must be replaced by $\alpha + \mu^2/3k_b T$ when the effect of the presence of permanent dipoles is taken into account. Thus, total molar polarisation,

$$\frac{k-1}{k+2} \cdot \frac{M}{\rho} = \frac{4}{3}\pi N\left(\alpha + \frac{\mu^2}{3k_b T}\right). \tag{11.8}$$

Equation (11.8) is known as the **Debye equation**. The Clausius-Mossotti equation, and consequently the Debye equation, hold only for molecules present in gases and in dilute solution in non-polar solvents.

METHODS OF MEASURING DIPOLE MOMENTS

In order to measure the permanent dipole moment of a substance it is necessary to devise a method which distinguishes between induced and permanent dipole moments.

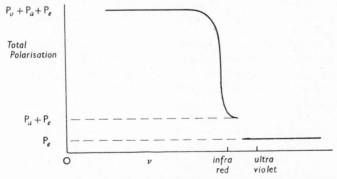

Fig. 11.4. Total polarisation plotted against values of field frequency.

If an alternating field is applied to the substance investigated, its dielectric constant for different frequencies of the field may be measured. A curve may then be drawn, showing the total polarisation as a function of the frequency of the field. The curve in Fig. 11.4 is a typical example. At low frequencies, such as those which are generally used in the measurement of dielectric constants, the polarisation is constant over a wide range. If the frequency is gradually increased it is found that as the infrared region is approached, the polarisation starts to drop and then shows a very sudden fall. As the frequency is increased, a further drop in polarisation takes place in the ultraviolet region. At still higher frequencies, the polarisation remains effectively constant.

The explanation of such a typical curve can best be made by considering the reverse process. At very high frequencies, the electrons are the only particles which are sufficiently light to follow the rapid alternations of the field. As the frequency is reduced, a point is reached somewhere in the infrared region where the nuclei of atoms or molecules are able to follow the oscillations of the field, and so the measured polarisation shows an increase. In this region absorption is likely to take place with change of vibration state of the molecule and consequent change of dipole moment and the curve becomes irregular. With still further reduction of frequency, the permanent dipoles also are able to orientate themselves with the field, and this corresponds to a large increase in the polarisation up to a saturation value. It is thus convenient to subdivide what has previously been called the *induced polarisation* into two parts, the *electronic polarisation* P_e, and the *atomic polarisation* P_a. The three stages of polarisation are therefore as follows:

(a) at low frequencies, $P = P_o + P_a + P_e$,

(b) in the infrared region, $P = P_a + P_e$,

(c) in the high-frequency region from the ultraviolet onwards $P = P_e$.

If it is possible to measure the dielectric constant accurately at different frequencies, the orientation polarisation, P_o, may be calculated. It is then possible to evaluate μ, the permanent molecular dipole moment, from the expression (p. 305),

$$P_o = \frac{n\mu^2 X}{3k_b T}.$$

MEASUREMENT OF DIELECTRIC CONSTANT

At low frequencies the dielectric constant may be accurately measured by electrical methods which are dependent on the change of capacity of a condenser used first with air as the dielectric and then with the substance which is being investigated. Particulars of these experiments may be found in textbooks on the subject. These methods are not suitable for the determination of dielectric constants at high frequencies. The most convenient method for such a determination is to make use of the relation between refractive index and dielectric constant which was deduced by Maxwell from his classical theory of electromagnetism. This theory shows that if μ is the permeability[†] and k the dielectric constant of a medium, the velocity of light in the medium may be expressed as $1/\sqrt{(\mu k)}$. For a transparent medium, the permeability is very nearly equal to unity. If n is the index of refraction of light passing from one medium to another,

$$n = \frac{\text{velocity of light in the first medium}}{\text{velocity of light in the second medium}}.$$

Therefore, to a first approximation,

$$n = \sqrt{\frac{k_2}{k_1}} \qquad \text{(see note ‡)}$$

where k_1 is the dielectric constant of the first medium, and k_2 is the dielectric constant

---

† The symbol μ is commonly used to denote permeability. It should not be confused with μ used for dipole moment.

‡ This relation holds when k and n are measured using radiation of the same frequency.

of the second medium. If the first medium is air or a vacuum, k_1 may be put equal to unity and

$$n^2 = k_2.$$

The expression for the molar polarisation then becomes (p. 303)

$$\frac{n^2-1}{n^2+1} \cdot \frac{M}{\rho}.$$

Unfortunately, the refractive index varies with the wave length of the radiation employed, and the above substitution cannot be made with any degree of accuracy unless the light is of infinite wave length. Use is made of a quantity R known as the molar refraction, where

$$R = \frac{n^2-1}{n^2+1} \cdot \frac{M}{\rho}. \tag{11.9}$$

Equation (11.9) is known as the *Lorenz-Lorentz* equation.

At infinite wave length, the molar refraction is equal to the molar polarisation, and to a fair degree of accuracy it may be assumed that they are equal in the region of infrared radiation. Even with this approximation the obstacles are not overcome, since it is very difficult to measure either the dielectric constant or the refractive index in this region. A measurement of one of these quantities for long wave length is necessary in order that the atomic polarisation P should be included. The following somewhat makeshift procedures have been suggested:

(a) The sodium D line is used to measure the refractive index. The molar refraction calculated from such an experiment is assumed to be P_e; P_a is then assumed to be a fixed percentage of P_e (from 5 to 15%).

(b) The molar refraction for a number of wave lengths in the region of the visible spectrum is determined, and from the graph so obtained the polarisation for light of infinite wave length is calculated by means of an extrapolation formula. The quantity so obtained is taken as P_I.

(c) It is assumed that when a substance is in the solid state there is no possibility that the permanent dipoles can orientate themselves in the direction of the applied field; the dielectric constant is measured, first in the solid, and then, if possible, in the gaseous state. It is also necessary to obtain the two corresponding determinations of the density. This method is obviously more suitable for certain substances than for others, and in many cases would be inapplicable.

(d) The polarisation at different temperatures is determined while the frequency is kept constant. Since P_e and P_a are independent of temperature, if the frequency is low the expression for the total polarisation may be written as $P = A + B/T$. If a graph is plotted of P against $1/T$, μ may be calculated. This method has been used for very dilute solutions of polar solutes in non-polar solvents, also for gases either at constant pressure, when the relation between density and temperature must be known accurately, or at constant density. At constant density the pressure must be adjusted so that the number of molecules in the volume under experiment is always the number that would be present if the gas were ideal. Unless this is done, the use of the Avogadro number N in the Debye equation is not justified. The method is not very reliable for solutions.

(e) A beam of molecules is passed through a non-uniform electric field. Where there is only induced polarisation, the beam is deflected towards the strongest part of the field. Where there is a permanent dipole, the beam is broadened by an amount which depends on the dipole moment. Though not capable of any great accuracy, the method has been useful in determining a value for the dipole moment of ion pairs which cannot be measured by other methods.

(f) If the dipole moment is determined in the infrared region by microwave methods it should be possible to determine P_a by combining the value so obtained with the total molecular polarisation calculated from measurements of the dielectric constant, and the electron polarisation calculated from measurements of refractive index. It is, however, uncertain whether the various moments so determined are all of the correct absolute magnitude. Measurements of absolute intensities of infrared absorption bands lead to an estimate of the rate of change of bond moment with internuclear distance, and so to an estimate of atom polarisation, but the experimental difficulties are considerable.

(g) The polarisation of a solution of a polar compound in a non-polar solvent is determined at different concentrations. The values of the polarisation differ because of the interaction of the dipoles with each other. A graph can be constructed of polarisation against concentration and extrapolated to zero concentration. A value for $P_e + P_a$ may be obtained from measurements of refractive index both for solute and solvent, and if this is subtracted from the total polarisation, a value may be obtained for the orientation polarisation of the polar solute when its molecules are quite independent of each other. If the experiment is repeated at different temperatures, a graph may be plotted of P_o at infinite dilution against $1/T$. The fact that reasonably straight lines are obtained on these graphs is a confirmation of the applicability of the Clausius-Mossotti equation to the case of a polar solute in a dilute non-polar solvent, especially when the dipole moment is small. When the dipole moment is large, it appears that *dipole association*, that is, interaction between the dipoles, starts at comparatively low concentrations.

There is evidence, however, that even at infinite dilution polarisation does depend to some extent on the character of the solvent, and so the temperature method cannot be considered to be really accurate. Various theories have been devised to account for the anomalous effects observed in liquids and solutions of polar solutes. Specialist textbooks should be consulted for details of these theories.

Microwave determination of dipole moments. This is the most accurate method available. It is chiefly used for gases, but some workers have been able to apply the technique to substances which are not gaseous at room temperature. The method consists in recording the Stark effect in the rotation spectrum of a substance placed in an electric field (p. 247). The high resolution achieved by the microwave technique makes it possible to measure the splitting accurately. Two cases may be distinguished:

Linear and diatomic molecules. These molecules do not show a primary Stark effect since the dipole moment always lies along the intermolecular axis which is at right angles to the total angular momentum vector (p. 226). They do show the secondary, or quadratic, Stark effect due to induced polarisation, and their dipole moments may be calculated from observation of the secondary splitting. The calculation required is complicated and will not be given here; a formula for the dipole moment in terms of the quantum numbers and properties of the molecule has been developed by Van Vleck.

Symmetric and asymmetric top molecules. These molecules show both primary and secondary Stark effects, but the latter is obscured by the former. The determination of the dipole moment of an asymmetric top molecule is very difficult but it has been carried out for a few cases; help is sometimes obtained from a consideration of the nuclear quadrupole coupling. The dipole moments of symmetric top molecules are more easily calculated than those of either linear or asymmetric top molecules.

For a symmetric top, K is the quantum number which determines the component of the angular momentum about the figure axis (p. 238); this axis is also the axis of the dipole moment (p. 239). If the figure axis makes an angle ϕ with the total angular momentum vector,

$$\cos\phi = \frac{K}{\sqrt{(J(J+1))}},$$

and the component of the dipole moment along the axis of total angular momentum is

$$\frac{\mu K}{\sqrt{(J(J+1))}}.$$

By similar reasoning, the component of the dipole moment along the axis of the electric field is

$$\frac{\mu K}{\sqrt{(J(J+1))}} \times \frac{M}{\sqrt{(J(J+1))}}.$$

M is here a quantum number for the electric field analogous to M, the magnetic quantum number for the magnetic field. The extra energy in the field due to the dipole is given by the product: component of dipole moment along the field × field (p. 101). Thus,

$$\text{extra energy due to dipole} = \frac{\mu KMX}{J(J+1)}$$

where $X =$ strength of applied electric field. If J changes by $+1$,

$$\text{extra energy due to dipole} = \frac{\mu KMX}{(J+1)(J+2)}.$$

Therefore a change of $+1$ in the value of J causes a line of frequency ν to appear in the spectrum where

$$h\nu = \mu KMX \left(\frac{1}{J(J+1)} - \frac{1}{(J+1)(J+2)} \right)$$

$$= \frac{2\mu KMX}{J(J+1)(J+2)}.$$

ν, K, M, and J may be determined from the spectrum, therefore μ may be calculated.

In general, liquids do not show well defined pure rotation infrared spectra as do gases. The close association of molecules in a pure polar liquid disturbs their individual rotation. The following method is suitable for the determination of the dipole moment of a polar liquid.

Determination of dipole moment from measurement of microwave absorption. The term *relaxation time* has been introduced in Chapter 9 in connection with paramagnetic resonance. It concerns the time taken for a dipole to orientate itself in the direction of an applied field. The term may be applied either to an electric dipole in an electric field, or to a magnetic dipole in a magnetic field. Since the relaxation time depends among other things on the value of the dipole moment, its determination forms the basis of a method for measuring the dipole moment.

The substance investigated acts as the dielectric of a condenser which is subjected to an alternating e.m.f. supplied by microwave radiation. In order to minimise dipole association, the polar substance is diluted with a non-polar solvent.

According to classical alternating current theory, if E is the field in the dielectric at any time t,

$$E = E_0 e^{i\omega t},$$

and

$$\omega = 2\pi\nu,$$

where E_0 is constant, and ν is the frequency in cycles per sec.

Since $kE = D$ (p. 301), D is also periodic and may be written as

$$D = D_0 e^{i(\omega t - \phi)}$$

where ϕ is the phase lag due to the time taken by the dipoles to orientate themselves in the direction of the field.

$$D = D_0 \cos(\omega t - \phi) + D_0 i \sin(\omega t - \phi)$$
$$= D_0(\cos \omega t \cos \phi + \sin \omega t \sin \phi) + i D_0(\sin \omega t \cos \phi - \cos \omega t \sin \phi).$$

If

$$D_1 = D_0 \cos \phi \quad \text{and} \quad D_2 = D_0 \sin \phi,$$

$$D = D_1(\cos \omega t + i \sin \omega t) + D_2(\sin \omega t - i \cos \omega t)$$
$$= (D_1 - i D_2) e^{i\omega t}.$$

If k^* is the effective dielectric constant and if $k' = D_1/E_0$ and $k'' = D_2/E_0$,

$$k^* E_0 e^{i\omega t} = (D_1 - i D_2) e^{i\omega t}$$

and

$$k^* = k' - ik''.$$

Thus, in an alternating field, the effective dielectric constant contains a real and an imaginary part and

$$\tan \phi = \frac{k''}{k'}.$$

Tan ϕ is known as the *loss tangent*.

Simple alternating current theory shows that in a circuit with capacity C and resistance R (no inductance) there is a phase difference ϕ between the current and e.m.f., and that

$$\tan \phi = \frac{1}{CR\omega}.$$

The dimensions of the product CR are those of time, and since, in the discharge of a condenser,

$$q = q_0 e^{-t/CR}.$$

CR may be replaced by a quantity τ which represents the time in which the charge, and thus the polarisation, is reduced to $1/e$ of its maximum value. τ is known as the *relaxation time* and is constant for a given dielectric at constant temperature. Hence

$$\tan \phi = \frac{1}{\omega \tau},$$

and

$$\frac{k''}{k'} = \frac{1}{\omega \tau}.$$

If the Debye equation is written for an alternating field, k^* is used instead of k, and the equation consists of both real and imaginary parts. There is no lag in the induced polarisation so that the term which concerns P_I is real. The orientation polarisation lags behind the field, so that the term concerning P_O contains both real and imaginary quantities. After a time t, if P_O is the polarisation which would have been built up if the field had been steady, and if P_O' is the polarisation which has actually been built up in the alternating field,

$$P_O' = P_O(1 - e^{-t/\tau}),$$

and

$$\frac{dP_O'}{dt} = \frac{1}{\tau}(P_O - P_O')$$

$$= \frac{1}{\tau}\left(\frac{n\mu^2 E_O e^{i\omega t}}{3k_b T} - P_O'\right) \text{ (see p. 305)}.$$

It may easily be verified that a solution of this differential equation is

$$P_O' = Ce^{-t/\tau} + \frac{n\mu^2 E_O e^{i\omega t}}{3k_b T(1 + i\omega\tau)}.$$

The first term may be neglected since it represents a quantity which dies away exponentially. Therefore

$$P_O' = \frac{P_O}{1 + i\omega\tau}.$$

The Debye equation for the alternating field must therefore be written:

$$\frac{k^* - 1}{k^* + 2} \cdot \frac{M}{\rho} = \frac{4}{3}\pi N\left(\alpha + \frac{\mu^2}{3k_b T(1 + i\omega\tau)}\right). \tag{11.11}$$

Substituting for k^*,

$$\frac{k' - ik'' - 1}{k' - ik'' + 2} \cdot \frac{M}{\rho} = \frac{4}{3}\pi N\alpha + \frac{4\pi\mu^2 N}{9k_b T(1 + i\omega\tau)}.$$

This equation may be rationalised by multiplying the top and bottom of the L.H.S by $(k' + ik'' + 2)$ and the top and bottom of the second term of the R.H.S. by $(1 - i\omega\tau)$. The real and imaginary parts of the equation may then be separated. From the imaginary part,

$$\frac{3k''}{(k' + 2)^2 + (k'')^2} = \frac{4\pi N\rho}{9Mk_b T}\frac{\mu^2\omega\tau}{(1 + \omega^2\tau^2)}.$$

$(k'')^2$ is small compared with $(k' + 2)^2$, therefore to a first approximation,

$$k'' = (k' + 2)^2\frac{4\pi N\rho\mu^2\omega\tau}{27Mk_b T(1 + \omega^2\tau^2)}.$$

When $\omega = 0$, $k'' = 0$, and when $\omega = \infty$, $k'' = 0$. When k'' is a maximum,

$$\frac{d}{d(\omega\tau)}\left(\frac{\omega\tau}{1 + \omega^2\tau^2}\right) = 0.$$

Hence $\omega\tau = 1$, and $k''_{max} = k'$, and

$$1 = \frac{(k' + 2)^2}{k'}\frac{4\pi N\rho\mu^2}{54Mk_b T}. \tag{11.12}$$

Since k'' has its maximum value, the maximum amount of energy is absorbed from the impinging radiation, therefore observations of the absorption are made to determine the critical frequency for which $1/\omega\tau = 1$. If k' is measured at this frequency, μ may be calculated from equation (11.12). Observation of the absorption is not easy and various refinements of technique must be employed for its measurement; for a comprehensive account of the method, the student should consult the works referred to at the end of the chapter.

Calculation of dipole moments using a model. The calculation of the dipole moments of some single bonds is carried out on p. 336.

COVALENT BOND LENGTHS

BOND LENGTHS OF SINGLE BONDS

The distance between the nuclei of two adjacent atoms linked together by forces due to their electrons is known as the *bond length*. The term is used whether the link is a single σ bond, or a multiple link of σ and π bonds. The bond length is often designated by an expression such as (C—O), and is measured in Angstrom units.

The measurement of a bond length can often be made very accurately. Bond lengths of heteronuclear diatomics and symmetric top molecules in the gaseous state are best determined by microwave spectroscopy (p. 256). Those of homonuclear diatomic molecules (which do not give a pure rotation spectrum (p. 206)) may be deduced from band spectra (p. 218), from Raman spectra (p. 252), or from electron diffraction experiments on gases (p. 289). Bond lengths in the solid state are best determined by means of X-ray diffraction analysis. The methods used are dealt with in Chapter 10 (p. 279 onwards). Estimates of bond lengths may also be obtained from electron and neutron diffraction experiments (pp. 294, 295), and these used alone or in conjunction with the results derived from X-ray diffraction are often sufficient to determine the dimensions of the molecule in question. Ideally, the equilibrium distance in the absence of vibration, r_e, should be determined, but if there is a zero-point vibration it is only possible to obtain a value for the mean internuclear distance, r_0.

Since Bragg made his first experiments in X-ray analysis, many investigators have made systematic studies of bond lengths to ascertain whether it is possible to assign a covalent radius, r, to the atoms of each element, so that the internuclear distances in covalent molecules may be computed by adding the covalent radii of atoms in contact. Covalent radii have been computed by four methods based on the independent assumptions:

    (i) that the covalent radius of an atom is half the interatomic distance in a diatomic molecule, such as Cl_2, in which no multiple bonds are present,

    (ii) that the covalent radius of the element A in the methyl derivative A—CH_3 is the bond length A—C less the covalent radius of the carbon atom,

    (iii) that the covalent radius of an element which crystallises with the diamond structure is half the interatomic distance in the crystal,

    (iv) that the covalent radius of an atom B which forms a compound BX which crystallises with the wurtzite or zinc blende structure is the interatomic distance B—X less the covalent radius of X.

In crystals with the diamond, zinc blende, or wurtzite structure, each atom exerts four tetrahedral bonds. Elements of Group IVN crystallise with the diamond structure in which all bonds are of equal length. The following substances crystallise with the zinc blende or wurtzite structures (p. 347): CSi, AlN, AlP, AlAs, AlSb, GaP, GaAs, GaSb, InSb, ZnO, ZnS, ZnSe, ZnTe, CdS, CdTe, HgS, HgSe, HgTe, CuCl, CuBr, CuI, AgI, MgTe, BeO, BeS, BeSe, BeTe. In all these substances the sum of the valency electrons in an atom pair is 8, but except in CSi each atom carries one or more formal charges. In CuCl and similar pairs the charges must be as high as three, $Cu^{3-}Cl^{3+}$.

Table 11.1 shows the covalent radii obtained using the four methods mentioned above. The results of the different methods agree well, except that in Period 4 the radius of an atom in the crystal is slightly shorter (by about 0·03) than the radius of the atom in a gaseous molecule, and in Period 5 it is shorter by about 0·05. The tetrahedral radii plotted against atomic numbers for elements in each Period give a

Table 11.1. *Covalent Radii Selected by Pauling†*

	C	N	O	F‡	Period 2
From methyl derivatives	0·77	0·70	0·66		
From elementary molecules	—	—	—	—	
From diamond structure	0·77	—	—	—	
From zinc blende or wurtzite crystal structures	0·77	0·70	0·66	—	

	Si	P	S	Cl	Period 3
From methyl derivatives	1·17	1·10	1·05	0·99	
From elementary molecules	—	1·10	1·05	0·99	
From diamond structure	1·17	—	—	—	
From zinc blende or wurtzite crystal structures	1·17	1·10	1·04	0·99	

	Ge	As	Se	Br	Period 4
From methyl derivatives	1·22	1·22	—	1·14	
From elementary molecules	—	1·22	1·16	1·14	
From diamond structure	1·22	—	—	—	
From zinc blende or wurtzite crystal structures	1·22	1·18	1·14	1·11	

	Sn	Sb	Te	I	Period 5
From methyl derivatives	1·41	—	—	1·33	
From elementary molecules	—	1·43	1·38	1·33	
From diamond structure	1·40	—	—	—	
From zinc blende or wurtzite crystal structures	1·40	1·36	1·32	1·28	

† All values except those from methyl derivatives are taken from *The Nature of the Chemical Bond* by L. C. Pauling, 3rd Edition, 1960, Chapter 7. Values from methyl derivatives are taken from the 2nd Edition, 1949, p. 162.

‡ The evidence on the covalent radius of F is conflicting; r_F is assumed to be 0·64.

consistent series of curves. Pauling§ collected together the radii of the atoms of the non-metallic elements as shown in Table 11.1, and by using these atomic radii he was able to predict the bond lengths in compounds of these elements to the accuracy shown in Table 11.5. He was also able to demonstrate that a single bond between two atoms is always longer than a multiple bond between the same atoms (p. 317). Table 11.1 also shows that the covalent radius of an atom of an element in Periods 2 and 3 is the same whether it is present in a crystal in which its valency shell contains four shared electron pairs, or in a molecule of one of its volatile derivatives, when, unless it is a member of Group IV, its valency shell must contain one or more lone electron pairs. Hence it may be concluded that the covalent radius of an atom in Periods 2 and 3 is not affected by the presence or absence of lone pairs in the valency shell.

Certain bond lengths, notably (C—C) and (C—O) in organic compounds, are remarkably constant. In the 18 compounds included in Table 11.2, (C—C) for two carbon atoms in the tetrahedral valence state linked by a single σ bond is consistently 1·54. Hence the covalent radius, r_C, of the carbon atom in this state may be taken as 0·77. Since (C—O) is 1·43 (Table 11.3) the covalent radius of the oxygen atom in the tetrahedral valence state with two lone pairs is 0·66.

Thus the concept of covalent radius is applicable with consistency at least over a limited field of chemical combination. Certain anomalies, however, must be mentioned.

(1) The covalent radius of hydrogen is uncertain. It is 0·37 in H_2, and it varies

§ L. Pauling, *Nature of the Chemical Bond* (Cornell University Press, 3rd Edition, 1960).

Table 11.2. *Observed lengths of C—C Bonds†*

Diamond	1·545‡	Tetramethylethylene	1·54 ± 0·02
Ethane	1·54 ± 0·03‡	Mesitylene	1·54 ± 0·01
Propane	1·54 ± 0·02	Hexamethylbenzene	1·54 ± 0·01
Isobutane	1·54 ± 0·02	Trans-2-butene	1·56 ± 0·02‡
Neopentane	1·54 ± 0·02	Cis-2-butene	1·54 ± 0·02
Cyclopropane	1·54 ± 0·03‡	Trans-2,3-epoxybutene	1·53 ± 0·02
Cyclopentane	1·54 ± 0·03‡	Cis-2,3-epoxybutene	1·54 ± 0·02
Cyclohexane	1·54 ± 0·03‡	Decaldehyde	1·54 ± 0·02
Isobutene	1·54 ± 0·02	Metaldehyde	1·54 ± 0·02

† Pauling, *op. cit.*, 2nd ed., p. 161. Values marked ‡ have been slightly adjusted to conform to those given in "Interatomic Distances", The Chemical Society, London, 1958.

Table 11.3. *Observed lengths of C—O Bonds‡*

Dimethyl ether	1·42 ± 0·03	Metaldehyde	1·43 ± 0·02
1-4 Dioxane	1·44 ± 0·04	Trans-2,3-epoxybutene	1·43 ± 0·02
O-methylhydroxylamine	1·44 ± 0·02	Cis-2,3-epoxybutene	1·43 ± 0·03
Paraldehyde	1·43 ± 0·02	Divinyl ether	1·43 ± 0·03

‡ Pauling, *op. cit.*, 2nd ed., p. 162.

between 0·32 and 0·28 in different hydrogen compounds. The standard radius chosen by Pauling was 0·30.

(2) The covalent radii of the highly electronegative elements N, O, F, in N_2H_4, H_2O_2, and F_2, are longer than the covalent radii exhibited by these elements in combination with methyl groups. The interatomic distances between pairs of these elements in other compounds are also longer than the sum of their covalent radii when in combination with methyl groups. The data are given in Table 11.4.

(3) The observed bond lengths in simple binary compounds in which one of the elements is in Period 3 or some higher Period are nearly always shorter than the sum of the covalent radii of the elements concerned. The data are given in Table 11.5.

Table 11.4. *Bond Lengths in Simple Covalent Compounds of* N, O, F

Bond			Observed Bond Length	$r_a + r_b$
F—F	in	F_2	1·44	—
N—N	in	$H_2N—NH_2$	1·48	1·40
O—O	in	H_2O_2	1·48	1·32
F—O	in	F_2O	1·41	1·30
F—O	in	$F—ONO_2$	1·42	1·30
F—N	in	$F—N=N—F$	1·44	1·34
N—Cl	in	$(CH_3)_2N—Cl$	1·77	1·69
N—Cl	in	CH_3NCl_2	1·74	1·69

Table 11.5. *Bond Lengths in Simple Covalent Compounds*

Column 2 gives the observed bond length. Column 3 gives the sum of the covalent radii as stated in Table 11.1, and Column 4 gives the difference between this sum and the observed bond length. Column 5 gives the bond length computed by Schomaker and Stevenson, and Column 6 gives the difference between this length and the observed bond length (Column 2). Column 7 gives the electronegativity correction. Column 8 gives the sum of the ionic radii of the elements.

1	2 $(x–y)$ obs.	3 Pauling $r_a + r_b$	4 Differ- ence	5 S & S† $r'_a + r'_b$	6 Differ- ence	7 $0·09\,(X_a \sim X_b)$	8 $r_A^+ + r_B^-$
B—C	1·56	1·65	−0·09	1·59	−0·03	0·05	2·80
Si—C	1·93	1·94	−0·01	—	—	0·06	3·01
Ge—C	1·98	1·99	−0·01	—	—	0·07	3·13
Sn—C	2·18	2·17	+0·01	—	—	0·07	3·31
N—C	1·47	1·47	0·00	1·51	−0·04	0·05	1·86
P—C	1·87	1·87	0·00	—	—	0·04	2·94
As—C	1·98	1·98	0·00	—	—	0·05	3·07
O—C	1·42	1·43	−0·01	1·51	−0·09	0·09	1·55
S—C	1·82	1·81	+0·01	—	—	0·00	1·99
F—C	1·39	1·41	−0·02	1·49	−0·10	0·14	1·51
Cl—C	1·76	1·76	0·00	—	—	0·05	1·96
Br—C	1·91	1·91	0·00	—	—	0·03	2·10
I—C	2·12	2·10	0·02	—	—	0·01	2·31
F—Si	1·54	1·81	−0·27	1·89	−0·35	0·20	1·77
Cl—Si	2·00	2·16	−0·16	—	—	0·11	2·22
Br—Si	2·14	2·31	−0·17	—	—	0·09	2·36
I—Si	2·43	2·50	−0·07	—	—	0·06	2·00
Cl—Ge	2·08	2·21	−0·13	—	—	0·12	2·34
Br—Ge	2·32	2·36	−0·04	—	—	0·10	2·48
I—Ge	2·48	2·55	−0·07	—	—	0·06	2·69
Cl—Sn	2·30	2·39	−0·09	—	—	0·12	2·52
Br—Sn	2·44	2·54	−0·10	—	—	0·10	2·66
I—Sn	2·64	2·73	−0·09	—	—	0·07	2·87
F—P	1·52	1·74	−0·22	1·82	−0·30	0·17	1·70
Cl—P	2·04	2·09	−0·05	—	—	0·08	2·15
Br—P	2·23	2·24	−0·01	—	—	0·06	2·29
I—P	2·47	2·43	+0·04	—	—	0·03	2·50
F—As	1·72	1·85	−0·13	1·93	−0·21	0·18	1·83
Cl—As	2·16	2·20	−0·04	—	—	0·09	2·28
Br—As	2·34	2·35	−0·01	—	—	0·07	2·42
I—As	2·54	2·54	0·00	—	—	0·04	2·63
Cl—Sb	2·37	2·40	−0·03	—	—	0·11	2·43
Br—Sb	2·50	2·55	−0·05	—	—	0·09	2·57
I—Sb	2·71	2·74	−0·03	—	—	0·06	2·78
F—O	1·41	1·30	+0·11	1·46	−0·05	0·05	1·45
Cl—O	1·68	1·65	+0·03	1·73	−0·05	0·05	1·66
Cl—S	1·99	2·03	−0·04	—	—	0·05	2·10
Cl—Te	2·36	2·36	0·00	—	—	0·08	2·37
F—Cl	1·64	1·63	+0·01	1·71	−0·07	0·09	1·62
I—Cl	2·32	2·32	0·00	—	—	0·05	2·31
F—B	1·30	1·48	−0·18	1·54	−0·24	0·18	1·56
Cl—B	1·74	1·87	−0·13	1·81	−0·07	0·09	2·01
Br—B	1·87	2·02	−0·15	1·96	−0·09	0·07	2·15

† V. Schomaker and D. P. Stevenson, *J. Amer. Chem. Soc.*, 1941, **63**, 37.

Anomalies such as these are to be expected because the force binding two atoms together depends largely on the piling up of negative charge between the nuclei, and the magnitude of this charge must depend on the wave functions of all the electrons in the molecule. Hence the length of a bond between two atoms depends not only on the natures of the two atoms, but also on the environment of the bond in the molecule. This effect is illustrated in Table 11.6. The constancy of the C—C bond length in Table 11.2 arises because the environment of the C—C bond is more or less the same in all the compounds considered.

Table 11.6. *Effect of Nature of the Molecule on a Particular Bond Length*†

Molecule	(Sn—Cl)	Molecule	(C—F)
$(CH_3)_3SnCl$	$2·37 \pm 0·03$	CF_4	$1·32‡$
$(CH_3)_2SnCl_2$	$2·34$	CHF_3	$1·33‡$
CH_3SnCl_3	$2·30$	CH_3F	$1·39‡$
$SnCl_4$	$2·30$	CCl_3F	$1·44$
$r_{Sn}+r_{Cl}$	$2·39$	r_C+r_F	$1·49$
with electronegativity correction	$2·27$	—	$1·36$

† A. F. Wells, *Structural Inorganic Chemistry* (Oxford, Clarendon Press, 1950), pp. 60, 61. Values marked ‡ have been slightly adjusted to conform to those given in "Interatomic Distances", The Chemical Society, London, 1958.

The Schomaker and Stevenson correction. Schomaker and Stevenson re-examined the data of covalent bond lengths and drew up a list of covalent radii adjusted by the assumptions:

(1) That the "true" covalent bond is found in the diatomic halogen molecules, and between the nitrogen atoms in N_2H_4, and between the oxygen atoms in H_2O_2; the "true covalent radii" of N, O, and F are deduced from the observed bond lengths given in Table 11.4.

(2) That an increase in the ionic character of a covalent bond decreases the bond length.

An adjustment based on the second assumption was applied by the use of the empirical formula§:

$$r_{ab} = r_a+r_b - 0·09(X_a \sim X_b) \tag{11.13}$$

where r_{ab} is the covalent bond length, r_a and r_b are the covalent radii of the atoms when purely covalent, X_a and X_b are the electronegativities of the atoms. The equation shows how the length of a covalent bond is diminished by a difference between the electronegativities of the atoms; the difference indicates the amount of ionic character in the bond. As an example, the bond length of the group CF may be computed. r_C for carbon is $0·77$, r_F for fluorine is $0·74$, X_C is $2·5$, X_F is $4·0$.

$$r_{CF} = 0·77+0·74-0·09(4·0-2·5)$$
$$= 1·49-0·135$$
$$= 1·35.$$

The observed value is $1·39$; Pauling's method gives $1·41$. Schomaker and Stevenson's method of computing bond lengths gives the results shown in Table 11.5. It has the merit of bringing the "true" covalent radii of N, O, and F, into the picture, but examination of the Table shows that this method of computing bond lengths is on the whole no more satisfactory than the original method of Pauling.

§$X_a \sim X_b$ represents the numerical difference between X_a and X_b; the sign is disregarded.

BOND LENGTHS OF MULTIPLE BONDS

Bond lengths of multiple bonds are always shorter than those of corresponding single bonds. Table 11.7 shows the bond lengths of certain compounds of carbon.

Table 11.7. *Bond Lengths of Multiple Bonds between Carbon Atoms*

Compound	Bond lengths			
	$\diagdown$C—C$\diagup$	$\diagdown$C=C$\diagup$	—C≡C—	C···C
Ethane	1·54			
Ethylene		1·34		
Acetylene			1·20	
Benzene				1·39
Graphite				1·42

It is seen from columns 2 and 3 that the distance between the carbon atoms in ethylene is shorter than that in ethane, and that the distance in acetylene (column 4) is shorter still. Table 11.8 shows that the bond length (C—C) is shorter than the normal distance, 1·54, if the carbon atoms concerned are exerting triple bonds.

Table 11.8. *Lengths of Bonds of Carbon Atoms Exerting Triple Bonds†*

Molecule	Bond lengths			
	C—C≡	C≡C	≡C—C≡	C≡N
H_3C—C≡CH	1·46	1·20		
H_3C—C≡C—CH_3	1·47	1·20		
H_3C—C≡C—C≡C—CH_3	1·47	1·20	1·38	
HC≡C—C≡CH		1·19	1·36	
N≡C—C≡N			1·37	1·16
H_3C—C≡N	1·49			1·16

† L. Pauling, H. D. Springall, and K. J. Palmer, *J. Amer. Chem. Soc.*, 1939, **61**, 927.

All lengths are estimated to be experimentally correct to $\pm 0·03$. The constancy of the length of each type of bond in similar environments is remarkable.

BOND LENGTHS OF CONJUGATED BONDS: BOND ORDER

The term *bond order* is used to express the multiplicity of the link between two atoms. It is used in several different ways, and its precise meaning has usually to be deduced from its connotation. When used in connection with molecular orbitals of diatomic molecules (p. 318) the bond order is the number of pairs of electrons having a resultant bonding effect. This is best made clear by examples given in Table 11.9. When used in connection with directed valence the meaning of the term "bond order" is different. It is used here to give information about the number of σ and π bonds which make up the link between two atoms. The *total bond order* is the total number of bonds between the atoms; the *mobile bond order* is the number of π bonds between the atoms. The total bond order of the C=C bond in ethylene is 2, and the mobile bond order is 1; the total bond order of the C≡C bond in acetylene is 3 and the

Table 11.9.   *Examples of Bond Order as Applied to Molecular Orbitals*

Molecule	Number of electrons		Bond order
	in bonding orbitals	in antibonding orbitals	
H_2	2	0	1
H_2^+	1	0	$\frac{1}{2}$
He_2	2	2	0
O_2	8	4	2
O_2^+	8	3	$2\frac{1}{2}$
F_2	8	6	1

mobile bond order is 2. In conjugated systems the bond orders are usually fractional, and the fraction has to be calculated from a knowledge of the conjugated structure. For example, graphite has a resonance structure, which is represented by

$$
\begin{array}{c}
C{=}C \\
C{=}C \qquad C{=}C \\
C{=}C \qquad C{=}C \qquad C \\
C{=}C \qquad C{=}C \\
C{=}C \qquad C{=}C
\end{array}
$$

and two other canonical forms in which the double bonds are written between other pairs of carbon atoms. Clearly there is a 33·3% chance that any given bond is a

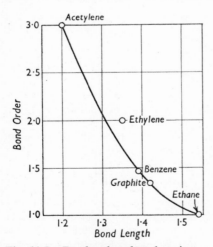

Fig. 11.5.   Bond order plotted against bond length.

double bond. The mobile bond order is 0·33, and the total bond order is 1·33. Benzene, however, is a resonance structure of two Kekulé and three Dewar forms (p. 171). If the Kekulé forms only are considered, the total bond order of each bond is 1·5. If both the Kekulé and the Dewar forms are taken into account, it is necessary to decide how much each form contributes to the resultant structure. The wave function of the resultant structure ψ is given by the combination of the component wave functions, thus

$$\psi = c_1(\psi_{1K}+\psi_{2K})+c_2(\psi_{3D}+\psi_{4D}+\psi_{5D}).$$

By wave mechanical methods it has been shown[†] that

$$c_2/c_1 = 0.4341,$$

and hence the relative weights of the Dewar and Kekulé forms are $(0.4341)^2:1$, or $0.19:1$. Expressed as percentages, the weight of each Dewar form is 7, and the weight of each Kekulé form is 39. The mobile bond order of any bond in the benzene molecule is therefore 0·46, and the total bond order is 1·46. The term bond order in this book means the total bond order of a directed bond.

† C. A. Coulson, *Valence*, p. 235.

If the bond length between two carbon atoms is plotted against the bond order, the curve in Fig. 11.5 is obtained. The data used in constructing the curve are:

Substance	Bond length	Bond order	Valence state of carbon atom
Ethane	1·54	1	Tetrahedral
Graphite	1·42	1·33	Trigonal
Benzene	1·39	1·46	Trigonal
Ethylene	1·34	2	Trigonal
Acetylene	1·20	3	Digonal

BOND LENGTHS OF πd BONDS

It is stated on p. 314 that covalent bonds in simple binary compounds in which the central element is in Period 3 or some higher Period, are nearly always shorter than the sum of the covalent radii (Table 11.5). Very short bond lengths are also present in the ions of certain oxyacids and some other oxygen compounds (Table 11.10).

Table 11.10. *Examples of "Short" Bond Lengths*

Ion or molecule	Bond	Bond length observed	Bond length of single bond (M—O)	Bond length of double bond (M=O)
CO_3^{2-}	C—O	1·27	1·43	1·23
NO_3^-	N—O	1·21	1·36	1·22
$(C_2H_5)_2SO$	S—O	1·47	1·70	1·50
$(C_2H_5)_2SO_2$	S—O	1·43	1·70	1·50
SO_4^{2-}	S—O	1·50	1·70	1·50
SeO_4^{2-}	Se—O	1·61	1·83	1·62
PO_4^{3-}	P—O	1·56	1·76	1·56
P_4O_{10}	P—O	1·39	1·76	1·56
$P_4O_6S_4$	P—S	1·85	2·14	1·94
AsO_4^{3-}	As—O	1·75	1·87	1·66
$B_3O_6^{3-}$	B—O	1·31	1·54	1·31

The ions CO_3^{2-} and NO_3^- consist of elements in Period 2. The valence shells of the atoms contain s and p orbitals only and the atoms can form π bonds but not πd bonds. The ions are resonance structures, and the bond order in both cases is 1·33. As would be expected by analogy with graphite and benzene the observed bond lengths are intermediate between (M—O) and (M=O).

The observed bond lengths in the remaining ions or molecules are either equal to or less than (M=O). The atoms of the element M in all cases contain d orbitals in the valency shell, and hence are capable of hybridisation to produce πd bonds (p. 156). Such bonds are characteristic of all the compounds or ions with very short bond lengths in Table 11.10 and their presence must be related to the bond shortening. It is easy to see, qualitatively, why this should be so. The SO_4^{2-} ion for example, written with a co-ionic bond structure (a) (p. 320) would have a considerable amount of negative charge in the lone pairs of the oxygen atoms remote from the sulphur atom. If, however, the two co-ionic bonds are replaced by σ and πd bonds (b) there is a transfer of negative charge from the outside of the oxygen atoms to positions between the oxygen atoms and the sulphur atom. The structure shown is one canonical form of a resonance system in which all the oxygen atoms are identically related to the sulphur atom. Hence all the atoms in the ion are more tightly bound than they would be in the co-ionic structure, and the bond length is shortened.

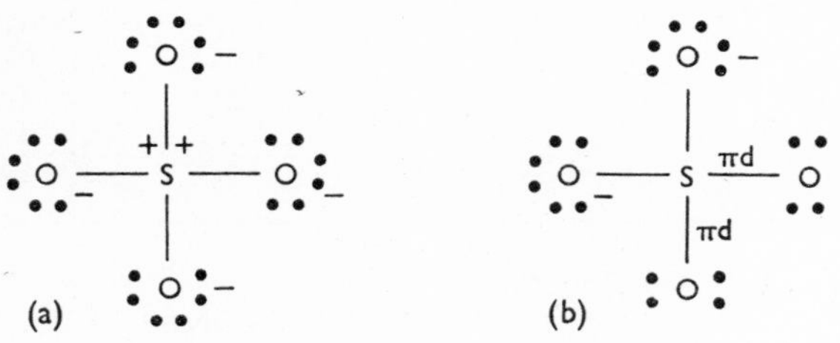

(a)   (b)

The metaborate ion is included in Table 11.10 because it shows a bond shortening comparable with that in the other ions. Although boron cannot form πd bonds it is conjectured that the shortening is produced by multiple bonding. Non-localised bonds probably embrace the whole of the ion to produce a more compact structure than that suggested by the formula on p. 499.

The effect of πd bonds on bond length can also be used to explain the short bond lengths in Table 11.5. Silicon tetrafluoride, for example, is usually described as a tetrahedral molecule (c). If the silicon atom, however, exerts three πd bonds in addition to the four σ tetrahedral bonds (p. 156), lone pairs from three of the fluorine atoms could be transferred to the πd orbitals to produce the structure (d). The high electronegativity of the fluorine atom would polarise the double bonds, but this would not diminish the concentration of charge in these bonds.

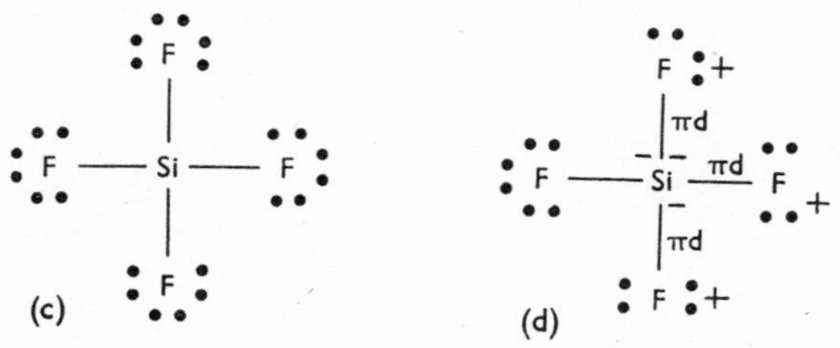

(c)   (d)

The bond length of sulphur hexafluoride (1·56) is very short; Pauling's bond lengths are (S—F) 1·68; (S=F) 1·48. This could be explained in just the same way by the superposition of three πd bonds on three of the octahedral σ bonds (pp. 154 and 161).

Calculation of bond lengths by means of a model. The calculation of certain bond lengths in terms of bond energies, ionisation potentials, and the valence states of the atoms is described on p. 327.

BOND ENERGY

The formation of a covalent bond is accompanied by release of energy, and the rupture of a bond is accompanied by the absorption of energy. The overall change of energy can be ascertained when, say, a C—C bond is broken by the dissociation of an ethane molecule into two methyl groups, but this energy change is, in fact, the resultant of changes in many energy terms concerning the structure and properties of the original ethane molecule, and those of the two fragments into which it has decomposed. The overall change which is observed when a molecule dissociates into fragments is an empirical quantity which can be observed or computed. It is known as the *bond dissociation energy*.

A covalent bond is formed by the overlapping of two atomic orbitals (p. 114). Its formation results in the concentration of negative charge between the atomic nuclei. This concentration of charge must have an effect on all the electrons in both atoms and must bring about changes in potential energy. Moreover, the kinetic energy of the original free atoms must be absorbed in some manner by the newly formed molecule. It is possible notionally to neglect these and other secondary energy changes, and to consider the energy change which results solely from the replacement of two atomic orbitals by one molecular orbital. This energy change is called the *bond energy* (p. 323).

The concepts used in the discussion of energy associated with bonds are considered in more detail in the following paragraphs.

BOND DISSOCIATION ENERGY

Bond dissociation energy is defined as the energy which is absorbed when a molecule is broken into two separate fragments, and hence one of the bonds originally in the molecule is ruptured. Bond dissociation energy is represented by the symbol $D(A—B)$ where A and B were linked by the bond in question in the original molecule, and are the fragments produced by dissociation. For example, if the bond to be dissociated is a C—H bond in methane, the bond dissociation energy is represented by $D(CH_3—H)$. The bond dissociation energy is identical with the heat change ΔH of the reaction:

$$CH_4 = CH_3 + H.$$

In principle, the bond dissociation energy is a quantity which can be measured precisely. The available methods of measurement vary in accuracy; they are briefly described in the following paragraphs. They may be classified as follows: spectroscopic methods, photochemical methods, electron impact methods, and thermochemical methods.

Spectroscopic method. This method is suitable only for the determination of the dissociation energy of diatomic molecules and radicals. In principle it is simple, but in practice it is limited in its application to substances with molecular spectra which are not too complex.

The dissociation energy of a diatomic molecule which dissociates into non-excited atoms can be obtained from the experimentally determined potential energy curve (Fig. 7.2, p. 210). The difference between the limiting value of the energy on the right-hand side of the curve and the energy corresponding to zero vibration quantum number (thus eliminating the zero point energy) measures the dissociation energy directly. The principle of the method is simple, but difficulties arise in its application because the absorption of energy necessary to set the molecule into vibration usually raises it to an excited electronic state, and at the same time changes of rotational energy may also take place. It is explained in the chapter on molecular spectra how these three effects may be identified (pp. 205, 206), but even with only moderately complex molecules it is not easy to separate the vibrational changes from the rest of the spectrum. To a first approximation the rotational changes may be ignored since they appear as the component lines of a band which denotes a vibrational change. By the application of the Franck-Condon principle (p. 213) potential energy curves for the ground and excited states can be plotted on the same diagram (Fig. 7.6, p. 215). The relative position of these curves shows the effect of electronic excitation on the dissociation energy. Since the vibrational energy levels for a given electronic state get

11 + A.T.I.C.

closer and closer together as the vibration quantum number increases, the vibration bands appear to converge to a more or less sharp edge known as the "convergence limit", corresponding to E_{lim} (Figs. 7.2 and 7.4). The energy change responsible for the dissociation is taken to be the change from E_{lim} of the excited state to $v=0$ of the ground state. In order to calculate the energy of dissociation it is necessary to be able to identify the products of dissociation, and to know their energy of electronic excitation. The accurate observation of the convergence limit of the excited vibrational level is facilitated if the line spectrum is followed by a continuous absorption spectrum due to the photodissociation of the molecule into atoms with kinetic energy. Even so there may be alternative interpretations of the state of the excited electron leading to different calculated bond energies.

Photochemical method. The object of the photochemical method is to subject the molecule to radiation of just the right frequency to set it into vibration of sufficient amplitude to break the molecular bond. Again, this method is one which is simple in principle but difficult in application. The products of dissociation are always excited, and these products and their state of excitation must be identified if the energy of dissociation is to be calculated.

It is difficult to relate the energy of the radiation absorbed to the dissociation energy if there is a wide gap between them. The method is sometimes varied by the use of a photosensitive substance, the atoms of which are excited by an impinging radiation, which is not directly absorbed by the dissociating molecule. On collision with an excited atom a molecule may absorb the energy of excitation to become dissociated; in consequence the excited atom returns to the ground state. Unfortunately the atoms of mercury, cadmium, and zinc are the only photosensitive bodies available for this method.

Electron impact methods. The substance investigated is subjected to a beam of electrons whose kinetic energy can be varied. If this kinetic energy is sufficient, the molecules dissociate with ionisation of one of the products, which may be identified in the mass spectrograph. To determine the dissociation energy it is normally necessary to know the ionisation potential of the radical produced; this may be measured independently.[†] It is difficult to estimate accurately the energy of the beam of electrons which is just sufficient to disrupt the molecule and ionise one of the products without giving kinetic energy to the products.

Thermochemical methods. The heat of dissociation ΔH (which is identical with the bond dissociation energy) is measured by observing the heat changes in a series of reactions, one of which is the dissociation under investigation. The method is illustrated by the computation of the heat of dissociation of the bond S—H by measuring the heat of combustion of hydrogen sulphide. The experimental result is expressed by the equation:

$$H_2S + 1\tfrac{1}{2}O_2 = H_2O + SO_2; \quad \Delta H = -122 \cdot 3 \text{ kcal}.$$

Other data which must also be known are:

$$
\begin{aligned}
S_{rhombic} + O_2 &= SO_2; & \Delta H &= -69 \cdot 3 \text{ kcal} \\
S_{rhombic} &= S_{gas}; & \Delta H &= +53 \cdot 3 \text{ kcal} \\
H_2 + \tfrac{1}{2}O_2 &= H_2O; & \Delta H &= -57 \cdot 8 \text{ kcal} \\
H_2 &= H + H; & \Delta H &= +104 \cdot 2 \text{ kcal}
\end{aligned}
$$

On multiplying the first and third equations in the data by -1, and adding all the equations together, it is found that $H_2S = S + H + H$; $\Delta H = +162 \cdot 3$ kcal. Hence the

† For a method which avoids the use of the ionisation energy of the radical produced, see M. Swarc, "Bond Dissociation Energies", *Quart. Rev.*, **5**, No. 1, 1951, 22.

bond dissociation energy $D(H-S)$, on the assumption[†] that it is one half of ΔH for this reaction, is 81·2 kcal.

The quantity ΔH can also be computed from measurement of the equilibrium constant, K, of the dissociation reaction at different temperatures, and applying Van't Hoff's relation:

$$\frac{d \log_e K}{dT} = \frac{\Delta H}{RT^2}.$$

The bond dissociation energies of many molecules can be ascertained by experiments involving a series of thermochemical reactions, as already illustrated for hydrogen sulphide. If the dissociation energy for a given bond can be measured by more than one method, the agreement is good.

AVERAGE BOND DISSOCIATION ENERGY

The bond dissociation energy of the bond C—H, which can be represented generally as $D(XC-H)$ (where X represents any radical with which carbon is combined in the molecule XCH) depends on the nature of X. Not only is the energy of the bond itself dependent on the nature of X, but there are also energy terms included in $D(XC-H)$ which represent the direct interaction of the hydrogen atom with all the electrons in the atoms constituting the radical X.

Consider the dissociation of methane. The bond dissociation energy $D(CH_3-H)$, which is the energy change accompanying the reaction

$$CH_4 = CH_3 + H,$$

is different from the bond dissociation energy $D(CH_2-H)$ for the reaction:

$$CH_3 = CH_2 + H,$$

and the values of the energies $D(CH-H)$, and $D(C-H)$, are again different. The *average bond dissociation energy* is defined as the "amount of work required for the rupture of the bond in question in a process in which all the other bonds are stretched independently and simultaneously with the particular bond, and thus the molecule swells infinitely without losing its shape" (Swarc). If this definition is adopted then the heat of atomisation of the molecule is equal to the sum of the average bond dissociation energies of the bonds.

BOND ENERGY

The *energy of a bond*, or *bond energy*, may be defined as *the energy required for the replacement of the molecular orbital constituting the bond by atomic orbitals*,[‡] and it may be designated ΔE. Bond energy is expressed in terms of bond dissociation rather than bond formation, because most of the experimental work on it is carried out on the dissociation of molecules.

The molecular heat of dissociation, ΔH, the energy absorbed when a gram molecule is dissociated into isolated atoms, is the resultant of a number of energy changes:

$$\Delta H = \Delta E + A - M + \Delta E_{electronic} + W. \tag{11.14}$$

ΔH is defined as the heat change which occurs when one gram molecule of the original compound in its standard state (that is, its normal state, gas, liquid, or crystal) is decomposed to the products of dissociation in their standard states: the physical conditions before and after dissociation are usually taken as 18° and 1 atmosphere pressure. ΔE is the bond energy, defined as above. M is the total kinetic energy

[†] This assumption is only approximately valid.

[‡] It should be noted that the atomic orbitals concerned may be those of the atom in an excited state.

(translational, vibrational, rotational) of the molecules before dissociation according to the classical kinetic theory in which atoms and molecules are treated as solid particles. A is the kinetic energy of the atoms produced by the dissociation. $\Delta E_{\text{electronic}}$ is the energy absorbed by any change in the electronic state of the atoms when the molecules dissociate. W includes the work done by any change of physical state (e.g. solid or liquid to gas) and by the expansion which occurs when the number of molecules in the system is doubled by the dissociation of the original diatomic molecules into monatomic molecules.

If the dissociation were deemed to be carried out at $0°K$, then W, A, and M (except for zero point energy) would be zero. The experimental work is usually conducted at room temperature, however, and the data for converting the results to $0°K$ very often do not exist. It is therefore convenient to modify the usual definition of ΔH by stating that both the original substance and the products of dissociation are to be in the gaseous state, and that only those reactions shall be considered in which there is no change in the electronic state of the atoms. By these modifications $\Delta E_{\text{electronic}}$ becomes zero, and the portion of W which concerns changes of physical state also becomes zero. If it could be assumed, either that A and M are insignificant compared to ΔE, or that A and M are nearly equal, ΔH (computed to conform to the above definition) could be accepted as an approximate measure of the bond energy. This means that the bond energy ΔE could be assumed to be very nearly equal in value to the bond dissociation energy ΔH.

If the effect of dissociation is first to change the molecule into unstable radicals, energy may be released or absorbed when the unstable radicals change into stable molecules or atoms, each possessing its appropriate kinetic energy. The energy associated with such a process is termed *reorganisation energy*. If equation (11.14) is applied to cases in which the dissociation produces radicals and not separate atoms, the term A must be replaced by the reorganisation energy. If this is large it would reduce the validity of regarding ΔH as equivalent to ΔE.

Attention must be drawn to the condition that bond energy is not to include any energy due to the change of electronic state of the atom (p. 323). This condition is important because an isolated atom frequently changes its electronic state when it combines with another atom. For example, the electron configuration of the isolated carbon atom in the ground state is $s^2 p_x p_y$, but when the carbon atom is combined with another atom, the configuration is based on the excited state $sp_x p_y p_z$. The change from the ground state to the excited state must involve the absorption of energy.

It has been found that the valence state of an atom in combination also influences the bond energy. An atom may adopt several valence states (p. 175) all based on the same electronic state. Table 11.11 shows how the bond energy increases as the proportion of the s contribution to the bond increases.

Table 11.11. *Relation between Bond Energy and the s Content of the Bond†*

Molecule	Hybridisation	Bond lengths C—H	k(C—H) Stretching force constant dynes/cm	Energy of C—H bond kcal/mole
CH radical	p	1·12	$4·09 \times 10^5$	80
CH_4	sp^3	1·094	$4·79 \times 10^5$	~99·3
C_2H_4	sp^2	1·087	$5·1 \times 10^5$	~106
C_2H_2	sp	1·059	$5·85 \times 10^5$	~121

†A. D. Walsh, *Discuss. Faraday Soc.*, 2, 1947, 181.

In view of the assumptions and approximations that have to be made in evaluating bond energies it is not possible to compile a table of bond energies with a reliability depending solely on experimental accuracy. In Table 11.12 values derived from the consideration of particular compounds are assigned to certain covalent bonds. These values are used in calculations made in this book.

Table 11.12. *Energies of Covalent Bonds*

Bond	Compound	Estimated Bond Energy kcal	Reference
H^+—H	H_2^+	61	C
H—H	H_2	104	C
O—O	H_2O_2	35	C
N—N	N_2H_4	64	W
C—C	general	83†	C
F—F	F_2	35	Co
Cl—Cl	Cl_2	58	W
P—P	P_4	53	C
S—S	S_8	54	C
C—H	CH_4	99·3†	C
N—H	NH_3	93·4	C
F—H	HF	135	C
O—H	H_2O_2	96	W
N—O	NH_2OH	50	C
C—O	CH_3OH	80·2†	C
H—Cl	HCl	103·1	C
P—Br	PBr_3	63	C
P—Cl	PCl_3	78	C
H—S	HS	66·3	C
H—Br	HBr	87·4	C
C—Br	C_2H_5Br	68	C
C—Cl	CCl_4	78·2	C
C—F	CF_4	121†	C
N—F	NF_3	65	C
P—H	PH_3	77	C
O=O	O_2	117	Co
C=C	general	146	C
N=O	CH_3NO_2	150	C
C=O	$(CH_3)_2CO$	179	C
S=O	SO_3	104	C
N≡N	N_2	226	C
C≡C	C_2H_2	194·3	C
C≡N	general	212·6	C

† These values, based on electron impact or photo-dissociation methods, do not include energy of excitation. Values for other bonds involving carbon atoms include excitation energy.

References: C = Cottrell, T. L., *The Strength of Chemical Bonds* (2nd ed. Butterworth, 1958)
Co = Coulson, C. A., *Valence* (Oxford University Press, 1952)
W = Walsh, A. D., *J. Chem. Soc.*, 1948, 331.
general = average of the values obtained by the investigation of several compounds.

BOND ENERGY AND RESONANCE

Although bond energies can be calculated only by the use of considerable approximation, discrepancies between the sum of the bond energies of certain compounds, and their observed heats of dissociation led to the concept of resonance (p. 168). For example, the heat of dissociation of benzene derived from experimental data is given in the equations:

$$\text{graphite} = 6C; \quad \Delta H = 6 \times 170 \text{ kcal}$$
$$3H_2 = 6H; \quad \Delta H = 3 \times 104 \text{ kcal}$$
$$C_6H_6 \text{ gas} = 6C \text{ (graphite)} + 3H_2; \quad \Delta H = 19 \cdot 7 \text{ kcal}$$

By addition,

$$C_6H_6 = 6C + 6H; \quad \Delta H = 1312 \text{ kcal}.$$

Using the data in Table 11.12, the total bond energy in one mole of benzene is

$$\left. \begin{array}{l} 6D(\text{C---H}) = 6 \times 99 \cdot 3 = 595 \cdot 8 \\ 3D(\text{C---C}) = 3 \times 83 \cdot 0 = 249 \cdot 0 \\ 3D(\text{C==C}) = 3 \times 146 = 438 \end{array} \right\} = 1283 \text{ kcal}.$$

Hence the observed heat of dissociation of benzene is 29 kcal per mole greater than expected (cf. p. 169). The difference is known as the *resonance energy*, and it indicates that benzene is more stable than it would be if the structure of the molecule were correctly represented by one of the Kekulé forms. Other examples of molecules showing resonance energy are given in Table 11.13.

Table 11.13. *Resonance Energy (kcal/mole)*

Compound	Resonance energy computed from heats of dissociation† (Pauling)	Resonance energy computed from heats of hydrogenation (Dewar)
Benzene	41	36
Naphthalene	77	62
Pyrene	152	107
Aniline	51	40
Pyridine	40	31

Dewar has pointed out that before the difference between the observed and computed dissociation energy can be taken as equal to the resonance energy, attention must be paid to the magnitude of the term M in equation (11.14).

The approximation $\Delta H = \Delta E$ is usually acceptable, either because the values of A and M are roughly the same for all dissociation reactions, or because A and M are insignificant in comparison with ΔE. If for any particular molecule M is unusually small numerically while A has a normal value, the heat of dissociation ΔH is increased, and on the assumption that $\Delta H = \Delta E$, the value assigned to ΔE is too great. The value of M is small if the number of mechanical degrees of freedom of the molecule is small, that is if, the number of modes of vibration of the molecules is restricted. A molecule with few degrees of freedom, even if it is not a resonance structure, therefore has a high heat of dissociation. By making observations on the heat of hydrogenation of conjugated and non-conjugated unsaturated molecules it is possible to compute the resonance energy without having to consider the kinetic energy of the dissociating molecule. The results are shown in Table 11.13. They indicate that Dewar's correction modifies the value of resonance energy, but it does not affect the general concept.

† The values of the resonance energies in the second column of Table 11.13 were calculated using bond energies slightly smaller than those given in Table 11.12 and used in the example above. Hence the discrepancy between the two values for the resonance energy of benzene. The change from 29 to 41 kcal per mole corresponds to a decrease of only 1 per cent. in the bond energies of the bonds C---H, C---C, and C==C.

Heteronuclear molecules have some ionic character, and must be represented as resonance structures of the canonical forms

$$A—B \qquad A^+B^-.$$

The molecule of such a system is more tightly bound than the molecule corresponding either to pure $A—B$ or pure A^+B^-. The observed bond energy of the compound is numerically greater than that corresponding to the pure covalent form. This effect was used by Pauling as a basis for his scale of electronegativity (p. 138). Table 11.14 shows the extra energy of bonds due to their ionic character as computed by Pauling‡.

Table 11.14. *Extra Energy of Bonds due to their Ionic Character*

Bond	Extra energy kcal per mole	Bond	Extra energy kcal per mole
C—H	6·3	Si—F	90·0
Si—H	2·1	Si—Cl	35·6
N—H	22·0	Si—Br	25·0
P—H	1·8	Si—I	11·7
As—H	− 12·0	Ge—Cl	53·9
O—H	41·0	N—F	27·0
S—H	3·9	N—Cl	− 0·5
Se—H	− 7·5	P—Cl	24·4
H—F	64·0	P—Br	16·7
H—Cl	22·1	P—I	7·6
H—Br	12·5	As—Cl	23·8
H—I	1·6	As—Br	17·4
C—Si	7·0	As—I	7·4
C—N	9·3	O—F	9·4
C—O	23·2	O—Cl	2·9
C—S	6·7	S—Cl	5·3
C—F	45·9	S—Br	2·2
C—Cl	8·3	Se—Cl	9·1
C—Br	1·6	Cl—F	25·7
C—I	− 1·9	Br—Cl	0·7
Si—O	50·6	I—Cl	4·0
Si—S	7·7	I—Br	1·7

‡ L. C. Pauling, *The Nature of The Chemical Bond* (Cornell University Press, 2nd Edition, p. 59).

CALCULATION OF BOND LENGTHS† FROM OBSERVED BOND ENERGIES, IONISATION POTENTIALS, AND THE VALENCE STATE OF THE ATOM

The lengths of bonds between atoms of the lighter elements may be calculated with the aid of a simple model. Except for bonds with high ionic character the values so obtained are close to the observed values. For the calculation it is necessary to know the bond energy, the extra energy due to the ionic character of the bond, the state of hybridisation of the atoms concerned, and the ionisation potentials of the valence electrons taking part in the bond. The ionisation potential of a particular electron represents the least energy required to remove it from the neutral atom (Table 11.15). The values given in this table are not quite the same as the values usually given in tables of physical constants, which refer to successive ionisations of the atom.

The model is based on the assumption that the bond concerned is strictly localised and concerns two electrons only for the single bond, four electrons for a double bond, and six electrons for a triple bond, half of the electrons being contributed by each

† The methods of calculating bond lengths and dipole moments described in the following pages have been devised by the authors, and have not been published elsewhere.

Dipole moments, bond lengths, and bond energies

Table 11.15. *Ionisation Potentials of the Lighter Elements (Rydbergs)†*

Element	K	L		M			N			O
	1s	2s	2p	3s	3p	3d	4s	4p	4d	5s
H	1·00									
He	1·81									
Li	4·80	0·40								
Be	(9·3)	0·69								
B	(15·2)	1·29	0·61							
C	(22·3)	1·51	0·83							
N	(31·1)	1·91	1·07							
O	(41·5)	2·10	1·00							
F	(53·0)	2·87	1·37							
Ne	(66·1)	3·56	1·59							
Na	(80·9)	(5·10)	2·79	0·38						
Mg	96·0	(6·96)	3·7	0·56						
Al	114·8	(9·05)	5·3	0·78	0·44					
Si	135·4	(11·5)	7·2	1·10	0·60					
P	157·8	(14·2)	9·4	(1·40)	(0·65)					
S	181·9	(17·2)	11·9	1·48	0·76					
Cl	207·9	(20·4)	14·8	1·81	0·96					
A	235·7	(23·9)	(18·2)	2·14	1·15					
K	265·6	(27·8)	21·5	(2·6)	1·2		0·32			
Ca	297·4	(31·9)	25·5	(3·1)	1·9		0·45			
Sc	331·2	(36·2)	30·0	(3·6)	2·7	0·54	0·50			
Ti	365·8	(41·0)	33·6	(4·2)	2·6	0·51	0·50			
V	402·7	(46·0)	37·9	(4·8)	3·0	0·50	0·52			
Cr	441·1	(51·2)	42·3	(5·4)	3·1	0·61	0·50			
Mn	481·9	(56·7)	47·4	(6·7)	3·8	0·68	0·55			
Fe	523·9	62·5	52·2	6·9	4·1	0·60	0·58			
Co	568·1	(68·5)	57·7	7·6	4·7	0·63	0·66			
Ni	614·1	74·8	63·2	8·2	5·4	(0·68)	0·64			
Cu	661·6	81·0	68·9	8·9	5·7	0·77	0·57			
Zn	711·7	88·4	75·4	10·1	6·7	1·26	0·69			
Ga	765·6	(96·0)	84·1	12·4	8·8	1·8	0·87	0·44		
Ge	817·6	(104·0)	89·3	13·4	9·5	3·2	1·39	0·60		
As	874·0	112·6	97·4	14·9	10·3	3·0	(1·6)	0·74		
Se	932·0	(121·9)	108·4	16·7	11·6	3·9	(1·7)	0·70		
Br	992·6	(131·5)	117·8	19·1	13·6	5·4	(1·9)	0·87		
Kr	(1055)	(141·6)	(127·2)	(21·4)	(15·4)	(6·8)	(2·1)	1·03		
Rb	1119·4	152·0	137·2	(23·7)	17·4	(8·3)	(2·3)	1·46		0·31
Sr	1186·0	162·9	147·6	26·2	19·6	9·7	2·5	(2·1)		0·42
Y	1256·1	175·8	159·9	30·3	23·3	13·0	4·7	2·9	0·48	0·49
Zr	1325·7	186·6	170·0	31·8	24·4	13·3	3·8	2·1	0·53	0·51
Cb	1398·5	198·9	181·7	34·7	26·9	15·2	4·3	2·5	(0·5)	(0·5)
Mo	1473·4	211·3	193·7	37·5	29·2	17·1	5·1	2·9	(0·5)	0·54

The ionisation potentials tabulated represent in each case the least energy, in Rydberg units, required to remove the electron in question from the atom. Interpolated or estimated values are given in parenthesis.

atom. The bond concerned is assumed to be isolated from the influence of other atoms in the molecule. An electron in the bond is treated as a particle in a ring (p. 22) subject to electrostatic forces. According to the uncertainty principle it is not possible for such a particle to have a sharp momentum and a sharp position simultaneously, but although both the energy of the particle and the radius of the ring appear in the

†J. G. Slater, *Quantum Theory of Matter* (McGraw-Hill, 1953), Table 6.4.1, p. 145.

calculation, there is in effect an uncertainty in the position of the charge due to spin (p. 58).

Although bond lengths have been measured with a high degree of accuracy, the same cannot be said of bond energies; this is one of the factors which limit the accuracy of the calculation. However, the data available are sufficient to enable the calculations to be made for many bonds, with enough precision to show that the method is of wide application.

HOMONUCLEAR BOND

Single bond. The system considered is that of two electrons in a ring whose centre lies on the mid-point of the line joining the two nuclei, each of which has effective nuclear charge $(Z_{\text{eff}})_{\text{mol}}$ (Fig. 11.6)†. The plane of the ring is at right angles to this line. The energy of the system is the sum of the kinetic energy of the electrons in the molecular orbital, the potential energy between the two electrons, between each electron and

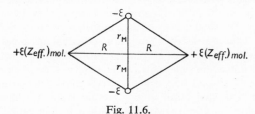

Fig. 11.6.

the two nuclei, and between the two nuclei, and the energy of interaction between the spins of the two electrons. Besides these terms there is also the thermal energy of the system.

When two electrons, say those in two hydrogen atoms, come together to form a bond between the two atoms, thus producing a hydrogen molecule, the energy of the whole system is lowered, and is less than the sum of the energies of the two separate atoms. After the formation of the molecule each electron rotates about the internuclear axis instead of a single nucleus; its distance r from the internuclear axis is such that the angular momentum is quantised.

If E is the total energy of the molecular system, r_M the radius of the ring in the molecular orbital, ϵ and m_0 the charge and mass of the electron, and $2R$ the length of the bond,‡

$$E = \frac{2h^2 n^2}{8\pi^2 m_0 r^2_M} - \frac{4\epsilon^2 Z_{\text{eff}}}{\sqrt{(r^2_M + R^2)}} + \frac{Z^2_{\text{eff}}\,\epsilon^2}{2R} + \frac{\epsilon^2}{2r_M} + Z' + S', \qquad (11.15)$$

where Z' is the zero point energy, and S' is the energy due to spin interaction.‡

For equilibrium,

$$\frac{\mathrm{d}E}{\mathrm{d}r_M} = 0,$$

and since $n = 1$, and $\dfrac{\epsilon^2}{2R}$, Z', and S' are independent of r_M,

$$\frac{-h^2}{2\pi^2 m_0 r^3_M} + \frac{4\epsilon^2 Z_{\text{eff}} r_M}{(r^2_M + R^2)^{3/2}} - \frac{\epsilon^2}{2r^2_M} = 0.$$

† See "Floating wave functions for H_2^+ and H_2", H. Shull and D. D. Ebbing, *J. Chem. Phys.*, **28**, 1958, 866, also E. G. Gurnee and J. L. Magee, *J. Chem. Phys.*, **18**, 1950, 142.

‡The system may be regarded as a stationary wave set up around the ring. Such a wave may always be described in terms of the angular motion of two particles moving in opposite directions; this corresponds to the σ orbital with no resultant angular momentum. In the π orbital the two particles move together in the same direction, and the whole wave pattern moves round the ring.

In equations (11.15) to (11.18) the term Z_{eff} is used to represent $(Z_{\text{eff}})_{\text{mol}}$ as defined on p. 136.

11*

Multiplying by $r_M/2$ and changing the signs throughout,

$$\frac{h^2}{4\pi^2 m_0 r^2{}_M} + \frac{\epsilon^2}{4r_M} = \frac{2\epsilon^2 r^2{}_M Z_{\text{eff}}}{(r^2{}_M + R^2)^{3/2}}. \tag{11.16}$$

If E_A and E_M are the kinetic energies of the electron in the atom and molecule respectively, and if B_E is the bond energy (heat given out in kcal per mole), it is assumed, since the bond is homonuclear, that

$$E_M = E_A - \frac{B_E}{2},$$

and since E_M is the kinetic energy of a particle in a ring of radius r_M,

$$r^2{}_M = \frac{h^2}{8\pi^2 m_0 (E_A - B_E/2)}. \tag{11.17}$$

E_A is evaluated from a knowledge of the state of hybridisation of the atom and the ionisation potentials. In the atom, the electron is assumed to be subject to Coulomb forces only, therefore the total energy of the electron is equal to its kinetic energy with the sign reversed. Thus the atomic ionisation potential of a particular electron is taken with a positive sign as the kinetic energy of the electron when in the atom.

For instance, the ionisation potentials of the s and p valence electrons of carbon in the ground state are 1·51 and 0·83 rydbergs respectively; when multiplied by 13·54 (the energy of the hydrogen atom in the ground state, 1 rydberg) the ionisation potentials are obtained in electron volts, and when further multiplied by the factor 23·053, the results are expressed as kcal/mole, 471·2 and 259·0 respectively. It is convenient to work in these units since bond energies are always expressed as kcal per mole.

Thus, E_A for carbon in the tetrahedral state (sp_3) is,

$$\frac{471\cdot2 + 3\times259\cdot0}{4} = 312\cdot1 \text{ kcal/gm-electron.}$$

Equation (11.16) may now be written in the form

$$r_M{}^2 + R^2 = \left[\frac{2\epsilon^2 r^2{}_M Z_{\text{eff}}}{2E_M + \epsilon^2/4r_M}\right]^{2/3}. \tag{11.18}$$

(see note †)

The steps taken in the calculation of a bond length are as follows.

(a) The screening constant for the nucleus is calculated (p. 136), and Z_{eff} is evaluated.

(b) The energy of the electron in the atomic orbital E_A is calculated from the ionisation potentials as above.

(c) The energy E_M of the electron in the molecular orbital is calculated from E_A and the bond energy B_E.

(d) The radius of the ring in the molecular orbital is calculated from equation (11.17).

(e) R^2 is calculated from equation (11.18).

As an example, the length of the bond O—O, such as is found in H_2O_2, may be calculated.

For the oxygen atom, $Z=8$; the screening constant $= 2\times0\cdot85 + 6\times0\cdot35 = 3\cdot8$, and therefore $Z_{\text{eff}} = 4\cdot2$.

For oxygen in the tetrahedral valence state,

$$E_A = \frac{655\cdot2 + 936}{4} = 397\cdot8 \text{ kcal/gm-electron.}$$

† In the evaluation of equations (11.17) and (11.18) kcal per mole must be converted to ergs per molecule; to do this, divide kcal by $1\cdot439 \times 10^{13}$.

For the O—O bond,

$$B_E = 35 \text{ kcal/two gm-electrons.}$$
$$E_M = 397 \cdot 8 - 17 \cdot 5 = 380 \cdot 3, \text{ kcal/gm-electron.}$$

therefore from equation (11.17)

$$r_M = 0 \cdot 4805 \text{ Å,}$$

and hence

$$\frac{\epsilon^2}{4r_M} = 172 \cdot 4 \text{ kcal/gm-electron.}$$

Therefore from equation (11.18) $2R = 1 \cdot 48$ Å.

By observation, $2R = 1 \cdot 48$ Å.

Double bond. The double bond is treated as a σ bond with a superposed π bond. The calculation is similar to that for the single bond, except that E_A is the sum of the energy of the electron in an atomic p orbital and the energy of an electron in the hybrid σ orbital, and there is a modification of the Coulomb energy term. The four electrons in the ring arrange themselves so that they are as far from each other as possible; this picture is consonant with that of "banana bonds" (p. 167). Instead of $\epsilon^2/4r_M$, the Coulomb energy term becomes $1 \cdot 915\epsilon^2/r_M$ (see Appendix).

As an example, the bond length C=C in ethylene may be calculated. In calculating the bond lengths of carbon compounds it is sometimes, but not always, necessary to include the energy of excitation of an electron from the $2s$ to the $2p$ state. For instance, the energy of excitation is not included in the calculation for ethane, since the bond dissociation energy was determined by the electron impact method which leaves the carbon atom in an excited state. The same applies to methane. In the cases of acetylene and ethylene, the numerical value of the calculated bond energy is based on heats of formation which include the excitation energy; in these cases the value of E_M is the value calculated as on p. 330 less the excitation energy. Shenstone has calculated[†] that the energy required to excite the carbon $2s$ electron to the $2p$ state is approximately $96 \cdot 4$ kcal per mole, and this value is used.

For the carbon atom, $Z = 6$, and the screening constant in the molecule is

$$2 \times 0 \cdot 85 + 4 \times 0 \cdot 35 = 3 \cdot 1,$$

therefore

$$(Z_{\text{eff}})_{\text{mol}} = 6 \cdot 0 - 3 \cdot 1 = 2 \cdot 9.$$

For a double bond, E_A represents the sum of the energies in the atom of one electron in the trigonal state (sp_2) and one in the p state. Since there is no means of distinguishing one electron from another, this energy is assumed to be shared equally between the two electrons contributed by the atom to the molecular bond.

$$E_A = \frac{471 \cdot 2 + 2 \times 259}{3} + 259 = 588 \cdot 7 \text{ kcal/two gm-electrons.}$$

The bond energy calculated from heats of formation is 146, the excitation energy per electron is 96/4.

$$E_M = E_A - \frac{146}{2} - \frac{96 \times 2}{4} = 467 \cdot 7 \text{ kcal/two gm-electrons.}$$

E_M represents the sum of the kinetic energies of two of the electrons in the molecular bond.

† A. G. Shenstone, *Phys. Review*, **72**, 1947, 411.

The kinetic energy of each electron in the bond $= E_M/2 = 233 \cdot 9$, therefore, from equation (11.17),

$$r_M = 0 \cdot 6127 \text{ Å,}$$

and hence,

$$\frac{1 \cdot 915\epsilon^2}{r_M} = 1038 \text{ kcal/two gm-electrons.}$$

From equation (11.18), $2R = 1 \cdot 32$ Å.

By observation, $2R = 1 \cdot 33$ Å.

Triple bond. The calculation is parallel to those for the single and double bonds, with again an alteration for the Coulomb term which becomes $15\epsilon^2/4r_M$ (see Appendix). The triple bond consists of one σ and two π bonds; three electrons are concerned in each half of the bond. As an example, the bond length in acetylene may be calculated. The carbon atom is in the digonal valence state, and therefore the energy of three electrons E_A is given by

$$E_A = \frac{471 \cdot 2 + 259}{2} + 2 \times 259$$

$$= 883 \cdot 1 \text{ kcal/three gm-electrons.}$$

The excitation energy must be included in the calculation; the calculated bond energy $= 194 \cdot 3$,

$$E_M = 883 \cdot 1 - \frac{194.3}{2} - \frac{96 \times 3}{4}$$

$$= 714 \text{ kcal/three gm-electrons.}$$

The energy of each electron in the bond $= 714/3 = 238$ nearly, therefore by equation (11.17),

$$r_M = 0 \cdot 6074 \text{ Å,}$$

and hence,

$$\frac{15\epsilon^2}{4r_M} = 2048 \text{ kcal/three gm-electrons.}$$

From equation (11.18), $2R = 1 \cdot 19$ Å.

By observation, $2R = 1 \cdot 20$ Å.

Oxygen molecule. Among the homonuclear bonds, oxygen presents a case which is of great interest since the molecule is paramagnetic and therefore contains two electrons with unpaired spins. The comparatively high value of the bond energy (117 kcal) as compared with the bond energy of fluorine (35 kcal) suggests that there is a large proportion of s in the σ bond; in fluorine, the s electron is so closely bound to the nucleus that the bond is all, or nearly all, p. The paramagnetism of the oxygen molecule can be explained if it is assumed that each oxygen atom is digonally hybridised and that an sp_z σ bond is formed between the oxygen atoms. In addition the oxygen nuclei are at the centres of two bonding interatomic π orbitals, and of two antibonding interatomic π^* orbitals. Each of the two π orbitals is occupied by two electrons, and each of the two π^* orbitals by a single electron. The presence of the two electrons with unpared spins in the π^* orbitals accounts for the paramagnetism of the molecule. If it be assumed as an approximation that the antibonding effect of the two unpaired electrons is equal to the bonding effect of one of the π orbitals the resultant bonding effect between the two oxygen atoms is one σ bond and one π bond. This conclusion derived from the valence bond theory is thus equivalent to that derived from the molecular orbital theory and represented by the cell diagram on p. 792.

If the oxygen molecule is thus regarded, the bond length calculated as for a double bond is found to be 1.22. The observed value is 1.21 (p. 335).

HETERONUCLEAR BONDS

The calculation of bond lengths in heteronuclear molecules may be carried out by a method parallel to that used for homonuclear molecules. There is always some ionic character in a bond between atoms of different effective nuclear charge. The electrons in the bond may again be viewed as particles in a ring, but the ring is no longer placed symmetrically with regard to the two nuclei; it takes up a position such that the energy of the system is a minimum, that is, it will lie in a potential well. The position of the well is determined by the values of $(Z_{eff})_{mol}$ for the two nuclei concerned. The

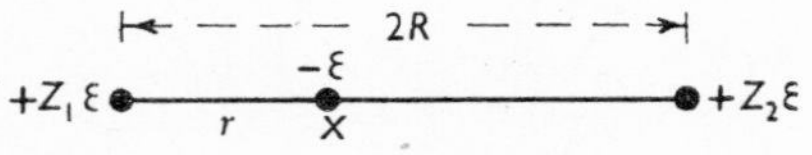

Fig. 11.7.

following simple example of a single electron situated between two nuclei provides an illustration (Fig. 11.7).

Suppose X is the position of the electron, at a distance r from Z_1 where $2R$ is the distance between the two nuclei of effective charge $Z_1\epsilon$ and $Z_2\epsilon$ ($Z_2 > Z_1$) where Z_1 and Z_2 represent $(Z_{1\ eff})_{mol}$ and $(Z_{2\ eff})_{mol}$ respectively.

Potential energy of $X = \dfrac{Z_1\epsilon^2}{r} + \dfrac{Z_2\epsilon^2}{2R-r}$.

If X is in a potential well,

$$\frac{dE}{dr} = 0, \quad \text{and} \quad \frac{Z_1\epsilon^2}{r^2} = \frac{Z_2\epsilon^2}{(2R-r)^2}.$$

Thus X takes up a position such that the force of attraction due to $Z_1\epsilon$ is balanced by the force of attraction due to $Z_2\epsilon$. The same argument applies to the case of particles in a ring which lies between Z_1 and Z_2. This leads to the unexpected conclusion that the electrons in a bond with some ionic character lie nearer the *less* electronegative nucleus. If electrostatic forces only are considered the molecule would be in unstable equilibrium, but although the electrostatic forces are largely responsible for the potential energy, the stability of the molecule depends also on other factors. It has been a puzzling feature of wave mechanics that Coulson's calculation[†] of the dipole moment of the C—H bond shows that the negative end is towards the H atom, and there is certain experimental evidence to support this conclusion.

Single heteronuclear bond. The model used for the calculation of bond length is essentially the same as that used for the homonuclear bond, but the distances x and y must be determined separately (Fig. 11.8). The extra ionic energy due to the difference between $(Z_{1,eff})_{mol}$ and $(Z_{2,eff})_{mol}$ must be subtracted from the bond energy calculated as for a homonuclear bond to give the heteronuclear bond energy. The values of the extra ionic energy are taken from Table 11.14. E_A for the particles in the ring is taken to be the mean value of E_A for the two overlapping atoms. In some cases the two values are the same; for instance, the value of E_A for carbon in the tetrahedral valence state is the same as that of hydrogen in the ground state (312). No doubt this fact contributes to the stability of the C—H bond. The sources of error in the calculation are numerous. In the first place, the ionisation potentials given in Table 11.15 are not likely to be accurate values of the energy of electrons in atomic orbitals, and many of the values given are extrapolated or estimated values. In many cases it is difficult to obtain a really firm value for the bond energy, and still more so for the extra ionic energy.

[†]C. A. Coulson., *Trans. Faraday Soc.*, **38** 1942, 433.

Added to this, the screening constants become less reliable with increasing atomic number. Nevertheless it is possible, for many bonds, to calculate a value for the bond length which is within a few per cent of the observed value.

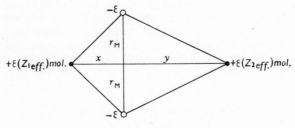

Fig. 11.8.

As an example, the bond length of H—Cl may be calculated.

$$E_A \text{ (hydrogen ground state)} = 312 \text{ kcal/gm-electron.}$$

$$E_A \text{ (chlorine } sp_3) = \frac{564 \cdot 8 + 3 \times 299 \cdot 5}{4}$$

$$= 365 \cdot 8 \text{ kcal/gm-electron.}$$
$$\text{Mean } E_A = 338 \cdot 9 \text{ kcal/gm-electron,}$$
$$B_E = 103 \cdot 1 \text{ kcal/two gm-electrons.}$$

Extra ionic energy $= 22 \cdot 1$ kcal

$$E_M = 338 \cdot 9 - \frac{(103 \cdot 1 - 22 \cdot 1)}{2} = 298 \cdot 4 \text{ kcal/gm-electron;}$$

therefore from equation (11.17),

$$r_M = 0 \cdot 5424,$$

and

$$\frac{\epsilon^2}{4r_M} = 153 \cdot 0 \text{ kcal/gm-electron.}$$

For hydrogen,

$$(Z_{\text{eff}})_{\text{mol}} = 0 \cdot 95,$$

and if x is the distance of the centre of the ring from the hydrogen atom (Fig. 11.8), using equation (11.18),

$$r^2_M + x^2 = 0 \cdot 3934,$$

and

$$x = 0 \cdot 3148.$$

For chlorine, $(Z_{\text{eff}})_{\text{mol}} = 5 \cdot 75$, and if y is the distance of the centre of the ring from the chlorine atom (Fig. 11.8),

$$r^2_M + y^2 = (5 \cdot 75/0 \cdot 95)^{2/3} \times 0 \cdot 3934$$
$$= 1 \cdot 306,$$

and

$$y = 1 \cdot 006.$$

Hence

$$2R = x + y = 1 \cdot 32 \text{ Å.}$$

By observation,

$$2R = 1 \cdot 27 \text{ Å.}$$

Double and triple heteronuclear bonds. The lengths of double and triple heteronuclear bonds for which the necessary values of the required parameters are known, may be calculated in a manner analogous to that used for the homonuclear double and triple bonds. Table 11.16 gives a list of thirty-two bonds, homonuclear and heteronuclear; the calculated and observed bond lengths are in close agreement. It is assumed that the halogen molecules, as exemplified in the Table by fluorine and chlorine, contain pure p bonds only. There is certain experimental evidence from pure quadrupole resonance spectra which supports this choice. The values taken for the bond energies in all cases include zero point energy, which is small except for bonds containing hydrogen.

It is interesting to see that the bond lengths of the hydrogen molecule and the hydrogen molecule-ion (with suitable adjustment of the formula to one electron) may be included in the Table. This implies that the electron in the s orbital has the property of rotation even though its resultant angular momentum is zero (Footnote, p. 329).

Table 11.16. *Comparison of Observed and Calculated Bond Lengths* (2R)

Bond	Å 2R (observed)	Å 2R (calculated)	Bond	Å 2R (observed)	Å 2R (calculated)
H—H$^+$	1·06	1·00	P—Br	2·23	2·30
H—H	0·742	0·725	P—Cl	2·04	2·17
O—O	1·48	1·48	H—S	1·35	1·37
N—N	1·46	1·40	H—Br	1·41	1·37
C—C	1·54	1·56	C—Br	1·91	1·85
F—F	1·42	1·50	C—Cl	1·76	1·6
Cl—Cl	2·00	2·15	O=O	1·21	1·22
P—P	2·21	2·12	C=C	1·33	1·32
S—S	2·04	2·06	N=O	1·22	1·24†
C—H	1·09	1·15	C=O	1·23	1·31
N—H	1·01	1·06	N≡N	1·095	1·08
F—H	0·917	1·14	C≡C	1·20	1·19
O—H	0·97	1·11	C≡N	1·15	1·11
N—O	1·46	1·44†	C—F	1·39	1·55
C—O	1·43	1·51	N—F	1·37	1·44
H—Cl	1·27	1·32	P—H	1·42	1·51

The calculated bond lengths are based on data from Tables 11.12, 11.14, and 11.15. The observed bond lengths are taken from *Interatomic Distances and Configurations in Molecules and Ions* (The Chemical Society, London, 1958).

† The ionic character of the bond (which is small) is disregarded.

CALCULATION OF DIPOLE MOMENTS†

An examination of a list of experimentally determined values of molecular dipole moments shows no obviously simple relation between dipole moment and bond length, nor between dipole moment and nuclear charge. Consideration of the orbital radii of the atoms concerned however, does throw some light on the subject, and it is possible, by means of a simple model, to calculate the dipole moments of certain single bonds with results which are in good agreement with the values generally assigned to these bonds. A full wave mechanical treatment would give more accurate results, but, with a few exceptions, it has not so far been possible to carry out the necessary calculations.

The significant quantities required for the simple calculation are the radii of the p orbitals of the atoms concerned (as determined by Slater's central field model) and the parameters x and y which appear in the model used for the calculation of bond lengths (Fig. 11.8, p. 334). It is assumed in the model that the dipole moment of the bond is caused by the movement into the molecular bond of a p electron from each atom concerned, and that such a movement leaves a positive "hole" on the molecular axis, the distance of the hole from the nucleus concerned being the radius of the p atomic orbital. It should be noted that although the concept of hybridisation has been used for the calculation of the energy of the electron before and after the formation of the molecular bond, the actual movement of charge envisaged is from an atomic orbital to a molecular orbital,‡ and the most easily detachable electron is, for the simple bonds considered, the p electron in the valence shell.

Table 11.17 gives a full list of the radii of the electronic orbitals of the atoms of the lighter elements. Atoms in these orbitals have ionisation potentials given in Table 11.15. If the atomic radii are introduced into Fig. 11.8, which gives a crude representation of a molecular bond, it is seen that the bonds fall into three classes which are depicted in Fig. 11.9, and may be described as follows:

Fig. 11.9(a). $(r_B - x) > (y - r_A)$. The bonds C—H, O—H, H—Br, C—F, H—P are examples of this type.

Fig. 11.9(b). $(r_B - x) < (y - r_A)$. The bonds H—Cl, H—S, and N—H are examples of this type.

Fig. 11.9(c). $x > r_B$. The bonds C—O, C—Cl, C—Br, P—Cl, P—Br, and N—F are examples of this type.

If the bond is considered in isolation, the calculation of the dipole moment is a very simple one. The resultant moment of the bond, μ, is the sum of the two dipole moments caused by the movement of the two electrons. These moments are measured by the products $\epsilon(y - r_A)$ and $\epsilon(r_B - x)$.

If the quantity $(y - r_A) + (r_B - x)$ is plotted against the values of observed dipole moments (Fig. 11.10), a straight line may be drawn through the points, but it does not cut the axis at the origin §. It can be seen from the graph that when $\mu_{obs} = 0$, $(y - r_A) + (r_B - x) = 0.235$, and if $(y - r_A) + (r_B - x) = X$

$$\mu = (X - 0.235)\epsilon$$
$$= (X - 0.235) \times 4.805 \text{ debyes.}$$

Table 11.18 shows a comparison between observed values and values of μ calculated on this simple model. For bonds of type (a) and (b) the observed and calculated values are in good agreement. Bonds of type (c) are interesting. The model in Fig. 11.9(c) shows the component dipoles opposed to each other, and it seems that in the case of N—F

†See Footnote on p. 327.
‡ The distance moved by the charge is, however, dependent on the hybridisation since this determines the value of y (p. 334).
§ The points are plotted regardless of the signs generally allotted to the moments.

these remain so in the electric field. The measured dipole N—F is very small which is what would be expected if the dipoles opposed one another. If X is given the value expected from Fig. 11.9(c), the point for N—F lies very near the line in Fig. 11.10. Of all the five molecules considered in type (c), N—F has the shortest bond length and therefore it would be the most likely to behave in the manner described above.

The points for C—O, P—Br, and P—Cl lie near the line if $(y - r_A)$ and $(x - r_B)$ are added; this suggests the possibility that, unlike N—F, the molecular dipole might have separated into its two component parts each of which has turned completely or partially in the field.

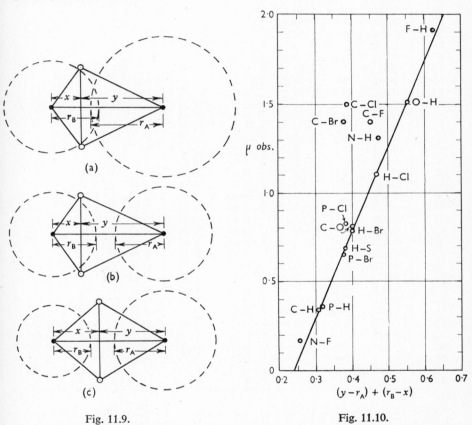

Fig. 11.9.   Fig. 11.10.

The positions of C—Cl and C—Br in Fig. 11.10 suggest that the large observed moments are due to the fields of lone pairs or those of other atoms in the molecule. It is customary to ascribe all anomalous dipole moments to lone pair effects; no doubt the fields of lone pairs and those of other atoms in the molecule do affect both the bond length and the dipole moment in many cases, as is shown by the behaviour of a single bond in different environments.

There has been considerable confusion concerning the direction of dipole moments. In the model used above, all dipole moments have (in the absence of a field) the negative end towards the nucleus with the *smaller* effective nuclear charge.† Such calculations as have been made on wave mechanical lines agree for the most part

---

† Such a moment is said to be *negative*. Coulson's value for the dipole moment of the C—H bond calculated from wave mechanical principles is −0·40 D. *Trans. Far. Soc.*, **38**, 1942, 433.

Table 11.17. *Radii of Electronic Orbits of the Lighter Atoms* (Å) †

Element	K	L		M			N	
	1s	2s	2p	3s	3p	3d	4s	4p
H	0·53							
He	0·30							
Li	0·20	1·50						
Be	0·143	1·19						
B	0·112	0·88	0·85					
C	0·090	0·67	0·66					
N	0·080	0·56	0·53					
O	0·069	0·48	0·45					
F	0·061	0·41	0·38					
Ne	0·055	0·37	0·32					
Na	0·050	0·32	0·28	1·55				
Mg	0·046	0·30	0·25	1·32				
Al	0·042	0·27	0·23	1·16	1·21			
Si	0·040	0·24	0·21	0·98	1·06			
P	0·037	0·23	0·19	0·88	0·92			
S	0·035	0·21	0·18	0·78	0·82			
Cl	0·032	0·20	0·16	0·72	0·75			
A	0·031	0·19	0·155	0·66	0·67			
K	0·029	0·18	0·145	0·60	0·63		2·20	
Ca	0·028	0·16	0·133	0·55	0·58		2·03	
Sc	0·026	0·16	0·127	0·52	0·54	0·61	1·80	
Ti	0·025	0·150	0·122	0·48	0·50	0·55	1·66	
V	0·024	0·143	0·117	0·46	0·47	0·49	1·52	
Cr	0·023	0·138	0·112	0·43	0·44	0·45	1·41	
Mn	0·022	0·133	0·106	0·40	0·41	0·42	1·31	
Fe	0·021	0·127	0·101	0·39	0·39	0·39	1·22	
Co	0·020	0·122	0·096	0·37	0·37	0·36	1·14	
Ni	0·019	0·117	0·090	0·35	0·36	0·34	1·07	
Cu	0·019	0·112	0·085	0·34	0·34	0·32	1·03	
Zn	0·018	0·106	0·081	0·32	0·32	0·30	0·97	
Ga	0·017	0·103	0·078	0·31	0·31	0·28	0·92	1·13
Ge	0·017	0·100	0·076	0·30	0·30	0·27	0·88	1·06
As	0·016	0·097	0·073	0·29	0·29	0·25	0·84	1·01
Se	0·016	0·095	0·071	0·28	0·28	0·24	0·81	0·95
Br	0·015	0·092	0·069	0·27	0·27	0·23	0·76	0·90
Kr	0·015	0·090	0·067	0·25	0·25	0·22	0·74	0·86

The radii tabulated represent the distance from the nucleus at which the radial charge density is a maximum and are computed from the calculations of Hartree and others. Since only a few atoms have been computed, most of the values tabulated are interpolated. The interpolation is likely to be much more accurate for the inner electrons than for the outer ones.

with this conclusion, but as it is contrary to the commonly accepted ideas on the meaning of "electronegativity", considerable effort has been made to turn the moment round by ascribing to the molecule a large moment of opposite sign due to lone pairs or other atoms in the molecule. Some attempts have been made to determine the "sense" of dipole moments experimentally, but the practical difficulties of the determination are considerable. It has been asserted by some workers and contradicted by others, that the negative end of the C—H bond is at the hydrogen atom. No doubt, when in an electric field, the measured overall effect in many molecules is a positive one; there is no general rule and each case must be considered on its own merits.

† J.G. Slater, *Quantum Theory of Matter* (McGraw-Hill, 1953), Table 6.4.2, p. 146.

Table 11.18.   *Dipole Moments† of some Single Bonds calculated from values of x and y and the Radii r_A and r_B of the outermost orbitals of the Atoms*

$$X = (y-r_A)+(r_B-x)$$

Bond	r_A Å	r_B Å	y Å	x Å	X Å	μ(calculated)	μ (observed)
C—H	0·66	0·53	0·794	0·355	0·309	0·36	0·35(B)
Cl—H‡	0·75	0·53	1·006	0·314	0·472	1·13	1·10(S)
S—H	0·82	0·53	1·017	0·346	0·381	0·70	0·68(P)
O—H‡	0·45	0·53	0·721	0·249	0·552	1·50	1·51(P)
N—H	0·53	0·53	0·769	0·293	0·476	1·16	1·31(P)
Br—H	0·90	0·53	1·071	0·299	0·402	0·80	0·78(P)
P—H‡	0·92	0·53	1·064	0·353	0·321	0·43	0·36(P)
F—H‡	0·38	0·53	0·693	0·224	0·619	1·84	1·91(H)
O—C	0·45	0·66	0·824	0·687	0·401	0·80	0·80(P)
F—C‡	0·38	0·66	0·740	0·578	0·443	1·00	1·4(P)
Cl—P‡	0·75	0·92	1·052	0·991	0·373	0·66	0·81(P)
Br—P‡	0·90	0·92	1·214	0·986	0·380	0·69	0·65
F—N	0·38	0·53	0·771	0·664	0·257	0·11	0·25
Cl—C	0·75	0·66	1·017	0·743	0·350	0·55	1·5(P)
Br—C‡	0·90	0·66	1·110	0·753	0·352	0·57	1·4(P)

† Values of dipole moments marked (P) are taken from a table of values assigned to single bonds by Pauling in *The Nature of the Chemical Bond*. The value marked (B) is from J. Barriol and J. Regnier (*J. Chim. phys.*, **51** (1954), 9); the value marked (H) is from N. B. Hannay and C. P. Smyth (*J. Amer. Chem. Soc.*, **68** (1946), 171); the value marked (S) is from J. W. Smith, *Electric Dipole Moments* (Butterworth, London, 1955). The values for P—Br and N—F are estimated from the observed values for whole molecules.

‡ Calculated values of x and y have been corrected to be in accordance with observed bond lengths.

BOOKS FOR FURTHER READING

BÖTTCHER, C. J. F., *Theory of Electric Polarisation* (Elsevier Publishing Company, 1952).
COULSON, C. A., *Valence* (Oxford University Press, 1952).
DEBYE, P., *Polar Molecules* (Dover, 1945).
FRÖHLICH, H., *Theory of Dielectrics* (Oxford University Press, 1949).
PAULING, L., *Nature of the Chemical Bond* (Cornell University Press, 3rd Edition, 1960).
SMITH, J. W., *Electric Dipole Moments* (Butterworth's Scientific Publications, 1955).
SMYTH, C. P., *Dielectrical Behaviour and Structure* (McGraw-Hill, 1955).
WELLS, A. F., *Structural Inorganic Chemistry* (Oxford University Press, 1950).

REVIEWS

LONG, L. H., *The Heats of Formation of Simple Inorganic Compounds* (*Quarterly Reviews*, **7**, No. 2, 1953, 134).
POTAPENKO, G., and WHEELER, D. JR., *A New Method of Determining the Relaxation Time and the Dipole Moment of Polar Substance* (*Rev. Mod. Phys.*, **20**, 1948, 143).
SAMUEL, R., *Dissociation Spectra of Covalent Molecules* (*Rev. Mod. Phys.*, **18**, 1946, 103).
SZWARC, M., *Bond Dissociation Energies* (*Quarterly Reviews*, **5**, No. 1, 1951, 22).

CHAPTER TWELVE

CRYSTAL STRUCTURES

The most obvious characteristic of a crystal is the symmetry of its external form. It was this symmetry which some 250 years ago attracted investigators to the study of crystallography. In 1912 the work of W. H. Bragg and W. L. Bragg on X-rays and crystal structure (see Chapter 10) initiated the study of the internal structure of crystals, and showed that the constituent particles are always arranged in regularly repeated patterns. For the chemist the aspect of crystallography which is chiefly concerned with the regular three-dimensional patterns developed by the arrangement of particles in crystals has now become of much greater interest than the study of external form. It is convenient in the first place to assume that the particles are spheres.

From purely geometrical considerations it may be decided how spheres can be packed together to form three-dimensional patterns. A single sphere can be surrounded

by a shell of twelve other similar spheres so that each sphere in the shell is in contact with the central sphere and with its own neighbours. This pattern can be extended indefinitely, and in the pile of spheres so obtained any sphere which is chosen as the central one will be surrounded by twelve others. As every sphere in the pile is in contact with its neighbours the system is said to be *close-packed*. It is found that there are two ways in which spheres can be assembled so that (i) any sphere is in contact with twelve others, and (ii) the three-dimensional pattern around any given sphere is the same as that around any other. These two ways

Fig. 12.1. One layer of close-packed spheres.

are known as *hexagonal close-packing* and *face-centred cubical close-packing*.

Hexagonal close-packing. The arrangement of spheres in a close-packed hexagonal lattice may be described starting from a single layer of identical spheres placed in mutual contact on a horizontal plane. The spheres form a pattern in which each sphere is surrounded by six others. The centres of the spheres are at the corners of a regular hexagon (Fig. 12.1). The element of pattern shown in Fig. 12.1 contains six gaps, each of which is situated between three contiguous spheres.

A second layer of spheres, conforming to a similar pattern, can be fitted on top of the first layer, by allowing the spheres of the second layer to rest in depressions corresponding to alternate gaps (marked X in Fig. 12.1) in the first layer. It is seen from Fig. 12.2 that alternate gaps in the second layer (marked a in Fig. 12.2) fall above the centres of the spheres of the first layer. A third layer of spheres may be added so that each sphere of this layer rests in a depression corresponding to a gap a, and is thus vertically above a sphere of the first layer. Similarly, each sphere of a fourth layer may be placed vertically above a sphere in the second layer, and so on. A vertical section through the extended pattern is shown in Fig. 12.3. Consideration of Fig. 12.3 shows that the centres of contiguous spheres lie in several series of parallel planes.

Three of the series may be mentioned: (1) planes parallel to that containing the

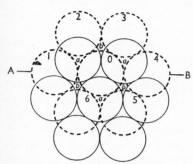

Fig. 12.2.   Two layers of close-packed spheres. Those in the upper layer are dotted and numbered 0 to 6. The layers are assumed to be horizontal.

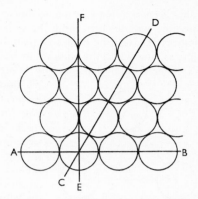

Fig. 12.3.   Vertical section of a close-packed structure.

centres of the first layer of spheres, (2) planes at 60° to this plane, (3) planes at 90° to this plane. In the vertical section shown in Fig. 12.3 these planes are respectively parallel to the lines AB, CD, and EF. If spheres labelled A are used for the first layer, and spheres labelled B for the second layer, then all the spheres in planes of types (1) and (3) are of one kind, either all A or all B, and spheres in planes of type (2) are of both kinds, A and B. Each sphere in the three-dimensional system has twelve nearest neighbours (Fig. 12.4). If r is the radius of each sphere, the volume of the structure containing n spheres is $5·66r^3n$.

From a structural point of view the gaps between the spheres are as important as the spheres themselves. Consideration of Fig. 12.2 shows that a gap X between the spheres of the first layer is not filled by the sphere of the second layer which lies above it. The three spheres round the gap, and the fourth sphere above it, lie at the apices of a regular tetrahedron (Fig. 12.5). The central part of this tetrahedron is a "three-dimensional gap" in the close-packed hexagonal structure, and it is known as a *tetrahedral hole*. In an indefinitely extended close-packed hexagonal structure there are twice as many tetrahedral holes as there are spheres.

Consideration of Fig. 12.2 shows that each gap b (the gaps other than those marked a) between the spheres in the second layer lies above a gap in the first layer, and below a gap in the third layer. Hence the gaps b are positions in a series of tunnels in the structure.

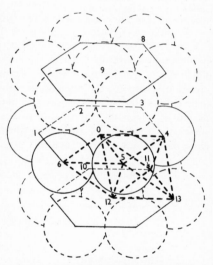

Fig. 12.4.   Three horizontal layers in a hexagonal close-packed structure. All the seven spheres in the uppermost layer are shown. In the middle layer the sphere 2 corresponding to sphere 7 in the uppermost layer is completely hidden, and the presence of spheres 3 and 0 corresponding to spheres 8 and 9 is indicated by very short lines only.

The central sphere is numbered 0; its twelve nearest neighbours are numbered 1 to 12. Spheres 0, 1, 2, 3, 4, 5, 6 correspond to the upper layer similarly numbered in Fig. 12.2. A tetrahedral hole is enclosed by spheres 0, 6, 5, 12; it corresponds to the gap marked a nearest to the number 6 in Fig. 12.2. An octahedral hole is enclosed by spheres 0, 5, 13, 11, 12, 4; it corresponds to the gap marked b nearest to the number 5 in Fig. 12.2.

It has been said that knitting needles could be passed through a close-packed hexagonal structure without disturbing the spheres. In each tunnel there are points which lie midway between the planes containing the centres of successive horizontal layers of spheres, and which are equidistant from the centres of the six nearest spheres. These six spheres lie at the apices of a regular octahedron with the point as centre, and the point is therefore said to be at the centre of an *octahedral hole* (Fig. 12.4). The number of octahedral holes in a close-packed hexagonal system is equal to the number of spheres. An even more densely packed structure may be obtained by filling the holes with smaller spheres. If the close-packed spheres have a radius of unity, the radius of spheres to fit the tetrahedral holes cannot exceed 0·41, and the radius of the spheres to fit the octahedral holes cannot exceed 0·59.

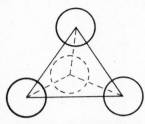

Fig. 12.5.   A tetrahedral hole enclosed by four spheres. In a close-packed structure the spheres are contiguous, but in the Figure they are separated for the sake of clarity.

Suppose each sphere of the close-packed structure is labelled M, each small sphere to fit a tetrahedral hole is labelled X, and each small sphere to fit an octahedral hole is labelled Y. The proportions in which the labelled spheres are present in the whole structure may be shown by a formula, such as MX_2. Since the pattern of spheres and holes is regular, the formula will be exact and constant for a given structure. If M and X represent atoms of elements, the crystalline substance would conform to the law of constant proportions, and in this respect would be indistinguishable from a chemical compound of which the formula MX_2 was determined by valency forces. Table 12.1 shows the formulae of structures which may arise through the filling of holes in a close-packed hexagonal structure.

Table 12.1.   *Formulae of Structures determined by Holes in Close-packed Crystals*

Holes filled	Formula of structure
None	M
Tetrahedral only	MX_2
Octahedral only	MY
Tetrahedral and octahedral	MX_2Y
(In ionic crystals (p. 346), ions of the same kind never occupy both the tetrahedral and the octahedral holes)	

Face-centred cubical close-packing. The face-centred cubical close-packed structure may be built up by the following imaginary procedure. The first two layers of spheres are arranged in the same way as the first two layers for the hexagonal close-packed structure, but the third layer is arranged differently. The spheres forming the third layer are so placed that they rest in alternate depressions, marked b (Fig. 12.2), of the second layer. The fourth layer is formed by placing spheres so that the centres are vertically above those of the first layer. The fifth and sixth layers repeat the pattern of the second and third, and so on. Fig. 12.6 shows the arrangement of the first three layers in plan. Fig. 12.7 is a perspective view of parts of six layers, A, B, C, D, E, F, of spheres stacked in the above manner. The spheres numbered 1, 2, 3, 4, 5, 6, 7, 8 are situated at the corners of three faces of a cube, sphere 4 being the nearest to the observer. In Fig. 12.8, which shows the arrangement in Fig. 12.7 canted through 45°, the same cube is heavily outlined. It will be seen that spheres 9, 10, 11, 12, 13, 14, are at the centres of the cube faces; there are no other spheres nearer to the cube centre than those numbered. Since sphere 1 (Fig. 12.7) is vertically above sphere 5, one of the cube diagonals is parallel to the vertical axis of the stack in its original position. The cubical arrangement of 14 spheres is more clearly shown in Fig. 12.9.†

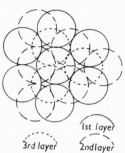

In face-centred cubical close-packing, as in hexagonal close-packing, each sphere is surrounded by twelve nearest neighbours. The volume of the structure containing n spheres of radius r is $5.66r^3n$. If there are n spheres in the system there are $2n$ tetrahedral holes and n octahedral holes. The positions of the holes lie as shown by the two examples in Fig. 12.9. The centres of the tetrahedral holes lie on the cube diagonals at one-quarter the diagonal length from the cube corners. The centres of the octahedral holes lie at the mid-points of the cube edges and at the cube centre; the octahedral holes are situated with regard to one another as if they were spheres in a cubical close-

Fig. 12.6. Plan of the first three layers of a cubical close-packed structure.

packed structure. The limiting dimensions of spheres which may occupy the holes are the same as for hexagonal close-packing.

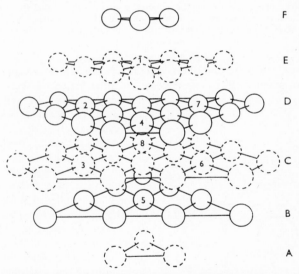

Fig. 12.7. A perspective drawing of a stack of six layers of spheres arranged in accordance with face-centred cubical close-packing. The cubical pattern is shown by the relative positions of spheres 1, 2, 3, 4, 5, 6, 7, 8, which are at the corners of a cube.

Mixed hexagonal and cubical close-packing. If the first, second, and third layers of identical spheres which were assembled in the first stage of building up the face-centred cubical close-packed structure are labelled *A*, *B*, and *C*, then the cubical arrangement

† Figs. 12.7 and 12.8 were prepared from photographs taken by the Crystallographic Laboratory in the Department of Physics of Cambridge University by the courtesy of Dr. W. H. Taylor.

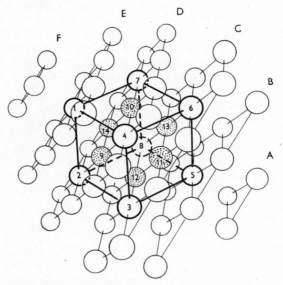

Fig. 12.8. The same stack as in Fig. 12.7 canted through 45°. One complete unit of the cubic structure is heavily outlined. A few of the spheres drawn in Fig. 12.7 have been omitted for the sake of clarity. The numbers on the spheres coincide with those in Fig. 12.7. Note that spheres 2, 9, 4, 10, 7, and 14 are all members of the layer *D* (Fig. 12.7). The spheres at the face centres of the cube are stippled.

may be designated *ABCABC*, and so on, and the hexagonal arrangement as *ABABAB*. It is possible to imagine other close-packed structures based on such arrangements of layers as *ABACAB*, *ABABCABABC*, and so on. The sequence may be regular or the introduction of *C* layers may be at random. Metallic cobalt below 500° displays a random structure of this kind.

Unit cell. The repeated three-dimensional pattern of a crystal system is indicated by a unit cell, so chosen that it includes, at least once, every element of the crystal pattern. Fig. 12.10 shows an example of such a cell for a face-centred cubic lattice. The lattice extends in three dimensions so that each face of the cell is also the face of a neighbouring cell; it may be said that each face is common to two cells. Similarly, each edge of the cell is common to four cells, and each corner of the cell is common to eight cells. Each particle at a face-centre is shared by the two cells having the face in common, and each particle at a cell corner is shared by the eight cells having the corner in common. Hence the number of particles in the cell is $6 \times \frac{1}{2} + 8 \times \frac{1}{8} = 4$.

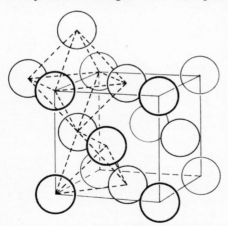

Fig. 12.9. Face-centred cubical close-packing, showing one tetrahedral and one octahedral hole.

The example illustrates the general principle by which the number of particles in a cell is computed. Any particle wholly contained within the cell is wholly assigned to it. If any particle is shared by adjoining cells, then the number it contributes to the cell under consideration is $1/n$ where n is the number of cells to which the particle is common.

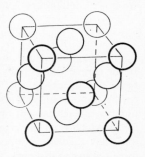

Co-ordination number. The co-ordination number of any given sphere in a crystalline structure is the number of other spheres by which it is immediately surrounded. In the hexagonal and face-centred cubical close-packed structures the co-ordination number is 12; in the body-centred cubical structure (see below) it is 8. The hexagonal and face-centred close-packed structures are attained only when the spheres are all of the same size. If two sets of spheres are employed to build up a structure, one set labelled A and the other B, and if the A spheres are the smaller, then the co-ordination number of A with respect to B (the number of B spheres that can form a shell round the A sphere) decreases as the ratio

Fig. 12.10. Unit cell of a face-centred cubic lattice.

$$\frac{\text{radius of sphere } A}{\text{radius of sphere } B}$$

decreases. In general, the expression

$$\frac{\text{radius of central sphere}}{\text{radius of spheres surrounding it}}$$

is known as the *radius ratio*. The dependence of the co-ordination number of A with respect to B on the radius ratio is shown in Table 12.2.

Table 12.2. *Relation between Co-ordination Number and Radius Ratio*

Radius of B sphere	Minimum radius of central A sphere	Radius ratio	Number of B spheres which can be packed round one A sphere	Arrangement	Co-ordination number of A
1	1	1	12	close-packed hexagonal, or close-packed face-centred cubic	12
1	0·732	0·732	8	body-centred cubic	8
1	0·414	0·414	6	octahedral	6
1	0·414	0·414	4	square planar	4
1	0·225	0·225	4	tetrahedral	4
1	0·155	0·155	3	triangular	3

Body-centred cubical packing. There is a second cubical structure which is often spoken of as close-packed, although it is less dense than the face-centred cubic structure. It is known as the *body-centred cubic structure*. The unit cell consists of a cube with one sphere at the centre, and one sphere at each of the eight cube corners (Fig. 12.11). The number of spheres per unit cell is $1 + 8/8 = 2$. Any given sphere in the structure is surrounded by eight equidistant nearest neighbours, and by another six neighbours 15% further away. If r is the radius of each sphere, the volume of the structure containing n spheres is $6 \cdot 16r^3 n$.

IONIC CRYSTALS

An ionic crystal is one in which the units of crystal structure are the ions of a salt. In the simplest cases both the cation, say A^+, and the anion, B^-, are univalent, and in order that the crystal shall be electrically neutral the number of A^+ ions must be equal to the number of B^- ions. If the cation and anion carry different charges, then the number of each present must again be such that the crystal is electrically neutral. The forces which hold the crystal together are the Coulomb forces between the ions; the ions may take up any positions with regard to one another provided the resultant force on any ion is zero. So far as the relative sizes of the ions permit they therefore

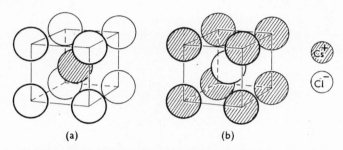

(a)   (b)

Fig. 12.11. The body centred cubic structure of caesium chloride; the structure is unaltered if the positions of all the Cs⁺ ions and all the Cl⁻ ions are interchanged.

tend to assemble in close-packed structures. If the positive and negative ions are not packed together as closely as possible the system has potential energy because the ions could release energy in moving closer together. Hence the co-ordination number of each ion tends to be as high as possible, because only then is the energy of the system a minimum.

The sizes of ions are given in the table of ionic radii (p. 361). It will be observed that the univalent anions have greater radii than the univalent cations in the same period of the periodic table; the radius of F^- is greater than that of Na^+, and the radius of Cl^- is greater than that of K^+, and so on. The radii of bivalent anions are also greater than the radii of bivalent cations in the same period. In close-packed crystal structures where the radius ratio is above 0·732 the anions and the cations both occupy close-packed positions. If the radius ratio is less than 0·732, the anions are close-packed and the cations fit into the octahedral or tetrahedral holes.

CRYSTALS CONTAINING TWO DIFFERENT ELEMENTS

Crystal structures of two kinds of ion, each having the same co-ordination number.

The caesium chloride structure. *8 : 8 co-ordination. Radius ratio > 0·732.* Two ions of nearly equal size, such as Cs^+ and Cl^-, tend to form a close-packed structure in which each ion plays an equal part. The hexagonal or cubical close-packed structure in which each ion would have the co-ordination number 12 cannot be formed, because a pattern is geometrically impossible in which an ion A^+ is surrounded by 12 B^- ions, while at the same time each ion B^- is surrounded by 12 A^+ ions. The highest co-ordination number to be found in an ionic crystal is 8, which corresponds to the body-centred cubic structure. In this structure the Cs^+ ions and the Cl^- ions occupy alternate points in the close-packed lattice. The unit cell may be represented either as (a) or (b) in Fig. 12.11. In (a) a Cs^+ ion occupies the central point, in (b) a Cl^- ion occupies the central point.   Substances crystallising with this structure are:

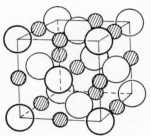

(1) CsCl, CsBr, CsI, TlCl.

(2) RbCl, RbBr, RbI under a pressure of 5000 kg/cm²; also RbCl at low temperatures.

(3) CsCN, TlCN, CsSH, CsNO₃.

(4) Some alloys.

The rock salt structure. *6:6 co-ordination. Radius ratio 0·732–0·414.* If the ions differ too much in size (that is, if the radius ratio falls to 0·732) the body-centred structure in which close-packed positions are occupied by both ions is unstable, and a lower degree of co-ordination must be accepted. The next lowest to the 8:8 co-ordination is the 6:6, which is found when the radius ratio lies between 0·732 and 0·414. In the crystal structures which correspond to 6:6 co-ordination the close-packed positions are occupied by the

Fig. 12.12. The rock salt structure. The Cl^- ions ($r= 1·81$) occupy positions on a face-centred cubic lattice; the Na^+ ions ($r=0·95$) occupy the octahedral holes. Compare Fig. 12.9.

anions only, which have the larger ionic radius, the smaller cations occupy the octahedral holes. In the rock salt crystal, the Cl^- anions ($r=1·81$) occupy the close-packed positions on a face-centred cubic lattice, and the Na^+ cations ($r=0·95$) are in the octahedral holes (Fig. 12.12).

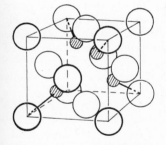

The rock salt structure is assumed at room temperature,

(1) by all the alkali halides except CsCl, CsBr, and CsI; CsCl has this structure above 445°,

(2) by AgF, AgCl, AgBr,

(3) by the oxides and sulphides of the alkaline earth metals, and by NiO,

(4) by certain other sulphides and nitrides,

(5) by some alloys.

Fig. 12.13. The zinc blende structure. The S^{2-} ions ($r= 1·84$) occupy positions on a face-centred cubic lattice. The Zn^{2+} ions ($r=0·74$) occupy one half of the tetrahedral holes, and are situated on cube diagonals at one quarter of the length of a cube diagonal from alternate cube corners.

The zinc blende structure. *4:4 co-ordination. Radius ratio 0·414–0·225.* This degree of co-ordination is found when the radius ratio lies between 0·414 and 0·225. The large S^{2-} ions ($r=1·84$) of zinc blende†, occupy the close-packed positions of a face-centred cubic lattice, and the Zn^{2+} ions ($r=0·74$) occupy one-half of the tetrahedral holes. Each S^{2-} ion is surrounded tetrahedrally by four Zn^{2+} ions, and each Zn^{2+} ion is surrounded tetrahedrally by four S^{2-} ions (Fig. 12.13). This structure is assumed by CuCl, CuBr, BeO.

The wurtzite structure. *4:4 co-ordination. Radius ratio 0·414–0·225.* The typical compound exhibiting this structure is wurtzite, ZnS. The sulphur atoms are in hexagonal close-packing (in contra-distinction to the cubical close-packing of the zinc blende

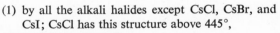

† Zinc sulphide, ZnS, is dimorphic; one crystal form is known as zinc blende and the other as wurtzite. Zinc blende is also known as *sphalerite*.

structure) and the zinc ions are in half the tetrahedral holes. This structure is assumed by ZnO and AlN.

Crystal structures of two kinds of ion, each having a different co-ordination number.
The fluorite structure. 8:4 *co-ordination. Radius ratio 0·732. The structure of fluorite.*

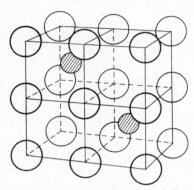

Fig. 12.14. The fluorite structure. The F^- ions ($r=1·36$) are at the cube corner positions of a body-centred cubic lattice; the Ca^{2+} ions ($r=0·99$) occupy one half of the positions at the cube centres.

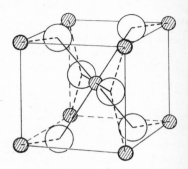

Fig. 12.15. The rutile structure. The Ti^{4+} ions ($r=0·64$) occupy positions corresponding to the points of a body-centred cubic lattice. Each O^{2-} ion ($r=1·32$) is equidistant from its three nearest Ti^{4+} neighbours. The group Ti_3O is planar.

CaF_2, is best regarded as a body-centred cubic lattice. The F^- ions ($r=1·36$) are at the cube corners; the Ca^{2+} ions ($r=0·99$) occupy one-half of the positions at the cube centres. Each F^- ion is surrounded tetrahedrally by four Ca^{2+} ions, and each Ca^{2+} ion by eight F^- ions (Fig. 12.14). The occupied points in the fluorite structure are in the same relative positions as if the Ca^{2+} ions were close-packed on a face-centred cubic

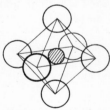

Fig. 12.16. The rhenium oxide structure. This structure is derived from that in Fig. 12.17 by removing the Ca^{2+} ions from the cube corners, and replacing the Ti^{4+} ion by a Re^{6+} ion.

lattice, and the F^- ions were in all the tetrahedral holes. Since the radius of the F^- ion is too great for it to be accommodated in the tetrahedral holes of a face-centred cubic lattice of Ca^{2+} ions, the body-centred lattice is adopted instead. Compounds exhibiting the fluorite structure are BaF_2, $SrCl_2$, ThO_2.

The antifluorite structure. 4:8 *co-ordination. Radius ratio* 0·732. The antifluorite structure, exemplified by sodium oxide, Na_2O, may also be regarded as a body-centred cubic lattice, but in this case the Na^+ ions occupy all the cube corners, and the O^{2-} ions occupy one-half of the cube centres. (A simple calculation shows that if O^- ions are close-packed on a face-centred cubic lattice, the Na^+ ions ($r=0·95$) are too big to be placed in the tetrahedral holes.)

The compounds exhibiting the antifluorite structure are the oxides, sulphides, selenides, tellurides of lithium, sodium, and potassium. Rb_2O, Be_2B, and Be_2C also exhibit this structure.

The rutile structure. 6:3 *co-ordination. Radius ratio 0·732 to 0·414.* The radius ratio of two kinds of atoms which crystallise in the rutile structure permits the inclusion of the smaller ions in the octahedral holes of a close-packed structure of the larger ions. In rutile, titanium dioxide, TiO_2 (r of Ti^{4+} is 0·64; of O^{2-} is 1·32) the O^{2-} ions are arranged in a close-packed hexagonal structure, and the Ti^{4+} ions are in one-half of the octahedral holes. In another way of regarding the rutile structure the Ti^{4+} ions are placed at the relative positions of a body-centred cubic structure (Fig. 12.15). The O^{2-} ions are arranged so that each is equidistant from its three nearest titanium neighbours.

PbO_2 adopts the rutile structure.

The rhenium oxide structure, ReO_3. *6:2 co-ordination.* If the calcium ions are removed from the perovskite unit cell p. 350, the structure left is shown in Fig. 12.16. If the titanium ions are replaced by rhenium ions this is the rhenium oxide structure. It is in effect a continuous structure of ReO_6 octahedra with oxygen atoms shared.

CrO_3 and WO_3 adopt the rhenium oxide structure.

CRYSTALS CONTAINING THREE DIFFERENT ELEMENTS

The co-ordination in crystals which contain more than two elements is too complex to be summarised in a short formula. The most numerous crystals of this kind are those of the complex oxides. The compositions of such oxides may be expressed generally as $A_xB_yO_n$. It is assumed that all the constituents are present as ions. The three most important complex oxide structures, all of which are described below, are:

Ilmenite	ABO_3
Spinel	AB_2O_4 and $B(AB)O_4$
Perovskite	ABO_3.

The ilmenite and spinel structures are based on close-packed arrays of oxygen ions. The perovskite structure is based on a face-centred close-packed array consisting of both oxygen ions and A ions.

The ilmenite structure, ABO_3. The oxygen ions are in a close-packed hexagonal lattice. The A ions and the B ions together occupy two-thirds of the octahedral holes (p. 342). Examples are furnished by the so-called titanates, $M^{2+}Ti^{4+}[O^{2-}]_3$, of Fe, Mg, Mn, Co, Ni, and (at low temperatures) Cd. A and B may represent the same kind of ion as in corundum, $\alpha-[Al^{3+}]_2[O^{2-}]_3$, and in haematite, $\alpha-Fe_2O_3$.

The spinel structure. The oxygen ions are on a face-centred cubic lattice. The unit cell contains 32 oxygen ions. There are two forms of the spinel structure:

	Close-packed positions	Tetrahedral positions	Octahedral positions
Normal spinel AB_2O_4	32 O^{2-}	8 A ions	16 B ions
Inversed spinel $B(AB)O_4$	32 O^{2-}	8 B ions	$\begin{cases} 8 \text{ B ions} \\ 8 \text{ A ions} \end{cases}$

The spinel must be electrically neutral, and therefore there must be 64 positive charges per unit cell of 32 O^{2-} ions. This condition can be satisfied by three different pairings of positive ions of different valency: (i) $A^{2+}B^{3+}$, (ii) $A^{4+}B^{2+}$, (iii) $A^{6+}B^+$. The 4:2 spinels are always inversed; the 2:3 may be either normal or inversed. A few examples may be quoted:

	Normal	Inversed
2:3	$MgCr_2O_4$ $NiCr_2O_4$ $ZnFe_2O_4$	$Fe(CuFe)O_4$ $Fe(MgFe)O_4$ $Fe(FeFe)O_4$ (magnetite)
4:2		$Zn(TiZn)O_4$ $Zn(SnZn)O_4$ $Co(SnCo)O_4$

The perovskite structure. In the structure of perovskite, $CaTiO_3$, the calcium ions and the oxygen ions are together in face-centred close-packing. The calcium ions

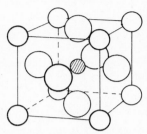

occupy the cube corners, and the oxygen ions the face-centres. Since in a unit cell there are 8/8 cube corner positions, and 6/2 face-centre positions, the proportions of calcium and oxygen ions are in the correct proportions for the formula CaO_3. The titanium ions are in the octahedral positions at the cube centres (the octahedral positions at the centres of the cube edges are unoccupied). This gives one titanium ion per unit cell, and completes the formula $CaTiO_3$ (Fig. 12.17)

Among the compounds crystallising with the perovskite structure are $CsCdCl_3$ and $CsHgCl_3$, and $KMgF_3$. The alkali metal iodates, such as $NaIO_3$, do not crystallise with the perovskite structure; the ion IO_3^- has a pyramidal structure.

Fig. 12.17. The perovskite structure. The O^{2-} ions (large white circles; $r=1.32$) occupy the face-centres of a face-centred cubic lattice. The Ca^{2+} ions (small white circles; $r=0.99$) occupy the cube corners. The Ti^{4+} ions (shaded circles; $r=0.64$) occupy the octahedral holes at the cube centres. The other octahedral holes are unoccupied.

Among other compounds which crystallise with the perovskite structure are

$BaTiO_3$	$LaFeO_3$
$BaZrO_3$	$NaNbO_3$
$KNiF_3$	$LaGeO_3$

NON-IONIC CRYSTALS

Non-ionic crystals may be divided into three types:

(a) Giant molecules, in which there is covalent bonding between all the atoms.

(b) Layer structures, in which there is covalent bonding between atoms in a given layer, but the layers are held in contact by van der Waals forces only.

(c) Crystals composed of discrete molecules. The atoms in each molecule are covalently bound. The structure of the crystal depends on the packing together of the molecules, and not on the forces between individual atoms. Crystals of this type are formed chiefly by organic compounds, and will not be discussed.

GIANT MOLECULES

If the interatomic bonding in a crystal is wholly covalent the crystal structure is determined by the lengths and directions of the bonds. A crystal such as diamond in which each atom is linked by covalent tetrahedral bonds to four other atoms has a structure related to that of zinc blende (p. 347). Carbon atoms are situated at the points on a face-centred cubic lattice and also in one-half of the tetrahedral holes.

Among the substances which crystallise as giant molecules are the elements of Group IV.

LAYER STRUCTURES

A crystal with a layer lattice is composed of layers of atoms. Each layer is capable of infinite extension in two dimensions, but is usually only two or three atoms thick. The layers are separated from one another by 3 or 4 Å, but the distance between atoms within each layer is 2 or 3 Å, which is the order of interatomic distance found in crystals. For example, in the cadmium chloride crystal described below the distance between layers is 3.68 Å, but the Cd—Cl distance within each layer is 2.74 Å.

Attention must be drawn to the use of the term *layer* in two different senses. In the description of the hexagonal close-packed structure on p. 340, the term *layer* was used to describe identical spheres in mutual contact all standing on the same horizontal plane; the complete structure was regarded as a number of such layers piled close-packed on top of one another. When applied to a layer lattice, however, the term *layer* must be understood to describe a structure of large area, two or three atoms thick. The layer is itself a close-packed structure composed of layers of atoms, and for

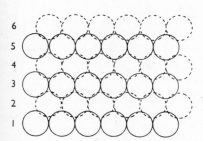

Fig. 12.18. Vertical elevation corresponding to the plan in Fig. 12.2. The elevation is along the line *AB* in in Fig. 12.2. It includes two vertical planes of spheres only.

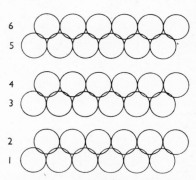

Fig. 12.19. The separation of pairs of horizontal planes shown end-on here and in Fig. 12.18.

clarity, a layer of atoms will be called a *plane* of atoms when it is a component of a crystal layer.

Many metallic oxides, sulphides, and halides crystallise with layer structures. Each layer consists of a close-packed structure of two planes of non-metal atoms, and the metallic atoms occupy holes in the lattice. The co-ordination number of the metal is 6; of the non-metal 3. As examples the structures of cadmium iodide crystals and cadmium chloride crystals will be described.

The cadmium iodide structure. The cadmium iodide structure is best envisaged by first imagining a hexagonal close-packed system of iodine atoms with planes of iodine atoms arranged as in Fig. 12.2. Fig. 12.18 shows an elevation of the structure on a vertical plane along the line *AB* in Fig. 12.2. The elevation shows that the atoms in the planes 1, 3, 5, 7 and so on, are vertically in line. The pairs of planes 1 and 2, 3 and 4, 5 and 6, and so on, are now imagined to be separated from one another by a vertical displacement so that the structure consists

Fig. 12.20. The cadmium iodide structure. One pair of horizontal planes of iodine atoms (shown end-on) with cadmium atoms occupying the octahedral holes.

of pairs of planes with a gap between each pair (Fig. 12.19). Each pair of planes is a *layer*. Finally, cadmium atoms are imagined to be placed in the octahedral holes between the iodine atoms in each layer (Fig. 12.20). In a layer each cadmium atom is surrounded by six iodine atoms, and each iodine atom has three cadmium atoms as its nearest neighbours (Fig. 12.21). It should be noted that the environment of the iodine atoms is asymmetric; as seen from Fig. 12·21 the upper plane of iodine atoms, for example, has cadmium atoms beneath it, but another plane of iodine atoms above it.

Compounds with the cadmium iodide layer structure are:

The di-iodides of Cd, Ca, Mg, Pb, Mn, Fe, Co;
the dibromides of Cd, Mg, Fe, Co, Ni, and also $TiCl_2$ and TiI_2;
the dihydroxides of Cd, Ca, Mn, Fe, Co, Ni;
the disulphides of Ti, Zr, Sn, Pt.

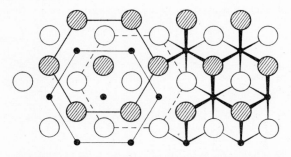

Fig. 12.21.   Plan of one closed-packed hexagonal layer of the cadmium iodide structure. The shaded circles represent iodine atoms above the plane of the paper; the open circles represent iodine atoms below the plane of the paper. The hexagonal arrangement of the iodine atoms and of the cadmium atoms (small black circles) is seen on the left.

The cadmium chloride structure. The cadmium chloride structure may be envisaged in the same way as the cadmium iodide structure, except that the arrangement of the planes of chlorine atoms is in accordance with cubical close-packing instead of hexagonal close-packing. It follows that the structure of a cadmium chloride layer is similar to that of a cadmium iodide layer; the difference in the two crystals lies in the relation of the halogen atoms in one layer to those in neighbouring layers.

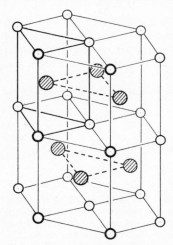

Compounds with the cadmium chloride layer structure are:

The dichlorides of Cd, Fe, Co, Ni, Mg, Zn, Mn.

The nickel arsenide, NiAs, structure. The nickel atoms are arranged in a series of planes each consisting of atoms arranged as in Fig. 12.22, but not close-packed. The nickel atoms in successive planes are vertically above one another. Arsenic atoms are inserted between the planes of nickel atoms so that each arsenic atom is the centre of a trigonal prism with nickel atoms at the corners. Each nickel atom is then surrounded by six arsenic atoms (the arsenic atoms are in the relative positions of hexagonal close-packing but are not close-packed) and each arsenic atom by six nickel atoms (Fig. 12.22). The figure shows that the six arsenic atoms are in octahedral formation. The distance Ni—As is 2·43. The distance between a nickel atom and its nickel neighbours vertically above and below it is 2·52, which is of the order of the length of a chemical bond.

Fig. 12.22.   The nickel arsenide structure. The arsenic atoms (shaded circles) are at the centres of alternate trigonal prisms, at the corners of which the nickel atoms (open circles) are situated.

The NiAs structure is adopted by substances AB, where A is a transition metal, and B is one of the elements S, Se, Te, Sn, Sb, As, or Bi. The more metallic the non-transition element, the more metallic are the properties of the crystals, which are frequently opaque and display metallic lustre. It is possible for the crystal to be found with a deficiency of the atom A; FeS often contains only about 45 atoms per cent of iron.

There is a close relation between the nickel arsenide and the cadmium iodide structures. If alternate planes of A atoms are removed from a crystal of the substance AB with the nickel arsenide structure, the cadmium iodide structure is obtained with the composition AB_2. This structure can be imagined if the middle plane of nickel (A) atoms is omitted from Fig. 12.22.

POTENTIAL ENERGY OF IONIC CRYSTALS

An ionic crystal is a regular system of oppositely charged ions. The system is a stable one, and it can be obtained experimentally either by the association of oppositely charged ions, or by reaction between non-ionised atoms. The potential energy of the system can be deduced by two methods. Method I considers, from the point of view of electrostatics, the energy changes which occur when oppositely charged ions are brought together, and Method II considers, from the point of view of thermochemistry, the energy changes which occur when two non-ionised atoms react.

METHOD I. CRYSTAL ENERGY CALCULATED FROM ELECTRICAL INTER-ACTIONS OF IONS OF OPPOSITE SIGN

When two oppositely charged ions approach one another there is an attractive Coulombic force between them, which increases as the distance of separation diminishes. When this distance is of the order of an atomic diameter the electron shells of the ions begin to overlap. The overlap results in a repulsion between the ions, the magnitude of which depends on the extent of the overlap. Equilibrium is reached when the attractive force is equal to the repulsive force. The distance between the nuclei at equilibrium is the interionic distance r_0, at which the energy is a minimum. The orbital overlap between the ions at the equilibrium interionic distance is illustrated in Fig. 12.23. In the figure the r-dependent wave functions of the orbitals of the isolated Li^+ and the isolated H^- ions are drawn, the centre of the Li^+ ion being at zero on the graph, and the centre

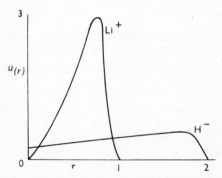

Fig. 12.23. Overlap of the electronic systems of the ions Li^+ and H^- in lithium hydride when the ions are separated by the normal internuclear distance.

of the H^- ion at 2·0. 2·0 is the interionic distance in the lithium hydride crystal. The diagram shows that if there is no distortion or polarisation of the electronic systems, the orbital of the H^- ion penetrates at least up to the nucleus of the Li^+ ion.

The potential energy of an ion pair separated by a distance r can be regarded as the sum of the potential energy due to the Coulomb forces, and of the potential energy due to the repulsive forces arising from the overlapping of the electron shells. The potential energy of a number of ion pairs forming a crystal can be regarded in the same way.

12 + A.T.I.C.

Potential energy of a crystal due to the Coulomb forces between ions. The potential energy of one isolated ion pair in which both ions are univalent, say K^+Cl^-, due to Coulomb forces is given by the expression:

$$E_I = -\frac{\epsilon^2}{r}$$

where r is the interionic distance. The potential energy which is negative increases numerically if the number of ion pairs in the system increases. If, for example, four ion pairs are arranged so that one ion is at each of the eight corners of a cube (Fig. 12.24), the potential energy of the system is given by

$$E'_I = -\frac{12\epsilon^2}{r} - \frac{4\epsilon^2}{r\sqrt{3}} + \frac{12\epsilon^2}{r\sqrt{2}}.$$

E'_I has greater negative value than E_I.

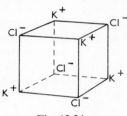

Fig. 12.24.

If n ion pairs are considered the potential energy remains a function of ϵ^2/r. For one gram molecule of K^+Cl^- the potential energy of the crystal due to ionic interaction can be expressed as

$$E_I = -NA\frac{\epsilon^2}{r}$$

where N is the Avogadro number and A is a constant for a given crystal known as *Madelung's constant*. (A is roughly $1\cdot7$ for crystals in which the two ions have equal co-ordination numbers, and 4–5 for crystals in which the co-ordination numbers of the two ions are different.)

If both ions are z-valent the expression for E_I is

$$E_I = -NA\frac{z^2\epsilon^2}{r}.$$

Potential energy of a crystal due to the overlap of the electron shells of the two ions. The repulsive forces due to the overlap of the electron shells of ions fall off very rapidly as the interionic distance increases. The potential energy of an ion pair due to these forces E_S is usually taken as $+B\epsilon^2/r^n$. Since the effect is small except between nearest neighbours, the potential energy of the system of one ion surrounded by its nearest neighbours in the crystal is $BK\epsilon^2/r^n$, where K is the co-ordination number of the ion. For a crystal containing one gram molecule of an ion pair, the potential energy due to the interaction between electron shells is given by:

$$E_S = +\frac{NBK\epsilon^2}{r^n}.$$

The total potential energy U_O of a crystal containing one gram molecule of an ion pair (both ions being z-valent) due to the Coulomb attraction and the electron overlap repulsion is given by:

$$U_O = E_I + E_S$$
$$= N\left(-\frac{A\epsilon^2 z^2}{r} + \frac{BK\epsilon^2}{r^n}\right). \tag{12.1}$$

In order to obtain agreement with experimental values of the energy and of the equilibrium interionic distance r_0 (p. 353), the following values for n are used: for ions with the helium structure, 5; the neon structure, 7; the argon structure, 9; the krypton structure, 10; the xenon structure, 12. For approximate purposes n is put equal to 9 in all cases.

The interactions between ions and between electron shells are not the only forces contributing to the potential energy of a crystal lattice. Additional sources of energy to be considered are:

(1) Zero point energy.
(2) Van der Waals forces between ions.
(3) Resonance energy which arises because all ionic bonds have some covalent character.

In the case of the alkali metal halides the inclusion of these additional energies introduces a correction amounting to about $\pm 3\%$ or less.

METHOD II. CRYSTAL ENERGY CALCULATED THERMOCHEMICALLY FROM THE REACTION OF SEPARATE ATOMS TO FORM AN IONIC CRYSTAL

The formation of an ionic crystal from atoms of two elements, for example sodium and chlorine, may be assumed to take place in three stages.

1. Conversion of the atoms to separate ions, $Na + Cl = Na^+ + Cl^-$.
2. Formation of ion pairs.
3. Assembly of the ion pairs in crystal array.

The energy changes associated with each of the stages are considered below.

Energy change in the formation of separated ions. The change

$$Na + Cl = Na^+ + Cl^-; \quad \Delta H = x \text{ kcal}$$

may be regarded as the sum of the two changes:

$$Na = Na^+ + e; \quad \Delta H = I_M$$
$$e + Cl = Cl^-; \quad \Delta H = E_X$$
$$Na + Cl = Na^+ + Cl^-; \quad \Delta H = I_M + E_X.$$

The quantity I_M is the **ionisation energy** of the sodium atom. It is *the energy in kcal required to convert 1 gram atom of sodium to 1 gram ion of* Na^+. I_M is always a positive quantity; it is determined by measuring the ionisation potential of sodium. **Ionisation potential** is defined as the *electrostatic potential between the limits of a field through which an electron must pass to acquire the speed necessary to remove one electron from the orbital system of the atom, both the original atom and the final ion being in the gas phase*. It is expressed in electron volts. The ionisation potential multiplied by $23 \cdot 06$ gives the ionisation energy in kcal per gram atom. The ionisation energies of certain atoms are given in Table 12.3.

Table 12.3. *Ionisation Energies,* I_M

The Table states the heat absorbed in kcal when 1 gram atom becomes a positive ion as, for example, in the reaction:

$$H = H^+ + e; \quad \Delta H = +312 \text{ kcal.}$$

Ion formed	I_M	Ion formed	I_M	Ion formed	I_M	Ion formed	I_M
H^+	312	Be^{2+}	594·5			C^+	259·0
Li^+	124·8	Mg^{2+}	520·8	B^{3+}	1648	N^+	333·9
Na^+	118·6	Ca^{2+}	412·9	Al^{3+}	1223	O^+	312·0
K^+	99·8	Sr^{2+}	383·7	Sc^{3+}	1019	F^+	427·5
Rb^+	96·7	Ba^{2+}	348·9	Y^{3+}	907	Ne^+	496·2
Cs^+	89·4			La^{3+}	831	A^+	365
		Zn^{2+}	313			Kr^+	324
Cu^+	177·8	Cd^{2+}	297				
Cu^{2+}	642						
Ag^+	174						

The quantity E_X is the **electron affinity** of the chlorine atom. It is the *energy in kcal required to convert 1 gram atom of chlorine to 1 gram ion of* Cl^-. The electron affinities of certain elements are given in Table 12.4 from which it is seen that E_X is positive in some cases, and negative in others.

Table 12.4.   *Electron Affinities,* E_X

The Table states the heat absorbed (+) or released (−) when one gram atom becomes a negative ion, as for example, in the reaction:

$$F + e = F^-; \quad \Delta H = -81 \cdot 7 \text{ kcal.}$$

Ion formed	E_X	Ion formed	E_X	Ion formed	E_X
H^-	−32·2	F^-	−81·7	O^-	−29·1
		Cl^-	−92·5	S^-	about −40
		Br^-	−87·1		
		I^-	−79·2	O^{2-}	+166
				S^{2-}	+79·5

Experimental values may now be inserted into the equation at the head of this section for the formation of Na^+ and Cl^- ions from separate atoms of sodium and chlorine.

$$Na = Na^+ + e; \qquad \Delta H = +118 \cdot 6 \text{ kcal}$$
$$e + Cl = Cl^-; \qquad \Delta H = -\ 92 \cdot 5 \text{ kcal}$$
$$Na + Cl = Na^+ + Cl^-; \quad \Delta H = +\ 25 \cdot 5 \text{ kcal}$$

The action takes place with the absorption of energy. Similar results may be obtained for the formation of all separated ions except those of the pair Cs^+Cl^-.

Energy change in the formation of ion pairs from separate ions. When two ions come together to form an ion pair, electrostatic energy is released. U_r denotes the energy which is liberated by the formation of an ion pair separated by the normal equilibrium distance, from free ions separated by a distance too great for interaction. U_r is of the order of -100 kcal per gram ion pair. Since U_r is negative the change from separate ions to an ion pair takes place spontaneously.

Energy change in the formation of crystals from ions. In the sodium chloride crystal each sodium ion is surrounded by six chlorine ions, and each chlorine ion by six sodium ions. The energy liberated per ion pair in the formation of a crystal is greater than that liberated in the formation of a single ion pair. The energy liberated when ions are brought into crystal array is known as the *lattice energy*, U_O:

$$Na^+ + Cl^- = NaCl_{cryst}; \quad \Delta H = U_O.$$

It is found that $U_O = AU_r$, where A is the Madelung constant (p. 354). This constant depends on the crystal type. For instance,

for crystals of the NaCl type, $A = 1 \cdot 7476,$
for crystals of the zinc blende type, $A = 1 \cdot 6381.$

The Born-Haber cycle. The lattice energy of a crystal may be conveniently calculated in terms of thermochemical quantities by means of the Born-Haber cycle. The formation of a crystal from two independent atoms and its subsequent disintegration into the two atoms again is represented as a thermodynamical cycle, each stage of which is associated with a definite quantity of energy. Suppose that the crystal of the ions M^+ and Y^- is formed from a metal consisting of atoms, M, and a gas consisting of molecules, Y_2, and that,

I_M is the ionisation potential of M
E_Y is the electron affinity of Y
S is the heat of sublimation of M
D is the dissociation energy of Y_2
U_O is the lattice energy of the crystal
ΔH is the heat change when the crystal is formed directly from the original substances in the metallic and gaseous states respectively.

The Born-Haber cycle is represented by a diagram, such as that in Fig. 12.25. Suppose the metal and the gas react directly to form 1 gram molecule of the crystal

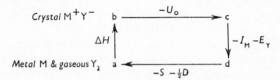

Fig. 12.25. The Born-Haber cycle.

M^+Y^-. ΔH kcal are liberated; the change on the diagram is represented by ab. 1 gram mole of the crystal can now be converted back to the original reagents by the following stages:

Stage	Route on Diagram	Energy change
Separation of ions	bc	$-U_O$
Conversion of ions to atoms	cd	$-I_M-E_Y$
Conversion of isolated atoms of M to the metallic crystal, and the combination of atoms of Y to give molecules Y_2	da	$-S-\frac{1}{2}D$

When the cycle is complete the relation holds

$$\Delta H - U_O - I_M - E_Y - S - \tfrac{1}{2}D = 0.$$

Hence,

$$U_O = -I_M - E_Y - S - \tfrac{1}{2}L + \Delta H.$$

The crystal energies of certain alkali halides have been determined by Method I and Method II. The results are compared in Table 12.5.

Table 12.5. *Crystal Energies of Alkali Halides*

Energies in kcal/mole (+indicates energy absorbed by the system)

Crystal	ΔH	I_M	S	D	E_Y	U_O by 1st method	U_O by 2nd method
NaCl	− 99	118·6	26	54	−92·5	−179	−178
NaBr	− 90	118·6	26	46	−87·1	−171	−171
NaI	− 77	118·6	26	34	−79·2	−160	−159
KCl	−104	99·8	21	54	−92·5	−163	−159
KBr	− 97	99·8	21	46	−87·1	−157	−154
KI	− 85	99·8	21	34	−79·2	−148	−144
RbCl	−105	96·7	20	54	−92·5	−158	−156
RbBr	− 99	96·7	20	46	−87·1	−151	−157
RbI	− 87	96·7	20	34	−79·2	−143	−152

The equilibrium ionic distance, r_0. Equation (12.1) (p. 354) states the relation between r, the interionic distance between two oppositely charged ions in a crystal, and U_O, the potential energy of the crystal. The equilibrium distance r_0 between the ions corresponds to a state of minimum energy for which

$$\frac{\mathrm{d}U_O}{\mathrm{d}r} = N\left(\frac{A\epsilon^2 z^2}{r^2} - \frac{nBK\epsilon^2}{r^{(n+1)}}\right) = 0.$$

Hence

$$r_0 = \left(\frac{nBK}{Az^2}\right)^{1/(n-1)}. \tag{12.2}$$

The value of n depends on the Period of the ion concerned, but it may be taken, approximately, as 9 (p. 354).

IONIC RADIUS

According to the concept of ionic radius the equilibrium distance between the two ions is the sum of the ionic radii of the two ions. The interionic distance in the crystal of lithium hydride, for example, would be the sum of two terms, one, r_A the radius of the H^- ion, and the other, r_C the radius of the Li^+ ion. At the equilibrium interionic distance $r_A + r_C = r_0$. It is pointed out on p. 353 that there is overlap between the electronic shells of the oppositely charged ions composing a crystal. The lack of any precise boundary between the charge clouds of electrons round the two nuclei makes it impossible to assign to ionic radii constant values which can be employed under all conditions without modification. Two modifications have been found valuable, the co-ordination number effect, and the radius ratio effect.

Co-ordination number effect. The dependence of the ionic radius on the co-ordination number of the ion is shown by equation (12.2). If a crystal undergoes a polymorphic change in which the co-ordination number of the ions alters from K_1 to K_2, then, on the assumption that the other constants in the equation do not vary significantly,

$$\frac{r_{A_1} + r_{C_1}}{r_{A_2} + r_{C_2}} = \frac{(nK_1B/Az^2)^{1/(n-1)}}{(nK_2B/Az^2)^{1/(n-1)}}$$

$$= \left(\frac{K_1}{K_2}\right)^{1/(n-1)}. \tag{12.3}$$

If $n=9$, and the ionic radius for co-ordination number 6 is taken as the standard, the data below at once follow from equation (12.3).

Co-ordination number	4	6	8
Radius	0·94	1·00	1·03

Pauling tabulated values for the radii of ions with 6:6 co-ordination. In most cases these values were experimental, but when the only crystals available were 8:8 co-ordinated he computed the 6:6 value by the above relation. For example, the value 3·85 for the interionic distance of caesium iodide was calculated by multiplying the observed value for the 8-co-ordinated body-centred crystal by 100/103.

Radius ratio effect. The limiting values of radius ratios for certain co-ordination numbers are stated in Table 12.2, p. 345. At those limiting values the surrounding spheres B just touch the central sphere A, and one another. If, for example, a 6-co-ordinated crystal is considered with radius ratio 0·414, the 6 surrounding spheres which just touch one another when the radius ratio is 0·414 must become more and more separated as the value of the radius ratio increases to 0·732. The interaction between the electron shells of the B spheres, therefore, greatly diminishes, and also to a less degree the mutual repulsion between the B ions. Pauling calculated corrections for the above effect; Table 12.6 shows how closely the corrected sum of the ionic radii in the lithium halides approaches the observed values.

Table 12.6. *Internuclear Distances in Crystalline Lithium Halides* (Å)

	LiF	LiCl	LiBr	LiI
Observed distance	2·009	2·566	2·747	3·022
Sum of radii as given in Table 12.7, p. 361	1·948	2·413	2·558	2·775
Correction for radius ratio effect	0·061	0·153	0·189	0·250
Corrected sum of radii	2·009	2·566	2·747	3·025

DETERMINATION OF IONIC RADII

The interionic distances in crystals are determined experimentally by X-ray analysis (p. 273). It may be supposed that the interionic distance is the sum of the ionic radii of the ions r_A and r_C. In order to compile a table of ionic radii it is necessary to know the ionic radius of one ion, say r_A, at least, so that it is then possible to find r_C by subtraction of r_A from the interionic distance. By determining the interionic distances in other crystals containing either the first or the second ion, and subtracting r_A or r_C, other ionic radii can be obtained, and so the radii of all ions can be found. Four methods have been used for determining or computing the ionic radii of certain ions.

Landé 1920. Landé determined the interionic distances, Li⁺Hal⁻ in the lithium halides. The lithium ion is so small that he was able to assume that in these compounds the halide ions are close-packed, and that the lithium ions are accommodated in the octahedral holes without disturbing the close-packing (Fig. 12.26). The internuclear distance (d in the diagram) was determined by

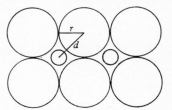

Fig. 12.26. Close-packed Cl⁻ ions (large circles) in a crystal of lithium chloride, showing how the packing is undisturbed by the presence of the Li⁺ ions (small circles).

X-ray analysis. It can be seen from the diagram that r_A, the radius of the halide ion, is equal to $(1/\sqrt{2})d$.

Bragg, 1927. Bragg used an argument similar to that of Landé, but he applied it to certain silicates in which the O^{2-} ions are close-packed, and the small silicon ions are in the tetrahedral holes. He used X-ray analysis to ascertain the Si—O distance. The radius of the O^{2-} ion is equal to $(1/\sqrt{2})d$.

Goldschmidt, 1926. Goldschmidt determined the internuclear distances in the crystals of the alkali halides, and of the alkaline earth oxides. He divided the internuclear distances, say Na^+Cl^-, or $Ca^{2+}O^{2-}$, in the proportions of the cube roots of the ionic refractivities. The employment of this principle is based on the arguments outlined in the following paragraphs.

From the Lorenz-Lorentz equation (p. 307)

$$R = \frac{n^2-1}{n^2+2} \cdot \frac{M}{\rho} \tag{12.4}$$

where n is the refractive index of a material, ρ is its density, M is its gram-molecular weight, and R is the *molar refraction*†. R is a constitutive property, and it is possible to assign values to quantities called the *refraction equivalents* of atoms and bonds, so that by the addition of the appropriate refraction equivalents the molar refraction of a compound may be predicted. The predictions are normally close to, but not identical with, the observed values. The discrepancies arise for the two principal reasons (a) that no atom in a molecule is independent of its environment in the molecule as a whole, and (b) that R is a constitutive property only when the light is of infinite wave length. In a corresponding manner the molar refraction of a salt may be assumed to be the sum of the ionic refractions of the component ions. It follows from equation (12.4) that R has the dimensions of volume, and therefore ionic refractions must also have the dimensions of volume. If R_1 is the ionic refraction of an ion with radius r_1, then the ionic radius can be written:

$$r_1 = k\sqrt[3]{R_1}.$$

If it be assumed that k is a constant for all ions, then

$$\frac{r_1}{r_2} = \frac{\sqrt[3]{R_1}}{\sqrt[3]{R_2}}. \tag{12.5}$$

For example, the interionic distance Na^+F^- is 2·31. The ionic refraction of Na^+ is 0·5, and of F^- is 2·5. The ionic radius of Na^+ is

$$\frac{\sqrt[3]{0\cdot5}}{\sqrt[3]{0\cdot5} + \sqrt[3]{2\cdot5}} \times 2\cdot31 = 0\cdot8525 \text{ Å.}$$

Since from Chapter 11 (p. 303 *et seq.*) the molar polarisation P, and the polarisability α of a material also have the dimensions of volume, either of these quantities may be used in equation (12.5) in place of R. The polarisability of Na^+ is $0\cdot19 \times 10^{-24}$ c.c., and that of F^- is $0\cdot96 \times 10^{-24}$ c.c. Hence the ionic radius of Na^+ is

$$\frac{\sqrt[3]{0\cdot19}}{\sqrt[3]{0\cdot19} + \sqrt[3]{0\cdot96}} \times 2\cdot31 = 0\cdot8505 \text{ Å.}$$

Pauling, 1934. Pauling based his system of ionic radii on the interionic distances

NaF	2·31
KCl	3·14
RbBr	3·43
(CsI)	3·85
LiO	2·00

He chose these compounds because (except for CsI) they all possess 6:6 co-ordination, and the radius ratio is about 0·73, which is the maximum value for 6:6 co-ordination. This value is so much greater than the minimum ratio, 0·414, that the radius ratio effect may be deemed absent. He divided the interionic distances into ionic radii on the assumption that the volumes of the ions are inversely proportional to an *effective nuclear charge*, which is the actual nuclear charge $Z\epsilon$ (where Z is the atomic number of the atom) less a screening constant calculated according to Slater's rules (p. 136).‡

† Molar refraction is defined in equation (12.4); the *refractivity*, R', of a substance refers to 1 gram, and is given by the expression

$$R' = \frac{n^2 - 1}{n^2 + 2} \cdot \frac{1}{\rho}.$$

‡ L. Pauling and J. Sherman, *Z. Krist.*, **81**, 1932, 1.

This computation predicts distances in crystals between univalent ions with inert gas structures, provided that the necessary corrections are made for the co-ordination number and radius ratio effects. If the ions are multivalent, however, the method predicts not the observed interionic distances, but the interionic distances which would be found (other conditions being unchanged) if the ions were univalent. An expression can be obtained from equation (12.2), p. 358, giving the relation between r_z, the interionic distance between the z-valent ions, and r_1, the interionic distance between the ions on the assumption that they are univalent.

From equation (12.2),

$$\frac{r_z}{r_1} = \frac{(nBK/Az^2)^{1/(n-1)}}{(nBK/A)^{1/(n-1)}}$$

$$= \left(\frac{1}{z^2}\right)^{1/(n-1)}.$$

If $n = 9$ (p. 354),

$$r_z = \frac{r_1}{\sqrt[4]{z}}.$$

The ionic radii of Pauling, determined for co-ordination number 6, and corrected for the valency of the ions, are known as Pauling's crystal radii. They are set out in Table 12.7.

Table 12.7. *Pauling's Crystal Radii* (Å)†

Radii of ions in crystals: ions formed by elements in normal sub-Groups

Li^+ 0·60	Be^{2+} 0·31	B^{3+} 0·20		N^{3-} 1·71	O^{2-} 1·40	F^- 1·36
Na^+ 0·95	Mg^{2+} 0·65	Al^{3+} 0·50	Si^{4+} 0·41	P^{3-} 2·12	S^{2-} 1·84	Cl^- 1·81
K^+ 1·33	Ca^{2+} 0·99	Ga^{3+} 0·62	Ge^{4+} 0·53	As^{3-} 2·22	Se^{2-} 1·98	Br^- 1·95
Rb^+ 1·48	Sr^{2+} 1·13	In^{3+} 0·81	Sn^{4+} 0·71	Sb^{3-} 2·45	Te^{2-} 2·21	I^- 2·16
Cs^+ 1·69	Ba^{2+} 1·35	Tl^{3+} 0·95	Pb^{4+} 0·84			
		Tl^+ 1·44	Pb^{2+} 1·21			

Radii of ions in crystals: ions formed by elements in transition sub-Groups

	Sc^{3+}	Ti^{3+}	V^{3+}	Cr^{3+}	Mn^{3+}	Fe^{3+}				
	0·83	0·76	0·74	0·69	0·66	0·64				
					Mn^{2+} 0·80	Fe^{2+} 0·76	Co^{2+} 0·74	Ni^{2+} 0·72	Cu^+ 0·96	Zn^{2+} 0·74
									Ag^+ 1·26	Cd^{2+} 0·97
									Au^+ 1·37	Hg^{2+} 1·10

† L. C. Pauling, *The Nature of the Chemical Bond*, Cornell University Press, 3rd Edition, 1960 pp. 514 and 518.

12*

The following points are to be noted in connection with Table 12.7.

(1) The radius of a positive ion is less than the radius of the corresponding atom in the covalent or the metallic state.

(2) The radius of a negative ion is greater than the radius of the corresponding atom in the covalent state.

(3) The radii of a series of isoelectronic positive ions decrease with increasing positive charge.

(4) The radii of the ions of the highly electronegative elements in the same Period (e.g. S, 1·84; Cl, 1·81) do not differ very much.

(5) Increase of positive charge on the nucleus, accompanied by the introduction of electrons to the inner d orbitals of atoms of the transition elements (e.g. in the building up of the series Mn^{2+}, Fe^{2+}, Co^{2+}, Ni^{2+}) causes a diminution of ionic radius.

The introduction of electrons to the inner f orbitals of atoms of the rare earth elements (e.g. in the series Ce^{3+} to Lu^{3+}) also causes a diminution of ionic radius. This effect is known as the lanthanide contraction (p. 1125).

BOOK FOR FURTHER READING

WELLS, A. F., *Structural Inorganic Chemistry* (Oxford University Press, 2nd Edition, 1950).

CHAPTER THIRTEEN

HYDROGEN

GENERAL CHEMISTRY

Hydrogen is a gas in normal conditions. Its physical properties are given in Table 13.3. Solid hydrogen has a hexagonal close-packed structure.

Hydrogen is present in the atmosphere, but only to the extent of 1 part in 1 million by volume. It is set free in many natural and industrial chemical reactions, but the speed of the molecule at the temperature of the atmosphere is sufficiently great to enable it to escape from the earth's gravitational field. Pure hydrogen for laboratory use is made by the electrolysis of barium hydroxide solution using nickel electrodes. Traces of oxygen are eliminated by passing the gas over heated platinum gauze, and the resultant water is absorbed in phosphorus pentoxide. Further purification may be effected by absorbing the gas on palladium at room temperature, and recovering it by reduction of pressure at 100°.

The chemistry of hydrogen is unique. The atom consists of a proton and one electron in the $1s$ shell. The energy required to expel the electron from the atom is very high, although less than the energy required to expel one electron from the atom of any inert gas except xenon, as is shown by the ionisation potentials in Table 11.15. The hydrogen atom does not lose its electron in any chemical process. It is therefore not analogous to the atoms of the alkali metals which readily lose their s electrons to form cations.

Hydrogen is a characteristically non-metallic element which shows no electropositive properties. When the atom reacts it does so by acquiring an electron, either to form the anion H^-, or to form an electron pair which it shares with another atom. Here again the hydrogen atom differs from the alkali metal atoms which do not form anions such as K^-.

Hydrogen forms binary compounds with many elements. It combines directly with the alkali metals, and with calcium, strontium, and barium, to form salt-like hydrides of the types LiH and CaH_2. Hydrogen does not combine directly with cadmium, zinc, or mercury, or with any of the elements of Group III. It combines directly with carbon, if an arc is struck between carbon poles in an atmosphere of hydrogen, to give mainly acetylene, but not with any other elements of sub-Group IV N. It combines directly with all the elements in the sub-Groups V N, VI N, and VII N to form covalent hydrides. These hydrides are gases or volatile liquids; the molecular formulae are given by the expression $XH_{(8-G)}$ where X is one atom of the element and G is the Group number. In the covalent hydrides the hydrogen atoms are usually linked to other atoms by σ two-centre bonds, but in a few cases, such as B_2H_6, three-centre bonds occur.

Hydrogen dissolves in the metals of sub-Groups IV T and V T to form interstitial compounds, but it dissolves only slightly in metals of the sub-Groups VI T, VII T, and of Groups VIII and IX. The metals in Group X, especially palladium, dissolve hydrogen freely, but the solubility of hydrogen in metals of Group XI is no greater than its solubility in the metals of sub-Groups VI T, VII T, and of Groups VIII and IX.

Hydrogen is usually regarded as a reducing agent because of its affinity for oxygen and the halogens. Hydrogen, however, acts as a catalytic rather than a reducing agent in reactions involving the transfer of electrons. The role of hydrogen in such reactions as the reduction of cupric oxide is to remove the oxygen atom which is liberated after the reduction of the cupric ion by the oxygen ion O^{2-}:

$$Cu^{2+}O^{2-} = Cu + O$$
$$O + H_2 = H—O—H.$$

(The reaction may be compared with the reduction of HgO and Ag_2O by heat alone.) Both in the hydrogen molecule and in the water molecule each hydrogen atom is sharing one electron pair: its mode of combination is unchanged by the reaction.

THE HYDROGEN ATOM

The isotopes of hydrogen. The atomic number of hydrogen is 1. There are three isotopes:

Ordinary hydrogen or protium	atomic weight	1·0078
Deuterium	„ „	2·01472
Tritium	„ „	3·0171

Deuterium and tritium are discussed later, deuterium on p. 391, and tritium on p. 397.

Atomic hydrogen. The structure of the hydrogen atom in terms of wave mechanics is discussed on p. 32.

The hydrogen atom is formed from the hydrogen molecule by the absorption of energy:

$$H_2 = H + H: \quad \Delta H = +104·2 \text{ kcal.}$$

The concentration of atomic hydrogen in hydrogen gas is therefore small. At a pressure of 1 atmosphere at 2000° there is 1% of atomic hydrogen in hydrogen gas, and at 3000° there is about 9%. Once produced, however, the atoms do not rapidly recombine at low pressures because the energy released by their union immediately causes them to separate again. The half-life of hydrogen atoms is about 1 second at 0·2 mm pressure. At higher pressures, or in the presence of an inert gas, three-body collisions occur, and recombination is rapid. Recombination is also rapid in the presence of certain metals.

If a jet of molecular hydrogen is forced through an electric arc struck between tungsten electrodes in an atmosphere of hydrogen, a considerable quantity of atomic hydrogen is present in the emergent gas stream. Tungsten placed in this stream is melted (m.p. 3400°) because the energy released by the recombination of the hydrogen atoms on the surface of the metal, raises its temperature to a very high degree. Iron, and alloys containing chromium, aluminium, silver or magnanese, can be melted by this process without undergoing surface oxidation. The process can be used for welding.

The efficiency of a metal in causing recombination of hydrogen atoms is related to the overvoltage of the metal. Metals with high overvoltage are the least effective. Sidgwick quotes the following series of metals in increasing order of catalytic efficiency:

$$Hg < Pb < Cu < Ag < Cr < Fe < W < Pd < Pt$$

The overvoltage falls steadily along the series as the catalytic activity increases.

Atomic hydrogen may be prepared by the thermal dissociation of molecular hydrogen as mentioned above, and also:

(1) By passing hydrogen gas at a low pressure (below 0·01 mm) over a tungsten, platinum, or palladium wire heated to 1000–2000°.

(2) By passing a mixture of an inert gas at 25 mm pressure and hydrogen at 1 mm pressure, through a long tube along which an electric discharge is passed.

(3) By exposing a mixture of hydrogen (up to $\frac{1}{2}$ atmosphere pressure) and mercury vapour to the resonance radiation ($\lambda = 2537$ Å) of a mercury arc; the energy of radiation per mercury atom, $h\nu$, is $112 \cdot 0/N$ kcal, which is greater than the value required ($104 \cdot 2/N$ kcal) to dissociate a hydrogen molecule (compare p. 322).

(4) By bombarding hydrogen with slow electrons (10–20 eV).

Atomic hydrogen has strong reducing properties. It converts oxygen to hydrogen peroxide, and ethylene to ethane. It initiates the explosive combination of hydrogen and oxygen. It reduces an aqueous solution of hydrogen peroxide to water, and aqueous solutions of silver nitrate, mercuric chloride, and copper acetate to the metals. It reduces aqueous solutions of chromates to chromic salts, permanganates to manganous salts, and iodine to hydrogen iodide. It converts sodium peroxide to sodium hydroxide. It reduces AgO, Ag_2O, CuO, PbO_2, and HgO to metals, and GeO_2 to metallic germanium and GeH_4; the hydride decomposes on the walls of the reaction vessel. It converts the higher oxides of Ti, V, Nb, Cr, Mo, W, and Mn to indefinite hydroxy compounds. The first stage of these reactions is probably an additive reaction to form a peroxide which dissociates, thus:

$$MnO_2 \rightarrow MnOOH \rightarrow Mn(OH)_2 \rightarrow MnO.$$

Benzene is reduced to dihydrobenzene when treated with hydrogen containing 60% of hydrogen atoms at $0 \cdot 5$ mm pressure and at $-180°$, and by a similar treatment mercury vapour is converted to a solid hydride, HgH, which decomposes below $-100°$.

THE PROTON H+

The proton, the nucleus of the hydrogen atom, has a mass $1 \cdot 0078$ ($O = 16$) and a radius of the order of 10^{-13} cm. In ordinary conditions its life is very short, as it soon combines with an electron to become a neutral hydrogen atom. It is produced:

(1) By ionising molecular hydrogen by an electric arc, or by a radiofrequency discharge.

(2) By the bombardment of, say, a solid paraffin by neutrons or deuterons.

(3) By the artificial disruption of certain nuclei, as, for example, in the reaction:

$$_7N^{14} + {}_2He^4 \rightarrow {}_8O^{17} + {}_1H^1$$

in which a fast-moving α particle reacts with an atom of nitrogen.

The proton in aqueous solution. In the chemistry of aqueous solutions the cation in neutral or acid solution is often written for simplicity as the proton H+, which is taken to be analogous to such cations as Li+ and Na+. The proton is in fact vastly different from a univalent metallic ion because:

(i) the energy of its formation from the atom (ionisation potential Table 11.15, p. 328) is unusually high,

(ii) the radius of H+ is only 1/50,000 that of Li+ and consequently,

(iii) the field strength at the boundary of the H+ ion (e/r^2, where r is the ionic radius, and $+e$ is the charge) is $2 \cdot 5 \times 10^9$ times as great as that of Li+, the ion of the most electronegative of the alkali metals.

The proton, therefore, when in contact with other atoms always passes into the covalent state.

The cation in neutral or acid aqueous solution is actually the hydronium ion, H_3O^+, a complex of oxygen; it is not a hydrated proton, just as formaldehyde is not hydrated carbon. The hydronium ion is formed directly from water molecules. Water is polymerised by the formation of hydroxyl bonds (p. 373). The hydrogen atom in the hydroxyl bond can occupy one of two positions of minimum energy at $1 \cdot 0$ from each

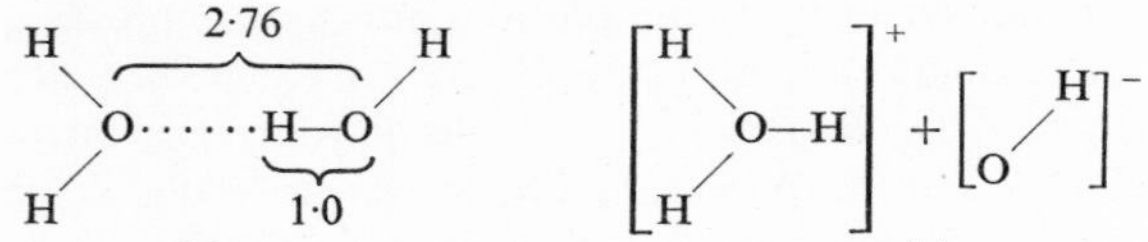

(a)   (b)

of the two oxygen atoms. If the central H atom in diagram (a) moves into the position in which it is shown in diagram (b), dissociation of the system may occur into H_3O^+ and OH^-. The dissociation of hydrogen chloride when dissolved in water probably takes place by a similar mechanism:

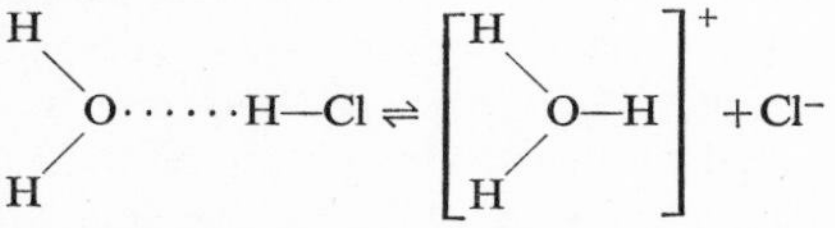

It is claimed[†] that during the electrolysis of water (at least in alkaline and weakly acid solutions) molecular water and not the hydronium ion is reduced at the cathode:

$$2\epsilon^- + 2H_2O = H_2 + 2OH^-.$$

The hydrogen anion, H⁻. The hydrogen anion consists of a proton associated with two electrons which occupy the $1s$ orbital. The electronic configuration is that of the helium atom. The H^- ion is present in the hydrides of the metals of Group I (p. 405), and in the hydrides of the metals, Ca, Sr, Ba (p. 449).

HYDROGEN MOLECULE-ION H₂⁺

The hydrogen molecule-ion consists of one electron bound to two protons. It is extremely unstable and its existence in the discharge tube is so transient that it is not possible to record its spectrum. Chemically it is not of great interest, but it is of theoretical importance as it provides the simplest possible example of a link between two atoms. The Schrödinger equation which describes the hydrogen molecule-ion can be solved if the wave function chosen for the ion is a linear combination of the wave functions of the isolated hydrogen atoms. The expression for the total energy E of the two-centre bond is given by equation (4.4), p. 118,

$$E_\pm = \frac{E_A \pm E_{AB}}{1 \pm S_{AB}}.$$

The system may be regarded as that of a hydrogen atom A in the neighbourhood of a proton B (Fig. 13.1). For this purpose the electron is considered to "belong" to A. If E_0 is the energy of the electron when A is in the ground state, the presence of B causes an increase of the potential energy by an amount ϵ^2/R and a decrease of potential energy by an amount ϵ^2/r_b, where R is the distance between the nuclei and r_b is the distance from the electron to nucleus B. The terms contained in equation (4.4) are given by the expressions:

$$E_A = \int \psi^2_A (T_p + V_p)\, d\tau \quad \text{(p. 117)}$$

$$= E_0 + \int \psi^2_A \left(-\frac{\epsilon^2}{r_b} + \frac{\epsilon^2}{R} \right) d\tau.$$

$$E_{AB} = \int \psi_A \psi_B \left(E_0 - \frac{\epsilon^2}{r_b} + \frac{\epsilon^2}{R} \right) d\tau.$$

$$S_{AB} = \int \psi_A \psi_B\, d\tau.$$

These integrals can be evaluated; they may also be expressed in terms of the inter-

† P. Delahay, *J. Amer. Chem. Soc.*, **74**, 1952, 3497.

nuclear distance R, and thus E_+ may be plotted against R. The form of the curve is that of a Morse curve (p. 211) showing a minimum value of E, for which the internuclear distance is the bond length. Since the Schrödinger equation can be solved, an expression for ψ_{mol} may be obtained, but for the chemist the chief interest lies in the values obtained for the energy of dissociation and the bond length; 41 kcal per mole and 1·32. Since the spectrum of the hydrogen molecule-ion cannot be recorded it is not possible to compare theoretical and experimental energy curves. Values for the dissociation energy, 61 kcal per mole, and bond length, 1·06, have been obtained indirectly from measurements of the ionisation potentials of H_2 and H, and extrapolation of the molecular Rydberg series of H_2. The bond length thus determined is twice the first Bohr radius and seems to be a more likely value than 1·32. The use of atomic wave functions in the molecule must introduce some inaccuracy, and various "improved" wave functions such as those of Hylleraas and Jaffé† have been devised in order to give a good correlation with the experimental value.‡

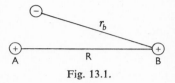

Fig. 13.1.

The charge contour diagrams for the hydrogen molecule-ion are similar to those given for the two-centre bond (Fig. 4.3, p. 122). Energy values for the repulsive and excited states of the hydrogen molecule-ion may also be calculated and the corresponding energy curves drawn.

The hydrogen triatomic molecule ion, H_3^+. This particle is found in the discharge tube. Its mass is 3·026, which clearly distinguishes it from tritium with mass 3·0171. It is comparatively stable as is shown by the equations:

$$H+H+H^+ = H_3^+; \quad \Delta H = -184 \text{ kcal}$$
$$H_2+H^+ = H_3^+; \quad \Delta H = -80·6 \text{ kcal}$$
$$H+H_2^+ = H_3^+; \quad \Delta H = -19·6 \text{ kcal}$$

H^+ and H_2^+ ions both tend to change into H_3^+. The structure is a linear three-centre orbital which is discussed on p. 120.

HYDROGEN MOLECULE H_2

The hydrogen molecule differs from the hydrogen molecule-ion in having two electrons instead of one, bound to the two protons. Both the molecule and molecule-ion are examples of the two-centre bond, and thus they both have the same expression for the energy of the molecular orbital if it is written in the form

$$E_\pm = \frac{E_A \pm E_{AB}}{1 \pm S_{AB}}.$$

The integrals, however, are different in the two cases. For the hydrogen molecule, the energy must be calculated in terms of both electrons (Fig. 13.2). Thus, the potential energy V of the whole system may be written as

$$V = -\frac{\epsilon^2}{r_{a_1}} - \frac{\epsilon^2}{r_{b_1}} - \frac{\epsilon^2}{r_{a_2}} - \frac{\epsilon^2}{r_{b_2}} + \frac{\epsilon^2}{r_{12}} + \frac{\epsilon^2}{R},$$

where r_{12} = distance of electron (1) from electron (2),
    r_{a_1} = distance of electron (1) from nucleus A,
    r_{b_1} = distance of electron (1) from nucleus B,
    r_{a_2} = distance of electron (2) from nucleus A,
    r_{b_2} = distance of electron (2) from nucleus B,
    R = distance of nucleus A from nucleus B.

† Hylleraas, E. A., *Z. Phys.*, **71**, 1931, 739; Jaffé, G., *Z. Phys.*, **87**, 1934, 535.
‡ Calculation using the concept of rotating charge (p. 327), and a value 61 kcal for the bond energy gives a bond length of 1·00.

The expression for the energy of the two-centre bond in terms of the valence bond theory is given on p. 134. This expression gives the energy of the hydrogen molecule and includes two possible values corresponding to the bonding and antibonding states respectively:

$$E_1 = 2E_0 + \frac{C+A}{1+S_{AB}}$$

and

$$E_2 = 2E_0 + \frac{C-A}{1-S_{AB}}.$$

It is possible to evaluate the integrals C and A; they both have negative values and A is larger than C; E_1 is less than the sum of the energies of two independent hydrogen atoms in the ground state, and therefore corresponds to the bonding state of a stable hydrogen molecule. The energy E_2 is greater than the sum of the energies of two independent hydrogen atoms in the ground state, and therefore corresponds to the antibonding state, with a deficiency of charge between the two nuclei. The calculated values of E_1 may be plotted as a function of the internuclear distance; the minimum value of E_1 corresponds to a dissociation energy of 72·3 kcal and a bond length of 0·86. An experimental energy curve may be plotted from the hydrogen spectrum; from this curve the values of dissociation energy and bond lengths are 104·18 kcal and 0·74, so the agreement is not close. Various workers have devised more complicated wave functions to fit the experimental values; this process culminated in the work of James and Coolidge who introduced more and more parameters until they achieved very close agreement between experiment and theory. It is, however, open to question whether this adjustment has much theoretical value.[†]

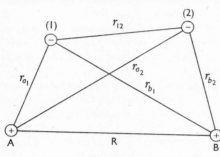

Fig. 13.2.

ORTHOHYDROGEN AND PARAHYDROGEN[‡]

There are two isomeric species of molecular hydrogen called orthohydrogen and parahydrogen. The isomerism is due to two possible couplings of the spin of the nuclei of the atoms in the molecule. It is supposed that the nuclei spin in planes at right angles to the molecular axis. In the molecule of orthohydrogen the spins of the two nuclei are parallel, in the molecule of parahydrogen they are antiparallel. The coupling of the resultant nuclear spin to the total angular momentum of the molecule excluding nuclear spin is mentioned in Chapter 7 (p. 223), where it is stated that orthohydrogen corresponds only to odd values of J and that parahydrogen corresponds only to even values of J.

Ordinary hydrogen gas is a tautomeric mixture of orthohydrogen and parahydrogen, of which the composition is determined by the laws of chemical equilibria. The compositions of equilibrium mixtures at certain temperatures are given in Table 13.1. This Table shows that the expected statistical ratio of three parts of orthohydrogen

---

† Calculation using the concept of rotating charge (p. 327) and a value 104 kcal for the bond energy gives a bond length of 0·73.

‡ For an account of orthohydrogen, parahydrogen, and deuterium see A. Farkas, *Orthohydrogen, Parahydrogen, and Heavy Hydrogen*, Cambridge University Press, 1935.

to one part of parahydrogen (p. 397) is shown at temperatures at and above 273°K. It should be noted that the percentage of orthohydrogen does not rise above 75.†

Table 13.1. *Proportions of Parahydrogen and Orthohydrogen present at Equilibrium at certain Temperatures*

Temp. °K	% of parahydrogen	% of orthohydrogen
20	99·8	0·2
50	76·9	23·1
100	38·5	61·5
200	26·0	74·0
273	25·13	74·87
298	25·1	74·9
Infinity	25·0	75·0

If the temperature of a given mixture is changed, however, there is no rapid adjustment of its composition to the appropriate equilibrium value. Pure parahydrogen in a glass vessel at room temperature undergoes no perceptible change in 3 weeks; its half life is about 3·years.

Transformation of one isomeric species into the other. If hydrogen gas is cooled to very low temperatures, the molecules tend to enter the lowest energy state possible. For the molecules of parahydrogen this state corresponds to $J=0$, for the molecules of orthohydrogen this state corresponds to $J=1$. Parahydrogen is therefore the more stable at low temperatures, and molecules of orthohydrogen tend to change into molecules of parahydrogen. It has been found experimentally that if the gas is kept at a low temperature for a very long time and is then heated to a normal temperature the spectrum shows only the lines equivalent to changes of even values of J, and the alternate lines in the spectrum are missing. This experiment was first performed by Bonhoeffer and Harteck.‡ The result confirms (i) the extreme slowness of the change from parahydrogen to the equilibrium mixture, and (ii) the deduction that the species stable at low temperatures is parahydrogen. To enable the transformation of one form of hydrogen into the other to take place at a normal rate the gas must either be activated by atomic hydrogen, or brought into contact with a catalyst. Atomic hydrogen may be introduced into molecular hydrogen

(i) by simple admixture,
(ii) by exposing molecular hydrogen to an electric discharge,
(iii) by heating molecular hydrogen to 800°.

If parahydrogen-enriched hydrogen (obtained by treating hydrogen with charcoal at the temperature of boiling liquid air, or liquid hydrogen) is mixed with hydrogen leaving a discharge tube and containing hydrogen atoms, partial conversion to the equilibrium para-ortho mixture occurs. By carrying out the reaction at different temperatures it is possible to deduce the heat of activation of the reaction:

$$\text{para } H_2 + H = \text{ortho } H_2 + H;$$

it is found to be 7·250 kcal. Exposure of molecular hydrogen to an electric discharge is clearly a more direct way of mixing it with atomic hydrogen. The effect of high

† Orthohydrogen of 99% purity has been obtained by a three-stage process of adsorption and desorption on γ-alumina at 20·4°K and 50 mm Hg. (C. M. Cunningham, D. S. Chaplin, and H. L. Johnston, *J. Amer. Chem. Soc.*, 1958, **80**, 2382).
‡ K. F. Bonhoeffer and P. Harteck, *Z. physikal. Chem.* **B4**, 1929 ,113.

temperatures in promoting the conversion of parahydrogen to the equilibrium mixture is probably due to the liberation of atoms of hydrogen by the thermal dissociation of the molecules.

Either homogeneous or heterogeneous catalysts may be used to promote the attainment of equilibrium. It is observed that paramagnetic substances are the most efficient catalysts. The paramagnetic gases oxygen, nitric oxide, and nitrogen dioxide are effective, but the diamagnetic gases N_2, N_2O, CO_2, NH_3, HI, SO_2 are not. Paramagnetic ions in solution also promote the conversion, and the rate of the change is related to the magnetic moment of the ion, thus:

Table 13.2.   *Effect of Paramagnetic Ions on the Rate of Conversion of Parahydrogen to the Equilibrium Mixture*

Ion	Magnetic moment (Bohr magnetons)	k, the velocity constant in mole^{-1} litre min^{-1}
Zn^{2+}	0	0
Cu^{2+}	1·9	1·15
Ni^{2+}	3·2	1·95
Co^{2+}	5·1	5·56
Fe^{2+}	5·3	6·05
Mn^{2+}	5·8	8·05

Charcoal is a good catalyst for bringing into equilibrium at the temperature of liquid air a mixture previously in equilibrium at room temperature, but if the mixture is raised to room temperature again it does not help to restore the original equilibrium; charcoal absorbs gases efficiently only at very low temperatures. The effectiveness of platinum black is opposite to that of charcoal. Platinum black is a good catalyst for

Table 13.3.   *Certain Physical Properties of Hydrogen*

	Orthohydrogen	Parahydrogen	Equilibrium mixture
m.p. °K	13·93	13·88	13·92
b.p. °K	20·41	20·29	20·38
Vapour pressure, mm, at:			
3·95°K		57	53·9
20·39°K		787	760·0
Rotational specific heat, cal/mole^{-1} degree^{-1}, at:			
50°K	0·00	0·040	0·010
100°K	0·073	1·504	0·431
200°K	1·151	2·767	1·555
298°K	1·838	2·186	1·925
Latent heat, cal/mole^{-1}, at 20°K:			
fusion		28·08	
vaporisation		215·0	219·3

bringing into equilibrium at room temperature a mixture previously in equilibrium at low temperatures, but it is not effective at liquid air temperatures. (Perhaps again it works in one direction only, parahydrogen to orthohydrogen.) The catalytic activity of various oxides reveals that at 86°K the paramagnetic ones are the more active.

Physical properties. Certain physical properties of orthohydrogen, parahydrogen, and of the equilibrium mixture which is "ordinary hydrogen" are given in Table 13.3.

Magnetic moment. The magnetic moment of the molecule of parahydrogen is zero because the anti-parallel spins compensate one another. The magnetic moment of the molecule of orthohydrogen is twice that of a proton.

Thermal conductivity. The thermal conductivities of orthohydrogen and parahydrogen are different. It can be shown that there is a linear relationship between the proportion of parahydrogen in a mixture of orthohydrogen and parahydrogen and the thermal conductivity of the mixture. This relationship can be used for determining the parahydrogen content of a given sample of hydrogen.

Uses of parahydrogen. The rate of conversion of parahydrogen to the equilibrium mixture has been used to measure the concentration of free hydrogen atoms in a gas, particularly the stationary concentration of hydrogen atoms in photochemical reactions.

THE HYDROGEN BRIDGE

A group consisting of a hydrogen atom linked to one of the highly electronegative atoms, F, O, or N, has peculiar properties, and it is able to form a link with another of these atoms or, much less readily, with a chlorine atom. Such links are found in all states of matter, for example, between fluorine atoms in hydrogen fluoride vapour, between oxygen atoms in liquid water, and between the oxygen atoms of oxy-ions in the crystals of certain salts, for instance sodium bicarbonate:

In the above examples the link F to F, or O to O is known as a *hydrogen bridge*. As represented in the diagrams it is made up of two sections, the original covalent bond F—H or O—H, and a new link H····F or O····H. There is evidence, to be discussed later, that the original covalent bond is little modified in the hydrogen bridge, and that the link represented by the dotted line is an electrostatic attraction. The high electronegativity of F, O, or N brings about polarisation of the hydrogen atom,[†]

$$\overset{\delta-\quad\delta+}{\text{F—H,}}$$

and the positive charge on the hydrogen atom, which thus tends to become a proton, exerts a Coulomb force on a negative group in its neighbourhood. There is an interesting contrast between the covalent bond in which an electron pair binds two positive nuclei $\oplus\overset{\circ}{\circ}\oplus$, and the hydrogen bridge in which a proton binds two negative atoms $\ominus H^+\ominus$.

According to the principles of valency discussed in Chapter 5, the atoms F, O, and

---

[†] A formula such as $\overset{\delta-\quad\delta+}{\text{F—H}}$ indicates a transfer of negative charge from the atom marked $\delta+$ to the atom marked $\delta-$, but it is to be understood that the quantity of electricity transferred is much smaller than that equivalent to 1 electron per atom.

N in combination are in the tetrahedral valence state.† Their hydrides may be formulated thus:

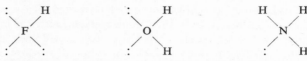

The tetrahedral orbitals which do not overlap the *s* orbitals of hydrogen atoms are occupied by lone pairs. The effect of polarisation of the hydrogen atoms by the electronegative central atom is to create dipoles. If it be assumed that the lone pairs are at the negative pole of the dipole, the formulae may be written:

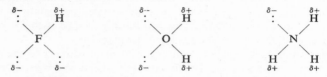

If, say, in the group FH, the polarisation of F—H were complete, the system would consist of a fluorine ion F⁻ of radius 1·36, and a proton of negligible radius. The dipole would remain, and the group could be represented by a sphere with three negative sectors corresponding to lone pairs in the formula, and one positive sector, corresponding to the presence of the proton:

By similar arguments the molecules of water and ammonia can be represented:

The hydrogen bridge on this notation results from the attraction between the positive sector of one sphere and a negative sector of another sphere.

Hydrogen bridges linking oxygen atoms are of especial interest. The oxygen atom may take part as a member of any of the four units:

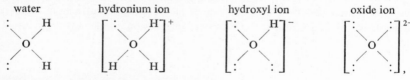

which, in the spherical notation are written:

It will be noted that the ionic valency of each unit is correctly ascertained if the magnitude of each + or − charge in a sector is taken to be one-half of an electronic

† Experiments on the polarised infrared spectrum of single crystals of CaCl₂,2H₂O, give support to the view that the orbitals of the oxygen atom in water are tetrahedrally arranged. Rundle et al. *J. Amer. Chem. Soc.*, 1958, 2450.

charge (this does not apply to fluorine or to nitrogen). The covalent groups, ROH, R_1R_2O, and $R\bar{O}$, can be represented in the same way as the above anions. (The group $R\bar{O}$ represents an oxy-ion such as SO_4^{2-}, ClO_4^-, or CO_3^{2-}; $\bar{O}$ represents one of the oxygen atoms, and R represents the remainder of the ion; e.g. if SO_4 is written O_3S—O, then R represents O_3S.) Since R represents an element or group other than hydrogen, on the spherical notation the sector of the oxygen atom to which R is linked is not marked $+$:

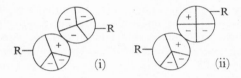

Two forms of hydrogen bridge requently found between two oxygen atoms are (i) the bridge between ROH and $R\bar{O}$, and (ii) the bridge between ROH and ROH:

One distinction between these two forms of hydrogen bridge is at once apparent; the right-hand oxygen atom in (i) has two free negative sectors, and can make an additional hydrogen bridge only by acting as electron donor, for example in $LiClO_4,3H_2O$, but the oxygen atom in (ii) has one negative and one positive sector, and can make additional hydrogen bridges either by acting as electron donor or as electron acceptor, as for example in boric acid.

The distinction between the two forms of hydrogen bridge between two oxygen atoms is sufficiently sharp for one to be called the hydrogen bond, and the other the hydroxyl bond:

Hydrogen bond R—O—H····$\bar{O}$—R; the distance O—H—O is 2·55

Hydroxyl bond R—O—H····O—R; the distance O—H—O is 2·75
$\qquad\qquad\qquad\qquad\quad |$
$\qquad\qquad\qquad\qquad\quad H$

The term *hydrogen bond* is used to describe any hydrogen bridge other than the hydroxyl bond between two electronegative atoms. The term *hydroxyl bond* is limited to the hydrogen bridge formed by two hydroxyl groups. The term *hydrogen bridge* includes both the hydrogen bond and the hydroxyl bond.

Normally only one hydrogen bridge terminates on each electronegative atom. This is true of polymers and of closed ring structures. In some crystal structures such as that of KHF_2, and in the chain structures of HCN and $NaHCO_3$, the fluorine, nitrogen, or oxygen atom takes part in the formation of one hydrogen bridge only. This is also true of the structures assigned to KH_2PO_4 and $(NH_4)_2H_3IO_6$. But in the layer lattices of $N_2H_6F_2$ and $B(OH)_3$, and in the infinite three-dimensional structures of NH_4F, NH_4HF_2, and ice, a given fluorine, oxygen, or nitrogen atom takes part in the formation of more than one hydrogen bridge.

CONDITIONS FOR THE FORMATION OF THE HYDROGEN BRIDGE

The conditions necessary for the formation of the hydrogen bridge $X—H\cdots Y$ between the atoms X and Y are:

(i) that both X and Y are highly electronegative,

(ii) that the distance between X and Y (which is determined by the molecular or crystal configuration of the substance concerned) is about 2·7.

Electronegativity. A hydrogen atom which forms a hydrogen bridge is nearly always covalently linked to one of the highly electronegative atoms, F, O, or N, and the atom to which the bridge extends is normally an atom of one of these elements. Examples are known, however, of hydrogen bridges in which atoms of lower electronegativity take part, as for instance the chlorine atom in *o*-chlorophenol

The electronegativity of an atom is increased if it acquires a positive ionic charge, or if it is the positive atom in a pair linked by a covalent bond with considerable ionic character. For example, the positive ammonium ion NH_4^+ forms strong hydrogen bonds in ammonium fluoride, but the hydrogen bonds between neutral ammonia molecules in the crystal of ammonia are only weak. The formation of hydrogen bonds between molecules of HCN is made possible by the molecular structure $H—C\frac{\pi}{\pi}N$, in which the triple bond enhances the electronegativity of the nitrogen atom and of the carbon atom, just as the triple bond in acetylene enhances the electronegativity of the two carbon atoms. Hence the polymerisation occurs:

$$H—C\frac{\pi}{\pi}N\cdots H—C\frac{\pi}{\pi}N\cdots H—C\frac{\pi}{\pi}N.$$

The formation of hydroxyl bonds in crystalline hydroxyl compounds is greatly influenced by the electronegativity of the element with which the hydroxyl group is combined. If it be assumed in the first place that crystalline hydroxides are ionic, then the ion OH^- must be electrically neutralised by the presence in its neighbourhood of some cation X. In a crystal each OH^- ion is surrounded by neighbour X ions according to its co-ordination number, and each X ion is correspondingly surrounded by OH^- ions. If in the crystal the ionic valency of X is low, and its co-ordination number with regard to OH^- is high, the polarising effect of X on OH^- is small. Conversely, if the ionic valency of X is high, and its co-ordination number is small, the polarising effect on the OH^- ion is high, and hence the tendency to form hydroxyl bonds is significant.

The polarising effect of the cation in the crystal of a hydroxyl compound, and hence the tendency to produce hydroxyl bonds, is measured by the ratio

$$\frac{\text{charge on cation}}{\text{co-ordination number of cation}}.$$

The magnitude of this polarising effect in a number of crystals is shown in Table 13.4. It is seen from Table 13.4 that the more basic the hydroxide, the less likely is the presence of hydroxyl bonds in its crystals. If the degree of polarisation is excessive the hydrogen atom may leave one ion to join another to produce a molecule of water:

$$X^+\left[H—\overset{..}{\underset{..}{O}}:\right]^-\cdots\cdots\left[H—\overset{..}{\underset{..}{O}}:\right]^- X^+ = X^+ + H_2O + :\overset{..}{\underset{..}{O}}:^{2-} + X^+$$

Such a mechanism may explain the instability of carbon compounds with more than one hydroxyl group attached to the same carbon atom.

Table 13.4.   *Bond Length O—O in Crystals of certain Metallic Hydroxides*

Compound (regarded as ionised)		Crystal structure	Co-ordination number of cation	Polarising effect on OH^-	Bond length O—O, Å
No OH bonds	LiOH	F.c.c. layer; Li^+ in tetrahedral holes	4	$\frac{1}{4}$	3·60
	KOH	Rock-salt	6	$\frac{1}{6}$	—
	$Ca(OH)_2$	CdI_2 layer	6	$\frac{1}{3}$	3·36
	$Mg(OH)_2$	CdI_2 layer	6	$\frac{1}{3}$	3·22
OH bonds	$Zn(OH)_2$†	Tetrahedral	4	$\frac{1}{2}$	2·83
	$Al(OH)_3$	Close-packed layer	6	$\frac{1}{2}$	2·78
	$B(OH)_3$	Layer	3	1	2·70
	$Te(OH)_6$		6	1	2·76
	Ice				2·76

The length of the hydrogen bridge. The length of the hydrogen bridge (Table 13.5) varies with the nature of the atoms bound to the hydrogen atom.

Table 13.5.   *The Length of the Hydrogen Bridge*

Bond	Compound in which bridge occurs	Length of bridge
F—H····F	H_2F_2	2·55
F—H····F	KHF_2	2·26
	NH_4HF_2	2·32
O—H····O	KH_2PO_4	2·54
	$(NH_4)_2H_3IO_6$	2·60
	$CO(NH_2)_2,H_2O_2$	2·63
	$B(OH)_3$	2·71 ⎫
	$Te(OH)_6$	
	$Zn(OH)_2$	
	$Al(OH)_3$	⎬ Hydroxyl bonds
	$AlO·OH$	2·71
	$FeO·OH$	2·70
	$C(CH_2OH)_4$	2·70
	Ice	2·76 ⎭
N—H····F	NH_4HF_2	2·80
	NH_4F	2·63
	$N_2H_6F_2$	2·62
N—H····O	CH_3CONH_2	2·86
	$CO(NH_2)_2,H_2O_2$	3·00
N—H····N	NH_3	3·38
	NH_4N_3	2·97

† It is interesting to note that the four hydroxides in Table 13.4 which form hydroxyl bonds are weak acids. None of them, however, gives rise to simple well-characterised salts. The aluminates and zincates are complex oxides, the borate ion is complex (p. 499) and orthotelluric acid, H_6TeO_6 is dibasic only.

Table 13.6. *Comparison of the Hydrogen Bridge Lengths with other dimensions of the Atoms or Ions concerned*

1	2	3	4	5	6	7
Nature of bridge	Rough mean value of bridge length from Table 13.5	Sum of covalent radii	Sum of ionic radii	Sum of van der Waals radii	See text	See text
N—H····N	3·0	1·40	5·94	3·0	2·55	3·45
N—H····O	2·9	1·36	4·23	2·9	2·45	3·35
N—H····F	2·7	1·34	3·83	2·85	2·40	3·30
O—H····O	2·7	1·32	3·52	2·80	2·14	3·04
O—H····F				2·75	2·09	2·99
F—H····F	2·3	1·28	2·72	2·70	2·07	2·97

The length of the hydrogen bridge may be compared with the lengths of other possible forms of bonds between the bridged atoms. Column 2 of Table 13.6 gives the approximate mean values of the lengths of the types of hydrogen bridge, X—H····Y, set out in Table 13.5. Columns 3, 4, and 5 in Table 13.6 give the bond lengths between the atoms X and Y computed respectively for covalent, ionic, and van der Waals bonds, neglecting the presence of the hydrogen atom. Column 6 gives the bridge length on the assumption that the bridge is made up of the sum of (i) the covalent bond length X—H, (ii) the covalent radius of the hydrogen atom, 0·3, (iii) an increase of 0·05 due to the influence of the hydrogen bond on the covalent bond, (iv) the van der Waals radius of the atom Y. The figures in column 7 are calculated in the same way as for column 6, except that the covalent radius of hydrogen, 0·3, is replaced by the van der Waals radius of 1·2. It is seen from Table 13.6 that the sums of the van der Waals radii of the atoms X and Y (column 5) approach most nearly and regularly the approximate mean values of hydrogen bridge lengths.

The position of a proton in a hydrogen bridge. It has been generally assumed that a hydrogen bridge, X—H····Y is formed with little change of the original bond length, X—H, and also that the three nuclei, X, H, and Y, are collinear. There is no evidence that these assumptions are correct, and in certain cases there is evidence that the assumptions require modification. In the highly symmetrical structure of ice, in which both X and Y represent O atoms, it has been argued that the arrangements X—H····Y and X····H—Y are both possible, and under certain conditions the proton may oscillate between them (p. 385). Electron diffraction analysis has shown that the three atoms in the hydroxyl bonds of boric acid (p. 498) are not collinear.

THE PHYSICAL PROPERTIES OF COMPOUNDS CONTAINING HYDROGEN BONDS

Melting points and boiling points. The effect of hydrogen bond formation on the physical properties of a compound can be seen by comparing the melting points and boiling points of a series of compounds which might contain molecules linked by hydrogen bonds, with those of compounds in which hydrogen bonds could not exist. This is done in Table 13.7.

The rise in the melting point or boiling point which occurs when there is a possibility of hydrogen bridge formation is striking.

Table 13.7. *The Effect of Hydrogen Bond Formation on Melting and Boiling Points*

Compound containing N or F and H	m.p. °C	b.p. °C	Corresponding compound not forming H bonds	m.p. °C	b.p. °C
H_3N	-77.7	-33.4	F_3N	-208.5	-129
$C_2H_5NH_2$	-81	19	C_2H_5Cl	-138.7	12.5
$C_6H_5NH_2$	6.2	182	C_6H_5Cl	-50	132
HCN	-12	25	C_2H_2	-81	-54
HF	-83.7	19.5	HCl	-114	-85

Table 13.8 sets out the melting points and boiling points of a number of hydroxyl compounds, and of the corresponding compounds in which OH has been replaced by chlorine. The higher atomic weight of chlorine (35·5), compared with the group weight of OH (17), should tend to make the physical constants of the chlorine compounds higher than those of the corresponding OH compounds.† The effect due to the

Table 13.8. *The Effect of Hydroxyl Bond Formation on Melting and Boiling Points*

OH compound	m.p. °C	b.p. °C	Chlorine compound	m.p. °C	b.p. °C
H_2O	0	100	Cl_2O	-11.6	2
CH_3OH	-97.8	64.5	CH_3Cl	-97.7	-27.3
C_2H_5OH	-117.3	78.5	C_2H_5Cl	-138.7	12.5
C_6H_5OH	41	181.4	C_6H_5Cl	-50	132
Resorcinol $m\text{-}C_6H_4(OH)_2$	110	276.5	$m\text{-}C_6H_4Cl_2$	53	173.4
Glycerol $C_3H_5(OH)_3$	17.9	290	$C_3H_5Cl_3$	-14.7	157

atomic weights, however, is completely masked by the much greater effect due to hydrogen bridge formation between molecules which contain hydroxyl groups. As a result of the bridge formation polymerisation occurs, thus:

$$nC_2H_5OH \rightleftharpoons \underset{\underset{C_2H_5}{|}}{O-H}\cdots\underset{\underset{C_2H_5}{|}}{O-H}\cdots\underset{\underset{C_2H_5}{|}}{O-H}\cdots$$

The presence of polymeric molecules in the liquid raises the boiling point and the melting point of the compound above the values that would be predicted for the monomeric substance, because energy is necessary to break the hydroxyl bonds. The elevation of the melting point is less marked than that of the boiling point because the rupture of a few bonds enables a crystal to liquefy, but all must be ruptured to enable the liquid to vaporise to a monomeric gas.

A hydrogen bond may be formed between, say, an OH group and an atom of oxygen, fluorine, or nitrogen in the same molecule, and a ring structure may be obtained, as for example:

† The dipole moments of the compounds listed must have an effect on their melting and boiling points, but this effect is not considered here.

salicyl aldehyde, or
o-hydroxy benzaldehyde

o-nitropheno

The formation of such intramolecular hydrogen bonds must diminish the formation of intermolecular bonds, and hence the above compounds would be expected to have lower melting points and boiling points than the corresponding *m*- and *p*-compounds, in which the distances of separation of the side-chains are too great for hydrogen bond formation. That this prediction is realised is shown by the data:

		m.p. °C	b.p. °C
Hydroxybenzaldehyde	*o*-	−7	197
	m-	106	240
	p-	116	sublimes
Nitrophenol	*o*-	45	214
	m-	96	194
	p-	114	279

Interesting curves are obtained by plotting the boiling points of the hydrides of the elements in the N sub-Groups of Groups IV, V, VI, and VII against the Period numbers 2, 3, 4, and 5 as shown in Fig. 13.3. The first three curves (Groups VI, V, and VII) show steady falls for the elements in Periods 5, 4, and 3, followed by a sharp rise for the elements O, F, and N in Period 2. These are the most electronegative of the elements, and the rise of the boiling point may be accounted for by the polymerisation of their hydrides by the formation of hydrogen bonds. The curve of the Group IV elements falls all the way from tin to carbon, since hydrogen bonds are not formed between methane molecules.

A somewhat similar set of curves is obtained by plotting the melting points of the same hydrides against the Period numbers, Fig. 13.4.

Dielectric constant. Compounds which undergo polymerisation by hydrogen bond formation have abnormally high dielectric constants. The relation between dipole moment and dielectric constant is given for gases by the equation for the total molar polarisation (p. 305)

$$\frac{k-1}{k+2} \cdot \frac{M}{\rho} = \frac{4}{3}\pi N \left(\alpha + \frac{\mu^2}{3k_b T} \cdot \right)$$

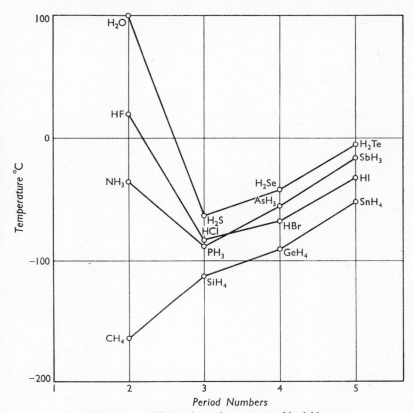

Fig. 13.3. Boiling points of sequences of hydrides.

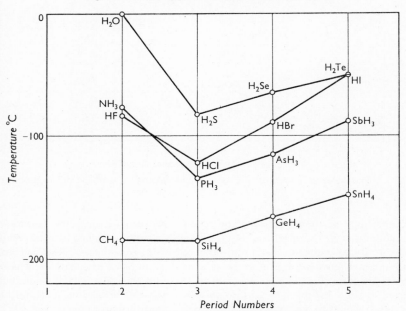

Fig. 13.4. Melting points of sequences of hydrides.

Since k is not much greater than 1, to a first approximation the equation for gases may be written

$$k-1 = \frac{4\pi N\rho}{M}\left(\alpha + \frac{\mu^2}{3k_bT}\right).$$

If the induced polarisation is neglected,

$$k = 1 + C\mu^2,$$

where C is a constant for a given temperature.

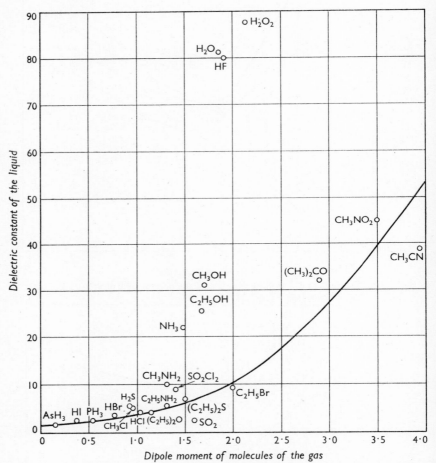

Fig. 13.5.   The dielectric constants of certain liquids plotted against the dipole moments of the molecules in the gaseous state.

A curve may be drawn showing the relation between the dielectric constants of certain liquids at 20°C (for HF and H_2O_2 the values must be obtained by extrapolation) and their dipole moments measured either when the substances concerned are in solution in non-polar solvents or in the gaseous state, in order to avoid dipole associa- tion. The diagram (Fig. 13.5) shows that the curve for molecules which would not be expected to show hydrogen bond formation is reasonably consistent, and that mole- cules which would be polymerised by hydrogen bond formation have dielectric constants which lie well above the curve. It is not possible to derive any simple relation for these deviations because the d.p.m. of a polymer depends on its configuration. If the polymer is linear, as for the trimer of HCN,

$$H-C{\equiv}N\cdots H{-}C{\equiv}N\cdots H{-}C{\equiv}N$$

the d.p.m. will be three times that of the monomer.
    Since

$$\mu_{trimer} = 3\mu_{monomer},$$

and

$$M_{trimer} = 3M_{monomer},$$

therefore $k-1$ for the trimer is three times that for the monomer. This is roughly in agreement with the observed value. But if polymerisation leads to a zig-zag chain or a ring structure, the d.p.m. of the polymer may be less than that of the monomer.

INFRARED SPECTROSCOPY AND THE HYDROGEN BRIDGE

For the discussion of the effect of hydrogen bridge formation on absorption spectra it is convenient to divide substances into two classes: those in which hydrogen bridges are so strong that they are not easily dissociated, and those in which the hydrogen bridges are weak, so that the substance is an equilibrium mixture of bridged and unbridged molecules.

Substances containing strong hydrogen bridges. Many substances containing the hydroxyl group when dissolved in carbon tetrachloride absorb light of long wave length. The fundamental frequency associated with the stretching of the OH group is 3700 cm^{-1}; the first overtone is 7400 cm^{-1}. The bands observed for substances containing the OH group are shown in Table 13.9. It is found that the substances can be differentiated by their absorption spectra into the classes A and B as shown in Table 13.10.

Table 13.9.   *Infrared Spectra of Compounds containing the OH Group*

Bands	(a) A band near 7400 cm^{-1} consisting of a single peak	Two bands near 3700 cm^{-1}:	
		(b) a narrow band near 3600 cm^{-1}	(c) a wide band near 3300 cm^{-1}
Band related to	(OH)	(OH)	(OH$\cdots$O)

Table 13.10.   *Compounds containing the OH Group classed according to their types of Absorption Spectra*

A Compounds which show bands (a), (b), and (c) (Table 13.9)		B Compounds which show band (c) only
Aldol	*o*-hydroxybenzonitrile	Acetyl acetone
acetyl benzoin oxime	methanol	2,4-dinitroresorcinol
benzaldioxime	*m*-nitrophenol	4,6-dinitroresorcinol
ethyl tartrate	*p*-nitrophenol	*o*-hydroxyacetophenone
hydroquinone	phenol	methyl salicylate
m-hydroxybenzaldehyde	resorcinol	salicyl aldehyde
p-hydroxybenzaldehyde	triphenol carbinol	

The compounds in Class A, whose spectra show all three bands, are capable of forming intermolecular hydrogen bridges, but their configurations prohibit the formation of intramolecular bridges; hence ring structures for their molecules are not possible. The spectra of these compounds reveal the presence of both OH groups and hydrogen bridges. If, for example, an alcohol dissolved in an inert solvent is examined for absorption in the range near 3000–3700 cm^{-1}, it is found that increase in temperature or increase in dilution strengthens absorption near 3600 cm^{-1}, and weakens absorption near 3300 cm^{-1}. This confirms that absorption near 3600 cm^{-1} is related to the unperturbed OH group, and that near 3300 cm^{-1} is related to the hydrogen bridge.

Examination of the wave numbers corresponding to maximum absorption for a particular substance shows that the restoring force governing the stretching of the OH bond is reduced by hydrogen bond formation. For instance, for ethyl alcohol, the maximum absorption corresponding to the monomeric substance is at 3638 cm^{-1}, and the peak of the broad band corresponding to hydrogen bond formation is at 3325 cm^{-1}. Since

$$\text{frequency of vibration} = \frac{1}{2\pi}\left(\frac{\text{restoring force per unit displacement}}{\text{mass}}\right)^{\frac{1}{2}}$$

the band with the lower peak wave number corresponds to a smaller restoring force.

The compounds in Class B are capable of forming either intermolecular or intra-molecular hydrogen bridges. The formation of intramolecular bridges, leading to ring structures, appears to be so complete that the bands at 7400 and at 3600 cm^{-1}, both relating to the group OH are suppressed, but the band at 3300 cm^{-1} relating to the hydrogen bridge is present.

Substances containing weak hydrogen bridges. Certain compounds (other than those mentioned in Table 13.10) show absorption in the region 7400 cm^{-1}, but the band shows not one peak, but two. Among the compounds which behave thus are *o*-chlorophenol and catechol (*o*-dihydroxy benzene). Pauling suggests that one peak is to be correlated with the stretching of the simple OH bond, and the other with the stretching of the OH bond modified by intramolecular hydrogen bridge formation. For example, for trichlorophenol (which shows only one peak at 6890 cm^{-1}) only one configuration of the molecule is possible; the apparently alternative forms are identical. The molecule of *o*-chlorophenol, however, has two possible non-equivalent configurations.

Two identical configurations of trichlorophenol

Two different configurations of *o*-chlorophenol

The absorption band of *o*-chlorophenol shows two peaks, one at 7050 cm^{-1} and the other at 6910 cm^{-1}. On Pauling's suggestion, the first peak is correlated with the trans form in which the OH group is unaffected by the Cl atom, and the second peak with the cis form, in which the OH group is modified by the presence of the chlorine atom, just as it is in trichlorophenol. The weak hydrogen bond in *o*-chlorophenol reduces the tendency of this substance to form intermolecular hydrogen bonds. Its melting and boiling points should therefore be lower than those of *m*- and *p*-chlorophenol. The experimental values are:

	m.p. °C	b.p. °C
o-chlorophenol†	7, 0, −4	176
m-	29	214
p-	41	217

It may be mentioned that the stabilisation of chloral hydrate, one of the few organic compounds in which two OH groups are found attached to the same carbon atom, is to be explained by the formation of an intramolecular hydrogen bond:

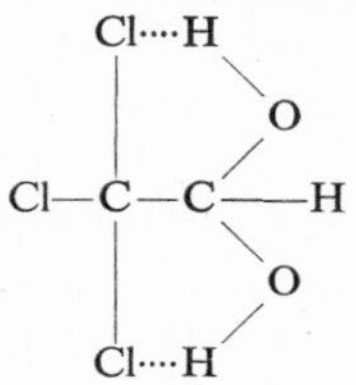

Correlation between length of hydrogen bond and change of frequency. The length of a hydrogen bond in a crystal can be determined from X-ray diffraction in many cases. If the change of stretching frequency consequent on the introduction of the hydrogen bond is plotted against the length of the bond, quite a good linear correlation is found, particularly where the hydrogen bonds are strong. Each type of hydrogen bond investigated, O—H····O, N—H····O and N—H····N, has its own linear correlation. The method is not so easily applied where the hydrogen bonds are short. The absorption bands are apt to be broad, and the spectrum may be confused.

THE HYDROGEN BRIDGE AND CRYSTAL STRUCTURE

The previous pages have described briefly how the properties of compounds in the liquid state or in solution are modified by the existence of hydrogen bridges. The presence of hydrogen bridges has equally important effects on the crystal structures of compounds in which they occur.

Ionic crystals. If the hydrogen bridge is present in the anion of a metallic salt the crystal may contain:

(i) finite ions, as the $(F—H····H)^-$ ion in potassium hydrogen fluoride,
(ii) infinite chains of ions as in $NaHCO_3$ (p. 371),
(iii) infinite three-dimensional structures as in KH_2PO_4 and in $(NH_4)_2H_3IO_6$.

If the hydrogen bridge extends between the cation and the anion of a salt, the crystal structure consists of an infinite complex in which the ionic close-packing is modified to give a more open structure which is not distinguishable from one based on covalent bonds. Examples are furnished by $N_2H_6F_2$, hydrazinium fluoride, which crystallises with a layer lattice, and by NH_4F and NH_4HF_2 (p. 693), which crystallise in three-dimensional complexes.

In all the above examples the hydrogen bridges are hydrogen bonds. The hydroxyl bond also occurs in ionic crystals, particularly in those in which the structural units are regarded as metal cations and OH^- anions. Here again one of the effects of the presence of hydroxyl bonds is the conversion of a close-packed lattice into a more open covalent structure. Of this the structures of $Al(OH)_3$ (p. 535), and of $Zn(OH)_2$ (p. 459), are good examples.

Covalent crystals. Covalent compounds capable of forming intermolecular hydrogen bridges crystallise in infinite complexes. Examples are crystalline ammonia, which

† The melting points are those of the three allotropic forms of o-chlorophenol.

contains hydrogen bonds, and crystallises in a three-dimensional complex, and ice (p. 385) and boric acid (p. 497), both of which form infinite complexes containing hydroxyl bonds.

WATER

The most familiar oxide of hydrogen is water. Certain physical constants of water are given in Table 13.12, p. 392. It is not thought necessary in this book to discuss the physical and chemical properties of water in detail and at length, and therefore only three aspects of water will be considered (i) its acid-base properties, (ii) the structure of ice and of liquid water, (iii) the part played by water as "water of crystallisation", and as a ligand in co-ordination compounds.

THE ACID-BASE PROPERTIES OF WATER

In liquid water the molecules are in equilibrium with ions, thus:
$$2H_2O \rightleftharpoons H_3O^+ + OH^-.$$

By a number of independent methods the degree of ionisation of water at 25° has been found to be $1 \cdot 81 \times 10^{-9}$, and the concentration of H_3O^+ ions to be $1 \cdot 00 \times 10^{-7}$ gram ion per litre. The ionic product of water, K_w (where $K_w =$ concentration in gram ions per litre of $[H_3O^+] \times$ concentration of $[OH^-]$) at 0° is $0 \cdot 113 \times 10^{-14}$, at 25° is $1 \cdot 008 \times 10^{-14}$, and at 50° is $5 \cdot 474 \times 10^{-14}$. Water is at the same time both an acid and a base according to all the principal proposals which have been put forward for defining acids and bases.

Lowry and Bronsted defined an acid as a proton donor, and a base as a proton acceptor. According to these definitions, water is at once an acid and a base because in the reaction:
$$H_2O + HOH = H_3O^+ + OH^-,$$

the first molecule of water acts as a base by accepting a proton from the second molecule, which thus acts as an acid. A compound such as acetic acid is an acid because on addition to water it transfers protons to water molecules:
$$CH_3COOH + H_2O = H_3O^+ + CH_3COO^-.$$

Ammonia is a base because it accepts protons from water molecules:
$$NH_3 + H_2O = NH_4^+ + OH^-,$$

and the ammonium ion is an acid because it donates protons to the base OH^-:
$$NH_4^+ + Na^+ + OH^- = NH_3 + H_2O + Na^+.$$

Lewis made the suggestion, in contrast to that of Lowry and Bronsted, that an acid be defined as an electron acceptor, and a base as an electron donor. Water on this definition is again an acid and a base, as in the reaction:
$$H_2O + HOH = H_3O^+ + OH^-;$$

the first molecule of water donates electrons to the second molecule to form a new acid, H_3O^+ and a new base OH^-. By the same outlook acetic acid is an acid, and the acetate radical is a base because it is ready to give up an electron. The equation for the dissociation of acetic acid is interpreted:
$$\underset{\text{acid}}{CH_3COOH} + \underset{\text{base}}{H_2O} = \underset{\text{acid}}{H_3O^+} + \underset{\text{base}}{CH_3COO^-}.$$

There are, however, acid-base systems in which hydrogen plays no part, for example, a reaction in the sulphur dioxide acid-base system is described by the equation:
$$\underset{\text{base}}{(Na^+)_2(SO_3{}^{2-})} + \underset{\text{acid}}{(SO^{2+})(Cl^-)_2} = \underset{\text{salt}}{2NaCl} + \underset{\text{solvent}}{2SO_2}.$$

This equation is analogous to that describing the neutralisation of sodium hydroxide by hydrochloric acid:
$$NaOH + HCl = NaCl + H_2O.$$

The Lewis definition has the advantage that it covers the neutralisation of thionyl chloride in sulphur dioxide, as well as the neutralisation of hydrochloric acid in water. The definition of Lowry and Bronsted cannot be applied to reactions in sulphur dioxide.

Both the Lowry and Bronsted definition and that of Lewis achieve generalisation, but at the cost of not being particularly helpful in any given instance; they are more useful in theoretical discussion than in the workaday affairs of the laboratory. For practical purposes the definitions of Cady and Elsey are at once precise, and also of wide application. They are as follows:

An *acid* is a substance which when dissolved in a solvent gives rise to cations which are identical with the cations yielded by the solvent.

A *base* is a substance which when dissolved in a solvent gives rise to anions which are identical with the anions yielded by the solvent.

These definitions again describe the dual nature of pure water, if water is taken to be both the substance dissolved and the solvent.

THE STRUCTURES OF ICE AND LIQUID WATER

Ice is polymorphic. The form of ice obtained by freezing water at atmospheric pressure is known as ice I. Ice I crystallises in the hexagonal system. The structure cannot be ionic; ionic crystals melt at high temperatures, and give highly conducting liquids, and ice shows neither of these properties. The arrangement of oxygen atoms in the ice crystals is clear and definite. X-ray analysis has shown that the oxygen nuclei are arranged in puckered layers; each layer consists of six-membered rings. Each oxygen nucleus is co-ordinated to four other oxygen nuclei, three in its own layer, and one in the next layer above or below (Fig. 13.6). In this structure the oxygen atoms occupy the positions of the silicon atoms in tridymite (p. 604).

The distance of separation of the oxygen nuclei is 2·76. The symmetry of the arrangement is hexagonal, and the point distribution is that of the wurtzite structure. The structure of ice, however, is not static; it is computed, for example, that thermal vibration at 0° causes the oxygen nuclei to move with a root mean square amplitude of 0·4. The positions of the hydrogen nuclei are not accurately known. It is assumed that the co-ordinated oxygen atoms are linked by hydroxyl bonds. The crystallisation of water vapour to ice takes place with very little distortion. In water vapour the OH distance is 0·958 and the angle HOH is 104° 31′. In ice the angle HOH is tetrahedral, 109° 28′, and the OH distance is 1·0; the decrease in the frequency of the infrared absorption band when the H—O····H bridge is formed, corresponds to an increase in the OH distance from 0·958 to 1·0. Hence it would appear at first sight to be satisfactory to assign hydrogen nuclei to points on each of the four lines joining the co-ordinated oxygen atoms, such that two hydrogen atoms are 1·0 from a given oxygen atom (position *A*) and two hydrogen atoms are 1·76 from the same oxygen atom (position *B*).

Although this arrangement appears to be static, it is possible for a hydrogen nucleus to oscillate along a given oxygen-oxygen linkage between positions *A* and *B*, but since any given oxygen atom can exert only two covalent bonds, it follows that the movement of one hydrogen atom involves corresponding movements of other hydrogen atoms throughout a portion of the crystal. The smallest unit in which such a co-operative movement of hydrogen nuclei can occur is a ring of six oxygen atoms (Fig. 13.6). It has been calculated that there is an energy barrier of 2·2 kcal/mole restricting the movement of a hydrogen nucleus between positions *A* and *B*, assuming that no other change occurs in the crystal at the same time. If the necessary co-operative movements take place in a ring of six oxygen atoms, but no other change occurs, then the energy barrier is about 10 kcal. It has been estimated that at 0° at any instant a movement of a hydrogen nucleus is occurring in only 1 in 10^9 of the water molecules in ice.

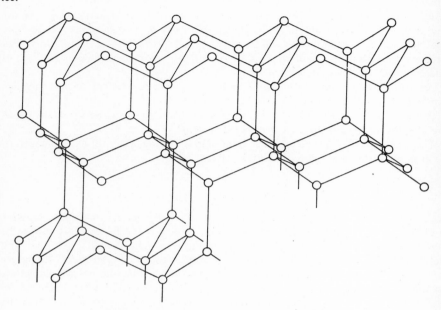

Fig. 13.6.   Arrangement of oxygen atoms in ice I.

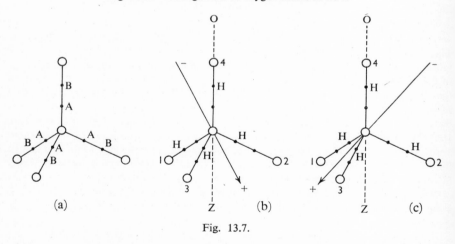

Fig. 13.7.

The movement of the hydrogen nuclei in ice causes the crystal to depart from complete symmetry, and accounts for the three following properties of ice:

(i) the absence of piezo- and pyro-electric properties,
(ii) the residual entropy of 0·82 cal/degree/mole,†
(iii) the high dielectric constant of ice at room temperature.

† This is not due to the rotation of the water molecules because deuterium oxide, D_2O, has almost the same value (0·77 cal/degree/mole).

At 0° ice has a dielectric constant of 80 when an oscillating potential of low frequency is used (300 c/s); the dielectric constant falls with temperature, reaching 4 at $-60°C$. Hence above $-60°C$ ice contains dipoles which are sufficiently free to rotate. The rotation of the *dipoles* does not require the rotation of the molecules; the effect is produced by movements of the hydrogen atoms along the lines joining the co-ordinated oxygen atoms, from positions A to positions B, or vice versa. For example, suppose hydrogen nuclei are at the four positions A^2, A^3, B^1, B^4, Fig. 13.7(a)(b). If the hydrogen nucleus at B^1 moves to A^1 (Fig. 13.7(c)), and the hydrogen nucleus at A^2 moves to B^2

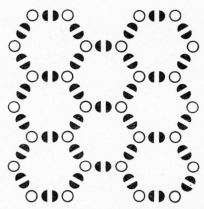

(Fig. 13.7(c)), since all hydrogen nuclei are equivalent, the effect is the same as a rotation of the structure through 120° about the axis OZ. If a hydrogen atom at position A is equivalent to a positive sector of the central oxygen atom, and a hydrogen atom at position B is equivalent to a negative sector of the central oxygen atom (p. 372), then the linear motion has produced a displacement of charge equivalent to the rotation of the original dipole through 120°.

A "mean structure" for ice may be depicted by representing half a hydrogen atom in every position A and B in the structure. The diagram in Fig. 13.8 shows such a

Fig. 13.8. A mean structure for ice.

representation for part of one layer of oxygen atoms in the crystal. The results of neutron diffraction experiments on ice made from heavy water agree closely with those predicted for a "mean structure".

Liquid water. Several careful studies have been made of the structure of liquid water, using X-ray, Raman spectra, and other techniques, but no model has been proposed which is universally accepted. It is likely that liquid water consists of mobile groups of molecules, each group having a pseudo-crystalline structure. Bernal and Fowler have suggested that the tridymite structure of ice I may be present in water, and that it is in equilibrium with a structure analogous to that of quartz (these structures are composed of SiO_4 tetrahedra with shared corners). Quartz has a higher density than tridymite, and hence the existence of variant forms of molecular arrangement in liquid water could account for the change of density of water with temperature. Later workers have suggested that the form regarded as quartz by Bernal and Fowler is better regarded as a close-packed structure of oxygen atoms, each of which has the co-ordination number 12.

WATER OF CONSTITUTION

The quantitative analysis of many crystalline substances suggests that they contain water. Sometimes water can be extracted from a substance by heating or reduction of pressure without any profound alteration in the properties of the substance, but more frequently the removal of water leads to disruption of the original substance. Water can be present in a crystalline material in the following ways:

(1) As molecules enclosed in the interstices of a rigid lattice framework in which the water molecules play no part. Dehydration and hydration have no effect on the structure.

(2) In a few instances a converse arrangement may be found in which molecules of an inert substance, such as methane or an inert gas, may be held in the open-work structure of ice.

(3) As molecules packed between the layers of a layer structure such as that of clay. On desiccation the layers come closer together; the structure becomes more compact, but its nature is not changed.

(4) As water of crystallisation in salts.

(5) As a ligand (p. 950) in co-ordination compounds.

The hydroxyl group also acts as a ligand in co-ordination compounds. The compounds do not contain water as H_2O molecules, but may often be caused to yield water by disproportionation:

$$6OH^- = 3H_2O + 3O^{2-}.$$

Quantitative analysis does not distinguish such co-ordination compounds from hydrated oxides, for example $Na_2[Sn(OH)_6]$ has been regarded as $Na_2SnO_3,3H_2O$.

Classes 1, 2, and 3 require no discussion. The remaining classes 4 and 5 will be briefly discussed.

The water molecule is a tetrahedral structure, and may be regarded as a sphere with two positive and two negative sectors (p. 372). The fundamental effect which accounts for the presence of water of crystallisation in salts, or as a ligand in co-ordination compounds (Classes 4 and 5 above) is the attraction of the positively charged metallic cation for the negative sectors of the oxygen atom in the water molecule. This attraction can result in the formation of two kinds of linkage (a) a covalent linkage present in aquo-complexes, and (b) an electrostatic attraction present in crystalline hydrates.

Aquo-complexes. Many examples are known of aquo-complexes in which a water molecule plays the part of a neutral ligand, as for example in the complex cation of trivalent chromium $[Cr(H_2O)_6]^{3+}[Cl^-]_3$. Aquo-complex ions retain their identity even in aqueous solution. The water molecules in such complexes can be replaced by other groups by chemical methods, and there is no doubt that there is a covalent link between the metal and the oxygen atom of the water molecule.

It is noteworthy that only the transition elements with partly occupied d orbitals in the valence shell form stable hydrates of this type. It is therefore reasonable to suppose that some form of double bonding (πd) takes place by the overlap of the d orbitals of the metal and the p orbitals of the oxygen atoms of the water molecules.

Water of crystallisation. The water present in salts as water of crystallisation is bound by the electrostatic attraction of the negative sectors of the oxygen atoms of the water molecules for the metallic cation. The metals which attract water in this way have no partly occupied d orbitals in their valence shells, and hence no πd bonds can be formed between the metallic atoms and the oxygen atoms. Examples of hydrated cations are found in the salts:

$$[Be,4H_2O]SO_4 \qquad [Zn,6H_2O](BrO_3)_2 \qquad [Nd,9H_2O](BrO_3)_3 \qquad [Li,3H_2O]ClO_4$$
$$[Li,3H_2O]BF_4 \qquad [Ca,2H_2O]SO_4 \qquad [R,6H_2O]ClO_4$$

R may be Mg, Mn, Fe, Co, Ni, Zn, and ClO_4 may be replaced by BF_4; all these hydrated salts are isomorphous. The structures of these hydrates are more elaborate than those produced by the simple grouping of water molecules round a metallic cation, because the existence of hydrogen bonds and hydroxyl bonds which are normally developed when oxygen and hydrogen atoms are in fairly close contact, has an important influence on the crystal structure. These bonds form links not only between neighbouring water molecules in the crystal, but also between water molecules and the salt anions if those contain oxygen or fluorine atoms.

Since the predominant force between the metallic cation and the oxygen atoms of the water molecules is one of electrostatic attraction, the oxygen atoms must be packed round the metal in accordance with its co-ordination number for oxygen. Many examples are known in which the ratio of the number of cations to the number of water molecules is just right to permit such packing, but there are also cases in which the number of water molecules present is less than, or greater than, the co-ordination number of the cation. Examples of the three cases are:

(a) The number of water molecules associated with each cation is equal to the co-ordination number of the cation: $[Be,4H_2O]SO_4$, $[Ni,6H_2O]SO_4$, $[Li,3H_2O]ClO_4$, $[K(H_2O)_6Al(H_2O)_6](SO_4)_2$, $[Sr,8H_2O]OH$.

(b) The number of water molecules in the hydated molecule is less than the co-ordination number of the cation: Li_2SO_4,H_2O, $CaSO_42H_2O$.

(c) The number of water molecules in the hydrated molecule is greater than the co-ordination number of the cation: $NiSO_4,7H_2O$, $CuSO_4,5H_2O$.

Some of these examples are studied further in the next paragraphs, where it will be shown that the correct co-ordination number with respect to oxygen is attained by

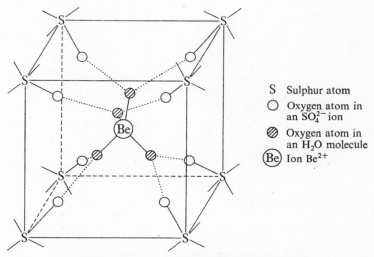

S   Sulphur atom

O   Oxygen atom in an SO_4^{2-} ion

⊘   Oxygen atom in an H_2O molecule

(Be)   Ion Be^{2+}

Fig. 13.9.   Structure of crystalline $BeSO_4,4H_2O$.

the metal cation in all cases, but the particular oxygen atoms concerned may be either those of the water molecules or those of the anions. In all cases the crystal is strapped together by the development of hydrogen and hydroxyl bonds between the water molecules and the anions.

(a) *The number of water molecules associated with each cation is equal to the co-ordination number of the cation.* In, say, the crystal of $BeSO_4,4H_2O$, there are two units, the tetrahedral $[Be,4H_2O]^{2+}$ cations, and the tetrahedral SO_4^{2-} anions. The cations and anions are situated as in a CsCl structure. Negative sectors of four water molecules are in contact with a Be^{2+} ion at the centre of the structure. The two positive sectors of each water molecule are in contact with the negative sectors of oxygen atoms of two SO_4^{2-} ions, one at each of two cube corners (Fig. 13.9). The links between the H_2O molecule and the SO_4^{2-} ions are in fact hydrogen bonds.

In the crystal of lithium perchlorate trihydrate $LiClO_4,3H_2O$, each Li^+ ion is surrounded by six water molecules. Each water molecule is in contact with two Li^+ ions, and is linked by two hydrogen bonds to oxygen atoms in different ClO_4^- tetrahedra. The co-ordination number of the ion Li^+ with respect to oxygen is six, although this is not revealed at all by the chemical formula. The structure of the hydrates, $RMX_4,6H_2O$, where R may be Mg, Mn, Fe, Co, Ni, Zn, and M may be Cl or B, when X is O or F, is identical with that of lithium perchlorate trihydrate, except that only one-half of the Li^+ sites are occupied by R^{2+}.

(b) *The number of molecules of water in the hydrated molecule is less than the coordination number of the cation.* Gypsum, $CaSO_4,2H_2O$, may be taken as an example of such a hydrate. Fig. 13.10 is a simplified diagram of the relations between the

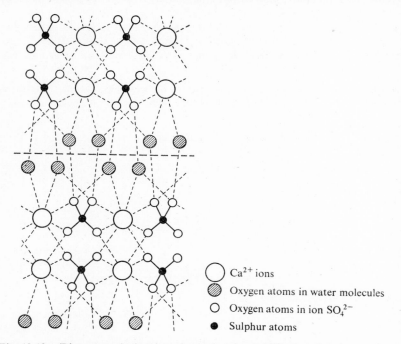

Ca^{2+} ions
Oxygen atoms in water molecules
Oxygen atoms in ion SO$_4^{2-}$
Sulphur atoms

Fig. 13.10. Diagrammatic drawing of a section through the crystal structure of gypsum through the layers. The heavy broken line indicates the cleavage, which breaks only O—H—O bonds. (Reproduced by permission from *Structural Inorganic Chemistry* by A. F. Wells, 2nd edition, 1950, Oxford University Press.)

ions Ca^{2+} and SO_4^{2-} and water molecules. Each Ca^{2+} ion is in contact with two water molecules, and with six oxygen atoms from SO_4^{2-} tetrahedra. The lattice is a layer lattice. Each layer consists of four planes: (a) one plane of water molecules, (b) and (c) two planes of alternate Ca^{2+} ions and SO_4^{2-} ions, and (d) one plane of water molecules. Each water molecule is orientated with a negative sector (lone pair) towards a Ca^{2+} ion, and the two positive sectors (hydrogen atoms) towards the oxygen atoms of SO_4^{2-} ions. The three lone pairs of an oxygen atom in a SO_4^{2-} ion are directed towards one Ca^{2+} ion, and two water molecules, or only two of the three are utilised, and these go to Ca^{2+} ions.

(c) *The number of water molecules in the hydrated molecule is greater than the co-ordination number of the cation.* An example of a hydrate of this kind is $CuSO_4,5H_2O$. This example is not a simple one, but it is chosen because of its familiarity. The co-ordination number of the ion Cu^{2+} is six, and in the crystal four of the six oxygen atoms are from water molecules and the other two from SO_4^{2-} ions. One water molecule per Cu^{2+} ion is *not directly bound* to the ion at all, but with its negative sector it forms two hydroxyl bonds with water molecules bound to the Cu^{2+} ion, and, with its positive sectors, two hydrogen bonds to the oxygen atoms of

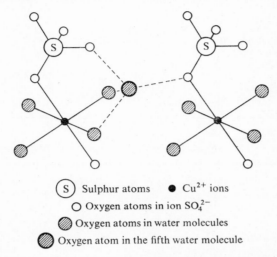

Ⓢ Sulphur atoms   ● Cu^{2+} ions

◯ Oxygen atoms in ion SO_4^{2-}

◑ Oxygen atoms in water molecules

◑ Oxygen atom in the fifth water molecule

Fig. 13.11. The position occupied by the fifth water molecule in crystalline $CuSO_4,5H_2O$. The oxygen atom in the molecule is co-ordinated to two other water molecules, and to two oxygen atoms in SO_4^{2-} ions.

the SO_4^{2-} ions. This arrangement is shown in the diagram (Fig. 13.11). The same principle, that the additional water molecule is bound to the other water molecules and to the oxygen atoms of the anion, also applies in nickel sulphate, $NiSO_4,7H_2O$.

DEUTERIUM

The nucleus of the ordinary hydrogen atom consists of one proton. Hydrogen consisting of atoms with this nuclear constitution is called protium. The nucleus of deuterium, known as a *deuteron*, consists of one neutron and one proton. Deuterium is an isotope of hydrogen, and the two isotopes, protium and deuterium, are related to one another in just the same way as the isotopes of any other element are related, that is the nuclei have the same atomic number but differ in the number of neutrons in the nuclei. Since the atomic numbers of protium and deuterium are the same, the atoms have the same electronic structures. Protium and deuterium have very nearly the same atomic volumes and molecular volumes, and therefore the electric fields about the nuclei must be nearly the same.

The isotopes of any given *heavy* element differ slightly in nuclear mass because of the difference in nuclear constitution. A gain of one neutron in a nucleus of mass number 100 results in a relative mass increase of one per cent. The chemical properties of all the isotopes of a heavy element are identical, since chemical properties depend on atomic number. The physical properties vary only in so far as they are dependent on differences of nuclear mass. Differences in mass spectra and in optical spectra are clearly detectable, but differences in other physical properties are too small to be detected experimentally.

Table 13.11. *Physical Properties of H_2, HD, and D_2*

Property	H_2	HD	D_2
m.p. °K	13·95	16·60	18·65
b.p. °K	20·38		23·6
Triple point, °K	—		18·72
Critical point, °K	33·24		38·35
Critical pressure, atm	12·807		16·432
Pressure at triple point, mm	53·8	95	128·5
Heat of fusion, cal mole^{-1}	28·0	37	47
Heat of evaporation, cal mole^{-1} at 195 mm	219·7	263	302·5
Zero point energy, cal	6184	5366	4395
Atomic weight	1·00813		2·01472

Table 13.12. *Physical Properties of Water and Deuterium Oxide*

Property	H_2O	D_2O
m.p. °C	0	3·82
b.p. °C	100	101·42
c.t. °C	374·2	371·5
Temperature of maximum density, °C	4·08	11·22
Molecular volume at 20°C	18·016	18·092
Dielectric constant at 0°C	81·5	80·7
D.P.M. in benzene at 25°C	1·76	1·78
,, in dioxan	1·86	1·87
Viscosity at 20°C	10·09	12·6
Solubility of NaCl, gm per 1000 gm	359	305

Table 13.13. *Effect of Replacement of H by D on the Melting and Boiling Points of certain Hydrides*

(Temperatures are in degrees K)

	m.p. X=H	m.p. X=D	Difference	b.p. X=H	b.p. X=D	Difference
Non-associated compounds						
CX_4	90·4	89	−1·4	—	—	—
C_6X_6	278·5	279·6	+1·1	353·1	352·2	−0·9
SX_2	187·5	187	−0·5	—	—	—
ClX	162·1	158·1	−4·0	188·1	191·6	+3·5
Compounds associated in the liquid, but not in the vapour						
NX_3	195·2	199·5	+4·3	239·7	242	+2·3
OX_2	273	276·8	+3·8	373	374·4	+1·4
XCN	259	261	+2·0	298·3	298·9	+0·6
Compound associated in the liquid and in the vapour						
FX				293·1	291·8	−1·3

The ratio of the mass numbers of deuterium and protium is approximately 2:1. The relative difference in mass numbers is sufficient to bring about big differences in physical properties between the molecules H_2 and D_2, and between corresponding compounds containing the atoms H and D.

The physical properties of the three molecules H_2, HD, and D_2 are given in Table 13.11.

ZERO-POINT ENERGY AND CHEMICAL REACTIVITY OF DEUTERIUM

The zero-point energy of a molecule is directly related to the mass of the atom. The energy of vibration of a diatomic molecule considered as a harmonic oscillator is given by

$$E = (n + \tfrac{1}{2})h\nu \quad \text{(p. 25)},$$

where n is an integer, h is Planck's constant, and ν is the frequency of vibration.

Now

$$\nu = \frac{1}{2\pi}\sqrt{\frac{k}{m}},$$

where k is the restoring force per unit displacement, and m is the mass of one of the atoms.

Hence

$$E = \frac{(n + \tfrac{1}{2})h}{2\pi}\sqrt{\frac{k}{m}}.$$

The molecule has zero point energy when $n = 0$. Hence

$$\text{Z.P.E.} = \frac{h}{4\pi}\sqrt{\frac{k}{m}},$$

which may be written as

$$\text{Z.P.E.} = k'\sqrt{\frac{1}{m}}.$$

The ratio of the Z.P.E.s for molecules of two isotopes differing in mass number by x is given by

$$\frac{E_1}{E_2} = \sqrt{\frac{m+x}{m}}.$$

For any fixed value of x the ratio will be greatest when m is small. Hence the difference in Z.P.E. between protium and deuterium (where $m = 1$, and $x = 1$) is greater than the difference between any other pair of isotopes differing in mass number by unity.

It follows at once that if 6184 cal is the Z.P.E. of protium, then the Z.P.E. for deuterium is

$$6184 \times \sqrt{\frac{1}{1+1}} = 6184 \times 0\cdot706$$

$$= 4372$$

which is close to the experimental value of 4395.

The Z.P.E. influences the rates of reaction of protium and deuterium with other molecules. The absolute energy of a molecule capable of taking part in a reaction is about the same for protium as for deuterium. The activation energy of a molecule, which is the energy to be acquired by thermal collision before it can react, is

Absolute energy necessary for reaction − Z.P.E.

Since the Z.P.E. of deuterium is only two-thirds that of protium, the activation energy of deuterium is greater than that of protium. Hence, at the same temperature, the rate of reaction of deuterium with other elements or compounds is slower than that of protium (Table 13.14).

Table 13.14. *Relative Rates of Reaction of Deuterium and Protium*

Reaction	Rate for deuterium compared with rate for protium
Addition to $\diagdown$C$=$C$\diagup$ at 500°	About 1/2
Addition to $\diagdown$C$=$C$\diagup$ in the presence of Ni or Cu	About 1/2
Reaction with chlorine in light at 30°	About 1/3
Reaction with bromine at 578°	About 1/3
Reaction with iodine at 750°	About 1/2

Although the rates of reactions vary in this manner the equilibrium constants are very little changed when deuterium is used instead of protium.

PREPARATION OF DEUTERIUM

Deuterium combined with oxygen is present in ordinary water in accordance with the equilibrium

$$H_2O + D_2O \rightleftharpoons 2HDO.$$

The ratio of the number of deuterium atoms to the number of protium atoms in water is about 1/6000. The first stage in the preparation of deuterium is the production of deuterium oxide, D_2O.

It is possible to enrich the deuterium content of water by electrolysis. If a solution of sodium hydroxide in ordinary water is electrolysed, using nickel electrodes, protium and deuterium are evolved at the cathode, but protium is discharged more rapidly than deuterium, and therefore the relative concentration of deuterium in the gas is less than that in the electrolyte. The water in the electrolyte thus gradually becomes enriched in deuterium oxide. The separation factor

$$\frac{(H/D)_{gas}}{(H/D)_{electrolyte}}$$

is about 6 for a nickel cathode. Starting from 610 gallons of water Taylor, Eyring, and Frost reduced the volume in seven stages of electrolysis, and finally obtained 82 c.c. of residual liquid containing 99% of deuterium.

Once deuterium oxide has been isolated, deuterium can be liberated from it by any of the reactions which liberate hydrogen from water. A form of molecular hydrogen, of which each molecule, HD, consists of one atom of protium and one atom of deuterium, is prepared by the interaction of D_2O and lithium aluminium hydride, $LiAlH_4$. The purity of the product is 98%. This may be increased to 99·8% by fractionation at the temperature of liquid hydrogen.

PREPARATION OF DEUTERIUM COMPOUNDS

Many compounds of deuterium can be prepared from deuterium oxide. Acidic and basic oxides dissolve in it to give deutero acids and bases:

$$SO_3 + D_2O = D_2SO_4$$
$$Na_2O + D_2O = 2NaOD.$$

The deutero acid can be used to form deuterides:

$$FeS + D_2SO_4 = D_2S + FeSO_4.$$

Other compounds of deuterium may be obtained by means of reactions in which an atom of deuterium replaces an atom of hydrogen in a molecule such as that of ammonia:

$$3D_2 + NH_3 = 2ND_3 + 3H_2.$$

Reactions of this kind are frequently referred to as *exchange reactions*.† The exchange reagent may be deuterium itself or deuterium oxide.

Deuterium in the purely molecular state does not react directly with hydrogen compounds, but it will do so in conditions in which it is slightly dissociated into atoms. Molecular deuterium reacts with H_2, CH_4, NH_3, and OH_2

(i) above 600°,
(ii) with the assistance of an electrical discharge (p. 364),
(iii) in the presence of a solid catalyst, such as nickel, platinum, silver, iron or copper.

The order of catalytic activity, $Pt > Ni > Fe > Cu > Au > Ag > Hg$, is the same as for promoting the recombination of atomic hydrogen, for overvoltage, and for hydrogenation. The rates of catalytic replacement of protium by deuterium are in the order $O—H > N—H > C—H$. The ionic character of the original covalent hydrogen link is no doubt related to the reactivity. This view is supported by the following sequence of reaction rates:

$$HC > H_2C > H_3C > H_4C.$$

Many exchange reactions are effected by the use of D_2O. If protium gas is bubbled through a solution of sodium hydroxide in deuterium oxide at 100° there is a slow formation of HD:

$$DO^- + HH + DOD = DOH + HD + OD^-.$$

Deuterium oxide reacts only with protium in the ionic state, and then the reaction is instantaneous. Protium attached to nitrogen, oxygen, sulphur or the halogens (in which cases the bonds possess some ionic character) is immediately replaced by deuterium when the compound is brought into contact with deuterium oxide. Protium linked to carbon is replaced only when the bond is capable of ionisation. If a sugar is treated with deuterium oxide, only the hydroxylic hydrogen is replaced.

Deuteration of paraffins and aromatic hydrocarbons is brought about at ordinary temperatures by the prolonged (12 hours) action of an equimolecular mixture of deuterium oxide and deuterosulphuric acid, D_2SO_4. Ingold has shown that the reaction with benzene shows all the characteristic behaviour of the substitution of a hydrogen atom in the aromatic nucleus by an electrophilic reagent.

If water and deuterium oxides are mixed the equilibrium is set up:

$$H_2O + D_2O \rightleftharpoons 2HDO.$$

The formation of HDO is complete within 20 seconds of mixing; the reverse reaction occurs so readily that HDO cannot be isolated from the mixture. When water and

† These must not be confused with exchange energy, which is a quantum effect.

deuterium oxide are mixed in molecular proportions 30 cal/mole are evolved. This may be due to the rearrangement of hydrogen and deuterium bonds,

$$
\begin{array}{ccc}
\text{H}\diagdown \quad \text{H}\diagdown \\
\quad \text{O} \cdots \quad \text{O} \\
\text{H}\diagup \quad \text{H}\diagup
\end{array}
+
\begin{array}{ccc}
\text{D}\diagdown \quad \text{D}\diagdown \\
\quad \text{O} \cdots \quad \text{O} \\
\text{D}\diagup \quad \text{D}\diagup
\end{array}
\rightarrow
\begin{array}{ccc}
\text{H}\diagdown \quad \text{H}\diagdown \\
\quad \text{O} \cdots \quad \text{O} \\
\text{D}\diagup \quad \text{D}\diagup
\end{array}
+
\begin{array}{ccc}
\text{D}\diagdown \quad \text{D}\diagdown \\
\quad \text{O} \cdots \quad \text{O} \\
\text{H}\diagup \quad \text{H}\diagup
\end{array}
$$

so that in the product only deuterium bonds are present.

THE EFFECT OF THE REPLACEMENT OF PROTIUM BY DEUTERIUM IN HYDRIDES AND OTHER COMPOUNDS

The changes in physical properties which occur when protium in water is replaced by deuterium are shown in Table 13.12. The changes in melting and boiling points of certain other hydrides are given in Table 13.13.

The crystal structure of solid deuterium oxide is the same as that of ice, and presumably the structure is determined by the existence of deuterium bonds (below). Water and deuterium oxide form a continuous series of solid solutions; the liquidus and solidus are never separated by more than 0·02°. The differences in physical constants between deuterium oxide and protium oxide are due to two effects:

(i) the greater nuclear mass of deuterium,
(ii) the greater degree of association of deuterium oxide.

The densities both of liquid water and of liquid deuterium oxide attain maximum values at temperatures a few degrees above their melting points. Hence when either of these liquids is cooled, a temperature is found below which the degree of association, which gives the liquid something of an open covalent crystalline structure, has a greater effect than the normal thermal contraction. For deuterium oxide this temperature is about 7° higher than for protium oxide, which indicates that the deuterium oxide is the more highly associated.

Associated hydrogen compounds contain protium or deuterium bonds. Since the deuterium bond is stronger than the protium bond, it would be predicted that the replacement of protium by deuterium in such compounds would raise the melting point and the boiling point. Table 13.13, however, gives no conclusive support to this prediction. The length of the deuterium bond X—D····Y may be considerably longer than that of the corresponding hydrogen bond, although the distances H—X and D—X differ but little.

In most cases salts are a little less soluble in deuterium oxide than in water, and the heats of solvation of ions are also smaller. Ionic mobilities are less in deuterium oxide than in water owing to the greater viscosity of deuterium oxide. The differences in properties of the hydrates and the corresponding deuterates of salts are small, for example, the transition temperature of $Na_2SO_4, 10H_2O$ is only 1·1° lower than that of $Na_2SO_4, 10D_2O$. Reactions involving deuterium compounds usually go more slowly than the corresponding reactions involving protium compounds. For example, water reacts with aluminium carbide in the cold, and at 80° 100 c.c. of methane are liberated in 2 min; deuterium oxide does not react in the cold, and at 80° 100 c.c. of deutero-methane are liberated in 45 min.

USES IN CHEMISTRY OF DEUTERIUM AND ITS COMPOUNDS

(i) The difference between the mass numbers of deuterium and protium makes it possible to test experimentally expressions which include atomic mass, such as those for the zero point energy of a molecule, and for the rates and the energies of activation of certain reactions.

(ii) If a particular hydrogen atom in a molecule can be differentiated from others, or *labelled*, the position which it takes up in a new molecule produced from the original one by a chemical change can often be ascertained. One method of labelling a hydrogen atom is to replace it by a deuterium atom. The use of deuterium for this purpose, however, is unreliable because of the ease with which it is exchanged for protium, and the use of radioactive isotopes of heavier elements is to be preferred.

Orthodeuterium and paradeuterium. Symmetry considerations show that as the space wave function of the ground state of the hydrogen molecule is symmetric, the even numbered rotational levels are symmetric and the odd ones anti-symmetric. Transitions can take place only from symmetric to symmetric levels, or from antisymmetric to antisymmetric levels. Symmetry considerations also show that the symmetric rotational levels occur with even values of total nuclear spin, and that the antisymmetric rotational levels occur with odd values of total nuclear spin. The same is true of the deuterium molecule as it has the same form of space function as the hydrogen molecule. There is however a difference in the relative intensities of the odd and even numbered rotational levels when nuclear spin is considered.

Since there is an equal probability of a transition to any of the possible energy levels, when the hyperfine structure is not resolved the transition to an energy level of the greatest multiplicity shows the greatest intensity, and has the greatest *statistical weight*. The ratio of statistical weights is measured by the ratio of multiplicities. Thus, for hydrogen, the possible total nuclear spin is 0 or 1, with respective statistical weights 1 and 3; the odd numbered total nuclear spin has the greater statistical weight. For deuterium, the possible total nuclear spin is 2, 1, 0, with respective statistical weights 5, 3, 1. The ratio of the statistical weights of even to odd is here 6:3, and it would be expected that transitions to even levels would have an intensity twice that of transitions to odd levels. Thus the effect of nuclear spin in the rotation spectrum of the *hydrogen* molecule is that lines corresponding to odd numbers of J are strong, and even numbers of J are weak. The opposite is true of *deuterium*. It should be noted that the name "ortho" is given to the modification which appears with the greatest statistical weight; thus orthodeuterium has nuclear spin 2 or 0; paradeuterium has nuclear spin 1. In hydrogen, the ortho modification has nuclear spin 1 and the para modification has nuclear spin 0.

At ordinary temperatures D_2 contains 33% paradeuterium; the rate of conversion of paradeuterium to this equilibrium mixture is less than the rate of conversion of parahydrogen at the same temperature. From 850°K–1000°K the rate of parahydrogen conversion is 2·4 times the rate for paradeuterium for thermal transformation; where the conversion is effected by the introduction of paramagnetic molecules such as NO or O_2, the ratio is 3·8/1. Owing to the larger mass of the deuterium nucleus, the quantum of energy required to change from one rotational state to another is smaller in the case of deuterium (p. 23).

In the case of the molecule HD there is no division into the ortho and para modifications, since an interchange of the nuclei produces a different configuration from the original. There is no distinction of intensity between even and odd levels since the distinction between symmetric and antisymmetric rotational states due to the interchange of identical nuclei is missing.

TRITIUM

The nucleus of tritium is composed of one proton and two neutrons. It is called a triton, and is designated either H^3 or T. It has been deduced that two of the spins are parallel and the third antiparallel; the resultant nuclear spin is thus $\frac{1}{2}$, as in the case of hydrogen. Since the triton is a spin $\frac{1}{2}$ particle, ortho- and paratritium have the same quantum states as ortho- and parahydrogen. The compositions of the equilibrium mixtures (Table 13.15) are, however, different at a given temperature, owing to the greater mass of the tritium nucleus.

Table 13.15.† *Percentage of Orthotritium present in Equilibrium Mixtures at certain Temperatures*

$T\,°K$	% orthotritium	$T\,°K$	% orthotritium
0	0·0000	50	71·272
10	2·823	100	74·928
20	33·814	150	74·999
30	56·694	175	75·000

Tritium is made by exposing lithium metal or a lithium compound to slow neutrons from a nuclear reactor. The nuclear equation‡ is:

$$_3Li^6 + _0n^1 = {}_2He^4 + {}_1H^3.$$

The nuclei of helium and tritium are the initial products, as is indicated by the equation, but these rapidly pick up electrons to form the normal molecules. If the tritium is oxidised to T_2O it is easily separated from the helium. Tritons are formed in many other nuclear reactions. Tritium is radioactive. The nuclear equation for its decay is:

$$_1T^3 = {}_2He^3 + {}_{-1}e^0.$$

The half-life period is 12·46 years.

The chemistry of tritium is very nearly identical with that of ordinary hydrogen; the molecule is T_2, and the principal oxide T_2O, and so on.

† W. M. Jones, *J. Chem. Phys.*, **16**, 1948, 1077.

‡The lithium atoms used in this reaction must have the mass number 6. The use of symbols in nuclear equations is explained in P. J. Durrant, *General and Inorganic Chemistry*, p. 605.

CHAPTER FOURTEEN

THE ALKALI METALS

The electronic configuration of an alkali metal atom in the ground state consists of a core with the electronic structure of an inert gas, and a single valence electron in an s orbital. The electronic configuration and the numerical values of the atomic, ionic, and molecular properties of the alkali metals are set out in Table 14.2. It will be seen that the direction of change of value from lithium to caesium is regular. The values of the atomic number, atomic weight, atomic radius, and ionic radius, all increase from lithium to caesium. The values of the ionisation potential and the electronegativity decrease from lithium to caesium, showing that the valency electron is removed with increasing ease as the atomic number of the metal increases. The heats of atomisation from the standard state show that caesium atoms are less firmly linked together in the crystal than are lithium atoms. The normal electrode potentials are irregular, probably because of the varying degrees of hydration of the metallic ions in aqueous solution.

The vapours of the alkali metals contain about 1% of diatomic molecules; otherwise they are monatomic; the internuclear distance in the molecule is less than twice the covalent radius (compare row 11 and row 12 in Table 14.2).

The alkali metals are soft, silver coloured, and have a high lustre when freshly cut. They all form body-centred lattices. Lithium is the least fusible, least volatile, least dense, and least soft, and the values of these properties change regularly down the Group to caesium (Table 14.3).

All the alkali metals are extremely reactive chemically (Table 14.4). They are easily tarnished by air. They combine with most elements, and react with reducible compounds. Lithium alone combines directly with nitrogen. All form oxides of the types Na_2O, Na_2O_2, and NaO_2. Lithium is relatively inert towards oxygen and the halogens. It does not react with oxygen below $100°$, and it alone gives the monoxide when heated in oxgyen. The other metals react with oxygen increasingly readily as the atomic number increases. Sodium yields the peroxide, Na_2O_2, and the metals of higher atomic number yield the superoxides, such as KO_2. The alkali metals react violently with water to form soluble hydroxides but they dissolve in liquid ammonia without liberating hydrogen; the metal appears to enter solution without suffering any immediate chemical change, but in the course of time the metallic amide is formed. The rate of formation of the amide increases from lithium to caesium. Hence although the alkali metals cannot be studied in aqueous solution, it is possible to examine their reactions when dissolved in liquid ammonia. Sodium also dissolves in methylamine (but not in di- or tri- methylamine) and in pyridine, without liberating hydrogen. From the pyridine solution the dark green compound $Na(C_5H_5N)_2$ may be obtained. This is oxidised to Na_2O_2 by air, and it reacts with nitric oxide to give sodium hyponitrite, $Na_2N_2O_2$.

SOLUTIONS OF THE ALKALI METALS IN LIQUID AMMONIA

The solutions of the alkali metals in liquid ammonia (Table 14.5) are dark blue. The behaviour of the solutions under the ultramicroscope, and many of their other

Table 14.1. Examples of Types of Compounds formed by the Alkali Metals

State of metal atom	Nature of bond	Examples of compounds
Compounds in which the metal atom is a univalent cation. The single bond exerted possesses both ionic and covalent character	The ionic character of the bond predominates	The salts of the alkali metals, particularly those of oxyacids, such as $NaClO_4$, $NaNO_3$, and Na_2CO_3. The hydroxides of the alkali metals, such as $NaOH$, and the oxides such as Na_2O, NaO_2, Na_2O_2
	The covalent character of the bond predominates	The hydrides of the alkali metals, such as NaH, the hydrocarbon derivatives, such as NaC_2H_5, $NaCH_2C_6H_5$, Na_2C_2, and the alkali metal molecules such as Na_2.

State of metal atom					Li	Na	K	Rb	Cs
Hybrid-isation	Formal charge	Bonds †	Nature of unit formed						
Tetrahedral	−3	4σ	Chelate neutral complex		[chelate structure: H_5C_6–C(H)=C–CH$_3$ diketonate with Li coordinated by two OH_2]	A compound corresponding to the lithium derivative	[chelate structure with K, OH_2, OH_2, H_3C]	A compound corresponding to the lithium derivative	A compound corresponding to the lithium derivative
					[bis-chelate Li structure]	[bis-chelate Na structure with O, N=O]		[bis-chelate Rb structure]	A compound corresponding to the lithium derivative
Octahedral	−5	6σ	Chelate neutral complex			[octahedral Na structure: H_5C_6–C(H)=C–CH_3 with OH_2, OH_2, OH_2, OH_2]	A compound corresponding to the rubidium derivative	[octahedral Rb structure]	A compound corresponding to the rubidium derivative
Digonal	−1	2σ	Complex anion			$K^+[H_2N\!-\!Na\!-\!NH_2]^-$			

† In this column the expression "4σ" indicates the presence of four bonds each of type σ; the other expressions have corresponding meanings

properties, show that the solutions are not colloidal. At $-33°$ the conductivity of a saturated solution of sodium in liquid ammonia is 0.5×10^{14} mhos, which is half that of metallic mercury. The mobility of the anion is 280 times that of the cation. To explain the properties of medium and dilute solutions of the alkali metals in ammonia two theories have been proposed: (i) the *cavity* theory which supposes that the cations

Table 14.2. *Atomic, Ionic, and Molecular Properties of the Alkali Metals*

	Li	Na	K	Rb	Cs
Atomic number	3	11	19	37	55
Electronic configuration	2, 1	2, 8, 1	2, 8, 8, 1	2, 8, 18, 8, 1	2, 8, 18 18, 8, 1
Atomic weight	6·940	22·997	39·096	85·48	132·91
Heat of atomisation from standard state, kcal/mole	39·0	25·9	19·8	18·9	
Heat of formation of molecules from atoms, kcal/mole	−27·2	−18·4	−12·6	−11·3	−10·4
Ionisation potential for gas, kcal	123·8	117·9	99·7	95·9	89·4
eV	5·36	5·18	4·41	4·16	3·96
Electron affinity, eV	(3s) 1·2	(4s) 0·7			
Normal electrode potential, V	3·038	2·71	2·92	2·92	2·93
Electronegativity	1·0	0·9	0·8	0·8	0·7
Ionic radius Å	0·68	0·97	1·33	1·47	1·67
Covalent radius for C.N. 12, Å	1·58	1·92	2·38	2·53	2·72
Internuclear distance in molecule, Å	2·67	3·08	3·91		4·55

are solvated metal cations $[Na(NH_3)_n]^+$, and the anions are electrons situated in cavities at the centres of groups of orientated ammonia molecules, (ii) the *expanded metal* theory which supposes that the metal cation is surrounded by ammonia molecules as ligands, and that the electron neutralising the cation occupies a metallic orbital of *s* character with maximum density on the surface of a sphere, on which also lie the

Table 14.3. *Properties of the Alkali Metals in the Metallic State*

	Li	Na	K	Rb	Cs
Appearance	Silvery white solid	Silvery white solid and liquid; purple vapour	Silvery white solid and liquid; green vapour	Silvery white solid	Silvery white solid
Lattice	Body centred cubic				
Hardness (Mohs' scale)	0·06	0·07	0·04		0·02
Specific gravity at 0°	0·5	0·972	0·859	1·525	1·903
m.p. °C	179·5	97·8	63·5	38·7	29·8
b.p. °C	1336	883	762	700	670
Heat of fusion, kcal/gm atom	0·69	0·63	0·57	0·53	0·50
Effective number of free electrons per atom	0·55	1·1	0·97	0·94	0·85

Table 14.4. The Chemical Properties of the Alkali Metals

Reagent	Li	Na	K	Rb†	Cs†
Air	Can be melted and poured in air without losing its brightness	Tarnishes but does not inflame	Inflames	Inflames	Inflames
O_2	No action below 100°; at 200° yields Li_2O, with incandescence	When heated yields a mixture of Na_2O and Na_2O_2	At 200° yields chiefly KO_2; at higher temperatures chiefly K_2O_2		
Compounds containing oxygen		Reduces CO and CO_2, silicates, tungstates, molybdates, chromites, and SnO_2	Reduces boric oxide to boron		
H_2 Cl_2 Compounds containing chlorine	At 700–800° yields LiH Yields LiCl	At about 400° yields NaH Yields NaCl	At about 360° yields KH Yields KCl with inflammation Reduces $AlCl_3$, BF_3, SiF_4 to the electropositive element		
Br_2	With liquid Br_2 reacts only superficially	With liquid Br_2 reacts only superficially	Explodes with liquid bromine		
C	At low red heat yields Li_2C_2	When heated yields small quantities of Na_2C_2	No reaction		
N_2	Yields Li_3N slowly; quickly on heating	No reaction	No reaction		
Water	Yields H_2 and LiOH (only slowly in the cold)	Yields H_2 and NaOH	Yields H_2 which ignites, and KOH		
C_2H_5OH Gaseous NH_3	When heated gives $LiNH_2$ and Li_2NH	Yields H_2 and $NaOC_2H_5$ At 300–400° yields $NaNH_2$	Yields H_2 Heated yields KNH_2		
Liquid NH_3	Yields a deep blue solution which slowly gives $LiNH_2$	As for lithium	As for lithium		
H_2S		Yields a mixture of Na_2S and NaHS (Liquid H_2S yields pure NaHS)			
C_2H_2	When heated yields Li_2C_2 and LiH	At 190° yields NaCCH At 210° yields NaCCNa	When heated gives HKC_2		
Fused NaOH or KOH		A solution is formed. 100 gr NaOH dissolve at: 480° 25·3 g Na 800° 6·9 g Na Yields amalgam	A solution is formed. 100 gr of KOH dissolve at: 450° 8–9 g K 700° 0·5 g K Yields amalgam		
Mercury		N.B. Heated sodium does *not* react with nitrogen, silicon, iron, or nickel	N.B. Heated potassium does *not* react with carbon (except to form interstitial compounds), nitrogen, boron, silicon, or iron		

† It is to be presumed that the reactions of rubidium and caesium are similar to those of potassium, but more vigorous.

hydrogen atoms of the ligand ammonia molecules. It is assumed that either the anionic cavities, or the expanded *s* orbitals, may be occupied by pairs of electrons.†

On evaporation of the ammonia the alkali metals (except lithium) are deposited as copper-coloured spongy solids which probably consist of crystals of the metal together with adsorbed liquid. Lithium crystallises as the ammoniate $Li,4NH_3$, and in this resembles the alkaline earth metals which crystallise as hexa-ammoniates such as $Ca,6NH_3$.

Table 14.5. *Solutions of the Alkali Metals in Liquid Ammonia*

Metal	Solubility, gm in 100 gm of ammonia at 0°	Notes on the equilibrium	Period required for formation of the amide, XNH_2‡
Li	9·41§	Forms two liquid phases below 60°	Several days
Na	18·7	Eutectic at −110° and 13% Na	Several days
K	32·7		1 hour
Rb	Sol.		30 min.
Cs	Sol.		15 min.

‡ These changes are catalysed by iron, platinum, ferric oxide, or by light of wave length 2150–2500 Å.
§ The heat of solution at −33° is 9·65 kcal/gm atom.

The alkali metals in liquid ammonia solution react with ammonium salts (which are acids in the solvent system, p. 692) to form salts. Ammonia and hydrogen are normally liberated:

$$2NH_4Cl + 2Na = 2NaCl + 2NH_3 + H_2.$$

Ammonium nitrate, however, produces the nitroxylate:

$$NH_4NO_3 + 3K = NH_3 + K_2NO_2 + KOH,$$

and there is no evolution of hydrogen or any other insoluble gas. The alkali metals in liquid ammonia solution react with certain elements as shown in Table 14.6.

The reactions of the alkali metals with certain non-metallic hydrides and oxides are given in Table 14.7. Potassium in liquid ammonia solution reduces oxides or salts of other metals. The result may be a reduction of the other metal to a lower valence state, the precipitation of the metal, or the formation of an intermetallic compound with potassium. For example, Cu^{II} goes to Cu^I; $Mo^{VI}O_3$ goes to $Mo_2^{III}O_3$ (the only method of preparation), and with excess of potassium yields metallic molybdenum. $Ge^{IV}O_2$ and $Mo^{IV}O_2$ are not reduced. The results of the reactions have been systematised thus:‖ If the liberated metal is in one of the Long Periods and more than four places prior to an inert gas it is precipitated as metal or as an alloy with potassium, e.g. Cu, Ag, Au, Zn, Cd, Hg, Ga, In, Tl react in this way. If the metal is in one of the Long Periods but is four or fewer places before an inert gas, it usually remains in solution as a highly coloured polyanionic salt; under the ultramicroscope these solutions are seen to be colloidal. Examples are furnished by the mercury, lead, antimony, and bismuth compounds of sodium in Table 14.6. It has been conjectured that solvation of the sodium cations weakens their field, so that the more electronegative metal is able to retain additional electrons in its crystal orbital system.

† For further explanation and many references see M.C.R. Symons, *Quart. Rev.*, **13**, 1959, 99.
‖ E. de Barry Barnett and C. L. Wilson, *Inorganic Chemistry*, Longmans, 1953, p. 323.

Table 14.6. *Additive Reactions of the Alkali Metals in Liquid Ammonia Solution*

Metal	Reagent	Product
Na	N_2	No reaction
K	P	K_3P_2
Li, Na	P	Li_2P, Na_2P
K	As	K_3As,NH_3 and K_2As_4,NH_3
Na	Sb	Na_3Sb_5, Na_3Sb_6, Na_3Sb_7
Na	Bi	Na_3Bi, Na_3Bi_3, Na_3Bi_{5-7}
Li	O_2	Li_2O, Li_2O_2
Na	O_2	Slow stream of oxygen: Na_2O, which is ammonolysed to $NaNH_2$, which is further oxidised to $NaNO_2$ and NH_3. If $NaNH_2$ is slowly added to liquid ammonia through which oxygen is passing rapidly a yellow product is obtained of composition Na_2O_3, which is probably a mixture of Na_2O_2 and NaO_2
K	O_2	As for sodium
Li	S	Li_2S, Li_2S_2, Li_2S_x
Na	S	Na_2S, Na_2S_x
Na	Se	Na_2Se, Na_2Se_2, Na_2Se_6
K	Te	K_2Te, K_2Te_3
Na	Pb	$NaPb$, $NaPb_2$, Na_4Pb_9
Na	Hg	$NaHg_8$
Rb	S	Rb_2S_x $x = 2, 3,$ or 5 but not 4 or 6
Cs	S	Cs_2S_x $x = 2, 3, 5$ or 6 but not 4
all	Graphite	Compounds of ideal formulae $C_{12}M(NH_3)_2$ and $C_{28}M(NH_3)_2$. The first consists of alternate layers of graphite and alkali metal ammoniate; the second of two layers of graphite to one of ammoniate

Table 14.7. *Reactions of the Alkali Metals in Liquid Ammonia Solution with certain Non-Metallic Hydrides and Oxides*

Metal	Reagent	Product
Na	Naphthalene	
Na	Acetylene	Sodium hydroacetylide, $NaC{\equiv}CH$
Na or K	PH_3	$NaPH_2$, which at 70° gives Na_2PH, at 100° H_2, and at 380° Na, leaving Na_2P_5
Li	PH_3	At 0° $LiPH_2$ which forms 4, 2, and 1-ammoniates At 50° Li_2PH which forms 5, 3, and 2-ammoniates
Li	AsH_3	$LiAsH_2,4NH_3 \xrightarrow{0°} LiAsH_2,2NH_3 \rightarrow Li_2AsH \xrightarrow{70°} Li_2As$, which is stable up to 450°
Na	GeH_4, Ge_2H_6	$NaGeH_3$ and H_2
Na	Ammonium di-borineamide	The reaction occurs (p. 519): $Na + NH_4(BH_3 \cdot NH_2 \cdot BH_3)$ $= NaBH_4 + \frac{1}{2}H_2 + NH_3 + BH_2NH_2$
All	CO	$LiCO$, $Na_2(CO)_2$, $K_2(CO)_2$, $RbCO$
Na	CO_2	NH_2COONa
Na	N_2O	The reactions occur in succession: $N_2O + 2K + NH_3 = KNH_2 + KOH + N_2$ $N_2O + 2KNH_2 = KN_3 + KOH + NH_3$
K, Na	NO	$NaNO$, KNO

COMPOUNDS OF THE ALKALI METALS

The types of compound formed by the alkali metals are summarised in Table 14.1. The alkali metals are the least electronegative of the elements. The atom of an alkali metal, therefore, readily loses one electron to become a cation with a single positive charge; by Fajans rule the atom of greatest radius (Cs) has the lowest electronegativity, and hence forms the most stable ionic bonds. The extreme improbability of the ionisation of more than one electron per atom is shown by the ionisation potentials of Ne, Na, and Na+:

		Ne	Na	Na+
Ionisation potential	ev/gm atom	21·5	5·18	47·0
	kcal/gm atom	496	119·5	1085

The compounds of the metals of low atomic number with hydrogen, nitrogen, carbon, and with the simple oxygen ion O^{2-}, appear to be more stable than the corresponding compounds of the metals of higher atomic number. On the other hand, compounds containing the oxygen ions $(O—O)^{2-}$ and $(O—O)^-$, and ions of the oxy-acids and of the halogens, increase in stability with rising atomic number of the metal.

There seems little doubt that in such molecules as Li_2, LiH, NaC_2H_5, in the neutral cationic complexes such as the benzoyl acetone derivative of sodium, and in the anionic complexes, such as $K(Na(NH_2)_2)$, an atom of an alkali metal is exerting at least one covalent bond. In the anti-$CdCl_2$ structure of Cs_2O the caesium ion is considerably polarised and hence the structure has covalent character. On this evidence it is reasonable to suppose that no bond exerted by an alkali metal is purely ionic. In Table 14.1 the univalent compounds of the alkali metals are therefore divided into two classes; in those in one class the ionic character of the bond predominates, and in those in the other class the covalent character predominates.

Nevertheless, to stress the covalent character of the bonds exerted by atoms of the alkali metals is to convey a false impression. The reactions of the metals given in Table 14.4 consist essentially of the ionisation of atoms of the metals. Once the metallic ion has been formed it may take part in numerous metatheses, but it retains its identity as a stable univalent cation, with the important property that its polarising influence on any anion with which it is associated is very small.

The interest of the chemistry of the majority of the alkali metal compounds lies not in the ion of the alkali metal but in the constitution and behaviour of the groups with which the ion is associated. The ionic compounds of the alkali metals are therefore discussed later in the book in the appropriate sections dealing with other elements, for example, the oxides are discussed under "oxygen".† A few types of alkali metal compounds, such as the hydrides, the hydrocarbon derivatives, and the neutral complexes, in which the proportion of covalent character of the alkali metal bonds becomes significant, are discussed in the following sections.

THE HYDRIDES OF THE ALKALI METALS

An account of the hydrides of the alkali metals is given in Table 14.8. They are colourless crystalline solids made by direct union of gaseous hydrogen and the metal. Lithium hydride is much more stable and less chemically reactive than sodium hydride. The stability of the hydrides decreases with increasing atomic weight of the metal. Lithium hydride undergoes useful reactions with trivalent metals of Group III, converting them to the four co-ordinate state.

The structures of the hydrides are of great interest. The electrolysis of fused lithium hydride yields lithium at the cathode, and hydrogen at the anode in the theoretical proportions. The crystals are much denser than the parent metals, and the apparent

† Table 21.2 (p. 782), Table 21.8 (p. 794), Table 21.9 (p. 796).

Table 14.8. *Alkali Metal Hydrides*

	LiH	NaH	KH	RbH	CsH
State	Colourless, crystalline solid. m.p. 680°	Colourless solid. m.p. with decomposition 700–800°. Begins to sublime with decomposition at 380°	White crystalline solid	←———— Dissociate below m.p. ————→	
Lattice	NaCl	NaCl	NaCl	NaCl	NaCl
Dissociation temperature	1000°	330°	200°		
Solubility	Reacts with water. Insoluble in ether, benzene, or liquid ammonia, or in lithium up to 150°	Reacts with water. Insoluble in ether, benzene, turpentine, or carbon tetrachloride, liquid ammonia, or in sodium up to 150°	Reacts with water. Insoluble in organic solvents, in liquid ammonia, or in potassium up to 150°		
Preparation	(i) Heat lithium and hydrogen at 700–800°. Reaction occurs with incandescence (ii) Heat lithium nitride in a current of hydrogen. The reaction is reversible: $2Li_3N + 3H_2 \rightleftharpoons 6LiH + N_2$ (iii) By the action of LiEt on LiAlH$_4$ in ether (iv) By the action of LiMe on Si(CH$_3$)$_3$H	(i) Heat sodium and hydrogen at 360–400° (i)a Heat sodium monoxide and hydrogen at 200° (ii) Warm sodium nitride in a current of hydrogen (ii)a Heat sodamide with hydrogen By the action of heat on NaC$_2$H$_5$ By the action of H$_2$ on NaC$_2$H$_5$	Heat potassium and hydrogen at 360°	Heat Rb and hydrogen at 400°	Heat Cs and hydrogen at 400° Heat caesium monoxide and hydrogen at 150°
Bond length M—H in solid	2·04	2·44	2·85	3·02	3·19
Apparent radius of H	1·26	1·46	1·52	1·53	1·54
Heat of formation of solid, kcal/mole	−21·6	−14	−14·1	−13	−13·5
Heat of dissociation of bond, kcal	57·7	47·0	44·5	About 40	About 40
Percentage change in density on formation from parent metal	+52·8	+44			

Reactions

Air	Stable	—	Inflames
O$_2$	Attacked only above red heat	Inflames at 230°	Inflames
N$_2$	No action	No action	
Cl$_2$	No reaction cold	Slowly attacked (Br$_2$ in cold, no reaction; iodine at 100°, reacts with incandescence)	Inflames
HCl gas	No reaction cold	—	Yields H$_2$
Alkali metal chloride	Reacts when heated at reduced pressure to yield metal and HCl		
Water	Yields hydrogen: LiH+H$_2$O = LiOH+H$_2$; $\Delta H = -31.7$ kcal	Yields H$_2$+NaOH	Yields H$_2$+KOH
Alcohol	Yields H$_2$+LiOC$_2$H$_5$	Yields H$_2$+NaOC$_2$H$_5$	Yields H$_2$+KOC$_2$H$_5$
Moist CO$_2$		Yields sodium formate NaH+CO$_2$=HCOONa	Yields HCOOK
Dry CO$_2$ Acetylene NH$_3$ gas		Yields Na$_2$CO$_3$+H$_2$ Yields NaC$_2$H Heated yields NaNH$_2$	Yields K$_2$CO$_3$ and H$_2$ At 100° forms KC$_2$H Heated yields KNH$_2$
SO$_2$			KH with SO$_2$ at low temp. thus: 2SO$_2$+2KH=K$_2$S$_2$O$_4$+H$_2$; at higher temp. yields a mixture of sulphide and sulphate
Diborane B$_2$H$_6$	Yields lithium borohydride, 2LiH+B$_2$H$_6$=2LiBH$_4$ (in ether only)		
Boron trifluoride etherate	Yields lithium borofluoride, 6LiH+8Et$_2$O·BF$_3$ =B$_2$H$_6$+6LiBF$_4$+8Et$_2$O	†	
Aluminium chloride in ether	Yields lithium aluminohydride LiAlH$_4$	Yields NaAl(OEt)$_3$H and ultimately NaAlH$_4$	
Al(OEt)$_3$	Yields LiAl(OEt)$_3$H, and ultimately LiAlH$_4$		
Gallium trichloride in ether	Yields LiGaH$_4$		

† It reduces BCl$_3$ at 200° to yield B$_2$H$_6$

radius of the H⁻ ion in the crystal varies from 1·26 in lithium hydride to 1·54 in caesium hydride (the radius of the first Bohr orbit of hydrogen is 0·53, and the ionic radius is 2·1). All the hydrides have been shown to crystallise with the sodium chloride lattice.

The sodium chloride structure is six co-ordinate. It is impossible for an alkali metal atom to find the number of valency electrons to form six covalent bonds, and therefore the bonding cannot be covalent. The examination of single crystal rotation X-ray photographs of lithium hydride has shown that the ionic character of the bond is only 25%. This is in conformity with the covalency of the hydrogen molecule, and with the presence of about 1% of diatomic molecules in the vapours of the alkali metals. As the ionic character of the M—H bond increases with increasing atomic number of the metal, it would appear that M^+H^- is a less stable structure than the covalent M—H. It seems probable, however, that the behaviour of the alkali metal hydrides is to be explained in terms of a general orbital system, such as that which applies to metal crystals (p. 179).

ALKALI METAL DERIVATIVES OF THE HYDROCARBONS

The alkali metal derivatives of the hydrocarbons can be grouped into three main classes:

(1) Derivatives of paraffins and of benzene. These are colourless.
(2) Derivatives of conjugated hydrocarbons, other than benzene. These are coloured.
(3) Derivatives of acetylene. These are colourless.

Alkali metal derivatives of the paraffins and of benzene. The simple alkyls of all the alkali metals are known. They cannot be made directly by the action of the metal on a hydrocarbon; the metal must be treated with mercury alkyl, or the halogen alkyl (say, ethyl iodide), in benzene or light petroleum. The alkali metal alkyls are colourless, and are spontaneously inflammable in air. Lithium ethyl melts without decomposition, and is soluble in organic solvents; sodium and potassium ethyls decompose on heating without melting, and are insoluble in organic solvents, with which they react. The preparations and properties of the alkali metal ethyls are briefly described in Table 14.9. In certain respects C_2H_5Na behaves in the same way as the Grignard reagent C_2H_5MgBr (p. 446). The reactivity of the alkyls decreases in the order:

$$Cs > Rb > K > Na > Li > MgBr.$$

In a hydrocarbon other than ethane, the replacement of a hydrogen atom by a sodium atom may be carried out experimentally by treating the hydrocarbon with sodium ethyl. Ethane is such an extremely weak acid that even benzene acts as a stronger acid, and expels ethane from sodium ethyl:

$$NaC_2H_5 + C_6H_6 = NaC_6H_5 + C_2H_6.$$

By observation of the effect of hydrocarbons on sodium ethyl it is possible to arrange them in order of acidity. The order of increasing acidity is: ethane: benzene, toluene, diphenylmethane: triphenylmethane: xanthene: aniline: fluorene: phenylacetylene: alcohols: phenol.

Other points of interest concerning the alkali metal alkyls are:

(1) Lithium methyl is almost insoluble in benzene or light petroleum, which makes possible the reaction:

$$2LiC_2H_5 \text{ (sol.)} + Hg(CH_3)_2\text{(sol.)} = 2LiCH_3\text{(ppt.)} + Hg(C_2H_5)_2\text{(sol.)}$$

(2) Lithium propyl, butyl, and heptyl, are liquid at room temperature.
(3) The d.p.m. of lithium butyl is 0·97D; this low value is evidence of the covalent nature of the C—Li bond.

Table 14.9. Alkali Metal Derivatives of Ethane and Benzene

Alkali metal ethyl	LiC_2H_5	NaC_2H_5	KC_2H_5, RbC_2H_5, CsC_2H_5
State	Colourless crystals, m.p. 95°. At higher temperatures distillation occurs with decomposition	Colourless powders which on heating decompose without melting or vapourising: e.g. $NaC_2H_5 = NaH + C_2H_4$ ⟶	⟶
Preparation	(i) Treat the metal with a warm solution of mercury diethyl in light petroleum (or, for lithium only, benzene) ⟶	⟶	
	(ii) Treat the metal with a solution of ethyl bromide in benzene ⟶		
Solubility	Soluble in benzene, ligroin, or ether	Insoluble in organic solvents ⟶	⟶
Reactions	The ethereal solution with oxygen gives carbonyls No reaction with benzene	Spontaneously inflammable in air	
		Reacts with any hydrogen compound which is a stronger acid than ethane. Thus:	
		with hydrogen $\quad H_2 + NaC_2H_5 = NaH + C_2H_6$	
		with boiling benzene $C_6H_6 + NaC_2H_5 = NaC_6H_5 + C_2H_6$	
		with alcohol $\quad C_2H_5OH + NaC_2H_5 = NaOC_2H_5 + C_2H_6$	
		with ether $\quad C_2H_5OC_2H_5 + NaC_2H_5 = NaOC_2H_5 + C_2H_4 + C_2H_6$	
		Reacts with compounds which part with hydrogen easily to give sodium hydride and ethane, e.g. with dihydronaphthalene	
	Reacts with zinc ethyl to give a conducting solution containing $Li[Zn(C_2H_5)_3]$	Reacts with zinc ethyl to give a conducting solution containing $Na[Zn(C_2H_5)_3]$. This can be obtained on evaporation as a colourless solid, m.p. 27°	

Table 14.10. Alkali Metal Derivatives of Certain Conjugated Hydrocarbons

Alkali metal benzyl	$LiCH_2C_6H_5$	$NaCH_2C_6H_5$	
State Preparation	Bright yellow powder. Act on lithium phenyl with mercury dibenzyl, or with benzyl magnesium bromide	Dark garnet red crystals	
Solubility	Does not attack ether	Insoluble in benzene or ligroin. Dissolves in ether to give a red conducting solution	
Reactions	Reacts with benzyl chloride: $C_6H_5CH_2Na + C_6H_5CH_2Cl = C_6H_5CH_2 \cdot CH_2C_6H_5 + NaCl$	Reacts with tetramethyl ammonium chloride: $[N(CH_3)_4]Cl + C_6H_5CH_2Na = [N(CH_3)_4]CH_2C_6H_5 + NaCl$	

Alkali metal triphenyl methyl	$LiC(C_6H_5)_3$	$NaC(C_6H_5)_3$	K, Rb, Cs, $C(C_6H_5)_3$
State Preparation	Pale yellow powder. Add lithium to the unsaturated free radical: $Li + C(C_6H_5)_3 = Li(C_6H_5)_3$	Red crystals. Add sodium to triphenyl methyl chloride: $2Na + C(C_6H_5)_3Cl = NaC(C_6H_5)_3 + NaCl$	Red powders
Solubility	Soluble in ether to give a yellow solution. Forms a bright red crystalline dietherate which at 90° in vacuo gives the original lithium triphenyl methyl	Soluble in ether to a deep red solution. Forms no etherate. Dissociation constant in ether 10^{-12}. Dissolves in pyridine to give a red conducting solution, but the colour fades, perhaps by the reaction:	Slightly soluble in ether but form no etherates

Pyridine reaction:

Reactions			
	———— Spontaneously inflammable in air ————→		
	———— With water yields the metallic hydroxide: $HOH + NaC(C_6H_5)_3 = NaOH + HC(C_6H_5)_3$ and triphenyl methane ————→		

With alcohol:

$$C_2H_5OH + NaC(C_6H_5)_3 = NaOC_2H_5 + HC(C_6H_5)_3$$

With acetone:

$$CH_3 \cdot \underset{\underset{CH_2}{\|}}{C} \cdot OH + NaC(C_6H_5)_3 = CH_3 \cdot \underset{\underset{CH_2}{\|}}{C} \cdot ONa + HC(C_6H_5)_3$$

It may be cautiously oxidised to sodium peroxide:

$$2NaC(C_6H_5)_3 + O_2 = 2C(C_6H_5)_3 + Na_2O_2$$

but excess of oxygen gives the peroxide:

$$(C_6H_5)_3C - O - O - C(C_6H_5)_3$$

With carbon dioxide, or sulphur dioxide, it behaves like a Grignard reagent:

$$\underset{\underset{O}{\|}}{C}\Big\langle{}_O + NaC(C_6H_5)_3 = \underset{\underset{O}{\|}}{C}\Big\langle{}^{ONa}_{C(C_6H_5)_3}$$

Carbon monoxide has no action

Alkali metal phenyl	LiC$_6$H$_5$	NaC$_6$H$_5$
State Preparation	Colourless powder Add lithium to phenyl bromide in ether: $C_6H_5Br + 2Li = LiC_6H_5 + LiBr$	White solid, infusible Add sodium to mercury diphenyl: $2Na + Hg(C_6H_5)_2 = 2NaC_6H_5 + Hg$
Properties Solubility Reactions	Soluble in ether, slightly soluble in benzene The ethereal solution is oxidised by oxygen, with chemiluminescence, to give diphenyl: $2LiC_6H_5 + O = C_6H_5 \cdot C_6H_5 + Li_2O$ Reacts with a peroxide to give $LiOC_6H_5$	Spontaneously inflammable in air

The aryl compounds of the type NaC_6H_5 are colourless, they are spontaneously inflammable in air, and in spite of the presence of the benzene ring they differ little in general properties from the ethyls.

The bond between the alkali metal atom and the carbon atom in all classes of alkali metal derivatives of the hydrocarbons is a bond with significant proportions both of ionic and covalent character. From the order of acidity of the hydrocarbons given on p. 408 the bond is most likely to be covalent in the simple alkyls and aryls. The covalent nature of the alkyls is shown by their behaviour. Lithium ethyl in benzene solution is associated to $(Li(C_2H_5))_6$, and the alkyl derivatives of the other metals are more associated still. Fused lithium ethyl is a non-conductor. Both lithium and sodium ethyls dissolve in zinc ethyl and, after warming, yield conducting solutions:

$$NaC_2H_5 + Zn(C_2H_5)_2 = Na^+ + Zn(C_2H_5)_3{}^-,$$

but this reaction does not indicate whether sodium ethyl is ionised or not.

Alkali metal derivatives of conjugated hydrocarbons. In compounds of this class an alkali metal atom has replaced a hydrogen atom on a carbon atom which is saturated, but which is attached to one or more conjugated rings. The carbon atom may be part of a short chain as in sodium benzyl, or it may form part of a ring as in sodium cyclopentadienyl or disodium anthracene. Compounds of this type may be made (a) by the elimination of hydrogen by the direct attack of an alkali metal on a hydrocarbon, (b) by the direct addition of an alkali metal to naphthalene or anthracene (in these cases the parent hydrocarbon from which the alkali metal compound is formed by *substitution* is dihydronaphthalene, or dihydroanthracene), (c) by the addition of the metal to an ethylene derivative as in the formation of disodium stilbene, or (d) by the separation of two radicals as in the formation of sodium benzyl from dibenzyl.

Derivatives of this class can also be made by reactions of the metal on certain derivatives of the hydrocarbons, for example:

$$C_6H_5CH_2I + 2Na = C_6H_5CH_2Na + NaI$$
$$(C_6H_5CH_2)_2Hg + 2Na = 2C_6H_5CH_2Na + Hg$$
$$2C_6H_5CH_2MgBr + 2Na = 2C_6H_5CH_2Na + Mg + MgBr_2$$
$$C_6H_5CH_2—O—Et + 2Na = C_6H_5CH_2Na + NaOEt$$
$$C(C_6H_5)_3 + Na = C(C_6H_5)_3Na$$
$$C_6H_5CH=CH_2 + NaEt = C_6H_5CHNa—CH_2Et.$$

Brief accounts of lithium benzyl and sodium benzyl and of the alkali metal derivatives of triphenyl methane are given in Table 14.10.

The bond between the alkali metal and the carbon atom in the alkali metal derivatives of conjugated hydrocarbons must possess a very considerable degree of ionic character. For example, in sodium benzyl the covalent form and the ionic form could be written:

If the lone electron pair on the carbon atom of the methylene group in the ionic form occupies a p orbital, then this orbital could be combined with the non-localised π orbitals in the benzene ring. Such a possibility is present in all alkali metal derivatives of the conjugated hydrocarbons. As the ionic structure is so important in these derivatives it will be used in equations describing their reactions.

The ring compound potassium cyclopentadienyl is formed by the action of potassium on cyclopentadiene in benzene solution. Hydrogen is liberated:

$$\text{(cyclopentadiene structure)} + K = K^+ + \text{(cyclopentadienyl structure)} + \tfrac{1}{2}H_2$$

The product is a yellow powder, insoluble, and inflammable in air; it has not been purified or analysed. It is of interest in comparison with ferrocene (p. 1118). Fluorene reacts with sodium at 200°, or with sodamide at 120°, to produce a brownish-yellow solid, insoluble, but not readily oxidised by air:

$$\text{(fluorene structure)} + Na$$

$$= \text{(fluorenyl sodium structure)} + Na^+ + \tfrac{1}{2}H_2.$$

With water or alcohol, the sodium compound reacts like a Grignard reagent and regenerates fluorene. The potassium derivative can be made by heating fluorene with potassium hydroxide at 260–280°; it is reactive, but not spontaneously inflammable in air.

Sodium also reacts directly *by addition* with naphthalene in methyl ether solution:

$$\text{(naphthalene structure)} + 2Na = \text{(naphthalene disodium structure)} + 2Na^+.$$

The product is a dark-green solid, soluble in ether to give a conducting solution. It is spontaneously inflammable in air, and with water and alcohol it reacts like a Grignard reagent, yielding dihydronaphthalene:

$$2Na^+ + \text{(structure)} + 2HOC_2H_5 = \text{(dihydronaphthalene structure)} + 2NaOC_2H_5$$

Anthracene reacts similarly to give a dark blue additive product which is less soluble in ether than the naphthalene compound. With alcohol it yields dihydroanthracene.

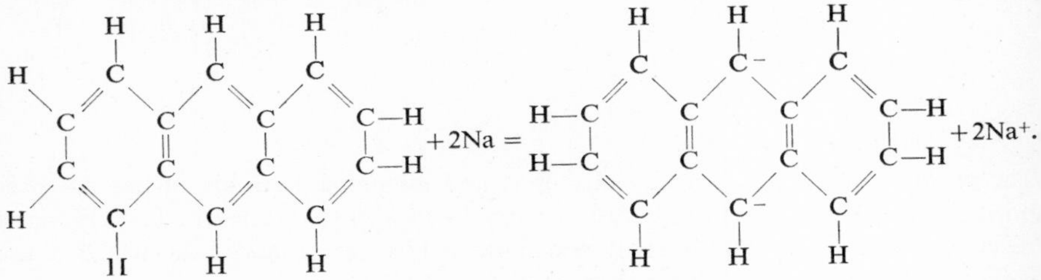

These alkali metal addition compounds may be regarded as substitution derivatives of dihydronaphthalene and dihydroanthracene, and as such they correspond to the alkali metal derivatives of cyclopentadiene and fluorene.

Lithium and sodium also form addition compounds with aromatic ethylene compounds. Lithium reacts with tetraphenyl ethylene thus:

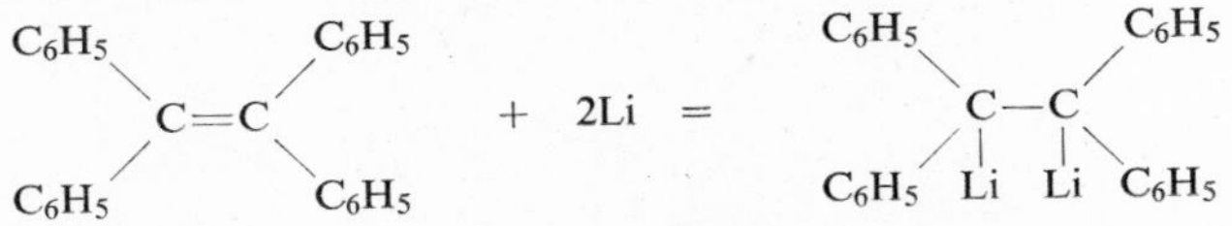

and sodium with stilbene in ethereal solution thus:

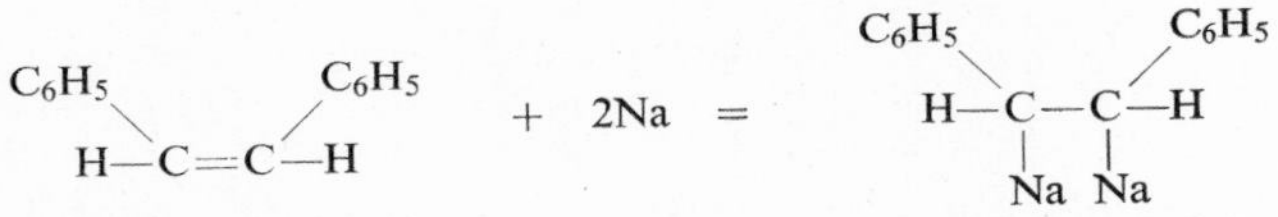

Disodium stilbene is a dark violet-brown powder, spontaneously inflammable in air. The sodium can be removed from disodium stilbene by cautious treatment with mercury, benzyl chloride, or oxygen. With water, alcohol, and carbon dioxide, however, the ethylene alkali metal compounds react like a Grignard reagent, thus:

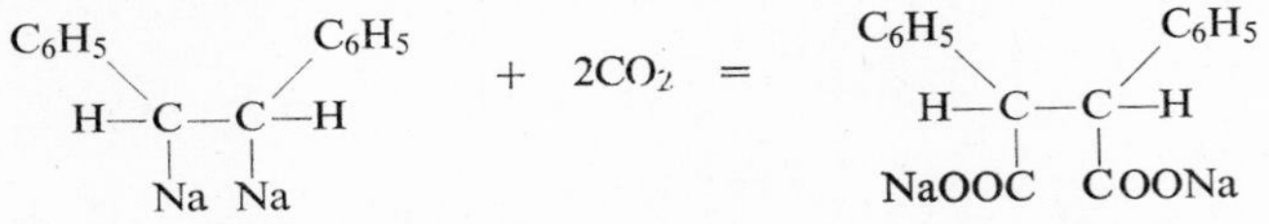

The alkali metal acetylides. The alkali metals invariably react with acetylene by replacing one or both of the hydrogen atoms in the acetylene molecule; they do not form addition compounds as they do with certain derivatives of ethylene. The acetylides and the hydroacetylides of all the alkali metals are known (Table 14.11). Lithium acetylide can be formed directly by heating lithium and carbon; sodium acetylide is formed in this way, but the reaction is reversible and the yield is small; potassium rubidium, and caesium react with carbon to form interstitial compounds such as C_8K (p. 591).

All the acetylides are formed by passing acetylene over the heated metal at a red heat. The hydroacetylides (except lithium) are made by heating the metal in acetylene at about 190°, or by passing acetylene into a solution of the metal in liquid ammonia The hydroacetylides are very easily converted into the acetylides by heating. The lithium compound (which has not been isolated) changes at −33°, the sodium compound at 200°.

Table 14.11. *The Hydroacetylides and the Acetylides of the Alkali Metals*

The hydroacetylides	$LiHC_2$	$NaHC_2$	K, Rb, Cs, HC_2
State		Colourless crystals	
Preparation	Has not been isolated. Is reported to be formed when acetylene is passed into a solution of lithium in liquid ammonia	(i) Pass acetylene over sodium at 190° (ii) Pass acetylene into a solution of sodium in liquid ammonia: $2NH_3Na + 2C_2H_2 = C_2HNa + NaNH_2 + C_2H_4 + NH_3$ (Moissan) (iii) Pass acetylene over sodium hydride at 210° (see below)	Pass acetylene over the heated metal or metal hydride
Reactions		Disproportionates at 210°. Is a vigorous reducing agent, and inflames in contact with oxidising substances. Reacts with water: $HOH + NaHC_2 = NaOH + C_2H_2$, and with alkyl halides: $C_2H_5Br + NaHC_2 = NaBr + C_2H_5HC_2$	

The acetylides	Li_2C_2	Na_2C_2	K_2, Rb_2, Cs_2, C_2
State	Colourless crystalline, non-conducting solids		
Preparation	(i) Heat lithium and carbon at a low red heat (ii) Pass C_2H_2 (or C_2H_4, or CO, or CO_2) over heated Li (iii) Pass C_2H_2 into a solution of lithium in liquid NH_3	Heat sodium hydroacetylide to 210°: $2NaC_2H = Na_2C_2 + C_2H_2$	Heat the hydro-acetylide
Reactions	Air: stable cold; oxidises if warmed. Water: Violent reactions yielding metallic hydroxide, carbon and hydrogen; acetylene is obtained if the reaction is moderated. Alkyl halides: Yields homologues of acetylene		
Structure	By analogy with calcium carbide the crystals are assumed to be ionic and to contain the ion $C \equiv C^{2-}$. No X-ray work appears to have been done		

The acetylides and hydroacetylides are strong reducing agents. They react with water with extreme violence to yield the metallic hydroxide, and free carbon and hydrogen. If the reaction is moderated by adding water to the acetylide suspended in ether, acetylene is evolved.

THE NITRIDES OF THE ALKALI METALS

Lithium nitride, Li_3N, exists as colourless transparent crystals with a hexagonal structure. It is made by passing nitrogen over lithium; the reaction takes place slowly at room temperature, and more rapidly as the temperature is raised.

Lithium nitride reacts readily with water to give lithium hydroxide and ammonia. If heated in a current of hydrogen it is reduced to lithium hydride; the reaction is reversible.

Lithium nitride forms double nitrides (which may be solid solutions) with certain other metallic nitrides. The double nitrides may be obtained (i) by heating lithium nitride with the second metal in an atmosphere of nitrogen or ammonia, (ii) by heating the lithium alloy of the second metal in an atmosphere of ammonia or nitrogen, or (iii) by heating a mixture of lithium nitride and the nitride of the second metal.

$(Li,Co)_3N$ is a black, brittle substance, decomposed by water or cold acids to give ammonia, nitrogen, hydrogen, and free cobalt. The double nitrides of nickel and copper behave similarly. Li_5SiN_3, Li_5TiN_3, Li_5GeN_3 are yellow, easily hydrolysed, salt-like substances with fluorite lattices. $LiMgN$, $LiZnN$, $LiAlN_2$, and the oxynitrides $Li_5MN_3,2Li_2O$ where $M = Ti$, Si, Ge, are also known.

Sodium nitride and potassium nitride. Neither sodium nitride nor potassium nitride can be made by the direct combination of the metal and molecular nitrogen under any conditions. These nitrides can be made:

  (i) by the action of active nitrogen on a film of the metal (continued action produces the azide; if, however, potassium azide is heated in vacuo, 20% remains behind as the nitride);

 (ii) by heating an intimate mixture of the metallic azide and the metal, prepared by the evaporation of a mixed solution of the metal and the azide in liquid ammonia.

Sodium nitride is red at room temperature, and darkens on heating to become black at 300°. It begins to dissociate at 300°. It is not affected by air or oxygen at room temperature, but it burns in oxygen if warmed. When treated with water (in which it is insoluble) it liberates ammonia. At slightly elevated temperatures it is reduced by hydrogen to sodium hydride and ammonia.

COMPLEX COMPOUNDS OF THE ALKALI METALS

Neutral complexes. Sodium ethylate reacts with benzoyl acetone to produce a compound $NaC_{10}H_9O_2$, which chars without melting, and dissolves in water but not in hydrocarbons. The structure is:

but the O^-Na^+ bond probably possesses considerable covalent character. On recrystallisation of this salt from 96% alcohol, crystals of a dihydrate are obtained which are perceptibly soluble in toluene, and the structure of the recrystallised material must be:

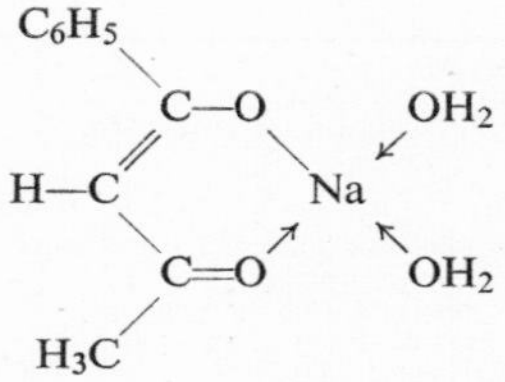

It is interesting to note that only two water molecules are taken up, and hence both the Na—O bonds to the benzoyl acetone radical are covalent, and the link O^-Na^+ in the anhydrous compound must have lost its ionic character. If one of the links in the hydrate were ionic, three water molecules would be necessary to complete the structure of four tetrahedral bonds. Further examples of both four and six co-ordinate neutral complexes of the alkali metals are given in Table 14.1.

Anionic complexes. It is not to be expected that the extremely electropositive alkali metals form anionic complexes. Nevertheless the addition of potassamide to sodium iodide in liquid ammonia solution precipitates the compound $KNa(NH_2)_2$, which might be written $K^+ [Na(NH_2)_2]^-$. The corresponding lithium compound, which should be more stable, does not appear to exist.

Cationic complexes. In many compounds a positive ion of an alkali metal is surrounded by four or six oxygen atoms. In hydrated compounds the oxygen atoms may be furnished by molecules of water of crystallisation. It is not always possible to decide whether the forces which hold such arrangements together are simple Coulomb forces, in which case the number of oxygen atoms in contact with the metal atom is decided by the co-ordination number of the metal, or whether there is interaction between the σ orbitals of the oxygen atom occupied by lone pairs, and the unoccupied atomic orbitals of the metal. Many salts of lithium and sodium are hydrated (according to Sidgwick, 76% of the lithium salts, and 74% of the sodium salts of 30 common inorganic acids form solid hydrates), but in few of these is the number of molecules of water of crystallisation either four or six, as would be expected if the oxygen atoms surrounding metal ions were solely contributed by water molecules. It has already been explained (p. 389) that in the hydrated salts of oxyacids the oxygen atoms surrounding the metal ions are furnished by the oxyacid anions as well as by the water molecules.

One of the few examples of a discrete cation present in a hydrated salt of an alkali metal is $[Na(H_2O)_3]_2[PtCl_6]$. The number of water molecules associated with one lithium ion never exceeds four. This limitation may arise because of the small size of the Li^+ cation, or because the absence of d orbitals in the valence shell of the lithium atom precludes octahedral hybridisation.

Table 15.1. *Examples of Types of Compo*

Oxidation Nu

	Compounds in which the atom is univalent	Be^+

Section	State of metal atom			Nature of unit formed	**Be**
	Hybrid-isation	Formal charge	Bonds †		
1		+2		Compounds in which the atom is present as a simple cation; the bonds may have both ionic and covalent character { Salts	None
				Giant molecules	Be_2B, $(BeC_2)_n$, Be_2C Be_3N_2, BeO BeX [X = S, Se, Te] BeF_2 $BeSO_4$ $Be(OH)_2$
2	Digonal	0	2σ	Non-chelate { Neutral complexes / Complex anions / Complex cations	$K_2[BeO_2]$
3	Trigonal	−1	3σ	Non-chelate { Neutral complexes / Complex anions / Complex cations	$(CH_3)_3N \cdot Be(iso-pr)_2$ $(CH_3)_3N \cdot Be(BH_4)_2$ cyclic [Be $CH_3 \cdot N(CH_3)_2]_3$ $NH_4[BeF_3]$, $Li[BeF_3]$
4	Tetra-hedral			Electron deficient compounds	$(BeH_2)_n$, $(Be(CH_3)_2)_n$, $(Be(C_2H_5)_2)$ $(BeCl_2)_n$, $Be(BH_4)_2$
		−2	4σ	Non-chelate { Neutral complexes / Complex anions / Complex cations	$BeCl_2, 2(C_2H_5)_2O$ $Be(CH_3)_2, 2N(CH_3)_3$ $K_2[Be(OH)_4]$, $K_2[Be(OC_2H_5)_4]$ $K_2[BeCl_4]$, $K_2[BeF_4]$ $K_2[Be_2F_7]$ $[Be(H_2O)_4]X_2$ [X = NO_3, ClO_4, $\frac{1}{2}SO_4$, $\frac{1}{2}CO_3$]
				Chelate { Neutral complexes / Complex anions / Complex cations	Acetylacetonate Hydroxyanthraquinone complex Normal acetate Basic acetate Alkali metal double sulphates Catechol complex Oxalate Salicylate $[Be\ en_2]Cl_2$
5	Octa-hedral	−4	6σ	Non-chelate { Neutral complexes / Complex anions / Complex cations	None

† In this column the expression "2σ" indicates the presence of two bonds each of type σ; the oth
pressions have corresponding meanings.

CHAPTER FIFTEEN

SUB-GROUP II N

THE ALKALINE EARTH METALS

The electronic configurations of the atoms, and the numerical values of the atomic and ionic properties, of the five alkaline earth metals are set out in Table 15.2. The electronic configurations of the atoms of the metals are similar; each atom possesses an inert gas core, and two electrons in the s orbital of the valency shell. By the loss of the two valency electrons the atom becomes a bivalent cation. The list of ionisation potentials given in Table 15.2 shows that the bivalent beryllium ion is formed much less readily than the barium ion. The ionisation potentials suggest that it might be *he Metal* = 1

| , $Mg(C_2H_5)^+$ | page 439 | CaCl,   CaH | page 449 | SrCl,   SrH | page 449 | BaCl,   BaH | page 449 |

he Metal = 2

Mg	page	Ca	page	Sr	page	Ba	page
$ClO_4)_2$, $Mg(NO_3)_2$, $NO_2)_2$, $MgCO_3$	440	$CaCO_3$, $Ca(NO_3)_2$ $CaSO_4$, $Ca(ClO_4)_2$		$SrCO_3$, $Sr(NO_3)_2$ $SrSO_4$, $Sr(ClO_4)_2$		$BaCO_3$, $Ba(NO_3)_2$ $BaSO_4$	
$_2$, MgB_2, MgC_2 $_3$, Mg_3N_2, $Mg(NH_2)_2$, MgO_2, MgS, $OH)_2$ $_2$ [X = F, Cl, Br, I]	441 442 443 443	CaH_2, CaHCl CaC_2, Ca_3N_2, CaO $Ca(OH)_2$, CaO_2 CaS CaX_2 [X = F, Cl, Br, I]	449 450 451 452	SrH_2, SrHCl SrC_2, Sr_3N_2, SrO $Sr(OH)_2$, SrO_2 SrS SrX_2 [X = F, Cl, Br, I]	449 450 451 452	BaH_2, BaHCl BaC_2, Ba_3N_2, BaO $Ba(OH)_2$, BaO_2 BaS BaX_2 [X = F, Cl, Br, I]	449 450 451 452
$C_2H_5)Br$	445	$Ca(C_2H_5)_2$	452	$Sr(C_2H_5)_2$	452	$Ba(C_2H_5)_2$	452
$NH_3)_2]X_2$ $X = Cl, ClO_4, NO_3, CN]$	444	$[Ca(H_2O)_2](ClO_4)_2$		$[Sr(H_2O)_2](ClO_4)_2$		$[Ba(H_2O)_2](ClO_4)_2$	
$_5)_2O \cdot Mg(C_2H_5)_2$	445						
$C_2H_5)_2)_n$	445						
$BH_4)_2$, $Mg(AlH_4)_2$	523						
$C_2H_5)Br, 2(C_2H_5)_2O$ $r_2, 2(C_2H_5)_2O$	446 444						
$MgCl_4]$, $K_2[MgF_4]$	446						
$H_2O)_4](ClO_4)_2$ $NH_3)_4]Cl_2$	447	$[Ca(NH_3)_4]Cl_2$ $[Ca(H_2O)_4](NO_3)_2$		$[Sr(H_2O)_4](NO_3)_2$ $[Sr(H_2O)_4](ClO_4)_2$		None	
$y$lacetonate nal acetate O_4	447 447 448	Acetylacetonate $CaC_2O_4, 3H_2O$	453 453	Acetylacetonate	453	Acetylacetonate	453
		$CaA_2, 2H_2O$	454				
$NH_3)_6](ClO_4)_2$ $H_2O)_6](ClO_4)_2$	448	$[Ca(H_2O)_6]Cl_2$	454	$[Sr(H_2O)_6]Cl_2$	454	$[Ba(H_2O)_6]I_2$	454

possible to form univalent ions of the metals, and, as the difference between the first and second ionisation potentials decreases on proceeding along the series from beryllium to barium, that the univalent Be^+ ion might be more stable than the univalent ion Ba^+. It is found, however, that exceptions to the rule that all the metals are consistently bivalent are very rare. There is some evidence for the univalency of beryllium, a little for the univalency of magnesium, and fairly good evidence for the existence of the subhalides CaCl, SrCl, and BaCl.

The different types of compounds formed by the metals are classified and illustrated in Table 15.1. A study of this Table indicates that the range of compounds formed by beryllium and magnesium is greater than the range of compounds formed by calcium, strontium, and barium. In particular, calcium, strontium, and barium do not form electron deficient compounds (Section 4, Table 15.1) and being more electropositive than beryllium or magnesium, their atoms are less likely to accept electrons from donor molecules and so form complexes. The diminution of co-ordinating power as the atomic number of the metal increases is shown by the degree of hydration of certain salts in Table 15.3, and also by the range of organic compounds containing oxygen with which the halides of calcium, strontium, and barium combine, as shown in the following list:

$CaCl_2$	$SrCl_2$	$BaCl_2$
Phenol, esters alcohol, acetone glycerol, sugars carboxylic acids	Alcohol, acetone glycerol, sugars carboxylic acids	Glycerol, sugars carboxylic acids

Table 15.2. *The Alkaline Earth Metals*

	Beryllium Be	Magnesium Mg	Calcium Ca	Strontium Sr	Barium Ba
Atomic number	4	12	20	38	56
Electronic configuration	2, 2	2, 8, 2	2, 8, 8, 2	2, 8, 18, 8, 2	2, 8, 18, 18, 8, 2
Atomic weight	9·02	24·32	40·08	87·63	137·36
Density	1·84	1·74	1·55	2·54	3·78
Crystal lattice	Hexagonal close-packed	Hexagonal close-packed	Hexagonal and F.c.c.	Below 235° F.c.c. 235–540° β 540–770° γ	Body centred cubic
m.p. °C	1278	649	810	770	830
b.p. °C	2970	1100	1439	1366	1737
Electrode potential on the hydrogen scale	1·69	2·40	2·87	2·92	2·90
Ionisation potential I	9·28	7·61	6·09	5·67	5·19
Ionisation potential II	18·12	14·96	11·82	10·98	9·95
Total	27·42	22·58	17·91	16·65	15·14
Atomic radius	1·06	1·40	1·74	1·92	1·98
Ionic radius	0·31	0·65	0·99	1·13	1·35
Deforming power†	17	3·3	1·8	1·2	1·0
Electronegativity	1·5	1·2	1·0	1·0	0·9
Ionic mobility at 25°	30	55·5	59·8	59·8	64·2

F.c.c. indicates face-centred cubical close-packed.
† The ionic charge divided by the square of the ionic radius.

Table 15.3. *Numbers of Molecules of Water of Crystallisation associated with one Molecule of certain Compounds of the Alkaline Earth Metals*

		Be	Mg	Ca	Sr	Ba
Hydroxides,	$M(OH)_2$				8, 1, 0	8, 1, 0
Peroxides,	MO_2			8, 2	8	8
Fluorides,	MF_2					
Chlorides,	MCl_2	4, 0	12, 8, 6, 4, 0	6, 4, 2, 1, 0	6, 2, 1	2, 0
Bromides,	MBr_2	4	10, 6, 4, 0	6, 0	6, 2, 0	2, 1, 0
Iodides,	MI_2		10, 8, 6, 0	8, 6, 0	6, 2, 1	6, 2, 1
Carbonates,	MCO_3	4	5, 3, 1	6, 1	0	0
Nitrates,	$M(NO_3)_2$	4	9, 6, 2, 0	4, 3, 2, 0	4, 0	0
Sulphates,	MSO_4	4, 2, 0	12, 7, 6, 1, 0	2, $\frac{1}{2}$, 0	0	0
Chlorates,	$M(ClO_3)_2$		6, 4	6, 4, 2	3, 0	1
Perchlorates,	$M(ClO_4)_2$	4	6, 4, 2, 0	2, 0	4, 2, $\frac{2}{3}$	3, 1, 0
Nitrites,	$M(NO_2)_2$		9, 6, 3, 0			

Table 15.4.   *The Halides of the Alkaline Earth Metals*   421

Fluorides

	BeF_2	MgF_2	CaF_2	SrF_2	BaF_2
Appearance	Colourless amorphous	Colourless tetragonal crystals	Colourless cubic crystals	Colourless cubic crystals	Colourless cubic crystals
Lattice	Cristobalite	Rutile	Fluorite	Fluorite	Fluorite
m.p. °C	800	About 1350	About 1350	About 1300	1285
b.p. °C	1159			2490	2140
Solubility: moles per 100 moles of water	10	346×10^{-5}	$58 \cdot 4 \times 10^{-5}$	168×10^{-5}	1675×10^{-5}

Chlorides

	$BeCl_2$	$MgCl_2$	$CaCl_2$	$SrCl_2$	$BaCl_2$
Appearance	Colourless needles Deliquescent	Colourless hexagonal crystals Deliquescent	Colourless cubic crystals Deliquescent	Colourless cubic crystals	Colourless monoclinic crystals
Lattice	Chain	$CdCl_2$	Slightly deformed rutile	Slightly deformed rutile	$PbCl_2$
m.p. °C	About 430	715	773	870	960
b.p. °C	488	1400			1560
Solubility: moles per 100 moles of water	Large	10·2	13·2	6·30	3·22
Hydrates	4, 0	12, 8, 6, 4, 0	6†, 4, 2, 1, 0	6†, 2, 1	2, 0
Solubility in organic compounds	Large if they contain O or N	Soluble in alcohol	Soluble in alcohol and in organic acids	Soluble in alcohol, but less than $CaCl_2$	Slightly soluble in methyl, but not in ethyl alcohol
Ammines	12‡, 6‡, 4	6, 4, 2	8, 4		
Temperature at which pressure of NH_3 over ammine is 100 mm			105·4°	71·9°	12·5°

Bromides

	$BeBr_2$	$MgBr_2$	$CaBr_2$	$SrBr_2$	$BaBr_2$
Appearance	White needles Deliquescent	Colourless hexagonal crystals Deliquescent	White needles Deliquescent	White needles Hygroscopic	Colourless crystals
Lattice		CdI_2	Slightly deformed rutile	Distorted $PbCl_2$	$PbCl_2$
m.p. °C	490	700	760	643	847
Solubility: moles per 100 moles of water		10	13·6	7·25	6·30
Hydrates	4	10, 6, 4, 0	6, 0	6, 2, 0	2, 1, 0
Solubility in organic compounds		Large if the compound contains oxygen	Soluble in alcohol	Soluble in alcohol	Soluble in alcohol

Iodides

	BeI_2	MgI_2	CaI_2	SrI_2	BaI_2
Appearance	Colourless needles	Hexagonal crystals Deliquescent	Colourless plates	Colourless plates	
Lattice		CdI_2	CdI_2		$PbCl_2$
m.p. °C	About 500	> 700	740		740
Solubility: moles per 100 moles of water		9·6	12·5	13·4	9·5
Hydrates		10, 8, 6, 0	8, 6, 0	6, 2, 1	6, 2, 1
Solubility in organic compounds		Soluble	Soluble	Soluble	Soluble

† Isomorphous.   ‡ Stable only below −50°.

The solubilities of the salts of the metals vary according to the same pattern as the degree of hydration. Usually the beryllium salt is the most soluble, and there is a fall in molecular solubility from beryllium to barium. This is well exemplified by the nitrates, sulphates, and chlorates. The same tendency is shown by other salts, but without the same regularity. The large difference between the molecular solubility of beryllium fluoride (10 moles per 100 moles of water) and the other fluorides (roughly 10^{-4} moles per 100 moles of water) is striking. The degree of hydration of the metallic ions in solution is indicated by the ionic mobilities at 25°. Here again the beryllium ion is associated with the greatest number of molecules of water of hydration, and the barium ion with the least. The solubility of the salts of these metals in organic compounds containing oxygen also decreases from beryllium to barium (see, for example, the chlorides, Table 15.4).

The tendency of the atom to exert ionic bonds is least in beryllium and greatest in barium. Stable anhydrous salts of the ions Ca^{2+}, Sr^{2+}, and Ba^{2+} are familiar; there is no evidence for the existence of Be^{2+}. The ionic character of corresponding compounds of the metals increases as the electronegativities of the metals decrease. This trend is illustrated by the nature of the crystal lattices of compounds of the alkaline earth metals as shown in Table 15.5.

Table 15.5.   *Crystal Lattices of certain Binary Compounds of the Alkaline Earth Metals*

Type of compound	Be	Mg	Ca	Sr	Ba
MO	Wurtzite	NaCl	NaCl	NaCl	NaCl
MS	Zincblende	NaCl	NaCl	NaCl	NaCl
MSe	Zincblende	NaCl	NaCl	NaCl	NaCl
MTe	Zincblende	Zincblende	NaCl	NaCl	NaCl
MF_2	Cristobalite	Rutile	Fluorite	Fluorite	Fluorite
MCl_2	Chain structure	$CdCl_2$	Rutile	Rutile	$PbCl_2$
MI_2			CdI_2		

The Table shows that all the beryllium compounds have covalent lattices. Compounds of the other metals have covalent lattices only if the anions are large and deformable. The diminution of deforming power with increase of atomic number is also shown by the increasing thermal stability of the hydroxides, peroxides, and carbonates of the metals on passing from beryllium to barium. The thermal stability is indicated by the temperature at which the dissociation pressure of the compound attains a certain value. Table 15.6 shows the temperatures at which certain dissociation pressures are reached by the dissociation products of the hydroxides, carbonates, and peroxides of the alkaline earth metals.

Table 15.6.   *Dissociation Pressures of certain Compounds of the Alkaline Earth Metals*

Compound	Dissociation pressure	Temperature at which dissociation pressure is reached, °C				
		Be	Mg	Ca	Sr	Ba
$M(OH)_2$	10 mm		300	390	466	700
MCO_3	1 atm	25	540	900	1289	1360
MO_2	1 atm				357	840

Calcium, strontium, and barium dissolve in cold water liberating hydrogen. The standard molar potentials of magnesium and beryllium suggest that these metals should react similarly, but they are in fact inert. This inertness must be due to the formation of a protective film of hydroxide on the surface of the metal.

All the metals burn in oxygen to give the oxide MO. Beryllium oxide is insoluble in water. The oxides of the other metals dissolve in water to give the hydroxides with increasing vigour as the atomic number of the metal increases. Beryllium oxide is amphoteric, but K_2BeO_2 has to be made in alcoholic solution as it is immediately hydrolysed by water. The oxides of the other metals show no acidic properties and become increasingly basic down the Group from magnesium to barium. Both beryllium and magnesium oxides possess the curious property of dissolving in aqueous solutions of beryllium salts; magnesium oxide also dissolves in an aqueous solution of magnesium chloride. This property is discussed on p. 426.

Calcium, strontium, and barium all form well-characterised peroxides of general formula MO_2, which can be precipitated from aqueous solutions of the salts of the metals as the octahydrates of general formula $MO_2,8H_2O$. Beryllium forms no oxide higher than BeO; magnesium oxide cannot be oxidised to MgO_2, but this unstable compound can be obtained indirectly.

BERYLLIUM

PROPERTIES OF THE METAL

Beryllium is a steel-grey metal, ductile only at high temperatures.

Table 15.7. *Reactions of Beryllium Metal*

Reagent	Conditions for reaction	Description of reaction	Product
H_2	Molecular H_2 at any temperature	No reaction	
	Atomic H_2		BeH_2
O_2		Burns brilliantly	BeO
Air	Massive metal		
	cold	No reaction	⎰Covered with layer of
	hot	No reaction	⎱ protective oxide
	Metal powder	Burns on ignition	Be_3N_2 and BeO
Steam	Cold, or red heat	No reaction	
C	Up to 1200°	No reaction	
N_2	1000°		Be_3N_2
S	Ignition in S vapour	Burns vigorously	BeS
Se and Te			BeSe and BeTe
Cl_2, Br_2, I_2	Cold	No reaction	
	Hot	Burns	$BeCl_2$, etc.
Water		No action	
HCl	Dilute	Dissolves	$BeCl_2$
H_2SO_4	Dilute	Dissolves	$BeSO_4$
HNO_3	Dilute or conc.	Rendered passive	
Alkali	Cold 50% NaOH	Dissolves	H_2
	Hot 10% NaOH	Dissolves	H_2
C_2H_5OH			$Be(OC_2H_5)_2$

GENERAL CHEMISTRY OF BERYLLIUM†

The general chemistry of beryllium is illustrated in Table 15.1. The table shows that, with the exception of simple ionic compounds, there are beryllium compounds which exemplify every mode of combination that the beryllium atom could adopt.

The electron configuration of the beryllium atom in the ground state is $1s^2$, $2s^2$. The configuration of the simple cation Be^{2+} would be $1s^2$. It would have a very small radius, 0·31, and a double charge; the penultimate shell of 2 electrons has a low screening power. Hence the Be^{2+} ion would polarise any atom with which it is in contact, and covalent bonds would be formed. It is extremely doubtful, therefore, whether the simple ion Be^{2+} exists in any stable beryllium compound. It might be sought in the beryllium salts. The perchlorate ion is one of the least easily deformable anions, but beryllium perchlorate in the solid state is known only as the tetrahydrate, $Be(ClO_4)_2,4H_2O$, which loses no water up to the temperature at which it begins to decompose. The formula is clearly $(Be,4H_2O)^{2+}(ClO_4^-)_2$. Anhydrous beryllium sulphate is well known, and it can be heated to 580° before sulphur trioxide is liberated. It is certain, however, that its structure is that of a sulphato-complex (p. 427). Beryllium fluoride, BeF_2, which might be expected to contain the ion Be^{2+}, crystallises with the typically covalent cristobalite structure, and in the fused state it is a very poor conductor of electricity. It may therefore be concluded that there is no salt in which the simple ion Be^{2+} is present.

There are a number of beryllium compounds including the methanide Be_2C, and the boride Be_2B, which crystallise with the antifluorite lattice, and might therefore be regarded as ionic. These are high-melting compounds, and in the solid state they almost certainly exist as giant molecules. Even if the bonding is to some extent ionic in character, the proportion of covalent bonding must be high, and the compounds may be classified with beryllium oxide, beryllium fluoride, and other beryllium compounds which have covalent giant molecule structures. Hence there is no evidence for the existence of compounds in which the simple cation Be^{2+} exerts pure ionic bonds.

A study of the hydrates of the so-called beryllium salts shows that the number of molecules of water of crystallisation associated with one atom of beryllium is consistently four. The complexes formed from beryllium chloride by the exertion of bonds between the beryllium atoms and oxygen or nitrogen atoms (Table 15.8, p. 431) can nearly all be formulated on the assumption that the beryllium atom exerts four covalent bonds. The beryllium atom is also four covalent in the neutral complexes such as the acetyl acetonate, the basic acetate, and in the complex anions $(BeO_2)^{2-}$ and $(BeF_4)^{2-}$. The co-ordination number four is also shown by the beryllium atom in the wurtzite structure of the oxide, in the zinc blende structure of the sulphide, in the cristobalite structure of the fluoride, in the antifluorite structures of the methanide, Be_2C, and the boride, Be_2B, and in the phenacite structure of the silicate Be_2SiO_4.

The maximum co-ordination number, four, is in accordance with the orbital structure of the beryllium atom, which consists of the K and L shells only. Those two shells are completely occupied by ten electrons ($1s^2$, $2s^2$, $2p^6$). If the beryllium atom were to be associated with more than ten electrons, those in excess of ten would have to occupy $3s$ or $3p$ orbitals of the M shell. These orbitals, however, have relatively high energy levels, and their occupation in a stable beryllium compound would be unlikely.

Since the valence shell of the beryllium atom (the L shell) has no d orbitals, the atom is incapable of octahedral hybridisation and there can be no beryllium compounds in Section 5 of Table 15.1.

†Beryllium compounds are extremely toxic when inhaled or injected into the blood stream.

The co-ordination number of the beryllium atom appears to be six, however, in the following complexes:

(i) in the unstable chloroberyllate ion $(BeCl_6)^{4-}$ which on conductometric evidence may exist in solution;

(ii) in the complexes $[Be(H_2O)_6](C_6H_5SO_3)_2$ and $[BePhen_3](ClO_4)_2$†;

(iii) in the following complexes formed from beryllium chloride:

$$BeCl_2,6NH_3, \quad BeCl_2,12NH_3,$$
$$BeCl_2,2NH_3,4CH_3COCH_3.$$

$$BeCl_2,2CH_3COCH_3,4C_6H_6, \quad Be(N_2H_4)_3Cl_2,$$
$$Be(NH_2 \cdot NHC_6H_5)_3Cl_2.$$

In the first three of the beryllium chloride complexes ammonia molecules may be linked to one another or to acetone molecules by hydrogen bonds (p. 431) and these complexes may, on this assumption, be assigned constitutions which do not require the co-ordination number of the beryllium atom to exceed four. For the second three of the beryllium complexes no such explanation is possible. The compounds of beryllium illustrating each Section of Table 15.1 are described and discussed in the following pages.

SECTION 1. BERYLLIUM COMPOUNDS WITH IONIC CHARACTER

The absence of beryllium compounds containing the simple ion Be^{2+} has already been discussed. Certain giant molecule compounds of beryllium probably contain bonds with a significant degree of ionic character; these compounds are considered in this Section.

The univalent ion Be^+. There is chemical evidence for the existence of the ion Be^+. If a conducting aqueous solution is electrolysed between beryllium electrodes in a divided cell, an anolyte is obtained which reduces potassium permanganate to manganese dioxide, and silver salts to silver.‡ It is assumed that Be^+ has been formed by anodic oxidation. If no oxidising agent is present the Be^+ ion is lost by one or both of the reactions:

$$Be^+ + 2H_2O = Be(OH)_2 + H + H^+$$
$$2Be^+ = Be + Be^{2+}.$$

BERYLLIUM COMPOUNDS CONSISTING OF GIANT MOLECULES IN WHICH THE BONDS HAVE SOME IONIC CHARACTER

Examples of beryllium compounds which consist of giant molecules are given in Table 15.1; there are no examples of layer lattices among beryllium compounds. Some of the more important giant molecule compounds are described below.

Beryllium boride, Be_2B, is formed from the elements at 1400°. It has an antifluorite lattice. The distance Be—B is 2·01, and B—B is 3·3.

Beryllium acetylide, BeC_2, is obtained by passing acetylene over metallic beryllium at 450°. If treated with water, alkalis, or acids it liberates acetylene.

Beryllium methanide, Be_2C, is a brick red compound, hard enough to scratch glass and quartz. It is made by heating the elements together at 1300°, or by heating BeO and carbon at 2000°. It reacts slowly with water, and rapidly with hot aqueous alkalis to give CH_4. With HF at 450°, or HCl at 600°, it yields the beryllium halide, hydrogen, and carbon. The lattice is antifluorite.

†The abbreviation *Phen* represents one molecule of *o*-phenanthroline.
‡ *Ann. Reports*, **53**, 1956, 85.

14*

Beryllium nitride, Be_3N_2, is a white crystalline powder with the anti-Mn_2O_3 lattice; m.p. about 2200°. It is made by heating the metal and nitrogen at 900°, or the metal and potassium cyanide at 700°:

$$3Be + 2KCN = Be_3N_2 + 2K + 2C,$$

or beryllium methanide and nitrogen at 1250°. When treated with water, acids, or alkalis it liberates ammonia.

Beryllium oxide, BeO, is the only oxide of beryllium. It is made by heating the hydroxide to 440°, or the basic carbonate to 600°. It is a white powder, with the wurtzite lattice, m.p. 2570°. It volatilises in steam at 1250°. It is unchanged by heating in air. When strongly heated with carbon, silicon, or boron it yields Be_2C, Be_2Si, or Be_2B. When heated with carbon in a current of chlorine it yields $BeCl_2$. With CS_2 at 1200° it yields BeS.

Beryllium oxide is insoluble in water. It is amphoteric, but it is an extremely weak base and an extremely weak acid. When freshly prepared it dissolves in acids, but after ignition its rate of solution is greatly reduced. The salts formed from BeO as a base are easily hydrolysed by water; the carbonate, nitrate, cyanide, and fluoride, hydrolyse so easily that they cannot be isolated by the evaporation of the warm aqueous solution. When treated with KHF_2 beryllium oxide forms potassium fluoro-beryllate, K_2BeF_4.

Beryllium oxide dissolves in aqueous solutions of beryllium salts, in some cases up to several molecular proportions. The presence of the dissolved beryllium oxide produces the following effects:

(i) there is a small increase in the electrical conductivity (3 to 7%); hence the number of ions does not change;

(ii) there is a slight increase in the freezing point depression, suggesting a fall in the concentration of water available as solvent;

(iii) the solubilities of the sulphate and the selenate are increased, and it is found that

$$\frac{\text{increased solubility (mole/litre)}}{\text{BeO dissolved (mole/litre)}} = \frac{1}{4},$$

suggesting that four molecules of beryllium oxide are associated with one $(Be(H_2O)_4)^{2+}$ ion.

Sidgwick has suggested that the beryllium oxide replaces the water in the hydrated beryllium ion of the original salt, thus

$$4BeO \;+\; \left[\begin{array}{c} OH_2 \\ \downarrow \\ H_2O\!\rightarrow\!Be\!\leftarrow\!OH_2 \\ \uparrow \\ OH_2 \end{array}\right]^{2+} \;=\; \left[\begin{array}{c} Be \\ \| \\ O \\ \downarrow \\ Be\!=\!O\!\rightarrow\!Be\!\leftarrow\!O\!=\!Be \\ \uparrow \\ O \\ \| \\ Be \end{array}\right]^{2+} \;+\; 4H_2O$$

There are, however, certain considerations against the above explanation of the solubility of beryllium oxide in a beryllium salt solution:

(i) there is some evidence for the existence of $BeSO_4,BeO$, but not of any sulphate containing a higher proportion of BeO;

(ii) in the anionic catechol complex (p. 437), the beryllium atom is tetracovalent, yet this complex dissolves beryllium hydroxide;

(iii) the structure of beryllium oxide is that of a giant molecule with a wurtzite lattice; the structure $Be^{II}O$ is otherwise unknown and is unlikely.

(iv) Magnesium oxide dissolves in an aqueous solution of beryllium sulphate until the ratio Mg:Be is 1:2. After this stage is reached solution is much slower and $Be(OH)_2$ and basic sulphates are precipitated. Metallic magnesium also dissolves rapidly in beryllium sulphate solution with the liberation of hydrogen until the same ratio is reached. Magnesium oxide also dissolves in an aqueous solution of magnesium chloride (p. 444). From the resultant solution the basic salt $Mg(OH)_3(Cl),4H_2O$ has been obtained and examined crystallographically. Clearly the property of beryllium oxide which enables it to dissolve in aqueous solutions of beryllium salts is not unique.

There is good evidence that beryllium oxide is not present in beryllium sulphate solution as a lyophobic colloid, but on balance it is probable that the product of the solution of beryllium oxide in beryllium chloride is a basic salt held in super-saturated solution, or a lyophilic colloidal system. The extreme ease by which a supersaturated solution of magnesium oxalate is prepared by dissolving magnesium oxide in oxalic acid solution may be significant.

Beryllium hydroxide, $Be(OH)_2$, is obtained as a gelatinous precipitate from solutions of beryllium salts by the introduction of the OH^- ion. The precipitate dissolves in excess of an alkali metal hydroxide, but if the solution stands, $Be(OH)_2$ is precipitated again in a crystalline and much less soluble form. The crystalline form, however, dissolves in very strong (10 Normal) sodium hydroxide solution, presumably as the beryllate, Na_2BeO_2.

The purest $Be(OH)_2$ is made by passing air containing ammonia through beryllium sulphate solution. If the precipitate is heated to 418° water is lost, and the residual BeO may be weighed for the gravimetric determination of beryllium.

Beryllium hydroxide does not absorb carbon dioxide, except in the presence of moisture, when it reacts slowly to give $BeCO_3,4H_2O$ (p. 435). Beryllium hydroxide is insoluble in water. It dissolves in ammonium carbonate solution, but a basic carbonate is precipitated on boiling. It is insoluble in solutions of other ammonium salts. It dissolves in a solution of ethylamine diamine, but not in solutions of other amines. Beryllium hydroxide, like the oxide, dissolves readily in solutions of beryllium salts (see above).

Beryllium sulphide, BeS, is made by the action of hydrogen sulphide on beryllium chloride at a red heat. It can also be made by burning beryllium in sulphur vapour, by the action of CS_2 on BeO at 1200°, or by the action of $BeSO_4$ on sulphur vapour at high temperatures, either alone or in the presence of a catalyst such as carbon, calcium carbide, or zinc. The separation of BeS from BeO cannot be effected. Beryllium sulphide burns in air to beryllium oxide and sulphur dioxide. It is almost insoluble in water to which it is very stable, but it is easily decomposed by acids. It ignites in concentrated nitric acid. It has the zinc blende structure; the distance Be—S is 2·10.

Beryllium selenide and telluride have been made from the elements. The solids also have the zinc blende structure.

Anhydrous beryllium sulphate $BeSO_4$. Beryllium sulphate tetrahydrate, $[Be,4H_2O]SO_4$, loses water at 400° to give the anhydrous salt. This does not decompose below 580°, and it is almost insoluble in cold water. With hot water, however, it reacts to form the tetrahydrate which dissolves freely. These properties suggest that the anhydrous sulphate is a sulphato complex, with the chain structure:

Beryllium fluoride, BeF$_2$, can be obtained by the ignition of beryllium oxide in gaseous hydrogen fluoride, or by the action of fluorine on the metal, or on beryllium carbide, Be$_2$C. It is best made by heating ammonium fluoroberyllate. The action takes place in two stages:

(i) at 230°, $\qquad$ (NH$_4$)$_2$BeF$_4$ = NH$_4$BeF$_3$ + NH$_4$F,

(ii) at 270°, $\qquad$ NH$_4$BeF$_3$ = NH$_3$ + HF + BeF$_2$.

Beryllium fluoride cannot be made by the action of hydrofluoric acid on beryllium hydroxide, because it is hydrolysed by water. It is hygroscopic and very soluble in water, but on account of hydrolysis, neither beryllium fluoride itself, nor its hydrate, can be isolated by crystallisation. It does not dissolve in anhydrous hydrogen fluoride, it is only very slightly soluble in absolute alcohol, and it absorbs ammonia to give only the unstable monammine BeF$_2$,NH$_3$. The small tendency of beryllium fluoride to combine with donor compounds implies that the beryllium atom is 4 covalent in the crystal. Beryllium fluoride fuses at the estimated temperature of 800° to a melt which crystallises with the cristobalite structure. The melt is a bad conductor of electricity.

SECTION 2. THE BERYLLIUM ATOM IN THE DIGONAL VALENCE STATE

There are no compounds which can be assigned to this Section with certainty. Beryllium hydride, the beryllium alkyls, and beryllium chloride (Table 15.1, Section 4) are polymerised; the atoms are linked into long chains by three-centre bonds. There seem to be no beryllium compounds corresponding to the co-ordination compound of magnesium [Mg,2NH$_3$]Cl$_2$. The beryllium atom may be digonally hybridised in potassium beryllate, K$_2$BeO$_2$. This salt is a very hygroscopic solid which is hydrolysed by water. It is made by treating freshly prepared beryllium hydroxide with an absolute alcohol solution of KOH in the complete absence of water and carbon dioxide.

SECTION 3. COMPOUNDS IN WHICH THE BERYLLIUM ATOM IS TRIGONALLY HYBRIDISED

Examples of compounds containing the trigonally hybridised beryllium atom are rare. Among the non-chelate neutral compounds are the additive compound of trimethylamine and beryllium borohydride, m.p. 35° (mentioned in Table 15.1, and described on p. 523), and the additive compound of trimethylamine and di-*iso*-propyl beryllium. There is also the interesting cyclic compound:

The complex anion (BeF$_3$)$^-$ is present in NH$_4$BeF$_3$, and in LiBeF$_3$.

SECTION 4. COMPOUNDS IN WHICH THE BERYLLIUM ATOM IS TETRAHEDRALLY HYBRIDISED

Beryllium compounds of this Section outnumber those in any other. The Section includes the electron deficient compounds such as $[Be(CH_3)_2]_n$ to which (with the exception of $[Mg(C_2H_5)_2]_n$) there are no corresponding compounds of the other metals of the sub-Group. Every type of beryllium complex, neutral, anionic, and cationic, chelate and non-chelate, is represented in the Section (Table 15.1). Examples of types of beryllium compounds included in the Section are discussed below.

ELECTRON-DEFICIENT COMPOUNDS

Among the beryllium compounds in this class are beryllium hydride BeH_2, beryllium dimethyl, $Be(CH_3)_2$, and beryllium chloride, $BeCl_2$. All these compounds are polymerised, and the formulae given are empirical. Beryllium borohydride (p. 523) is a member of this class; it differs from the compounds described in the following paragraphs in having a discrete molecule.

Beryllium hydride, BeH_2, is a white non-volatile compound. It is formed:

(i) by treating beryllium dimethyl, $Be(CH_3)_2$, or beryllium dichloride, $BeCl_2$, with lithium aluminium hydride in ethereal solution:

$$Be(CH_3)_2 + 2LiAlH_4 = BeH_2 + 2LiAlH_3(CH_3),$$

(ii) by heating di-*tert.*-butyl beryllium at 210°:

$$((CH_3)_3C)_2Be = BeH_2 + 2(CH_3)_2C{=}CH_2,$$

(iii) by the action of atomic hydrogen on metallic beryllium.

Beryllium hydride is stable at room temperature, but it dissociates above 125°. It reacts with diborane to give beryllium borohydride:

$$BeH_2 + B_2H_6 = Be(BH_4)_2,$$

and with dimethylamine to give the nitride derivative $[(CH_3)_2NBeN(CH_3)_2]_3$.

For a discussion on the structure of beryllium hydride, see p. 433.

The beryllium alkyls.

$Be(CH_3)_2$	$Be(C_2H_5)_2$	$Be(C_3H_7)_2$	$Be(C_4H_9)_2$	Be di-*iso*-propyl
White crystalline solid which sublimes without melting at 200°	Colourless liquid; b.p. about 200° with some decomposition	Colourless liquid	Colourless liquid	Colourless liquid, m.p. −9.5°

The low volatility of $Be(CH_3)_2$ and $Be(C_2H_5)_2$ compared with the low b.p. of the corresponding zinc compounds ($Zn(CH_3)_2$, 46° and $Zn(C_2H_5)_2$, 118°) shows that the beryllium compounds are polymerised.

Beryllium dimethyl, $Be(CH_3)_2$, is made by the action of methyl magnesium iodide on beryllium dichloride:

$$BeCl_2 + 2MgCH_3I = Be(CH_3)_2 + MgI_2 + MgCl_2.$$

It is extremely reactive, and its preparation must be conducted in an atmosphere of pure hydrogen or nitrogen; air, water, and carbon dioxide must be entirely excluded. It is spontaneously inflammable in air; a concentrated solution in ether also ignites spontaneously in air. The crystalline compound ignites in carbon dioxide, but the ethereal solution reacts with carbon dioxide to yield acetic acid. It reacts with diborane at 95° to give beryllium borohydride, and with lithium aluminium hydride to give the hydride, BeH_2. It is quantitatively hydrolysed by water:†

$$Be(CH_3)_2 + 2H_2O = Be(OH)_2 + 2CH_4.$$

Beryllium dimethyl forms co-ordination compounds with $N(CH_3)_3$, $P(CH_3)_3$, $(CH_3)_2O$, $(C_2H_5)_2O$, but not with $As(CH_3)_3$ or with $S(CH_3)_2$. The stability of the complexes is in the order $N > P > O$. If the donor molecule contains a hydrogen atom which is not part of an alkyl group, as for example, H_2NCH_3, $HN(CH_3)_2$, $HP(CH_3)_2$, CH_3OH, CH_3SH, HCl, a reaction occurs in which methane is evolved, and a polymerised residue remains. Dimethylamine reacts to give the trimeric compound $(Be(CH_3) \cdot N(CH_3)_2)_3$, which may be cyclic. The structures of the beryllium alkyls are discussed on p. 432.

The beryllium halides. The physical properties of the beryllium halides are set out in Table 15.4. Beryllium fluoride is described on p. 428.

Beryllium chloride. Anhydrous $BeCl_2$ is a colourless crystalline compound which sublimes and fumes in moist air. The vapour is associated, and the fused compound is a very poor conductor. The specific conductivity at 451° is 0·00319 mho cm^{-1}, which is about 1/1000 that of fused sodium chloride.

Beryllium chloride is made:

(i) by the action of chlorine or hydrogen chloride on the metal,
(ii) by the action of chlorine at high temperature on a mixture of beryllium oxide and carbon,
(iii) by heating the oxide to 800° in the vapour of CCl_4, S_2Cl_2, PCl_3 or PCl_5,
(iv) by heating the acetylide BeC_2 in chlorine to about 280°.

Beryllium chloride dissolves freely in water with the evolution of heat. The ion $(Be,4H_2O)^{2+}$ is formed, and on crystallisation the salt $(Be,4H_2O)Cl_2$ is deposited. This holds its water so strongly that it is not dehydrated at all by several months exposure to P_2O_5. The chloride of the hydrated ion is not soluble in donating organic solvents. Anhydrous beryllium chloride is insoluble in chloroform, carbon tetrachloride, carbon disulphide, and benzene, but it dissolves freely in organic liquids containing oxygen atoms or nitrogen atoms with lone electron pairs. It is easily soluble in ether, acetone, nitromethane, benzaldehyde, anisole, in liquid ammonia, and in many amines and nitriles. Beryllium chloride forms many complexes with donor molecules. The formulae of certain of these complexes are given in Table 15.8.

Complexes of one molecule of beryllium chloride with two donor groups can be formulated thus:

$$
\begin{array}{c}
Cl \\
| \\
(C_2H_5)_2\overset{+}{O}-\overset{-}{Be}-\overset{+}{O}(C_2H_5)_2 \\
| \\
Cl
\end{array}
$$

A complex of one molecule of beryllium chloride with four donor groups can be

† It may be noted that when beryllium diethyl reacts with a small quantity of water, no beryllium hydroxide is precipitated. In this reaction complexes such as

$$
\begin{array}{c}
C_2H_5 \\
| \\
H_2O \rightarrow Be \leftarrow OH_2 \\
| \\
C_2H_5
\end{array}
$$

may be formed.

Table 15.8.   *Certain Complexes of Beryllium Chloride*

Ligand	Complex	Notes
Alcohols	{constitution unknown}	
Phenols		
Ether	$BeCl_2,2(C_2H_5)_2O$	White crystals, m.p. 330°
		Decomposes in air. Soluble in C_6H_6, CS_2, CCl_4
Aldehydes	$BeCl_2,2CH_3CHO$	
Ketones	$BeCl_2,2CH_3COCH_3$	
	$BeCl_2,2CH_3COCH_3,4C_6H_6$	m.p. 40°, loses C_6H_6 easily
Nitrobenzene	$BeCl_2,2C_6H_5NO_2$	
Ammonia	$BeCl_2,4NH_3$	Stable at room temperature. Pressure of NH_3 at 156° is only 6 mm
	$BeCl_2,6NH_3$	Decomposes in air at $-50°$
	$BeCl_2,12NH_3$	Decomposes in air at $-50°$
	$BeCl_2,2NH_3,4CH_3COCH_3$	In dry air loses acetone, but not ammonia
Amines	$BeCl_2,4CH_3NH_2$	
$NH_2CH_2CH_2NH_2$	$BeCl_2,2C_2N_2H_8$	Insoluble in water
	$BeCl_2,3C_2N_2H_8$	
$NH_2NHC_6H_5$	$BeCl_2,3NH_2NHC_6H_5$	
Hydrocyanic acid	$BeCl_2,4HCN$	
Nitriles	$BeCl_2,2CH_3CN$	

The strengths of the bonds Be—X, where X is H_2O, NH_3, or $(C_2H_5)_2O$, decrease in that order; amines expel ether from complexes, and water expels ammonia.

formulated in two ways, (a) as a covalent structure in which two molecules of the ligand are linked by hydrogen bonds (p. 371), thus:

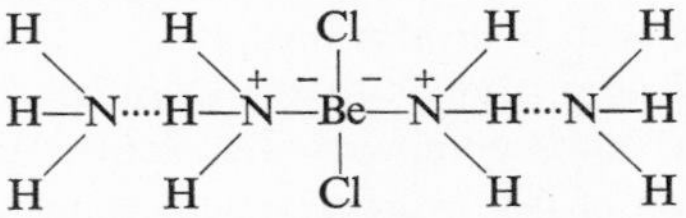

or, (b) as an ionic structure in which the ligand has expelled the chlorine atoms from covalent bonds with the beryllium atom, thus:

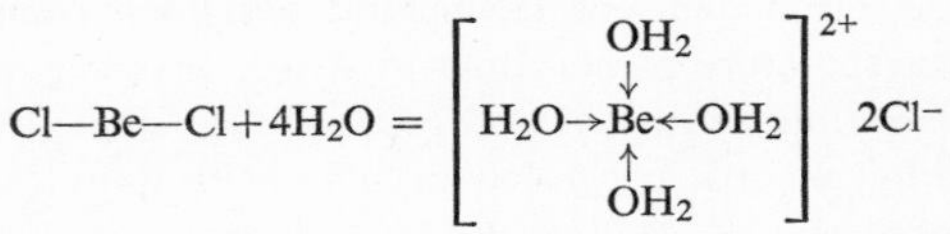

$$Cl—Be—Cl+4H_2O = \left[\begin{array}{c} OH_2 \\ \downarrow \\ H_2O \rightarrow Be \leftarrow OH_2 \\ \uparrow \\ OH_2 \end{array} \right]^{2+} 2Cl^-$$

The ionic type is probably formed when the ligand is strongly binding like H_2O or NH_3; the very small dissociation pressures of the tetrahydrate and tetra-ammoniate confirm this. More weakly bonding ligands such as HCN may form the covalent type:

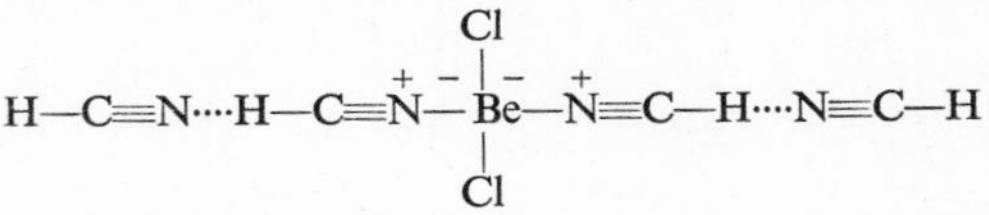

It is interesting to note that the complex with methyl cyanide, which could not develop hydrogen bonds, contains only two molecules of ligand per atom of beryllium.

Complexes with 6 or 12 molecules of ligand (one molecule of ethylene diamine counts as two for this purpose, because it contains two donor nitrogen atoms) per atom of beryllium are unstable, and may be formulated using hydrogen bonds, for example:

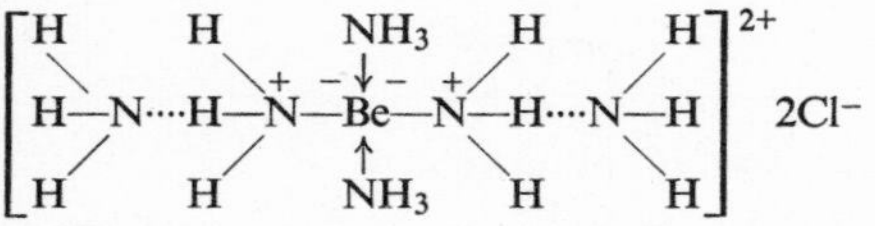

$$\begin{bmatrix} H & H & NH_3 & H & H \\ \diagdown & \diagdown{}^+ \ ^- \downarrow{}^- \ ^+\diagup & \diagup & \\ H-N\cdots H-N-Be-N-H\cdots N-H \\ \diagup & \diagup & \uparrow & \diagdown & \diagdown \\ H & H & NH_3 & H & H \end{bmatrix}^{2+} \ 2Cl^-$$

The double complex with ammonia and acetone could be formulated:

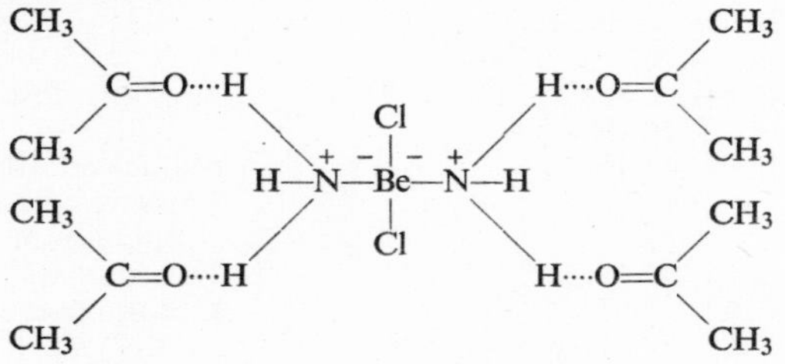

The hydrogen bond formation would be favoured both by the positive charge on the nitrogen atom and by the electrophobic nature of the methyl groups which would increase the negative charge on the oxygen atom.

Beryllium chloride can be used instead of aluminium chloride as a catalyst in certain organic reactions. It is a little less efficient, and the reactions take place at somewhat higher temperatures. It reacts at room temperature with a solution of a monocarboxylic acid in benzene, thus:

$$BeCl_2 + 2CH_3COOH = 2HCl + Be(CH_3COO)_2,$$

but if a trace of water is present the basic acetate is obtained (p. 436).

Beryllium bromide is similar to the chloride in methods of preparation and in all its properties. The tetrahydrate can be made by crystallisation of the concentrated aqueous solution saturated with hydrogen bromide.

Beryllium iodide is, in general, similar to the chloride and bromide, but it is much more reactive to water, which decomposes it violently, liberating hydrogen iodide. It is best made by the action of dry hydrogen iodide on the carbide at 700°. It can be purified by sublimation in vacuo.

The structures of the beryllium halides are discussed in the next paragraph.

Structures of the electron deficient tetrahedral beryllium compounds. There is no direct evidence on the structure of beryllium hydride. Investigations have been made on the structure of beryllium dimethyl and of beryllium chloride.† It has been found that beryllium dimethyl is isostructural with silicon disulphide, and that it consists of a chain structure:

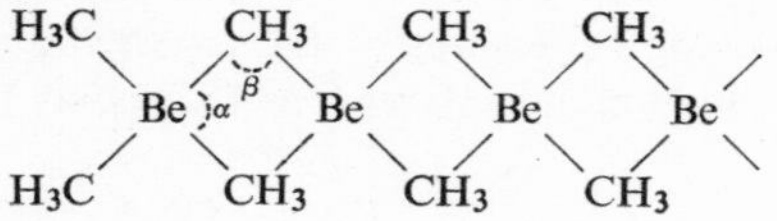

Be—C	1.93 ± 0.02	Be—Be	2.09 ± 0.01
	α 114°		β 66°

Each beryllium atom in the chain is linked to four carbon atoms. Eight electrons in four shared pairs would normally be required for these links, but each carbon atom

† Snow and Rundle, *Act. Cryst.*, **4**, 1954, 348; *J. Chem. Phys.*, **18**, 1950, 1125.

has only one disposable electron, and the beryllium atom has only two, making a total of six. The structure can be formulated in terms of three-centre bonds (p. 118):

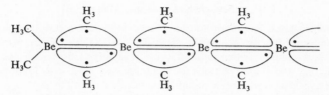

The three-centre bond refers to three nuclei, one carbon atom and two beryllium atoms, but it is occupied by two electrons only, one contributed by the carbon atom, and the other by one of the beryllium atoms. The contributed electrons are represented by dots in the formula. The $Be(CH_3)_2$ units linked in this way may produce chains of indefinite length. (The ends of the chain possibly consist of single CH_3 groups, unless the polymers are negatively charged so that the bonding of two extra CH_3 groups becomes possible.)

Beryllium chloride is also isostructural with silicon disulphide,† and consists of chains:

$$
\begin{array}{c}
\text{Cl} \quad\quad \text{Cl} \quad\quad \text{Cl} \\
\diagdown\diagup \quad \diagup \diagup \quad \diagup \diagup \quad \diagup \\
\text{Be}\,)\alpha \quad \text{Be} \quad\quad \text{Be} \quad\quad \text{Be} \quad\quad \alpha = 98.2°. \\
\diagup \quad \diagdown\diagup \quad \diagdown\diagup \quad \diagdown \\
\text{Cl} \quad\quad \text{Cl} \quad\quad \text{Cl}
\end{array}
$$

This chain structure might be based on one of two alternative orbital structures, (a) a completely two-centre bond structure in which each covalently bound chlorine etom donates a lone electron pair to a beryllium atom thus:

$$
\begin{array}{c}
\text{Cl} \quad\quad \text{Cl} \quad\quad \text{Cl} \\
\diagdown\diagup \searrow \diagup \diagup \searrow \diagup \diagup \searrow \diagup \\
\text{Be} \quad \text{Be} \quad\quad \text{Be} \quad\quad \text{Be} \\
\diagup \nwarrow \diagdown\diagup \nwarrow \diagdown\diagup \nwarrow \diagdown \\
\text{Cl} \quad\quad \text{Cl} \quad\quad \text{Cl}
\end{array}
$$

or (b) a three-centre bond structure in which BeClBe bonds correspond to the bond BaCBe in beryllium dimethyl, thus:

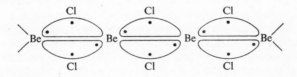

The electronegativities of chlorine and beryllium do not favour the completely two-centre bond structure, and unless experimental evidence indicates otherwise it is best to assume that three-centre bonds are present in the chloride, bromide, and iodide of beryllium, as well as in the hydride and the alkyls.

NON-CHELATE COMPLEXES

Non-chelate complexes formed by the beryllium atom in the tetrahedral valence state may be neutral, anionic, or cationic. The adducts formed by the addition of donor molecules to molecules of the beryllium halides (Table 15.1) are examples of neutral complexes. The fluoroberyllates and the chloroberyllates are examples of

† Rundle and Lewis, *J. Chem. Phys.*, **20**, 1952, 132.

anionic complexes, and the tetrahydrated beryllium salts are examples of cationic complexes.

Non-chelate Complex Anions

The fluoroberyllates. Beryllium fluoride reacts with alkali metal fluorides to produce fluoroberyllates of the types X_2BeF_4, $X_2Be_2F_7$, and $XBeF_3$, where X represents an atom of the alkali metal. Beryllium fluoride itself crystallises with the cristobalite (SiO_2) structure, and these reactions are analogous to those of a high melting acidic oxide, such as silica, with a basic metallic oxide.

Lithium fluoroberyllate, Li_2BeF_4, m.p. 475°, is made by dissolving beryllium fluoride in fused lithium fluoride in the correct proportions. The other compounds, $Li_2Be_2F_7$ and $LiBeF_3$, have incongruent m.p. at 445° and 365° respectively. Potassium fluoroberyllate, K_2BeF_4, is best made either by dissolving beryllium oxide in potassium hydrogen fluoride:

$$BeO + 2KHF_2 = K_2BeF_4 + H_2O,$$

or, by heating potassium fluosilicate, K_2SiF_6, with beryllium oxide to 700°. Fluoroberyllates of the alkaline earth metals, and of the transition metals, are also known.

The fluoroberyllate ion $BeF_4{}^{2-}$ bears certain resemblances to the sulphate ion $SO_4{}^{2-}$, and to the silicate group SiO_4. Fluoroberyllates containing the ion $BeF_4{}^{2-}$ behave like the sulphates and selenates in their solubilities, and in the formation of certain types of double salts. For example, the alkali metal fluoroberyllates are soluble, and those of the alkaline earth metals are relatively insoluble. Cobaltous, nickel, and zinc fluoroberyllates crystallise with 6 or 7 molecules of water; cupric fluoroberyllate crystallises with 5 molecules of water. The constitution of the double fluoroberyllate $Fe(NH_4)_2(BeF_4)_2$ is parallel to that of ferrous ammonium sulphate. A difference between the fluoroberyllates and the sulphates is found in the silver salts; silver fluoroberyllate is very soluble, whereas silver sulphate is relatively insoluble.

It is found that the equilibria of the system LiF/BeF_2 are analogous to those of the system MgO/SiO_2, and that those of the system NaF/BeF_2 are analogous to those of the system CaO/SiO_2.† The eutectic in the system LiF/BeF_2 is at the composition 31 mol % of BeF_2, and the eutectic in the system MgO/SiO_2 is at the composition 31 mol % of SiO_2. The absolute temperature of the MgO/SiO_2 liquidus at any given composition is 2·88 times that of the LiF/BeF_2 liquidus at the corresponding composition. The absolute temperatures of the invariant points in the system CaO/SiO_2 are 2·82 times those of the corresponding points in the system NaF/BeF_2. $LiNaBeF_4$ has strong crystallographic resemblance to monticellate $CaMgSiO_4$.

The analogies between $BeF_4{}^{2-}$ and $SO_4{}^{2-}$ and SiO_4 imply that the ion $BeF_4{}^{2-}$ is tetrahedral, and that the ion $Be_2F_7{}^{2-}$ consists of two BeF_4 tetrahedra linked by the holding of one fluorine atom in common.

Chloroberyllates. From the conductances of mixtures of NH_4Cl and $BeCl_2$ in aqueous solution the existence of $BeCl_3{}^-$, $BeCl_4{}^{2-}$, $BeCl_5{}^{3-}$, and $BeCl_6{}^{4-}$ is deduced. From the freezing point diagrams the existence of Li_2BeCl_4, Na_2BeCl_4, Tl_2BeCl_4, $BaBeCl_4$, is deduced. The chloroberyllates are less stable than the fluoroberyllates.

Non-chelate Complex Cations

In the non-chelate complex cation the beryllium atom has accepted four electron pairs from four donor molecules such as water or ammonia. These complexes are extremely stable. It has already been mentioned (p. 424) that $(Be,4H_2O)(ClO_4)$ when

† *Z. physikal Chem.*, **197**, 1951, 39–62.

heated decomposes altogether before water is lost, and (p. 431) that the pressure of ammonia over the tetra-ammoniate of beryllium chloride at 156° is only 6 mm.

Beryllium sulphate tetrahydrate, [Be,4H$_2$O]SO$_4$. Beryllium oxide dissolves in hot concentrated sulphuric acid, and the solution on cooling deposits the tetrahydrate. The solubility of the tetrahydrate in water is 42·5 gm in 100 gm at 25°. The solution is that of a normal electrolyte. The solution of beryllium oxide in an aqueous solution of beryllium sulphate is discussed on p. 426, and the crystal structure of the tetrahydrate is discussed on p. 389.

The tetrahydrate loses water when heated. The transition temperature corresponding to the equilibrium

$$BeSO_4,4H_2O \rightleftharpoons BeSO_4,2H_2O + 2H_2O$$

is 89·0°. There is another transition at 270° and 9·38 atm which may indicate the change to the anhydrous salt (p. 427). X-ray diffraction shows that there is no monohydrate.

Beryllium carbonate tetrahydrate, [Be,4H$_2$O]CO$_3$, is obtained by treating an aqueous suspension of beryllium hydroxide with carbon dioxide for a long time, and evaporating the resulting solution at room temperature in an atmosphere of carbon dioxide. The solubility of the tetrahydrate in water is 0·36 gm in 100 c.c. at 0°.

The commercial basic carbonate is precipitated by adding a soluble carbonate to beryllium sulphate in aqueous solution. It is probably a mixture of the carbonate and hydroxide. It leaves a residue of BeO when heated to 600°.

CHELATE COMPLEXES

Chelate complexes formed by the beryllium atom in the tetrahedral valence state may be neutral, anionic, or cationic. Among the neutral complexes are the beryllium acetyl acetonate, the hydroxyanthraquinone complex, normal beryllium acetate, and the so-called basic beryllium salts of organic acids, such as the basic acetate, Be$_4$O(OCOCH$_3$)$_6$. The basic salts are best regarded as derivatives of oxygen, and they are discussed on p. 809. The complex anions include the double sulphates of beryllium and one of the alkali metals, and the catechol complex. The cationic complexes are represented by the ethylenediamine compound, [Be en$_2$]Cl$_2$.

Chelate Neutral Complexes

Beryllium acetylacetonate.

This is a typical chelate neutral complex of beryllium. It is made by the action of acetylacetone on a solution of beryllium hydroxide in dilute acetic acid, or on a solution of the chloride in the presence of ammonia. It is insoluble in water; m.p. 108°, b.p. 270°. The vapour is monomeric. It does not form hydrates or absorb ammonia; it dissolves in carbon disulphide and benzene. The beryllium derivative of benzoyl pyruvic acid exhibits optical isomerism, and hence the tetrahedral valency of the beryllium atom is confirmed.

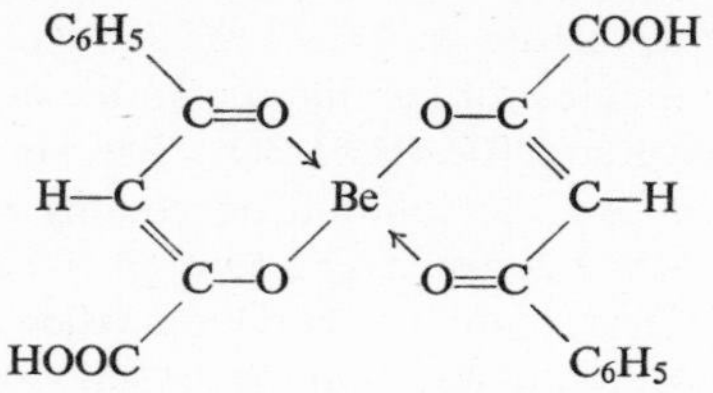

The hydroxyanthraquinone complex,

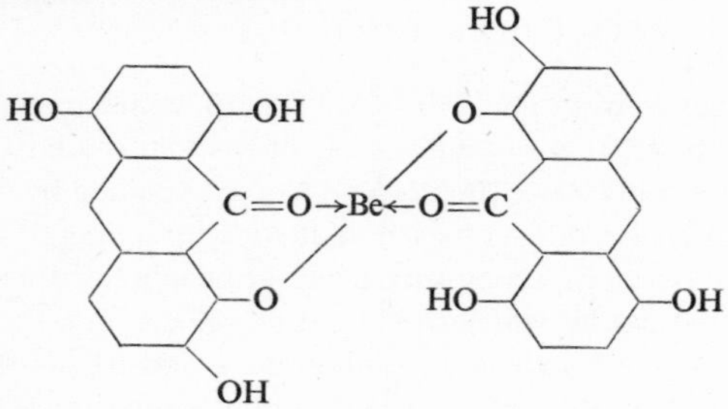

is an insoluble "lake", and is used as a delicate test for beryllium. The colourimetric determination of beryllium by use of this complex has been shown to be unsatisfactory.

Normal beryllium acetate,

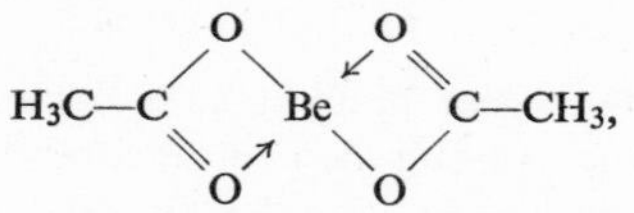

is made: (a) by the action of anhydrous acetic acid in benzene solution on beryllium chloride, or, (b) by the action of acetic anhydride on the basic acetate at 140°. The basic acetate is obtained if an attempt is made to prepare the normal acetate in aqueous solution. The normal acetate melts, with decomposition, at 295°. It is insoluble in water, but is hydrolysed on boiling. It is insoluble in organic solvents. On slow sublimation it is converted to the basic acetate:

$$4Be(OAc)_2 = Be_4O(OAc)_6 + Ac_2O.$$

Basic beryllium acetate and similar compounds. If beryllium chloride is treated with a benzene solution of a monobasic organic acid in the presence of a trace of water, a complex is obtained of general formula $Be_4O(OCOR)_6$. The most familiar of these complexes is the so-called basic beryllium acetate (p. 809).

Chelate Complex Anions

The double sulphates of the alkali metals and beryllium have the constitution:

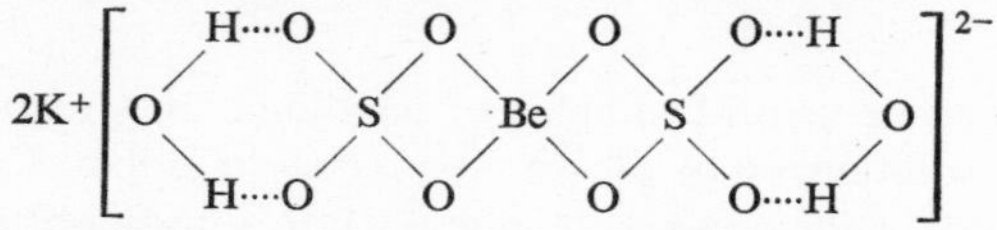

The ammonium and potassium salts have been prepared. The presence of only two molecules of water per beryllium atom shows the absence of the hydrated ion $[Be,4H_2O]^{2+}$.

The catechol complex. A complex with catechol is obtained by dissolving beryllium hydroxide in an alkaline solution of catechol. The potassium salt,

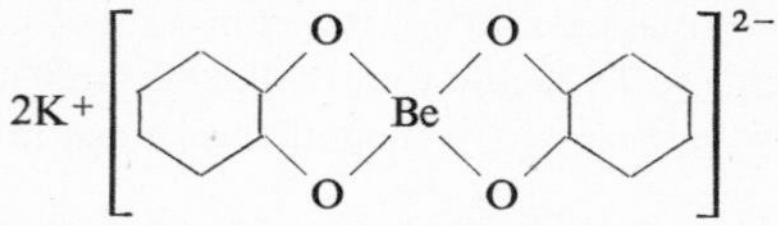

and the corresponding salts of Na, NH_4 and Ba have been prepared. Excess of beryllium hydroxide dissolves in a solution of the potassium salt to give $K_2[Be \cdot BeO(C_6H_4O_2)_2]$, $5H_2O$. The structure of this compound is not understood, but its existence appears to undermine Sidgwick's explanation of the solution of BeO in $BeSO_4$ (p. 426)

Beryllium oxalate. The composition of beryllium oxalate is $BeC_2O_4, 3H_2O$. The degree of hydration suggests the probable absence of the ion $(Be, 4H_2O)^{2+}$. Both the molecular conductivity and the depression of the freezing point of water show that the oxalate is very little ionised in solution. Moreover, beryllium oxalate differs from oxalates of all other bivalent metals by being soluble in water (27·8% anhydrous salt at 25°). These properties are explained if the condition of beryllium oxalate in aqueous solution is represented by the equilibrium:

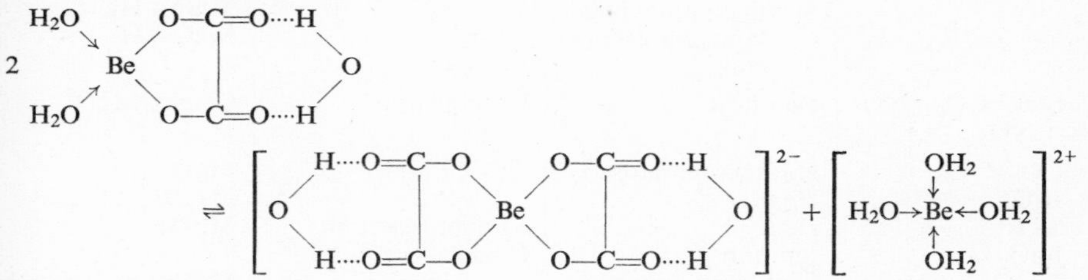

The degree of dissociation of the neutral complex is independent of the dilution, since the number of particles is the same on both sides of the equation. This is in accordance with the observation that the molar conductivity and the van't Hoff coefficient are very little affected by the dilution. The sodium salt of the oxalate anion has been obtained.

Beryllium salicylate, $Be(C_6H_4O \cdot CO_2), 2H_2O$. Salicylic acid is here behaving as a dibasic acid, and beryllium salicylate must be a salt of the two ions:

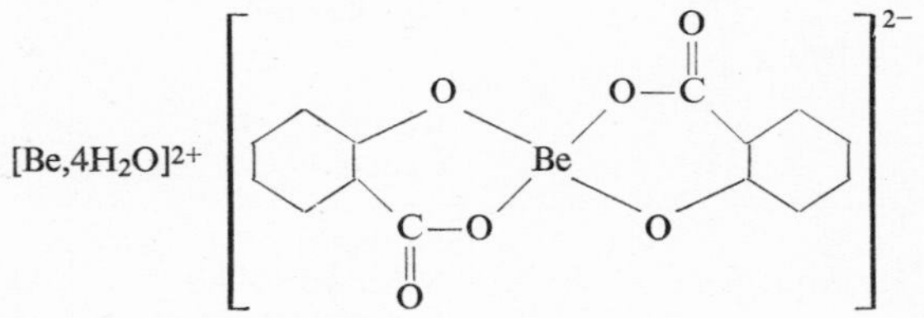

Chelate Complex Cations

Beryllium ethylenediamine chloride is insoluble in water and in ether. It may be made by precipitating an ethereal solution of beryllium chloride with two equivalents of ethylenediamine

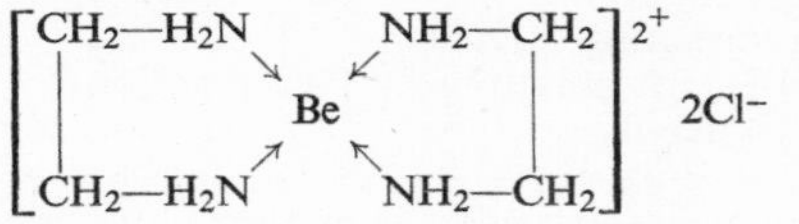

MAGNESIUM

PROPERTIES OF THE METAL

The physical properties of magnesium are stated in Table 15.2. It is a white metal with a brilliant lustre. It is light, soft, ductile and malleable, and may be obtained as ribbon or wire. It is chemically reactive; its principal reactions are collected in Table 15.9.

Table 15.9. *The Reactions of Magnesium Metal*

Reagent	Conditions for reaction	Description of reaction	Product
H_2	570°, 200 atm presence of MgI_2		MgH_2
O_2	Above m.p. 651°	Brilliant combustion	MgO
Air	(i) Room conditions	Apparently none	Superficial film of MgO which impedes further reaction
	(ii) High temperature	Brilliant combustion	MgO and Mg_3N_2
Water	Cold on pure metal	No reaction	
	Steam on pure metal		$MgO + H_2$
	Cold on amalgamated metal		$MgO + H_2$
SO_2, CO_2, NO, NO_2	Red heat	Combustion	Chiefly MgO
CO	High temperature		MgO
B_2O_3	Heat		Mg_3B_2
SiO_2	Heat	Violent reaction	Mg_2Si
BaO_2	Ignition	Explosive	
Na_2O, K_2O	High temperature		MgO and Na or K
$KClO_3$	Ignition	Explosive	
Phosphates	Heat		Mg_3P_2 (test)
N_2	800–850°		Mg_3N_2†
NH_3	Heat		Mg_3N_2
NH_3	Activated with iodine at 350–400°		$Mg(NH_2)_2$
$NaNH_2$ or KNH_2	Heat		$Mg(NH_2)_2 + Na(K)$
C		No reaction	
S	600°		MgS
P	Heat		Mg_3P_2
As		Reacts	
Si		Reacts	
HF	Dry	No action	
	Aqueous	Metal dissolves	MgF_2
F_2		Brilliant combustion	MgF_2
Cl_2		Brilliant combustion	$MgCl_2$
Br_2	Bromine in anhydrous ether		$MgBr_2$
I_2	(i) Pure vapour up to 600°	Little reaction	
	(ii) Moist iodine	Violent reaction	MgI_2
	(iii) I_2 in non-donating solvents	Slow reaction	MgI_2
	(iv) I_2 in donating solvents	Fast reaction	MgI_2

† A mixture of magnesium powder and liquid nitrogen burns brilliantly.

Table 15.9—*continued*

Reagent	Conditions for reaction	Description of reaction	Product
Dilute acids		Rapid solution	Mg salt; the acid is not reduced
Alkalis		No reaction	
C_2H_5OH	Activation by iodine		$Mg(OC_2H_5)_2$
CH_3OH	200°		$Mg(OCH_3)_2$
C_2H_2	(i) 500°		MgC_2
	(ii) 600°		$MgC_2 + Mg_2C_3$
CH_4	750°		Mg_2C_3 only
Alkyl or aryl halides†	Ether solution		Grignard reagent
$Hg(CH_3)_2$	Ether solution		$Mg(CH_3)_2$

† Fluorine compounds do not react.

THE GENERAL CHEMISTRY OF MAGNESIUM

The electron configuration of the magnesium atom in the ground state is $1s^2$, $2s^2$, $2p^6$, $3s^2$. Magnesium closely resembles beryllium in the range and variety of its compounds (Table 15.1). Magnesium is more electropositive than beryllium, hence its simple ionic compounds, such as $Mg(NO_3)_2$ are stable, and the degree of ionic character of its covalent compounds is more pronounced. The increased tendency towards ionic bonding is shown by comparing its giant molecule compounds with those of beryllium (Section 1 of Table 15.1): BeO has the wurtzite structure, MgO has the rutile structure; BeS has the zinc blende structure, MgS has the rock salt structure, and so on. The comparison of the crystal structures of the magnesium halides with those of the beryllium halides is interesting. BeF_2 has the cristobalite structure; $BeCl_2$ and $BeBr_2$ have electron deficient chain structures (p. 421). MgF_2 has the rutile structure which indicates considerable ionic character, but the other magnesium halides have covalent layer structures. Decrease in electronegativity of the metallic atom appears to favour normal covalency in place of three-centre bonds, and ionic bonding in place of covalency. Among the giant molecule compounds is Mg_2C_3; no other member of the sub-Group forms a carbide of this composition.

Magnesium, unlike beryllium, but like all the heavier members of the sub-Group, forms complex cations with the atom in the digonal valence state. The tetrahedral electron deficient compounds, which are fairly numerous in the case of beryllium, Section 4, Table 15.1, are represented only by the magnesium alkyls, the magnesium borohydrides, and the magnesium aluminium hydrides. Since the magnesium atom possesses d orbitals in the valency shell, octahedral hybridisation is possible, and is attained in the hexammino cations such as $(Mg,6NH_3)(ClO_4)_2$.

The cations Mg^+ and $Mg(C_2H_5)^+$. The evidence for the existence of compounds in which magnesium is univalent is slender and inferential. Acetone is reduced to pinacol by treatment with a mixture of magnesium turnings and mercuric chloride, and the action is thought to proceed by the intermediate formation of MgCl, thus:

$$2HgCl_2 + 2Mg = Hg_2Cl_2 + 2MgCl$$

$$\begin{array}{c} (CH_3)_2CO \\ (CH_3)_2CO \end{array} + 2MgCl = \begin{array}{c} (CH_3)_2C\text{—}O\text{—}MgCl \\ | \\ (CH_3)_2C\text{—}O\text{—}MgCl \end{array}$$

$$\begin{array}{c} (CH_3)_2C\!-\!O\!-\!MgCl \\ | \\ (CH_3)_2C\!-\!O\!-\!MgCl \end{array} +2H_2O = \begin{array}{c} (CH_3)_2C\!-\!OH \\ | \\ (CH_3)_2C\!-\!OH \end{array} +2MgOHCl.$$

Benzophenone, $C_6H_5COC_6H_5$, may be reduced to $(C_6H_5)_2COH \cdot COH(C_6H_5)_2$ by treatment with magnesium and magnesium bromide in ethereal solution; this reaction might proceed by the intermediate formation of MgBr. In the presence of a ketone, magnesium dissolves in magnesium iodide.

When a solution of sodium iodide in pyridine is electrolysed between magnesium electrodes in a divided cell, the anolyte becomes a reducing agent, and it is deduced that Mg^+ has been formed.

Magnesium ethyl bromide dissolves in ether to give a solution which has a small conductivity; at 20° the specific conductivity of a normal ethereal solution is $6 \cdot 14 \times 10^{-5}$ ohm^{-1} cm^{-1}, which although only 1/1000 that of a normal aqueous solution of potassium chloride, is twice as great as that of a normal ethereal solution of magnesium bromide at the same temperature. It must therefore be accepted that magnesium ethyl bromide undergoes electrolytic dissociation:

$$MgC_2H_5Br \rightleftharpoons (MgC_2H_5)^+ + Br^-.$$

SECTION 1. MAGNESIUM COMPOUNDS WITH IONIC CHARACTER

THE SIMPLE BIVALENT CATION Mg^{2+}

The configuration of the cation Mg^{2+} is $1s^2 2s^2 2p^6$. The radius, $0 \cdot 78$, is more than twice that of the ion Be^{2+}; its deforming power is only one-fifth that of the ion Be^{2+}. It is therefore to be anticipated that at least a few compounds of magnesium would show characteristics indicating the presence of the ion Mg^{2+}. Among them should be found the anhydrous salts of the oxyacids, and the oxide, MgO, the sulphide MgS, and the fluoride MgF_2. Nevertheless, the ionic bond between the ion Mg^{2+} and other atoms possesses varying degrees of covalent character; for example, it has been deduced by X-ray Fourier analysis that the bonding in magnesium oxide, which crystallises with the sodium chloride lattice, is predominantly covalent.

Magnesium perchlorate, $Mg(ClO_4)_2$, forms three hydrates, $Mg(ClO_4)_2, 2H_2O$, $Mg(ClO_4)_2, 4H_2O$, and $Mg(ClO_4)_2, 6H_2O$, any of which, if heated to 250°, loses water, and (in contrast to the behaviour of the tetrahydrate of beryllium perchlorate) yields the anhydrous salt. Anhydrous magnesium perchlorate absorbs water very readily to give the hexahydrate, and it is used as a dehydrating agent. It also absorbs ammonia to form a hexa- and a di-ammoniate.

Magnesium nitrate, $Mg(NO_3)_2$, cannot be made by the dehydration of its hydrates, but it has been prepared by the reaction:

$$2N_2O_5 + Mg(OH)_2 = Mg(NO_3)_2 + 2HNO_3.$$

If heated above 90° the anion decomposes, and basic nitrates are formed. The anhydrous salt with water at low vapour pressure gives the dihydrate, and at higher vapour pressures the hexahydrate.

Magnesium nitrite, $Mg(NO_2)_2$, is made from silver nitrite and magnesium chloride. On gentle heating it decomposes to N_2O_3, NO, and a little N_2, leaving a residue of nitrite, nitrate, and magnesium oxide. It is soluble in water, and is not much hydrolysed in the cold. It forms hydrates, 9, 6, and 3.

Magnesium carbonates. Anhydrous magnesium carbonate is found as the mineral magnesite. It loses carbon dioxide on heating. A clear solution of the bicarbonate, $MgHCO_3$, is obtained by passing carbon dioxide into a suspension of either magnesium oxide or the basic carbonate precipitated when sodium carbonate or potassium carbonate is added to the solution of a magnesium salt.

If the solution of the bicarbonate is crystallised at 50°, heated with magnesium hydroxide, or violently agitated at 18°, crystals of magnesium carbonate trihydrate separate. The trihydrate is more reactive than the anhydrous salt, and is used in the Engel-Precht process.

Magnesium sulphate, MgSO₄, melts at 1120°, and is almost certainly a sulphato-complex like anhydrous beryllium sulphate. It is therefore described on p. 448.

MAGNESIUM COMPOUNDS CONSISTING OF GIANT MOLECULES IN WHICH THE BONDS HAVE SOME IONIC CHARACTER

Examples of magnesium compounds which consist of giant molecules are given in Table 15.1, Section 1. The compounds have crystal lattices which indicate a considerable degree of ionic character. $Mg(OH)_2$, $MgCl_2$, $MgBr_2$, and MgI_2 crystallise in covalent layer lattices; magnesium is the only element in the sub-Group which forms compounds with this type of lattice.

Magnesium hydride, MgH₂, may be prepared by the direct combination of the elements in the presence of magnesium iodide at 570° and 200 atm. The yield is 60%. It may also be prepared:

(i) by the action of lithium aluminium hydride on magnesium dimethyl, or magnesium dichloride, in ethereal solution,

(ii) by heating magnesium diethyl in vacuo at 175°:

$$Mg(C_2H_5)_2 = MgH_2 + 2C_2H_4;$$

in this reaction some MgC_2H_4 is produced.

As obtained by direct synthesis magnesium hydride is a light grey powder, stable to air, and only slowly hydrolysed by water. It decomposes to the elements at 280–300°. It reacts with diborane in ether to give magnesium borohydride, $Mg(BH_4)_2$, and with aluminium chloride in ether to give magnesium aluminium hydride, $Mg(AlH_4)_2$. Magnesium hydride is more stable than the hydrides of beryllium, zinc, or cadmium.

It has been shown by X-ray methods that magnesium hydride, prepared either by direct synthesis or by the pyrolysis of magnesium diethyl, has the rutile structure. This requires that each magnesium atom is equidistant from six hydrogen atoms, and each hydrogen atom is equidistant from three magnesium atoms. Such a structure is incompatible with the electron deficient chain structure assigned to beryllium hydride.

Magnesium boride, MgB₂, is prepared from the elements at 800° in an atmosphere of hydrogen.† It is isomorphous with AlB_2. There is also a crystalline phase MgB_4.

Magnesium acetylide, MgC₂, is a tetragonal crystalline solid, made by heating magnesium in acetylene at 500°. The acetylide is unstable at high temperatures; if heated for 2 hours at 550° it is converted to Mg_2C_3:

$$2MgC_2 \rightarrow Mg_2C_3 + C.$$

Magnesium acetylide may also be obtained by the action of acetylene on an ethereal solution of magnesium diethyl, or by the action of acetylene on ethyl magnesium bromide. The product of the last reaction is an oil, formed according to the equation:

$$2C_2H_5MgBr + HC \vdots CH = 2C_2H_6 + Br—Mg—C \vdots C—Mg—Br.$$

The oil on long standing changes to a crystalline substance, which is a mixture of magnesium bromide and acetylide:

$$Br—Mg—C \vdots C—Mg—Br = MgBr_2 + MgC_2.$$

Magnesium acetylide yields acetylene on treatment with water.

† *Ann. Reports*, **51**, 1954, 124.

Magnesium carbide, Mg_2C_3, a hexagonal crystalline solid, is obtained (without the formation of MgC_2) by the action of methane or pentane on magnesium at 700°. It is also formed if magnesium reacts with acetylene at 600°. With water it yields allylene, $CH_3 \cdot C \equiv CH$. The ionic character of the crystal structure may include the form $[Mg^{2+}]_2(C = C = C)^{4-}$. In this case reaction with water would yield allene, $H_2C = C = CH_2$ as the immediate product, and this on isomeric conversion would yield allylene. Mg_2C_3 is decomposed into its elements if heated to 750°. Magnesium is the only member of the sub-Group to form a carbide of composition Mg_2C_3.

Magnesium nitride, Mg_3N_2, is best made by heating magnesium in nitrogen at 800–850° for 4 or 5 hours. It can also be made by heating magnesium in ammonia. A mixture of magnesium oxide and carbon may be used instead of magnesium for both these reactions. When magnesium burns in air some nitride is formed. Magnesium nitride is also obtained by heating the diamide $Mg(NH_2)_2$.

Magnesium nitride is a colourless crystalline substance with the anti-A-Mn_2O_3 crystal structure. When heated alone to 1000° or more it decomposes. It burns in oxygen to magnesium oxide. With water it is readily hydrolysed to magnesium hydroxide and ammonia.

Mg_3N_2 heated with CO gives the oxide:

$$Mg_3N_2 + 3CO = 3MgO + N_2 + 3C.$$

Mg_3P_2 and Mg_3As_2 are similar; Mg_3Sb_2, Mg_3Bi_2 have the anti-C-Mn_2O_3 lattice.

Magnesium diamide, $Mg(NH_2)_2$, is made:

  (i) by the action of ammonia at 350–400° on magnesium activated with iodine,
 (ii) by heating magnesium with $NaNH_2$ or KNH_2,
(iii) by the action of ammonia on an ethereal solution of magnesium diethyl.

It is a white powder, it decomposes at a red heat to give Mg_3N_2 and ammonia, it catches fire in air, and it reacts violently with water giving ammonia.

Magnesium cyanide, $Mg(CN)_2$, is made by heating the diammine, $[Mg(NH_3)_2](CN)_2$, in vacuo. The diammine is precipitated when magnesium nitrate is treated with hydrocyanic acid in the presence of ammonia. At 200° magnesium cyanide yields magnesium cyanamide, $MgNC \vdots N$.

Magnesium oxide, MgO, is made most conveniently by heating magnesite in air. It can also be made by heating magnesium hydroxide, nitrate, or sulphate, or by burning magnesium in oxygen. As ordinarily obtained it is a white powder, m.p. 2850°. It occurs as octahedral crystals in periclase, and the powder may be rendered crystalline by heating it strongly in a current of hydrogen chloride. It is sparingly soluble in water with which it combines very slowly to form the hydroxide, $Mg(OH)_2$. Magnesium oxide is basic in its reactions. It is easily soluble in acids, but it is unaffected by alkalis or ammonia. It dissolves in aqueous solutions of magnesium chloride or bromide to give basic salts such as $MgBr_2,9Mg(OH)_2,5H_2O$.

Magnesium oxide is not converted by oxygen or oxidising agents to any higher oxide (the unstable magnesium peroxide can be obtained indirectly (p. 443); chlorine passed through a suspension of magnesium oxide in water yields magnesium chlorate, $Mg(ClO_3)_2$. It remains unaffected at high temperatures by reducing agents such as carbon, carbon monoxide, hydrogen or metals, but it undergoes the following reactions:

$$MgO + C + S = MgS + CO,$$
$$2MgO + CS_2 = 2MgS + CO_2, \quad \text{carried out at 700–900° in nitrogen,}$$
$$MgO + CaC_2 = Mg + CaO + 2C, \quad \text{carried out at 1300° in argon,}$$
$$MgO + CO + Cl_2 = MgCl_2 + CO_2, \quad \text{carried out at 750°.}$$

Crystalline magnesium oxide has the sodium chloride lattice. The minimum value for the electron density between magnesium and oxygen atoms has been determined by X-ray Fourier analysis. The value is 0·6 electron per cubic Å; the corresponding value for sodium chloride is 0·23. Hence it is assumed that the bonding is predominantly covalent.

Magnesium hydroxide, $Mg(OH)_2$, is made by the action of water on magnesium oxide, or by the action of alkalis on a solution of a magnesium salt. It is very slightly soluble in water (19 mg/litre at 18°) and is a strong electrolyte. It dissolves in acids, but shows no tendency at all to form salts with bases. On heating it loses water, not very readily, to yield magnesium oxide. Magnesium hydroxide has a CdI_2 layer lattice in which the oxygen atoms are close-packed, and the magnesium atoms are in the octahedral holes. This structure enables $Mg(OH)_2$ to form layers with $MgSiO_4$ in chondrodite (p. 608).

Magnesium ethoxide, $Mg(OC_2H_5)_2$, is made by the action of ethanol on magnesium activated with iodine, or on magnesium amalgam. It is a white powder soluble in alcohol.

Magnesium peroxide, MgO_2, has not been isolated, and it cannot be made by the action of oxygen on magnesium oxide. If, however, sodium hydroxide is added to an aqueous solution of magnesium sulphate containing hydrogen peroxide, a precipitate is formed of composition $MgO,MgO_2,2H_2O$, but of unknown structure. The precipitate loses hydrogen peroxide easily. The product obtained by the action of hydrogen peroxide on magnesium diethyl in ethereal solution appears to contain a high proportion of MgO_2.

Magnesium sulphide, MgS. Pure magnesium sulphide, free from magnesium oxide, is made by heating $MgCl_2,NH_4Cl$ in a stream of hydrogen sulphide. The anhydrous double salt $MgCl_2,NH_4Cl$ is made by heating the ammonium analogue of carnallite:

$$MgCl_2,NH_4Cl,6H_2O = MgCl_2,NH_4Cl + 6H_2O.$$

Magnesium sulphide can also be obtained by the action of

(i) sulphur vapour on the metal above 600°,
(ii) sulphur vapour on a mixture of magnesium oxide and carbon,
(iii) a mixture of carbon disulphide and nitrogen on the oxide or sulphate at 700–900°.

Magnesium sulphide is a colourless crystalline substance with the sodium chloride lattice; m.p. above 2000°. It is rapidly decomposed by water to magnesium hydrosulphide, $Mg(SH)_2$, which is known only in solution; the warm solution decomposes to yield $Mg(OH)_2$ and H_2S.

Magnesium selenide also has the NaCl lattice. *Magnesium telluride* is made from the elements which combine at a red heat with explosive violence. The lattice differs from those of the oxide, sulphide, and selenide in having the zinc blende structure instead of the sodium chloride. The change is due to the greater size and deformability of the telluride ion.

The magnesium halides. Table 15.4 sets out the principal properties of the magnesium halides.† Magnesium fluoride differs sharply from the other magnesium halides in (i) its much higher melting point, (ii) its small solubility in water, (iii) its inability to form hydrates, (iv) its rutile crystal structure. The chloride, bromide, and iodide are closely similar. Their melting points are near 700°, their solubilities are near 10 molecules of salt per 100 molecules of water, they form hydrates, and the crystal lattices are of the layer type of cadmium chloride or cadmium iodide. The chloride and the bromide form basic salts of parallel composition.

† Accounts of these properties are not repeated in the text.

Magnesium fluoride, MgF$_2$, is made by dissolving magnesium in aqueous hydrofluoric acid. It is very sparingly soluble in water.

Magnesium chloride, MgCl$_2$. Anhydrous magnesium chloride is made by:

(i) heating MgCl$_2$,6H$_2$O in vacuo, or in a current of hydrogen chloride,
(ii) passing a mixture of chlorine and carbon monoxide over magnesium oxide at 750°,
(iii) passing a current of chlorine over a heated mixture of magnesium oxide and carbon,
(iv) heating the double salt, MgCl$_2$,NH$_4$Cl,6H$_2$O. This salt decomposes in two stages:

$$MgCl_2,NH_4Cl,6H_2O = MgCl_2,NH_4Cl + 6H_2O$$
$$MgCl_2,NH_4Cl = MgCl_2 + NH_3 + HCl.$$

Method (iv) is the most convenient for laboratory use.

Anhydrous magnesium chloride can be distilled in a current of hydrogen. Magnesium chloride reacts with oxygen when hot:

$$2MgCl_2 + O_2 = 2MgO + 2Cl_2.$$

Magnesium chloride hexahydrate, MgCl$_2$,6H$_2$O, is obtained by dissolving magnesium carbonate in hydrochloric acid and crystallising the solution. On ignition it undergoes hydrolysis, and a residue of Mg$_2$OCl$_2$ is obtained.

A neutral solution of magnesium chloride reacts slowly with magnesium oxide to yield the compounds:

$$MgCl_2,2Mg(OH)_2,4H_2O \quad \text{and} \quad MgCl_2,9Mg(OH)_2,5H_2O.$$

The second compound is stable; the first changes in a week to MgCl$_2$,3Mg(OH)$_2$,8H$_2$O.

Magnesium bromide, MgBr$_2$. The anhydrous salt can be made by the action of bromine on magnesium suspended in anhydrous ether. It reacts with ethyl magnesium bromide in ether or benzene saturated with ammonia to give the slightly soluble amide MgNH$_2$Br which is stable up to 200°. Magnesium bromamide forms two ammoniates MgNH$_2$Br,NH$_3$ and MgNH$_2$Br,2NH$_3$.

Magnesium bromide is very hygroscopic. It is soluble in water and in organic solvents containing oxygen (alcohols, ketones, ethers). From the alcoholic solution the solid compound MgBr$_2$(C$_2$H$_5$OH)$_6$ may be obtained, and from the ethereal solution the dietherate, 2Et$_2$O,MgBr$_2$. The existence of the dietherate confirms the explanation of the Grignard reaction given on p. 446. If magnesium oxide is digested with an aqueous solution of magnesium bromide the salt MgBr$_2$,9Mg(OH)$_2$,5H$_2$O is obtained. This is isomorphous with the corresponding compound of magnesium chloride.

Magnesium iodide, MgI$_2$, is made by treating magnesium with excess of iodine vapour at 600°. It is soluble in water, and it is more soluble than the bromide in organic solvents containing oxygen. Magnesium iodide forms a dietherate.

SECTION 2. THE MAGNESIUM ATOM IN THE DIGONAL VALENCE STATE

The only covalent compounds of magnesium that might be assigned to this Section are the magnesium alkyl halides, such as (C$_2$H$_5$)MgBr. The compounds Mg(BH$_4$)$_2$, Mg(AlH$_4$)$_2$, and Mg(Al(OEt)$_4$)$_2$, with formulae which suggest that the magnesium atom might be bivalent, are certainly bridge compounds, in which the magnesium atom is in the tetrahedral valence state. There is no magnesium compound corresponding to K$_2$BeO$_2$, but there are several diammino magnesium cations, such as [Mg,2NH$_3$](ClO$_4$)$_2$, in which the Mg^{2+} ion has accepted two electron pairs from donor molecules; the magnesium atom may be digonally hybridised in these cationic complexes. In forming cationic complexes of this type magnesium differs from beryllium, but resembles calcium, strontium, and barium.

Magnesium ethyl bromide, $Mg(C_2H_5)Br$. Magnesium reacts very slowly with pure ethyl bromide to give magnesium ethyl bromide:

$$Mg + C_2H_5Br = C_2H_5MgBr.$$

The compound is produced somewhat more readily if the ethyl bromide is run into a suspension of magnesium in pure dry benzene or toluene. Magnesium ethyl bromide is not volatile, but it can be distilled in a stream of ether vapour. It is stable to heat, and only 14% of a sample decomposes if heated to 300° for 1 hour. It combines with ether to form a dietherate (p. 446). The ionisation of $(C_2H_5)MgBr$ is considered on p. 440.

SECTION 3. THE MAGNESIUM ATOM IN THE TRIGONAL VALENCE STATE

Compounds containing the trigonally hybridised magnesium atom are less common than the corresponding beryllium compounds. Magnesium diethyl monoetherate, $Mg(C_2H_5)_2,(C_2H_5)_2O$, must be assigned to this Section. It is made by the action of metallic magnesium on mercury diethyl in ether. It is a solid at 0°, but it melts at higher temperatures. It inflames on exposure to air, and it explodes on contact with water. When heated in vacuo ether is lost, and magnesium diethyl is left. Magnesium diethyl monoetherate is very soluble in ether. In ethereal solution it reacts with ammonia to yield $Mg(NH_2)_2$.

The empirical formulae of potassium and rubidium fluoromagnesates, $KMgF_3$ and $RbMgF_3$, suggest the presence of the anion $[MgF_3]^-$. These compounds, however, have the perovskite structure (p. 350), and the crystals must be regarded as giant molecules in which no discrete ions are present.

SECTION 4. COMPOUNDS IN WHICH THE MAGNESIUM ATOM IS TETRAHEDRALLY HYBRIDISED

The magnesium atom in the tetrahedral valence state forms neutral, anionic, and cationic complexes, both chelate and non-chelate, but examples are less numerous and less well-established than they are among the corresponding beryllium compounds.

Magnesium, like beryllium, forms electron deficient tetrahedral compounds. Certain of these compounds, such as $Mg(C_2H_5)_2$, have polymerised molecules, consisting of chains of indefinite length, with structures analogous to those of the corresponding beryllium compounds described on p. 432. Others, such as $Mg(BH_4)_2$, have discrete molecules.

ELECTRON-DEFICIENT COMPOUNDS

Magnesium diethyl, $Mg(C_2H_5)_2$. When magnesium diethyl monoetherate (above) is heated in vacuo, magnesium diethyl is left. It is a non-volatile white substance, and can be heated to 150° without decomposition, but at 175° in vacuo it yields magnesium hydride. Magnesium diethyl is extremely reactive and ignites in carbon dioxide. It can be handled in an atmosphere of dry nitrogen or hydrogen. It reacts violently with water, alcohols, or ammonia:

$$Mg(C_2H_5)_2 + H_2O = MgO + 2C_2H_6.$$

It reacts with hydrogen peroxide to give an oxide rich in MgO_2. It is insoluble in common solvents except ether.

The structure of magnesium diethyl has not been experimentally determined, but the properties of magnesium diethyl and beryllium dimethyl (p. 429) are so similar that it is reasonable to suppose that their structures are parallel.

NON-CHELATE COMPLEXES

Non-chelate Neutral Complexes

Magnesium ethyl bromide dietherate, $Mg(C_2H_5)Br,2(C_2H_5)_2O$. In ethereal solution magnesium ethyl bromide is familiar to organic chemists as a member of a class of compounds known as Grignard reagents which have extensive use in organic synthesis. The reactions of a Grignard reagent are set out in detail in any text-book of organic chemistry and there is no need to discuss them here. In the ethereal solution the equilibrium:

$$2((Et_2O)_2MgC_2H_5Br) \rightleftharpoons Mg(C_2H_5)_2 + MgBr_2 + 4Et_2O,$$

is attained. The two halogen compounds separate as insoluble precipitates when the solution is treated with dioxane $(CH_2)_4O_2$. By filtering off the precipitate and determining the magnesium in the filtrate, the proportions of the constituents present at equilibrium can be ascertained if the concentration of the original solution is known. The active reagent in organic synthesis is ethyl magnesium bromide, and its activity is correlated with the greater strength of the bonds Mg—O, Mg—N, Mg—Cl compared with that of Mg—C. The mechanism of the reaction can be illustrated by the conversion of acetone to ethyldimethyl carbinol:

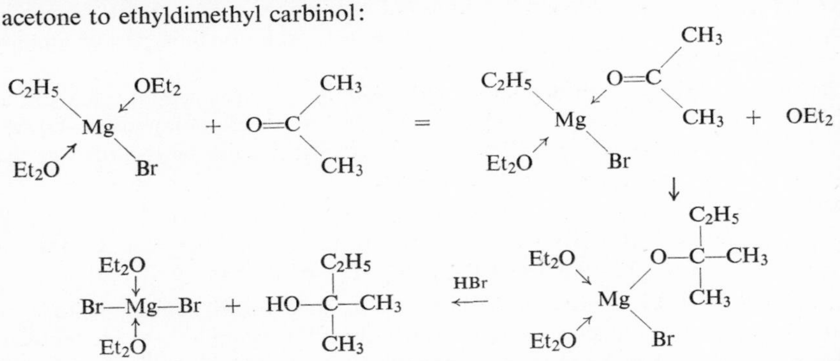

Magnesium ethyl bromide also forms complexes with ethers other than diethyl, with tertiary amines, and with the diethyl ethers of sulphur, selenium, and tellurium.

Ethyl chloride, ethyl bromide, and ethyl iodide react with magnesium in ether to form Grignard reagents, but ethyl fluoride does not do so. The differences in reactivity are to be correlated with the energies of the bonds (Table 11.12):

C—F	C—Cl	C—Br	C—I
121	78·2	68	51 kcal

Evidence for the existence of the ion $Mg(C_2H_5)^+$ is discussed on p. 440.

Magnesium dicyclopentadienyl, $(C_5H_5)_2Mg$, is made by the action of cyclopentadiene on magnesium ethyl bromide. It is mentioned along with the corresponding compounds of the transition metals in Chapter 25, p. 1117.

Non-chelate Complex Anions

The fluoromagnesates of potassium, K_2MgF_4, and rubidium, Rb_2MgF_4, have been reported, but their structures are unknown. The equilibrium diagrams of the systems $KCl/MgCl_2$ and $RbCl/MgCl_2$ indicate the existence of the corresponding compounds of chlorine, which have congruent melting points. Sodium iodide, however, forms a solid solution with magnesium iodide, and at lower temperatures a eutectic system. It is claimed that the ionic radius of the original anion is the determining factor in complex anion formation, which takes place more readily if the original anion is small. Hence the stability of the fluorine compounds, and the non-existence of the iodine compounds.

Non-chelate Complex Cations

The tetrahydrated and tetra-ammoniated magnesium salts, such as $(Mg,4H_2O)(ClO_4)_2$ and $(Mg,4NH_3)Cl_2$, contain cations in this class.

CHELATE COMPLEXES

It is difficult to believe that magnesium does not follow all the other members of the sub-Group in combining with β-diketones, β-ketoesters, and α-dicarboxylic esters to form chelate neutral complexes. Records of such magnesium compounds, however, are scanty. The acetylacetonate

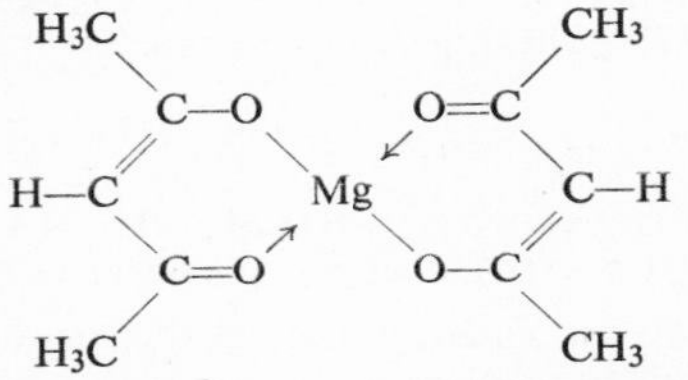

has been described. It is anhydrous and soluble in alcohol. Its molecular weight in solution is normal. Anhydrous magnesium acetate, magnesium oxalate dihydrate, and anhydrous magnesium sulphate are assumed to be chelate complexes, but there is evidence for the assumption only in the case of **magnesium acetate**. This evidence is as follows:

(a) the solid retains acetic acid tenaciously,
(b) at a concentration of 5·4 moles per litre the viscosity of the aqueous solution is 155 times that of water,
(c) the depression of the freezing point of a 2-molar solution of magnesium acetate is only one-third of that of a 2-molar solution of magnesium chloride,
(d) the conductivity of the aqueous solution has a maximum at 1-normal; the conductivity of the aqueous solution of magnesium chloride has a maximum at 2·5 normal; the magnitude of the maximum conductivity of the chloride is 5 times that of the acetate.

Anhydrous magnesium acetate is made by heating magnesium nitrate hexahydrate with acetic anhydride, washing the precipitate with ether, and drying at 60°. It has been suggested that the structure of anhydrous magnesium acetate consists of chains of indefinite length, made up of rings, thus:

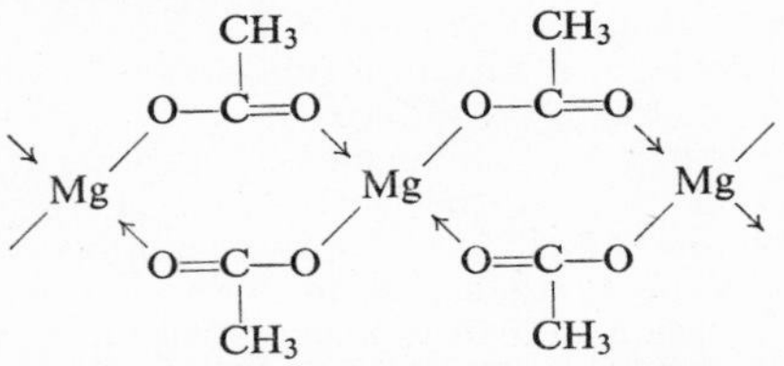

Magnesium oxalate dihydrate, $MgC_2O_4,2H_2O$, is extremely insoluble in water, but supersaturated solutions can be obtained by dissolving magnesium oxide in aqueous oxalic acid.

Anhydrous magnesium sulphate, MgSO$_4$, is obtained by heating any hydrate of magnesium sulphate to 200°. At a white heat the anhydrous salt decomposes, evolving sulphur dioxide and trioxide and oxygen, and leaving a residue of magnesium oxide; m.p. (with some decomposition) 1120°. Anhydrous magnesium sulphate is slightly soluble in methyl and ethyl alcohol. It is reduced by lampblack at 800°:

$$2MgSO_4 + C = 2MgO + 2SO_2 + CO_2,$$

with some reduction to sulphide,

$$MgSO_4 + 2C = MgS + 2CO_2.$$

Magnesium sulphate forms the hydrates:

$$\text{ice} \rightleftharpoons 12H_2O \rightleftharpoons 7H_2O \rightleftharpoons 6H_2O \rightleftharpoons 1H_2O \rightleftharpoons \text{anhyd.}$$
$$\quad -4° \qquad 1·8° \qquad 48·3° \qquad 68° \qquad 200°$$

There are two crystal forms of the heptahydrate, MgSO$_4$,7H$_2$O. One is isomorphous with the rhombic crystals of zinc sulphate heptahydrate, and the other is isomorphous with the monoclinic crystals of ferrous sulphate heptahydrate. Many double salts are known, such as schönite, K$_2$SO$_4$,MgSO$_4$,6H$_2$O, astrakanite Na$_2$SO$_4$,MgSO$_4$,4H$_2$O, and kainite KCl,MgSO$_4$,3H$_2$O. Magnesium selenate is similar to the sulphate, and forms the hydrates 7, 6, 2, 1.

SECTION 5. COMPOUNDS IN WHICH THE MAGNESIUM ATOM IS OCTAHEDRALLY HYBRIDISED

The existence of d orbitals in the valency shell of the magnesium atom (the M shell) enables the atom to adopt the octahedral valence state. The only examples of compounds containing the magnesium atom in this state appear to be the hexahydrates and hexammino complexes, such as:

$$(Mg,6H_2O)(ClO_4)_2$$
$$(Mg,6NH_3)Cl_2$$
$$(Mg,6NH_3)(ClO_4)_2$$
$$(Mg,2pyr,4H_2O)(NO_3)_2$$
$$(Mg,4pyr,2Et_2O)Br_2$$
$$(Mg,5pyr,Et_2O)I_2$$
$$(Mg,6CH_3CN)I_2$$

CALCIUM, STRONTIUM, AND BARIUM

THE PROPERTIES OF THE METALS

The three metals are all silver white. They are softer than beryllium or magnesium and are about as hard as lead.

Table 15.10. *The Reactions of Calcium, Strontium, and Barium*

Air	All the metals react to form nitrides and oxides; calcium forms chiefly calcium nitride, and barium forms chiefly barium oxide
O$_2$	All the metals burn to the monoxide
N$_2$	Nitrogen combines with all the metals on gentle heating
H$_2$O	All metals react to give the hydroxide and hydrogen. The violence of the reaction increases with the atomic number of the metal, but barium reacts less violently than sodium
H$_2$	Direct combination to hydrides occurs with all metals on gentle heating. Calcium reacts more readily than barium
NH$_3$	Calcium absorbs ammonia to give Ca(NH$_3$)$_6$, which on heating gives Ca(NH$_2$)$_2$ and Ca(NH)

GENERAL CHEMISTRY OF CALCIUM, STRONTIUM, AND BARIUM

The electron configurations of the two outermost shells of the atoms of calcium, strontium, and barium in the ground state are s^2, p^6, s^2; there are two electrons in the s orbital of the external shell, and eight electrons in the penultimate shell. Almost without exception both the external s electrons take part together in bond formation whether the bond is ionic or covalent; the somewhat scanty evidence for the existence of alkaline earth metals in the univalent state in the subhydrides and subhalides is mentioned below. From Table 15.2 it can be seen that the elements do not differ greatly in the magnitudes of properties which determine chemical behaviour. The values of the ionisation potentials, deforming powers, and electronegativities fall steadily along the series beryllium, magnesium, calcium, but there is little further change from calcium to barium; the electrode potentials behave similarly except that the values rise along the series.

The electronegativity (1·0) is only slightly greater than that of the alkali metals, and in accordance with this value the oxides of calcium, strontium, and barium are strongly basic, and the simple metal ions are present in stable salts. The tendency of the salts to be hydrated falls from calcium to barium (Table 15.3). Giant molecules are formed by such compounds as the hydrides, nitrides, sulphides, and fluorides of the metals, but the ability to form simple covalent compounds is much less than that of beryllium or magnesium. There are no electron deficient tetrahedral compounds (Table 15.1, Section 4), but alkyls and chelate compounds of β-diketones and similar ligands are known for all the elements. The metals form no anionic complexes, but digonal, tetrahedral, and octahedral cationic complexes are common.

SECTION 1. CALCIUM, STRONTIUM, AND BARIUM COMPOUNDS WITH IONIC CHARACTER

The metals in the univalent state. The band spectra of the hydrides, MH, of each of the metals can be observed in a vacuum tube containing the vapour of the metal and hydrogen. The band spectra of the fluorides, MF, can be observed in a vacuum tube containing a mixture of the vapours of the metal and the normal metallic fluoride. A grey subchloride of calcium, CaCl, is obtained by heating to 1000° the appropriate proportions of calcium metal and calcium chloride; X-ray diffraction has shown that it is an individual substance, and not a mixture.

The simple bivalent cations, Ca^{2+}, Sr^{2+}, Ba^{2+}. Calcium, strontium, and barium are the next most electropositive metals after the alkali metals. Like the alkali metals they form stable salts of which the anions are the chief points of interest: the alkaline earth metal cations in the salts have little deforming power, and hence they stabilise the anions. Nevertheless, the deforming power is greater than that of the alkali metals. This effect is seen in the thermal instability of the carbonates and peroxides, and in the reduced solubility of many salts, including the carbonates, sulphates, and phosphates.

GIANT MOLECULES IN WHICH THE BONDS HAVE SOME IONIC CHARACTER

The hydrides of calcium, strontium, and barium are white crystalline compounds with high melting points. They are all formed by the direct union of the elements more readily than the hydrides of beryllium and magnesium. The crystal structures of the hydrides are unknown, but since MgH_2 is more ionic than BeH_2, it is probable that the metal-hydrogen bonds in CaH_2, SrH_2, and BaH_2 are largely ionic in character. The hydrides are stable in air, but are violently decomposed by cold water:

$$CaH_2 + 2H_2O = Ca(OH)_2 + 2H_2.$$

Metallic calcium dissolves in calcium hydride at 800°. Both strontium hydride and barium hydride absorb hydrogen at 0°, up to the composition MH_4, but much of the additional hydrogen can be pumped off.

The hydridechlorides. Calcium hydride chloride, CaHCl (m.p. 700°) resembles mica in appearance. It is made by melting together calcium hydride and anhydrous calcium chloride, or by heating the chloride in an atmosphere of hydrogen. It is stable at high temperatures under vacuum. It has the PbClF crystal structure. SrHCl (m.p. 840°) and BaHCl (m.p. 850°) are made by analogous reactions and are similar in properties.

The acetylides. All the metals form acetylides, MC_2. Calcium acetylide (colloquially called calcium carbide) is obtained commercially as a soft, grey, solid by heating coke and lime in an electric furnace to 2000°. Calcium acetylide reacts with water to yield acetylene. At a red heat it absorbs nitrogen to form calcium cyanamide (traces of calcium chloride facilitate the reaction):

$$CaC_2 + N_2 = Ca^{2+}(NC \equiv N)^{2-} + C.$$

Calcium acetylide is a reducing agent; it reduces magnesium oxide to magnesium (p. 442). A powdered mixture of calcium acetylide, ferric chloride, and ferric oxide burns when gently ignited, and yields metallic iron. Calcium acetylide reacts with bromine to give C_2Br_6 and $CaBr_2$. The crystal structure of calcium acetylide (p. 580) is closely related to that of sodium chloride.

The acetylides of strontium and barium resemble those of calcium. Barium acetylide ignites in contact with water, and decomposes with incandescence in contact with absolute alcohol, with air, or when heated in hydrogen or in vacuo above 150°. It absorbs nitrogen when heated to yield barium cyanide, $Ba(CN)_2$. (Calcium acetylide yields $CaCN_2$ in similar conditions.)

Barium hydroacetylide tetra-ammoniate, $(C_2H)_2Ba,4NH_3$, a white crystalline compound, is prepared by passing acetylene through a solution of barium in liquid ammonia at −34°. If heated to 120° in vacuo, barium hydroacetylide leaves a solid residue containing 97% of BaC_2.

The nitrides of calcium, strontium, and barium, M_3N_2, are colourless crystalline compounds which are prepared by heating the metals in nitrogen at 300–400°. The action is autocatalytic and is promoted by the presence of more electropositive metals.

Metallic calcium absorbs ammonia gas to form $Ca(NH_3)_6$, which on heating gives the amide:

$$Ca(NH_3)_6 = Ca(NH_2)_2 + 4NH_3 + H_2.$$

At 400° the imide is formed:

$$Ca(NH_2)_2 = CaNH + NH_3,$$

and on further heating, the nitride, Ca_3N_2, m.p. 900°.

With carbon monoxide, calcium nitride and strontium nitride behave like magnesium nitride (p. 442), but barium nitride at a red heat yields the cyanide:

$$Ba_3N_2 + 2CO = Ba(CN)_2 + 2BaO.$$

With graphite at about 1000°, Ca_3N_2 gives a mixture of $Ca(CN)_2$ and $CaNC \equiv N$, but Ba_3N_2 gives $Ba(CN)_2$ only.

Oxides. The oxides of calcium, strontium and barium are white solids with very high melting points. All have the sodium chloride lattice. Calcium oxide is made by heating the carbonate, but the dissociation of barium carbonate takes place with difficulty

(Table 15.6) and to obtain barium oxide it is necessary to heat a mixture of the carbonate and carbon. Strontium oxide is obtained most readily in a similar manner. Red crystals of barium oxide have been grown in a vacuum furnace at 900° with 0·1% excess of barium. The colour is due to lattice defects.

The oxides are strongly basic, and react with water to form the hydroxides. Calcium oxide (quicklime) exposed to the atmosphere absorbs water and carbon dioxide, and is converted to a mixture of the hydroxide and carbonate. Dry calcium oxide does not absorb carbon dioxide, chlorine, hydrogen sulphide, sulphur dioxide or nitrogen dioxide.

Hydroxides. Calcium hydroxide is obtained as a fine powder by the action of a limited quantity of water on calcium oxide. It is slightly soluble in water, and less soluble in hot than in cold. Its solubility is reduced if NaOH or KOH is present in the solution. At a dull red heat it yields calcium oxide. Like magnesium hydroxide, calcium hydroxide crystallises with a layer lattice. Strontium hydroxide is formed with the evolution of heat when strontium oxide combines with water. The addition of sufficient water yields the crystalline hydrate, $Sr(OH)_2,8H_2O$, which effloresces to $Sr(OH)_2,H_2O$, and at 100° yields the anhydrous hydroxide. At a dull red heat this yields strontium oxide.

Barium hydroxide behaves in the same way as strontium hydroxide with the exception that on heating, even to high temperatures, the formation of barium oxide is incomplete.

Peroxides. It is seen from the dissociation pressures and from the method of preparation (Tables 15.6 and 21.9) that the stability of the peroxides increases from calcium to barium.

Calcium peroxide cannot be made by the direct action of oxygen on calcium oxide. The octahydrate is precipitated when hydrogen peroxide is added to lime water below 40°: above 40° the anhydrous peroxide is precipitated. The octahydrate is also precipitated when sodium peroxide is added to a solution of a calcium salt. At 130° the octahydrate loses water to yield the anhydrous peroxide.

Strontium and barium peroxides can also be made by the precipitation of the octahydrates by the action of hydrogen peroxide or sodium peroxide on a solution of a strontium or barium salt, followed by dehydration of the octahydrate.

Sidgwick notes the curious reaction:

$$BaO_2 + 2K_3(Fe(CN)_6) = K_6Ba(Fe(CN)_6)_2 + O_2.$$

The crystal structure of barium peroxide has been shown to be of the calcium carbide type, which suggests the presence of the ions Ba^{2+} and $[O—O]^{2-}$. This structure is analogous to that of potassium tetroxide, $K^+[O—O]^-$. CaO_4 and BaO_4 are mentioned in the literature, but there is no certain evidence of their existence.

Sulphides. The sulphides of calcium, strontium, and barium are white or colourless solids. They may be prepared by the reduction of the sulphates at 900°. They may also be prepared by passing hydrogen sulphide over the gently heated hydroxide:

$$Ca(OH)_2 + H_2S = CaS + 2H_2O.$$

The sulphides are sparingly soluble in water, but react with it to yield the soluble hydrosulphides:

$$2CaS + 2H_2O = Ca(SH)_2 + Ca(OH)_2.$$

The sulphides are easily oxidised by air. If air is blown through a suspension of calcium sulphide in water, calcium thiosulphate is obtained:

$$H_2O + 2CaS + 2O_2 = CaS_2O_3 + Ca(OH)_2.$$

The three sulphides have the NaCl lattice.

Polysulphides. Calcium polysulphides of indefinite composition are formed by boiling sulphur with a suspension of calcium hydroxide in water. From the solution obtained $CaS_4,3Ca(OH)_2,9H_2O$ crystallises. $SrS_4,4H_2O$ and $SrS_4,2H_2O$ are obtained by boiling a suspension of strontium sulphide and sulphur, and evaporating in the cold in vacuo. BaS_4,H_2O, a red solid, is formed by the oxidation of a solution of barium hydrosulphide. It is soluble in water, 41 gm in 100 gm at 15°: the solution is red and alkaline.

The halides of calcium, strontium, and barium. Certain properties of these compounds are set out in Table 15.4. From the Table it is seen that the fluorides all crystallise with the fluorite lattice, and that the chlorides also have lattices which indicate considerable ionic character. The bromides and iodides have covalent lattices. The melting points of all the compounds are high. The solubility of the fluorides in water is very much lower than the solubilities of the other halides. The fluorides are not hydrated; each of the other halides forms several hydrates, but the degree of hydration is not so high as that of the corresponding magnesium compounds. X-ray analysis has shown that the hexahydrates, $[Ca,6H_2O]Cl_2$, $[Sr,6H_2O]Cl_2$, $[Ca,6H_2O]Br_2$, $[Sr,6H_2O]Br_2$ are isomorphous, and that the six water molecules are arranged octahedrally round the metal atom.

The fluorides when heated in air to about 1000° are converted to oxides. Calcium fluoride in the condition in which it occurs naturally as fluorspar or fluorite is phosphorescent, but this property is ascribed to the presence of traces of heavy metals such as bismuth. Calcium fluoride is transparent to ultraviolet light.

SECTIONS 2 AND 3. CALCIUM, STRONTIUM, AND BARIUM ATOMS IN THE DIGONAL AND TRIGONAL VALENCE STATES

The calcium, strontium, and barium atoms in the digonal valence state are found in certain dihydrates of the salts of strong acids, such as $[Ca,2H_2O](ClO_4)_2$ (Table 15.1, Section 2), and in the dialkyls. Each of the metals reacts with methyl iodide or ethyl iodide in pyridine to yield a dialkyl such as $Ca(C_2H_5)_2$. The ethereal solutions of double alkyls of the type $(C_2H_5)_2Sr—Zn(C_2H_5)_2$ give the reactions expected for $(C_2H_5)_2Sr$. The double alkyls are colourless, crystalline bodies, made by treating the metal with boiling zinc diethyl in the absence of air. If calcium, strontium, or barium is treated in ether with an alkyl or aryl iodide, a solution is obtained which reacts in the same way as a Grignard reagent, a property which suggests the presence of, say, $CaI(C_2H_5)$. The reaction between the metal and the iodide, however, is very much slower than the corresponding reaction with magnesium, and the existence of a compound such as $CaI(C_2H_5)$ containing an alkaline earth metal in the digonal valance state is by no means certain.

It is doubtful whether the metals ever adopt the trigonal valence state. Equilibrium diagrams indicate the existence of the double chlorides, $KCaCl_3$ m.p. 754°, $RbCaCl_3$ m.p. 930°, $CsCaCl_3$ m.p. 1030°, but there is no evidence that the group $CaCl_3$ is an ion.

SECTION 4. THE CALCIUM, STRONTIUM, AND BARIUM ATOMS IN THE TETRAHEDRAL VALENCE STATE

NON-CHELATE COMPLEXES

The atoms of calcium, strontium, and barium in the tetrahedral valence state are present in compounds containing non-chelate cationic complexes such as $[Ca,4NH_3]Cl_2$. Complex cations present in hydrates such as $[Ca,4H_2O](NO_3)_2$ are formed by certain calcium salts, and to a less degree by strontium salts (Table 15.3), but barium salts form no such hydrates.

Electron deficient tetrahedral compounds which are a prominent feature of the chemistry of beryllium, and which, on a more restricted scale, are part of the chemistry of magnesium, are not formed by calcium, strontium, or barium. The compounds most likely to be electron deficient and to contain the metal atoms in the tetrahedral valence state are the alkyls and aryls, but these compounds are not well characterised, and probably contain the metal in the digonal valence state. There is very slender evidence, based on the change of transport number with concentration, for the presence in solution of $Ba(BaCl_4)$, but otherwise there is no indication of the existence of complex anions of the type $[MCl_4]^{2-}$.

CHELATE COMPLEXES

Chelate Neutral Complexes

The alkaline earth metals form complexes of this type with β-diketones, β-ketoesters, and α-dicarboxylic esters.

The dichelate acetylacetonates, such as

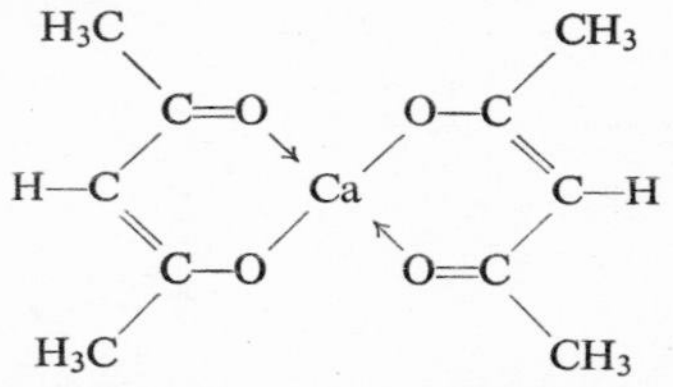

are made by the action of acetylacetone on the hydroxide, or on an aqueous solution of the cyanide.

They are insoluble in water, but they crystallise with two molecules of water of hydration from solvents containing a little water. The two water molecules are easily removed by warming in vacuo. Derivatives of acetoacetic and malonic esters can be made by corresponding reactions; they do not form hydrates.

Calcium oxalate forms a trihydrate which may be:

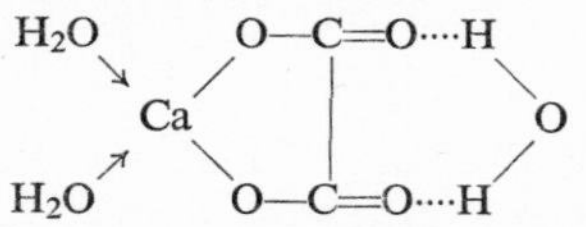

At 120° it yields the monohydrate, and at 200° the anhydrous salt. At 560° this produces the carbonate: $CaC_2O_4 = CaCO_3 + CO$. Strontium and barium oxalates also form hydrates.

Chelate Complex Anions and Complex Cations

Examples of these two classes cannot be given. It may be noted, however, that calcium sulphate dissolves in a concentrated aqueous solution of ammonium sulphate. This solubility may indicate the existence of the salt:

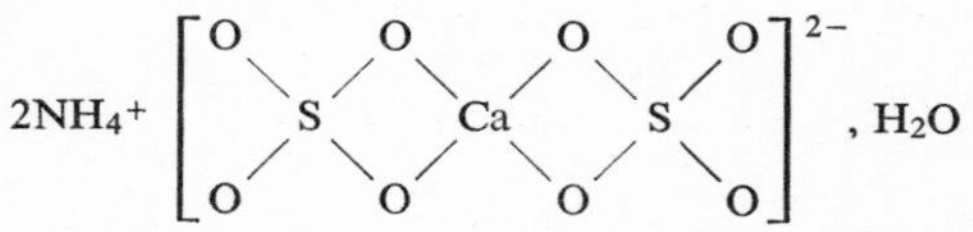

Strontium and barium sulphates do not dissolve in ammonium sulphate solution. The conductivities of solutions of the oxalates of Ca, Sr, and Ba give no indication of auto-complex formation.

SECTION 5. COMPOUNDS IN WHICH CALCIUM, STRONTIUM, AND BARIUM ARE OCTAHEDRALLY HYBRIDISED

The valence shells of the atoms of calcium, strontium, and barium contain d orbitals, but examples of octahedral hybridisation are not numerous. Complex cations are found in the hexahydrates (Table 15.1, Section 5). The dihydrates of the acetylacetonate complexes belong to this Section.

CHAPTER SIXTEEN

SUB-GROUP II T

THE TRANSITION METALS, ZINC, CADMIUM, AND MERCURY

The electronic configurations of the atoms of the three metals are shown in Table 16.2. In each case the valency shell contains one pair of s electrons, and the penultimate shell contains 18 electrons which completely occupy the s, p, and d orbitals of that shell.

$(Z_{eff})_{mol}$ for an atom with 18 electrons in the penultimate shell is greater than $(Z_{eff})_{mol}$ for an atom in the same Group and in the same Period with 8 electrons in the penultimate shell; for example, $(Z_{eff})_{mol}$ for zinc is 4·0, and for calcium is 2·5. In fact, the electronegativity of zinc, cadmium, and mercury is higher than that of beryllium, which has the highest electronegativity of all the normal elements in Group II. The first and second ionisation potentials of zinc, cadmium, and mercury are higher than those of the normal elements of the Group, and the values are roughly the same as that of beryllium. The general chemistry of zinc, cadmium, and mercury therefore resembles that of beryllium and magnesium, rather than that of calcium or barium. There is no evidence of any compound in which either zinc or cadmium, or mercury is univalent; when an atom of one of these metals enters into chemical combination both the electrons in the valency shell take part.

Zinc, cadmium, and mercury occupy positions in Periods 4, 5 and 6 in the periodic table which enable them to be regarded either as the final members of three transition series otherwise ending at copper, silver, and gold, or as the first members of the three series of normal elements otherwise beginning with gallium, indium, and thallium. The atoms of copper, silver, and gold have electron configurations $d^{10}s^1$; the d orbitals are those of the penultimate shell, and the s orbital is that of the outermost shell. Copper, silver, and gold all form univalent compounds which are colourless; in these only the s electron is used in bond formation. Copper, silver, and gold also form coloured compounds in which one or two of the d electrons of the penultimate shell as well as the s electron are used for bond formation. The d orbitals in the penultimate shells of the atoms of zinc, cadmium, and mercury are never used in bond formation, and hence these metals do not show the variable valency which is one of the characteristics of transition elements. The complete inertness of the penultimate shells of the atoms of zinc, cadmium, and mercury is a characteristic property of a normal element, which is shown by gallium, indium, and thallium and the succeeding normal elements in Periods 4, 5, and 6.

The tendency of the metals to form complexes by co-ordination is in the order $Hg > Cd > Zn$. This order, in which the greatest co-ordinating power is shown by the atom of highest atomic number, is opposite to that of the normal elements in Group II.

The vapours of the metals are nearly completely monatomic above 1000°, but there are sufficient diatomic molecules present to produce a characteristic band spectrum. Vaporised mixtures of zinc, cadmium, and mercury with each other or with the alkali metals, also give characteristic band spectra.

Table 16.1.   *Examples of Types of Compounds formed by Metals in Group II T.*

Oxidation State of the Metal = 1

Nature of compound	page	Zn	page	Cd	page	Hg	page
Ionic compounds	466	None		$CdAlCl_4$		Hg_2F_2, Hg_2Cl_2, $Hg_2(NO_3)_2$	485
Covalent compounds		None		None		$Hg_2(Cl_3CO_2)_2$, $Hg_2(S_7N)_2$	486
Cationic complexes		None		None		$[Hg_2(H_2NNH_2)](NO_3)_2$ $[Hg_2(H_2O)_2](NO_3)_2$	486

Oxidation State of the Metal = 2

Section	Hybridisation	Formal charge	Bonds ‡	Nature of unit formed	Zn	page	Cd	page	Hg	page
1				**Salts** — Compounds in which the atom is present as a simple cation; the bonds may have both ionic and covalent character	$Zn(NO_3)_2$, $ZnSO_4$	459	$Cd(NO_3)_2$, $CdSO_4$	467	$[HgC_2H_5]NO_3$ $Hg(NO_3)_2$, $HgSO_4$	467
				Giant molecules	ZnC_2, Zn_3N_2, $Zn(NH_2)_2$ ZnO, $Zn(OH)_2$, ZnS ZnS_2, ZnX_2 [$X = F$, Cl, Br, I]	459 459 460	CdC_2, $Cd(NH_2)_2$, CdS CdO, $Cd(OH)_2$, CdX_2 [$X = F$, Cl, Br, I]	467 468	HgC_2, $Hg(CN)_2$, Hg_3N_2 $HgNH_2Cl$†, $Hg_2NOH·2H_2O$† HgO†, HgS† HgX_2 [$X = F$, Cl, Br, I]	472 473 474 476
2	Digonal	0	2σ	Neutral compounds	$Zn(C_2H_5)_2$, $Zn(C_2H_5)I$ $Zn(BH_4)_2$, ZnI_2(vapour)	462	$Cd(C_2H_5)_2$ CdX_2(vapour) [$X = Cl$, Br, I]	468	$Hg(C_2H_5)_2$, $Hg(C_6H_5)_2$, $Hg(C_2H_5)Cl$ HgO, HgS, $HgCl_2$ $HgBr_2$ (vapour), HgI_2 (vapour)	468 480 473

					Zn compounds	p.	Cd compounds — [CdC5H5N](NO3)2	p.	Hg compounds — Na2[HgS2]	p.
3	Trigonal	−1	3σ	Complex anions						
				Complex cations					[Hg(H2O)2]F2, (HgNH2)mClm, (Hg2ONH2)mCln	476 / 473
4	Tetrahedral	−2	4σ	Neutral compounds	Na[Zn(OH)3], Na[Zn(C2H5)3]	462	K[Cd(NO2)3]	468	(C2H5)SHgCl2, ClHgOCH3CO	476 / 481
				Complex anions					K[HgCl3], K[Hg(CN)2Cl]	481
				Electron deficient compounds	(ZnH2)n	463	(CdH2)n	468	None	
				Non-chelate — Neutral complexes	(C2H5N)2ZnCl2, ((CH3)2S)2ZnBr2, [CH3(C6H5)2As]2ZnCl2	463	((CH3)2S)2CdI2, (R3P)2CdCl2, (R3P2CdCl2)	469	[Hg(NH3)2]Cl2	482
				Non-chelate — Complex anions	Na2[Zn(CN)4], Na2[Zn(OH)4]	464	K2[Cd(CN)4], K2[Cd(NO2)4]	469	K2[HgI4], K2[Hg(CN)4]	482
				Non-chelate — Complex cations	K2[Zn(NH2)4], [Zn(NH3)4]Cl2	464	[Cd(NH3)4](OH)2, {[(CH2NH)2CS]4Cd}Cl2, [Cd(C5H5N)4](NO3)2	470	[Hg(NH3)4](NO3)2	482
				Chelate — Neutral complexes	ZnA2, Basic zinc acetate	464	CdA2	470	HgA2, Hg3Cl6(PR3)2	482
				Chelate — Complex anions	K2[Zn(C2O4)2], K6[Zn(P2O7)2]	465	K2[Cd(C2O4)2]	470	(NH4)2[Hg(C2O4)2(H2O)4]	483
				Chelate — Complex cations			[Cd(o-phen)2](NO3)2	470	[Hg en2]Cl2	483
5	Octahedral	−4	6σ	Neutral complexes	K2Zn[Zn(C6N6)]	465	CdCl2,2NH3	470	K3[Hg(NO2)5H2O]	483
				Complex anions	[Zn(NH3)6]Cl2, [Zn(H2O)6](ClO4)2	466	[Cd(NH3)6]Cl2, [Cd en3]Cl2	470	[Hg en3]Cl2	483

† The mercury atom in these compounds has been shown to have digonal configuration

‡ In the column the expression "2σ" indicates the presence of two bonds each of type σ; the other expressions have corresponding meanings.

Table 16.2.   *The Properties of the Metals in sub-Group II T*

	Zn	Cd	Hg
Atomic number	30	48	80
Electron configuration	2, 8, 18, 2	2, 8, 18, 18, 2	2, 8, 18, 32, 18, 2
Atomic weight	65·38	112·41	200·61
Density	7·1	8·64	13·6
Crystal lattice	Distorted hexagonal close-packed	Distorted hexagonal close-packed	Distorted cubical close-packed
m.p. °C	419	321	−39
b.p. °C	910	778	356·9
Electrode potential on H scale	+0·762	+0·401	−0·799
Ionisation potential I	9·36	8·96	10·39
II	17·89	16·84	18·65
Total	27·25	25·80	29·04
Atomic radius	1·31	1·48	1·48
Ionic radius, M^{2+}	0·83	1·03	1·12
Electronegativity	1·6	1·6	1·6

The chemistry of zinc and cadmium is what would be expected for bivalent moderately electronegative elements. The chemistry of mercury is unique in several respects. The peculiar properties of mercury are related to the tendency for the *s* electrons in the valency shell of the atoms of heavy elements to be inert. This subject is discussed on p. 487.

GENERAL CHEMISTRY OF ZINC

The chemistry of zinc on the whole closely follows that of magnesium. It is seen from Tables 15.1 and 16.1 that there is a zinc compound corresponding to every type of compound formed by magnesium. The principal differences between zinc and magnesium are:

 (i) Zinc is less electropositive than magnesium; zinc dissolves in aqueous potassium hydroxide (as does beryllium), but magnesium and all the other metals in sub-Groups II N and II T are unattacked by alkalis. The structure of potassium zincate is uncertain (p. 460).

 (ii) The co-ordination number of the zinc atom in combination tends to be lower than that of magnesium. Both magnesium oxide and magnesium sulphide have sodium chloride lattices in which the co-ordination number of the magnesium atom is 6; zinc oxide and zinc sulphide have the wurtzite structure in which the co-ordination number of the zinc atom is 4. The co-ordination number of magnesium in Mg_2SiO_4 is 6, but in Zn_2SiO_4, although the chemical formula corresponds to that of the magnesium compound, the co-ordination number of zinc is 4.

 (iii) The only zinc compound which might have an electron deficient structure is the hydride, ZnH_2. Magnesium forms several electron deficient compounds, such as the polymeric $Mg(C_2H_5)_2$, but $Zn(C_2H_5)_2$ is monomeric in the vapour and in solution, and the molecule almost certainly has a simple linear structure.

 (iv) There are no zinc compounds corresponding to the Grignard reagents such as $Mg(C_2H_5)Br$.

The range of compounds formed by zinc is seen from Table 16.1. The compounds included in each section of the table are discussed in the following paragraphs.

SECTION 1. ZINC COMPOUNDS WITH IONIC CHARACTER

It is not certain whether the simple ion Zn^{2+} is present in any zinc compound. Anhydrous zinc nitrate and anhydrous zinc sulphate can be obtained, but these compounds may be auto-complexes.

Zinc nitrate, $Zn(NO_3)_2$, is best prepared in the anhydrous condition by the action of liquid nitrogen dioxide on the metal. A zinc nitrate complex is formed in the cold:

$$Zn + 4N_2O_4 \text{ (liq.)} = Zn(NO_3)_2,2N_2O_4 + 2NO,$$

but this decomposes on raising the temperature to 100°:

$$Zn(NO_3)_2,2N_2O_4 = Zn(NO_3)_2 + 2N_2O_4.$$

Zinc sulphate. If the aqueous solution of zinc sulphate is crystallised below 38·12° $ZnSO_4,7H_2O$ is obtained. This is isomorphous with the corresponding sulphates of Mg, Cd, Fe, Ni, Co, Mn, Cr. The heptahydrate is efflorescent and loses all its water at 450° to yield the anhydrous salt, which on further heating yields the oxide. The sulphate forms vitriols of the type $K_2SO_4,ZnSO_4,6H_2O$.

ZINC COMPOUNDS CONSISTING OF GIANT MOLECULES IN WHICH THE BONDS HAVE SOME IONIC CHARACTER

Zinc compounds in this class are numerous, like the corresponding compounds of beryllium and magnesium (Table 15.1). In lattice structure, ZnO (wurtzite) and ZnS (zinc blende) resemble the beryllium compounds, but ZnF_2 (rutile), and $Zn(OH)_2$ and $ZnCl_2$ (both layer lattices) resemble the magnesium compounds. The compounds $ZnCO_3$, $ZnWO_4$, and $ZnSb_2O_6$ are isomorphous with the corresponding magnesium compounds. Certain zinc compounds forming giant molecules are described below.

Zinc carbide. Acetylides. The white powder obtained by passing acetylene into a solution of zinc diethyl in ligroin is said to be ZnC_2. It is decomposed by water to $Zn(OH)_2$.

Zinc nitride, Zn_3N_2, can be made by heating zinc dust to 600° in a stream of ammonia, or by heating zinc amide to 330°. It is grey, definitely crystalline, with a clear X-ray diffraction pattern. Its heat of formation is given by the equation:

$$3Zn + N_2 = Zn_3N_2; \qquad \Delta H = -5\cdot3 \text{ kcal.}$$

It decomposes water vigorously to give ammonia.

Zinc amide, $Zn(NH_2)_2$, is made by heating an ethereal solution of zinc diethyl with ammonia at 150°. It is a white powder, decomposed by water and acids. At 200–300° it gives zinc nitride.

If treated with H_2O_2 in ethereal solution it gives a compound rich in ZnO_2.

Zinc oxide, ZnO, is obtained by burning zinc in air, or by heating the carbonate or nitrate. It is a solid with a wurtzite lattice. It is white when cold, but yellow above 250°, m.p. above 2000°. It sublimes (1 atm) at 1720°. Zinc oxide does not take up oxygen, even under 12 atm pressure. It is reduced by carbon at a red heat to metal, but the reactions with carbon monoxide and with hydrogen are reversible. Below 39° it reacts slowly with water to give zinc hydroxide.

Zinc hydroxide, $Zn(OH)_2$, is a crystalline compound which exists in two forms, one with a CdI_2 layer lattice, and the other with a tetrahedral structure with hydroxyl bonds. Zinc hydroxide is stable in contact with water below 39°; above this temperature zinc oxide is stable. Zinc hydroxide is nearly insoluble in water, but it dissolves in aqueous ammonia to form ammines. It also dissolves in acids and in alkalis. Its solubility in acids is no doubt to be explained by the formation of soluble zinc salts of the acids, but the reason for its solubility in alkalis is not clear. The zinc hydroxide may form a sol which is stabilised by the OH$^-$ ions, or the solubility may be due to the formation of zincates, since the following zincates may be crystallised from concentrated alkali solution after the addition of alcohol; $Na(Zn(OH)_3)$, $Na(Zn(OH)_3),3H_2O$, $Na_2(Zn(OH)_4)$, $Na_2(Zn(OH)_4),2H_2O$.

Zinc peroxide. Hydrated zinc peroxides of indefinite composition can be obtained by the action of H_2O_2 on zinc hydroxide, but no compound ZnO_2 has been isolated. Ethereal hydrogen peroxide reacts with zinc diethyl or zinc amide to produce a substance containing 86% of ZnO_2.

Zinc sulphide, ZnS, occurs naturally as zinc blende, or sphalerite, which is the chief ore of zinc. It is typical of an important crystal lattice. Above 1020° this structure changes to wurtzite:

$$ZnS_{blende} \rightarrow ZnS_{wurtz.} ; \qquad \Delta H = -3 \cdot 19 \text{ cal.}$$

Wurtzite melts under pressure at 1800° to 1900°, but it begins to sublime at 1200° In the laboratory zinc sulphide is made by heating zinc or zinc oxide with sulphur, or by adding ammonium sulphide to a solution of a zinc salt at pH 2 to 3.

Zinc sulphide is white, but it darkens on exposure to light, probably because it dissociates to zinc and sulphur. When ignited in air it burns to zinc oxide. It is insoluble in water, in alkaline solutions or in acetic acid, but it dissolves in mineral acids with the evolution of hydrogen sulphide.

Zinc persulphide, ZnS$_2$, is precipitated in a reaction between a zinc salt and a thiosulphate in water at 100°:

$$Zn^{2+} + 2S_2O_3{}^{2-} = ZnS_2 + S_2O_6{}^{2-}$$

In the course of 10 minutes the hexathionate ion breaks down:

$$S_2O_6{}^{2-} + H_2O = SO_4{}^{2-} + SO_3{}^{2-} + 2H^+$$
$$S_2O_3{}^{2-} + 2H^+ = H_2O + SO_2 + S.$$

If ZnS_2 is heated above 120° it decomposes to $ZnS + S$; the decomposition is incomplete after 2 hours at 500°. ZnS thus prepared is free from zinc oxide.

The structure of ZnS_2 has not been determined.

The zinc halides. Certain properties of the zinc halides are set out in Table 16.3. It is clear from the Table that all the halides are covalent, and that zinc fluoride has the highest degree of ionic character. Zinc fluoride is made by the action of fluorine on zinc, zinc oxide, zinc bromide, or zinc sulphide.

Zinc chloride, ZnCl$_2$. The anhydrous salt may be made:

   (a) by the action of chlorine at 700° on zinc, zinc oxide, or zinc sulphide,

   (b) by heating zinc oxide at 450° in a mixture of chlorine and sulphur chloride (S_2Cl_2), or in carbonyl chloride,

   (c) by passing hydrogen chloride over heated zinc, or by evaporating zinc chloride solution in a current of hydrogen chloride,

   (d) by heating zinc with mercuric chloride.

It is made industrially by heating zinc sulphide with chlorine.

Anhydrous zinc chloride is a white deliquescent substance with a great affinity for water. The concentrated solution obtained by heating zinc, zinc oxide, or zinc carbonate with hydrochloric acid deposits $ZnCl_2,H_2O$. The other hydrates are mentioned in Table 16.3. Zinc chloride in aqueous solution is only very slightly hydrolysed.

The basic chlorides $ZnCl_2,4Zn(OH)_2$ and $ZnCl_2,3Zn(OH)_2$ have structures corresponding to the layer lattices of the hydroxide in which certain OH groups are replaced by Cl$^-$ ions.

Zinc iodide in the solid state has a layer lattice, but in the vapour the molecules ZnI_2 have been shown to be linear.

Table 16.3. *The Halides of Zinc, Cadmium, and Mercury*

Fluorides

	ZnF_2	CdF_2	HgF_2
Appearance	Colourless mono-clinic crystals	White cubic crystals	Colourless octa-hedral crystals
Lattice	Rutile	Fluorite	Fluorite
m.p. °C	875	1110	645
b.p. °C		1758	650
Solubility: moles per 100 moles of water	0·28 (20°)	0·52 (25°)	
Hydrates	4, 0	0	2, 0

Chlorides

	$ZnCl_2$	$CdCl_2$	$HgCl_2$
Appearance	White cubic crystals Deliquescent	Colourless hexa-gonal crystals	Colourless rhombic needles
Lattice	$CdCl_2$	$CdCl_2$	(See below)†
m.p. °C	270	568	280
b.p. °C	730	964	303
Solubility: moles per 100 moles of water	55·5 (25°)	11·32 (20°)	0·47 (25°)
Hydrates	4, 3, 2½, 1½, 1, 0	4, 2½‡, 1, 0	2, 0

Bromides

	$ZnBr_2$	$CdBr_2$	$HgBr_2$
Appearance	Colourless rhombic crystals Hygroscopic	Colourless crystals	Colourless rhombic crystals
Lattice		CdI_2	Distorted CdI_2
m.p. °C	390	585	237
b.p. °C	670	963	320
Solubility: moles per 100 moles of water	39·0 (25°)	7·6 (20°)	0·031 (25°)
Hydrates	3, 2, 0	4, 1, 0	

Iodides

	ZnI_2	CdI_2	HgI_2
Appearance	Colourless cubic crystals	Colourless hexagonal crystals	Below 127°: scarlet Above 127°: yellow
Lattice	CdI_2	CdI_2	Scarlet, tetrahedral: yellow, as $HgBr_2$
m.p. °C	446	388	259
b.p. °C	624	713	354
Solubility: moles per 100 moles of water	41·2 (25°)	4·2 (25°)	0·0019 (25°)
Hydrates	4, 2, 0	0	

† Mercuric chloride crystallises in discrete linear molecules. Each molecule is at the site of a point on a face-centred cubic lattice.
‡ Efflorescent; not hydrolysed by water.

SECTION 2. COMPOUNDS IN WHICH THE ZINC ATOM
IS DIGONALLY HYBRIDISED

The zinc compounds included in this Section are $Zn(C_2H_5)_2$, $Zn(CH_3)_2$, $Zn(C_2H_5)I$, $Zn(BH_4)_2$, and ZnI_2 in the vapour state. $Zn(C_2H_5)_2$ is monomeric and the molecule is probably linear. Beryllium and magnesium form compounds of corresponding empirical formulae (Table 15.1, Section 4) but they are polymerised and must be tetrahedral electron deficient compounds.

Zinc dialkyls. Zinc diethyl, $(C_2H_5)_2Zn$, a mobile liquid, m.p. $-30°$, b.p. $118°$, is made in two stages. Zinc is heated with ethyl iodide at the b.p. $(72\cdot3°)$ when ethyl zinc iodide is formed. The temperature is then raised, and the following reaction takes place:

$$2EtZnI = Zn(Et)_2 + ZnI_2$$

The reactions are carried out in the complete absence of air. Carbon dioxide is generally used as the inert atmosphere. The zinc–copper couple reacts more readily than pure zinc. Iodine and ethyl acetate have a catalytic effect, but ether has none.

Other reactions by which zinc diethyl can be made are:

$$Zn + Hg(C_2H_5)_2 = Zn(C_2H_5)_2 + Hg$$
$$ZnCl_2 + 2Mg(C_2H_5)I = Zn(C_2H_5)_2 + MgI_2 + MgCl_2$$

Zinc diethyl is stable but reactive. It can be kept indefinitely, and may be heated to over $200°$ without decomposition. It catches fire in air, but if the oxidation is carried out slowly the compound $Zn(C_2H_5)_2O_2$ is formed. This compound has oxidising properties. In ethereal solution H_2O_2 converts zinc diethyl into a body rich in ZnO_2.

Zinc diethyl reacts with water, alcohol, ammonia, and organic compounds containing oxygen, in a manner parallel to that of a Grignard reagent:

$$Zn(C_2H_5)_2 + 2H_2O = 2C_2H_6 + Zn(OH)_2$$

It differs, however, from a Grignard reagent in failing to react with carbon dioxide. Zinc diethyl dissolves in and reacts with alkyls of the alkali metals (p. 463), and it reacts with ethereal ammonia (p. 459). It is monomolecular in the vapour state and in solution in benzene. It has a low dielectric constant $(2\cdot55)$ and is a non-conductor in the pure state. Infrared and Raman spectra indicate that zinc dimethyl has a linear structure.

Zinc diphenyl is made from mercury diphenyl and metallic zinc. It is a white crystalline substance, m.p. $107°$, b.p. $283°$.

Zinc ethyl iodide, C_2H_5ZnI, is made by heating zinc and ethyl iodide at the b.p. $(72\cdot3°)$ in an atmosphere of carbon dioxide. It is a white crystalline solid, stable in carbon dioxide, but decomposed by air or water. It does not undergo the wide variety of reactions for which C_2H_5MgI is remarkable. Zinc ethyl iodide, however, dissolves in a mixture of ethyl acetate and toluene and, provided that an electronegative group is attached to the active group in each case, it reacts in the cold with organic halides, ethers, ketones, or with compounds containing the ethylenic double bond:

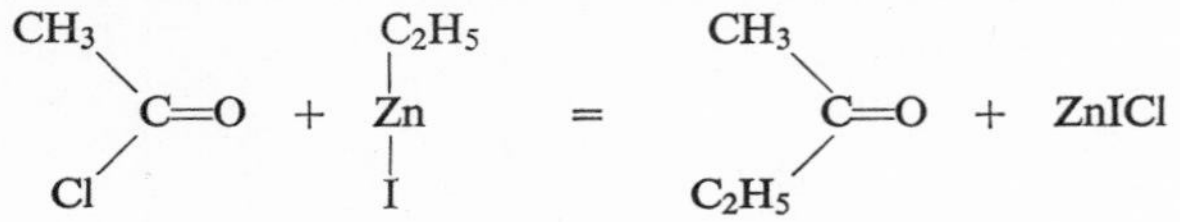

SECTION 3. COMPOUNDS IN WHICH THE ZINC ATOM
IS TRIGONALLY HYBRIDISED

Neither neutral compounds nor complex cations of this class exist, but the zinc atom may be trigonally hybridised in the complex anions in $Na[Zn(OH)_3]$ (p. 460), and in

$Na[Zn(C_2H_5)_3]$. Complex anions in which the metal is in the trigonal valence state are formed only by zinc and aluminium. $KZnF_3$ has the perovskite structure (p. 350), and therefore is not to be included in this Section.

Sodium triethylzincate, $Na[Zn(C_2H_5)_3]$, is a colourless solid, m.p. 27°. It is obtained by dissolving sodium in zinc diethyl:

$$2Na + 3Zn(C_2H_5)_2 = 2NaZn(C_2H_5)_3 + Zn,$$

and evaporating the solution. It may also be obtained by dissolving sodium ethyl in zinc diethyl; the solution becomes conducting after warming. As the conductivity depends on the presence of the anion $[Zn(C_2H_5)_3]^-$, it seems that the formation of this ion does not occur immediately after the reagents are mixed.

The electrolysis of lithium triethyl zincate has been studied. The primary change on discharge is:

$$Li^+[Zn(C_2H_5)_3]^- \rightarrow \overset{cathode}{Li} + \overbrace{Zn(C_2H_5)_2 + C_2H_5}^{anode}.$$

After discharge the lithium reacts with zinc ethyl, liberating zinc and reforming lithium triethyl zincate, and the ethyl radical partly disproportionates to ethylene (40%) and ethane (40%), and partly polymerises to butane (17%) and propane (3%).

Zinc diethyl also reacts with lithium methyl, lithium phenyl, and lithium benzyl, with potassium ethyl, and with caesium ethyl to produce compounds of the type $M[ZnR_3]$.

SECTION 4. COMPOUNDS IN WHICH THE ZINC ATOM IS TETRAHEDRALLY HYBRIDISED

Zinc compounds in this Section are numerous; all possible types are represented (Table 16.1).

ELECTRON-DEFICIENT COMPOUNDS

The only representative of this class is zinc hydride. Its structure is unknown, but its properties show that it is related to beryllium hydride rather than to magnesium hydride, and therefore it is regarded as an electron-deficient compound.

Zinc hydride, ZnH_2, is prepared by the action of lithium aluminium hydride on zinc dimethyl in solution in diethyl ether:

$$Zn(CH_3)_2 + 2LiAlH_4 = ZnH_2 + 2LiAl(CH_3)H_3$$

Zinc iodide may be used in place of zinc dimethyl.

Zinc hydride is a white, non-volatile solid which decomposes into its elements above 80°. It is insoluble in ether, and is slowly decomposed by water. With diborane it gives zinc borohydride:

$$B_2H_6 + ZnH_2 = Zn(BH_4)_2$$

NON-CHELATE COMPLEXES

Non-chelate Neutral Complexes

The zinc compounds of this type are adducts of the zinc halides with donor molecules, for example:

The molecular weights of zinc chloride, zinc bromide, and zinc iodide, dissolved in dimethyl sulphide are normal which indicates that the complexes formed are covalent and monomeric.

Non-chelate Complex Anions and Complex Cations

Among the tetrahedral non-chelate anions are $[Zn(CN)_4]^{2-}$ and $[Zn(NH_2)_4]^{2-}$. The tetrahedral configuration of the anion in $Na_2[Zn(CN)_4]$ has been established. The dissociation constant of the reaction: $Zn(CN)_4{}^{2-} \rightleftharpoons Zn(CN)_2 + 2CN^-$, is 1.3×10^{-17}. Potassium tetra-ammino zincate, $K_2[Zn(NH_2)_4]$, is made by dissolving zinc amide or metallic zinc in a solution of KNH_2 in liquid ammonia. It is not hydrolysed by liquid ammonia. Sodium zincate, $Na_2[Zn(OH)_4]$ has been mentioned under zinc hydroxide (p. 459). The tetrahydrate $[Zn(H_2O)_4]Cl_2$ and the tetra-ammoniate $[Zn(NH_3)_4]Cl_2$ are zinc compounds containing non-chelate complex cations.

CHELATE COMPLEXES

Chelate Neutral Complexes

Zinc diacetylacetonate,

is a colourless solid, m.p. 138°. It can be distilled. The vapour density indicates that the vapour is monomeric. It is easily soluble in benzene. It is soluble in water which does not hydrolyse it except on boiling. It does not form hydrates, and hence it crystallises from aqueous solution in the anhydrous condition. In all these properties it resembles the beryllium analogue (p. 435). Zinc benzoyl pyruvate (like the beryllium compound) has been resolved into optical antimers.

Basic zinc acetate, $Zn_4O(CH_3COO)_6$, is described on p. 810. The complex

is related to the dimethyl sulphide complex of zinc bromide (p. 457).

Chelate Complex Anions

Potassium zinc oxalate, $K_2[Zn(C_2O_4)_2]$. The anion in this salt may have the constitution:

The salt forms the hydrate $K_2[Zn(C_2O_4)_2],7H_2O$.

Zinc pyrophosphate. The existence of the ion

$$\left[\begin{array}{c} \overset{O}{\underset{O}{\|}} \overset{O}{\underset{P}{\|}} -O \quad\quad O-\overset{O}{\underset{P}{\|}}\overset{O}{\underset{\|}{}} \\ Zn \\ \overset{O}{\underset{O}{\|}}\overset{}{P}-O \quad\quad O-P\overset{O}{\underset{O}{}} \end{array}\right]^{6-}$$

has been proved by physico-chemical methods. The stability constant of the ion, K_s, is given by the expression

$$K_s = \frac{[Zn^{2+}][P_2O_7{}^{4-}]^2}{[Zn(P_2O_7)_2{}^{6-}]}$$

The value of K_s at $35°$ is $3\cdot17 \times 10^{-7}$.

SECTION 5. COMPOUNDS IN WHICH THE ZINC ATOM IS OCTAHEDRALLY HYBRIDISED

NON-CHELATE COMPLEXES

There are no non-chelate neutral compounds. Examples of non-chelate complex anions and cations are given below.

Non-chelate Complex Anions

An interesting compound is potassium zinc zincocyanide, $K_2Zn[Zn(CN)_6]$ (sometimes written as $KZn(CN)_3$). The inner group $Zn(CN)_6$ contains six bonds:

$$\left[\begin{array}{c} CN \\ CN\quad | \quad CN \\ Zn \\ CN \quad | \quad CN \\ CN \end{array}\right]^{4-}$$

Each Zn^{2+} ion which is not part of the complex $Zn(CN)_6$ is co-ordinated to four CN groups by use of the lone pairs on the nitrogen atoms:

$$\begin{array}{c} CN \\ CN\quad | \quad CN\rightarrow Zn\leftarrow \\ Zn \\ CN \quad | \quad CN \\ CN \end{array}$$

The resultant charge is neutralised by two K^+ ions. The structure is three-dimensional and continuous throughout the crystal, and is known as a *super complex*. The salt crystallises as the pentahydrate, $K_2Zn[Zn(CN)_6],5H_2O$. The potassium zinc nitrites, $K_2[Zn(NO_2)_4],2H_2O$ and $K_3[Zn(NO_2)_5],3H_2O$, may belong to this class of compound.

Non-chelate Complex Cations

The zinc halides form ammines of the type $(Zn,6NH_3)Cl_2$. These compounds are fairly easily decomposed by heat. The temperatures at which the dissociation pressure of ammonia reaches 100 mm are

	$ZnCl_2,6NH_3$	$ZnBr_2,6NH_3$	$ZnI_2,6NH_3$
	$23°$	$31°$	$28°$
(Temperatures for the corresponding cadmium salts	$24°$	$45°$	$65°$)

The complexes formed by the zinc halides with methylamine, $ZnX_2,5CH_3NH_2$, and with ethylenediamine, $ZnX_2,3C_2H_4(NH_2)_2$, are probably cationic, but the ethylamine derivatives appear to be covalent (p. 463).

CADMIUM

GENERAL CHEMISTRY

The chemistry of cadmium is close to that of zinc, but cadmium shows a greater tendency towards complex formation which makes it difficult to decide exactly what part a cadmium atom is playing in a molecule or crystal of one of its compounds. It is not clear whether the simple cadmium ion, Cd^{2+}, is present in any cadmium compound. The ion is most likely to be present in the perchlorate or the nitrate. These salts are briefly described below; both can be obtained in the anhydrous condition, and show no abnormalities. Cadmium fluoride has a fluorite lattice. It is somewhat soluble in water. It forms no hydrate. There is nothing in these properties to disprove the presence of the ion Cd^{2+} in the fluoride. The behaviour of the other cadmium halides is unusual and merits discussion here. The falls in molecular conductivity of aqueous solutions of $CdCl_2$, $CdBr_2$, and CdI_2 with increasing concentration of the solution, are very much more rapid than those of $Cd(NO_3)_2$, $MgCl_2$, or $ZnCl_2$. (The rates of fall of the last three compounds are roughly equal.) This rapid fall has been attributed to the formation of a complex, such as $Cd[CdCl_4]$. By several different physical methods it has been estimated that in a 0·01 molar solution of each of the cadmium halides the percentage proportions of the various species are present as follows:

	$CdCl_2$	$CdBr_2$	CdI_2
Cd^{2+}	41·0	32·8	23·1
$[Cdhal]^+$	56·3	60·6	66·4
$Cdhal_2$	3·9	6·5	6·9
$[Cdhal_3]^-$ $[Cdhal_4]^{2-}$ }	0·05	0·17	0·47

These results indicate that the fall in molecular conductivity is due to the aggregation of the two ions, Cd^{2+} and hal^- to give one ion, $[Cdhal^+]$. The very low proportions of the complex anions $[Cdhal_3^-]$ and $[Cdhal_4^{2-}]$, and the high proportion assigned to the simple ion Cd^{2+}, should be noted. Polarographic study of 0·004 molar cadmium nitrate in 1 molar sodium iodide solution indicates the existence of the ion $[CdI_4^{2-}]$ with the decomposition constant $1·2 \times 10^{-6}$. The formation of this ion may be responsible for the solubility in potassium iodide solution of insoluble salts such as CdS.

Equilibrium diagrams based on thermal analysis have established the existence of the following compounds:

$$Na_2[CdCl_4] \quad K_2[CdCl_4] \quad Rb_2[CdCl_4] \quad Cs_2[CdCl_4]$$
$$\text{tr. pt. } 433° \quad \text{tr. pt. } 450° \quad \text{max. } 440° \quad \text{max. } 462°$$

$$K[CdCl_3] \quad Rb[CdCl_3] \quad Cs[CdCl_3]$$
$$\text{max. } 430° \quad \text{max. } 500° \quad \text{max. } 545°$$

$CdCl_2$ and LiCl do not form a compound of this type. The $CdCl_2$–LiCl system consists of a continuous series of solid solutions, with a liquidus minimum at 502° and 40 mol % LiCl. The Rb and Cs compounds are completely isomorphous. It has been shown experimentally that $NH_4[CdCl_3]$, which is isomorphous with $RCb[dCl_3]$, has a chain structure. The chains consist of portions of the $CdCl_2$ layer structure with the composition $CdCl_3$. The chains are held together by the NH_4^+ ions.

SECTION 1. CADMIUM COMPOUNDS WITH IONIC CHARACTER

SALTS WHICH MAY CONTAIN THE SIMPLE ION Cd^{2+}

Cadmium nitrate, $Cd(NO_3)_2$, is a colourless, crystalline compound. It is soluble in water; at 25°, 134·4 gm dissolve in 100 gm of water. It forms three hydrates: 9, 4, and 2. The anhydrous salt melts at 360°, and at higher temperatures yields the oxide.

Cadmium sulphate, $CdSO_4$, is a colourless salt. It is soluble in water and forms the hydrates 7, 8/3, and 1. The anhydrous salt melts at 1000°.

Cadmium perchlorate, $Cd(ClO_4)_2$, can be obtained as the anhydrous salt, or as the dihydrate or hexahydrate (m.p. 129·4°). It is deliquescent, and soluble in alcohol.

Cadmium fluoride, CdF_2, is described on p. 468.

CADMIUM COMPOUNDS CONSISTING OF GIANT MOLECULES IN WHICH THE BONDS HAVE SOME IONIC CHARACTER

Cadmium acetylide has been reported, and is said to be stable to water.

Cadmium cyanide, $Cd(CN)_2$, is very similar to the zinc compound with which it is isomorphous.

Cadmium amide, $Cd(NH_2)_2$, a white compound, is made by the action of potassamide on cadmium cyanide in liquid ammonia. It reacts violently with water. On heating it explodes with the deposition of cadmium; it does not give the nitride.

Cadmium oxide, CdO, is a brown solid.† It is made by burning cadmium in air, or by heating the hydroxide, carbonate, or nitrate. It has the sodium chloride lattice.

Cadmium hydroxide, $Cd(OH)_2$, is a white crystalline compound, which is sparingly soluble in water. It does not dissolve in alkaline solution, but it is easily soluble in aqueous ammonia to give the cation $[Cd(NH_3)_4]^{2+}$. It does not take up carbon dioxide. On heating it yields the oxide. It has a cadmium iodide lattice.

Cadmium peroxide, CdO_2, is detectable in the product obtained by burning the metal in air. Otherwise the reactions which yield products containing cadmium peroxide correspond to those of zinc.

Cadmium sulphide, CdS, is a yellow compound with the wurtzite lattice. It melts at about 1750°, and sublimes at lower temperatures; it is very sparingly soluble in water (0·13 mg/100 gm at 18°). Cadmium selenide is brown and has a wurtzite structure. It

† There is no suboxide. The product of the thermal decomposition of cadmium oxalate is a mixture of CdO and the metal.

melts at 1350°. Cadmium telluride is black, and has a zinc blende structure. It melts with decomposition at 1050°.

Cadmium halides. The properties of the cadmium halides are summarised in Table 16.3. Cadmium fluoride is a high-melting solid with the fluorite lattice which may contain the simple ion Cd^{2+}. It can be made by adding ammonium fluoride to a solution of the much more soluble cadmium chloride. The chloride, bromide, and iodide are fairly soluble in water, they melt at lower temperatures than the fluoride, and they have covalent layer lattices. The lattices of cadmium chloride and iodide are typical of layer lattices based on cubic and hexagonal close-packing (p. 340). In the vapours of these three compounds the molecules are linear. The behaviour of the cadmium halides in aqueous solution is discussed on p. 466.

SECTION 2. COMPOUNDS IN WHICH THE CADMIUM ATOM IS DIGONALLY HYBRIDISED

Cadmium diethyl, $Cd(C_2H_5)_2$, is a liquid, denser than water, m.p. $-21°$, b.p. 64° at 19·5 mm. It is made by the action of cadmium on ethyl iodide, or by the action of cadmium chloride on a Grignard reagent in ethereal solution. Air must be absent from the apparatus.

It decomposes if heated to 150°, and in light it gives a black deposit of metallic cadmium. If exposed to the air, oxidation occurs with the formation of brown cadmium oxide. It is insoluble in water, but the two layers react with intermittent explosions. It dissolves lithium ethyl and sodium ethyl, but the solutions are non-conducting (cf. $Zn(C_2H_5)_2$).

The mean bond dissociation energy of Cd—C, deduced from experiments on $(CH_3)_2Cd$, is 31·1 kcal.

Cadmium ethyl iodide has not been prepared.

SECTION 3. COMPOUNDS IN WHICH THE CADMIUM ATOM IS TRIGONALLY HYBRIDISED

The range of compounds in which the cadmium atom is trigonally hybridised is interesting. The cadmium atom in this state forms no neutral complexes, and no hydroxyl or ethyl complexes corresponding to the zinc compounds $Na[Zn(OH)_3]$ and $Na[Zn(C_2H_5)_3]$, but the nitrite complex $K[Cd(NO_2)_3]$ appears to be well established. The potassium, rubidium, and caesium salts of the ion $[CdCl_3]^{-1}$ are mentioned on p. 467, but the anion in $NH_4[CdCl_3]$ has a chain structure, in which the valency of the cadmium atom is not certain.

$K[Cd(NO_2)_3]$ is stable in air. It is anhydrous, but is very soluble in water. It does not decompose if the solution is boiled. It is insoluble in alcohol.

SECTION 4. COMPOUNDS IN WHICH THE CADMIUM ATOM IS TETRAHEDRALLY HYBRIDISED

Like zinc, cadmium forms numerous compounds with the atom in the tetrahedral valence state, and all possible classes of compounds are represented.

ELECTRON-DEFICIENT COMPOUNDS

Cadmium hydride, CdH_2, is prepared by the action of lithium aluminium hydride on cadmium dimethyl in diethyl ether:

$$Cd(CH_3)_2 + 2LiAlH_4 = CdH_2 + 2LiAl(CH_3)H_3.$$

It is a white non-volatile solid, stable only below $0°$. It does not dissolve in ether, and it is slowly decomposed by water. Its structure is uncertain, but it closely resembles zinc hydride and is therefore assumed to be electron deficient and to contain three-centre bonds (p. 463).

NON-CHELATE COMPLEXES

Non-chelate Neutral Complexes

A molecule of a cadmium halide accepts two molecules, each capable of donating one electron pair, to form a tetrahedral complex such as

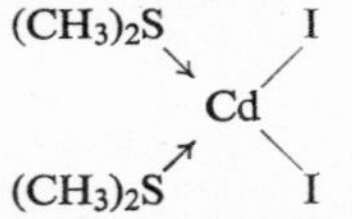

Cadmium iodide has the normal molecular weight when dissolved in dimethyl sulphide, and hence the complex must be monomeric. The adduct, however, is not always such a simple structure. According to Mann and Purdie, tertiary phosphines and arsines give compounds of three types:

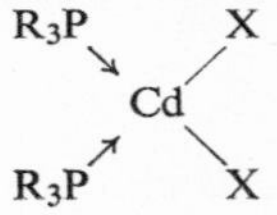

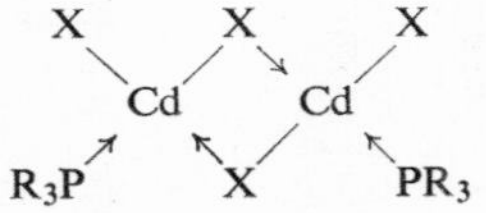

The structure of compound III is uncertain. Cadmium chloride diammoniate, $CdCl_2,2NH_3$, has been shown to have a chain structure in which the cadmium atoms are in the octahedral valence state:

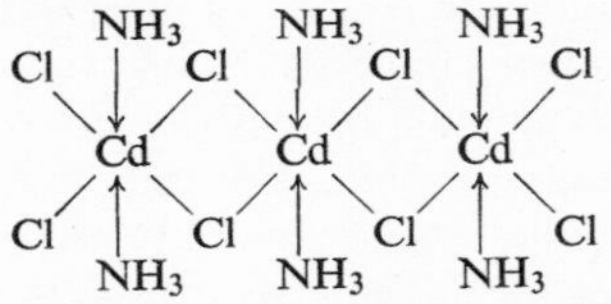

Two other stable complexes of uncertain structure may be mentioned, $CdI_2,(N_2H_4)_2$, which is precipitated quantitatively when potassium iodide and hydrazine are added to the solution of a cadmium salt, and $CdCl_2,C_5H_5N$, which is precipitated when pyridine and ammonium chloride are added to the solution of a cadmium salt. These precipitates may be dried at about $150°$ and weighed.

Non-chelate Complex Anions

Tetrahedral complex anions containing cadmium are well known. $K_2[Cd(CN)_4]$ resembles the corresponding zinc compound; the decomposition constant of the anion is $1·4 \times 10^{-7}$. $K_2[Cd(NO_2)_4]$ has been prepared as anhydrous yellow crystals, very soluble in water. The aqueous solution is not decomposed by boiling. The halogen complexes such as $K_2[CdCl_4]$ are mentioned on p. 467. There is no compound $K_2[Cd(OH)_4]$.

Non-chelate Complex Cations

Two examples of complex cations formed by cadmium are furnished by cadmium tetrammine hydroxide, and by the salts of cadmium ethylene thiocarbimide. Cadmium tetrammine hydroxide, $[Cd(NH_3)_4](OH)_2$, is prepared by dissolving cadmium hydroxide in ammonia solution. The decomposition constant of the ion $[Cd(NH_3)_4]^{2+}$ is $1 \cdot 0 \times 10^{-7}$. Cadmium ethylene thiocarbimide chloride has the formula

$$\left\{ \left[\begin{array}{c} CH_2-NH \\ | \qquad\quad \diagdown \\ \qquad\qquad\quad C=S \\ | \qquad\quad \diagup \\ CH_2-NH \end{array} \right]_4 Cd \right\} Cl_2$$

The corresponding bromide, iodide, and nitrate are known. The chloride, bromide, and iodide melt respectively at 220°, 208° and 165°. The compounds are insoluble in organic solvents, but soluble in water. The aqueous solution of the nitrate is a good conductor. The pyridine complex $[Cd(C_5H_5N)_4](NO_3)_2$ is known.

CHELATE COMPLEXES

The neutral complex cadmium acetylacetonate is similar to the zinc compound, but is less soluble in water. There is no "basic acetate" of cadmium. Among the chelate complex anions are the thiosulphate, and the oxalate complexes:

$$2K^+ \left[\begin{array}{ccccc} O & & S & & O \quad\quad O \\ \diagdown & & & & \diagup \\ & S & & Cd & & S \\ \diagup & & & & \diagdown \\ O & & O & & S \quad\quad O \end{array} \right]^{2-} \qquad 2K^+ \left[\begin{array}{ccc} O=C-O & & O-C=O \\ | \qquad \diagdown & & \diagup \quad | \\ & Cd & \\ | \qquad \diagup & & \diagdown \quad | \\ O=C-O & & O-C=O \end{array} \right]^{2-}$$

A chelate complex cation $[Cd(o\text{-phen})_2]^{2+}$ is formed when o-phenanthroline is added to an aqueous-alcohol solution of cadmium nitrate.

SECTION 5. COMPOUNDS IN WHICH THE CADMIUM ATOM IS OCTAHEDRALLY HYBRIDISED

There are not many cadmium compounds in this Section. The donating atom in complex formation is nearly always nitrogen. Non-chelate complex cations of cadmium are found in the hexammino cadmium halides which are slightly more stable than the corresponding zinc compounds (p. 466). The cadmium atom in cadmium chloride diammoniate is in the octahedral valence state (p. 469). The polarographic study of cadmium nitrate in the presence of a large excess of the complexing reagent has established the existence of the following cation complexes of cadmium:

$[Cd(o\text{-phen})_3]^{2+}, \qquad [Cd(dipyr)_3]^{2+},$

$$\left[Cd \left(\begin{array}{c} NH_2-CH_2 \\ | \\ NH_2-CH_2 \end{array} \right)_3 \right]^{2+}, \quad \left[Cd \left(\begin{array}{c} NH_2-CH_2 \\ \qquad\qquad\diagdown \\ \qquad\qquad\quad CH_2 \\ \qquad\qquad\diagup \\ NH_2-CH_2 \end{array} \right)_3 \right]^{2+}, \quad \left[Cd \left(\begin{array}{c} \qquad\quad CH_2 \\ \qquad\diagup \quad\diagdown \\ NH_2 \qquad\quad CH_2 \\ \qquad\qquad\quad | \\ \qquad\quad NH \\ \qquad\qquad\quad | \\ NH_2 \qquad\quad CH_2 \\ \qquad\diagdown \quad\diagup \\ \qquad\quad CH_2 \end{array} \right)_2 \right]^{2+}$$

In the last complex cation each of the three nitrogen atoms of a ligand molecule donates one electron pair to the cadmium atom.

MERCURY

GENERAL CHEMISTRY

The penultimate shell ($n = 5$) of the mercury atom is completely occupied by 18 electrons. $(Z_{eff})_{mol}$ for the mercury atom is relatively high, and hence the two electrons in the valency shell ($n = 6$) tend to form covalencies. The electronegativity of mercury is about 1·6, which is the normal value for a transition element. These properties are bound up with, but in themselves fail to explain, four properties of the mercury atom which differentiate its relation to cadmium from that of gold to silver, or thallium to indium:

(i) Mercury is unexpectedly volatile. The b.p. is 357°. The metal with the next lowest b.p. is caesium (670°). The vapour is monatomic. Mercury is the only element outside the group of the inert gases which yields a monatomic gas at moderate temperatures.

(ii) The mercury atom forms covalent rather than ionic bonds; the degree of ionisation of mercuric chloride, for example, is extremely small.

(iii) The mercury atom is saturated by the formation of two covalent bonds, that is, with four electrons in the valency shell.

(iv) Two mercury atoms combine by means of a single covalency to yield the bivalent unit (Hg—Hg).

Mercury forms two series of compounds, the mercuric compounds in which the atom is bicovalent, and in which its behaviour is in general analogous to that of the cadmium atom, and the mercurous compounds which contain the ion (Hg—Hg)$^{2+}$. The mercurous compounds have no analogues among the compounds of any other element. The evidence which establishes that the mercurous ion is (Hg—Hg)$^{2+}$ and not Hg$^+$ is summarised on p. 483. It is not to be expected that the ion Hg$^+$ would be stable. This hypothetical ion has one electron only in the valency shell. It is related to the dimeric ion [Hg$_2$]$^{2+}$ as the hydrogen atom is related to the hydrogen *molecule*.

Metal to metal bonds are rare. They must be present in the very small proportion of diatomic molecules of the alkali metals present in their vapours, and there is strong circumstantial evidence of the presence of these bonds in the molecules of certain metallic carbonyls, nitrosyls, and ferrocenes (Chapter 25). The metal-to-metal bond in these compounds is thought to be due to the overlapping of d orbitals of the two metallic atoms. It is possible that the two mercury atoms in the mercurous ion are held together by the overlapping of p orbitals of parallel orientation, but work on the orbital structure of the mercurous ion is still awaited.

Univalent mercury. A black, very impure substance, thought to be HgH, has been made by injecting mercury vapour at low pressure into a stream of atomised hydrogen at the temperature of liquid air. It decomposes into mercury and hydrogen at $-125°$. The same hydride has been detected in the spectrum of hydrogen containing mercury vapour, and in the mass spectrometer to which mercury and hydrogen have been admitted.

THE MERCURIC COMPOUNDS

Mercury in the mercuric state forms stable compounds with nitrogen, chlorine, bromine, iodine, and sulphur. It also forms compounds with oxygen and fluorine, but the bonds in these compounds are easily ruptured. There is no stable hydride of mercury. It is not certain whether the simple mercuric ion Hg^{2+} is present in any mercury compound. Mercury forms a large number of giant molecule compounds. In some of these, as for example in HgF$_2$ which has a rutile lattice, the bonds must possess a high degree of ionic character.

SECTION 1. MERCURIC COMPOUNDS WITH IONIC CHARACTER

The mercuric ion Hg^{2+}. Mercury salts which would be expected to contain the mercuric ion resemble salts of the hydroxonium ion, H$_3$O$^+$, in that their degree of ionisation varies with the nature of the anion. In aqueous solution the mercuric salts (with the exception of the halides, the fluoride, and the thiocyanate) are ionised to about the same extent as the acids from which they are derived. The mercuric salts of strong oxyacids, such as nitric, sulphuric, and perchloric acids, are strong electrolytes, but owing to the weakness of the hydroxide $Hg(OH)_2$ as a base, are considerably hydrolysed in solution. These salts are nearly always hydrated.† Mercuric salts of weak oxyacids, like the carboxylic acids, are "half strong" electrolytes, and because of their small ionisation are not greatly hydrolysed.

MERCURIC COMPOUNDS CONSISTING OF GIANT MOLECULES IN WHICH THE BONDS HAVE SOME IONIC CHARACTER

In many mercuric compounds the atom of mercury is digonally hybridised. In some of the giant molecule compounds the presence of the mercury atom exerting two collinear valencies has been established by experiment. These are marked "digonal" in Table 16.1, Section 2. In other giant molecule compounds the co-ordination of the mercury atom is high, and the bonding is partly ionic. Compounds in which the mercury atom is in the digonal valence state, and which have monomeric molecules, are discussed in Section 2 (p. 477).

Mercuric acetylide, like the acetylides of zinc and cadmium, is very ill-defined. It is reported that:

(i) when acetylene is passed into an aqueous solution of mercuric cyanide a highly explosive white solid of composition HgC_2 is obtained,

(ii) when acetylene is passed into mercurous acetate solution a compound Hg_2C_2,H_2O is obtained, which cannot be dehydrated,

(iii) when acetylene is passed into an alkaline solution of potassium mercuri-iodide, or an ammoniacal solution of mercuric oxide containing ammonium carbonate, a compound $3HgC_2,H_2O$ is obtained, which can be dehydrated.

On treatment with hydrochloric acid the above compounds yield acetaldehyde.

It is not surprising that mercuric acetylide (like the zinc and cadmium acetylides) is ill-defined, because the metal–carbon bonds in the stable acetylides of the alkali and alkaline earth metals are largely ionic in character. The unstable nature of the mercuric ion must hinder its union with the anion of so weak an acid as acetylene to produce a salt. It is shown in Section 3 that the *covalent* bond Hg—C in such a molecule as $Hg(C_2H_5)_2$ is broken only with difficulty.

Mercuric cyanide, $Hg(CN)_2$, is made by adding mercuric oxide to aqueous hydrocyanic acid. The reaction is vigorous. Mercuric cyanide is soluble in water (11·3 gm in 100 gm at 25°), but it is only very slightly ionised; at 25° the ionisation of a $N/32$ solution is about 2%. Hence it can be made by the action of mercuric oxide on a complex cyanide such as Prussian blue, and slightly soluble mercuric salts like the sulphate dissolve in it. The concentration of Hg^{2+} ions in the aqueous solution is so low that they are not precipitated by hydroxyl or iodine ions; the concentration of CN^- ions is so low that they are not precipitated by silver nitrate. Hg^{2+} ions are precipitated as HgS by the addition of hydrogen sulphide. Mercuric cyanide is decomposed by heat into mercury and cyanogen. It is hardly affected by hydrochloric acid or nitric acid. An aqueous solution of mercuric cyanide reacts with acetylene (above), with *cis*-dichloroethylene to give $(ClC{\equiv}C)_2Hg$, a highly explosive white solid, and with *trans*-dichloroethylene to give $(CHCl{=}CCl)_2Hg$.

The crystal structure has not been definitely established.

† For example, $Hg(NO_3)_2$ 1 and $8H_2O$, $HgSO_4,H_2O$, $Hg(ClO_4)_2,6H_2O$.

Mercuric nitrite, $Hg(NO_2)_2$, is deliquescent and very soluble, and is very slightly onised. The structure is probably O_2N—Hg—NO_2. Complex mercuric nitrites which probably also contain Hg—N bonds are mentioned on p. 483.

Mercuric nitride, Hg_3N_2, is a highly explosive chocolate coloured powder, made by the action of potassamide on mercuric iodide dissolved in liquid ammonia.

Mercuric chloramide $(HgNH_2Cl)_x$. A white solid known as *infusible white precipitate* is precipitated by the action of ammonia on a solution of mercuric chloride in pure water. The equation may be written in the simplest terms:

$$Cl—Hg—Cl + 2NH_3 = Cl—Hg—NH_2 + NH_4Cl$$

Ethylamine forms a similar compound. Mercuric salts of oxyacids do not undergo parallel reactions, but instead give salts of Millon's base (see below). Infusible white precipitate appears to be a purely covalent substance; when heated it volatilises without fusion.

The composition and the constitution of the substance have been under much discussion. Possible formulae are NHg_2Cl,NH_4Cl, or $xHgO(1-x)HgCl_2,2NH_3$, or $HgNH_2Cl$. The third formula is chosen on the evidence of proton resonance spectra. The first formula would give a broad flat-topped absorption curve of mean square width about 50 gauss^2, the second a triple-peaked curve of mean square width 36 gauss^2, and the third a double-peaked curve of about 20 gauss^2. The observed value is 18·3 gauss^2, which corresponds to a theoretical curve for a pair of protons 1·69 apart and an N—H distance of 1·03. The presence of NH_2 units is thus established, but the substance must be polymerised. It has been concluded from the powder diffraction of X-rays that the powder consists of infinite chains of $(HgNH_2)^+$ units between which lie chlorine ions. The chains are:

$$
\begin{array}{ccccc}
H & & H & & H \\
| & & | & & | \\
N—Hg—N & —Hg— & N—Hg \\
| & & | & & | \\
H & & H & & H
\end{array}
$$

the bond angle Hg—N—Hg is 109°, and the bond angle N—Hg—N is 180°; the distance Hg—N—Hg is 3·345, and the distance N—Hg is 2·05.

Other mercury amino-halides have been examined. $HgNH_2Br$ is assigned a structure corresponding to that of infusible white precipitate. The compound often described as $HgNH_2F$ has the constitution Hg_2NF,NH_4F. Hg_2NHBr_2 has a layer lattice of $Hg_3(NH_2)$ units: Br^- ions are in the holes in these layers, and $HgBr_3^-$ ions are between the layers.

Millon's Base, $Hg_2NOH,2H_2O$, is a yellow powder made by the action of yellow mercuric oxide on aqueous ammonia solution (a process which is reminiscent of the action of mercuric acetate on benzene), or by digesting infusible white precipitate with water for 12 hours at 60–70°. On heating it loses water to give Hg_2NOH,H_2O, and at 125° it gives a dark-brown powder which is very dense (Sp. Gr. = 8·52), and which explodes if touched or heated to 130°. This might be Hg_2NOH, or perhaps a mixture containing the explosive Hg_3N_2. Millon's base with mineral acids forms a series of salts of composition Hg_2NX,H_2O, where $X = Cl$, Br, NO_3.†

There appears to be little evidence in favour of any one of the structures that might be proposed to explain the relations of these compounds to one another. If it be taken that the bonds of bivalent mercury are collinear, ring structures which contain a mercury atom must be ruled out. X-ray diffraction experiments show that the structures are probably based on that of infusible white precipitate, that the group Hg_2N has the

† Mercurous nitrate and mercurous perchlorate react with dilute aqueous ammonia to give metallic mercury and $(Hg_2N)NO_3$ or $(Hg_2N)ClO_4$. By treatment with aqueous KCl, KBr, KI or KOH pure solid $(Hg_2N)NO_3$ yields $(Hg_2N)Cl,H_2O$, $(Hg_2N)Br,H_2O$, $(Hg_2N)I$, or $(Hg_2N)OH,2H_2O$.

cristobalite structure, with the modification that the Hg bonds are collinear. The nitrogen bonds are tetrahedral and the distance Hg—N is 2·07.

The chloride of Millon's base can be made by the slow hydrolysis of infusible white precipitate, and hence it might be hazarded that the NH_2 groups in the chain —Hg—NH_2—Hg—NH_2— are replaced in part by oxygen atoms to give Hg—O—Hg—NH_2, and that for every replacement of NH_2^+ by oxygen one Cl^- is removed from the structure. This gives a pattern of the composition Hg—O—Hg—NH_2—Hg—O—Hg—NH_2. If the Cl^- ions are replaced by OH^- ions the composition of the structure becomes that of the partially dehydrated Millon's base, Hg_2NOH,H_2O.

Mercuric derivatives of amides and imides. Mercuric oxide dissolves in fused acetamide or in an aqueous solution of acetamide to give $Hg(NHCOCH_3)_2$. Cyclic imides also dissolve mercuric oxide easily. Succinimide, for example, gives:

$$
\begin{array}{ccc}
& O \qquad\qquad O & \\
CH_2-C & & C-CH_2 \\
| & N-Hg-N & | \\
CH_2-C & & C-CH_2 \\
& O \qquad\qquad O &
\end{array}
$$

Solutions of the amide and imide derivatives can be titrated with hydrochloric acid in the presence of methyl orange, because hydrolysis occurs, giving perhaps:

$$
\text{HO—Hg—N} \overset{\displaystyle H}{\underset{\displaystyle CO\cdot CH_3}{\big<}}.
$$

Mercuric oxide, HgO, is an infusible red or yellow powder. Red orthorhombic mercuric oxide is obtained by the action of heat on mercurous nitrate or mercuric nitrate, or of air or oxygen on mercury above 300°. An orange rhombohedral form of mercuric oxide in crystalline condition is obtained from an aqueous solution of mercuric nitrate by slow precipitation. If heated above 200° it is immediately changed to the orthorhombic form. The yellow mercuric oxide as ordinarily obtained by precipitating a solution of a mercuric salt with alkali is probably the rhombohedral form in a finely divided condition.

Mercuric oxide is decomposed by heat; the pressure of oxygen at 400° is a few mm; at 610° is 1240 mm. It is a basic oxide soluble in dilute acids but insoluble in water. It reacts with dilute ammonia solution to yield Millon's base. It attacks amides and imides more readily than it does ammonia. Mercuric oxide in contact with water must give rise to a significant concentration of Hg^{2+} ions, because the reactions:

$$HgO + 2NaCl + H_2O \rightarrow HgCl_2 + 2NaOH,$$

$$HgO + 4KI + H_2O \rightarrow K_2HgI_4 + 2KOH,$$

proceed from left to right. Mercuric oxide reacts with mercaptans to yield compounds of the type $Hg(SC_2H_5)_2$ (p. 475).

The crystal structure consists of infinite planar zig-zag chains, Hg—O—Hg—O—. The angle Hg—O—Hg is 109°, and the angle O—Hg—O is 179°. The distance Hg—O is 2·03 in the chains, and 2·82 between the chains. The radius of the bicovalent mercury atom from Table 11.1 is $2\cdot03 - 0\cdot66 = 1\cdot37$. The bond angles in the structure indicate that the oxygen atoms are tetrahedrally hybridised, and the mercury atoms are digonally hybridised, and hence provide support for the assumptions made on p. 473.

Mercuric hydroxide, Hg(OH)₂, exists in aqueous solution, but it has not been isolated. It is amphoteric but more basic than acidic.

$$K_b = \frac{[Hg^{2+}][OH^-]^2}{[Hg(OH)_2]} = 1\cdot8 \times 10^{-22}, \qquad K_a = \frac{[H^+][HgOOH^-]}{[Hg(OH)_2]} = 1\cdot4 \times 10^{-15}.$$

An orange yellow precipitate formed when sodium methylate is mixed with mercuric chloride in methyl alcohol is said to be *mercury dimethylate*, $Hg(OCH_3)_2$, but no analysis has been made. Ethyl alcohol and propyl alcohol are said to react similarly.

Mercuric sulphide, HgS, occurs in the red form as cinnabar or vermilion. Above 386° a black form is stable:

$$HgS\ (black) \rightarrow HgS\ (red); \qquad \Delta H = -0\cdot381\ kcal.$$

The black form sublimes at 58·0°. By means of e.m.f. measurements the standard free energy of formation of the black variety at 25° has been calculated to be $-10\cdot22$ kcal/mole, and the solubility product to be 9×10^{-25}. The red form is prepared by triturating mercury and sulphur with a little potassium hydroxide solution; the black form is obtained by passing hydrogen sulphide through a solution of mercuric chloride.

On account of its very low solubility product mercuric sulphide is precipitated by hydrogen sulphide even from the most stable complexes. It is not dissolved by boiling hydrochloric acid, or by boiling nitric acid, but it dissolves very easily in a mixture of these acids even if dilute. It dissolves in concentrated solutions of the sulphides of the alkali metals:

$$Na_2S + HgS = Na_2(HgS_2).$$

This sodium salt can be crystallised from the solution.† If S^{2-} ions are removed from the solution (say, by the passage of hydrogen sulphide which removes S^{2-} as HS^-) the mercuric sulphide is precipitated. The concentration of S^{2-} in ammonium sulphide solution is too low to effect the solution of mercuric sulphide.

The crystal of cinnabar consists of infinite spiral chains, S—Hg—S—Hg, running parallel to the *c* axis of the hexagonal unit cell. The bond angles are S—Hg—S 172·4°, Hg—S—Hg 105·2°, the distance Hg—S is 2·36. The bond angles do not deviate greatly from the digonal angle (180°) and the tetrahedral angle (109°). The bond length indicates that the radius of the bicovalent mercury atom is about 1·27.

Another form of mercuric sulphide (metacinnabarite, which is black) and mercuric selenide and telluride have the zinc blende lattice.

Mercury thioalkylates, Hg(SAlk)₂. Mercury very easily forms covalent links with sulphur which do not readily suffer chemical attack; in this respect the bond Hg—S resembles the bond Hg—C. The formation from HgO of derivatives of the type $Hg(SAlk)_2$ has already been mentioned. These compounds are low melting solids, which decompose on heating, thus:

$$Hg(SAlk)_2 = Hg + S_2(Alk)_2.$$

$Hg(SC_2H_5)_2$ has m.p. 76°, and is soluble in organic solvents. Treatment with hydrogen chloride yields C₂H₅—S—Hg—Cl, consisting of colourless crystals not affected by water or alcohol. The chlorine atom can be replaced by iodine or the nitrate group without disturbing the Hg—S link. Alkaline salts of mercury disulphonic acid are known:

$$
\begin{array}{ccc}
O & & O \\
\diagdown & & \diagup \\
O\!-\!Hg\!-\!S\!-\!O \\
\diagup & & \diagdown \\
HO & & OH.
\end{array}
$$

† If the structure of the anion in Na₂(HgS₂) is [S—Hg—S]²⁻, this anion is an example of a complex anion containing digonally hybridised mercury.

The mercuric halides. Certain properties of the mercuric halides are set out in Table 16.3. The properties indicate the transition from mercuric fluoride, in which the bonding is predominantly ionic, to mercuric iodide in which it is predominatly covalent. The fluoride has a fluorite lattice (co-ordination 8:4), the scarlet form of the iodide has a wurtzite lattice (co-ordination 4:4). The chloride and the bromide both have covalent lattices, but the bond lengths show that the lattice of the chloride is the more distorted. The steady fall in the solubility of the halides in water and in other donating solvents marks the diminishing ability of the halogen ions, in the order F^-, Cl^-, Br^-, I^-, to stabilise the cation $[Hg,2H_2O]^{2+}$; all the compounds except the fluoride, however, readily form complex ions such as that in the salt $K_2[HgI_4]$.

Mercuric fluoride, HgF_2, is made by heating mercurous fluoride to 450° when disproportionation occurs:

$$Hg_2F_2 = HgF_2 + Hg,$$

or by passing chlorine over mercurous fluoride:

$$Hg_2F_2 + Cl_2 = HgF_2 + HgCl_2,$$

or by passing fluorine over powdered mercuric chloride. The ionic character of the bonds in the crystal is indicated by the fluorite lattice, and by the Hg—F distance, 2·40, which is nearly equal to the sum of the ionic radii, 2·45. In solution mercuric fluoride is a strong electrolyte, but it is hydrolysed, giving a basic fluoride which is further hydrolysed to mercuric oxide. The solubility of mercuric fluoride in water is diminished by the addition of potassium fluoride, thus showing that F^- ions are produced by both salts; the other mercuric halides have their solubilities increased as the result of complex formation when the potassium halide is added. Mercuric fluoride dihydrate, a yellow crystalline substance, probably contains the cation $[Hg,2H_2O]^{2+}$, in which the mercury atom is bicovalent.

Mercuric chloride, $HgCl_2$, or corrosive sublimate, is obtained as a white sublimate (i) by heating a mixture of sodium chloride and mercuric sulphate with a little manganese dioxide in a long-necked flask, (ii) by the action of chlorine on metallic mercury. It is freely soluble in hot water, but less so in cold, and may be purified by re-crystallisation. It is soluble in organic solvents which act as donors. It is inert towards acids; it is not attacked either by nitric acid or by boiling sulphuric acid, but it reacts reversibly with sodium hydroxide solution thus:

$$HgCl_2 + 2NaOH \rightleftharpoons HgO + 2NaCl + H_2O.$$

It is easily reduced to mercurous chloride, or to the metal. It reacts with ammonia to give infusible white precipitate $ClHgNH_2$ (p. 473), or fusible white precipitate $HgCl_2,2NH_3$ (p. 482), according to the conditions. It combines with dialkyl sulphides to give complexes of the types:

$$(C_2H_5)_2S,2HgCl_2, \qquad (C_2H_5)_2S,HgCl_2, \qquad [(C_2H_5)_2S]_2HgCl_2.$$

Much attention has been paid to the structure of mercuric chloride. Evidence that the molecule has a symmetrical linear structure is furnished by (i) the photodissociation of the chloride into $Cl + (Hg—Cl)$†, (ii) the Raman spectra of the vapour, liquid and solid states, (iii) electron diffraction by the vapour (also for the iodide), and (iv) X-ray analysis. The Hg—Cl bonds appear to be predominantly covalent.

Mercuric bromide, $HgBr_2$, resembles the chloride. The covalent Br-Hg-Br molecule is shown by experimental methods to be present in the vapour, the liquid, and the solid. There is a slight dissociation in the melt, either:

$$2HgBr_2 \rightleftharpoons (HgBr)^+ + (HgBr_3)^-,$$

or,

$$HgBr_2 \rightleftharpoons Hg^{2+} + 2Br^-.$$

† The group Hg—Cl is in an excited energy state.

At 250° the degree of dissociation is 2×10^{-8}. At 252° the specific conductance is $1 \cdot 45 \times 10^{-4}$ ohm^{-1}cm^{-1}.

In the fused state mercuric bromide acts as the solvent of an acid base system. Metallic bromides act as bases; mercuric salts act as acids. Neutralisation is expressed by an equation such as:

$$2KBr + Hg(ClO_4)_2 = 2KClO_4 + HgBr_2$$

$$\text{base} \qquad \text{acid} \qquad\quad \text{salt} \qquad \text{solvent}$$

The acids vary in strength: $Hg(ClO_4)_2 > Hg(NO_3)_2 > HgSO_4$. If $Hg(ClO_4)_2,6H_2O$ is melted carefully with $HgBr_2$, it loses water of crystallisation without decomposition.

The compounds HgO, HgS, HgSe, HgTe, dissolve in fused $HgBr_2$ and function as weak Lewis bases (p. 384). The relations between the specific conductances of the solutions so formed show similarities to those of H_2S, H_2Se, H_2Te in water, and indicate that the ionisation increases with atomic weight.

Mercuric iodide, HgI_2, is made by adding potassium iodide solution to a solution of mercuric chloride. Although almost insoluble in water it dissolves easily in excess of potassium iodide solution to form the salt $K_2[HgI_4]$. The molecule I—Hg—I is linear in the vapour, but in the solid the structure is tetrahedral.

SECTION 2. COMPOUNDS IN WHICH THE MERCURY ATOM IS DIGONALLY HYBRIDISED

The mercury atom in combination is in the stable mercuric condition when it possesses four shared electrons (two pairs) in the valency shell. The atom is then bicovalent. There is a considerable amount of experimental evidence that the bond angle X—Hg—X in compounds containing the mercury atom in this state is 180°. This has been proved for H_2NHgCl, HgS (cinnabar), $HgCl_2$, $HgBr_2$, HgI_2 (vapour), and $HgO,HgCl_2$. The very small d.p.m. of mercury diphenyl in inert solvents (about $0 \cdot 42$ at 25°) is also evidence that the bond angle C—Hg—C is 180°. This bond angle indicates that the bond orbitals are *sp* hybrids. Why this condition of the mercury atom should be stable, and why the tendency to change to a tetrahedral state by the formation of two co-ionic bonds is so small, is not clear. In some compounds containing the digonally hybridised mercury atom the molecule may be polymerised and the bonds may be largely ionic. Such compounds have already been discussed in Section 1. In other digonal mercury compounds the molecule is monomeric and bonding is wholly covalent. Compounds of this type such as $Hg(C_2H_5)_2$ are discussed in this Section. It may be mentioned here that no mercury hydride, HgH_2, has been prepared.

The stability of the bond Hg—C. The covalent bond between a mercury and a carbon atom is remarkable for its inertness; it is broken with difficulty and is chemically inactive. The mercury atom in mercury dimethyl takes on certain of the characteristics of the methylene group in propane:

$$H_3C—Hg—CH_3, \qquad H_3C—CH_2—CH_3.$$

An explanation of the structural stability of the mercury-carbon bond may perhaps be found in the high energy of activation associated with its rupture, and in the reluctance of the mercury atom to accept electrons from donating molecules. The bond dissociation energy of the bond Hg—C, however, is not high. The bond dissociation energy of the reaction† :

$$H_3C—Hg—CH_3 = H_3C—Hg + CH_3$$

at 300° is $51 \cdot 3$ kcal mole^{-1}, and for the reaction

$$H_3C—Hg = H_3C + Hg$$

is $5 \cdot 5$ kcal mole^{-1}.

† Ann. Reports, 1955, **52**, 11.

The bond dissociation energy required to rupture the bond $ClHg$—Cl is 81 kcal, and the order of magnitude for the rupture of the bond X—C, where X is an atom of a metal or non-metal, is in many cases about 70 kcal. It is to be noted that almost any metal removes the hydrocarbon radical from combination with mercury, and the mercury dialkyls spontaneously decompose to metallic mercury and the paraffin.

The heat of formation of a bond from atoms, however, cannot be a complete statement of the stability of a compound. The correct criterion is the change in the free energy brought about by any rearrangement of the bonds, and this depends on many variables, including the nature, physical state, and concentration of the products of the change.

Compounds containing the mercury-carbon link often undergo reactions in which the link is not broken. For example, by the action of moist silver oxide on mercury ethyl chloride the base *mercury ethyl hydroxide*, HgC_2H_5OH, is obtained. This is a mobile liquid readily soluble in water. It is alkaline, it neutralises acids, it liberates ammonia from ammonium salts, and it precipitates hydroxides from metallic salts. The nitrate, sulphate, acetate, and carbonate of the base have been prepared. As with the mercuric salts (p. 471), the relative degrees of ionisation of these salts in aqueous solution are roughly proportional to the strengths of acids from which they are derived.

Many other compounds could be mentioned which contain mercury-carbon links which remain undisturbed during certain chemical reactions. In mercurated phenol

the OH group can be acetylated, or coupled with a diazonium salt, and in mercurated aniline

the NH_2 group can be acetylated or alkylated, or diazotised and coupled. Both these compounds dissolve in ammonia, but they are reprecipitated unchanged by acids. The compound $HOCH_2CH_2HgCl$ does not begin to decompose until 154°. Alkalis or silver oxide merely replace Cl by OH. Na_2S precipitates $(HOCH_2CH_2Hg)_2S$. The OH group can be benzoylated, and iodine gives the iodohydrin. With acids, however, ethylene is liberated.

Formation of the mercury-carbon bond, Hg—C. On account of its stability the mercury-carbon bond is readily established. A mercury-oxygen bond or a mercury-halogen bond is usually broken in its favour when appropriate reagents are brought together. The general methods for its formation are:

(i) by a reaction which results in the replacement of a particular element in a carbon compound by mercury; the particular element may be H, Mg, B, Al, Sn, Sb, N, O, or a halogen; mercury is introduced into the reaction as the metal, or as sodium amalgam, or as mercuric halide, acetate, or oxide;

(ii) by the action of mercuric acetate on an olefine.

Particular examples of these generalisations are given below.

Mercury replaces hydrogen. This process is known as "mercuration". In the aromatic compounds it is brought about by treating the compound, say benzene, with mercuric acetate under pressure at 100–110°:

$$\text{benzene} + Hg(OCOCH_3)_2 = \text{benzene-HgOCOCH}_3 + HCOOCH_3.$$

The di-derivatives formed are always *ortho* and *para*. The heterocyclic compounds react most readily. Thiophene can be removed from benzene as $C_4H_3S.HgOCOCH_3$ by one hour's boiling with mercuric oxide suspended in aqueous acetic acid; the benzene is not attacked under these conditions.

In the aliphatic compounds the reaction is carried out using mercuric oxide in the presence of an alkali. If ethyl alcohol is the organic reagent *ethane hexamercarbide* is formed. The formula is given as $C_2Hg_6O_4H_2$, but the substance must be highly polymerised. It is yellow powder. It forms insoluble salts with acids. It is entirely unaffected by H_2S, aqua regia, $KMnO_4$, $K_2Cr_2O_7$, or $NaOCl$. However, SO_2, NH_4OH, and NH_2NH_2 react slowly with it. If heated above 230°, it detonates with violence.

Mercury replaces another metal. The action of mercuric bromide on methyl magnesium bromide, boron trimethyl, tin tetramethyl, or antimony pentamethyl produces mercury dimethyl:

$$Sn(CH_3)_4 + 2HgBr_2 = 2Hg(CH_3)_2 + SnBr_4.$$

Al_4C_3 in the presence of dilute HCl in the cold reacts according to the equation:

$$2Al_4C_3 + 3HgCl_2 + 18HCl = 3Hg(CH_3)_2 + 8AlCl_3.$$

Mercury replaces nitrogen. The double salt of benzene diazonium chloride and mercuric chloride can be decomposed by copper powder:

$$C_6H_5N_2Cl.HgCl_2 + 2Cu = C_6H_5HgCl + 2CuCl + N_2.$$

Mercury replaces oxygen. Sodium amalgam reacts with diethyl sulphate thus:

ethyl acetate acts as a catalyst.

Mercury replaces a halogen. Metallic mercury reacts only with CH_3I, ICH_2CH_2I, $C_6H_5CH_2I$, and $CH_3.CH=CHI$. The reactions take place at ordinary temperature, and are assisted by sunlight. Mercury reacts less easily with alkyl halides than either zinc or magnesium. Mercury diphenyl can be made by reaction between bromobenzene, sodium, and mercuric chloride in benzene solution.

Addition of a mercury compound to ethylene. Ethylene is passed into mercuric acetate in methyl alcohol solution, where it is probably in the basic form $CH_3COOHgOH$:

The dimer is made by the elimination of one molecule of water.

The alkyl and aryl derivatives of mercury. Certain properties of a few of these derivatives are given in Table 16.4.

Table 16.4.   *Alkyl and Aryl Derivatives of Mercury*
(All compounds are monomeric; tol indicates $CH_3C_6H_4$)

	m.p.		m.p.		b.p.		m.p.	b.p.
CH_3HgOH	137°	CH_3HgCl	167°	$(CH_3)_2Hg$	92°	$(C_6H_5)_2Hg$	125°	204°/13·5 mm
C_2H_5HgOH	37°	C_2H_5HgCl	192°	$(C_2H_5)_2Hg$	159°	$(o\text{-tol})_2Hg$	107°	219°/14 mm

Mercury diethyl, $Hg(C_2H_5)_2$, is a mobile liquid, b.p. 159°, soluble in benzene and chloroform. It can be made directly:

(i) by the action of mercuric halides on the Grignard reagent:

$$2C_2H_5MgBr + HgCl_2 = MgBr_2 + Hg(C_2H_5)_2 + MgCl_2.$$

(ii) by shaking ethyl iodide with sodium amalgam:

$$HgNa_2 + 2C_2H_5I = Hg(C_2H_5)_2 + 2NaI.$$

(iii) by the reduction of the monohalogen derivatives with sodium, or with copper powder:

$$2C_2H_5HgCl + 2Na = Hg(C_2H_5)_2 + 2NaCl + Hg.$$

The equilibrium, $R_2Hg + HgX_2 \rightleftharpoons 2RHgX$, favours the forward reaction. The dialkyl derivative is stable, however, if the compound HgX_2 is removed from the sphere of action by precipitation, as in the reaction:

$$(RHg)_2S = R_2Hg + HgS,$$

or by complex formation, as in the reaction:

$$2RHgI + 2KI = R_2Hg + K_2HgI_4.$$

Mercury diethyl is poisonous and a vesicant. It is inert to most common reagents, but it undergoes the following reactions:

(a) In the cold on standing, or more rapidly on heating, mercury diethyl breaks down to give mercury and butane:

$$Hg(C_2H_5)_2 = Hg + C_4H_{10}.$$

(b) With hydrogen under pressure (say, 50 atm) and a fairly high temperature (200°) mercury diethyl is reduced to ethane:

$$H_2 + Hg(C_2H_5)_2 = Hg + C_2H_6.$$

(c) With the metals Li, Na, Be, Mg, Zn, Cd, Al, Si, Sb, Bi, Te, an exchange occurs, for instance:

$$2Li + Hg(C_2H_5)_2 = Hg + 2LiC_2H_5.$$

(d) With the halogens, non-metallic chlorides, or acyl halides reactions occur as follows:

$$Hg(C_2H_5)_2 + 2Cl_2 = HgCl_2 + 2C_2H_5Cl$$
$$Hg(C_2H_5)_2 + 2HCl = HgCl_2 + 2C_2H_6$$
$$3Hg(C_2H_5)_2 + 2PCl_3 = 2P(C_2H_5)_3 + 3HgCl_2$$
$$Hg(C_2H_5)_2 + CH_3COCl = HgClC_2H_5 + CH_3COC_2H_5.$$

The chlorides BCl_3, $SiCl_4$, $AsCl_3$, and $SbCl_3$ react similarly.

(e) Reaction takes place with the oxides N_2O_3, N_2O_4, SO_3, Cl_2O, but not with NO.

Mercury diethyl does not react with air, water, ethers, amines, alcohols, organic carbonyl compounds, hydrocarbons, olefines, alkyl chlorides. Alkalis usually have no action. The reaction with acyl halides is said to be slow.

Mercury ethyl chloride, HgC_2H_5Cl, is a solid, m.p. 192°, made by the action of hydrochloric acid on mercury diethyl:

$$Hg(C_2H_5)_2 + HCl = C_2H_5HgCl + C_2H_6.$$

It is far less reactive than a Grignard reagent such as C_2H_5MgCl. It is not affected by water, alcohol, amines, or carbonyl compounds, and it will not react with an alkyl halide such as methyl chloride to give the hydrocarbon and mercury chloride in the manner of the corresponding magnesium compound:

$$C_2H_5MgCl + CH_3Cl = C_3H_8 + MgCl_2.$$

Mercury ethyl chloride is attacked by hot concentrated acids, but not by dilute acids. If it is treated with acetylene in alkaline solution an ethyl mercury derivative of acetylene is very readily obtained, $C_2H_5—Hg—C{\equiv}C—Hg—C_2H_5$, which is volatile, soluble in benzene, and hence covalent.

SECTION 3. COMPOUNDS IN WHICH THE MERCURY ATOM IS TRIGONALLY HYBRIDISED

A *neutral complex*, $(C_2H_5)_2S{\rightarrow}HgCl_2$, is formed when diethyl sulphide reacts with mercurous chloride (p. 485). An ethylenediamine-mercuric chloride complex is reported of which the formula might be $Cl_2Hg—NH_2CH_2CH_2NH_2—HgCl_2$.

A solution of mercury acetate in methyl alcohol absorbs carbon monoxide at 1 atm in the cold. The reaction occurs

$$CO \ + \ CH_3CO.O.Hg\diagdown_{O.COCH_3} \ = \ CH_3CO.O.Hg{\underset{OCH_3}{\overset{CO}{\diagup}}} \ + \ CO$$

The mercury compound thus produced melts at 110°. Potassium chloride converts it to:

$$Cl—Hg{\underset{OCH_3}{\overset{CO}{\diagup}}}$$

Hydrochloric acid expels the CO giving a complex mercuric chloride, thus showing that the CO is co-ordinated to the mercury atom.

The *anionic complexes*, $[HgCl_3]^-$ and $[HgCl_4]^{2-}$ are formed when mercuric chloride reacts with an alkali chloride in solution; in the presence of excess alkali halide the tetrahedral anion is the stable one. $NH_4[HgCl_3]$ is reported to have a layer lattice. Other examples of the trigonal complex anion are found in $Ca[Hg(CN)_3]_2$, and in mixed salts of the type $K[Hg(CN)_2X]$ where X is Cl, Br, or I.

The group $[HgCl_3]^-$ often changes from trigonal to tetrahedral hybridisation by co-ordination. Thus $K[HgCl_3]$ forms $K[HgCl_3,H_2O]$ and $K[HgCl_3,C_2H_5OH]$. The complex ion in a 1:1 solution of mercuric iodide and potassium iodide is $[HgI_3,OH_2]^-$.

SECTION 4. COMPOUNDS IN WHICH THE MERCURY ATOM IS TETRAHEDRALLY HYBRIDISED

Like cadmium, mercury forms no electron deficient tetrahedral compounds. The absence of a hydride of mercury, HgH_2, is mentioned on p. 477. The mercuric atom, however, forms all other classes of compound in this Section.

16+A.T.I.C.

NON-CHELATE COMPLEXES

Non-chelate Neutral Complexes

The ammines of mercuric salts. In conditions in which hydrolysis is impossible ammonia reacts with the mercuric halides to give complexes of the type $(NH_3)_2HgCl_2$. The conditions are attained:

   (i) by treating the mercuric halide with aqueous ammonia in the presence of excess of an ammonium salt which depresses the ionisation of ammonium hydroxide,

   (ii) by allowing pure ammonia (liquid or gaseous) to act on the dry mercuric halide, or on its solution in acetonitrile.

The chloride derivative is the most stable; the iodide the least. Ethylamine gives the corresponding diammine $Hg(EtNH_2)_2Cl_2$.

If instead of a mercuric halide the mercuric salt of an oxyacid is used, the tetrammine, say $[Hg(NH_3)_4](NO_3)_2$, is obtained. If sodium chloride is added to the tetrammine, mercuric chloride diammine is obtained. Sodium bromide and iodide (but not the fluoride) react similarly.

The structure of the mercuric halide diammines is probably in the form:

$$\begin{array}{ccc} Cl & & NH_3 \\ & \diagdown \quad \diagup & \\ & Hg & \\ & \diagup \quad \diagdown & \\ Cl & & NH_3 \end{array}$$

and, if so, the mercury atom is tetrahedrally hybridised, and the diammines are correctly placed in the present class. There is, however, no experimental evidence for this structure, and the ionic form $[H_3N—Hg—NH_3]Cl_2$ is not ruled out.

Mercuric chloride diammine is the familiar *fusible white precipitate.*

Non-chelate Complex Anions

Complex cyanides, $M_2[Hg(CN)_4]$. In the potassium salt the anion is tetrahedral (as in the zinc and cadmium complexes). $M_2[Hg(NO_2)_4]$ and $M_2[Hg(CNS)_4]$ are reported.

Complex halides. Mercuric chloride, bromide, and iodide form the complexes $M_2[HgX_4]$ and $M[HgX_3]$ when treated with aqueous solutions of alkaline halides. The fluorides do not produce complexes (note the reluctance of fluorine, as of oxygen, to form a covalent link with mercury). Experiments show that the predominant type in the presence of excess alkaline halide is $M_2[HgX_4]$, and that the stability is in the order $Cl < Br < I$. The $[HgX_4]^{2-}$ ion has a tetrahedral structure.

Experiments using a radioactive isotope of bromine shows that all four bromine atoms in $K_2[HgBr_4]$ are equally strongly bound to the mercury atom.

Non-chelate Complex Cations

If ammonia is passed into a saturated solution of ammonium nitrate containing mercuric nitrate in suspension, a salt having a non-chelate complex cation is obtained, $[Hg(NH_3)_4](NO_3)_2$. The tetrammines of the sulphate, perchlorate, cyanide, acetate, have been made by corresponding reactions.

CHELATE COMPLEXES

The neutral complex. Mercuric acetylacetonate is made by the action of sodium acetylacetonate on aqueous mercuric chloride. It is a white solid, slightly soluble in water, and almost insoluble in organic solvents. The mercury is not precipitated by KOH. Hg_2Cl_2 forms the same complex with the precipitation of metallic mercury.

With phosphine and arsine three compounds like those of cadmium are formed, and in addition compounds with structures of the types:

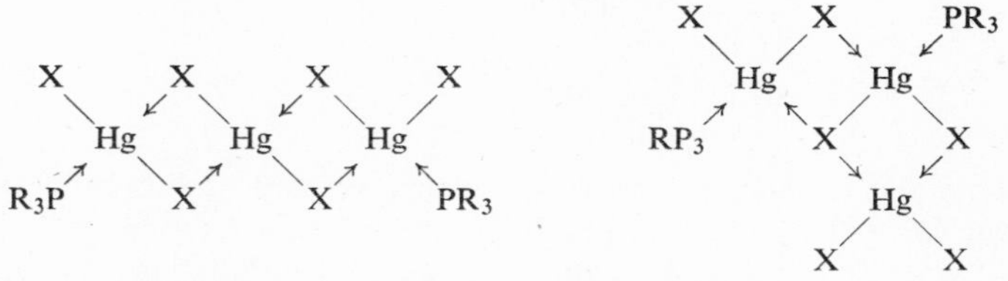

These structures have been established by X-ray analysis.

Ammonium mercuric-oxalate with the structure:

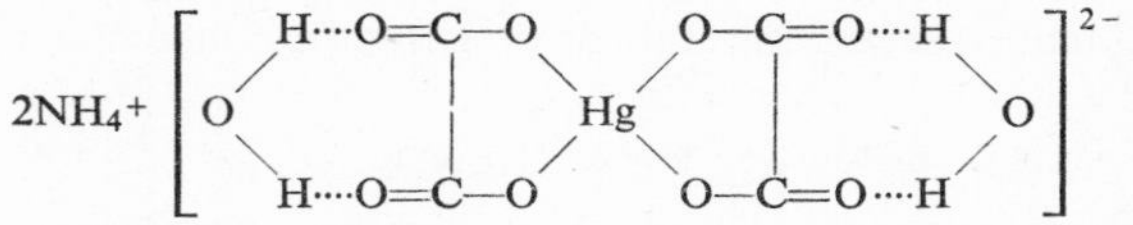

contains the mercuric-oxalate *complex anion*. Mercuric oxalate is readily soluble in solutions of alkaline oxalates, and the solution obtained does not respond to tests for the mercuric or oxalate ions. The freezing point of the solution confirms the presence of a complex.

Complex cations are known of the type $[Hg(\text{diamine})_2]^{2+}$, where the diamine is ethylenediamine, propane-1:2-diamine, or diethylenetriamine.

SECTION 5. COMPOUNDS IN WHICH THE MERCURY ATOM IS OCTAHEDRALLY HYBRIDISED

The mercury atom in this valence state does not appear to form neutral complexes. Three examples of non-chelate complex anions can be given: $M_3[Hg(NO_2)_5,H_2O]$, $M_2Hg[Hg(NO_2)_6]$, and $(en2H)_2[HgCl_6]$. No complex cations are known, but it has been observed that the salts $[Hg(NH_3)_4](ClO_4)_2$ and $[Hg(NH_3)_4](NO_3)_2$ are more soluble in aqueous ammonia than they are in water.

The only chelate complexes appear to be the complex cations $[Hg\ en_3]X_2$ and $[Hg\ en_2(H_2O)_2]SO_4$.

THE MERCUROUS COMPOUNDS

Nearly all the mercurous compounds are salts. Mercurous salts in solution are highly ionised. The hydroxide, $Hg_2(OH)_2$, has not been isolated, but it may be present in the yellow precipitate which appears transitorily when alkali is added to a solution of mercurous nitrate. It is a stronger base than mercuric hydroxide. Mercurous salts are hydrolysed in solution, but less so than mercuric salts. The sulphate, chloride, bromide, and iodide, and the salts of organic acids are less soluble than the corresponding mercuric salts; the chlorate, nitrate, and perchlorate are more soluble. The formula of the mercurous ion is $[Hg—Hg^{2+}]$. In the following paragraphs five proofs for the diatomicity of the ion are outlined.

(1) Ogg treated silver nitrate solution with metallic mercury, and determined the equilibrium concentrations of Ag^+ and mercurous ion in solution, and the concentration of silver in the amalgam. The reaction is either

$$\text{(a)}\quad AgNO_3 + Hg = HgNO_3 + Ag(Hg)$$

or
$$\text{(b)}\quad 2AgNO_3 + Hg = Hg_2(NO_3)_2 + 2Ag(Hg).$$

For (a)

$$K_a = \frac{[Hg^+][Ag]}{[Ag^+][Hg]}$$

for (b)

$$K_b = \frac{[Hg_2^{2+}][Ag]^2}{[Ag^+]^2[Hg]}$$

On the assumptions (i) that the term [Hg] remains constant (the concentration of the amalgam was only 0·05% of silver) and that the term [Ag] is proportional to the concentration of silver in the amalgam, Ogg found that for a variation in the concentration of mercurous ion from 8:1, K_a varied in the ratio 3:1, whereas K_b was constant to within 20%.

(2) Ogg, and also Abel, treated mercuric nitrate solution with metallic mercury and determined the equilibrium concentration of mercurous and mercuric ions. The reaction is either

(a) $Hg(NO_3)_2 + Hg = 2HgNO_3,$

or

(b) $Hg(NO_3)_2 + Hg = (Hg_2^{2+})(NO_3)_2.$

For (a)

$$K_a = \frac{[Hg^+]^2}{[Hg^{2+}][Hg]},$$

for (b)

$$K_b = \frac{[Hg_2^{2+}]}{[Hg^{2+}][Hg]}$$

K_b was found to be constant, and hence the reaction (b) is the one that occurs. At 18° the ratio $[Hg_2^{2+}]/[Hg^{2+}]$ in the presence of mercury may be taken to be 116.

(3) Ogg also compared the change of equivalent conductance with dilution of mercurous nitrate in aqueous solution with the corresponding changes for lead nitrate and silver nitrate. He found at 10°:

Dilution, litre mole^{-1}	Equivalent conductance, ohm^{-1} cm^2		
	$Hg_2(NO_3)_2$	$Pb(NO_3)_2$	$AgNO_3$
250	69·58	102·16	84·04
5	51·85	76·82	63·55
Ratio	0·66	0·67	0·73

Hence Hg_2^{2+} behaves as a bivalent ion.

(4) The X-ray analysis of crystalline mercurous chloride shows that it is built up of units Cl—Hg—Hg—Cl. All compounds MCl have a succession of alternate M and Cl atoms in the crystal.

(5) The Raman spectrum of mercurous nitrate in water (0·6N) in the presence of excess nitric acid shows a strong line in addition to the NO_3 lines. This must be due to Hg—Hg, as a monatomic ion can show no Raman spectrum.

It is difficult to say whether the mercurous unit, Hg—Hg, forms covalent compounds or complexes of the type X—Hg—Hg—X. Neither mercurous oxide nor mercurous sulphide can be obtained. A study of the reaction:

$$[Hg^{2+}] + Hg_{metal} = [Hg_2^{2+}],$$

however, shows that in the presence of moisture these mercurous compounds would disproportionate. For this reaction:

$$K = \frac{[Hg_2^{2+}]}{[Hg^{2+}][Hg]} = \frac{116}{[Hg]}$$

The solubility of metallic mercury in water is 1 gm atom in 10^7 litres. Hence:

$$K = \frac{116}{10^{-7}} = 1.16 \times 10^9.$$

Hence the mercurous ion is stable in the presence of mercury unless the concentration of (Hg^{2+}) is reduced to vanishing point. This occurs when the mercuric compound produced is (a) wholly covalent, (b) a stable complex, or (c) highly insoluble. Examples of disproportionations according to these categories are:

> (a) $Hg_2I_2 = HgI_2 + Hg$
> $Hg_2(CN)_2 = Hg(CN)_2 + Hg$
> (b) $Hg_2Cl_2 + (C_2H_5)_2S = Hg + (C_2H_5)_2S, HgCl_2$
> $NH_3 + Hg_2Cl_2 = NH_2HgHgCl = Hg + NH_2\text{---}Hg\text{---}Cl$
> (c) $Hg_2O = HgO + Hg$
> $Hg_2S = HgS + Hg.$

The correctness of the first equation under category (c) has been confirmed by the X-ray analysis of the black powder into which yellow precipitated mercurous hydroxide rapidly decomposes; it has been found that the black powder is a mixture of mercuric oxide and metallic mercury.

The mercurous halogen compounds might be expected to show both ionic and covalent character. Except for its solubility in water mercurous fluoride resembles the other mercurous halides, and there is no evidence that any of these compounds is ionic. Their molecular formulae and crystal lattices are unknown, although X-ray experiments show that the unit X—Hg—Hg—X is present in the crystals.

Mercurous fluoride, $(Hg_2F_2)_n$ forms tetragonal crystals. It is very soluble in water which rapidly hydrolyses it thus:

$$Hg_2F_2 + 2H_2O = Hg_2(OH)_2 + 2HF,$$
$$Hg_2(OH)_2 = Hg + H_2O + HgO.$$

Mercurous chloride, $(Hg_2Cl_2)_n$, is a white insoluble substance. It sublimes at low temperatures, and the observed vapour density corresponds to that of the monomer HgCl, but by several methods it has been shown that this result is due to thermal dissociation:

$$Hg_2Cl_2 \rightleftharpoons Hg + HgCl_2.$$

Mercurous chloride disproportionates to yield metallic mercury and a mercuric compound if the conditions are such that mercuric ions are removed from the sphere of action as rapidly as they are formed. The equations for its reactions with diethyl sulphide and with ammonia are given above. It has been established by X-ray diffraction data that the only products of the action of ammonia on mercurous chloride are metallic mercury and infusible white precipitate $Hg(NH_2)Cl$, fusible white precipitate $Hg(NH_3)_2Cl_2$, and the chloride of Millon's base Hg_2NCl, which may be present as the hydrate Hg_2NCl,H_2O (p. 473). All the compounds are derivatives of mercuric mercury.

The nature of the product depends on the conditions of the reaction:

> 0·1 to 0·7N aq. ammonia $\rightarrow Hg + Hg_2NCl,H_2O$
> Dry ammonia gas $\rightarrow Hg + Hg(NH_3)_2Cl_2$
> Liquid ammonia $\rightarrow Hg + HgNH_2Cl \rightarrow Hg(NH_3)_2Cl_2.$

Mercurous bromide is very similar to the chloride; the iodide is less stable, and, if moist, slowly disproportionates to mercuric iodide and mercury at room temperature.

Mercurous nitrate is one of the most familiar salts of the mercurous ion. It is soluble in water from which it crystallises as the dihydrate, which might suggest the existence of the ion $[H_2O \rightarrow Hg-Hg \leftarrow OH_2]^{2+}$. If such a structure is admitted it becomes possible to accept the covalent structure for the trichloroacetate:

$$Cl_3C \diagdown \qquad\qquad\qquad Cl_3 \diagup$$
$$C-O-Hg-Hg-O-C$$
$$O^{\diagup} \qquad\qquad\qquad\qquad O^{\diagdown}$$

which has d.p.m. $2 \cdot 65 D$, comparable with that $(1 \cdot 50 D)$ of the ester of hydroquinone $CCl_3CO.O \langle\rangle O.COCCl_3$. Mercurous nitrate reacts with heptasulphur imide, S_7NH, to give a yellow product which darkens in air and light, and has been formulated $S_7N-Hg-Hg-NS_7$. These covalent formulae are all open to the objection that each mercury atom is in the bicovalent *mercuric* state, and there appears to be no evidence that oxidation of the mercurous to the mercuric state has occurred.

Mercurous nitrate and mercurous perchlorate react with dilute ammonia solution to give metallic mercury and derivatives of Millon's base (p. 473).

Mercurous complexes. Only one mercurous complex is reported, $N_2H_4.Hg_2(NO_3)_2$, which may have the structure:

$$\begin{bmatrix} H_2N\text{---}NH_2 \\ \downarrow \quad\; \downarrow \\ Hg\text{---}Hg \end{bmatrix}^{2+} \quad (NO_3^-)_2.$$

CHAPTER SEVENTEEN

SUB-GROUP III N

BORON, ALUMINIUM, GALLIUM, INDIUM, AND THALLIUM

The valency shells of all the atoms of the elements in the sub-Group have the configuration s^2p^1. The similarities and differences in the types and numbers of compounds formed by the elements are shown in Table 17.1.

The great majority of the compounds of the elements in the sub-Group contain the element in oxidation state 3†. The most stable and best characterised compounds of thallium, however, are the thallous compounds in which the metal is in oxidation state 1. The heavier elements of later Groups also show to a marked degree an ability to form stable compounds in which the valency of the element is two units less than the Group valency. Sidgwick was the first to recognise this tendency which he ascribed to the presence of the *inert electron pair*. He explained the existence of the thallous compounds by postulating that the $6s$ electrons of the thallium atom may become inert and form a closed shell like the $1s$ shell of the helium atom.‡ The single $6p$ electron of the thallium atom in this state then behaves more or less as the $2s$ electron in the lithium atom, or as the $4s$ electron in the copper atom in the cuprous state. The alternative explanation for the existence of the thallous compounds, that the thallium atom is digonally hybridised and one hybrid orbital is occupied by a lone electron pair, is not acceptable (i) because it is difficult to apply such a structure to the ion Tl^+, and (ii) because compounds such as TlCl or TlA (on this hypothesis) would be ready donors, giving rise to such complexes as $ClTl{\rightarrow}B(CH_3)_3$ and $AClTl{\rightarrow}B(CH_3)_3$, but compounds of this type are unknown.

All the metals of the sub-Group except boron form compounds in which their valencies are less than three. Aluminium, gallium and indium form a number of univalent compounds (Table 17.1). The constitutions of these compounds are unknown; it is possible that they may be explained in terms of the inert pair. Aluminium forms the unstable AlO in which it is bivalent, but there is no other compound in which any member of the sub-Group is bivalent.

The pattern of compound formation by the elements in oxidation state 3 is apparent from an overall study of Table 17.1. None of the elements forms a simple trivalent cation, but all form a number of giant molecule non-volatile compounds in which the bonding must have some ionic character. The crystal structures of these compounds become more ionic with increase of atomic number of the element. Digonal hybridisation is almost unknown, but indium in a few cases forms anions and thallium forms cations which may have such a structure. Gallium forms a remarkable compound, Ga_2S_2, in structure comparable to mercurous chloride. Trigonal hybridisation is

†The *oxidation state* of an element indicates the number of *its own* electrons which the atom of the element is using to form covalent, co-ionic, or ionic bonds.

‡ The behaviour of the $6s$ electrons is not predicted by the ionisation potentials of indium and thallium (Table 17.2). The difference between the first and second ionisation potentials is of the same order for Al, Ga, In, and Tl.

Table 17.1. *Examples of Types of Compoun*
Oxidation Sta

Nature of compound	B	page	Al	pa
Simple ionic or covalent compounds			AlH, Al$_2$O, Al$_2$S, Al$_2$Se, AlF, AlCl, AlBr	5.
Complexes				

Oxidation Sta

Section	Hybrid-isation	Formal charge	Bonds†	Nature of unit formed	B	page	Al	pa
1				Giant molecules in which the bonds have both ionic and covalent character	B$_{12}$C$_3$, B$_2$O$_3$, B$_2$S$_3$, BPO$_4$ BAsO$_4$, metallic borides	494	(AlH$_3$)$_n$, Al$_4$C$_3$ Al$_2$(C$_2$)$_3$ AlN, AlP, Al$_2$O$_3$ Al(OH)$_3$ Al$_2$S$_3$, AlF$_3$	5.
2	Digonal			Neutral compounds Complex anions Complex cations	None		None	
3	Trigonal	0	3σ	Neutral compounds	B(CH$_3$)$_3$, B(C$_6$H$_5$)$_3$ B(CH$_3$)$_2$Cl, B(CH$_3$)Cl$_2$ B[N(CH$_3$)$_2$]$_3$ BCl$_2$[N(CH$_3$)$_2$], H$_3$BO$_3$ B(OC$_2$H$_5$)$_3$, B(OC$_2$H$_5$)$_2$CH$_3$ B(OC$_2$H$_5$)$_2$Cl B(OCOCH$_3$)$_3$ BX$_3$ [X=F, Cl, Br, I]	495 496 496 497 500 500		
				Anions	B$_2$(OH)$_4$, B$_2$Cl$_4$, B$_2$I$_4$ [BO$_3$]$^{3-}$, [B$_3$O$_6$]$^{3-}$, [BO$_2{}^-$]$_n$	503 499		
		−1	3σ 1π	Aromatic ring compounds	(BN)$_n$, [B$_3$O$_6$]$^{3-}$	505 506 529	None	
4	Tetrahedral		2 three centre	Electron deficient compounds	B$_2$H$_6$, B$_4$H$_{10}$, B$_5$H$_9$, B$_5$H$_{11}$ B$_{10}$H$_{14}$ Methyl derivatives of B$_2$H$_6$ B$_2$H$_5$X [X=Cl, Br, I] H$_2$B[NH$_2$,H]BH$_2$, H$_2$B[N(CH$_3$)$_2$,H]BH$_2$ H$_2$B[N(SiH$_3$)$_2$,H]BH$_2$ Be(BH$_4$)$_2$, Al(BH$_4$)$_3$, Ti(BH$_4$)$_3$	510 517 520 523	Al$_2$(CH$_3$)$_6$ Al$_2$X$_6$ [X=Cl, Br, I]	5 5
		−1	4σ	Non-chelate { Neutral complexes	(CH$_3$)$_3$N·BH$_3$, OC·BH$_3$ H$_3$N·BF$_3$, (C$_2$H$_5$)$_2$O·BCl$_3$ Saturated borazole compounds	521 501 507	X$_3$Al←D [X=Cl or Br, D=NH$_3$, NCCH$_3$, PH$_3$, O(C$_6$H$_5$)$_2$,SH$_2$] (C$_6$H$_5$)$_3$Al·NH$_3$, (C$_6$H$_5$)$_3$AlO(C$_2$H$_5$)$_2$	5 5
				Complex anions	M(BH$_4$) [M=Li, Na, K, R$_4$N] HBF$_4$, H[BF$_3$OH], H[BF$_2$(OH)$_2$] K$_2$[H$_2$OHB·BH$_2$OH]	525 527 528	M[AlH$_4$] [M=Li, Na, ½Ca] M[Al(OC$_2$H$_5$)$_4$] K[AlX$_4$] [X=Cl, Br, I]	5 5 5
				Complex cations	None		None	
				Chelate { Neutral complexes Complex anions	BF$_2$A Borotungstates	501 529	None None	
				Complex cations	[BA$_2{}^+$][FeCl$_4{}^-$]	530	None	
5	Octahedral		6 three centre	Electron deficient compounds	None		Al(BH$_4$)$_3$, Al$_2$(BH$_4$)$_4$	5
		−3	6σ	Non-chelate { Neutral complexes Complex anions	None		M$_3$[AlF$_6$][M=Li, Na, K, NH$_4$]	5
				Complex cations			[Al(H$_2$O)$_6$]Cl$_3$ [Al(NH$_3$)$_6$]Cl$_3$	5
				Chelate { Neutral complexes Complex anions	None		AlA$_3$ (NH$_4$)$_3$[Al(C$_2$O$_4$)$_3$]	5
				Complex cations				

† In this column the expression "3σ" indicates the presence of three bon

Ga	page	In	page	Tl	page
O, Ga₂S Cl, GaBr, GaI GaCl₄], Ga[AlCl₄]	547	In₂X [X=O, S, Se, Te] InY [Y=Cl, Br, I] In[InCl₄], In₃[InCl₆]	533	TlN₃, Tl₃N, Tl₂O, TlOH Tl₂S, Tl₂S₅, Tl(NO₃) TlX [X=F, Cl, Br, I]	558
				(TlOC₂H₅)₄, TlA, [Fe(SC(NH₂)₂)₄]Cl	562

the Metal=3

Ga	page	In	page	Tl	page
N, Ga₂O₃, Ga₂S₃ F₃	548	InN, In₂O₃, In(OH)₃ In₂S₃, InF₃	554	Tl₂O₃, Tl₂S₃, TlF₃	563
Ga—Ga—S	548	H[OInO], NH₄[SInS]	554	[I—Tl—I]I, [C₆H₅·Tl·C₆H₅]Cl	563
CH₃)₃ above 100°	549	In(CH₃)₃ in vapour	555	Tl(CH₃)₃, Tl(C₂H₅)₃, Tl(C₆H₅)₃	564
Cl₃, GaBr₃, GaI₃, all above 800°	551				
e		None		None	
H₆, GaH₂(CH₃)₄, (CH₃)₆, Ga₂(CH₃)₄(NH₂)₂ X₆ [X=Cl, Br, I]	549 549	In(CH₃)₃, In(C₆H₅)₃ In₂X₆ [X=Cl, Br, I]	555 556	[(C₂H₅)₂Tl(OC₂H₅)]₂	566
₃)₃Ga←NH₃	550	[In(CH₃)₃]₂O(C₂H₅)₂	556	(CH₃)₃Tl←O(C₂H₅)₂	
GaH₄], Tl[GaH₄] CH₃)₃Ga·NH₂·Ga(CH₃)₃	551 552	In[InCl₄]	553	Tl[TlCl₄], H₂[TlOCl₃],3H₂O	565
e				(C₂H₅)₂TlA	567
				NH₄[Tl(C₂O₄)₂],H₂O	567
₃(H₂O)₃, GaF₃(NH₃)₃ GaF₆] [M=Li, Na, NH₄] H₂O)₆](ClO₄)₃	552 552 552	(NH₄)₃[InF₆], (NH₄)₂[InF₅,H₂O] [In(H₂O)₆](ClO₄)₃,2H₂O	556 557	K₃[TlCl₆], Cs₃[TlCl₉]	568
A₃ Ga(C₂O₄)₃],3H₂O M=Na, K, NH₄]	552 552	InA₃ NH₄[In(C₂O₄)₂(H₂O)₂] [In en₃]Cl₃ [In en₂Cl₂]Cl	557 557 557	(NH₄)₃[Tl(C₂O₄)₃] [Tl en₃]Br₃,2H₂O	568 568

n of type σ; the other expressions have corresponding meanings.

6*

adopted by boron, but scarcely by any other of the elements; the aromatic ring compounds of boron are unique in the sub-Group. Tetrahedral hybridisation is common to all the elements, but whereas boron forms many tetrahedral complexes, the other elements tend to form complexes by adopting octahedral hybridisation. The tendency to form tetrahedral complexes, which falls off steadily from boron to indium, is revived again by thallium, probably because the presence of a potentially inert electron pair in the thallium atom causes it to become 4 co-ordinate rather than 6 co-ordinate.

Electron deficient compounds containing three-centre bonds are characteristic of the sub-Group. Boron forms many compounds of this type, including the boron hydrides and the borohydrides. Aluminium and gallium also form compounds containing three-centre bonds, but it is less certain whether such structures should be assigned to any compounds of indium and thallium. It is interesting to note that the trihalides and trialkyls of boron are simple monomeric compounds, but the corresponding compounds of aluminium are dimeric and contain three-centre bonds.

Certain properties of the elements of sub-Group III N are given in Table 17.2.

Table 17.2.   *Properties of the Elements in sub-Group III N*

	B	Al	Ga	In	Tl
Atomic number	5	13	31	49	81
Electronic configuration	2, 3	2, 8, 3	2, 8, 18, 3	2, 8, 18, 18, 3	2, 8, 18, 32, 18, 3
Atomic weight	10·82	26·97	69·72	114·76	204·39
Density	2·13	2·70			
Crystal lattice	Complex, see p. 491	Close-packed	Complex	Slightly distorted close-packed	Close-packed
m.p. °C	2300	659·7	29·75	155	303·5
b.p. °C	2550	1800	about 2000	1450	1650
Electrode potential on the hydrogen scale, $M \rightarrow M^{3+}$	—	+1·7	+0·5	+0·34	$\begin{cases} Tl \rightarrow Tl^+ \\ \quad +0·34 \\ Tl^+ \rightarrow Tl^{3+} \\ \quad -1·25 \end{cases}$
Ionisation potential (volts)					
I	8·26	5·96	5·97	5·76	6·07
II	25·00	18·74	20·43	18·79	20·32
III	37·75	28·31	30·6	27·9	29·7
Covalent radius (tetrahedral)	0·88	1·26	1·26	1·44	1·47
Ionic radius, M^{3+}	0·20	0·50	0·62	0·81	0·95
$(Z_{eff})_{mol}$	2·25	3·14	4·65	4·65	4·65

BORON

Pure boron is best made by passing a mixture of boron tribromide and hydrogen over an electrically heated tantalum filament. The temperature may vary from 600 to 1600° (tantalum does not combine with boron below 1800°). A macrocrystalline deposit is favoured by a high temperature and a low partial pressure of boron tribromide (about 20 mm). Impure boron is obtained by heating boric oxide, or potassium fluoroborate, with Na, K, Mg, Ca, Al, or Fe:

$$KBF_4 + 3K = 4KF + B,$$
$$B_2O_3 + 3Mg = 3MgO + 2B.$$

Impure boron (Moissan's boron) is a brown finely-divided powder, containing about 98% of boron.

Pure crystalline boron is black. It has great opacity and metallic lustre. Its electrical properties are those of a semi-metal. It is a poor electrical conductor; the conductivity increases rather less than 100 fold between 20° and 600°. The density is 2·130. The hardness is 9·3 (Moh's scale). The crystal structure of the needle form has been determined from Weissenberg X-ray data and the density. The structural unit is tetragonal and contains 50 atoms, 48 atoms are arranged at the vertices of four nearly regular icosahedra; the icosahedra are linked together so that each boron atom is co-ordinated to six others situated at the corners of a pentagonal pyramid. Each of the remaining two boron atoms has tetrahedral co-ordination. The average internuclear distance is 1·75 to 1·80.

Boron is found in the periodic table between beryllium, which has a truly metallic close-packed hexagonal lattice, and carbon, which has a giant molecule covalent lattice. In terms of the wave-mechanical theory of valency, beryllium crystals have a Bloch

Table 17.3. *Reactions of Boron*

Reagent	Conditions	Reaction of Amorphous boron	Reaction of Crystalline boron
Air	Heated	Burns to oxide and nitride	No action
Oxygen	Heated	Burns to oxide	Superficially oxidised only when heated to incandescence
Sulphur	Vapour over boron at 1200°	Yields B_2S_3	
Selenium	Heat elements	Yields B_2Se_3	
Steam	Red heat	Yields boric acid and H_2	
Fluorine	Room temp.	Inflames	
Chlorine	Heated to 410°	Yields BCl_3	
Bromine	Heated to 700°	Yields BBr_3	
Iodine	Heated to 1250°	Yields BI_3	
Hydrogen fluoride	Boiling concentrated	No action	No action
Hydrogen chloride	Boiling concentrated	No action	No action
Sulphuric acid	Hot, concentrated	Oxidation at 250°	Very slight attack
Chromic acid in sulphuric acid			Very slight attack
Nitric acid	Dilute	Vigorous attack	No action
	Concentrated	Inflames	Scarcely attacked
Hydrogen peroxide	Concentrated	Oxidised to boric acid	Slowly oxidised
Ammonium persulphate	Hot aq. solution		Slight action
Sodium hydroxide	Boiling conc. soln.	Attacked	No action
Sodium hydroxide	Fused	Dissolves, liberating H_2	Slight action about 500°
Sodium peroxide	Fused		Vigorously attacked
$Na_2CO_3 + KNO_3$	Fused		Vigorously attacked
Carbon dioxide	Heated	Yields B_2O_3 and C	
Silicon dioxide	Heated	Yields B_2O_3 and Si	
H_3PO_4	Heated to 800°	Yields B_2O_3 and P	

structure of generalised orbitals (p. 179), but the carbon atoms in diamond are linked by localised covalent bonds. The structure of the boron crystal suggests a continuous covalent structure which is dissociated into the large icosahedral units.

It is shown on p. 495 that the octahedral group B_6 occurs in certain metallic borides. Both the icosahedral and the octahedral arrangements of boron atoms, and also (except for diborane) the molecules of the boron hydrides which are derived from them, are marged by the presence of triangular groups of three boron atoms.

Pure crystalline boron is chemically almost inert, but impure amorphous boron is active. Table 17.3 illustrates the difference in chemical activity.

GENERAL CHEMISTRY OF BORON

The electron configuration of the boron atom in the ground state is $1s^2$, $2s^2$, $2p^1$. The ionisation potentials of the boron atom are:

$1s$	$1s$	$2s$	$2s$	$2p$	
338·5	258·1	37·75	25·0	8·3	volts

Under the ordinary conditions of a chemical reaction no electrons are removed from the boron atom; boron is never present in chemical combination as a simple positive ion. Unlike all the other elements in sub-Group III N, boron is never univalent; when the boron atom is in combination all three electrons in the valency shell are used in the formation of covalencies. The boron atom does not undergo digonal hybridisation, and hence there are no boron compounds in Section 2 of Table 17.1.

The boron atom undergoes trigonal (sp^2) hybridisation (Section 3 of Table 17.1) and either does not use the third $2p$ orbital at all, or uses it to form a π bond which becomes part of a non-localised orbital system of a six-membered ring.

Among the compounds in which the boron atom is trigonally hybridised and the third p orbital is unused are BF_3, BCl_3, BBr_3, and $B(N(CH_3)_2)_3$. The molecules of all these compounds have been shown experimentally to have planar structures with the angle XBX 120°. Six-membered ring systems containing non-localised orbitals are found in boron nitride, BN, which has a graphitic lattice, in borazole and its derivatives, which have a six-membered ring analogous to that in the benzene molecule, and in methyl boric anhydride, $(BOCH_3)_3$, and in the ion $(B_3O_6)^{3-}$ of the alkali metal metaborates. It is possible that the boron atom may form a π bond which is not part of a ring structure in such compounds as BI_3, $(CH_3)_3B$, and $(CH_3O)_3B$. These compounds do not readily act as acceptors when treated with ammonia, ether, and such reagents, and their inertness may be explained if the fourth boron orbital is used in forming a π bond, either with the iodine atom of low electronegativity, or with the hyperconjugated groups, CH_3 and CH_3O. If (as has been suggested) π bonds play some part in certain types of hydrogen bonds, the boron atoms in crystalline boric acid may be exerting π bonds. It should be noted that among the elements of sub-Group III N boron alone is able to adopt the bonding configuration of three σ bonds and one π bond. Boron is the only element to form compounds with the structure of borazole. Attempts to make $Al_3N_3H_6$, $Al_3P_3H_6$, $Be_3O_3H_6$, and $B_3P_3H_6$ have failed.

The group BX_3 containing a trigonally hybridised boron atom has three electron pairs only. The boron atom readily accepts another electron pair from a donor molecule, and becomes tetrahedrally hybridised. If the original group BX_3 and the donor molecule each contain at least one hydrogen atom, the formation of the addition compound may be followed by the elimination of hydrogen and the production of a π bond between the boron atom and the central atom of the donor molecule. For example, dimethylamine reacts with diborane to give at $-42°$ *NN*-dimethylamine borine, which on heating gives *NN*-dimethylaminoborine:

$$2H(CH_3)_2N + B_2H_6 = 2H_3B \cdot N(CH_3)_2H$$
$$H_3B \cdot N(CH_3)_2H = H_2 + H_2B \overset{\pi}{-} N(CH_3)_2.$$

This type of reaction is explained by the tendency of the hydrogen atom in the B—H group to be hydridic. This hydrogen atom is ready to unite with a protonic hydrogen atom in the donor group to yield molecular hydrogen.

The borine group, BH_3, has no free existence, but the reactions of the dimer, diborane B_2H_6, frequently suggest the presence of two loosely linked borine groups, H_3B—BH_3.

The boron atom is the typical example of what is known as an "electron deficient" atom. The term implies a comparison of other atoms with the carbon atom. The carbon atom has four electrons in the valency shell, and it is therefore able to adopt the very stable tetrahedral valence state by forming four σ two-centre bonds without ionisation or the formation of π bonds. Because the boron atom has only three valency electrons it cannot imitate the carbon atom in adopting the tetrahedral valence state in a direct and simple manner. It is for this reason that the boron atom is called electron deficient. The term could be applied to any element in Groups I, II, or III, but it is usually reserved for those elements which compensate for the deficiency by the formation of three-centre bonds.

Since the boron atom contains only three valency electrons, the tetrahedrally hybridised atom must either acquire a formal negative charge, or form three-centre bonds. Compounds in which the boron atom acquires a formal negative charge are numerous. They may be non-chelate neutral compounds such as $F_3B \cdot N(C_2H_5)_3$ and $(C_2H_5)_3B \cdot NH_3$ formed by acceptor-donor reactions, or compounds containing non-chelate tetrahedral anions such as $(BH_4)^-$ in $Na^+(BH_4)^-$. As might be predicted from the electronegativity of boron, no compounds are found in which the atom is part of a non-chelate tetrahedral cation, such as would be present in the hypothetical compound, $[B,4H_2O^{3+}](Cl^-)_3$. Chelation stabilises all types of compound in which a tetrahedrally hybridised boron atom is present, and the chelated boron atom is found in neutral, anionic, and cationic complexes.

The three-centre bond was conceived to explain the structures of diborane and the other boron hydrides. Each three-centre bond is a molecular orbital occupied by two electrons; the orbital is compounded of contributions from the atomic orbitals of *three* atoms. By the use of three-centre bonds an atom can attain a valence state for which it would have too few electrons if these were to occupy normal two-centre bonds. The nature of three-centre bonds is discussed on p. 118, and the part they play in the structure of the boron hydrides and other boron compounds is described on p. 511.

Although boron in combination with nitrogen or oxygen forms sheet structures analogous to those of graphite and benzene, boron differs markedly from carbon in rarely forming chains of B—B bonds. Only a few compounds such as B_2Cl_4 and $Be_2(OH)_4$ are known to contain single B—B bonds. In crystalline boron, in $B_{10}H_{14}$, and in C_3B_{12}, boron atoms are arranged at the vertices of a nearly regular icosahedron. The relation between the structures of crystalline boron and $B_{10}H_{14}$ is explained on p. 515.

COMPOUNDS IN WHICH THE OXIDATION STATE OF BORON IS 3

SECTION 1. BORON COMPOUNDS WITH IONIC CHARACTER

The boron atom gives rise to no monatomic ion, and hence the only boron compounds in this Section are those which form giant molecules. Beryllium, the element preceding boron in Period 2, forms many compounds of this kind, but the corresponding compounds of boron are few, and their structures are complex and obscure. Carbon, the element following boron in Period 2, forms still fewer giant molecule compounds; CO_2, CS_2, CCl_4, and $(CN)_2$ are all gases at room temperature. Boron nitride, which might well be included in this Section, is discussed in Section 3 (p. 505), and the boron hydrides are discussed in Section 4.

BORON COMPOUNDS CONSISTING OF GIANT MOLECULES IN WHICH THE BONDS HAVE SOME IONIC CHARACTER

Boron carbide, $B_{12}C_3$, is made by heating boron with carbon in the electric furnace. It is a black, very hard substance. It shows considerable electrical conductivity, but at room temperature its specific conductivity is only 1/100 that of polycrystalline graphite; at 500° this ratio has increased to 1/10.

The chief interest of boron carbide lies in its structure. Clark and Hoard (1943) established that the structural units in boron carbide are a straight chain of three carbon atoms, and a group of twelve boron atoms arranged at the vertices of a nearly regular icosahedron. These two units are distributed in the crystal in a structure which is related to that of sodium chloride; the centre of each icosahedron is at the position of a Na^+ ion, and the central carbon atom of the chain is at the position of a Cl^- ion. Each boron atom is attached to five other boron atoms in the icosahedral group, and either to a carbon atom, or to a boron atom in an adjacent icosahedron. Thus a continuous three-dimensional network of boron atoms extends throughout the crystal. A carbon at the end of a carbon chain is attached to the central carbon atom, and to three boron atoms; the central carbon atom is attached only to the other two carbon atoms of the chain.

There is some evidence that boron carbide dissolves boron, but not carbon.

Boric oxide, B_2O_3, is a white solid, which exists in both a crystalline and a glassy form. It is formed when amorphous boron is heated in air, or when boric acid is heated to a low red heat. It has no basic properties. It combines with water to form boric acid, which is soluble, and it dissolves in alkalis to form borates. It is reduced to boron when heated with certain metals (p. 490); it is not reduced by carbon. X-ray analysis shows that the crystalline form consists of linked spiral chains of tetrahedra of BO_4, of two types. The Raman spectrum of boric oxide includes the line at 806 cm^{-1} characteristic of the boroxole ring (p. 509).

Boron sulphide, B_2S_3, is a solid, m.p. 310°; it sublimes at 200°. It burns in air or in chlorine, and it is hydrolysed by water to boric acid and hydrogen sulphide. It is insoluble in organic solvents. It combines with ammonia to form a hexammoniate.

Boron sulphide can be made by heating the elements together, or by the action of hydrogen sulphide on boron tribromide (BCl_3 does not react) in carbon disulphide or benzene solution. In the course of some days crystals are formed from the solution. The crystals have the molecular formula (by cryoscopic determination) $H_2S_4B_2$. When heated they yield B_2S_3.

The metallic borides consist of atoms of the metal associated with boron atoms which may be present as single atoms, chains, hexagonal sheets, or in three-dimensional networks. The following examples may be given:

Single atoms	Chains	Hexagonal sheets		Three-dimensional networks
Mo_2B	CrB	AlB_2	WB_2	CaB_6 and similar compounds
W_2B	MoB	CrB_2	MnB_2	of Sr, Ba, La, Ce, Nd, Er,
	WB	Mo_2B_5	CoB_2	C, Th
		W_2B_5	NiB_2	

The metallic borides are made by heating a mixture of the metal and boron to 2000°. The structure of calcium boride may be regarded as cubic. A group of six boron atoms arranged octahedrally is situated at each corner of the cube; calcium atoms are at the cube centres. The bonding, if covalent, must be polycentred, as there are only twenty electrons available per unit cube. In AlB_2 the boron atoms are arranged on a graphitic layer lattice and the aluminium atoms are between the layers. The distance B—B is 1·73. Each boron atom has six aluminium atoms at the apices of a trigonal prism as its equivalent nearest neighbours. Like BN, AlB_2 is able to act as host to intercalated atoms.

Boron phosphate and arsenate. These compounds are prepared by the evaporation of an aqueous solution of boric acid containing phosphoric acid, or arsenic acid. They do not dissolve in organic solvents; they are hydrolysed by water. They possess cristobalite lattices. The boron atom, and the phosphorus or arsenic atoms, are each surrounded by four oxygen atoms arranged at the apices of a tetrahedron.

SECTION 3. COMPOUNDS IN WHICH THE BORON ATOM IS TRIGONALLY HYBRIDISED†

Boron forms many compounds in which the atom is present in the trigonal valence state. Like the beryllium atom, however, the boron atom readily becomes tetravalent, either by forming neutral complexes such as $H_3N{\rightarrow}BF_3$, or complex anions such as $[BF_4^-]$. Although the simplest hydride of boron is B_2H_6 (p. 510), and the monomer BH_3 does not exist, many derivatives of the borine radical, BH_3, among them the trihalides and trialkyls, are monomeric and well-known. The boron atom in the trigonal valence state in a ring system is ready to acquire an additional electron and to exert a π bond in addition to the three σ bonds; the π bond becomes part of the non-localised orbital system of the ring (p. 505).

COMPOUNDS IN WHICH THE BORON ATOM EXERTS THREE σ BONDS ONLY

A list of certain of these compounds is given in Table 17.1. The compounds are of two types, BX_3 and X_2B—BX_2.

Boron trialkyls and triaryls. The physical properties of a few of these compounds are given in Table 17.4. They are prepared by the action of boron trifluoride on a Grignard reagent:

$$3C_2H_5MgBr + BF_3 = (C_2H_5)_3B + 3MgFBr.$$

Boron trimethyl is spontaneously inflammable in air or chlorine, but it does not react with water or iodine. The aryl compounds are not spontaneously inflammable, but are readily oxidised by atmospheric oxygen. With hydrogen peroxide the rapid and quantitative reaction occurs:

$$(C_2H_5)_3B + 3H_2O_2 = 3C_2H_5OH + H_3BO_3.$$

Boron trimethyl reacts with acetaldehyde and with acetone to liberate ethylene with the formation of alkyloxy compounds:

$$CH_3CHO + (C_2H_5)_3B = C_2H_5O \cdot B(C_2H_5)_2 + C_2H_4,$$
$$CH_3COCH_3 + (C_2H_5)_3B = (CH_3)_2CH \cdot O \cdot B(C_2H_5)_2 + C_2H_4$$

† The boron atom does not attain the digonal valence state, and hence there are no boron compounds in Section 2.

Table 17.4.   *Boron Trialkyls and Triaryls, and their Halogen Derivatives*

Compound	m.p. °C	b.p. °C	Notes
$(CH_3)_3B$	−161·5	−20·2	⎫ Monomeric in the vapour and in
$(C_2H_5)_3B$	−92·5	+95	⎬ solution. Molecules planar and
$(C_6H_5.CH_2)_3B$	+47		symmetrical by electron diffrac-
$(C_6H_5)_3B$	142	203/15 mm	⎭ tion
$B(CH_3)_2F$	−147·2	*ca.* 44	Molecule planar by electron diffraction
$B(C_6H_5)_2Cl$		270	
$B(C_6H_5)_2Br$	24	*ca.* 155/8 mm	
$B(CH_3)F_2$		−62·3	Molecule planar by electron diffraction
$B(C_6H_5)Cl_2$		178	
$B(C_6H_5)Br_2$	3·3	100/20 mm	

The boron trialkyls with hydrogen bromide give monobromides, e.g. $(C_2H_5)_2BBr$, and with bromine in the absence of a solvent, mono- and di-bromides.

The trialkyls and triaryls co-ordinate readily with donor compounds containing a nitrogen atom, but not with phosphine, water, or ether. With alkalis they also form addition compounds, but the boron atom becomes the central atom of a complex anion. For example, boron trimethyl is absorbed in concentrated aqueous KOH to give a gummy mass containing $K[B(CH_3)_3OH]$. It reacts similarly with NaOH, $Ca(OH)_2$, and $Ba(OH)_2$. Boron triphenyl reacts with tetramethyl ammonium hydroxide in alcoholic solution to give $(CH_3)_4N[(C_6H_5)_3BOH]\cdot C_2H_5OH$. The alcohol in this derivative can be replaced by water to give a salt, m.p. 186°. Boron trimethyl is absorbed by lithium ethyl to give a solid $Li[B(CH_3)_3C_2H_5]$ soluble in benzene from which it can be recrystallised. Boron triphenyl and boron tribenzyl react with alkali metals to form coloured additive compounds:

$$K + (C_6H_5)_3B = K[B(C_6H_5)_3].$$

The anion is isoelectronic with the radical $C(C_6H_5)_3$. The boron trialkyls undergo no parallel reactions. One, two, or three alkyl or aryl groups in $B(CH_3)_3$ or $B(C_6H_5)_3$ may be replaced by the group OH, thus giving a series such as:

$$B(CH_3)_3, \quad B(CH_3)_2OH, \quad B(CH_3)(OH)_2, \quad B(OH)_3.$$

Nitrogen compounds of boron in the trigonal valence state. The aminoborines $BH_2(NH_2)$, $BH(NH_2)_2$, and $B(NH_2)_3$ have no stable existence. $B(NH_2)_3$ is said to be present when boron trichloride is introduced into liquid ammonia at −50°. Conditions which would be expected to produce $BH_2(NH_2)$ yield borazole, probably through the intermediate formation of $H_2B\overset{\pi}{-}NH_2$.

The N-alkyl derivatives of the aminoborines, however, are well-characterised (Table 17.5).

Compound I is made almost quantitatively by the pyrolysis at 130° of borine dimethylamine, $H(CH_3)_2N{\rightarrow}BH_3$, which is itself obtained by the action of dimethylamine on diborane at low temperatures. Compound II is also obtained from diborane. Compound III cannot be made from diborane; it is obtained by the action of dimethylamine on boron trichloride.

Table 17.5.   *Certain N-alkyl Derivatives of Aminoborine*

		m.p. °C	b.p. °C	Notes
I	$(CH_3)_2N \cdot BH_2$			Monomeric at 110°, dimeric at room temperature
II	$((CH_3)_2N)_2BH$	−45	109 extr.	Colourless mobile liquid which shows no tendency to dimerise or disproportionate
III	$((CH_3)_2N)_3B$	−40	147·5	
IV	$((CH_3)_2N)BCl_2$	monomeric −46 dimeric +142	111·9	Sublimes in vacuo
V	$((CH_3)_2N)_2BCl$	−54	146·1	

The monomeric forms of compounds I and IV are more reactive than the dimeric forms. Hydrochloric acid, for example, hydrolyses the monomers to dimethylamine and boric acid, but it has no reaction on the dimers. The monomers may be formulated as canonical forms in resonance, for example:

The dimeric forms may contain three-centre bonds (p. 118), thus:

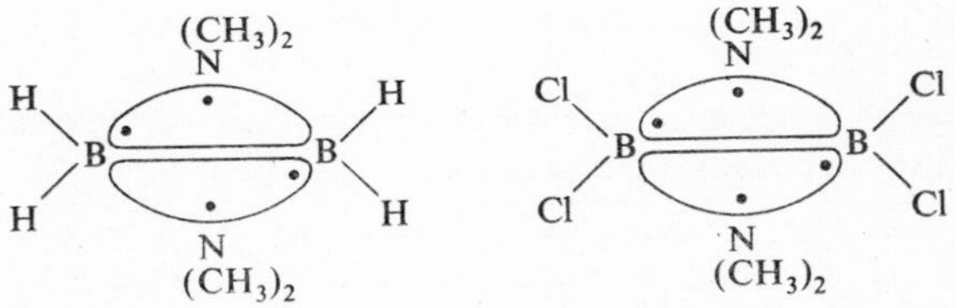

Oxygen compounds of boron in the trigonal valence state. These compounds include boric acid, H_3BO_3, which possesses a continuous layer structure in which the $B(OH)_3$ units are held together by hydroxyl bonds, the metaborate ions which have either a ring structure or a chain structure, the boric esters such as $B(OC_2H_5)_3$ which are monomeric, and the alkyl and aryl boric acids, such as $CH_3B(OH)_2$.

Boric acid, $B(OH)_3$, is made by adding hydrochloric acid to a hot saturated solution of borax until the solution is strongly acid:

$$Na_2B_4O_7 + 2HCl + 5H_2O = 2NaCl + 4H_3BO_3.$$

On cooling, boric acid separates; it may be recrystallised from hot water. The triclinic crystals are soft, pearly white, and have a greasy feel due to the gliding of the $B(OH)_3$ sheets over one another. The structure of crystalline boric acid, as deduced by X-ray analysis, is a layer lattice in which the groups $B(OH)_3$ are linked by hydroxyl bonds. The distances are: B—O, 1·37: O—O, 2·71. (The distances given by Pauling's covalent radii are B—O, 1·54; B=O, 1·31.) The sheets are 3·18 apart.

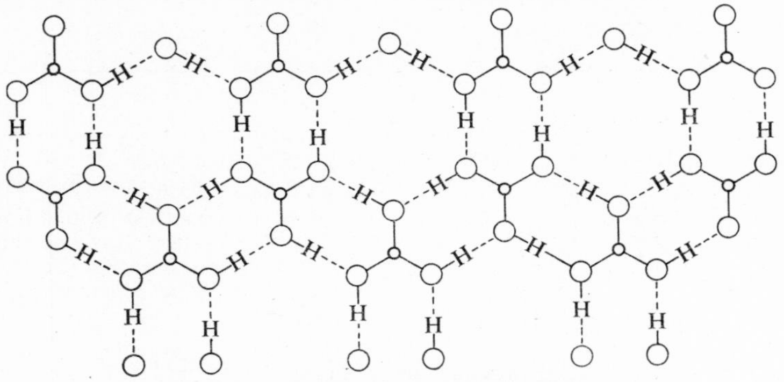

Fig. 17.1. Structure of boric acid, $B(OH)_3$.

This elegant structure is highly plausible. It assumes (i) that the hydrogen atoms are situated at points on straight lines joining the oxygen atoms, and (ii) that the oxygen atoms are in the trigonal valence state. If the oxygen atoms are in the trigonal valence state it is possible that the structure of boric acid may contain non-localised orbitals. From a study of infrared and ultraviolet data it has been concluded that in a molecule which possesses an intramolecular hydrogen bond, and a $C=O$ bond conjugated with other double bonds, for example, in salicyl aldehyde

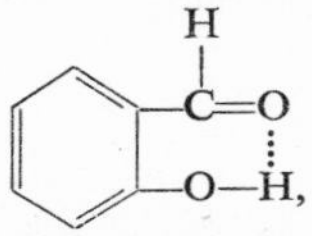

conjugation occurs across the hydrogen bond. On this conclusion hydrogen bonds are associated with π electrons. If this is acceptable, it would be reasonable to assume that the oxygen atoms in boric acid are trigonally hybridised, and that one p orbital per oxygen atom is available for the formation of non-localised π bonds, either in a hexagon of six oxygen atoms, or embracing the boron atoms also, and so the whole structure.

Electron diffraction evidence, however, suggests that the hydrogen atoms are displaced towards the centres of the oxygen rectangles, thus:

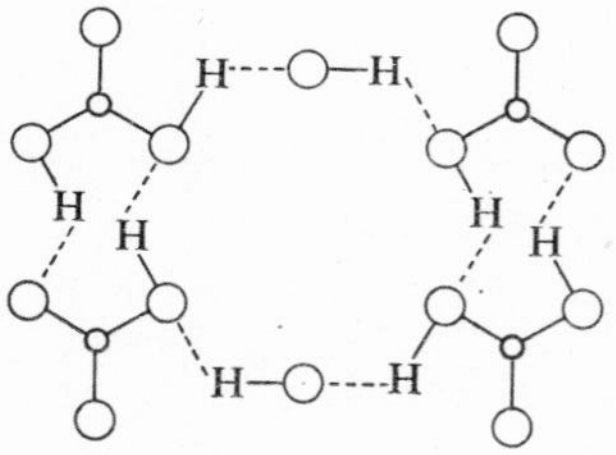

If the hydrogen atoms are in the same plane as the other atoms, the hybridisation of the oxygen atoms in the modified arrangement may still be trigonal with somewhat distorted angles. If the hydrogen atoms are not in the same plane as the other atoms, the valence state of the oxygen atoms may be tetrahedral, which would be in accord with the general conclusion that the angles at a given atom between hydrogen or hydroxyl bonds and any other bonds are tetrahedral angles.

In the boric acid lattice (in contrast to that of $Al(OH)_3$ which also forms hydroxyl bonds, and to that of $Mg(OH)_2$ which does not) no OH^- ions are held in common by B^{3+} ions. The $B(OH)_3$ units are recognisable and are held together by hydroxyl bonds.

Boric acid is soluble in cold water (1·95 gm in 100 gm at 0°) and more soluble in hot water (16·82 gm/100 gm at 80°). It is slightly volatile in steam. The equilibrium diagram of the system, B_2O_3—H_2O shows that the solid phases are ice, B_2O_3, H_3BO_3, and HBO_2 which may be present as one of three monotropic modifications. On heating, H_3BO_3 passes to HBO_2 at 100°, and at higher temperatures yields B_2O_3. The results of molecular weight determinations (by freezing point, boiling point, and osmotic pressure methods) of boric acid in solution all agree with the molecular formula, H_3BO_3.

Boric acid is a very weak acid; the dissociation constant at 25° is 6×10^{-11}. The ionisation may occur in one of several ways:

1. $H_3BO_3 \rightleftharpoons H^+ + (H_2BO_3)^-$
2. $H_3BO_3 \rightleftharpoons H^+ + BO_2^- + H_2O$; $3BO_2^- = (B_3O_6)^{3-}$
3. $H_3BO_3 + H_2O \rightleftharpoons H^+ + (B(OH)_4)^-$ (p. 500).

The formulae assigned to metallic borates are of the following types: borates $ScBO_3$, metaborates $Na_3B_3O_6$, pyroborates $Na_2B_4O_7$, and salts of more highly condensed acids such as NaB_5O_8. Borates of the type MBO_3 are known only where M is a trivalent metal. The BO_3^{3-} ions in the compounds, $ScBO_3$, YBO_3, and $InBO_3$ are planar and symmetrical like the ions CO_3^{3-} and NO_3^{3-}.

The unit BO_2 in the crystal structures of the metaborates is not present as a simple ion. When the cation is that of an alkali metal the unit BO_2 is part of a hexagonal ring:

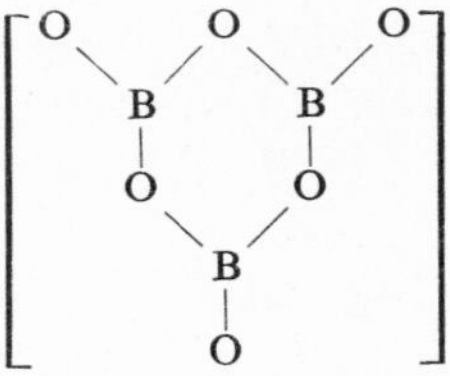

The ring is no doubt "aromatic", as it is in boroxole (p. 509). The bond lengths are B—O (in the ring) 1·38, B—O (outside the ring) 1·33. When the cation is bivalent, the BO_2 units form part of an infinite chain (cf. the pyroxenes which contain a chain of SiO_2 units):

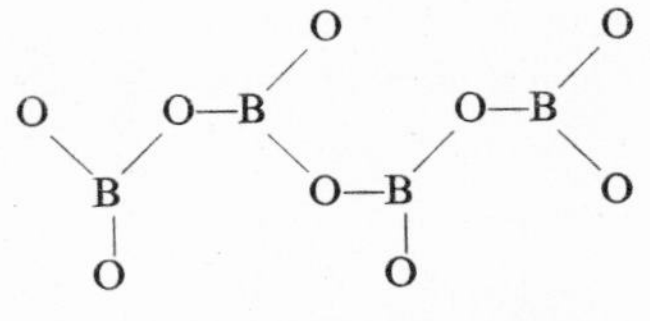

The structures of the simpler borates may be expressed in terms of the group BO_3, thus:

Cation	Anion
Trivalent metal	Discrete BO_3 groups (no oxygen atom shared)
Bivalent metal	Groups BO_3, each sharing two oxygen atoms
Univalent metal	Groups BO_3, each sharing three oxygen atoms.

Boric acid is so weak that the soluble salts are easily hydrolysed. Sodium borate may be titrated as an alkali against a mineral acid using methyl orange as indicator. If, however, glycerol or mannitol is present in the solution the strength of boric acid is so much increased that it may be titrated against sodium hydroxide using phenolphthalein as indicator. The increase in ionisation may be due to the formation of a chelate compound (p. 529), thus:

$$HB(OH)_4 + 2 \begin{array}{c} R \\ | \\ H-C-OH \\ | \\ H-C-OH \\ | \\ R \end{array} = \left[\begin{array}{c} R \quad\quad\quad R \\ | \quad\quad\quad | \\ H-C-O \quad\quad O-C-H \\ \diagdown \quad\quad \diagup \\ B \\ \diagup \quad\quad \diagdown \\ H-C-O \quad\quad O-C-H \\ | \quad\quad\quad | \\ R \quad\quad\quad R \end{array} \right]^{-} + H^+ + 4H_2O$$

The product would be a strong acid because the complex anion could not accept an H^+ ion without undergoing decomposition†. In much the same way $(CH_3)_4NOH$ is a strong base because the group $(CH_3)_4N$ cannot accept an OH^- ion. The strength of boric acid is also increased by saturating its aqueous solution with a salt, such as calcium chloride, which has a highly hydrated cation; the mechanism of the change here is uncertain.

Boric acid forms derivatives in which either the H atoms, or the OH groups in $B(OH)_3$ are replaced by other atoms or groups such as halogen atoms or alkyl or aryl groups. Boric acid acts as an acid by forming esters such as $B(OC_2H_5)_3$, and as an alcohol by forming esters such as $B(OCOCH_3)_3$.

Esters of boric acid, for example $B(OC_2H_5)_3$, a liquid, b.p. 118°. The lower esters of boric acid are volatile, non-associated liquids. They are made by the action of boric acid, or its anhydride, or boron triacetate, on the appropriate alcohol. They are at once hydrolysed by water. Electron diffraction shows that the BO_3 group in trimethyl borate is planar, and that the angle OBO is 120°. The halogen derivatives of the esters of boric acid are made by the action of the alcohol on the boron trihalide, for example:

$$C_2H_5OH + BCl_3 = Cl_3B \leftarrow OHC_2H_5 = BCl_2OC_2H_5 + HCl,$$

and by other methods. $BCl_2OC_2H_5$ is a liquid, b.p. 78°. Like all the halide esters of boric acid it is readily hydrolysed by water to boric acid, alcohol, and the halogen acid. The halide esters of boric acid are monomeric in the vapour.

Boron triacetate, $B(OCOCH_3)_3$, m.p. 147·8°, is made by heating boric oxide with acetic anhydride. When heated it dissociates into these compounds. It is rapidly hydrolysed by water; with alcohol it gives boric esters. It is soluble in chloroform or acetone, and it yields an interesting anthraquinone derivative (p. 529).

Boron trihalides.

	BF_3	BCl_3	BBr_3	BI_3	B_2Cl_4	B_4Cl_4
m.p. °C	$-130·7$	-107	-46	$+43$	-100	
b.p. °C	-101	$+12·5$	91	210	*ca.* $+55$	

Boron trifluoride, BF_3, is a gas which fumes strongly in moist air. It reacts with water, but it is soluble in many organic liquids. Boron has a greater affinity for fluorine than for any other element. On the assumption that the heat of atomisation of boron is 115 kcal, the values for certain heats of linkage (kcal per bond) are:

B—F	140·6	B—Cl	96·7	B—Br	76·9
C—F	103·4	C—Cl	78·0	C—Br	65·5
Difference	37·2		18·7		11·4

† Orthotelluric acid also becomes a strong acid in the presence of mannitol.

Boron trifluoride may be obtained by passing fluorine over amorphous boron; the boron spontaneously inflames. It may be made by heating a mixture of calcium fluoride, boric oxide, and concentrated sulphuric acid:

$$B_2O_3 + 3CaF_2 + 3H_2SO_4 = 2BF_3 + 3CaSO_4 + 3H_2O.$$

It is better, however, to use potassium fluoroborate in place of calcium fluoride:

$$6KBF_4 + B_2O_3 + 3H_2SO_4 = 8BF_3 + 3K_2SO_4 + 3H_2O.†$$

The original materials should be free from silicon, as SiF_4 (sublimation point $-95 \cdot 7°$) cannot easily be separated from BF_3. The gas may be collected over mercury.

Boron trifluoride forms additive compounds with ammonia and its derivatives, and with ethers, esters, and phosphine; with nitric oxide it gives $NOBF_3$. It has been shown by electron diffraction that the bonds of the boron atom in $F_3B \cdot O(CH_3)_2$ are tetrahedral. With water, alcohols, and acids, however, any complexes that may be formed break down immediately. If boron trifluoride is passed into water it first gives a precipitate of boric acid, and then a solution of fluoroboric acid (p. 527):

$$BF_3 + 3H_2O = B(OH)_3 + 3HF$$
$$BF_3 + HF = HBF_4.$$

In this solution fluoroboric acid is in equilibrium with hydroxyfluoroboric acid (p. 527). Boron trifluoride combines with alcohols to form acids such as $(C_2H_5OH_2)(BF_3OC_2H_5)$, which gives rise to the salt $Na(BF_3OC_2H_5)$, the structure of which has been determined by X-ray analysis. Boron trifluoride reacts with β-diketones such as acetylacetone in benzene solution to form semi-chelate neutral compounds of the type (p. 528):

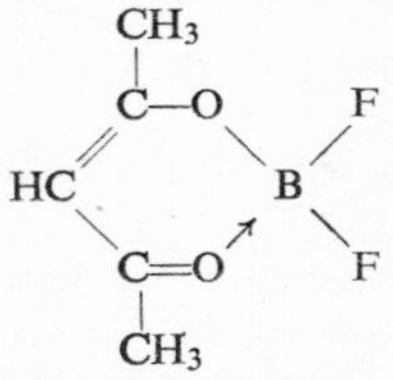

m.p. 43°

The completion of the reaction at this stage is an indication of the high affinity of boron for fluorine (compare the corresponding reactions of boron trichloride (p. 530)).

Boron trifluoride reacts with trimethyl boroxole at $-45°$ thus:

$$(CH_3OB)_3 + 2BF_3 = 3CH_3 \cdot BF_2 + B_2O_3.$$

With a Grignard reagent it gives a trialkyl or triaryl boron:

$$BF_3 + 3MgC_6H_5Br = B(C_6H_5)_3 + 3MgFBr.$$

A mixture of BF_3 and HNO_3 in molar proportions is a strong nitrating agent. Raman spectroscopy indicates the prescence of NO_2^+ in the mixture, probably as $[NO_2^+][BF_3OH^-]$ or $[NO_2^+][BF_3NO_2^-]$. BF_3 acts as a catalyst in many organic reactions, of which the following are examples:

1. The formation of esters from alcohols and acids.
2. The formation of diacetoacetic anhydride from acetic anhydride:

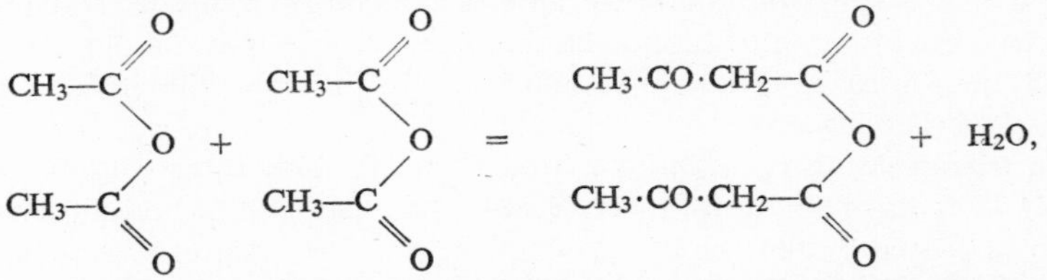

† It is also obtained by heating BCl_3 with CaF_2 to 200°, or by treating BCl_3 with SbF_3 and $SbCl_5$ at any temperature down to $-78°$, or by the action of fluorosulphonic acid, $HFSO_3$, on boric acid.

or of ethyl benzene from ethyl alcohol and benzene:

$$C_2H_5OH + C_6H_6 = C_2H_5 \cdot C_6H_5 + H_2O.$$

3. The addition of ethylene to benzene to give ethylbenzene:

$$CH_2{=}CH_2 + C_6H_6 = CH_3CH_2 \cdot C_6H_5.$$

4. The promotion of isomeric change, for example, the benzidine transformation:

The vapour density of boron trifluoride is normal down to $-75°$. Electron diffraction studies show that the molecule in the vapour has a planar structure, the angle F—B—F being $120°$. The B—F distance is 1·31 (Pauling's covalent radii predict 1·52). This structure is confirmed by the infrared and the Raman spectra.

Boron trichloride, BCl_3, is a very volatile liquid. It is made:

(i) by passing chlorine over a strongly heated mixture of boric oxide and charcoal:

$$B_2O_3 + 3C + 3Cl_2 = 2BCl_3 + 3CO,$$

(ii) by passing chlorine over heated amorphous boron,

(iii) by heating boric oxide with phosphorus pentachloride in a sealed tube at $150°$:

$$B_2O_3 + 3PCl_5 = 2BCl_3 + 3POCl_3.$$

The product is freed from chlorine by shaking with metallic mercury, and is fractionated to remove HCl and $SiCl_4$.

Boron trichloride reacts with water, alcohols, acids, ammonia, monoalkylamines and dialkylamines to produce compounds in which the boron atom is in the trigonal valence state. With water, boron trichloride gives boric acid. Water does not react with boron trichloride as it does with boron trifluoride; chloroboric acid does not exist. With alcohols boron trichloride gives boric chloroesters:

$$BCl_3 + C_2H_5OH = BCl_2(OC_2H_5) + HCl.$$

With liquid ammonia at $-50°$ it gives $B(NH_2)_3$, and with dimethylamine it gives successively $(CH_3)_2NBCl_2$, $((CH_3)_2N)_2BCl$, and $((CH_3)_2N)_3B$. Boron trichloride is reduced by lithium aluminium hydride to diborane, B_2H_6 (p. 543).

The acceptor-donor reactions in which boron trichloride acts as acceptor to give stable addition compounds are discussed generally on p. 504. It will be seen that boron trichloride forms additive compounds with trialkylamines and with ethers, and also with phosphine, and hydrogen sulphide. Boron trichloride reacts with nitrosyl chloride to give $[NO][BCl_4]$, and with β-diketones in ethereal solution to give complexes, described on p. 530, in which the boron atom is the centre of a chelate cationic complex.

The structure of boron trichloride has been deduced, by electron diffraction studies and from the Raman spectrum, to be similar to that of boron trifluoride. The distance B—Cl is 1·75 (Pauling's covalent radii predict 1·87).

Boron tribromide, BBr_3, a fairly volatile liquid, is made by passing bromine over boron at $700°$. Its ability to form complexes is less than that of boron trichloride. Its structure is proved by electron diffraction to be similar to that of the trichloride. The distance B—Br is 1·87 (Pauling, 2·02). The reaction of hydrogen sulphide on boron tribromide is mentioned on p. 494.

Boron tri-iodide, BI_3, can be made by passing hydrogen iodide mixed with the vapour of BCl_3 or BBr_3 through a red hot tube, or by the action of iodine on $LiBH_4$ at 120°, or on $NaBH_4$ at 200°. It consists of colourless needles soluble in CS_2, CCl_4, and benzene. It burns when heated in oxygen. It is violently hydrolysed by water. It is unable to form adducts by co-ordination. If the vapour of boron tri-iodide at low pressure is subjected to an electric discharge, B_2I_4 is obtained.

Diboron tetrahalides. The compounds B_2F_4†, B_2Cl_4, B_2Br_4, and B_2I_4 are known.

B_2F_4 is a gas, m.p. $-56 \cdot 1°$. It forms a very explosive mixture with oxygen. X-ray diffraction has shown that the molecule B_2F_4 is planar and centrosymmetric. The distance B—F is $1 \cdot 32$ and B—B is $1 \cdot 67$. The angle FBF is 120°. The distance B—B is shorter than the corresponding distance in B_2Cl_4 which is $1 \cdot 75$. The replacement of some other atom in a molecule by highly electronegative fluorine atoms normally shortens the lengths of bonds which do not involve the fluorine atom.

B_2Cl_4. If BCl_3 is passed several times at 1–2 mm pressure through a glow discharge between mercury electrodes, B_2Cl_4 is obtained in 50% yield, m.p. $-98°$, b.p. (extr.) $+55°$. In the absence of air it decomposes to boron and BCl_3 to the extent of 21% in 72 hours. Water hydrolyses it to sub-boric acid, $B_2(OH)_4$, but it reacts with alkalis to yield sodium borate:

$$3B_2Cl_4 + 6NaOH + 6H_2O = 2Na_3B_3O_6 + 12HCl + 3H_2.$$

B_2Cl_4 reacts with BBr_3 to give B_2Br_4; it does not react with BF_3. It forms mono- and di-etherates, and tetra-alkoxy derivatives with alcohols. It gives boron hydrides with hydrogen at room temperature, or with $LiBH_4$ or $Al(BH_4)_3$. Its reaction with NH_3 is complex. By X-ray analysis B_2Cl_4 is a planar, centrosymmetric molecule. The distance B—Cl is $1 \cdot 73$ and B—B is $1 \cdot 75$.

B_2I_4. If an electrodeless electric discharge is passed through BI_3 at 1–3 mm pressure at room temperature, B_2I_4 is obtained. It is a pale yellow crystalline substance, which undergoes the change:

$$B_2I_4 = BI_3 + (BI)_n,$$

slowly at room temperature, and more quickly on heating.

Sub-boric acid, $(HO)_2B \cdot B(OH)_2$. A solution of sub-boric acid (containing hydrogen chloride) is made by the hydrolysis of the chloride, B_2Cl_4:

$$B_2Cl_4 + 4H_2O = B_2(OH)_4 + 4HCl.$$

The acid itself is made by the formation and hydrolysis of its ester. The ester is made from dimethoxyboron chloride by a reaction analogous to that of Wurtz:

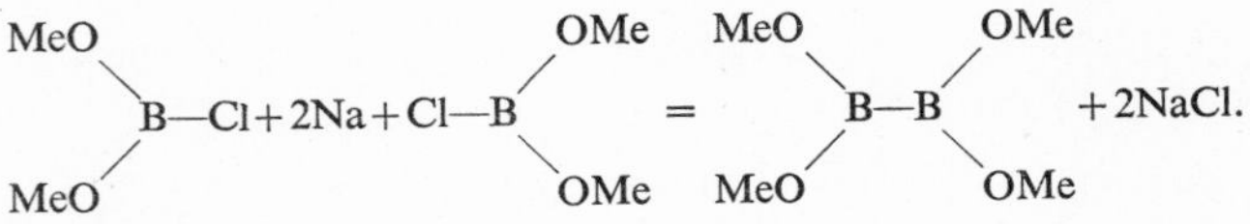

The reaction proceeds slowly in the cold. The ester is a liquid, m.p. $-24°$, b.p. (extr.) 93°. On standing in the cold it deposits a very active form of boron:

$$3B_2(OCH_3)_4 = 4B(OCH_3)_3 + 2B.$$

The ester is hydrolysed by water in vacuo at room temperature. The acid is a white solid. Sub-boric acid is a reducing agent, but a weaker one than hypoboric acid (for

† L. Trefonas and W. N Lipscomb, *J. Chem. Phys.*, **28**, 1958, 54.

a comparison (p. 528). Unlike hypoboric acid it has no reaction on the solution of a nickel salt. When oxidised it is converted to boric acid:

$$B_2(OH)_4 + H_2O + O = 2B(OH)_3.$$

Acceptor properties of molecules containing boron atoms in the trigonal valence state. Compounds having the general formula BX_3 which contain a boron atom in the trigonal valence state bonded to H, F, Cl, Br, alkyl or aryl groups, or in a few cases to an oxygen atom, are powerful electron acceptors. They react with donor molecules, such as, NH_3, $N(CH_3)_3$, HCN, CH_3CN, ethers, esters, aldehydes, and ketones, and in a few cases phosphine, arsine, and hydrogen sulphide, to form stable adducts. The reaction is carried out by bringing together the acceptor and donor molecules, either at a suitably low temperature, or in solution in benzene or ether. A boron atom in the trigonal valence state is most ready to act as an acceptor when its fourth valency orbital has no tendency to form a π bond by co-ordination with one of the three atoms to which it is linked by σ bonds. This is the case when the boron atom is combined with electronegative atoms such as fluorine or chlorine. The high electronegativity of fluorine hinders the formation of a π bond by the overlapping of the unoccupied third p orbital of the boron atom and one of the p orbitals of the fluorine atom occupied by a lone pair. The fourth orbital of the boron atom in BF_3 is therefore fully available to receive a lone electron pair from a donor molecule. By a parallel argument, compounds such as $B(CH_3)_3$ and $B(CH_3O)_3$ form additive compounds which are not very stable, because the third p orbital of the boron atom can be utilised in forming a π bond by hyperconjugation with the methyl or methoxy group†.

Some confirmation of the correctness of this point of view is afforded by the temperature of dissociation of certain adducts. $F_3B{\leftarrow}N(CH_3)_3$ dissociates above $230°$: $F_2(CH_3)B{\leftarrow}N(CH_3)_3$ is 90% dissociated at $230°$: $(CH_3)_3B{\leftarrow}NH_3$ is 90% dissociated at $30°$. It may be stated generally that a boron atom does not act as an acceptor if it is combined with atoms or groups with electronic configurations which permit the development of a system of non-localised π bonds which includes the fourth boron orbital. The boron atom has decreasing acceptor power in the groups:‡

$$BH_3 > BF_3 > BCl_3 > BBr_3 > (CH_3)_3B > (CH_3O)_3B.$$

The reactions of the adducts are frequently identical with those of a mixture of the component acceptor and donor molecules. Examples may be given, however, of pairs of reactions in which the behaviour of the adduct is different from that of its component molecules:

1 $\begin{cases} 8(F_3B \cdot O(C_2H_5)_2) + 6NaBH(OCH_3)_3 = 6NaBF_4 + 6B(OCH_3)_3 + B_2H_6 + 8(C_2H_5)_2O \\ BF_3 + NaBH(OCH_3)_3 = NaHBF_3 + B(OCH_3)_3. \end{cases}$

2 $\begin{cases} F_3B \cdot O(C_2H_5)_2 + NaH = Na(HBF_3) + O(C_2H_5)_2; \text{ at room temperature.} \\ \text{The reaction of NaH on pure } BF_3 \text{ is complex.} \end{cases}$

3 $\begin{cases} 8(F_3B \cdot O(C_2H_5)_2) + 6LiH = B_2H_6 + 6LiBF_4 + 8(C_2H_5)_2O. \text{ This reaction is rapid} \\ \text{at room temperature. Pure } BF_3 \text{ acts only slowly with LiH at about } 150°. \end{cases}$

†By the linear combination of the $1s$ atomic orbitals of three hydrogen atoms it is possible to construct one combined orbital with s symmetry, and two combined orbitals with p symmetry. The group H_3 by this treatment may in certain respects be regarded as a digonally hybridised carbon atom. The p orbitals may contribute towards a system of non-localised π bonds in a molecule in which the group H_3 is present. This effect is known as *hyperconjugation* (C. A. Coulson, *Valence*, p. 312).

‡ This order has been disputed. F. G. A. Stone states (*Chem. Rev.*, 1958, **581**, 110) that when BF_3, BCl_3, or BBr_3 (in the liquid state) is added to pyridine, the values of ΔH observed are respectively -32, -40, or -45 kcal mole^{-1}. From these results he infers that BBr_3 is a more powerful acceptor than BF_3.

COMPOUNDS IN WHICH THE BORON ATOM EXERTS THREE
σ BONDS AND CONTRIBUTES TO A GENERALISED π BOND
SYSTEM

Boron nitride, $(BN)_n$, is made by the action of nitrogen or ammonia on boron at 1000°. It may also be prepared by the unusual reaction which occurs when borax is heated with ammonium chloride:

$$Na_2B_4O_7 + 2NH_4Cl = 2NaCl + 2BN + B_2O_3 + 4H_2O.$$

It melts under pressure at 3000° and sublimes below this temperature. Boron nitride is decomposed by heating with acids, but otherwise it is non-reactive. It is unchanged by heating in air, oxygen, hydrogen, chloride, iodine, or carbon disulphide. Water is without effect below a red heat, when reaction takes place with the formation of boron trioxide and ammonia. Hydrogen fluoride reacts slowly with boron nitride, thus:

$$BN + 4HF = NH_4BF_4,$$

and fluorine reacts to give BF_3 and N_2. When boron nitride is fused with potassium hydroxide or with potassium carbonate, the reactions occur:

$$3H_2O + 3KOH + 3BN = K_3B_3O_6 + 3NH_3,$$
$$3K_2CO_3 + 3BN = K_3B_3O_6 + 3KCNO.$$

Boron nitride has a layer lattice. Each layer consists of a hexagonal arrangement of boron and nitrogen atoms (Fig. 17.2). The group BN is isoelectronic with the group C_2. Hence groups BN, in which each atom is in the trigonal valence state, form a hexagonal layer similar to that of graphite in which the carbon atoms are in the trigonal valence state. The trigonal hybridisation is a combination of the atomic orbitals sp_xp_y.

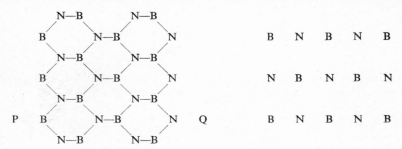

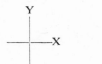

Fig. 17.2. One layer of B and N atoms consisting of hexagonal rings. (XY plane)

Fig. 17.3. The positions of the B and N atoms when the layers are superimposed. (XZ plane including the line PQ in Fig. 17.2.)

The p_z orbitals of all the atoms in a layer form a generalised π bond system, extending throughout the ring structure. The layers are superimposed on one another so that boron and nitrogen atoms are alternately above one another. In this the structure differs from graphite in which the layers are so arranged that a carbon atom of one layer is above the centre of a hexagonal ring of the layer next below it. The distance B—N is 1·45. Boron nitride, like graphite, is able to act as host to intercalated atoms; it is able to occlude oxides, sulphides, oxyhalides, and chlorides in the same way that graphite does.

Borazole is a colourless volatile liquid, m.p. $-58°$, b.p. $55°$. Its molecular formula is $B_3N_3H_6$. Electron diffraction studies supported by infrared and Raman spectra show that the borazole molecule has a planar structure. The B—N distance is 1·44, and the angles are 120°. These facts are in accordance with hexagonal ring structure:

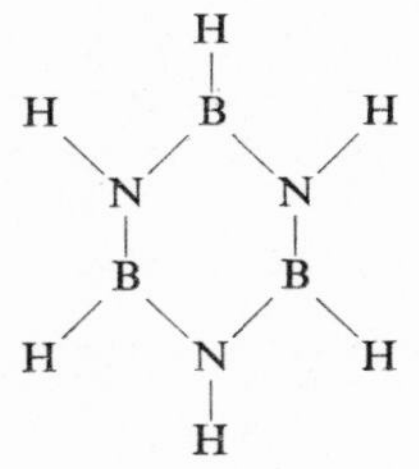

This ring structure is related to the layer lattice of boron nitride in the same way as the ring structure of benzene is related to the layer lattice of graphite. Just as the isolation of a ring of six carbon atoms from graphite, followed by the saturation of unattached valencies with hydrogen atoms gives a molecule of benzene:

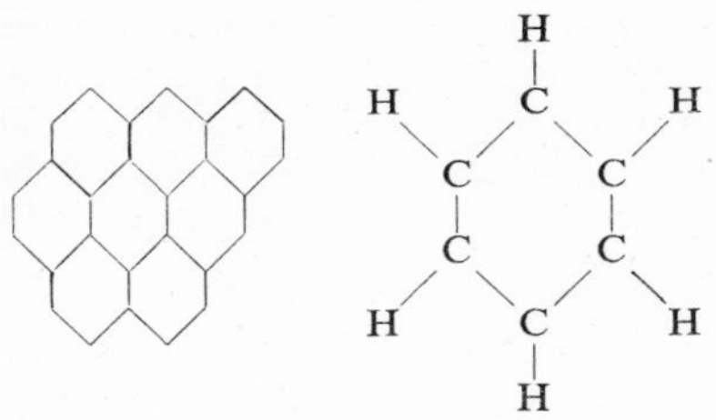

so the isolation of a six-membered ring, B_3N_3, from boron nitride and the saturation of free valencies with hydrogen atoms, produces a molecule of borazole:

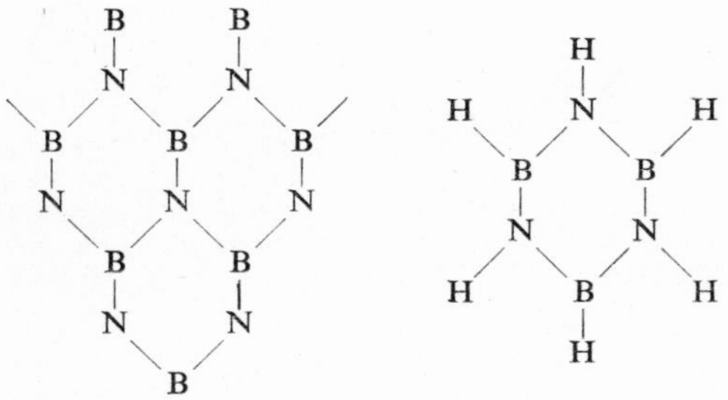

Borazole can be made in 90% yield by reducing B-trichloroborazole with lithium borohydride at room temperature:

$$2B_3N_3H_3Cl_3 + 6LiBH_4 = 2B_3N_3H_6 + 6LiCl + 3B_2H_6.$$

Borazole can be made in 40% yield (i) by heating together diborane and ammonia, or (ii) by heating tetraborane tetra-ammoniate to 200°, and in 30% yield by heating a mixture of lithium borohydride and ammonium chloride in vacuo at 230°.

Borazole decomposes very slowly at room temperature in the liquid phase, and even more slowly in the gas phase, producing H_2, B_2H_6, and non-volatile solids. Air at room temperature has no action on it; oxygen has no action unless a mixture of oxygen and the vapour be sparked. With water, borazole very slowly hydrolyses to hydrogen, boric acid and ammonia; the reaction is favoured by increase of temperature:

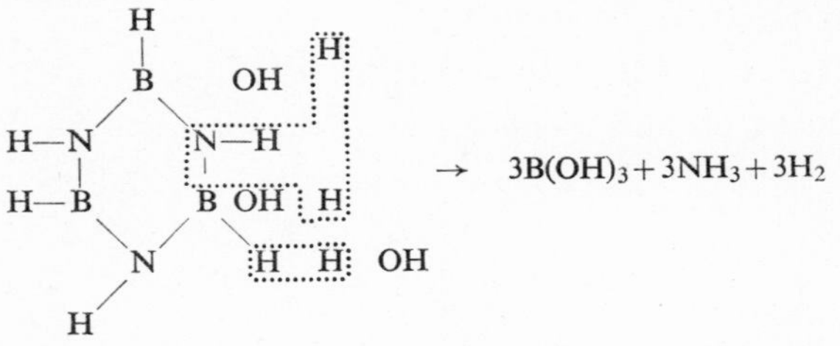

$$\rightarrow \quad 3B(OH)_3 + 3NH_3 + 3H_2$$

Many of the reactions of borazole are reminiscent of those of benzene. It combines in the cold and without a catalyst with three molecular proportions of HCl, HBr, CH_3I, H_2O, and CH_3OH, thus:

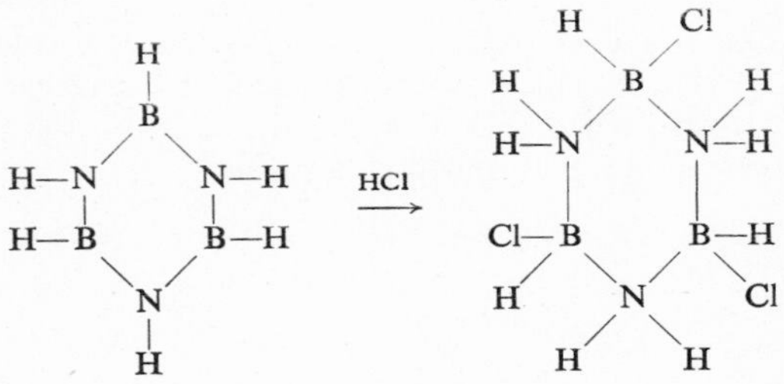

The hydrogen chloride derivative, if heated to 50–100°, loses three molecules of hydrogen to give B-trichloroborazole:

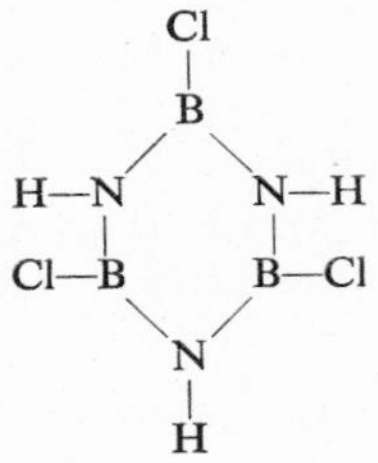

At 0° borazole takes up two molecules of bromine, and at 60° the molecule produced loses two molecules of hydrogen bromide:

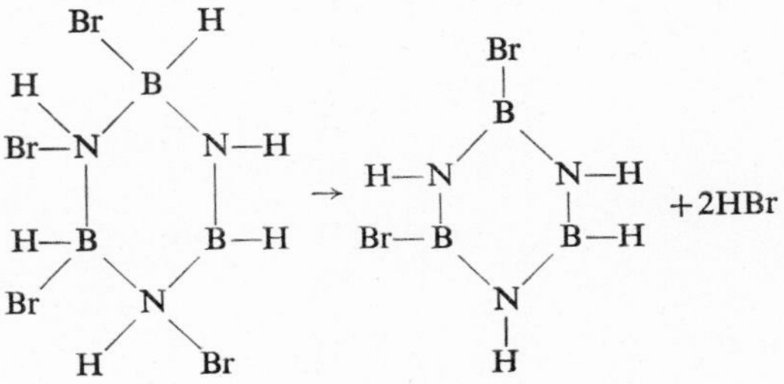

B-trichloroborazole. One method of preparing this compound is mentioned above. A better method consists in adding boron trichloride to a suspension of ammonium chloride in chlorobenzene in the presence of an iron, nickel, or cobalt catalyst at about 120°. The yield is 50–60%.

B-trimethyl borazole is prepared by heating $(CH_3)_3B$, (p. 495) with ammonia at 320–340° at 20 atm for 2 hours. There are a number of stages to the reaction, and the intermediate products can be isolated:

$$B(CH_3)_3 + NH_3 = (CH_3)_3B{\leftarrow}NH_3 = (CH_3)_2B{\overset{\pi}{-}}NH_2 + CH_4 = CH_3B{\overset{2\pi}{=}}NH + 2CH_4.$$

The final product crystallises spontaneously to the trimer:

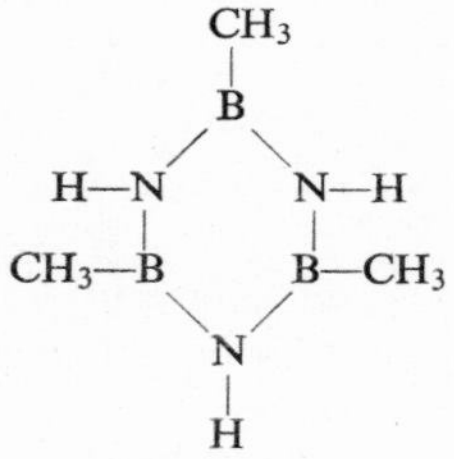

At room temperature this compound consists of colourless, volatile crystals, m.p. 31·8°, b.p. (extr.) 127°. It is stable in vacuo to 350°. It is sensitive to moisture but is insoluble in water. It is soluble in many organic solvents. At 100° water replaces the NH groups by oxygen and gives B-trimethyl boroxole:

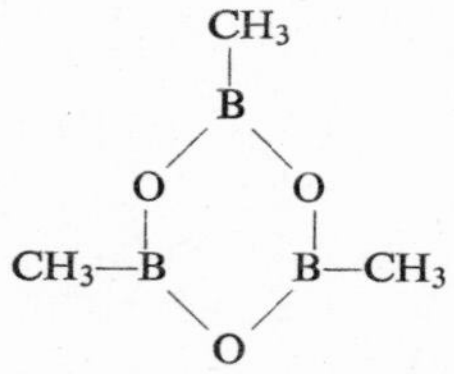

N-trimethyl borazole is obtained in 90% yield by heating a mixture of B_2H_6 and CH_3NH_2 in the correct proportions at 180–200° for 2 hours:

$$BH_3 + CH_3NH_2 = H_3B{\leftarrow}NH_2CH_3 = H_2B{\overset{\pi}{-}}NHCH_3 + H_2 = HB{\overset{2\pi}{=}}NCH_3 + 2H_2$$

The final product polymerises to the trimer which is N-trimethyl borazole. N-trimethyl borazole can also be prepared by reducing monomethyl ammonium chloride with lithium borohydride:

$$3CH_3NH_3Cl + 3LiBH_4 = B_3N_3H_3(CH_3)_3 + 3LiCl + 9H_2.$$

By treating N-trimethyl borazole with $B(CH_3)_3$ at 450° and 20 atm pressure hydrogen atoms linked to the boron atoms are replaced by methyl groups. N-trimethyl borazole is a colourless mobile liquid, m.p. −9°, b.p. (extr.) 132°. It is stable up to 300°. With water at 60° the B—H link is attacked and the product is:

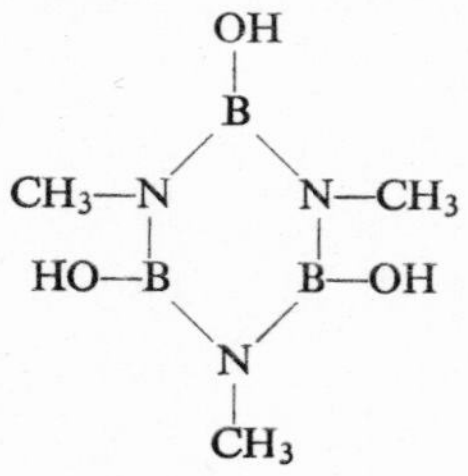

Boroxole. The molecule of boroxole,

$$
\begin{array}{c}
H \\
| \\
B \\
\diagup \quad \diagdown \\
O \qquad O \\
| \qquad | \\
B \qquad B \\
\diagup \quad \diagdown \quad \diagup \quad \diagdown \\
H \qquad O \qquad H
\end{array}
$$

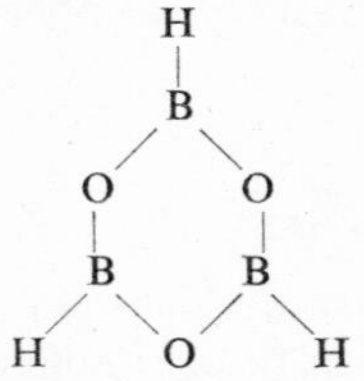

is isoelectronic with that of borazole. In the molecule of boroxole the oxygen atoms are trigonally hybridised; one of the trigonal orbitals is occupied by a lone electron pair. In the boroxole ring the distance B—O is 1·38. The characteristic Raman frequency of the ring is 807 cm^{-1}. Borazole and boroxole exhibit aromatic properties characteristic of benzene; it has been stated that if the aromatic character of benzene is 100, that of borazole is 50, and that of boroxole is 15. The following derivatives of boroxole are known:

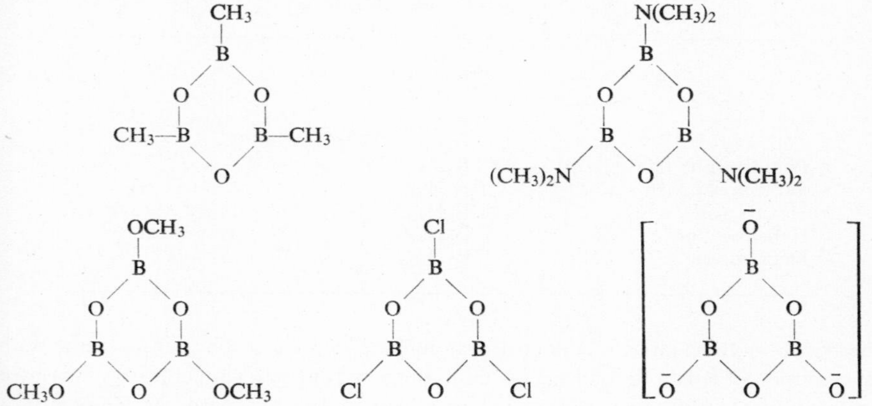

Trimethyl boroxole, m.p. − 68°, b.p. (extr.) 79°, can be made by the dehydration of monomethyl boric acid (p. 496) with anhydrous calcium sulphate:

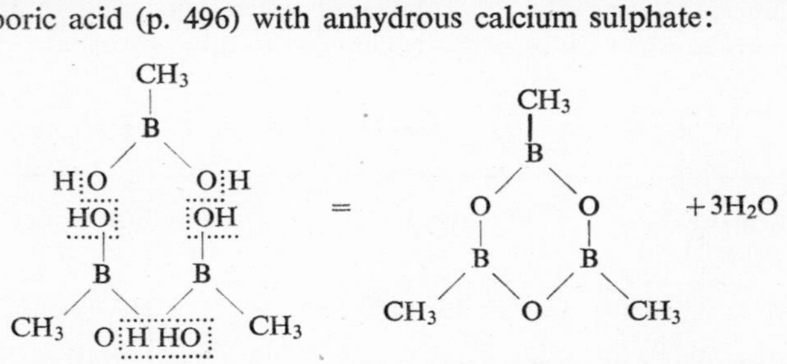

The reaction is reversible. The structure of the trimethyl boroxole molecule has been determined. The distance B—O is 1·39, and B—C is 1·57. The angle OBO is 128°, and the angle BOB is 112°. The action of trimethyl boroxole on BF$_3$ is described on p. 501.

SECTION 4. COMPOUNDS IN WHICH THE BORON ATOM IS TETRAHEDRALLY HYBRIDISED

The tetrahedral valence state is the highest attained by the boron atom. All types of tetrahedral compounds (Section 4, Table 17.1) except non-chelate complex cations are formed by boron. The hydrides of boron are of particular interest because their molecular formulae cannot be accounted for in terms of two-centre bonds. The need to reconcile the formulae with the numbers of valency electrons in the molecules led to the concept of the three-centre bond.

ELECTRON-DEFICIENT COMPOUNDS

The boron hydrides. The tricovalency of boron suggests that a hydride should exist of molecular formula BH_3. This hydride does not exist in the free condition, although the borine radical BH_3 is found in several compounds such as $OC \cdot BH_3$ and $(CH_3)_3N \cdot BH_3$. There is a break at boron in the series of hydrides:

$$LiH \quad BeH_2 \quad - \quad CH_4 \quad NH_3 \quad OH_2 \quad FH.$$

Boron, however, forms a hydride, B_2H_6, and other volatile hydrides of which the names, molecular formulae, and certain of their properties are given in Table 17.6.

Table 17.6.   *The Boron Hydrides*

Name	Formula	m.p. °C	b.p. °C
Diborane	B_2H_6	$-165 \cdot 5$	$-92 \cdot 5$
Tetraborane	B_4H_{10}	-120	18
Pentaborane (stable)	B_5H_9	$-46 \cdot 6$	48
Pentaborane (unstable)	B_5H_{11}	-123	63
Hexaborane	B_6H_{10}	-65	110 (extr.)
Enneaborane	B_9H_{15}	-20	
Decaborane	$B_{10}H_{14}$	$99 \cdot 7$	213

The boron hydrides do not spontaneously inflame in air at room temperature. With the exception of B_5H_{11} they all remain undecomposed at room temperature, at least for several days. At 300° they all decompose to boron and hydrogen. At temperatures between 50 and 300° it is probable that the hydrides play their parts in a series of equilibria. Table 17.7 sets out the conditions under which diborane, pentaborane (B_5H_{11}) and tetraborane may be partially changed to other hydrides.

Table 17.7.   *The Pyrolysis of certain Boron Hydrides*

Boron hydride	Treatment†	Product
B_2H_6	Heat to 180° at 150–450 mm Heat to 100–200° Heat to 225° for 15 sec Heat to 115–120° for 48 hours	B_5H_{11} (yield 75%) B_4H_{10} B_5H_9 $B_{10}H_{14}$
B_5H_{11}	Allow to stand in the cold Heat with hydrogen at 100°	$B_{10}H_{14} + H_2$ B_4H_{10}
B_4H_{10}	Heat to 90° Heat to 180° Heat to 200°	B_2H_6 B_5H_{11} B_5H_9

† Unless otherwise stated the pressure is atmospheric.

Structure of the boron hydrides. The structures of the boron hydrides have been determined mainly by experiments on X-ray diffraction, electron diffraction, and nuclear magnetic resonance, and the bonding of the atoms has been interpreted by wave mechanics. The structures assigned to the compounds are not revealed by their chemical behaviour, and hence it is logical to discuss their structures first, and afterwards to give some account of their preparations and chemical properties. With the exceptions of B_6H_{10} (of which the structure is uncertain) and $B_{10}H_{14}$, the structures of all the boron hydrides in Table 17.6 are related to that of the octahedral B_6^{2-} ion in calcium boride (p. 495). The derivation of a molecule of a boron hydride from the boride ion may be compared to that of a paraffin molecule from diamond. The paraffin molecule is imagined to be derived from the diamond crystal by the separation of the correct group of carbon atoms, followed by the saturation of the broken bonds by hydrogen atoms. By analogy, a boron hydride molecule may be derived from the boride ion by the isolation of a group of boron atoms, followed by saturation of the severed valency bonds by hydrogen atoms; in the case of boron the process would require a readjustment of polycentre bonds which are absent in the diamond crystal. The structure of $B_{10}H_{14}$ is related to that of crystalline boron in the manner described on p. 515.

Structure of diborane. The composition of diborane is B_2H_6. The gas shows no sign of thermal dissociation up to 100°. It is diamagnetic, hence the molecule contains no unpaired electrons. The molecule is electron deficient. It has 12 valency electrons, but its formula corresponds to that of ethane, C_2H_6, which has 14 electrons, all of which are in shared pairs. Two types of structure might be possible:

(i) an ethane-like structure, in which the boron atoms would be linked by a single bond, and two hydrogen atoms would be linked to each boron atom. This would use up all the boron valency electrons, and so each of the remaining hydrogen atoms would have to be attached to a boron atom, say, by a one-electron link:

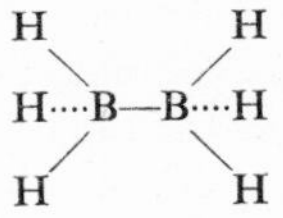

(ii) a bridged structure containing two three-centre bonds† :

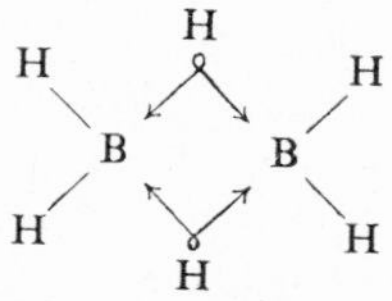

The bridge structure has been postulated on wave-mechanical principles as explained on p. 118. In this particular case each boron atom is tetrahedrally hybridised. Two of the tetrahedral orbitals on each boron atom are used for forming normal σ bonds with hydrogen atoms; the remaining two orbitals on each boron atom take part in forming three-centre bonds. Each three-centre bond consists of two electrons occupying a molecular orbital constructed from the atomic orbitals of two boron atoms and one hydrogen atom.

†There is no generally recognised symbol for a three-centre bond. In this book the arrangement

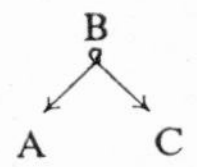

is used to indicate that the atoms A, B, and C are linked by one open three-centre bond.

Only four of the six hydrogen atoms in the molecule of diborane can be methylated (p. 517), which suggests that four of the hydrogen atoms are constitutionally different from the remaining two. Electron diffraction studies of tetramethyl boron show that the four methyl groups and the two boron atoms are coplanar, and the Raman spectrum below 0° shows no frequencies characteristic of terminal B—H stretching. All this favours the structure for tetramethyl boron:

$$
\begin{array}{ccc}
 & H & \\
H_3C & & CH_3 \\
 & B \quad B & \\
H_3C & & CH_3 \\
 & H &
\end{array}
$$

The infrared and Raman spectra of diborane can be successfully interpreted in terms of the bridge structure, but not in terms of the ethane-like model. Price's work on the rotation spectrum shows that there is a two-fold symmetry axis through the boron atoms. A conclusive argument for the bridge structure is furnished by experiments on the nuclear magnetic resonance of diborane. In order to simplify the argument, the boron atoms in diborane are assumed to be the pure isotope ^{11}B. If each nucleus in the diborane molecule is imagined to be situated in a uniform magnetic field H, when irradiated its absorption spectrum would consist of a single peak of frequency ν_0 given by the expression:

$$h\nu_0 = Hg\mu \quad \text{(p. 263)}.$$

The field in which each nucleus is situated, however, is modified by the magnetic fields generated by the spins of the other nuclei to which it is bonded (p. 266). The boron nucleus, ^{11}B, has four possible spin values, $3/2, 1/2, -1/2, -3/2$. The field experienced by one of the *terminal* protons is H with the addition of the field due to one of these spin values. When the whole sample of diborane is considered each of the spin values of the boron nucleus affects some of the terminal protons, and what would be the single peak due to the magnetic resonance of the isolated proton is split into four peaks. Each *bridge* proton is bound to two boron atoms of which the nuclei have possible combined spins $3, 2, 1, 0, -1, -2, -3$, and hence the spectral line corresponding to the absorption of energy by a bridge proton is split into seven peaks. Each boron nucleus is affected by the combined spins of the two terminal protons $(1, 0, -1)$ which produce a triplet, and the triplet again splits into three triplets under the influence of the combined fields of the bridge protons. The spectrum thus predicted agrees entirely with the spectrum observed, and leaves no doubt on the structure of diborane. The parameters of the diborane molecule deduced from electron diffraction studies[†] are: distance B—B $1\cdot770\pm0\cdot013$: distance B—H (normal covalent bond) $1\cdot87\pm0\cdot03$: distance B—H (in three-centre bond) $1\cdot334\pm0\cdot027$: angle HBH (normal covalent bonds) $121\cdot5°\pm7\cdot5$: angle BHB (in three-centre bond) $100°$.

Structure of tetraborane. The molecular formula of tetraborane is B_4H_{10}. The structure of the tetraborane molecule has been deduced from X-ray diffraction studies[‡] (Fig. 17.4). The group of four boron atoms may be regarded as a fragment of a slightly distorted octahedron; atoms labelled B_{II} are at the poles, atoms labelled B_I lie in the equatorial plane. The bonds are arranged as follows:

Normal covalent bonds: two from each boron atom.

From boron atoms B_I: one to a hydrogen atom and one to the other B_I.

From boron atoms B_{II}: both to hydrogen atoms.

† K. Hedberg and V. Schomaker, *J. Amer. Chem. S.*, **73**, 1951, 1482.
‡ C. E. Nordman and W. N. Lipscomb, *J. Amer. Chem. Soc.*, **75**, 1953, 4116, and *J. Chem. Phys.*, **21**, 1953, 1856.

Three-centre bonds: four in the molecule, each of the type B_IHB_{II}. The hydrogen atoms are not symmetrically placed but are nearer to the B_I atoms. A boron atom contributes $\frac{1}{2}$ electron to a three-centre bond.

The structure described conforms to the physical evidence, and to the requirements of wave mechanics, but it does little or nothing to explain the reactions of tetraborane.

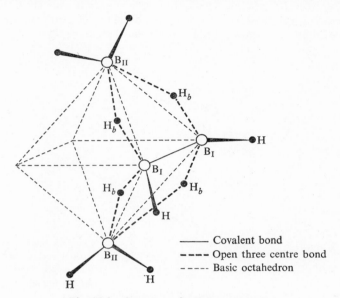

——— Covalent bond
- - - - Open three centre bond
- - - - - Basic octahedron

Fig. 17.4. Structure of tetraborane, B_4H_{10}

B_I—B_{II} = 1·85	B_I—H_b = 1·33
B_I—B_I = 1·75	B_{II}—H_b = 1·43
B—H = 1·19	Angle B_{II}—B_I—B_{II} = 98°

Structure of pentaborane. The molecular formula of pentaborane is B_5H_9. The structure of the pentaborane molecule has been investigated by Buerger precession photographs (p. 277) of single crystals at $-115°$. It was deduced† that the five boron atoms in the molecule are at the corners of a tetragonal pyramid, which may be regarded as part of a slightly distorted octahedron (Fig. 17.5). The atom labelled B_I is at a pole, atoms labelled B_{II} lie in the equatorial plane. The bonds are arranged as follows:

Normal covalent bonds: one from each boron atom to a hydrogen atom.

Three-centre bonds: four in the molecule, each of the type $B_{II}HB_{II}$. The hydrogen atoms lie below the equatorial plane, remote from B_I.

Five-centre delocalised orbital system: one in the molecule, linking B_I to the B_{II} atoms.

Four orbitals are supplied by each B_{II} atom, tetrahedrally hybridised. Four orbitals are also supplied by the B_I atom, but for covenience these are assumed to be two digonally hybridised orbitals lying at right angles to the equatorial plane, and two p orbitals in that plane. The combination of one tetrahedral orbital from each B_{II} atom together with one digonal orbital and two p atomic orbitals from the B_I atom forms a set of seven molecular orbitals of which three are bonding. B_{II} atoms contribute charge equivalent to half an electron each to a three-centre bond, and one electron

† W. J. Dulmage and W. N. Lipscomb, *Acta Cryst.*, **5**, 1952, 260–264.

each to the five-centre system. B_I contributes *two* electrons to the five-centre system. The six electrons available for the five-centre system just fill the three bonding molecular orbitals.

It is convenient to visualise the pentaborane molecule in terms of the bonds described above, but it is possible to choose other sets, or to describe the molecule in terms of resonating structures. These are alternative ways of stating that concentrations of electron density in the molecule are found just outside the apex and the corners of the base of the pyramid, just below the edges of the base, and at the centre of the pyramid.

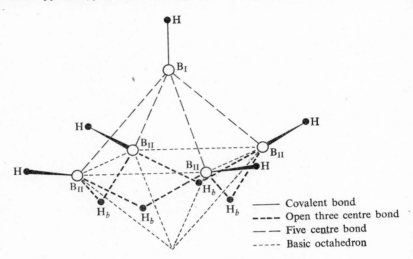

Fig. 17.5. Structure of pentaborane, B_5H_9

$B_I—B_{II} = 1.66$	Angle plane of pyramid base
$B_{II}—B_{II} = 1.77$	to plane $B_{II}—B_{II}—H_{II} = 119 \pm 5°$
$B_{II}—H_b = 1.35$	Non-bonded distances $H_b—H_b = 1.95 \pm 0.09$
$B_I—H = 1.20$	$H_{II}—H_b = 2.17 \pm 0.09$
$B_{II}—H = 1.20$	Close intermolecular distances $H_{II}—H_{II} = 2.46$ and 2.96
Altitude of pyramid $= 1.09$	$H_I—H_b = 2.59$ all
Angle $B_I—B_{II}—H_{II} = 115 \pm 5°$	$B_{II}—H_b = 3.40$ ± 0.09

Structure of unstable pentaborane. The molecular formula of the unstable pentaborane is B_5H_{11}. The most reliable method for the determination of the structure is that of X-ray diffraction†. The positions of the boron atoms have been established with certainty, and those of the hydrogen atoms with a high probability. The first boron atoms occupy relative positions which resemble those in the molecule of B_5H_9; but in the B_5H_{11} one side of the equatorial plane of the basic octahedron is opened out and the hydrogen bridge on this side is missing. There are therefore two types of boron atoms in the equatorial plane, B_{II} and B_{III}, differentiated by slightly different bonding. The bonds are arranged as follows (Fig. 17.6):

Normal covalent bonds: Each of the atoms B_{III} and the atom B_I has a bond to each of two hydrogen atoms. Each of the atoms B_{II} has a bond to one hydrogen atom.

Three-centre bonds: There are in the molecule three of the B—H—B type, one $B_{II}—H—B_{II}$ and two $B_{II}—H—B_{III}$. They lie below the equatorial plane, remote from B_I. There are in the molecule two of the B—B—B type, one is open, the other

† L. R. Lavine and W. N. Lipscomb, *J. Chem. Phys.*, **22**, 1954, 614; W. N. Lipscomb, *J. Chem. Phys.*, **22**, 1954, 985.

closed (p. 120). From the point of view of charge distribution the B—B—B bonds form a single system, but mathematically it is convenient to separate them. B_I and the B_{II} atoms contribute one electron each and the B_{III} atoms half an electron each to the B—B—B system. Six orbitals are available, two from the B_I atom, and one each from the B_{II} and B_{III} atoms. There are thus six orbitals and four electrons. If one orbital from B_I is taken with one orbital each from the B_{III} atoms to form an open three-centre bond, two of the available electrons can fill the bonding molecular orbital. If the other available orbital from B_I forms a closed three-centre bond with the two available orbitals from the B_{II} atoms, the other two electrons can fill the bonding molecular orbital of this arrangement. The available electrons thus just fill the available bonding molecular orbitals, and the formation of two three-centre bonds is consonant with the known geometry of the molecule. This method of description may therefore be conveniently adopted.

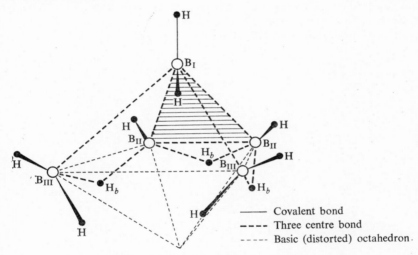

Fig. 17.6.   Structure of unstable pentaborane, B_5H_{11}

B_I—B_{II} = 1·72	Angles B_{II}—B_{III}—B_I = 57·5°
B_I—B_{III} = 1·86	B_{III}—B_{II}—B_I = 65°
B_{II}—B_{II} = 1·77	B_{III}—B_{II}—B_{II} = 112°
B—H = 1·07	B_I—B_{II}—B_{II} = 60°
B—H_b = 1·24	B_{III}—B_I—B_{II} = 57° and 108°
B_{II}—H_I = 1·67	B_{II}—B_I—B_{II} = 62°

Structure of decaborane. The molecular formula of decaborane is $B_{10}H_{14}$. The structure of the molecule has been determined by† X-ray diffraction and the positions of the boron and hydrogen atoms established with certainty. The boron atoms are arranged in two pentagonal pyramids with one edge of the bases in common; the bases of the pyramids make an angle of 76° with each other (Fig. 17.7). The structure of decaborane is therefore related to the icosahedral structure of crystalline boron rather than to the octahedral structure of the boride ion. Each pentagonal pyramid contains four types of boron atoms, distinguished by their bonding. B_I atoms are at the poles of the pyramids; two B_{II}, one B_{III}, and two B_{IV} lie in the equatorial plane of each pyramid. The bonds are arranged as follows:

Normal covalent bonds: one from each boron atom to a hydrogen atom; one in each pyramid from B_I to B_{III}.

† Kasper, Lucht, and Harker, *Acta. Crist.*, **3**, 1950, 436, and *J. Amer. Chem. Soc.*, **70**, 1948, 881.

Three-centre bonds: there are in the molecule four of the B—H—B type; all of these are of the form B_{II}—H—B_{III}. They lie below the equatorial plane remote from B_I. In all of them the arms of the bridge are unequal, the longest arm being attached to B_{III} which is sometimes described as the "outer" boron atom. There are in the molecule six three-centre bonds of the B—B—B type: these form one system of charge distribution, but it is mathematically convenient to separate them into three-centre bonds. There are two closed bonds of the form B_{IV}—B_I—B_{IV}, two, probably closed, of the form B_{II}—B_{IV}—B_{II}. There are two open bonds of the form B_{II}—B_I—B_{II}.

Atoms B_I contribute two electrons each to covalent bonds and one each to the B—B—B system. Atoms B_{II} contribute one electron each to covalent bonds, one and a half electrons each to the B—B—B system and half an electron each to a bridge bond. Atoms B_{III} contribute two electrons each to covalent bonds and one electron each to bridge bonds. Atoms B_{IV} contribute one electron each to covalent bonds and two electrons each to the B—B—B system. There are thus twelve electrons to fill exactly the bonding orbitals of the six three-centre bonds. Each boron atom contributes one orbital to each three-centre bond with which it is concerned.

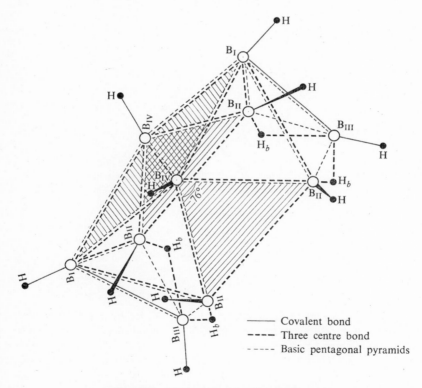

Fig. 17.7.   Structure of decaborane, $B_{10}H_{14}$

Properties of Diborane

Diborane, B_2H_6, is made by the action of a metallic hydride on a halide of boron. Sodium hydride or calcium hydride is allowed to react on boron trichloride at 200°, or the vapour of boron trifluoride, trichloride or tribromide mixed with hydrogen is passed over Al, Mg, Zn, or Ni at the same temperature. These reactions may be regarded as reductions, but it is also possible to regard them as donor-acceptor reactions in which the negative H^- ion is the donor, and the boron halide molecule is the acceptor:

$$H^- + BCl_3 = (HBCl_3)^- = HBCl_2 + Cl^-.$$

By two further replacements of Cl by H, BH_3 is formed which dimerises to B_2H_6. The use of high temperatures, however, is inconvenient, and the yield in the above reactions is low. Diborane is best made by donor-acceptor reactions carried out either in ethereal solution, or in suspension in ether. The acceptor in these reactions is the ethereate of boron trifluoride; the donor is the negative H^- ion present in lithium hydride or in lithium borohydride, sodium borohydride, or in sodium trimethoxy-borohydride. The equations for these reactions are:

(1) $6LiH + 8(C_2H_5)_2O \cdot BF_3 = B_2H_6 + 6LiBF_4 + 8(C_2H_5)_2O.$

(2) $3LiBH_4 + (C_2H_5)_2O \cdot BF_3 = 2B_2H_6 + 3LiF + (C_2H_5)_2O.$

(3) $3NaBH_4 + 4(C_2H_5)_2O \cdot BF_3 = 2B_2H_6 + 3NaBF_4 + 4(C_2H_5)_2O.$

(4) $6NaBH(OCH_3)_3 + 8(C_2H_5)_2O \cdot BF_3$
$$= B_2H_6 + 6NaBF_4 + 8(C_2H_5)_2O + 6B(OCH_3)_3.$$

All these reactions are smooth, rapid, and efficient. They may be employed for making diborane on a considerable scale; reaction (4) has been used to furnish 20 litres of diborane in one run. For small scale preparations reaction (2) is probably the most convenient because $LiBH_4$ is soluble in ether; for large-scale operations the use of finely divided LiH suspended in ether is more economic. Diborane is a very reactive gas. When heated to $300°$ it yields boron and hydrogen. Films of boron 0.25 mm thick may be deposited on glass and on certain metals by the thermal decomposition of borane at $500–600°$. When heated at lower temperatures under controlled conditions diborane yields other boron hydrides (Table 17.7). Pure diborane undergoes no change when mixed with dry air or oxygen at room temperature, but it may ignite if impure. A mixture of diborane and oxygen when heated or sparked explodes with the formation of boric oxide and water. Chlorine reacts vigorously with diborane to yield boron trichloride and hydrogen chloride. Bromine reacts slowly to give hydrogen bromide and a mixture of boron tribromide and monobromodiborane. Iodine does not react at all.

The remaining reactions of diborane can be grouped into three classes: (i) reactions in which the three-centre bonds are undisturbed, (ii) a reaction in which the three-centre bonds are replaced by normal covalencies, and (iii) reactions in which the molecule appears to dissociate into two borine radicals, BH_3, so that the product contains only one atom of boron per molecule unless the reaction is followed by polymerisation. Hydrogen atoms covalently bound to a boron atom are easily replaced by the hydroxyl group or by a halogen atom.

Reaction in which the three-centre bonds are undisturbed. Reaction with boron trimethyl. Diborane reacts at ordinary temperatures with boron trimethyl to produce a series of methyl derivatives:

$$(CH_3)H_2B \cdot BH_3, \quad (CH_3)_2HB \cdot BH(CH_3)_2, \quad (CH_3)_2HB \cdot BH_3, \quad (CH_3)_2HB \cdot BH_2(CH_3).$$

The compound $(CH_3)H_2B \cdot BH_2(CH_3)$ is not formed in this reaction, but it can be made by heating the monomethyl derivative with dimethyl ether. The reaction appears to be:

$$(CH_3)_2O + CH_3BH_2 \cdot BH_3 = (CH_3)_2O \rightarrow BH_3 + CH_3BH_2,$$
$$2CH_3BH_2 = CH_3BH_2 \cdot BH_2CH_3.$$

Not more than four hydrogen atoms in the diborane molecule can be replaced by methyl or any other alkyl group.

Reaction in which the three-centre bonds are replaced by a normal covalency. Reaction with concentrated aqueous potassium hydroxide solution. If diborane is passed into a concentrated aqueous solution of potassium hydroxide at 0° a reaction occurs, and the solution on evaporation in vacuo deposits potassium hypoborate, $K_2(BH_2OH \cdot BH_2OH)$, (p. 528):

$$\begin{array}{c} H \\ B \quad\quad B \\ H \quad\quad\quad H \\ H \end{array} + 2OH^- = \left[\begin{array}{c} OH\ OH \\ H-B-B-H \\ H\ \ H \end{array}\right]^{2-}$$

The salt, $Na_2[HB(CH_3)_2 \cdot B(CH_3)_3]$, made indirectly from tetramethyl diborane and stable up to 100°, has been reported.

Reactions which are preceded by the dissociation of diborane into two borine radicals.
Reaction with sodium or potassium amalgam. If diborane is exposed to dilute sodium or potassium amalgam in the cold, an alkali metal derivative of composition $Na_2B_2H_6$ is produced, which is white, crystalline, and stable up to 300°. The white derivative is an equimolar mixture of sodium borohydride, $NaBH_4$, and a new borohydride, NaB_3H_8. The mixture dissolves in water; the solution reduces a nickel salt to nickel boride, and hence must contain sodium hypoborate (p. 528).

Reaction with water. Diborane is readily hydrolysed by water, or by dilute alkalis, to boric acid or its salts, and hydrogen:

$$B_2H_6 + 6H_2O = 2H_3BO_3 + 6H_2.$$

Reactions with alcohols, aldehydes, and ketones to yield boron alkyl oxides. At temperatures of about $-80°$ the terminal hydrogen atoms in diborane are replaced by alkoxy groups by the action of alcohol, aldehydes, and ketones. Equations may be written:

$$\begin{array}{c} H \\ B \quad\quad B \\ H \quad\quad\quad H \\ H \end{array} + 4CH_3OH = \begin{array}{c} CH_3O \quad\quad OCH_3 \\ B \quad\quad B \\ CH_3O \quad\quad OCH_3 \\ H \end{array} \rightarrow 2BH(OCH_3)_2. \\ + 4H_2$$

$$\begin{array}{c} H \\ B \quad\quad B \\ H \quad\quad\quad H \\ H \end{array} + 4R_1R_2CO = \begin{array}{c} R_1R_2HC-O \quad\quad O-CHR_1R_2 \\ B \quad\quad B \\ R_1R_2HC-O \quad\quad O-CHR_1R_2 \\ H \end{array} = 2BH(OCHR_1R_2)_2$$

Ethylene oxide and propylene oxide react similarly.

Reactions with ammonia and the amines. The initial reaction of diborane with ammonia or an amine results in the formation of an adduct, such as $H_3B{\leftarrow}N(CH_3)_3$ (p. 493). The adducts of the three methylamines are stable with sharp melting points; the adduct of ammonia immediately disproportionates to ammonium diborineamide (p. 519):

$$H_3B{\leftarrow}\ \overline{NH_3 + H}\ NH_2{\rightarrow}BH_3 = NH_4[H_3B-NH_2-BH_3].$$

Ammonium diborineamide on treatment with excess diborane yields aminodiborane (p. 520). The adducts of mono- and di-methylamine behave similarly yielding the mono- and di-methyl derivatives of aminodiborane.

Reaction with phosphine. At ordinary temperatures diborane reacts with PH_3 to give a non-volatile white solid of approximate composition $(H_2PBH_2)_x$. It is insoluble in organic solvents, is hydrolysed with difficulty, and slowly yields hydrogen on heating

At $-110°$ diborane reacts with phosphine to yield an unstable product with the composition, $PH_3 \cdot BH_3$. The structure of the product is unlikely to be $PH_4(BH_3 \cdot PH_2 \cdot BH_3)$ because it does not liberate PH_3 when treated with ammonia at $-77°$. (Such a reaction is normally shown by phosphonium compounds.) Trimethylamine, however, liberates PH_3 at $-40°$:

$$PH_3 \cdot BH_3 + (CH_3)_3N = PH_3 + (CH_3)_3N \cdot BH_3.$$

Hence the evidence is in favour of the structure, $PH_3 \cdot BH_3$.

Certain Derivatives of Diborane

The methyl boranes. The methyl boranes are gases or volatile liquids (Table 17.8). On treatment with water every hydrogen atom directly linked to a boron atom is replaced by hydroxyl, for example:

$$(CH_3)_2BH \cdot BH(CH_3)_2 + 2H_2O = 2(CH_3)_2BOH + 2H_2.$$

Table 17.8.   *The Methyl Boranes*

	m.p. °C	b.p. °C
$H_3B \cdot BH_3$	$-165 \cdot 5$	$-92 \cdot 5$
$CH_3BH_2 \cdot BH_3$		ca. -15
$CH_3BH_2 \cdot BH_2CH_3$	$-124 \cdot 9$	$+4 \cdot 9$
$(CH_3)_2BH \cdot BH_3$	$-150 \cdot 2$	$-2 \cdot 6$
$(CH_3)_2BH \cdot BH_2CH_3$	$-122 \cdot 9$	$+45 \cdot 5$
$(CH_3)_2BH \cdot BH(CH_3)_2$	$-72 \cdot 5$	$68 \cdot 6$

The group, XBH_2, is always unstable, and methyl diboranes containing this group in the molecule readily disproportionate, thus:

$$CH_3BH_2 \cdot BH_2CH_3 = BH_3 \cdot BH(CH_3)_2.$$

On treatment with ammonia, ammonium salts such as $NH_4[(CH_3)H_2B \cdot NH_2 \cdot BH_3]$ are produced (cf. reaction of diborane with ammonia, p. 493).

Ammonium diborineamide, $NH_4(H_3B \cdot NH_2 \cdot BH_3)$, is white, water soluble, and non-volatile; m.p. 90° with the evolution of hydrogen. It burns if heated in air. It is best made by adding liquid diborane to solid ammonia at $-120°$.

It is very soluble in liquid ammonia from which it can be crystallised. The solution in ammonia is conducting, but less so than would be expected for a di-ionic salt. When ammonium diborineamide is dissolved in heavy ammonia only the H atoms attached to N are replaced by D. The solution in liquid ammonia at $-77°$ reacts with metallic sodium to liberate hydrogen; one equivalent of hydrogen is liberated for each equivalent of sodium dissolved. The equation may be written:

$$2Na + 2NH_4(BH_3 \cdot NH_2 \cdot BH_3) = 2NaBH_4 + H_2 + 2NH_3 + 2BH_2NH_2.$$

Ammonium diborineamide reacts vigorously with hydrogen chloride at $-60°$ to give $NH_4(BH_2Cl \cdot NH_2 \cdot BH_2Cl)$.

Aminodiborane.

Diborane reacts with ammonium diborineamide at 80° to yield aminodiborane. The reaction may be explained by the following equations:

$$NH_4(BH_3 \cdot NH_2 \cdot BH_3) \rightleftharpoons 2H_3N \rightarrow BH_3 \rightleftharpoons 2H_2N \overset{\pi}{-} BH_2 + 2H_2,$$

$$BH_3 + H_2N \overset{\pi}{-} BH_2 = BH_2(NH_2,H)BH_2.$$

Aminodiborane is a liquid, m.p. $-66°$, b.p. $76 \cdot 2°$. It is fairly stable, and can be left for some days at room temperature, but it ultimately decomposes into diborane and a solid substance $(H_2B \cdot NH_2)_x$. When in solution in liquid ammonia it reacts with sodium to yield a compound $Na(B_2N_2H_9)$. The reaction may take place in two stages:

$$H_2B(NH_2,H)BH_2 + 2NH_3 = NH_4(BH_3 \cdot NH_2 \cdot BH_2NH_2),$$

which is analogous to the action of liquid ammonia on diborane, followed by:

$$2Na + 2NH_4(BH_3 \cdot NH_2 \cdot BH_2NH_2) = 2Na(BH_3 \cdot NH_2 \cdot BH_2NH_2) + H_2 + 2NH_3.$$

When heated to about 200° aminodiborane yields borazole (p. 506). The vapour density of aminodiborane shows that it is monomeric in the vapour. Hedberg and Stosick carried out electron diffraction experiments in 1952 on aminodiborane and its dimethyl derivative, and concluded that both these compounds have bridge structures in which the nitrogen atom takes part in three-centre bond formation.[†]

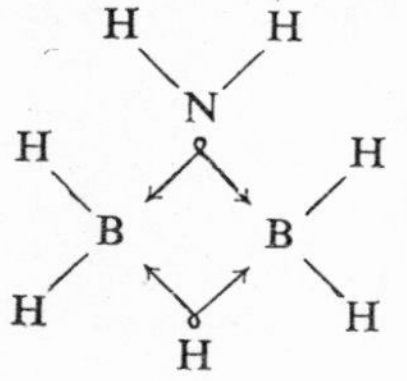

aminodiborane, m.p. $-66°$,
b.p. $76 \cdot 2°$

Distance B—B $1 \cdot 93$:
distance N—B $1 \cdot 56$:
distance B—H $1 \cdot 15$:
angle BNB $76°$.

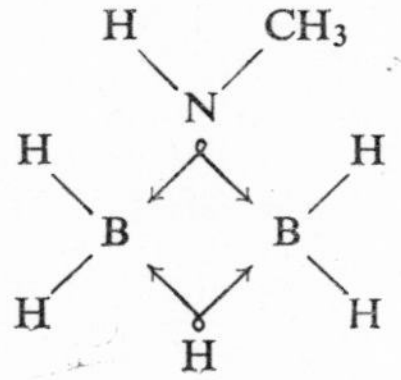

monomethylaminodiborane
m.p. $-33°$, b.p. $66 \cdot 8°$

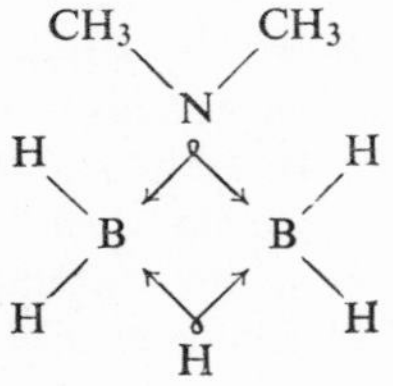

dimethylaminodiborane
m.p. $-54 \cdot 4°$, b.p. $50 \cdot 3°$

Distance B—B $1 \cdot 92$:
distance N—B $1 \cdot 55$:
distance N—C $1 \cdot 48$:
angle BNB $76 \cdot 4°$.

† The disilylamine derivative is also known:

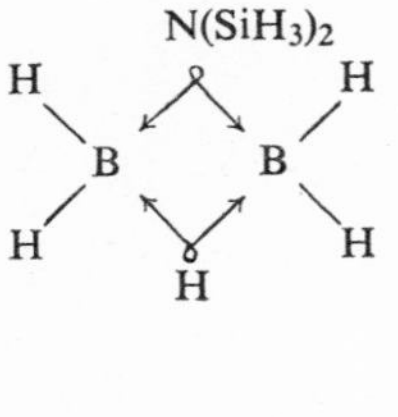

Diborane trimethylamine complex, $(CH_3)_3N{\to}BH_3$. Diborane reacts with trimethyl-amine rapidly and completely to give the co-ordination complex $(CH_3)_3N \cdot BH_3$, m.p. 94°, b.p. (extr.) 171°. The complex is monomeric in the vapour. Electron diffraction experiments have shown the grouping round the nitrogen atom to be tetrahedral. The distance B—N is 1·62. The crystal structure has been determined.

Diborane hydrazine complex. Diborane reacts with hydrazine at 0° to yield a white hygroscopic non-volatile solid with the composition, $BN_{1.2}H_{4.8}$. It is insoluble in organic solvents and in liquid ammonia. It does not form borazole on heating to 180°. Hydrolysis gives hydrazine but not ammonia, and hence the compound has been formed without breaking the N—N bond in the hydrazine molecule.

Borine carbonyl, $OC{\to}BH_3$. Diborane reacts with carbon monoxide to give borine carbonyl, a gas, m.p. −137°, b.p. −64°. The action is reversible and proceeds rapidly at 100°; the conditions chosen for preparation are 20° and 20 atm.

Trimethylamine expels carbon monoxide from the molecule to give $H_3B{\leftarrow}N(CH_3)_3$. Ammonia gives $OC{\to}BH_3 \cdot 2NH_3$, a white solid. This compound dissolves in liquid ammonia to form a conducting solution which reacts with sodium thus:

$$OC{\to}BH_3 \cdot 2NH_3 + 2Na = Na_2(OCBH) + 2NH_3 + H_2.$$

Hence the ammonium compound appears to be a salt, $(NH_4)_2[O{\overset{2\pi}{=}}C\!-\!B\!-\!H]$. If this be the correct structure of the anion, the boron atom is digonally hybridised. There is no other boron compound with this orbital structure (Table 17.1).

The structure of borine carbonyl has been determined by microwave methods. The dimensions of the non-planar molecule are:

$$
\begin{array}{c}
\mathrm{H} \\
\overset{1 \cdot 194\ |\ 1\cdot 54}{\mathrm{H}\!-\!\mathrm{B}\!-\!\mathrm{C}\!-\!\mathrm{O}} \qquad \alpha = 113°\,52' \\
\underset{\mathrm{H}}{\diagdown\ \alpha\,|}
\end{array}
$$

The Properties of the Higher Hydrides of Boron

Tetraborane, B_4H_{10}, can be made by the following three methods:

(1) Finely divided magnesium boride is heated with 8N phosphoric acid; the yield is only 0·1%. Other borides may be used, and beryllium boride is recommended if the contamination of the tetraborane with silicanes is to be avoided. A useful modification of the method is the treatment of magnesium boride with ammonium bromide in liquid ammonia solution.

(2) Monoiododiborane is agitated with dilute sodium amalgam:

$$B_2H_5I + 2Na + IB_2H_5 = B_4H_{10} + 2NaI.$$

The volatile boron hydrides are distilled off. Tetraborane can be freed from diborane by treatment with water, which hydrolyses diborane rapidly and tetraborane only slowly.

(3) B_5H_{11} is treated with hydrogen at 100°; the principal product is B_4H_{10}.

Tetraborane is a volatile liquid which decomposes slowly in the cold and more rapidly if gently heated, giving chiefly B_2H_6 (Table 17.7). A mixture of tetraborane vapour and oxygen explodes when sparked. Tetraborane reacts with water to form boric acid, but so much less quickly than does diborane that water may be used to free it from diborane. With concentrated KOH tetraborane reacts like diborane, yielding a solution which contains a hypoborate. Hydrogen chloride reacts with tetraborane to yield diborane and boron trichloride. Tetraborane combines with ammonia at −70° to

17*

yield a tetra-ammoniate, $B_4H_{10} \cdot 4NH_3$, which, by analogy with diborane di-ammoniate, would have the structure:

$$(NH_4)_2(BH_3 \cdot NH_2 \cdot BH_2 \cdot BH_2 \cdot NH_2 \cdot BH_3).$$

At 200° this compound is converted to borazole (p. 506). Tetraborane reacts with sodium amalgam to yield the compound $Na_2B_4H_{10}$, which on heating loses hydrogen, and at 450° gives the stable compound $Na_2B_4H_6$. It is possible, however, that one or other of these two hydrogen compounds is the borohydride, $NaBH_4$. (Compare the corresponding diborane compound, p. 518.)

Pentaborane, B_5H_9, is made by heating either B_4H_{10} or B_2H_6 at about 200°. If diborane is passed through a reactor at 225° with 15 sec residence time, 66% conversion occurs and the product consists of 35% of the pentaborane and 65% of solid hydrides. Pentaborane is also produced by heating diborane to 250–300° in the presence of mercury vapour, or to 120–130° for 48 hours in the presence of hydrogen chloride.

Pentaborane is a liquid, m.p. $-46 \cdot 9°$, b.p. 48°. It is one of the stablest of the boron hydrides.

On standing pentaborane changes very slowly into hydrogen and a solid hydride. If passed through a tube heated to 300°, 50% comes through unchanged; the remainder is decomposed to boron and hydrogen. Pentaborane has no action with hydrogen chloride, even in the presence of aluminium chloride. It is hydrolysed by water only very slowly; it is not completely hydrolysed in three days at 90°. It dissolves in 30% sodium hydroxide solution. The ultimate product is sodium hypoborate. With ammonia, pentaborane yields the tetra-ammoniate, $B_5H_9,4NH_3$. With hydrogen chloride at room temperature the tetra-ammoniate yields $B_5H_5Cl_4,4NH_3$ and ultimately $B_5H_2Cl_7,4NH_3$.

Unstable pentaborane, B_5H_{11}, is made by passing B_2H_6 at 150–450 mm pressure at 180° through a heated tube. The yield is 75%. B_5H_{11} is known as the "unstable pentaborane" because it decomposes in a few hours in the cold, mainly to H_2, $B_{10}H_{14}$, and a solid hydride. If heated with excess of hydrogen it is quantitatively converted to B_2H_6 and B_4H_{10}. B_5H_{11} reacts with ammonia with the evolution of hydrogen, to give the same product as that prepared from B_5H_9.

Hexaborane, B_6H_{10}, is made by the fractionation of the gases given off by the action of phosphoric acid on magnesium boride; 1 kg of the boride gives 150 c.c. of the hydride in the gaseous state.

Hexaborane decomposes slowly at ordinary temperatures, but if passed through a tube at 300° most of it comes through unchanged; hydrolysis by water is slow. Hexaborane dissolves in 30% NaOH solution without the evolution of hydrogen, but H_2 comes off at once quantitatively if the solution is acidified.

Decaborane, $B_{10}H_{14}$, is made by heating diborane at 115–120° for 48 hours. Decaborane has a peculiar and unpleasant smell. It is very stable and it can be kept in air or oxygen at 50–60° for several days without perceptible change; it decomposes slowly at 200–250°. Decaborane is insoluble in water, but water hydrolyses it very slowly in the cold and more rapidly at 100°. Decaborane is soluble in alcohol, ether, benzene, and carbon disulphide. In alcohol or dioxan solution decaborane forms a monobasic acid without the evolution of hydrogen; the solution can be titrated potentiometrically against aqueous sodium hydroxide solution.

Chlorine, bromine, and iodine react slowly with decaborane in the cold, and probably yield $B_{10}H_{12}Hal_2$. Hydrogen chloride has no action, even at 100° in the presence of aluminium chloride. With ammonia at $-75°$ decaborane forms the solid compound, $B_{10}H_{14},6NH_3$, which completely dissociates at room temperature. The solution in liquid ammonia conducts electricity. Hydrogen is evolved if decaborane is heated with ammonia to 120°.

The Borohydrides

The borohydrides contain the group BH_4 attached to a metallic atom or a basic radical. The metals which form borohydrides are:

Li, Na, K, Rb, Cs, Be, Mg, Zn, Ca, Al, Ti, Zr, Hf, Th, U.

The borohydrides,

$(CH_3)_4NBH_4$, $(C_2H_5)_4NBH_4$, $(C_6H_5CH_2)_4NBH_4$, and $(CH_3)_2GaBH_4$,

have also been prepared and examined.

The alkali metal borohydrides and thorium borohydride are crystalline substances, stable in air. The decomposition temperatures in vacuo are:

K	Na	Li	Th
500°	400°	275°	204°

The borohydrides of beryllium, aluminium, hafnium, and zirconium inflame in air and are volatile. $U(BH_4)_4$ and $U(BCH_3 \cdot H_3)_4$ are among the most volatile compounds of U^{IV}. The volatile borohydrides are thermally unstable. Both classes of borohydrides react with water, giving hydrogen, boric acid, and the metallic hydroxide, and with hydrogen chloride at $-80°$ to give hydrogen, diborane, and the metallic chloride.

Trimethylamine has no action on the non-volatile borohydrides, but it forms addition compounds with the volatile borohydrides. The physical properties of the two types of borohydrides suggest that the non-volatile borohydrides are ionic, and that the volatile borohydrides are covalent. A few examples are:

Ionic	Covalent
$LiBH_4$	$Be(BH_4)_2$
$NaBH_4$	$Al(BH_4)_3$
KBH_4	$Ti(BH_4)_3$
$Th(BH_4)_4$	$U(BH_4)_4$

The borohydrides of nitrogen bases must be ionic. The ion BH_4^- is not electron deficient, and therefore the borohydrides of lithium and sodium are classed as non-chelate anions containing boron, and they are described on p. 525. The electron deficient covalent borohydrides are described in the following paragraphs.

Beryllium borohydride, $Be(BH_4)_2$, is a solid which sublimes at 91·3°. m.p. 123° under pressure. The vapour pressure at 0° is 0·5 mm. Beryllium borohydride is made by the method mentioned on p. 527, or by the action of beryllium hydride, or of beryllium dimethyl, on diborane:

$$4B_2H_6 + 3Be(CH_3)_2 = 3Be(BH_4)_2 + 2B(CH_3)_3.$$

Beryllium borohydride is spontaneously inflammable in air. It reacts violently with water to form the oxides of boron and beryllium, and molecular hydrogen. Beryllium borohydride with trimethylamine forms a stable addition compound, $(CH_3)_3N \rightarrow Be(BH_4)_2$. This compound has m.p. $+35°$, and b.p. (extr.) 260°. It is spontaneously inflammable in air. Its vapour density up to 140° is normal.

Beryllium borohydride is a covalent compound. The beryllium atom and the two boron atoms are in the tetrahedral valence state. The molecule contains four three-centre bonds which constitute four hydrogen bridges. The bridges are in two pairs in planes at right angles to one another. Each pair links the beryllium atom to one of the boron atoms:

The presence of the bridge structure in beryllium borohydride is indicated by the infrared and Raman spectra. The bond lengths show that the hydrogen atoms in the bridges are not equidistant from the beryllium and the boron atoms. The distance B—H is 1·28, Be—H is 1·63, and B—Be is 1·74. The addition compound $(CH_3)_3N{\rightarrow}Be(BH_4)_2$, however, cannot be formulated in terms of such a structure.

Aluminium borohydride, $Al(BH_4)_3$, is a liquid, m.p. $-64.5°$, b.p. $44.5°$. The vapour pressure at $0°$ is 119 mm. It is made from $Li(BH_4)$ by the reaction mentioned above, and also by the action of aluminium trimethyl on diborane:

$$2B_2H_6 + Al(CH_3)_3 = Al(BH_4)_3 + B(CH_3)_3.$$

The use of aluminium borohydride for preparing borohydrides of certain heavy metals is exemplified by reactions mentioned on p. 527. Aluminium borohydride forms addition compounds with trimethylamine and with ether. The trimethylamine complex has m.p. 79°, and can be sublimed in vacuo, but the ether complex decomposes at 50°.

The structure of the aluminium borohydride molecule is similar to that of beryllium borohydride, and there are three pairs of hydrogen bridges. The distance B—H is 1·28, Al—H is 2·1, and Al—B is 2·15.

A condensed form of aluminium borohydride has also been reported with the structure

NON-CHELATE COMPLEXES

Non-chelate Neutral Complexes

Many of the neutral complexes of boron are adducts formed by the union of a donor molecule, such as $(CH_3)_3N$, with a compound such as BF_3 which contains a boron atom in the trigonal valence state. $(CH_3)_3N{\rightarrow}BH_3$ and $OC{\rightarrow}BH_3$ are described among the derivatives of diborane on p. 521. The properties of certain other complexes of this kind are discussed generally on p. 504. Other interesting compounds containing four-covalent boron are the adducts of borazole formed by the direct addition of HCl, HBr, CH_3I, H_2O, CH_3OH, and Br_2 to borazole (p. 507). The structures of these adducts probably consist of six-membered rings, each containing three boron atoms and three nitrogen atoms arranged alternately; all the boron and the nitrogen atoms are in the tetravalent state. It is conjectured that the ring has the form of the chair structure of cyclohexane. All these compounds are readily decomposed by a slight rise of temperature to yield a substitution derivative of borazole.

Somewhat similar six-membered ring compounds may be prepared in which the nitrogen atoms are replaced by atoms of phosphorus or arsenic. Dimethylphosphine borine, $(CH_3)_2PH,BH_3$, if heated to 150°, yields polymers of PP-dimethylphosphino-borine, $[(CH_3)_2P \cdot BH_2]_n$. The corresponding arsenic compound behaves similarly. The trimers (and the tetramers also) are marked by extreme chemical inactivity. Their mode of formation shows that they are thermally stable. They are hydrolysed only very slowly indeed by concentrated hydrochloric acid at 300°. X-ray diffraction experiments have shown the PP-dimethylphosphinoborine trimer has a ring structure like the chair structure of cyclohexane. The inertness of the phosphorus and arsenic compounds compared with the activity of the nitrogen compounds may be due to resonance in the molecule of the phosphorus derivative. Burg and Wagner have suggested that non-localised orbitals may be formed using the d orbitals of the phosphorus atoms.

The completely methylated compound $[P(CH_3)_2B(CH_3)_2]$, m.p. 334° has been prepared; it is as stable as the compound $[P(CH_3)_2BH_2]$.

Non-chelate Complex Anions

The principal anions containing the boron atom in the tetrahedral valence state are BH_4^-, BF_4^-, BF_3OH^-, $BF_2(OH)_2^-$, and $BH(OCH_3)_3^-$. The borohydrides, MBH_4 (p. 523), are either covalent compounds containing hydrogen bridges, or ionic compounds such as $Na^+BH_4^-$. The covalent $Be(BH_4)_2$ and $Al(BH_4)_3$ are described on p. 523; the ionic compounds are described below.

Lithium borohydride, $LiBH_4$, is a white solid which melts at 275° with the evolution of hydrogen. Its vapour pressure at 0° is less than 10^{-4} mm. It is made:

 (i) by the action of sodium borohydride on lithium chloride, already mentioned,
 (ii) by the action of diborane on lithium ethyl, lithium ethoxide, or on lithium hydride suspended in ether:

$$2B_2H_6 + 3LiC_2H_5 = 3LiBH_4 + B(C_2H_5)_3,$$
$$2B_2H_6 + 3LiC_2H_5O = 3LiBH_4 + B(OC_2H_5)_3,$$
$$B_2H_6 + 2LiH = 2LiBH_4,$$

(iii) by the action of aluminium borohydride on lithium ethyl in benzene:

$$Al(BH_4)_3 + 3LiC_2H_5 = 3LiBH_4 \downarrow + Al(C_2H_5)_3.$$

Lithium borohydride is stable towards air, and towards trimethylamine. It dissolves in water at 0° without evolution of hydrogen; at 20° $LiBH_3(OH)$ is formed, and at 100° $LiBH_2(OH)_2$. It reacts with methyl alcohol down to $-100°$:

$$LiBH_4 + 4CH_3OH = LiOCH_3 + B(OCH_3)_3 + 4H_2,$$

and with hydrogen chloride down to $-80°$:

$$2LiBH_4 + 2HCl = 2LiCl + B_2H_6 + 2H_2.$$

With iodine at 120° it yields (in 66% yield) BI_3. It forms a very well-defined etherate at 0°, which decomposes at 70–100°. The reactions of lithium borohydride are those of a powerful reducing agent.

The crystal of $LiBH_4$ has an orthorhombic lattice. Each Li^+ ion is associated with four tetrahedral BH_4^- ions; two of the Li^+ ions are separated from B by 2·56 and two by

2·47. The overall structure is that of strings of borohydride tetrahedra stacked edge to edge in the crystal. $LiBH_4$ does not appear to be isomorphous with $LiAlH_4$, $LiClO_4$, $LiBF_4$, $MgSO_4$, or $BeSO_4$.

Sodium borohydride, $NaBH_4$, a white salt-like substance, is made either (a) by a reaction involving an electron transfer from a H^- ion to a (OCH_3) group by a sequence of changes, thus:

$$H^- + B(OCH_3)_3 = HB(OCH_3)_3{}^- = HB(OCH_3)_2 + OCH_3{}^-,$$
$$H^- + HB(OCH_3)_2 = H_2B(OCH_3)_2{}^- = H_2B(OCH_3) + OCH_3{}^-,$$

and so on, or, (b) by the action of a $(OCH_3{}^-)$ ion on the borine radical, for example:

$$3(OCH_3{}^-) + 4BH_3 = 3BH_4{}^- + B(OCH_3)_3.$$

Reactions based on process (a) are:

$$4NaH + B(OCH_3)_3 = NaBH_4 + 3NaOCH_3,$$
$$4NaH + NaB(OCH_3)_4 = NaBH_4 + 4NaOCH_3,$$
$$3NaH + NaBH(OCH_3)_3 = NaBH_4 + 3NaOCH_3.$$

The reaction of sodium hydride on trimethyl borate is carried out by adding methyl borate to a well-stirred mass of sodium hydride powder at 250°. The cooled product is treated with liquid ammonia or isopropylamine, either of which dissolves sodium borohydride, but not sodium methoxide. Reactions exemplifying process (b) are:†

$$NaBH(OCH_3)_3 + BH_3 = NaBH_4 + B(OCH_3)_3,$$
$$3NaB(OCH_3)_4 + 4BH_3 = 3NaBH_4 + 4B(OCH_3)_3,$$
$$3NaOCH_3 + 4BH_3 = 3NaBH_4 + B(OCH_3)_3.‡$$

The first reaction proceeds so rapidly that it may be used to remove diborane from a stream of gas passing over solid sodium trimethoxyborohydride; the second § and third reactions also take place very rapidly, and quantitatively.

Sodium borohydride is stable up to 400° in vacuo, and up to 300° in air. It is soluble in isopropylamine and in liquid ammonia; it crystallises from liquid ammonia as the diammoniate. Sodium borohydride is insoluble in ether or dioxane. It is slowly decomposed by cold water, but it is rapidly hydrolysed by hot water. It is attacked by acids. Some of the principal reactions of sodium borohydride are given by the equations:

$$3NaBH_4 + 6H_2O = 12H_2 + Na_3[B_3O_6],\|$$
$$2NaBH_4 + 2HCl = 2NaCl + B_2H_6 + 2H_2,$$
$$NaBH_4 + 4CH_3OH = NaB(OCH_3)_4 + 4H_2; \text{ this reaction proceeds}$$

even at $-40°$:

$$3NaBH_4 + 4BF_3 \cdot O(C_2H_5)_2 = 3NaBF_4 + 2B_2H_6 + 4(C_2H_5)_2O.$$

Sodium borohydride reacts with iodine at 200° giving BI_3.

Sodium borohydride is useful as a reducing agent in weakly alkaline solution, as it can be subsequently destroyed by the addition of acid. It is less powerful, and therefore more selective, than $LiBH_4$ or $LiAlH_4$. It reduces aldehydes and ketones to alcohols, but it is without action on acids, esters, nitriles, anhydrides, or nitro compounds. It reduces Fe^{III} to Fe^{II}, V^V to V^{IV}, Tl^{III} to Tl^I, and Ag^I to metal.

---

† Sodium hydride does not react with diborane, either alone or in the presence of ether.
‡ $KOCH_3$ does not react.
§ The corresponding reaction with $LiB(OCH_3)_4$ is very sluggish.
‖ This reaction is a better means of obtaining hydrogen than the action of water on lithium hydride. $CoCl_2$ is used as a catalyst.

X-ray analysis shows that sodium borohydride possesses a sodium chloride lattice in which the group BH_4 plays the part of a chlorine ion. The distance Na—B is 3·07, B—B is 4·35.

The preparation of metallic borohydrides starting from sodium borohydride. $NaBH_4$ is a commercial product, and other borohydrides are made from it, directly or indirectly. In general, when the halide of one metal and the borohydride of another are brought into contact an exchange of radicals occurs if the conditions ensure that one of the products is removed from the sphere of action. $LiBH_4$ is made by treating LiCl with $NaBH_4$ in isopropylamine solution, when the NaCl is precipitated:

$$NaBH_4 + LiCl = LiBH_4 + NaCl \downarrow.$$

$BeBr_2$ and $AlCl_3$ react with $LiBH_4$ to produce the volatile $Be(BH_4)_2$ and $Al(BH_4)_3$. UF_4 and ThF_4 react with $Al(BH_4)_3$ at room temperature:

$$UF_4 + 2Al(BH_4)_3 = U(BH_4)_4 + 2Al(BH_4)F_2.$$

$NaHfF_5$ and $NaZrF_5$ also react with $Al(BH_4)_3$ to yield $Hf(BH_4)_4$ and $Zr(BH_4)_4$:

$$NaHfF_5 + 2Al(BH_4)_3 = Hf(BH_4)_4 + 2Al(BH_4)F_2 + NaF.$$

KBH_4 is made by the reaction in methanol:

$$KOCH_3 + NaBH_4 = KBH_4 + NaOCH_3.$$

Fluoroboric acid, HBF_4, is known only in solution. It is formed when boron trifluoride dissolves in water. A solution containing 30% of HBF_4 is made by adding boric acid in slight excess to a 40% aqueous solution of HF:

$$H_3BO_3 + 4F^- + 3H^+ = BF_4^- + 3H_2O.$$

If the resulting solution is distilled the distillate has the composition, $BF_3 \cdot 2H_2O$. Fluoroboric acid is a strong acid, but the ion BF_4 is slowly hydrolysed by water; a freshly prepared solution of $Ca(BF_4)_2$ is clear, but it becomes turbid owing to the separation of CaF_2. The aqueous solution of fluoroboric acid attacks glass when hot but not when cold.

Potassium fluoroborate is precipitated as an amorphous white compound on the addition of a potassium salt to a solution of the acid. The fluoroborates of the alkali metals, and of Tl^+ and NH_4^+ have essentially the same crystal structure as $BaSO_4$. The BF_4^- ion is tetrahedral, and it shows a remarkable resemblance to the ClO_4^- ion. The distance B—F is 1·53; the distance Cl—O is 1·63. The alkali metal salts of both ions are isodimorphous, being rhombic at low temperatures and cubic at higher temperatures. The uni- and bi-valent metal salts are very soluble in water; the hexammines of Ni^{2+}, Mn^{2+}, Cd^{2+}, and Co^{2+} are very much less soluble. The $(CH_3)_4N$, $(C_2H_5)_4N$, pyridinium, strychnine, and diazonium salts are highly insoluble. Both ions with nitric oxide form compounds, $NOBF_4$ and $NOClO_4$. Diazonium fluoroborate, however, decomposes quietly when heated, whereas diazonium perchlorate explodes violently. In the crystals of the potassium salts both the ions BF_4^- and ClO_4^- are rotating.

HBF_3OH. This acid is known only as the so-called monohydrate, $(H_3O)(BF_3OH)$, which is prepared by distilling the solution obtained by adding boric oxide to 40% aqueous hydrofluoric acid, or by adding one molecular proportion of boron trifluoride to two molecular proportions of water. The monohydrate has a sharp m.p. of 6°. The b.p. is 59°/1·2 mm. It forms an addition compound with dioxane, $(H_3O)(BF_3OH) \cdot C_4H_8O_2$, m.p. 128–130°. It forms the compound $2BF_3 \cdot H_2O$ which decomposes on distillation.

X-ray analysis shows that the monohydrate is isomorphous with $NH_4(ClO_4)$, and hence with $(H_3O)(ClO_4)$. The structure, therefore, must be $(H_3O)(BF_3OH)$. As determined by nuclear magnetic resonance the quickly cooled monohydrate has this ionic structure, but the slowly crystallised compound is $BF_3,2H_2O$.

$HBF_2(OH)_2$. This acid can be isolated as a syrupy liquid, b.p. 160° which sets to a glass at $-20°$. It is stable in dry air. It is a strong acid.

$HBF_2(OH)_2$ is insoluble in CCl_4, CS_2, C_6H_6, but it dissolves in the co-ordination compounds of BF_3 with ethers, esters or alcohols. In solution in $BF_3 \cdot OEt_2$ it is so strong an acid that it expels HCl from sodium chloride.

It reacts with alcohols, ethers, esters, organic acids, aldehydes, and ketones, to give boric acid and a co-ordination compound of BF_3:

$$2C_2H_5OC_2H_5 + 3HBF_2(OH)_2 = 2(C_2H_5)_2O \cdot BF_3 + B(OH)_3 + 3H_2O.$$

It has catalytic powers similar to, but weaker than, those of BF_3. Neither the acids $HBF(OH)_3$ and $HB(OH)_4$ nor their salts are known.

Anions containing more than one boron atom are known. One anion of this type is present in ammonium diborineamide, described on p. 519. Another is present in the potassium salt of hypoboric acid described below.

Hypoboric acid. The acid itself has not been obtained; only the potassium salt $K_2[H_2OHB \cdot BH_2OH]$ is known. This is made by treating diborane or tetraborane with concentrated KOH solution at 0°, and evaporating off the water in vacuo. The salt is stable to heat. It begins to lose water at 100° and at 400–500° hydrogen is liberated and potassium distils in vacuo. It is unaffected by dry air, but is hygroscopic. In water it gives an alkaline solution from which hydrogen is slowly evolved; the evolution of hydrogen becomes rapid on the addition of acid. The negative charge on the hypoborate ion is so loosely held that the ion has the reducing properties associated with an alkali metal. It is a much stronger reducing agent than the sub-borate ion (p. 503), as is shown by a comparison of its action, in aqueous solution, on salts of certain other metals.

Table 17.9.   *Comparison of the Reducing Properties of Hypoboric and Sub-boric Acids*

Salt to be reduced	Product using potassium hypoborate	Product using potassium sub-borate
Silver salts	Metallic silver	Metallic silver
Mercuric chloride	Metallic mercury	Mercurous chloride
Cupric sulphate	Copper hydride	Metallic copper
Nickel sulphate	Black ppt of Ni_2B	No reaction
Arsenic salts	Arsenic	
Bismuth salts	Metallic bismuth	

CHELATE COMPLEXES

Chelate Neutral Complexes

The reaction of boron trifluoride with acetylacetone to yield a semi-chelate complex has already been mentioned on p. 501. Other derivatives of similar structure are made from benzoylacetone, m.p. 155°, and from dibenzoyl methane, m.p. 191°. All these compounds are soluble in benzene to give solutions in which they are monomeric.

Boron triacetate reacts with 1-hydroxy anthraquinone to give compound I:

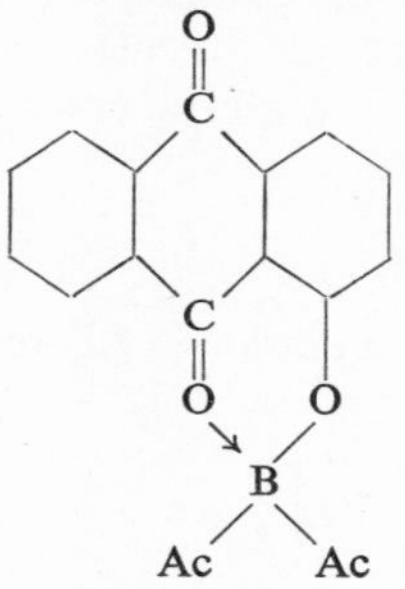

I

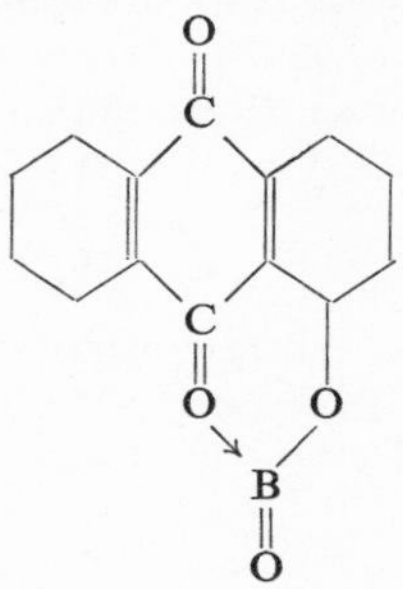

II

Compound I on warming in vacuo gives compound II in which the environment of the boron atom is similar to that in the metaborate ion (p. 499).

Chelate Complex Anions

Boric acid in aqueous solution in the presence of glycerol or mannitol behaves as a strong acid. This may be due to the formation of a chelate anion (p. 500):

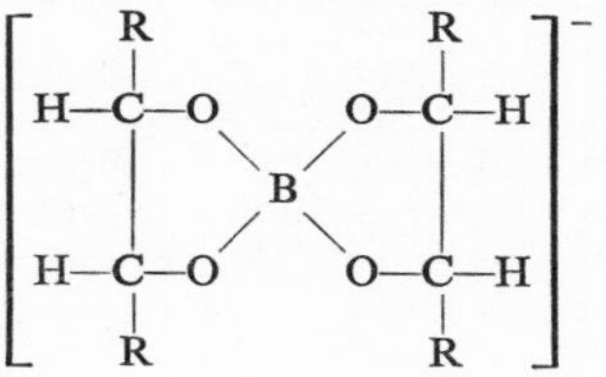

Many examples of this type of chelate anion are known. It has been shown, however, that such an anion is produced only when the molecular structure of the polyhydric alcohol or sugar is such that similarly orientated hydroxyl groups are present on adjacent carbon atoms. Glycerol and mannitol react with boric acid, but glycol does not, and hence it has been deduced that the two hydroxyl groups in glycol are in the *trans* position:

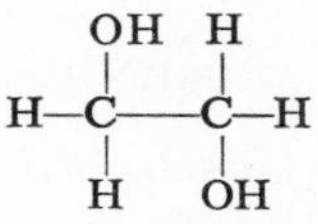

Catechol and salicylic acid form compounds with similar structures. The free acid of the catechol derivative:

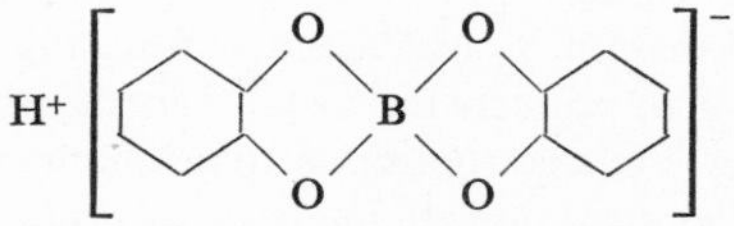

has been made by heating the aniline or pyridine salt to 100° in vacuo, and subliming the residue at 180–200° under 1–2 mm pressure. The tetrahedral arrangement of the boron bonds in the salicylic acid derivative has been established by resolution of the brucine and strychnine salts. The boron atom in anions of this class may be one atom of a five-membered or six-membered ring.

Borotungstic acid, $H_5[BW_{12}O_{40}]$, 24 and $30H_2O$. Borotungstic acid is an example of a 12 heteropoly acid. Its structure is similar to that of phosphomolybdic acid which is described on p. 999. The boron atom is in a tetrahedral hole of oxygen atoms, and the borotungstate ion is therefore a complicated example of a chelate anion.

Chelate Complex Cations

Acetylacetone and benzoylacetone react with boron trichloride in ethereal solution to yield salts of the type:

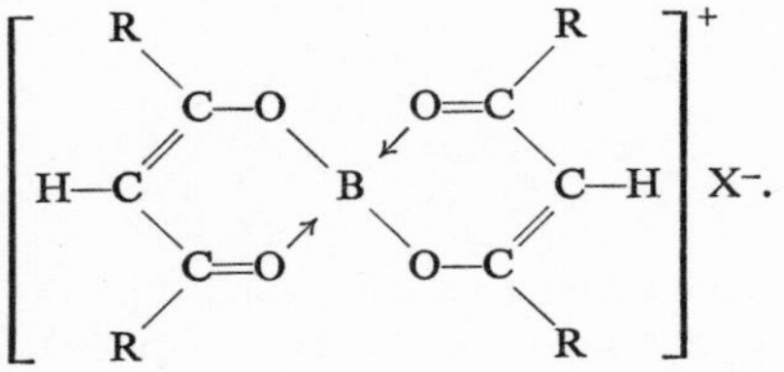

The iodide of the benzoylacetone derivative, m.p. 210°, is the only stable simple salt; in all other cases X^- represents a complex anion such as $[FeCl_4^-]$. The melting points of certain salts in which the cations are chelate boron derivatives, and the anions are complex anions containing an atom of a heavy metal, are given below:

	m.p. of salt °C	
Anion	Acetylacetone boron cation	Benzoylacetone boron cation
$FeCl_4^-$	137	
$AuCl_4^-$	135	
$ZnCl_3^-$		208
$SnCl_6^{2-}$	210	
$PtCl_6^{2-}$	180	

The salts dissolve readily in chloroform and are precipitated by ether. They are decomposed by water.

ALUMINIUM

PROPERTIES OF THE METAL

Aluminium is a silver-grey metal. Its electrical conductivity is about one-third that of silver. It is sufficiently malleable and ductile to be rolled into leaf or drawn into wire.

Pure aluminium reacts initially with boiling distilled water, but the reaction is almost arrested by the formation of a coherent self-healing film of α-OAlOH on the surface of the metal. This film protects the metal from attack by dilute acids, by solutions of metals which are less electropositive than aluminium, and by atmospheric oxygen. Amalgamation of aluminium with mercury, or contact with solutions of certain salts such as sodium chloride, destroys the coherence of the film, and reaction then occurs with all the above reagents. Oxidation by moist air in the presence of sodium chloride solution is inhibited if the aluminium contains a small quantity of copper, iron, or silicon. In spite of the presence of the oxide film, aluminium is attacked by oxygen or by air at 800°; with air the nitride as well as the oxide is formed.

Aluminium absorbs hydrogen at high temperatures. 100 gm of aluminium absorb the following volumes of hydrogen reduced to N.T.P.:

Temperature	700°	800°	900°	1000°
Vol. in c.c.	0·23	0·89	1·87	3·86

The reactions of metallic aluminium in the manufactured condition, i.e. covered with protective film of oxide, are set out in Table 17.10:

Table 17.10. *Reactions of Aluminium*

Reagent	Conditions of reaction	Product
Air	Room temperature	No action
Air	Room temperature in presence of sodium chloride solution	$Al(OH)_3$
Air	800°	$Al_2O_3 + AlN$
Oxygen	800°	Al_2O_3
C	Heated above 1000°	Al_4C_3
N	Heated	AlN
P	Heated	AlP
S	Heated	Al_2S_3
As	Strongly heated	AlAs
F		AlF_3
Cl		$AlCl_3$
C_2H_2	At 500°	$Al_2(C_2)_3$
H_2S	Room temperature	No action
Fe_2O_3	Ignited by a fuse of magnesium	$Al_2O_3 + Fe$†
Water		No action
HCl gas		$AlCl_3$
Hydrochloric acid	Warm, nearly conc.	$AlCl_3 + H_2$
Nitric acid	Any conditions	Almost no action
Sulphuric acid	Dilute	No action
Sulphuric acid	Hot, concentrated	$2Al + 6H_2SO_4$ $= Al_2(SO_4)_3 + 3SO_2 + 6H_2O$
NaOH or KOH in solution	Room temperature	$2Al + 2NaOH + 2H_2O$ $= 2NaAlO_2 + 3H_2$‡
Ethyl iodide		$EtAlI_2$ and Et_2AlI
Anhydrous alcohol	(Trace of water stops the reaction)	$(EtO)_3Al$ $(MeO)_3Al$

† MnO_2 and Cr_2O_3 react similarly. $Fe_2O_3 + 2Al = Al_2O_3 + 2Fe$; $\Delta H = -199$ kcal. Temperature attained is about 2500°.
‡ Maximum rate of solution is at $5·5N$ NaOH.

GENERAL CHEMISTRY OF ALUMINIUM

The electron configuration of the aluminium atom in the ground state is $1s^2$, $2s^2$, $2p^6$, $3s^2$, $3p^1$. The ionisation potentials of the five outermost electrons of the aluminium atom are:

2p	2p	3s	3s	3p	
153·4	119·4	28·31	18·74	5·96	volts

The valency shell of the aluminium atom has the principal quantum number 3. The penultimate shell ($n=2$) contains 8 electrons. The effective nuclear charge $(Z_{\text{eff}})_{\text{mol}}$ (p. 136) of the aluminium atom is greater than that of the boron atom (Table 17.2). It will be seen from Fig. 4.9 (p. 140), however, that owing to the greater atomic radius of aluminium, the "surface charge density" for aluminium is less than that for boron. Hence it is to be predicted that aluminium has a slightly greater tendency to ionisation than boron, but there is no clear evidence for the existence of the ion Al^{3+}.

Table 17.1 shows the classes of compound formed by aluminium. There are seven compounds in which aluminium is apparently univalent: AlH, Al_2O, Al_2S, Al_2Se, AlF, AlCl, AlBr. Knowledge of these compounds is too scanty to show whether they are ionic or covalent, or to furnish any basis for conjectures on their orbital structures.

There is no aluminium compound which contains a digonally hybridised aluminium atom. The aluminium atom rarely adopts the trigonal valence state. In marked and sudden contrast to boron there are no aluminium compounds comparable with borazole and boroxole (p. 506). Definite attempts to obtain such compounds have failed. Aluminium nitride has a wurtzite structure, and not the graphitic lattice adopted by boron nitride.

The aluminium atom may be tetrahedrally hybridised, but since it is electron deficient, it can enter into chemical combination in this state only by forming three-centre bonds, or by acquiring a formal negative charge. There are no aluminium hydrides analogous to the boron hydrides (the only stable hydride of aluminium is the solid $(AlH_3)_n$), but the compounds mentioned in the first row of Section 4 of Table 17.1 probably contain aluminium atoms which take part in the formation of three-centre bonds. The neutral non-chelate compounds of aluminium formed by donor-acceptor reactions are not numerous, but aluminium is present in a range of anions of the type (AlX_4^-). It is noteworthy that the tetrahedrally hybridised aluminium atom is not present in any cation or in any chelate complex.

The valency shell of the aluminium atom ($n=3$) contains d orbitals, and octahedral hybridisation is possible. Five of the seven possible classes of compounds based on the octahedrally hybridised aluminium atom are represented by compounds mentioned in Table 17.1. Among them are aluminium borohydrides in which the aluminium atom is exerting six three-centre bonds. There appear to be no neutral non-chelate compounds, and no chelate cations. All the chelate complexes of aluminium contain the octahedrally hydridised aluminium atom; the effect of chelation is to produce the maximum co-ordination number for aluminium.

COMPOUNDS IN WHICH THE OXIDATION STATE OF ALUMINIUM IS 1

Univalent aluminium. There is good evidence for the existence of the univalent compounds of aluminium: AlH, Al_2O, Al_2S, Al_2Se, AlCl, AlBr. There is some evidence for the existence of AlF in the vapour. Aluminium behaves like beryllium (p. 425) when subjected to anodic oxidation.

AlH. When aluminium is heated at 1500° with hydrogen at a pressure of 1 atm the partial pressure of AlH is 0·35 mm.

Al_2O is made by heating a mixture of Al_2O_3 and silicon to 1800° in a high vacuum. The sublimation product contains SiO and Al_2O.

Al_2S is made by heating a mixture of Al_2S_3 and aluminium shavings to 1300° in vacuo. Gaseous Al_2S is obtained, which condenses to a brown-black solid. X-ray examination reveals the presence of metallic aluminium resulting from the disproportionation:

$$3Al_2S = Al_2S_3 + 4Al.$$

Al₂Se is made from Al_2Se_3 by a method parallel to that used for making Al_2S. Al_2Te has not been obtained.

AlF, AlCl, or AlBr, is present when metallic aluminium is heated with the appropriate aluminium trihalide. If AlF_3 and Al are heated to 650–850°, which is well below the sublimation temperature of AlF_3, 1291°, a white sublimate is obtained. AlF may exist in the vapour, but X-ray examination of the sublimate reveals only AlF_3 and Al.

At 1115° and 74 mm the reaction:

$$2Al + AlCl_3 = 3AlCl,$$

proceeds to the extent of 13·4%. AlBr is detectable in a mixture of Al and $AlBr_3$ at 500°.

COMPOUNDS IN WHICH THE OXIDATION STATE OF ALUMINIUM IS 2

Aluminium suboxide, AlO. When aluminium powder burns in oxygen the temperature attained in 3260°, and spectroscopic examination shows that under these conditions AlO is present.

COMPOUNDS IN WHICH THE OXIDATION STATE OF ALUMINIUM IS 3
SECTION 1. ALUMINIUM COMPOUNDS WITH IONIC CHARACTER

The simple trivalent cation, Al^{3+}. The deforming power of the cation Al^{3+}, 10·8, is three times that of the cation Mg^{2+}. It is therefore not expected that the simple ion Al^{3+} will be found in anhydrous salts, or in binary compounds such as Al_2O_3, or AlN. Aluminium hydroxide is a weak base, and the aluminium salts of weak acids such as the carbonate, nitrite, cyanide, formate, and acetate, either cannot be prepared, or are at once hydrolysed in solution. The salts of strong acids, such as the chlorate, perchlorate, nitrate, and sulphate are stable. They are soluble in water, and form hydrates with six or more molecules of water of crystallisation. The compound most likely to contain the ion Al^{3+} would be anhydrous aluminium perchlorate. This compound can be made by treating aluminium trichloride with anhydrous perchloric acid, and evaporating away, first excess of the acid, and then as much as possible of the aluminium trichloride. The product, however, contains about 10% of aluminium chloride as impurity. Aluminium perchlorate is very soluble in water, and it crystallises from the solution with 6, 9, and $15H_2O$.

ALUMINIUM COMPOUNDS CONSISTING OF GIANT MOLECULES IN WHICH THE BONDS HAVE SOME IONIC CHARACTER

Aluminium, like beryllium and boron, forms a number of binary compounds which are crystalline solids with high melting points, and in which the bonding has both ionic and covalent character. Among these compounds are the carbides, the nitride, the oxide Al_2O_3, and the sulphide. The non-volatile hydride, although its structure is unknown, is also included here.

Aluminium hydride, $(AlH_3)_n$. If aluminium trimethyl is mixed with a large excess of hydrogen and passed through a glow discharge, the product includes mixed alkylhydrides, such as $Al_2(CH_3)_3H_3$, and $(AlH_3)_n$, which burn explosively in air and are attacked by water. If the product is treated with trimethylamine, $(AlH_3)_nN(CH_3)_3$ is formed, and this on distillation at 100–135° yields $(AlH_3)_n$, a white, amorphous, non-volatile substance, stable up to 100° in vacuo, but at higher temperatures giving aluminium and hydrogen. Its structure is unknown.

When an ethereal solution of aluminium chloride is added to lithium hydride suspended in ether, lithium aluminohydride is formed:

$$AlCl_3 + 4LiH = LiAlH_4 + 3LiCl.$$

If the aluminium chloride is in excess, aluminium hydride is formed in solution:

$$AlCl_3 + 3LiH = AlH_3 + 3LiCl.$$

The preparation of aluminium hydride is most efficient if the lithium aluminohydride is first isolated and is then treated with the requisite quantity of aluminium chloride dissolved in ether. When the ethereal solution of aluminium hydride is allowed to stand, a solid compound of the composition $(AlH_3)_x(Et_2O)_y$ is deposited. It is not possible to prepare the polymer $(AlH_3)_x$ free from ether.

It is not known whether the two substances prepared by the above procedures, if pure, would be identical.

At low temperature, $(AlH_3)_n$ forms adducts with NH_3, NH_2Me, $NHMe_2$, NMe_3, and $(C_2H_5)_3P$. The ammoniate loses hydrogen to give ultimately AlN.

Aluminium carbide, Al_4C_3, is made by heating the elements together above 1000°. It consists of pale yellow crystals, m.p. 2200°. It is hard. With water or dilute acids it gives methane and a little hydrogen. With N_2 at 1800° it gives Al_5C_3N.

The lattice is complex. Each carbon atom is surrounded by Al atoms at distances 1·90 to 2·22. The shortest C—C distance is 3·16. The carbon atoms, therefore, are not linked directly to one another.

Aluminium acetylide, $Al_2(C_2)_3$, is made by passing acetylene over aluminium at 450–500°. It reacts with water to yield pure acetylene.

Aluminium nitride, AlN, is made by heating aluminium in nitrogen at 800°. The reaction is exothermic. Aluminium nitride can also be made by heating a mixture of aluminium and carbon in nitrogen in the electric furnace:

$$Al_2O_3 + N_2 + 3C = 2AlN + 3CO.$$

Aluminium nitride is thermally stable up to 1800°, and it melts under 4 atm at 2200° with some decomposition. Aluminium nitride is hydrolysed by cold water to aluminium hydroxide and ammonia. It yields aluminium chloride and ammonia when heated in hydrogen chloride at 900°, and aluminium chloride and nitrogen when heated in chlorine at 300°. Crystalline aluminium nitride has the wurtzite lattice.

Aluminium phosphide, AlP, is formed by heating aluminium with red phosphorus. The reaction is exothermic. Aluminium phosphide forms yellow or dark grey crystals with the wurtzite structure which neither melt nor decompose when heated to 2000°. Aluminium phosphide is readily hydrolysed to give phosphine.

Aluminium oxide, Al_2O_3, occurs naturally as *corundum*, m.p. about 2020°, b.p. (extr.) about 3000°. Corundum is made by burning aluminium in oxygen, or by heating the hydroxide, nitrate, or sulphate to a high temperature. Various precious stones consist of corundum contaminated with traces of other metals. The hardness of corundum is exceeded only by that of diamond, boron nitride, and carborundum. Corundum is almost insoluble in water (1 mg dissolves in 1 litre at 29°), and it is insoluble in acids or bases. There is an amorphous form of aluminium oxide which is made by the gentle ignition of aluminium hydroxide. It is soluble in acids and bases, but ignition converts it to insoluble corundum.

X-ray diffraction patterns show that there are not less than seven crystalline modifications of nearly anhydrous Al_2O_3 between 200° and 1200°. Of these the familiar modifications are corundum or α-Al_2O_3, and γ-Al_2O_3†. γ-Al_2O_3 is stable below 1100°.

† The so-called β-Al_2O_3 is not aluminium oxide at all, but has the composition $Na_2O,11Al_2O_3$, and is closely related to the spinels. Its composition has been definitely established. The potassium compound is made by heating at 1100° a mixture of potassium nitrate and aluminium nitrate in the required proportions. The potassium compound is isomorphous with $K_2O,11Fe_2O_3$. These two substances form a range of solid solutions which is continuous save for a gap in the middle.

In α-Al_2O_3 the oxygen atoms are hexagonally close-packed and the aluminium atoms occupy two-thirds of the octahedral holes; each aluminium atom is surrounded by six octahedrally arranged oxygen atoms, and each oxygen atom by four aluminium atoms. γ-Al_2O_3 is cubic; the crystal lattice is a defect rock-salt structure.

Aluminium hydroxide. A gelatinous precipitate of aluminium hydroxide is obtained by adding ammonia solution to the aqueous solution of an aluminium salt. The hydroxide is amphoteric. It is the base of the aluminium salts, which are highly hydrolysed. When the concentration of aluminium in the solution is $> 1 \times 10^{-2}$ M the predominant basic ionic form is $(AlOH)_2^{4+}$, which dissociates in solution to the simple basic ion $(AlOH)^{2+}$ when the concentration falls to $< 5 \times 10^{-3}$ M. Aluminium hydroxide is a very weak acid with a first dissociation constant, $K_1 = 6 \times 10^{-12}$. The aluminates are mentioned on p. 543.

Hydroxides of aluminium occur naturally with the two different compositions, $OAlOH$ and $Al(OH)_3$. Both exist in several modifications. Their relations are set out in Table 17.12.

Table 17.12.　*Forms of Aluminium Hydroxide*

Name and empirical formula	Properties and preparation	Form of Al_2O_3 to which the hydroxide is related
Diaspore OAlOH	Stable 280–450°. With steam at 400° yields Al_2O_3.	α
Böhmite OAlOH	Stable 155–280°; stable in steam at 400°. Obtained by action of pure H_2O on Al—Hg at $> 80°$. Precipitated by boiling NH_3 solution from $Al_2(SO_4)_3$ solution. First product of ageing of amorphous gel. Ages to bayerite at room temperature.	γ
Bayerite $Al(OH)_3$	Stable below 155°. Obtained by action of pure H_2O on Al—Hg at $< 40°$ Produced when böhmite gel ages under dilute alkali.	γ
Gibbsite or hydragillite $Al(OH)_3$	Stable below 155°. Most stable form of $Al(OH)_3$. Formed from bayerite by long shaking with fairly dilute alkali at 60°. Pure crystals are produced by the electrolysis of $Al(NO_3)_3$ in KOH. Dehydration at 100° gives böhmite; at 150° anhydrous γ-Al_2O. Ignition above 800° yields α-Al_2O_3	γ

The lattice of *diaspore* is a layer structure in which the oxygen atoms are close-packed and the aluminium atoms are in certain of the octahedral holes. Each layer is continuous in one dimension only, and hence the structure consists of a series of parallel chains. The chains are bound together by hydroxyl bonds.

Gibbsite (hydragillite) also consists of a layer structure. Each layer consists of two planes of OH groups; the aluminium atoms are in two-thirds of the octahedral holes (Fig. 17.8). The layers are packed on top of one another so that the centres of the oxygen atoms in the lower plane in one layer are vertically above the centres of the oxygen atoms in the upper plane in the layer beneath (Fig. 17.9). This arrangement is not close-packing (p. 340). The open nature of the structure depends on the presence of hydroxyl bonds which link oxygen atoms in a given layer, and also link the oxygen atoms in one layer to those in the next, and thus prevent the structure from becoming uniformly close-packed.

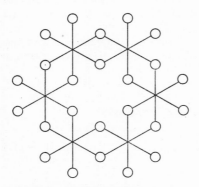

Fig. 17.8. Plan of layer of Al(OH)$_3$
(Gibbsite).

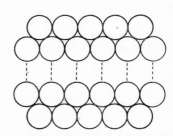

Fig. 17.9. Two layers of the Gibbsite structure. The centres of the oxygen atoms in the lower plane of the top layer are vertically above the centres of the oxygen atoms in the upper plane of the bottom layer (cf. Fig. 12.3).

Aluminium sulphide, Al$_2$S$_3$, a white solid, is obtained:

(i) by passing hydrogen sulphide over aluminium powder at 850–1350°, or over Al$_2$O$_3$ at about 1600° for 2 to 8 hours; the product is pure α-Al$_2$S$_3$;

(ii) by igniting the theoretical amounts of aluminium powder and precipitated sulphur in a carbon crucible in an atmosphere of dry carbon dioxide; impurities are removed by heating for six hours at 1200° in vacuo.

If the product is slowly cooled from high temperatures it is obtained as a white or transparent monocrystal.

Aluminium sulphide is polymorphic. The transformations occur:

$$\alpha\text{-Al}_2\text{S}_3 \leftarrow 1000° \rightarrow \gamma\text{-Al}_2\text{S}_3 \leftarrow \text{in presence of Al}_4\text{C}_3 \text{ at } 1000° \rightarrow \beta\text{-Al}_2\text{S}_3$$

γ-Al$_2$S$_3$ has a hexagonal lattice of the wurtzite type. Double sulphides are known of the general formula MAl$_2$S$_4$, where M may be Mg, Cr, Mn, Fe, Zn, or Pb.

Aluminium fluoride, AlF$_3$, on account of its high melting point, is included among the giant molecule compounds. The other aluminium halides with much lower melting points possess tetrahedral covalent structures and are described on p. 539. For convenience the properties of aluminium fluoride are included in Table 17.14, p. 540.

Aluminium fluoride, a white solid which sublimes without melting at 1291°, is made by treating Al(OH)$_3$ with hydrogen fluoride either in the gaseous phase or in aqueous solution. It can also be made by the direct combination of the elements. Aluminium fluoride is very inert; it does not react with cold water in which it is almost insoluble, or with boiling sulphuric acid. Water at 400° and fused KOH attack it only slowly (contrast BF$_3$, p. 500). Aluminium fluoride reacts with sodium fluoride in the presence of a weak acid to give Na$_3$AlF$_6$. Aluminium fluoride is soluble in hydrofluoric acid, from which it may be obtained in the crystalline state by evaporating the solution.

Crystalline aluminium fluoride has the ReO_3 structure (p. 349). The F^- ions occupy the face-centre positions (but not the corner positions) on a close-packed cubic lattice, and the Al^{3+} ions occupy the octahedral holes at the cube centres; each Al^{3+} ion is surrounded by six octahedrally arranged F^- ions, and each of these is common to another octahedral group.

SECTION 3.† THE ALUMINIUM ATOM IN THE TRIGONAL VALENCE STATE

There are many compounds of aluminium with empirical formulae AlX_3, where X may be a halogen atom, an alkyl or aryl group, or an alkoxy group. AlH_3 and AlF_3 have giant molecule structures (p. 533). Other compounds of the type AlX_3, if not giant molecules, are at least polymerised to dimeric or trimeric forms. The structures of these polymers are uncertain. $Al(CH_3)_3$ has been the subject of X-ray diffraction experiments on a single crystal from which it has been concluded that the molecule is dimeric and has a bridge structure; a simple model gives the correct order of magnitude for the heat of dimerisation, which at about $100°$ is -20.2 kcal. Bridge models have been accepted for the structures of $(Be(CH_3)_3)_2$, $(BeCl_3)_2$, and the boron hydrides, and certain other boron compounds, and there seems no reason why they should not be applied to the dimeric aluminium compounds $(AlX_3)_2$. These compounds therefore are discussed in Section 4, although it must be admitted that there is no clear evidence that they contain the aluminium atom in the tetrahedral valence state.

Whatever their structure, these polymerised compounds must retain some relation to the trigonally hybridised aluminium atom, for they undergo numerous reactions with ions or molecules containing donor atoms. The donor may be F^-, Cl^-, H^-, a nitrogen atom in NH_3, NR_3, NCR, a phosphorus atom in PH_3, an oxygen atom in H_2O, ROH, R_2O, a sulphur atom in H_2S. or a carbon atom in certain unsaturated organic compounds. In these reactions the aluminium atom behaves as an electron acceptor, and it must be present, at least as an intermediate, in the trigonally hybridised state. When aluminium is combined with F, Cl, I, alkyl, aryl, or ethoxy groups, it undergoes donor-acceptor reactions, and the product is either a simple addition compound, such as $Br_3Al{\leftarrow}NH_3$, or a univalent ion of the type (AlX_4^-). The aluminium atom in the addition compound or in the ion is tetrahedrally hybridised. It must also be admitted that above $800°$ aluminium chloride is monomeric, and in these conditions it is an example of a compound containing the aluminium atom in the trigonal valence state.

Boron forms many well-characterised compounds in which it exerts three σ bonds and one non-localised π bond, among them boron nitride, borazole, and boroxole, but aluminium forms no compound with this orbital structure; definite attempts to prepare such compounds have been unsuccessful.

SECTION 4. COMPOUNDS IN WHICH THE ALUMINIUM ATOM IS TETRAHEDRALLY HYBRIDISED

Examples of compounds containing an aluminium atom in the tetrahedral valence state are found in electron deficient compounds, in non-chelate complex neutral compounds, and in non-chelate complex anions. There are, however, no non-chelate complex cations, and no chelate compounds at all in which the aluminium atom is present in the tetrahedral valence state.

† The aluminium atom does not attain the digonal valence state, and hence there are no aluminium compounds in Section 2.

ELECTRON-DEFICIENT POLYMERS. BRIDGE COMPOUNDS

Some of the polymerised aluminium compounds which for convenience are arbitrarily assigned to this class are mentioned in Table 17.13.

Aluminium alkyls and aryls. The aluminium alkyls and aryls are colourless volatile liquids. They are made by the action of aluminium on the mercury alkyl. (Ether must not be present or the etherate will be formed which cannot be dissociated). Aluminium trimethyl is obtained in 80% yield by heating aluminium amalgam with methyl iodide at 170°. Aluminium triethyl can be made from ethylene by the reaction:

$$Al + 3C_2H_4 + 1\tfrac{1}{2}H_2 = Al(C_2H_5)_3.$$

Table 17.13. *The Aluminium Alkyls, Aryls, and their Derivatives*

		m.p. °C	b.p. °C	
	$Al(CH_3)_3$	$+15$	$126 \cdot 1$	Dimeric at 70°
	$Al(C_2H_5)_3$	$-52 \cdot 5$	$185 \cdot 6$	12% dimeric at 150°
	$Al(n\text{-}C_3H_7)_3$	-107	*ca.* 250	
	$Al(C_6H_5)_3$	230		
	$Al(CH_3)_2N(CH_3)_2$	154	228	
	$Al(CH_3)_2SCH_3$	103		
Dimeric	$Al(CH_3)_2Cl$	$\begin{cases} -21 \\ -45 \end{cases}$	$119 \cdot 4$	Dimorphic
	$Al(CH_3)_2Br$	0	150	
	$Al(CH_3)Br_2$	79		
	$Al(C_6H_5)Cl_2$	94		
	$Al(CH_3)Cl_2$	73		
	$Al(CH_3)I_2$	70		
	$Al(C_2H_5)Cl_2$	32		
	$Al(C_2H_5)I_2$	39	158/4 mm	
Trimeric	$Al(CH_3)_2 \cdot P(CH_3)_2$	220	*ca.* 250	
	$Al(CH_3)_2 \cdot OCH_3$		*ca.* 140	
Tetrameric	$Al(OCH_3)_3$			
	$Al(OC_2H_5)_3$	139	320	
	$Al(O\ iso\text{-}C_3H_7)_3$	125	242/10 mm	
	$Al(OC_6H_5CH_2)_3$	81		

The dimeric and trimeric compounds in this list are reluctant to become monomeric; they are little dissociated at 150° and 30 mm.

Aluminium trimethyl slowly decomposes at 300°, one of the products being methane. The lower alkyls are spontaneously inflammable in air, and they are violently attacked by water to give saturated hydrocarbons:

$$Al(CH_3)_3 + 3H_2O = Al(OH)_3 + 3CH_4.$$

They readily form adducts with donor molecules such as ether. The etherates are very stable; $(C_2H_5)_2O \rightarrow Al(C_2H_5)_3$ can be distilled without decomposition. The affinities of the donors $R(CH_3)_n$ towards aluminium trimethyl are in the order:

$$N(CH_3)_3 > P(CH_3)_3 > O(CH_3)_2 > S(CH_3)_2 > Se(CH_3)_2 > Te(CH_3)_2 > ClCH_3.$$

The affinity of $ClCH_3$ towards aluminium trimethyl is very small indeed. If the donor molecule contains a hydrogen atom linked to the atom of the electronegative element, decomposition with the elimination of methane occurs on heating, as, for example, in the reaction:

$$Al(CH_3)_3 + NH(CH_3)_2 = (CH_3)_2Al\!\!-\!\!N(CH_3)_2 + CH_4.$$

$(CH_3)_2PH$, CH_3OH, and CH_3SH behave similarly. The product other than the hydrocarbon is dimeric or trimeric.

The aluminium alkyls (like the boron alkyls) react with ketones thus:

On hydrolysis the product gives the secondary alcohol. At 110–115° aluminium ethyl dissolves alkyls of the alkali metals to give conducting solutions, probably containing salts such as $Na[Al(C_2H_5)_4]$.

Aluminium triphenyl is easily soluble in benzene. It is oxidised by air in the solid state and in solution, but less readily than the alkyl compounds. It forms an etherate, m.p. 112°, which loses ether on being heated in vacuo. Sodium dissolves in the ethereal solution to give a reddish-brown solution which on evaporation leaves a brown powder, presumably $Na[Al(C_6H_5)_3]$.

Aluminium alkyl halides such as $Al(C_2H_5)Cl_2$ *and* $Al(C_2H_5)_2Cl$. Compounds of this type are made by dissolving aluminium in the alkyl halide and fractionating the product. They are low-melting and fairly volatile, easily inflammable, and violently reactive with air or water. They form monoetherates. They are dimeric in solution.

Aluminic esters, $Al(OR)_3$. The aluminic esters are solids. They are made by the action of aluminium on the warm anhydrous alcohol; a trace of mercuric chloride promotes the reaction, probably by breaking the oxide film on the aluminium:

$$Al + 3C_2H_5OH = Al(C_2H_5O)_3 + 1\tfrac{1}{2}H_2.$$

The esters are insoluble in alcohol, but easily soluble in benzene. They form salts $M[Al(OEt)_4]$ indirectly, but they do not form additive compounds. They react with water to yield aluminium hydroxide and the alcohol. A mixture of the aluminic ester and the corresponding alcohol reduces aldehydes and ketones (the *iso*-propylate is the most efficient):

$$RRC:O + HOCH(CH_3)_3 = RRCHOH + CH_3COCH_3.$$

If the aldehyde or ketone contains a $C\!=\!C$ bond this is unaffected. The conversion is complete, and no pinacols are formed.

Aluminium halides. Certain properties of the aluminium halides are stated in Table 17.14. Aluminium fluoride is a giant molecule compound, and is described on p. 536; the other aluminium halides exist in the dimeric form except at high temperatures. They are described in the following paragraphs.

Aluminium chloride, Al_2Cl_6, is a white, stable, volatile solid. It is made by the action of chlorine or hydrogen chloride on aluminium foil. The heat of the reaction causes aluminium chloride to sublime as soon as it is formed. On the manufacturing scale, a mixture of bauxite and carbon is heated at 1000° in chlorine:

$$Al_2O_3 + 3C + 3Cl_2 = Al_2Cl_6 + 3CO.$$

Aluminium chloride is very hygroscopic and fumes in moist air. In aqueous solution it is so much hydrolysed that the liberated hydrochloric acid can be titrated against sodium hydroxide solution. The hexahydrate, $AlCl_3,6H_2O$, can be made by dissolving aluminium hydroxide in hydrochloric acid, and saturating the solution with HCl gas. With anhydrous ammonia aluminium chloride forms the ammines $AlCl_3,nNH_3$, where n is 2, 5, 6, 7, or 14. With nitric acid at room temperature it gives Al_2Cl_6,NO.

Table 17.14 *The Aluminium Halides*

	AlF_3	$AlCl_3$	$AlBr_3$	AlI_3
Appearance	Colourless, transparent triclinic crystals	Colourless hexagonal crystals. Very deliquescent	Colourless rhombic plates. Deliquescent	White crystals. Deliquescent
Lattice	ReO_3 structure	Slightly distorted $CrCl_3$ structure	Close-packed Br atoms with Al atoms in pairs of adjacent tetrahedral holes; hence a molecular lattice	
m.p. °C	1290	193	98	About 180
b.p. °C	Sublimes at 1290	Sublimes at 180	About 260	About 380
Structure of molecule in vapour		Dimeric; tetrahedral	Dimeric; tetrahedral	Dimeric; tetrahedral
Distance Al—X in ring		2·21	2·33	2·58
Distance Al—X in terminal positions		2·06	2·21	2·53
Solubility in water	0·56 gm in 100 gm at 25°	Soluble with violence	Soluble with violence	Soluble with decomposition
Hydrates (in terms of monomeric formulae)	0, $\frac{1}{2}$, 3, 9	0, 6	0, 6, 15	0, 6
Specific conductivity $\times 10^6$ ohm^{-1} cm^{-1} of liquid at m.p.		0·45	0·09	1·2

The vapour density up to 400° corresponds to the formula Al_2Cl_6; above 800° to $AlCl_3$. In solution in non-donating solvents such as benzene, aluminium chloride is dimeric. Solutions of aluminium chloride in alcohol or benzene absorb ethylene, butylene, amylene, and acetylene.

Aluminium bromide, Al_2Br_6. Aluminium reacts slowly with bromine vapour at room temperature, rapidly at a red heat. It reacts violently with liquid bromine at room temperature after a short period of induction, which probably corresponds to the breaking of the oxide film on the surface of the metal. Al_2Br_6 is a non-conductor in both the solid and the liquid states. Al_2Br_6 is soluble in normal hexane and in cyclohexane.

The molecular weight in the vapour and in solution in bromine corresponds to Al_2Br_6.

Aluminium iodide, Al_2I_6, is formed from the elements by heating aluminium and iodine in a sealed tube, or by the action of aluminium on iodine in carbon disulphide solution. It is a non-conductor in both the solid and the liquid states. It is soluble in normal hexane and in cyclohexane.

When heated with CCl_4, the following exchange occurs:

$$4AlI_3 + 3CCl_4 = 4AlCl_3 + 3CI_4.$$

The molecular weight in solution in iodine and in the vapour corresponds to Al_2I_6.

Structures of aluminium bridge compounds. The polymeric compounds of aluminium dealt with in this section are those included in Table 17.13, p. 538, and also aluminium chloride, bromide and iodide, Table 17.14. Compounds containing only alkyl groups or halogen atoms are dimeric; trimeric or tetrameric compounds appear to contain alkoxy groups.

The structures of the aluminium trihalides in the vapour have been studied by electron diffraction. Below about 400° the molecules have the form

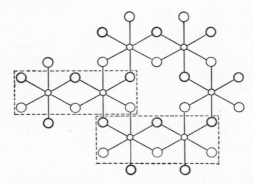

Crystalline aluminium tribromide contains Al_2Br_6 molecules of this type. Crystalline Al_2Cl_6 has a layer lattice. The rectangles show how such layers on evaporation might split up into Al_2Cl_6 molecules.

Plan of a layer in the crystal of aluminium chloride.
The small circles represent Al atoms.

The orbital structure of the isolated molecule Al_2Cl_6 might consist of tetrahedrally hybridised aluminium atoms, each exerting three covalent bonds and one co-ionic bond as in the figure.

The orbital structure might equally well contain three-centre bonds, thus:

Table 17.14 shows that the distance Al—Cl in the bridge (2·21) is greater than the distance Al—Cl for the terminal atoms (2·06). This relation corresponds to that for the H—B distances in diborane which quite certainly possesses a bridge structure.

In the *crystal* of Al_2Cl_6 each Al atom is six co-ordinate, and each Cl atom is two co-ordinate. The structure can again be interpreted by assuming either (i) that every

Cl atom exerts one covalent bond to one Al atom and a co-ionic bond to a second Al atom, or (ii) that every Cl atom is the central atom of a three-centre bond. Raman spectra experiments have shown that aluminium compounds of the type $AlMeX_2$ and Me_2AlX (where $X = Cl$, Br, or I) are dimeric, and that the bridging occurs by the methyl group and not by the Cl atoms. The properties and structure of aluminium borohydride, which contains the three-centre bonds AlHB, are discussed on p. 524.

NON-CHELATE COMPLEXES

Non-chelate Neutral Complexes

The neutral complexes containing aluminium atoms in the tetrahedral valence state are chiefly represented by the adducts formed by the combination of such compounds as $Al(CH_3)_3$ and $AlCl_3$ with ether, ammonia, or the amines. The aluminium alkyls and aryls readily form stable etherates. $(C_2H_5)_3Al \leftarrow O(C_2H_5)_2$ is made by the action of aluminium magnesium alloy on an ethereal solution of ethyl iodide:

$$(C_2H_5)_2O + 2Al + 3C_2H_5I = (C_2H_5)_3Al \leftarrow O(C_2H_5)_2 + AlI_3.$$

It can be distilled (b.p. 217°) without decomposition. The ether cannot be removed without complete disruption of the molecule. The etherates, however, are as sensitive to air and water as the alkyls and aryls from which they are derived. Examples of neutral tetrahedral complexes of aluminium derived from the aluminium alkyls and aluminium chloride are set out in Table 17.1.

Non-chelate Complex Anions

The principal salts containing anions in which the aluminium atom is in the tetrahedral valence state are:

$M[AlH_4]$	$M = Li$, Na, Ca, Ti^{IV}, Sn^{IV}, In^{III}, $[TlCl]^{2+}$.
$M[Al[C_2H_5]_4]$	$M = K$.
$M[Al[OH]_4]$	$M = Na$, K in solution only.
$M[Al[OEt]_4]$	$M = Li$, Na, K, Tl^+, Mg, Cu^{2+}, Ni.
$M[AlCl_4]$	$M = Li$, Na, K, NH_4, NO, I.
$M[AlBr_4]$	$M = Li$, Na, K, NH_4, Cu.
$M[AlI_4]$	$M = K$.

The **aluminohydrides** of the electropositive metals Li, Na, and Ca are salt-like and stable but very reactive. The aluminohydrides of titanium, tin, and indium decompose at room temperature. The aluminohydrides, in contrast to the borohydrides (p. 523) are not divided into a covalent class and an ionic class.

Lithium aluminohydride, $Li[AlH_4]$, a colourless solid, is made by the action of aluminium chloride on lithium hydride suspended in ether. The lithium aluminohydride remains in solution in the ether. The precipitated lithium chloride is filtered off, the ether is evaporated, and the lithium aluminohydride remains. It is stable to air in the cold.

Lithium aluminohydride decomposes if heated to 150°:

$$2LiAlH_4 = 2LiH + 2Al + 3H_2.$$

It reacts so vigorously with a small quantity of water that it becomes incandescent:

$$LiAlH_4 + 4H_2O = LiOH + Al(OH)_3 + 4H_2.$$

Lithium aluminohydride reacts with deuterium oxide to give 98% HD, which is used as a starting point for making 99·8% HD.

Lithium aluminohydride generates hydrogen when treated with liquid ammonia, or with primary and secondary amines, for example:

$$LiAlH_4 + 4NR_1R_2H = LiAl(NR_1R_2)_4 + 4H_2.$$

With boron trichloride it gives diborane:

$$3LiAlH_4 + 4BCl_3 = 2B_2H_6 + 3LiCl + 3AlCl_3.$$

A solution of lithium aluminohydride in ether† (prepared and used after the manner of a Grignard reagent) is an important reducing agent. It reduces aldehydes, ketones, carboxylic acids, and their esters to alcohols, and nitrocompounds, amides, oximes, and nitriles to amines. It does *not* react with an ethylenic linkage unless this is bonded to a phenyl group and a reducible group, as in C_6H_5—C=C—C=O. It will also bring

$$\begin{array}{ccc} | & | & | \\ H & H & CH_3 \end{array}$$

about the reductions:

$SiCl_4$ to SiH_4.
$SnCl_4$ to SnH_4.
$ZnMe_2$ to ZnH_2
ZnI_2 to ZnH_2
$BeMe_2$ or $BeCl_2$ to BeH_2.
NO   to $H_2N_2O_2$ (isolated as $Ag_2N_2O_2$).

Lithium aluminohydride reacts with water and alcohols more readily than does $LiBH_4$, and it appears to be the less polar. The Raman and infrared spectra of the solution in ether are consistent with a tetrahedral $[AlH_4^-]$ ion.

The alkali aluminates are soluble and are formed when metallic aluminium dissolves in aqueous alkalis. The solid phases of the sodium and potassium salts are $Na(AlO_2)$, 5/4, and $3H_2O$, and $K(AlO_2),3/2H_2O$. In solution the ions may be:

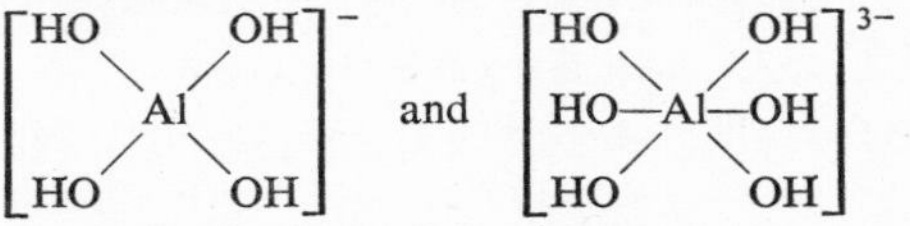

$$\begin{bmatrix} HO & OH \\ & Al \\ HO & OH \end{bmatrix}^- \quad \text{and} \quad \begin{bmatrix} HO & OH \\ HO—Al—OH \\ HO & OH \end{bmatrix}^{3-}$$

Raman spectra confirm the existence of $[Al(OH)_4]^-$. Dialysis methods, however, suggest that the aluminate ion is a binuclear complex:

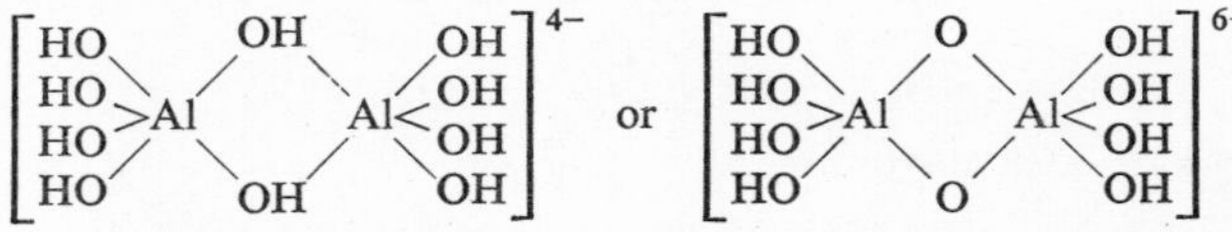

$$\begin{bmatrix} HO & OH & OH \\ HO & & OH \\ HO{>}Al & Al{<}OH \\ HO & OH & OH \end{bmatrix}^{4-} \quad \text{or} \quad \begin{bmatrix} HO & O & OH \\ HO & & OH \\ HO{>}Al & Al{<}OH \\ HO & O & OH \end{bmatrix}^{6-}$$

The aluminium ion precipitates Al_2O_3 from the solution of an aluminate:

$$Al^{3+} + 3AlO_2^- = 2Al_2O_3.$$

Besides being easily hydrolysed, the aluminates decompose spontaneously in the presence of suspended $Al(OH)_3$ or Al_2O_3 gel. The instability is greatest at a concentration of 130 gm of Na_2O per litre (mol. ratio of $Na_2O/Al_2O_3 = 1.4$). Use is made of this effect in the purification of bauxite; the effective seeding agent is gibbsite. There is no analogy between the aluminates and the borates, probably because of the strong tendency of the aluminium atom to adopt the octahedral valence state.

The aluminohalides. In contrast to boron, aluminium forms no tetrafluoroaluminates. The compound NH_4AlF_4 appears to contain the $[AlF_4]^-$ ion, but the crystal consists of AlF_6 octahedra with certain fluorine atoms common to two or more octahedra. The absence of the ion $[AlF_4]^-$ is evidence of the tendency of aluminium to adopt the

† The evaporation of dimethyl ether solutions of AlH_3, $LiAlH_4$ or $NaAlH_4$ may lead to explosion if the solvent contains carbon dioxide.

octahedral rather than the tetrahedral valence state. The aluminochlorides are well-known. The salts $M[AlCl_4]$ are made from melts of the constituent chlorides, or by reaction of $AlCl_3$ with the chloride of the other metal in benzene; the aluminochlorides cannot be made in aqueous solution. The acid $H[AlCl_4]$ does not exist; a definite search for combination between HCl and $AlCl_3$ down to $-80°$ has yielded no result. Nitrosyl aluminochloride, $NO[AlCl_4]$, is made by treating pure solid $AlCl_3$ with NOCl vapour in the presence of dry nitrogen. It melts at $180°$ without decomposition. The interesting compounds $CdAlCl_4$, $GaAlCl_4$, m.p. $175°$, $BiAlCl_4$, m.p. $253°$, are made by reducing MCl_2 or MCl_3 with metallic M in the presence of aluminium trichloride.

Sodium aluminochloride, $Na[AlCl_4]$, m.p. $156°$, is made by heating $AlCl_3$ and NaCl at $200–240°$ in vacuo. The crystal structure, as determined by X-ray diffraction, consists of the ions Na^+ and $[AlCl_4^-]$. The $[AlCl_4^-]$ ion is tetrahedral. There are four $[AlCl_4^-]$ ions per unit cell, and the Na^+ ions are in the spaces between them. Each Na^+ ion has eight chlorine atom neighbours at distances varying from 2·79 to 3·72. Within each tetrahedron the distance Cl—Cl is 3·48, and the distance Al—Cl is 2·13.

SECTION 5. COMPOUNDS IN WHICH THE ALUMINIUM ATOM IS OCTAHEDRALLY HYBRIDISED

The d orbitals in the valency shell $(n=3)$ of the aluminium atom enable the atom to adopt the octahedral valence state. Examples of compounds in which the aluminium atom is in this valence state are included in Table 17.1, Section 5. With the exception of neutral non-chelate complexes and of chelate cationic complexes, all possible classes of compound are represented. The electron deficient compounds include the aluminium borohydrides which have already been discussed on p. 524.

NON-CHELATE COMPLEXES

Non-chelate Complex Anions

The fluoroaluminates, M_3AlF_6, where $M = Li, Na, K, NH_4$. When sodium fluoride or sodium carbonate is added to a solution of aluminium fluoride in hydrofluoric acid containing sufficient acid to give the empirical composition H_3AlF_6, two compounds, Na_3AlF_6 and $5NaF,3AlF_3$, are formed. Their existence has been established by X-ray examination. Na_3AlF_6 is the mineral cryolite. It can be made in solution by the reaction:

$$AlF_3 + 3NH_4F + 3NaNO_3 = Na_3AlF_6 + 3NH_4NO_3.$$

It is decomposed if heated with lime:

$$Na_3AlF_6 + 3CaO = 3CaF_2 + Na_2O + NaAlO_2.$$

The crystal of Na_3AlF_6 contains Na^+ ions and $[AlF_6^{3-}]$ ions. The $[AlF_6^{3-}]$ ions are somewhat distorted octahedra. If ammonium fluoroaluminate is heated, the following changes occur:

$$(NH_4)_3AlF_6 \xrightarrow{350°} NH_4AlF_4 \xrightarrow{\text{higher temperature}} NH_4F + AlF_3.$$

The crystal of NH_4AlF_4 consists of AlF_6 octahedra with certain fluorine atoms common to two or more octahedra (compare p. 537).

Non-chelate Complex Cations

The crystalline halides and sulphates of aluminium probably contain the hydrated ion $[Al,6H_2O]^{3+}$. The hexa-ammoniate of aluminium chloride probably contains the ion $[Al,6NH_3]^{3+}$. The alums have the general formula $M^+M^{3+}(SO_4)_3,12H_2O$, where M^+ is a univalent cation, and M^{3+} is a trivalent cation. It has been shown experimentally that six molecules of water surround each metal cation; there is no evidence of complex formation in which the sulphate ion plays a part. Lithium does not form an alum, perhaps because it cannot become six co-ordinate.

CHELATE COMPLEXES

Chelate Neutral Complexes

Neutral aluminium chelate complexes are derived from acetylacetone, acetoacetic ester, diethyl malonate, and salicylic ester. The structure of the acetylacetonate is:

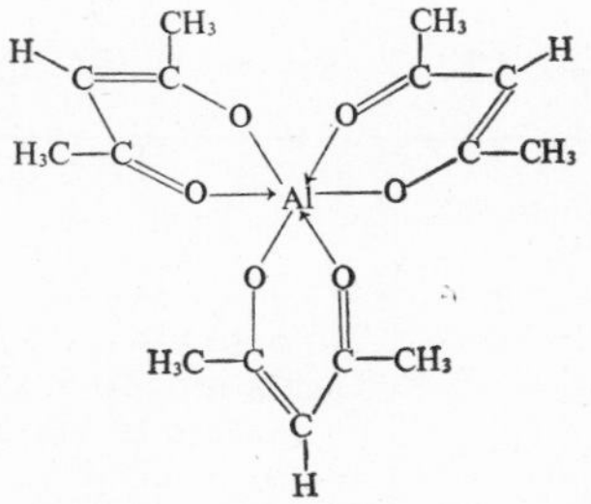

It is a volatile compound which melts at 192° and boils at 315°. Compounds of this type are nearly insoluble in water, easily soluble in alcohol, ether, and benzene. They are monomeric in the vapour and in benzene solution.

Chelate Complex Anions

Examples of chelate complex anions containing the aluminium atom in the octahedral valence state are present in the ammonium salts of the oxalato derivative, and of the catechol derivative:

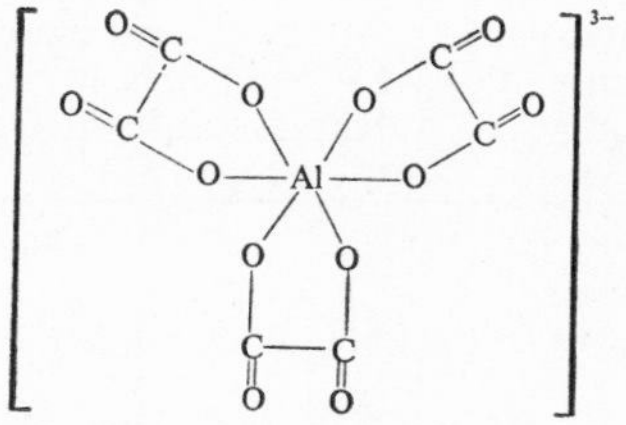

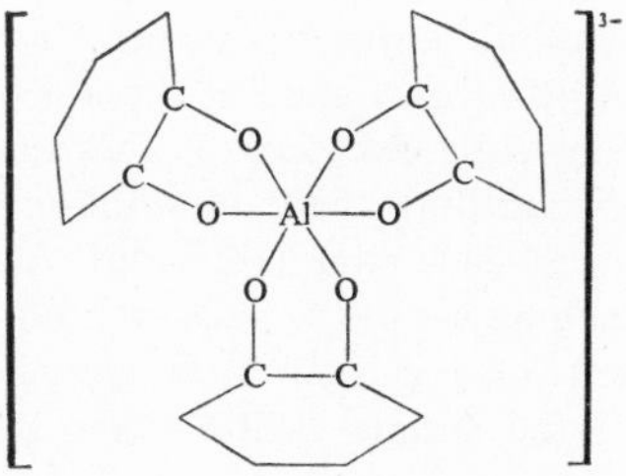

GALLIUM

PROPERTIES OF THE METAL

The colour of metallic gallium is white with a slight bluish tinge. Gallium is softer than lead. Its low m.p. 29·75° is remarkable. The liquid has a brilliant mirror surface like mercury. Gallium (like water, germanium, and bismuth) expands on freezing. The crystal has a complicated structure; one atom is near one neighbour, and less near six others. This arrangement persists in the liquid. Gallium alloys with many metals, but its solubility in mercury is only 1·3% at 25°. Aqua regia is one of the best solvents for the metal.

Table 17.15.   *Reactions of Gallium*

Reagent	Conditions of reaction	Result
Air	Cold	No action
Air	Hot	Oxidation to "GaO" which is probably a mixture of Ga and Ga_2O_3
Oxygen	Heated	Burns to Ga_2O_3
Hydrogen		No action
Nitrogen		No action
Sulphur	1300°	Ga_2S_3
Fluorine		
Chlorine		Burns to $GaCl_3$
Water	Hot or cold in absence of oxygen	No action
Ammonia	1200°	GaN
H_2S	800°	Ga_2S_3
Mercury alkyls and aryls		$Ga(C_2H_5)_3$, etc.
HCl	Dilute and cold	Slow attack
H_2SO_4	Dilute and cold	Slow attack
HCl	Conc.	Rapid attack
HNO_3	Dilute and warm	Attacked and dissolved
Alkali	Dilute aq.	H_2 evolved
$HClO_4$	Hot conc.	Rapid solution: $Ga(ClO_4)_3,6H_2O$ crystallises

Reactions are slow if the metal is very pure, 99·9%

GENERAL CHEMISTRY OF GALLIUM

The ionisation potentials of the electrons in the valency shell ($n = 4$) of the gallium atom are:

$4s$	$4s$	$4p$
30·6	20·43	5·97

The valency shell of the gallium atom is outside the shell ($n = 3$) which contains eighteen electrons, whereas the valency shell of the aluminium atom ($n = 3$) is outside the shell ($n = 2$) which contains eight electrons. The effective nuclear charge $(Z_{eff})_{mol}$ of the gallium atom is greater than that of the aluminium atom (Table 17.2). It will be seen from Fig. 4.9 that the "surface charge density" for gallium is greater than that for aluminium. The deforming power of the gallium atom is therefore greater than that of the aluminium atom. Hence the gallium atom shows a smaller tendency to ionise than the aluminium atom; the simple cation Ga^{3+} is not present in any gallium compound.

The gallium atom is electron deficient, and like the atoms of boron and aluminium, must either receive electrons or develop three-centre bonds before it attains a stable arrangement of bonding orbitals. The valency shell of the gallium atom includes d orbitals, and hence the atom can undergo octahedral hybridisation.

Table 17.1 shows the types of compounds formed by gallium. There are seven compounds in which the gallium atom is univalent; the so-called gallium dichloride has the structure $Ga[GaCl_4]$ in which one gallium atom is present as a univalent cation. The principal hydrated oxide of gallium, $HGaO_2$, has the same lattice as diaspore.

Compounds which contain the trigonally hybridised gallium atom are closely parallel to those of aluminium. There are no gallium compounds analogous to borazole and boroxole. Gallium forms compounds in which the atom is tetrahedrally hybridised. These compounds may be electron deficient bridge compounds, non-chelate neutral compounds, or complex anions; there are neither complex non-chelate cations, nor any chelate complexes. Digallane, Ga_2H_6, is of interest because it is probably analogous to diborane, which is remarkable since no analogous aluminium hydride has been obtained. In the octahedrally hybridised state the gallium atom is present in complexes, but no chelate cationic complexes have been found.

COMPOUNDS IN WHICH THE OXIDATION STATE OF GALLIUM IS 1

Univalent gallium. A number of binary compounds in which gallium is thought to be univalent have been reported. Ga_2O is a dark-coloured solid, made by reducing Ga_2O_3 with gallium at $500°$, Ga_2S, made by heating the metal with hydrogen sulphide at a high temperature, is a black solid which may be sublimed. It may be, however, that these substances are mixtures of Ga_2O_3, or Ga_2S_3, with the metal. There is spectroscopic evidence for GaCl, GaBr, and GaI. GaCl can be made by heating the metal in argon containing 1% of chlorine. Its absorption spectrum has been observed.

The univalent Ga^+ ion is present in the well-characterised compound, $Ga[GaCl_4]$, known as gallium dichloride. Gallium dichloride consists of colourless crystals, m.p. $170.5°$. It disproportionates to Ga and $GaCl_3$ if heated in vacuo at $200°$. Gallium dichloride is made: (i) by heating gallium metal in anhydrous hydrogen chloride, (ii) by heating gallium metal with gallium trichloride at $175°$. It may be purified by distillation in vacuo. It dissolves in benzene without change. It liberates hydrogen from water, and at $-78°$ it reacts with liquid ammonia, thus:

$$3GaCl_2 + nNH_3 = Ga + 2GaCl_3, nNH_3.$$

It is diamagnetic. The structure $Ga^+[GaCl_4]^-$ has been confirmed; for the molten state by Raman spectra, and for the solid state by X-ray diffraction.

If the dichloride is treated with metallic gallium in the presence of aluminium chloride, the reaction occurs:

$$Ga[GaCl_4] + 2Ga + 4AlCl_3 = 4Ga[AlCl_4].$$

The aluminium compound thus formed, m.p. $175°$, is similar to gallium dichloride.

COMPOUNDS IN WHICH THE OXIDATION STATE OF GALLIUM IS 3

SECTION 1. GALLIUM COMPOUNDS WITH IONIC CHARACTER

The simple cation, Ga^{3+}. There is no definite evidence for the existence of the cation Ga^{3+}. The oxyacid salts of gallium are deliquescent, and crystallise with water of crystallisation. They probably contain the metal as an aquo-complex. Gallium salts are usually prepared from the metal. Metallic gallium is dissolved in aqua regia, and the solution is precipitated with ammonium carbonate. The precipitate is dissolved in the acid of the salt required.

GALLIUM COMPOUNDS CONSISTING OF GIANT MOLECULES IN WHICH
THE BONDS HAVE SOME IONIC CHARACTER

Gallium nitride, GaN, is made (i) by heating the metal in ammonia gas at 1200°, (ii) by heating $(NH_4)_3[GaF_6]$ in ammonia gas. It is a grey powder, stable to air, water, and dilute acids. It is only very slowly attacked by hot concentrated HCl or aqueous alkali. It has the wurtzite lattice.

Gallium oxide, Ga_2O_3, is formed when the nitrate, sulphate or alum, or the hydrated oxide is ignited. It cannot be made by heating the metal in air as the reaction stops when a mixture of the composition GaO is obtained. Gallium trioxide is a white solid. It exists in at least five polymorphic forms. The form stable at room temperature is β which melts at 1740°. The ignited substance is insoluble in both acids and alkalis. If heated with fluorine it is converted to GaF_3.

The material obtained by precipitating a gallic salt with an alkali is a Ga_2O_3–H_2O complex. On ageing this changes to $GaO.OH$, which has a diaspore lattice. $GaO.OH$ is stable in contact with water up to 300°, but at higher temperatures β-Ga_2O_3 is stable.

Gallium hydroxide, $Ga(OH)_3$, is a colourless gelatinous substance. It is amphoteric, and it is a weaker alkali and a stronger acid than $Al(OH)_3$, because the deforming power of the gallium atom is greater than that of the aluminium atom. Gallium hydroxide is soluble in sodium hydroxide solution sufficiently concentrated (10·3N) to convert gallium hydroxide to Na_3GaO_3. Less concentrated sodium hydroxide solution precipitates the insoluble compounds Na_2HGaO_3 and NaH_2GaO_3. Gallium hydroxide is very soluble in aqueous ammonia solution.

Gallic sulphide, Ga_2S_3, a yellow solid, m.p. 1250°, is made by heating gallium with sulphur vapour at 1300°, or with hydrogen sulphide at 800°. It is decomposed by water. Gallic sulphide is dimorphic; the α-form with the zinc blende lattice exists at room temperature, but at 600° it changes to the β-form with the wurtzite lattice.

Gallium trifluoride, GaF_3, is a high-melting solid (950°) which starts to sublime at 800°, and does so freely at 1000°. It is quite different from the highly volatile and soluble gallium chloride, bromide, and iodide (see Table 17.17, p. 551). It is made (i) by heating Ga_2O_3 in fluorine, (ii) by heating $(NH_4)_3GaF_6$ in fluorine at 250–400°. It is very slightly soluble in water. The trihydrate is prepared indirectly by treating gallium hydroxide with hydrofluoric acid. It gives a basic salt on heating. The triammoniate, $GaF_3,3NH_3$, is made by the action of ammonia on the trihydrate; the high crystal energy of the anhydrous fluoride prevents its direct combination with ammonia. The crystal structure of GaF_3, and the orbital structure of $GaF_3,3NH_3$, are unknown.

SECTION 2. COMPOUNDS IN WHICH THE GALLIUM ATOM IS DIGONALLY HYBRIDISED

The only compound which might be assigned to this Section is the sulphide S—Ga—Ga—S which has a structure parallel to that of mercurous chloride.†

SECTION 3. COMPOUNDS IN WHICH THE GALLIUM ATOM IS TRIGONALLY HYBRIDISED

Gallium follows aluminium (p. 537) in forming very few compounds which belong to this Section. Among them are the monomeric forms of $GaCl_3$, $GaBr_3$, GaI_3, which are stable above about 800°, and the monomeric forms of the gallium trialkyls, which are stable above about 100°. At room temperatures all these compounds are dimeric.

† *Proc. Chem. Soc.*, May, 1958, p. 130.

There are no gallium compounds in which the gallium atom exerts three σ bonds and one non-localised π bond.

SECTION 4. COMPOUNDS IN WHICH THE GALLIUM ATOM IS TETRAHEDRALLY HYBRIDISED

ELECTRON DEFICIENT POLYMERS. BRIDGE COMPOUNDS

By analogy with aluminium the dimeric forms of the compounds GaH_3, $GaH(CH_3)_2$, $Ga(CH_3)_3$, $GaCl_3$, $GaBr_3$, and GaI_3, are assigned to this Section. The dimeric molecules are assumed to have a bridge structure, but there is no direct experimental evidence to support this assumption.

Digallane, gallium hydride, Ga_2H_6, is a volatile liquid, m.p. $-21\cdot4°$, b.p. (extr.) $139°$. It decomposes at $130°$. It is obtained by treating tetramethyl digallane with triethylamine:

$$3Ga_2H_2(CH_3)_4 + 4N(C_2H_5)_3 = Ga_2H_6 + 4Ga(CH_3)_3 \leftarrow N(C_2H_5)_3.$$

The volatility of digallane suggests that its structure may be analogous to that of diborane:

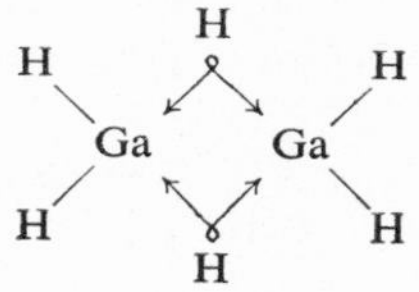

but there is no direct evidence for this bridge structure.

Tetramethyl digallane, $Ga_2H_2(CH_3)_4$, is a volatile liquid (b.p. extr. $172°$). It is obtained by subjecting a mixture of gallium trimethyl vapour and hydrogen to a glow discharge. At $130°$ it decomposes to give $Ga(CH_3)_3$, metallic gallium, and hydrogen. It reacts readily with air and with moisture. With ethylamine it gives digallane by the reaction shown above. The conjectured structure is:

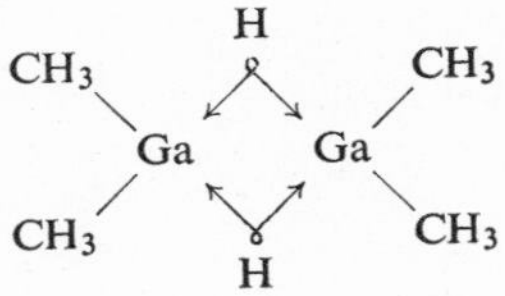

The gallium trialkyls are reactive volatile liquids. They are dimeric in the vapour at low temperature and in benzene solution.

	m.p. °C	b.p. °C
$Ga(CH_3)_3$	-19	$55\cdot7$
$Ga(C_2H_5)_3$	$-83\cdot2$	$142\cdot8$
$Ga(C_6H_5)_3$	166	

Gallium trimethyl is made by the action of gallium metal on mercury diethyl. It is spontaneously inflammable in air, even at $-78°$. It is hydrolysed by cold water ($25°$) to $(CH_3)_2GaOH$, and by hot water to $CH_3Ga(OH)_2$. It is readily chlorinated by hydrogen chloride in ether to $(CH_3)_2GaCl$ and $(CH_3)GaCl_2$. It forms numerous addition compounds, some of which are included in Table 17.16.

Table 17.16.   *Adducts Formed by* $Ga(CH_3)_3$

Donor	Adduct	m.p. of adduct, °C	b.p. (extr.) of adduct, °C	% dissociation of adduct in vapour phase at 100°
NH_3	$H_3N{\rightarrow}Ga(CH_3)_3$	31	179	For reactions on
$NH_2(CH_3)$	$(CH_3)H_2N{\rightarrow}Ga(CH_3)_3$	37	169	warming see below
$N(CH_3)_3$	$(CH_3)_3N{\rightarrow}Ga(CH_3)_3$	96·2	164	0
$P(CH_3)_3$	$CH_3)_3P{\rightarrow}Ga(CH_3)_3$	56·4	173	<10
$O(CH_3)_2$	$(CH_3)_2O{\rightarrow}Ga(CH_3)_3$		100	70
$O(C_2H_5)_2$	$(C_2H_5)_2O{\rightarrow}Ga(CH_3)_3$	−76	98	(70 at 25°)
$S(CH_3)_2$	$(CH_3)_2S{\rightarrow}Ga(CH_3)_3$		116	90

With $Ga(Me)_3$ as acceptor the donor properties of $X(CH_3)_3$ diminish in the order:

$$X = N > P > As > Sb > Bi,$$

and the donor properties of $X(CH_3)_2$ diminish in the order:

$$X = O > Se > S = Te.$$

If the group NH is present in the molecule of the donor, the effect of heating the adduct is to liberate CH_4, and to form a dimeric derivative containing three-centre bonds:

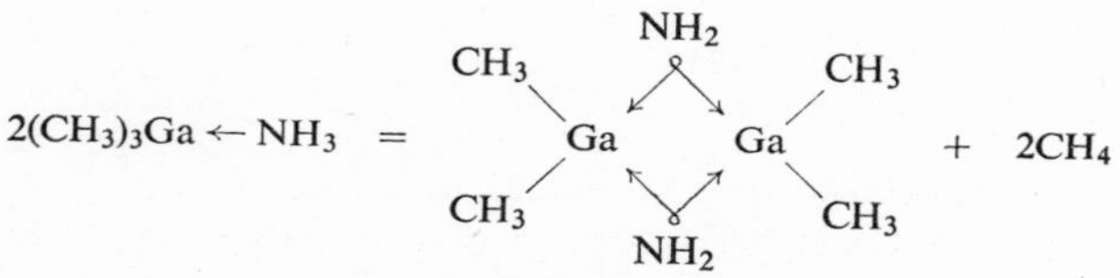

m.p. 97·2°, b.p. 212°

Similarly, $(CH_3)_3Ga{\leftarrow}NH_2(CH_3)_3$ yields:

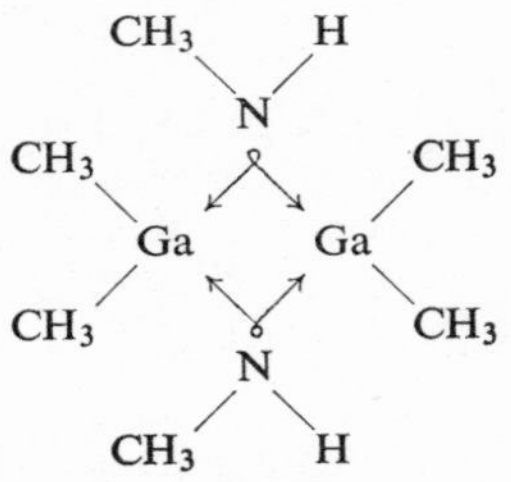

b.p. 226°

and $(CH_3)_3Ga{\leftarrow}NH(CH_3)_2$ yields:

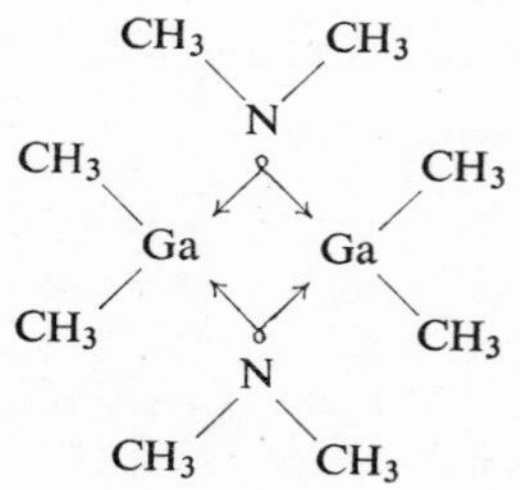

These reactions are parallel to those leading to the formation of aminodiborane (p. 519), and the aluminium compound $[(CH_3)_2Al—N(CH_3)_2]_2$ (p. 539).

Gallium triphenyl is made by the action of gallium metal on mercury diphenyl at 130°.

Gallium halides. Gallium trifluoride has a giant molecule structure, and is discussed on p. 548. Accounts of the chloride, bromide, and iodide are given below.

Gallium trichloride, Ga_2Cl_6, is a low-melting solid; the liquid boils at 201°. Gallium trichloride is made by heating the metal in chlorine, or in hydrogen chloride. It dissolves in hydrochloric acid as $HGaCl_4$, and it may be extracted from the solution by diethyl ether or *iso*-propyl ether. It is hygroscopic and fumes in moist air; it hisses when added to water. It forms ammines with ammonia. When it is added to lithium hydride suspended in ether, lithium gallium hydride is formed, $Li[GaH_4]$.

The vapour of gallium chloride does not attack Au, Pt, W, or Mo, but it attacks and chlorinates Ag, Cu, Zn, Cd. If the product of the attack on silver is heated, crystals of silver are formed and $GaCl_3$ sublimes. Hence there must be an equilibrium:

$$AgCl + GaCl_2 \rightleftharpoons Ag + GaCl_3.$$

The reaction might be used for making pure $GaCl_3$. Ga_2Cl_6 is more efficient than Al_2Cl_6 as a catalyst in the Friedel-Crafts' reaction.

Analysis of the Raman spectrum of solid gallium trichloride at 20° and of the liquid at 90°, and of the results of electron diffraction experiments on the vapour, indicate that the molecule is dimeric. In non-polar organic solvents the d.p.m. is zero.

Table 17.17. *Properties of the Gallium Trihalides*

	GaF_3	$GaCl_3$	$GaBr_3$	GaI_3
Appearance	White powder	Colourless crystals. Deliquescent	Colourless crystals. Deliquescent	Lemon yellow crystals. Hygroscopic
m.p. °C	About 1000	77·9	122	212
b.p. °C		201	280	346
Solubility in water	Slight (24 mg/litre)	Very soluble	Soluble	
% of monomer in vapour at b.p. under 1 atm pressure		2	30	87

NON-CHELATE COMPLEXES

Non-chelate Neutral Complexes

Compounds of this class are represented by the adducts formed by the union of donor compounds with gallium trichloride or gallium trimethyl (Table 17.16).

Non-chelate Complex Anions

This type of anion is present in the gallohydrides $LiGaH_4$ and $TlGaH_4$. $LiGaH_4$ is made by adding $GaCl_3$ to lithium hydride suspended in ether. The remarkable compound:

which is stable to 90°, is made by a reaction between trimethyl gallium ammoniate (Table 17.16) and sodamide:

$$NaNH_2 + 2(CH_3)_3GaNH_3 = 2NH_3 + [(CH_3)_3GaNH_2Ga(CH_3)_3]Na.$$

The anion furnishes an example of the donation of two lone pairs by one nitrogen atom.

SECTION 5. COMPOUNDS IN WHICH THE GALLIUM ATOM IS OCTAHEDRALLY HYBRIDISED

Examples may be found of gallium compounds representing the six classes of compounds included in this Section, Table 17.1. The trihydrate and triammoniate of gallium trifluoride (p. 548) are probably to be regarded as octahedral non-chelate neutral complexes:

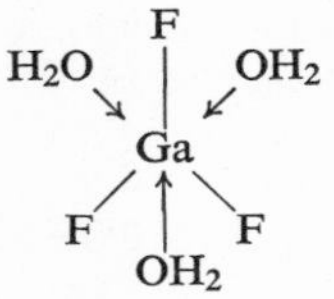

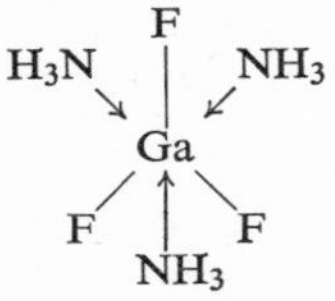

The **fluorogallates** are examples of salts containing a gallium atom in a non-chelate complex anion. There are two types (a) $M'_3[GaF_6]$, xH_2O, and (b) $M''[GaF_5,H_2O]$, $6H_2O$. M' may be Li, Na, K, Rb, Cs, or NH_4, and M'' may be Mn, Co, Ni, Cu, Zn, Cd. x is zero for the salts of Li, Na, and NH_4, 1 for the K salt, and 2 for the salts of Rb and Cs. Gallium forms no parallel complex anions containing chlorine, bromine, or iodine. The hydrated oxyacid salts such as $Ga(ClO_4)_3$, $6H_2O$, or $[Ga,6H_2O](ClO_4)_3$, contain an octahedral non-chelate complex cation.

Gallium acetylacetonate, $Ga(CO \cdot C_3H_7 \cdot CO)_3$, a volatile solid, m.p. 194°, is an example of a chelate neutral complex of the gallium atom in the octahedral valence state. The oxalato compounds, $M_3[Ga(C_2O_4)_3]$, $3H_2O$, where M may be K, Na, or NH_4, are examples of complex anions containing the gallium atom in the octahedral valence state. The chelate anion has neither plane nor centre of symmetry and no fourfold alternating axis of symmetry, and hence is optically active. The optically inactive salts may be resolved by preparation of the strychnine salt, from which the optically active alkali metal salts may be prepared.

INDIUM

PROPERTIES OF THE METAL

Indium is a white soft metal. The crystal is cubic close-packed with some distortion; each atom has four nearest neighbours at 3·24, and four next nearest neighbours at 3·36.

GENERAL CHEMISTRY OF INDIUM

The general chemistry of indium is very similar to that of gallium. The existence of many univalent compounds of indium indicates that the $5s$ electrons in the indium atom may become inert. Indium forms an anionic complex with sulphur, $Na(S \overset{\pi}{-} In \overset{\pi}{-} S)$ which has no analogue among the lighter elements in the sub-Group. The numbers of compounds in which the indium atom is digonally, trigonally, or tetrahedrally hybridised is small, but the range of octahedral compounds is greater than that of any other element in the sub-Group.

Table 17.18. *Reactions of Indium*

Reagent	Conditions of reaction	Result
Air	Cold	No action
Air	Hot	Burns to In_2O_3
Hydrogen		No action (from 0° to 900° indium absorbs less than 1 mgm of H_2 per 1000 gm)
Nitrogen		No action
Sulphur	Heat	In_2S_3 (red)
Chlorine		Burns to $InCl_3$
Water		Action only if oxygen is present
Mercury alkyls and aryls		$In(CH_3)_3$, $In(C_6H_5)_3$, etc.
HCl	200°	$InCl_2$
HCl	Dilute and cold	Slow attack
H_2SO_4	Dilute and cold	Slow attack
HCl	Concentrated solution	Rapid attack
HNO_3	Warm dilute solution	Attacked and dissolved
KOH		No attack, even with boiling concentrated solution

COMPOUNDS IN WHICH THE OXIDATION NUMBER OF INDIUM IS 1

Univalent indium. A number of binary compounds in which indium is thought to be univalent have been reported, including In_2O, In_2S, In_2Se, In_2Te, $InCl$, $InBr$, InI, $In[InCl_4]$, $In[AlCl_4]$, $In_3[InCl_6]$.

In_2O is made by the reduction of In_2O_3 with hydrogen below 400°. The fairly volatile In_2O is separated from the In_2O_3 by sublimation in vacuo at 750°. In_2O has its own X-ray pattern. It is not hygroscopic and does not turn red litmus blue. It is not acted on by cold water, but dilute hydrochloric acid dissolves it with the evolution of hydrogen.

$InCl$ is made by treating $In_3[InCl_6]$ with indium; the reaction is quick, and the $InCl$ can be distilled over in vacuo. It can also be obtained by extracting $In_3[InCl_6]$ or $In[AlCl_4]$ with ether; the etherate of the metal in the anion is formed:

$$In_3[InCl_6] + (C_2H_5)_2O = 3InCl + InCl_3,O(C_2H_5)_2.$$

There are two solid forms of $InCl$, one yellow and one red; the red form melts at 225° to a blood red liquid. In the presence of water $InCl$ disproportionates to $InCl_3$, and metallic indium. The vapour density at 1100–1400° is 1·05 times the value calculated for $InCl$. $InCl$ is diamagnetic.

Indium hexadichloroindate is described on p. 557.

$InBr$ is made by treating indium dibromide (probably $In[InBr_4]$) with indium. Both solid and liquid $InBr$ are red. With hot water $InBr$ disproportionates to $InBr_3$ and metallic indium. The vapour density at 1300° is 1·06 times the value calculated for $InBr$. The crystal structure is a layer structure similar to that of TlI. Each In atom has five Br atoms arranged round it at the corners of a rectangular pyramid. One distance In—Br is 2·80, and four others are 3·29. The indium atoms are similarly arranged about each bromine atom.

InI is the most stable of the indium univalent halides. It is a brown solid which liberates hydrogen very slowly from acids, and is scarcely attacked by hot water in the absence of oxygen. In the presence of oxygen it reacts:

$$2InI + 4H_2O + O_2 = 2In(OH)_3 + 2HI.$$

18*

COMPOUNDS IN WHICH THE OXIDATION NUMBER OF INDIUM IS 3†

SECTION 1. INDIUM COMPOUNDS WITH IONIC CHARACTER

The simple cation, In^{3+}, may perhaps be present in the indium salts of oxyacids such as $In(NO_3)_3,4\frac{1}{2}H_2O$, $In_2(SO_4)_3$, $In(ClO_4)_3,8H_2O$, but there is no definite evidence for its existence.

INDIUM COMPOUNDS CONSISTING OF GIANT MOLECULES IN WHICH THE BONDS HAVE SOME IONIC CHARACTER

Indium nitride, InN, is made by heating $(NH_4)_3[InF_6]$ in ammonia to 600°. It is a grey powder, with a wurtzite lattice, and resembles GaN.

Indium trioxide, In_2O_3, can be made by heating the metal in air; or by heating $In(OH)_3$, In_2CO_3, $In(NO_3)_3$, $In_2(SO_4)_3$. Indium trioxide is yellow at room temperature. It is soluble in acids but not in alkalis; the salt $Mg(InO_2)_2$ is obtained, however, by the action of magnesium oxide on boiling $InCl_3$ solution.

The crystal structure of indium trioxide is that of the A-M_2O_3 oxides (p. 1011).

Indium trihydroxide, $In(OH)_3$, is formed as a colourless, gelatinous precipitate when alkali is added to a solution of an indic salt. It loses water to yield In_2O_3 at 170°. Its solubility in water at 20° is 0.37×10^{-3} mg/litre. It is amphoteric and is soluble in acids and in alkalis, but the alkaline solution deposits $In(OH)_3$ on standing.

Indium trisulphide, In_2S_3. A yellow precipitate of In_2S_3 is obtained by passing hydrogen sulphide through a feebly acid solution of an indic salt; the precipitate is insoluble in yellow ammonium sulphide. A red form of In_2S_3 is obtained by heating indium in sulphur vapour. The red form, m.p. 1090–1100°, is non-volatile and stable to water. The red form, if heated in air to about 400°, is oxidised to a mixture of $In_2(SO_4)_3$ and In_2O_3.

In_2S_3 exists in two crystalline modifications: a low temperature, α-form, which has a cubic face-centred lattice of sulphur atoms, and contains $\frac{2}{3}$ of the In atoms in the octahedral holes, and $\frac{1}{3}$ in the tetrahedral holes, and a high temperature β-form which has a spinel-like lattice, similar to that of γ-Al_2O_3.

Indium trifluoride, InF_3, is made by heating In_2O_3 with fluorine at 500°, or by heating $(NH_4)_3InF_6$ in fluorine. The anhydrous compound is sparingly soluble in water at room temperature, and does not react with it. When it is heated with hydrogen or with indium it forms InF_2.

The trihydrate $InF_3,3H_2O$ is made by dissolving indic hydroxide in aqueous hydrofluoric acid. Its solubility in water is much greater than that of anhydrous indic fluoride, and hence it may be argued that the hydrated compound is complex.

SECTION 2. COMPOUNDS IN WHICH THE INDIUM ATOM IS DIGONALLY HYBRIDISED

There are two types of compound which may be assigned to this Section, the alkali metal salts of the oxide O—In—OH, and the corresponding sulphur compounds such as $Na(InS_2)$. If an indic salt in aqueous solution is treated with sodium sulphide the complex, $Na(InS_2),4H_2O$, which is only slightly soluble in water, is precipitated. Potassium sulphide reacts similarly, but ammonium sulphide yields the anhydrous compound, $NH_4(InS_2)$. All the compounds are oxidised by air to indium sulphate. The

†There are no compounds in which the oxidation number of indium is 2. Compounds have been described to which the compositions InF_2, $InCl_2$, $InBr_2$, and InI_2 were assigned. It has now been shown (R. J. Clark, E. Griswold, and J. Kleinberg, *J. Amer. Chem. Soc.*, 1958, **80**, 4764) that the chlorine and iodine compounds have the respective constitutions $In_3[InCl_6]$ and $In[InI_4]$; the structures of the fluorine and bromine compounds are not certain.

structure of the ion InS_2 is probably $(S—In—S)^-$, and it may be compared with that of the ions $(S—Hg—S)^{2-}$, $(S—Tl—S)^-$, and $(O—In—O)^-$.

SECTION 3. THE INDIUM ATOM IN THE TRIGONAL VALENCE STATE

Indium resembles gallium in forming trialkyls and trihalides which are monomeric only at high temperatures. It is assumed that at room temperature these compounds are polymers with bridge structures but there is no definite evidence for this assumption. The trialkyls and trihalides are discussed in Section 4.

SECTION 4. COMPOUNDS IN WHICH THE INDIUM ATOM IS TETRAHEDRALLY HYBRIDISED

ELECTRON-DEFICIENT POLYMERS. BRIDGE COMPOUNDS

The indium alkyls and aryls. Indium trimethyl, $In(CH_3)_3$, is made by heating metallic indium with mercury dimethyl at 100° for eight days. It is very readily oxidised, and at ordinary temperatures reacts with water thus:

$$In(CH_3)_3 + 2H_2O = In(CH_3)(OH)_2 + 2CH_4$$

and with dilute acid:

$$In(CH_3)_3 + 3HCl = InCl_3 + 3CH_4.$$

Indium trimethyl forms no amines at $-35°$ or any higher temperature. The indium alkyl etherates are mentioned on p. 556.

Table 17.19.   *The Alkyls and Aryls of Indium*

	m.p., °C	b.p., °C	
$In(CH_3)_3$	88·4	135·8	Sublimes at room temperature in vacuo. Monomeric in vapour at 80–139°. Tetrameric in benzene at f.p.
$In(C_2H_5)_3$	−32	144	
$In(C_3H_7)_3$	−51	178	
$In(Nonyl)_3$			Decomp. at b.p.
$2In(CH_3)_3 \cdot (C_2H_5)_2O$	−15	139	
$In(OCH_3)_3$	250		Insoluble in benzene
$In(C_6H_5)_3$	208		Easily soluble in chloroform or benzene

Indium triphenyl, $In(C_6H_5)_3$, is made from metallic indium and mercury diphenyl. Indium triphenyl is easily soluble in organic solvents. It reacts quickly and quantitatively with bromine and iodine to yield, with bromine, the derivatives $In(C_6H_5)_2Br$, $In(C_6H_5)Br_2$, and $InBr_3$. On oxidation indium triphenyl yields phenol and p-monohydroxydiphenyl. It is not attacked by mercury in boiling benzene.

Indium halides. The properties of the indium halides are summarised in Table 17.20. Indium trifluoride is briefly discussed on p. 554.

Indic chloride, $InCl_3$, can be obtained by burning indium in chlorine, or by heating indic oxide with chlorine and carbon, or with chlorine and carbon tetrachloride. It is hygroscopic, fumes in moist air, and hisses when brought into contact with water.

Indic iodide, InI_3. X-ray analysis of the fused compound indicates a tetrahedral configuration of iodine atoms round indium atoms. In—I is 2·70. It could not be established whether InI_3 is monomeric or dimeric.

Table 17.20.   *Indium Halides*

	InF_3	$InCl_3$	$InBr_3$	InI_3
m.p. °C	1170	586	436	210
b.p. °C	1200	Volatilises at 600	Volatilises easily	
Equiv. cond. of liquid at m.p., ohm^{-1} cm^{-1} c.c.		14·7	6·4	2·3
Solubility of anhydrous trihalide at 15°	40 mgm/100 gm			
Solubility of trihydrated trihalides at 22° gm/100 gm	8·49	183·3	557	1091
State in vapour		Dimeric	Dimeric	Dimeric
Distances (electron diffraction)		2·46	2·57	2·76
Colour, solid		Colourless	Colourless	Yellow
liquid		Yellow	Pale brown	Pale brown

Range of Stability of Indium Halide Hydrates

Halide	Hydrate	Temperature range, °C	Halide	Hydrate	Temperature range, °C	Halide	Hydrate	Temperature range, °C
$InCl_3$	$4H_2O$	< 27·5	$InBr_3$	$5H_2O$	< 21	InI_3	Anhydrous salt	0–70
	$3H_2O$	27·5–76		$2H_2O$	22–33			
	$2\frac{1}{2}H_2O$	76–98		Anhydrous salt	> 33			
	$2H_2O$	> 98						

The chloride, bromide, and iodide form a number of double salts with lithium halides, thallium halides, and the halides of the alkaline earth metals. These double salts, e.g. $MgCl_2,2InCl_3,10H_2O$, contain large numbers of molecules of water of crystallisation.

OTHER COMPOUNDS WHICH CONTAIN THE INDIUM ATOM IN THE TETRAHEDRAL VALENCE STATE

The indium alkyl etherates are examples of a class of compounds which contain the indium atom in the tetrahedral valence state. The etherates of the indium alkyls are made by the action of $InCl_3$ or $InBr_3$ on the appropriate Grignard reagent in ethereal solution. They all inflame in dry air, and are decomposed by water. $2In(CH_3)_3 \cdot O(C_2H_5)_2$ is a rare example of a compound in which an oxygen atom donates both lone pairs. The indium alkyl etherates are not electron deficient.

Indium tetraiodoindate, $In[InI_4]$, has been prepared; the anion $[InI_4]^-$ is an example of a tetrahedral complex anion formed by indium.

SECTION 5. COMPOUNDS IN WHICH THE INDIUM ATOM IS OCTAHEDRALLY HYBRIDISED

There are no non-chelate neutral complexes of indium in the octahedral valence state.

Non-chelate complex anions. Three representatives of this class of compound are $(NH_4)_3[InF_6]$, $K_3[InCl_6]$, and $(NH_4)_2[InCl_5,H_2O]$. $(NH_4)_3[InF_6]$, when heated with ammonia, gives InN; when heated with fluorine gives InF_3. X-ray diffraction experiments on single crystals show that the anion $[InCl_5,H_2O]^{2-}$ is octahedral, but distorted to include the water molecule. $(NH_4)_2[InCl_5,H_2O]$ and $(NH_4)_2[FeCl_5,H_2O]$ are isomorphous.

Indium hexachloroindate, $In_3[InCl_6]$, has been made by heating mercuric chloride with indium metal in vacuo at 350°. It is an orange-coloured solid which melts at 314° to a red liquid.

Non-chelate complex cations. Complex cations may be present in the hydrates of the oxyacid salts such as $In_2(SO_4)_3,6H_2O$ or $In(ClO_4)_3,8H_2O$.

Chelate neutral complexes. Indium acetylacetonate, InA_3, is known, m.p. 186° sublimation point 140° under 10 mm pressure. It exists in two crystalline forms.

Chelate complex anions. The oxalato compounds have the general formula:

$$M \begin{bmatrix} C_2O_4 & C_2O_4 \\ & In & \\ H_2O & OH_2 \end{bmatrix} (x-2)H_2O. \qquad \begin{matrix} \text{If } M = \text{Na} & x = 3 \\ \text{K} & x = 4 \\ \text{NH}_4 & x = 2. \end{matrix}$$

Chelate complex cations. $(In\ en_3)Cl_3$ is formed by the direct action of anhydrous ethylenediamine on indic chloride. It is sparingly soluble in EtOH, MeOH, $CHCl_3$, and in 1:4 dioxane. It is soluble in water, which readily hydrolyses it to $In(OH)_3$. On heating the changes occur:

$$(In\ en_3)Cl_3 \xrightarrow{140°} (In\ en_2Cl_2)Cl \xrightarrow{280-420°} InCl_3.$$

THALLIUM

PROPERTIES OF THE METAL

Thallium is a white soft metal.

Table 17.21. *Reactions of Thallium*

Reagent	Conditions of reaction	Result
Air	Room temperature	Oxide
	Heated	Burns to Tl_2O_3
Hydrogen		No action
Nitrogen		No action
Sulphur	Heated	Tl_2S_3
Chlorine		$TlCl_3$
Water	Cold in the absence of oxygen	No action
Steam	Red heat	Tl_2O
HCl $\left.\begin{matrix} \\ \\ \end{matrix}\right\}$		
H_2SO_4	Dilute	Metal is dissolved
HNO_3		

The ionisation potentials of the four outermost electrons in the thallium atom are:

$5d$	$6s$	$6s$	$6p$
50·5	29·7	20·72	6·07

The thallium atom uses the three electrons in the valency shell ($n = 6$) for bond formation. When all three electrons are so used the bonding is always covalent; there is no evidence for the existence of the simple trivalent cation, Tl^{3+}.

One of the remarkable aspects of the chemistry of thallium is the prominence of the univalent, or thallous, compounds. Univalent boron does not exist. There is some evidence for the existence of univalent aluminium and univalent gallium, and much more for the existence of univalent indium; the indous halides (p. 553) are fairly well characterised. At thallium, the next member of sub-Group III N, there is a striking change. The thallous compounds are numerous and as sharply defined as the corresponding compounds of the alkali metals. The existence of the thallous compounds must be due to a condition of the thallium atom in which the $6s$ electrons are inert, and form a closed shell like the $1s$ shell of the helium atom. The single $6p$ electron in the thallium atom in this state then behaves more or less as the $2s$ electron in the lithium atom, or as the $4s$ electron in the copper atom.

COMPOUNDS IN WHICH THE OXIDATION STATE OF THALLIUM IS 1

UNIVALENT THALLIUM COMPOUNDS (THALLOUS COMPOUNDS)

In the univalent thallium compounds the two $6s$ electrons of the valency shell of the thallium atom are part of the atomic core, and only the $6p$ electron is used for bond formation. The bond formed by the thallium atom in this state may be covalent, as for example in thallium acetylacetonate, but more frequently it is ionic. In the thallous state, therefore, the thallium atom has analogies with the atom of an alkali metal such as sodium, or a coinage metal such as copper.

It is interesting to compare the properties of univalent thallium with those of an alkali metal and a coinage metal having ionic radii as near as possible to that of the thallous ion Tl^+. The aurous ion is probably closest in properties to the thallous ion, but it is unstable, and the argentous ion is therefore chosen instead; of the alkali metals the rubidium ion is closest in radius to the thallous ion. The following tables set out some of the properties of univalent thallium, the alkali metals, and the coinage metals.

Table 17.22. *Ionic Radii and Mobilities of certain Univalent Ions*

	Tl	K	Rb	Cs	Ag	Cu
Ionic radius	1·44	1·33	1·49	1·65	1·13	1·0
Mobility at 18°	65·6	64·7	67·5	68·0	54·3	

Table 17.23. *Crystal Structures of the Halides of certain Univalent Metals*

	Rb		Tl		Ag	
	Radius ratio†	Structure	Radius ratio†	Structure	Radius ratio†	Structure
F	1·12	NaCl	1·09	NaCl	0·85	NaCl
Cl	0·83	NaCl	0·80	CsCl	0·63	NaCl
Br	0·76	NaCl	0·74	CsCl	0·58	NaCl
I	0·68	NaCl	0·66	CsCl	0·53	Wurtzite

†The standard limits for the radius ratios of the structures are (p. 345):

CsCl, 1 and 0·73,   NaCl, 0·73 and 0·41,   Wurtzite, 0·41 and 0·23.

The discrepancy between these values and those in Table 17.23 shows that the deductions on pp. 346–9 are only approximate.

Table 17.24. *Melting Points of the Halides of certain Univalent Metals,* °C

	K	Rb	Tl	Ag	Cu
F	846	760	327	435	908
Cl	768	715	430	449	430
Br	730	682	460	434	504
I	723	642	440	552	605

Table 17.25. *Boiling Points of the Halides of certain Univalent metals,* °C

	K	Rb	Tl	Ag	Cu
Fluoride	1490	1410	655	—	—
Chloride	1411	1390	806	1554	1367
Bromide	ca. 1400	1340	815	700 (decomp.)	1345
Iodide	ca. 1400	1300	824	—	1290

Table 17.26. *Solubilities of the Salts of certain Univalent Metals*

(The solubilities are expressed as moles of salt per 100 moles of water. Temperatures are indicated by superscripts)

	Rb		Tl		Ag	
Fluoride	[18]	22·5	[15]	6·06	[15]	25·8
Chloride	[20]	13·6	[20]	$2·4 \times 10^{-2}$	[10]	$1·12 \times 10^{-5}$
Bromide	[15]	10·7	[25]	$3·2 \times 10^{-4}$		$8·05 \times 10^{-7}$
Iodide	[17]	12·9	[20]	$3·48 \times 10^{-4}$		$2·30 \times 10^{-8}$
Carbonate	[20]	35·1	[15]	$1·55 \times 10^{-1}$	[20]	$2·09 \times 10^{-4}$
Nitrate	[20]	4·25	[0]	$6·45 \times 10^{-1}$	[0]	1·29
Sulphate	[10]	2·87	[20]	$1·74 \times 10^{-1}$	[0]	$3·3 \times 10^{-2}$
Hydroxide	[15]	31·6		2·11		—
Chromate	[0]	3·90	[60]	$1·03 \times 10^{-3}$	[0]	$7·60 \times 10^{-5}$
Sulphide		very soluble	[20]	$8·2 \times 10^{-4}$	[20]	$1·02 \times 10^{-6}$

From Table 17.24 it is seen that the melting points of the thallous halides are nearer to those of the silver halides than to those of the halides of potassium or rubidium. From Table 17.25 it is seen that the boiling points of the thallous halides are several hundred degrees lower than those of the halides of the other metals.

The solubilities of the corresponding salts of rubidium, thallium, and silver in the neighbourhood of room temperature are set out in Table 17.26. The solubilities of the rubidium salts are all roughly of the order of 15 moles of salt to 100 of water. For thallium the solubilities of the fluoride, carbonate, nitrate, sulphate, and hydroxide, do not greatly differ from the average value of 1 mole of salt per 100 moles of water: the solubilities of the chloride, bromide, iodide, sulphide, and chromate, however, are of the order 10^{-3} moles per 100 moles of water. A parallel, but greater, difference is observed between the solubilities of the two groups of corresponding silver salts. The solubilities of the alkali metal salts show no such sudden variation.

The following resemblances are apparent:

(a) *between thallous salts and both rubidium and silver salts,*
    (i) the ions are colourless,
    (ii) the salts are nearly all anhydrous;
(b) *between thallous thallium and an alkali metal,*
    (i) the ionic mobilities are about 66,
    (ii) the hydroxides are soluble and strong bases,
    (iii) the azides are not explosive,
    (iv) the metallic ions have little power of forming complexes,
    (v) the metals form polysulphides, Tl_2S_5 and K_2S_5,
    (vi) the salts are often isomorphous:
        thallous nitrate is isodimorphic with potassium nitrate
        thallous chlorate is isomorphous with potassium chlorate
        thallous perchlorate is isomorphous with potassium perchlorate
        thallous chromate is isomorphous with potassium chromate
        $Tl_2LiBi(NO_2)_6$ is isomorphous with $K_2LiBi(NO_2)_6$
        the thallous ion can replace an alkali metal ion in an alum;
(c) *between thallous salts and silver salts,*
    (i) the melting points of the halides are close,
    (ii) the solubilities of the chloride, bromide, iodide, sulphide, and chromate are low.

Certain of the more important thallous compounds are described in the following paragraphs. In the solid state several of the compounds have giant molecule structures.

Thallous azide, TlN_3, is easily soluble in water. Like the alkali metal azides it is not explosive.

Thallous nitride, Tl_3N, is made by the action of thallous chloride on potassamide dissolved in liquid ammonia.

Thallous oxide, Tl_2O, is made by passing air and steam over granulated thallium. It is a black, hygroscopic solid, m.p. about 300°. The fused oxide attacks glass. It reacts with water to yield the hydroxide which dissolves.

Thallous hydroxide, TlOH, is made by the action of water on thallous oxide. The reaction is reversible, and if thallous hydroxide is allowed to stand in vacuo at room temperature, or is heated to 100° in the atmosphere, it yields the oxide:

$$Tl_2O + H_2O = 2TlOH; \qquad \Delta H = -2 \times 3 \cdot 12 \text{ kcal.}$$

Thallous hydroxide is a yellow solid. It is a fairly strong base and it absorbs carbon dioxide from the air. It attacks the skin and glass. The aqueous solution is readily oxidised by air to Tl_2O_3, which is precipitated. Thallous hydroxide hydrolyses ethyl iodide to ethyl alcohol, but with alcohol in excess the reaction occurs:

$$4C_2H_5OH + 4TlOH = [TlOC_2H_5]_4 + 4H_2O.$$

With acetylacetone in alcohol it gives the acetylacetonate (p. 562).

Thallous sulphide, Tl_2S, is made (i) by the precipitation of a solution of a thallous salt with ammonium sulphide, or (ii) by the reduction with hydrogen of thallous sulphate at the m.p. 632°.

Thallous sulphide is insoluble in ammonium sulphide, sodium hydroxide, or acetic acid solution, but it is soluble in mineral acids. It is a black solid, m.p. 433°. Its crystal structure is a layered lattice like that of lead iodide. It reacts with carbon disulphide to give Tl_2CS_3 (p. 561). It is only sparingly soluble in water (Table 17.26). Tl_2Se, m.p. 340° (grey), and Tl_2Te have been made.

Thallous pentasulphide, Tl_2S_5, is made by adding thallous chloride to a solution of ammonium polysulphide. It exists as black shining crystals, m.p. 310°.

Thallous halides. Some of the properties of these compounds are given in Table 17.27.

Table 17.27. The Thallous Halides

	TlF	TlCl	TlBr	TlI
m.p. °C	327	430	456	440
b.p. °C	655 ± 10	806	815	824
Solubility moles per 100 moles of water	$^{15°}$ 6·06	$^{20°}$ $2·4 \times 10^{-2}$	$^{25°}$ $3·2 \times 10^{-4}$	$^{20°}$ $3·48 \times 10^{-4}$
Hydrates	None			
Crystal structure	Deformed NaCl lattice	CsCl lattice	CsCl lattice	Above 170°: CsCl lattice Below 170°: layer lattice
Colour	None	None	None	Above 170°: red Below 170°: yellow

The low solubilities of the chloride, bromide, and iodide enable these compounds to be made by adding the appropriate acid to a solution of thallous nitrate.

Thallous chloride is not soluble in hydrochloric acid solution, and only slightly soluble in aqueous ammonia or aqueous potassium cyanide; this behaviour is evidence of the reluctance of the thallous ion to act as an electron acceptor. If thallous chloride is treated with chlorine at 160° and 7 atm it yields thallic chloride.

Thallous iodide is polymorphic. Below 170° the crystals are yellow and have a layer lattice; above 170° the crystals are red and have a CsCl lattice. At 440° the crystals melt to a black liquid.

The action of bromine or chlorine on the thallous halide ultimately yields the thallic compound, but well-defined intermediate compounds may be isolated:

Tl_2Cl_3 or $(Tl^+)_3(TlCl_6{}^{3-})$. The existence of this compound is revealed by phase-rule studies of the system $TlCl—TlCl_3—H_2O$ from 30–90°. The substance is yellow and is unaffected by water. If a potential gradient is applied to the solution, thallium migrates both to the anode and to the cathode, thus showing that it is present in both anion and cation.

$TlCl_2$ or $(Tl^+)(TlCl_4{}^-)$. The existence of this compound is revealed by phase-rule studies. It is colourless. It is decomposed by water.

$(Tl^+)_3(TlBr_6{}^{3-})$ is bright red and is decomposed by water.

$(Tl^+)(TlBr_4{}^-)$ is yellow and is decomposed by water.

Thallous halides with lithium ethyl and methyl iodide in ether give thallium trimethyl.

The thallous oxysalts mentioned below are well characterised:

Tl_2CO_3, m.p. 272°. Its aqueous solution is alkaline.

Tl_2CS_3 is made by the action of carbon disulphide on a suspension of Tl_2S in alkali. Its colour is vermilion. Is stable in the cold, but all the CS_2 is lost in vacuo at 100°. Its formation is used as a delicate test for thallium.

$TlNO_3$ is trimorphic, m.p. 206°. At 300° it decomposes yielding Tl_2O_3 and oxides of nitrogen.

Tl_2SO_4, m.p. 632°, at which temperature it is reduced by H_2 to Tl_2S and metal.

$TlClO_4$, m.p. 500°.

$TlClO_3$, $TlBrO_3$, $TlIO_3$, are known.

The blue *thallous perchromate* is highly explosive.

Thallous phosphate is soluble in water.

COMPLEX THALLOUS COMPOUNDS

The univalent thallous atom has acceptor properties, but they appear to be weak because, for instance, thallous chloride does not dissolve in an aqueous solution of ammonia, or in alcohol, and it is only very slightly soluble in hydrochloric acid.

Three compounds in which the thallous atom is behaving as an acceptor call for special comment, thallous ethoxide, thallous acetylacetonate, and the thiourea complex, $[Tl(SC(NH_2)_2)_4]Cl$. These are undoubtedly thallous derivatives, but the orbital structures assigned to them are unusual and must be regarded as provisional.

Thallous ethoxide, $[Tl(OC_2H_5)]_4$, is tetrameric. It is a liquid, m.p. $-30°$. It is made by the action of ethyl alcohol on thallous hydroxide, or by oxidising thallium in the presence of alcohol. It is only partially miscible with ethyl alcohol, but it is soluble in benzene. This behaviour suggests that it is covalent, and that the thallium atom is in a state in which it does not easily become an electron acceptor. The molecular weight of this compound in benzene as determined by the freezing point, and in methyl and ethyl alcohol as determined by the boiling point, shows that it is tetrameric, even in $0.2M$ solution. The configuration of the molecule is taken to be cubic;

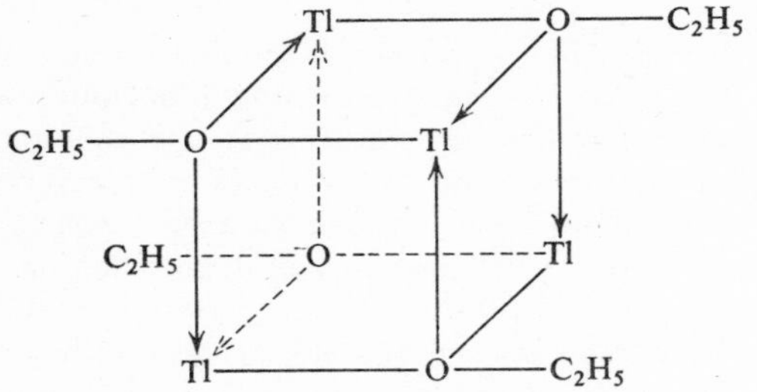

The molecule is built of four groups, $Tl—O—C_2H_5$. Each oxygen atom is assumed to be linked by π bonds to two neighbouring thallium atoms. If this is so, each oxygen atom is digonally hybridised, and exerts two σ bonds and two π bonds. Inspection of the figure shows that the cubic structure can be attained without distortion of the natural inter-orbital angles.

This structure requires that π bonds are formed between thallium atoms and oxygen atoms not linked by σ bonds. The rarity of such an arrangement is pointed out on p. 126. If it is the correct orbital structure for thallium ethyl oxide, it is strange that it is not more frequently encountered.

Thallous acetylacetonate, m.p. 161°, with the structure

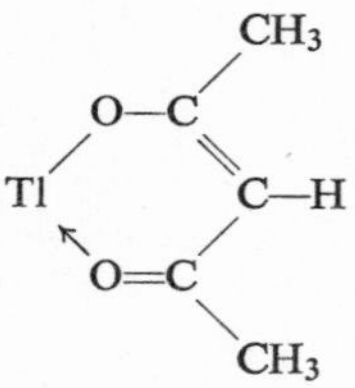

is a member of a fairly extensive class of compounds. In this class are found the thallous derivatives of propionylacetone (m.p. 86° with decomposition), dipropionyl methane (m.p. 68.5°), benzoylacetone, methyl acetylacetone, methyl benzoylacetone, acetoacetic ester, and salicylaldehyde. There is evidence, from the b.p. of the alcoholic solution, that the acetoacetic ester derivative is dimeric in 10% solution.

Thallous acetylacetonate exists as white crystals. It is soluble in benzene. In contact with water it is hydrolysed so that the solution can be titrated against an acid. Thallous acetylacetonate is made by the action of acetylacetone on thallous hydroxide in alcohol. It differs from the sodium derivative of benzoylacetone (p. 416). The sodium compound chars without melting when heated, it does not dissolve in non-polar solvents, and while it dissolves in water it reacts only to form the dihydrate. In general, the sodium compound is the more ionic in character, which would be expected if in the sodium compound the bonding electron from the sodium atom is an *s* electron, while in the thallium compound the bonding electron from the thallium atom is a *p* electron. The covalent bonding of the thallium atom cannot result from *sp* digonal hybridisation, because the 6*s* electrons are inert. The hybridisation must result from the combination of two *p* orbitals unless the molecule is in a highly excited state, for which there is no evidence.

X-ray examination of the salts of the thallium thiourea complex such as $[Tl(SC(NH_2)_2)_4]Cl$, shows that the cation is square planar. It is difficult to assign an orbital structure to the cation which is in accordance with this result.

COMPOUNDS IN WHICH THE OXIDATION NUMBER OF THALLIUM IS 3

SECTION 1. THALLIC COMPOUNDS HAVING GIANT MOLECULE STRUCTURES IN WHICH THE BONDS HAVE SOME IONIC CHARACTER

By analogy with the other members of sub-Group III N thallic oxide, thallic sulphide, and thallic fluoride (which differs sharply in properties from the chloride) are regarded as having giant molecule structures. Thallic oxide has the Mn_2O_3 structure; there is no experimental evidence on the crystal lattices of the other two compounds.

Thallic oxide, Tl_2O_3, is made (i) by heating the metal in air, (ii) by heating the thallic salt of a volatile oxyacid, (iii) by precipitating the solution of a thallic salt with alkali. Thallic oxide is a black powder. It begins to dissociate to thallous oxide when heated to 100°. Under a pressure of 25 cm of oxygen it melts at 717°. It is scarcely soluble in water (0.251×10^{-5} mg/litre at 25°). It forms no hydrates; the precipitate obtained by method (iii) above has been shown by X-ray analysis to be the anhydrous oxide.

Thallic oxide reacts with fluorine at 300° to yield TlF_3, and with chlorine to yield $TlCl_3$.

Thallic sulphide, Tl_2S_3, can be made by fusing a mixture of thallium and sulphur, and distilling off the excess of sulphur. If hydrogen sulphide is passed into the aqueous solution of a thallic salt, thallous sulphide Tl_2S, and sulphur are produced. Thallic sulphide, nevertheless, dissolves in warm dilute sulphuric acid to give a solution of thallic sulphate.

Thallic fluoride, TlF_3, is made by passing fluorine over thallic oxide at 300°. It is white or colourless, and can be heated in fluorine up to its m.p. 550° without decomposition, but it decomposes if heated alone. It is hygroscopic and is hydrolysed by moist air.

SECTION 2. THE THALLIUM ATOM IN THE DIGONAL VALENCE STATE

No thallium compound can be assigned with certainty to this Section. The complex anion in the dark red powder, $KTlS_2$, obtained by fusing thallous sulphate with potassium carbonate and sulphur, is isoelectronic with carbon dioxide, and may have the structure $[S\overset{\pi}{-}Tl\overset{\pi}{-}S]^-$. There are several compounds with the general formula

TlX$_3$ which probably consist of the tautomeric forms, TlX$_3 \rightleftharpoons$ [X—Tl—X]$^+$X$^-$. Among them are (written in the ionic form):

[I—Tl—I]I	[(C$_2$H$_5$)$_2$Tl]Cl
[Cl—Tl—Br]Cl	[(C$_6$H$_5$)$_2$Tl]Cl
[Br—Tl—Br]Cl	[(C$_6$H$_5$)$_2$Tl]Br
[(C$_2$H$_5$)$_2$Tl]OH	[(C$_6$H$_5$)TlBr]Br

There is no clear evidence on the relative stability of the ionic and the covalent forms, and for convenience all these compounds are included in Section 3.

SECTION 3. COMPOUNDS IN WHICH THE THALLIUM ATOM IS TRIGONALLY HYBRIDISED

Compounds in this Section include the thallium trialkyls and triaryls (of which at least thallium trimethyl is monomeric in benzene solution), the thallium alkyl and aryl halides, and the thallium trihalides if they are simple covalent compounds. As explained under Section 2, the alkyl halides and the halides can exist either in a covalent form which places them in this Section, or in an ionic form which places them in Section 2. Thallium hydride has not been reported.

Thallium alkyls and aryls. Thallium trimethyl in benzene solution is found to be monomeric by the freezing point method. There is no definite evidence on the structures of the other trialkyl or triaryl derivatives, but they are regarded as simple tri-covalent compounds by analogy. The methods of preparation and properties of these compounds are presented in Table 17.28.

Table 17.28.   *Thallic Alkyls and Aryls*

		Tl(CH$_3$)$_3$	Tl(C$_2$H$_5$)$_3$	Tl(C$_6$H$_5$)$_3$
	Prepara-tion	Made quantitatively by reaction: 2CH$_3$Li+CH$_3$I+TlCl =(CH$_3$)$_3$Tl+LiCl +LiI	(i) Made quantitatively by reaction: (C$_2$H$_5$)$_2$TlCl+LiC$_2$H$_5$ =(C$_2$H$_5$)$_3$Tl+LiCl (ii) Made by reaction: 3C$_2$H$_5$Cl+TlNa alloy =(C$_2$H$_5$)$_3$Tl+3NaCl Solid, colourless; liquid, yellow	Made by the reaction (C$_6$H$_5$)$_2$TlCl+ Li(C$_6$H$_5$) =(C$_6$H$_5$)$_3$Tl +LiCl
	Colour	None		
	m.p. °C	38·5	−63	169
	b.p. °C	147 (extr.)	192 (extr.); 55/1·5 mm	—
Reaction with	Heat	Explodes above 90°	Gives thallium and hydrocarbons	
	Air	Spontaneously inflammable	Not spontaneously inflammable; fumes	Oxidised
	Water	Hydrolysed to (CH$_3$)$_2$TlOH	Hydrolysed to (C$_2$H$_5$)$_2$TlOH	Hydrolysed to (C$_6$H$_5$)$_2$TlOH
	Acids	All hydrolysed to salts of the above bases		
	Organic solvents	Miscible in benzene in which it is mono-meric. Forms unstable etherate	Soluble in ether but forms no etherates	Treated with CO$_2$ in boiling xylene (not benzene) it gives diphenyl and benzoic acid.

The thallium alkyl and aryl halides and hydroxides.

(C$_2$H$_5$)$_2$TlCl, is made by the action of hydrochloric acid on thallium triethyl, or by the action of magnesium ethyl chloride on thallium trichloride. It is stable and is not attacked by air or water. If the ethyl group is replaced by a secondary alkyl group the stability of the compound is much reduced. $(C_2H_5)_2TlCl$ reacts with lithium ethyl to regenerate the triethyl compound.

$(C_2H_5)_2TlOH$, is made by the action of water on thallium triethyl. It is soluble in water and is quite a strong base; it is 60% dissociated in $N/10$ aqueous solution, and hence the ionic form is important.

$(C_6H_5)_2TlCl$ and $(C_6H_5)_2TlOH$, are made by reactions parallel to those which produce the corresponding ethyl compounds.

$(C_6H_5)TlCl_2$, m.p. 234°, is made by boiling excess of thallium trichloride in water with phenyl boric acid, $C_6H_5B(OH)_2$. $(C_6H_5)TlBr_2$ is made similarly using thallium tribromide. These compounds tend to disproportionate, yielding $(C_6H_5)_2TlCl$ or $(C_6H_5)_2TlBr$ and thallium trihalide.

Thallic halides. The anhydrous compounds (Table 17.29) all have the same empirical formula TlX_3, but their constitutions are different. The apparently simple compound TlX_3 may actually be a mixture of two compounds having more complex structures.

The fluoride is considered on p. 563.

Table 17.29. *Thallic Halides*

	TlF_3	$TlCl_3$	$TlBr_3$	TlI_3
Preparation and m.p. °C	Fluorine on Tl_2O_3 at 300; m.p. 550 in fluorine	(i) Chlorine on Tl_2O_3; m.p. 60–70 in Cl_2 (ii) Dehydrate tetrahydrate over P_2O_5; m.p. 25 in Cl_2		(i) Treat TlI with alcoholic solution of iodine (ii) Add KI to solution of thallic sulphate
Colours	White	Colourless		Black
Action of heat	Loses fluorine	Loses chlorine at at 40°		Loses iodine readily
Water Solubility	Hygroscopic	Hygroscopic		Very sparing (0·4 gm/litre)
Hydrates		$TlCl_3,4H_2O$ $TlCl_3,H_2O$	$TlBr_3,4H_2O$ $TlBr_3,H_2O$	
Structure of anhydrous compound	Ionic	Tricovalent		$Tl^+(I_3)^-$ $\rightleftharpoons (I—Tl—I)^+I^-$

The chloride is dimorphic; one form, made by the action of chlorine on thallic oxide, has m.p. 60–70° in chlorine under pressure, and the other form, made by the dehydration of the tetrahydrate over phosphorus pentoxide in vacuo, has m.p. about 25° under chlorine at pressure. The existence of the bromide is doubtful; dehydration of the tetrahydrate yields $Tl^+(Tl^{III}Br_4)^-$. The iodide may be either thallous per-iodide $Tl^+[I_3]^-$, or $(I—Tl—I)^+I^-$.

The structures of the hydrates of the chloride and bromide call for attention. The tetrahydrates are made by the action of chlorine or bromine on a suspension of thallous chloride or bromide in water. Thallic chloride tetrahydrate on treatment with hydrogen chloride yields $H(TlCl_4),3H_2O$, which if dried in vacuo over P_2O_5 yields the monohydrate to which is assigned the constitution $(H^+)_2(TlOCl_3^{2-})$. Thallic bromide monohydrate probably has a parallel constitution. Thallic chloride tetrahydrate, therefore, probably has the constitution $(H^+)_2[TlOCl_3^{2-}],3H_2O$.

The mixed halides $TlCl_2Br$ and $TlClBr_2$ and the corresponding tetrahydrates are known. The anhydrous mixed halides lose halogen very readily.

Thallic iodide, TlI_3, is thought to be thallous periodide because (i) of its deep colour, (ii) TlI_3 is isomorphous with RbI_3 and CsI_3. On the other hand an alcoholic solution of TlI_3 does not give the spectrum of I_3^- ions, and the ethylenediamine complex, [TlI_3 en], made by precipitating a solution of $TlCl_3$,en$_3$ with KI, is brick red. Thallic iodide is soluble in $C_2H_4Br_2$ and in $NO_2 \cdot C_6H_5$. In the last solvent it is less than 10% dissociated. The constitution of the complex might be (TlI_2,en)I, and of thallic iodide $(I-Tl-I)^+I^-$.

SECTION 4. COMPOUNDS IN WHICH THE THALLIUM ATOM IS TETRAHEDRALLY HYBRIDISED

ELECTRON-DEFICIENT POLYMERS. BRIDGE COMPOUNDS

There are no certain examples of thallium compounds containing three-centre bonds. It has been suggested that **thallium diethyl ethoxide**, which is dimeric in benzene solution, has the bridge structure:

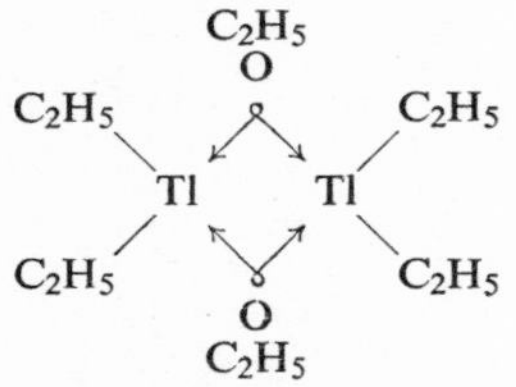

This formula indicates that each three-centre bond embraces two thallium atoms and one oxygen atom. The three-centre bonds formed by other members of sub-Group III N embrace two atoms of the Group III metal, and one atom of hydrogen, carbon, nitrogen, or halogen; in Group II three-centre bonds embrace two atoms of beryllium or magnesium, and one atom of hydrogen, carbon, or halogen. The use of the oxygen atom as a member of a three-centre bond is new, and if in thallium diethyl ethoxide the oxygen atom plays such a part, it is surprising that no other example can be given.

Thallium diethyl ethoxide is a liquid, b.p. 110–120°/15 mm. It is made by the reaction between diethyl thallium bromide and thallous ethoxide:

$$(C_2H_5)_2TlBr + TlOC_2H_5 = (C_2H_5)_2TlOC_2H_5 + TlBr.$$

It is miscible in benzene and hexane. The methyl derivative is crystalline, m.p. 179°.

OTHER COMPOUNDS IN WHICH THE THALLIUM ATOM IS IN THE TETRAHEDRAL VALENCE STATE

The thallium atom shows little tendency to act as an electron acceptor, and if the general trend of the periodic sub-Group III N from boron to indium were to continue to thallium it would be expected that thallium would form no compounds in which the thallium atom is the centre of a tetrahedral complex. In fact, however, the thallium atom in the tetrahedral valence state is present in the unstable thallium trimethyl etherate, which is a neutral non-chelate complex, in non-chelate complex anions, and in chelate neutral and anionic complexes. This reversal of the general trend of members of sub-Group III N is no doubt related to the reluctance of the heaviest atoms in each Group to make full use of their possible bonding orbitals. This reluctance has been seen in mercury, which forms stable compounds in which the mercury atom has only four electrons in its valency shell, and it will be seen again in lead (p. 638), and in bismuth (p. 647).

The non-chelate complex anions are represented by the anions of the so-called thallium dihalides which should be written $Tl^+[TlCl_4^-]$, and by the anions of the hydrated halides which should be written $[H^+]_2[TlOCl_3^{2-}],3H_2O$. No cationic non-chelate complexes are known.

Chelate complexes of the thallium atom in the tetrahedral valence state are fairly numerous. There are no complex cations, but examples are found of neutral complexes and of complex anions.

Chelate neutral complexes. The compound,

m.p. 200°, is made from thallium diethyl ethoxide and acetylacetone in petroleum ether. Many other similar compounds can be made, including those mentioned in Table 17.30.

Table 17.30.   *Chelate Neutral Complexes of Thallium*

Alkyl group attached to thallium atom	Ligand		
	Acetyl acetone	Propionyl acetone	Dipropionyl methane
	m.p. of complex °C	m.p. of complex °C	m.p. of complex °C
CH_3	214	162	121
C_2H_5	200	147	116
$n\text{-}C_3H_7$	181	108	89
$n\text{-}C_4H_9$	138	72	41

These compounds are soluble in benzene, in which they may be up to 40% associated. They are hydrolysed by water, presumably to thallium dialkyl hydroxide, and they can be titrated against acid in aqueous solution. The compounds of the β-keto-esters are similar, but they are less stable and more highly associated in solution.

Chelate complex anions. Ammonium thallium oxalate,

which crystallises with one molecule of water of crystallisation, is an example of a compound containing a chelate complex anion centred on a thallium atom in the tetrahedral valence state. Potassium thallium oxalate, and the parent acid itself, crystallise as trihydrates, and probably contain the thallium atom in the octahedral valence state.

SECTION 5. COMPOUNDS IN WHICH THE THALLIUM ATOM IS OCTAHEDRALLY HYBRIDISED

The octahedrally hybridised thallium atom is most stable (a) as an anion, (b) when chelated. There are no non-chelate neutral complexes or complex cations, and no chelate neutral complexes.

Non-chelate complex anions. The presence of octahedral configuration in $K_3(TlCl_6)$, $2H_2O$, and in $Rb_3(TlBr_6)7/8H_2O$ has been proved experimentally. The anion of the salt $Cs_3(Tl_2Cl_9)$ consists of two $TlCl_6$ octahedra having three chlorine atoms of one face in common.

Certain complex thallium chlorides or bromides in which the thallium atom may have octahedral configuration are:

$H(TlCl_4),3H_2O$
$M_2(TlCl_5),xH_2O$ for K $x=1$ or 2; for Rb $x=1$; for Cs $x=1$ or 0,
$M_3(TlCl_6),yH_2O$ for Li $y=8$; for Na $y=12$; for K $y=2$ or 0; for Rb $y=2$, 1 or 0,
$Rb_3(TlBr_6),zH_2O$ $z=0$ or 7/8,
$Cs_3(Tl_2Cl_9)$.

Chelate complex anions. The ammonium thallic oxalate $(NH_4)_3(Tl(C_2O_4)_3)$ and the corresponding pyridinium salt belong to this class. On the grounds that octahedral bonds are stronger than tetrahedral bonds the following are also assigned to this class:

$$H(Tl(C_2O_4)_2),3H_2O$$
$$K(Tl(C_2O_4)_2),3H_2O.$$

The acid is a crystalline powder, stable to cold water.

Chelate complex cations. The following ethylene diamine compounds are known:

$TlCl_3 \cdot en \cdot H_2O$ $TlBr_3 \cdot en_2$
$TlCl_3 \cdot en_2 \cdot H_2O$
$TlCl_3 \cdot en_3 \cdot 3H_2O$ $TlBr_3 \cdot en_3 \cdot 2H_2O.$

The stability of these compounds indicates that they are chelate, but there is no experimental evidence of their structure.

CHAPTER EIGHTEEN

SUB-GROUP IV N

CARBON, SILICON, GERMANIUM, TIN, AND LEAD

The properties of the elements of sub-Group IV N are given in Table 18.2. Carbon and silicon are non-metals; tin and lead are typical metals. Carbon, silicon, and germanium crystallise with the diamond structure, but carbon alone adopts the graphite structure.† Graphite forms certain peculiar derivatives, such as graphitic oxide, graphite fluorine compounds, graphite potassium compounds, and graphitic salts.

The elements of sub-Group IV N are not electron deficient, and hence differ sharply from the elements in the first three Groups. The four valency electrons in the neutral atoms of sub-Group IV N elements are exactly sufficient for forming four covalent bonds to give the stable tetrahedral configuration. The increased electronegativity of the sub-Group IV N elements rules out any likelihood of the formation of simple cations by carbon and silicon; the tendency is always for these elements to be anionic.

All the elements of sub-Group IV N form compounds in which the oxidation state of the element is 4. The carbon atom is never found in any other oxidation state. Silicon forms one compound SiO in which its oxidation state is 2, germanium forms a few compounds, GeO, GeS, and GeI_2, in which it may be in this oxidation state, but for both tin and lead the oxidation states 4 and 2 are equally important. The existence of stable compounds of tin and lead in which the metal is present in oxidation state 2 is to be explained by the ability of one electron pair in the valency shells of the tin and lead atoms to become inert (p. 487).

Carbon is unique in forming the large range of "organic" compounds. It is of interest to see whether the other elements in sub-Group IV N form corresponding compounds. It may be stated at once that they do not do so. There are three properties of carbon which enable it to form "organic" compounds: (i) it forms a very stable C—H link, (ii) it forms a very stable C—C link which makes possible the development of unbranched and branched chains of carbon atoms, and (iii) the carbon atom is able to form non-localised π bonds with nitrogen, oxygen, and other carbon atoms.

All the elements of the sub-Group IV N form the link X—H in the hydrides XH_4, but the tetrahydrides of germanium, tin, and lead are unstable and act as strong reducing agents. All the elements of the sub-Group IV N, however, give rise to alkyl and aryl derivatives of hydrides corresponding to the lower members of the paraffin series, although the parent hydrides cannot in all cases be isolated.

The affinity of the atom X for hydrogen in the molecule XH_4 is shown in Table 18.3. Clearly methane is more stable than the other hydrides.

The comparative weakness of the bond X—X in the ethane-like hydrides of the elements other than carbon is shown by the heats of linkage:

Bond X—X	C—C	Si—Si	Ge—Ge	Si—C‡
Heat of linkage (kcal)	81·6	42·5	42·5	69·1

† The only other layer lattice of the graphite type is that of boron nitride, BN (p. 505), but boron nitride differs from graphite in the way the layers are assembled in the crystal.

‡ For comparison.

Table 18.1. *Examples of Types of Compou...*

Oxidation St...

Nature of unit formed	C		Si
Simple ionic compounds, or compounds in which the bonds have ionic character			SiO
Simple covalent compounds			
Neutral complexes			
Complex anions			
Complex cations			

Oxidation S...

Section	State of atom of element			Nature of unit formed	C	page	Si
	Hybridisation	Formal charge	Bonds ‡				
1				Giant molecules in which the bonds have both ionic and covalent character	Be_2C, $B_{12}C_3$, Al_4C_3	375	Si_3N_4, SiO_2 Silicates SiS_2
2	Digonal		2σ 2π	Neutral compounds	$H—C\overset{\pi}{\underset{\pi}{}}C—H$ $C\overset{\pi}{\underset{\pi}{}}O$ $O—C\overset{\pi}{\underset{\pi}{}}O$ and the compounds on p. 578		None
3	Trigonal		3σ 1π	Neutral compounds	Graphite, $H_2C\overset{\pi}{=}CH_2$ C_6H_6, $(CH_3)_2CO$ $CH_3CO·OH$, $C(C_6H_5)_3$ $(NH_2)_2CNH$	590 594 596 596	None
				Complex anions	$[CO_3^{2-}]$		
		+1	3σ	Complex cations	$K[PtCl_3C_2H_4]$	1054	$[(CH_3)_3Si]_2SO_4$†
4	Tetrahedral		4σ	Neutral compounds	CH_4 and the aliphatic organic compounds CF_4, CCl_4, CBr_4	598	SiH_4 and its derivatives in Table 18.16 SiX_4 [X = F, Cl, Br, I] $(SiH_3)_2O$, $(SiH_3)_3N$
				Covalent giant molecules	Diamond, SiC	599	Silicon, SiC
		−1	3σ 1 lone pair	Complex anions	$Na[C(C_6H_5)_3]$		$Li[Si(C_2H_5)_3]$ $Li[Si(C_6H_5)_3]$
5	Trigonal bipyramidal	−1	5σ				
6	Octahedral	−2	6σ	Non-chelate {Neutral compounds, Complex anions, Complex cations}	None		$Na_2[SiF_6]$
				Chelate {Neutral compounds, Complex anions, Complex cations}	None		$[A_3Si]Cl$
7	Dodecahedral	−4	8σ				

† These compounds are included here because they could perhaps be assigned io...
‡ In this column the expression "2σ" indicates the presence of two bonds each of ty...

…he Element = 2

Ge	page	Sn	page	Pb	page
H, GeO, GeS …$_2$ [X=F, Cl, Br, I]	621 622	Sn(NO$_3$)$_2$, SnSO$_4$, SnNH, SnO, SnS SnX$_2$ [X=F, Cl, Br, I]	629 630	Pb(NO$_3$)$_2$, PbSO$_4$, PbCrO$_4$ PbO, PbS, PbX$_2$, [X=F, Cl, Br, I]	638 639
		Sn(C$_2$H$_5$)$_2$, Sn(C$_6$H$_5$)$_2$	631	Pb(CH$_3$)$_2$, Pb(C$_6$H$_5$)$_2$, Pb(C$_2$H$_5$S)$_2$, Pb(C$_4$H$_9$S)$_2$	640 640
				PbA$_2$	640
…eCl$_3$]	622	K$_2$[SnCl$_4$],H$_2$O K$_2$[Sn(HCO$_2$)$_4$]	631	K$_2$[PbCl$_4$] K$_2$[Pb(HCO$_2$)$_4$] K$_4$[PbCl$_6$]	640

…he Element = 4

Ge	page	Sn	page	Pb	page
…N$_4$, GeP, GeO$_2$, GeS$_2$	622	Sn$_3$N$_4$, SnO$_2$, SnS$_2$	631	PbO$_2$, Pb$_3$O$_4$	641
…ne		None		None	
…ne		None		None	
…H$_5$)$_3$Ge]Br†	626	[(CH$_3$)$_3$Sn]F†	635	[(CH$_3$)$_3$Pb]F†	643
…H$_4$ and its derivatives in Tables 18.19 and 18.21 …X$_4$ [X=F, Cl, Br, I]	624 626	SnH$_4$ and its derivatives in Table 18.24 SnX$_4$ [X=F, Cl, Br, I] Polystannanes	633 635 633	PbH$_4$ and its derivatives in Tables 18.29 and 18.30 PbCl$_4$ Diplumbanes	641 643 642
…[GeH$_3$], Li[Ge(C$_2$H$_5$)$_3$] …Ge(C$_6$H$_5$)$_3$],3NH$_3$	625	Na[Sn(CH$_3$)$_3$] Na[Sn(C$_6$H$_5$)$_3$]	635	Na[Pb(C$_6$H$_5$)$_3$]	643
		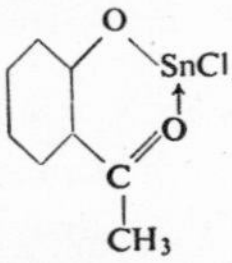	636		
		SnCl$_4$(OHC$_2$H$_5$)$_2$	636		
…[GeF$_6$], Cs$_2$[GeCl$_6$]	628	K$_2$[Sn(OH)$_6$], K$_2$[SnCl$_6$] K$_2$[SnF$_4$(C$_2$H$_5$)$_2$]	637 637	K$_2$[Pb(OH)$_6$], (NH$_4$)$_2$[PbCl$_6$]	644
…A$_2$Cl$_2$	627				
…Ge]CuCl$_2$	627			K$_2$[Pb(SO$_4$)$_3$]	644
				K$_3$H[PbF$_8$] Pb[CH$_3$CO$_2$]$_4$	644

…mulae, but in the text they are assumed to be covalent, and are considered in Section 4.
…the other expressions have corresponding meanings.

The properties of the ethane-like hydrides are in accord with these figures. Ethane is thermally stable and resistant to chemical attack, disilane is very reactive, digermane is extremely unstable, and the corresponding compounds of tin and lead are non-existent.

Table 18.2.   *Properties of the Elements in Sub-Group IV N*

	C	Si	Ge	Sn	Pb
Atomic number	6	14	32	50	82
Electron configuration	2, 4	2, 8, 4	2, 8, 18, 4	2, 8, 18, 18, 4	2, 8, 18, 32, 18, 4
Atomic weight	12·01	28·06	72·60	118·7	207·2
Density	Diamond 3·52 Graphite 2·25	2·49	5·36	Grey 5·77 White 7·29	11·37
Crystal lattice	Diamond Graphite	Diamond	Diamond	Grey, diamond; White, distorted close-packed	Close-packed
m.p. °C	3500	1420	958	232	327·4
b.p. °C	4200	2600	2700	2260	1620
Electrode potential on hydrogen scale	—	—	—	$Sn \to Sn^{2+}$ 0·136	$Pb \to Pb^{2+}$ 0·122
Ionisation potentials I	11·2	8·12	8·1	7·3	7·4
II	24·3	16·3	15·9	14·5	15·0
III	47·7	33·4	34·1	30·5	32·0
Covalent atomic radius	0·771	1·17		1·40	1·46
Ionic radius				Sn^{4+} 0·74	Pb^{2+} 1·32 Pb^{4+} 0·84
Electronegativity	2·5	1·8		1·7	

Table 18.3.   *Stability of the Link X—H in the Molecule XH$_4$*

	CH$_4$	SiH$_4$	GeH$_4$	SnH$_4$	PbH$_4$
Temperature of decomposition of the hydride	800°	450°	285°	150°	0°
Affinity of X for H in the hydride	98·8	75·1			

If six alkyl or aryl groups are bonded to the chain X—X to give a substituted ethane-like structure, the compounds of the elements so represented other than those of carbon show a fair thermal stability, but they are for the most part oxidised by air or the halogens. Oxidation occurs by the breaking of the bond X—X to yield compounds in which the element X remains in the tetrahedral valence state. When the compound $(C_6H_5)_3C—C(C_6H_5)_3$ is dissolved in benzene it is partly dissociated into the radical $(C_6H_5)_3C$. The hexaphenyl compounds of the elements of sub-Group IV N other than carbon do not undergo a corresponding dissociation. The absence of triphenyl radicals of the other elements may be due to their inability to exert π bonds, or to take part in molecular structures which include non-localised π bonds.

The reactivity of the bond X—C increases from silicon to lead. Chlorine and bromine attack the C—H bond in both carbon tetramethyl and in silicon tetramethyl, but in the tetramethyls of germanium, tin, and lead, it is the X—C bond and not the C—H bond that is attacked. In $Si(C_6H_5)_4$ (b.p. 530°) the hydrogen atoms in the phenyl groups are attacked by certain reagents, but the Si—C bonds are not broken, whereas in $Pb(C_6H_5)_4$

(decomposed at 270°) the phenyl groups are detached from the lead atom by boiling with glacial acetic acid.

The hexa-alkyl ethane-like derivatives of the elements of the sub-Group IV N other than carbon, for example $(C_2H_5)_3Ge—Ge(C_2H_5)_3$, are attacked by reagents in such a way that the X—X link is broken, thus indicating that this link is more reactive than the X—C link. The hexa-phenyl compounds show similar behaviour.

In Group IV localised π bonds linking the atoms of the lighter elements become common for the first time.† These bonds are superposed on the σ bonds which link atoms in digonal or trigonal valence states. Boron in Group III is present in many ring systems in which the bonding is probably non-localised as it is in benzene, but there are only a few boron compounds of the type:

$$\begin{array}{cc} H & H \\ \diagdown & \diagup \\ \overset{-}{B}\overset{\pi}{-}\overset{+}{N} \\ \diagup & \diagdown \\ H & H \end{array}$$

and none of the type

$$H_3C—B\overset{\pi}{-}C\begin{array}{c} H \\ \diagup \\ \diagdown \\ H. \end{array}$$

It seems therefore that π bonds are formed by the bonded atoms only if by doing so both atoms are able to complete their octets of valency electrons. There are many compounds of carbon of which the molecules contain a trigonally hybridised carbon atom linked by one σ bond and one π bond either to another carbon atom, or to a nitrogen atom, or to an oxygen atom. If the π bonds are alternating the orbitals become delocalised, as in butadiene or benzene. There are also many carbon compounds in which the carbon atoms are digonally hybridised and exert in addition to the two σ bonds two π bonds as in acetylene $H—C\overset{\pi}{\underset{\pi}{-}}C—H$. The second carbon atom may be replaced by a nitrogen atom, as in $H—C\overset{\pi}{\underset{\pi}{-}}N$, or by an oxygen atom as in $C\overset{\pi}{\underset{\pi}{-}}O$. There is general evidence that π bonds are formed only by atoms with $2p$ orbitals in the valency shell. In confirmation of this rule, it is observed that Si, Ge, Sn, Pb, do not form any compounds analogous to ethylene, acetylene, benzene, or their derivatives (($C_6H_5)_6Ge_6$, if correctly formulated, is an exception). There is a remarkable jump in properties from carbon nitride (cyanogen, C_2N_2) a colourless gas, b.p. $-21°$ to silicon nitride, a solid with the phenacite structure. The jump would be explained if the silicon atom does not form π bonds.

All the elements of sub-Group IV N form oxides of empirical formulae XO and XO_2, but the oxides of carbon differ markedly from those of the other elements. The properties are given in Table 18.4.

All the dioxides are acidic. Stannous and plumbous oxides are basic, but the other monoxides are nondescript. It is likely that the distinctive properties of the oxides of carbon are due to the presence of π bonds in the molecules of these compounds.

The very important tetrahedral group XO_4, in which X may be any of the elements in the third, fourth, or fifth Periods of sub-Groups IV N to VII N, appears for the first time in sub-Group IV N. Elements in sub-Group III N do not form this tetrahedral unit. Boron in combination with oxygen forms the metaborates $Na_3(B_3O_6)$ and $Ca_n(BO_2)_n$, in which ring and chain structures are developed by boron atoms linked

† In Group III N localised π bonds are present only in the not very well characterised anions $[O\overset{\pi}{-}M\overset{\pi}{-}O^-]$ and $[S\overset{\pi}{-}M\overset{\pi}{-}S^-]$ where M is gallium, indium, or thallium.

Table 18.4. *Oxides of the Elements in Sub-Group IV N*

	CO_2	SiO_2	GeO_2	SnO_2	PbO_2
Crystal structure	Molecular	Tetra-hedral SiO_4 groups	Quartz or rutile	Rutile	Rutile
Co-ordination	2:1	4:2	4:2 6:3	6:3	6:3
m.p. °C	−56·5	1710	1116	1900	
b.p. °C	−78·5 Sublimes	2590	1200	1900 Sublimes	
	CO	(SiO)	GeO	SnO	PbO
Crystal structure	Molecular			Square pyramid	Square pyramid
m.p. °C	−207				888
b.p. °C	−190		Sublimes at 710	Decom-poses about 800	

through oxygen atoms, but in these structures the boron atom is trigonally hybridised. Carbon, in Period 2 of sub-Group IV N, forms the carbonate ion CO_3^{2-}, but not CO_4^{4-}, although the tetrahedral hybridisation required for such a structure is readily assumed by the carbon atom in CH_4, CCl_4, and a multitude of other compounds. (Similarly nitrogen gives only NO_3^-, and neither oxygen nor fluorine form oxyacid anions at all, although all these elements form tetrahedral derivatives.)

It might be suggested that the XO_4 unit is formed by those atoms which possess d orbitals in the valency shell. If it be assumed that the negative charges on an anion XO_4^{n-} reside on the oxygen atoms, then the XO_4 ions for the last four elements in Period 3 may be formulated:

| atomic radius of central atom | 1·17 | 1·10 | 1·04 | 0·99 |

The number of πd bonds actually formed depends on the number of valency electrons present in the uncombined atom of the central element. In the ion $[SiO_4]^{4-}$ the four valency electrons of the silicon atom are the exact number required for making four σ bonds with the oxygen atoms. In the ion $[PO_4]^{3-}$ the five valency electrons of the phosphorus atom enable it to form four σ bonds with the oxygen atoms, and in addition one πd bond. By similar considerations two πd bonds are present in the ion $[SO_4]^{2-}$, and three in the ion $[ClO_4]^-$. The absence of πd bonds in the group SiO_4 thus differentiates silicon from phosphorus, sulphur, and chlorine. The chemistry of the group SiO_4 is, in fact, noticeably different from that of the ions PO_4^{3-}, SO_4^{2-}, and ClO_4^-. In the silicates the group SiO_4 is an arbitrary unit in a continuous structure of close-packed oxygen atoms with silicon atoms in certain of the tetrahedral holes. In many silicates a number of SiO_4 groups are linked through the oxygen atoms to form chains, rings, sheets, and three-dimensional structures. In contrast, each of the ions PO_4^{3-}, SO_4^{2-}, and ClO_4^- has a recognisable existence as a discrete particle. The ions PO_4^{3-} and SO_4^{2-} are able to condense to give the ions $P_2O_7^{4-}$ and $S_2O_7^{2-}$; the ionic valency becomes zero for chlorine which forms the oxide Cl_2O_7. Both the thermal stability and the stability towards reducing agents decrease along the series silicon to chlorine.

The silicates are types of giant molecule structures, and have much in common with the oxides, sulphides, nitrides, and carbides of elements of the earlier Groups. They are therefore included in the giant molecule class in Section 1, Table 18.1. It is difficult to subdivide the giant molecule class because it is not easy to ascertain either the numerical valency of the Group IV element in such a molecule, or to decide whether the bonding is ionic or covalent. Table 18.5 states the crystal structures of the compounds mentioned in Section 1, Table 18.1, and the co-ordination numbers of the Group IV elements in these structures.

Table 18.5   *Crystal structures of certain giant molecule compounds formed by elements in Group IV N, and the co-ordination numbers of the Group IV elements in these structures.*

Be_2C	$B_{12}C_3$	Al_4C_3	SiC	Si_3N_4	SiO_2
antifluorite	complex	complex	diamond	phenacite	quartz
8	4		4	4	4

the silicates		SiS_2		Ge_3N_4	GeP	GeS_2
		chains of tetrahedra		phenacite	rock salt	quartz
4		4		4	6	4

GeO_2	SnO_2	SnS_2	PbO_2
quartz rutile	rutile	cadmium iodide	rutile
4 6	6	6	6

The antifluorite structure of beryllium carbide appears anomalous. If this is disregarded, carbon has the co-ordination number 4, silicon 4, germanium either 4 or 6, and tin and lead 6. These numbers suggest that in the compounds in Table 18.5 carbon and silicon are tetrahedrally hybridised, germanium may adopt either the tetrahedral or the octahedral valence state, and tin and lead adopt the octahedral valence state. This sequence is to be expected, since the d orbitals make increasing contributions to the hybrid orbitals as the atomic numbers of the elements increase. The rutile structures of GeO_2, SnO_2, and PbO_2 indicate that the ionic character of these compounds is important.

GENERAL CHEMISTRY OF CARBON

The electron configuration of the carbon atom is $1s^2$, $2s^2$, $2p^2$. The atom adopts the three valence states:

Digonal hybridisation forming two σ bonds and two π bonds,
Trigonal hybridisation forming three σ bonds and one π bond,
Tetrahedral hybridisation forming four σ bonds.

The absence of d orbitals in the carbon atom precludes the adoption of higher valence states. Carbon–carbon bonds may be formed from all three of the valence states. The bond distances and heats of formation are:

	Distance	Heat of formation (the heat of atomisation of carbon is taken as 170·4 kcal per gm atom)
C—C	1·542	−81·6 kcal per mole
C$\overset{\pi}{=}$C	1·326	−146·1 ,, ,,
C$\overset{\pi}{\underset{\pi}{=}}$C	1·204	−192·1 ,, ,,

The digonal valence state. The two σ bonds at 180° must necessarily be directed from the carbon atom to two other atoms. The two π bonds may be directed from the carbon atom to one of these two atoms, as in ethyl cyanide C_2H_5—C$\overset{\pi}{\underset{\pi}{=}}$N, or one π bond may be directed to each of the two atoms as in carbon dioxide, O$\overset{\pi}{=}$C$\underset{\pi}{=}$O. Compounds containing digonally hybridised carbon atoms cannot be divided into two classes, one containing double π bonds and the other single π bonds, because the canonical forms representing any given molecule may contain representatives of both classes. For example, the canonical forms of carbon dioxide are:

$$O\overset{\pi}{=}C\underset{\pi}{=}O \qquad \overset{-}{O}—C\overset{\pi}{\underset{\pi}{=}}\overset{+}{O} \qquad \overset{+}{O}\overset{\pi}{\underset{\pi}{=}}C—\overset{-}{O}.$$

In certain compounds containing digonal carbon (among them carbon monoxide, O$\overset{\pi}{\underset{\pi}{=}}$C: and the isocyanides, R—N$\overset{\pi}{\underset{\pi}{=}}$C:), one of the two digonal orbitals is occupied by a lone pair. The acetylide ion, $[:C\overset{\pi}{\underset{\pi}{=}}C:]^{2-}$, contains two carbon atoms with this electronic arrangement. In compounds containing a carbon atom in the digonal valence state, the localised π bonds formed between the carbon atom and other atoms may become conjugated to form a non-localised π orbital system. The C—C distances in a chain of carbon atoms in the digonal valence state, as for example, in diacetylene, show that in such structures the π bonds are non-localised.

The trigonal valence state. In carbon compounds formed from the carbon atom in the trigonal valence state three σ bonds, making angles of approximately 120° with one another, are directed from the carbon atom to other atoms, and one of these atoms is linked to the carbon atom by a π bond. Some of the important carbon compounds of this type are ethylene $H_2C\overset{\pi}{=}CH_2$, and its derivatives,
the oximes,

$$\begin{matrix} R & & OH \\ & \diagdown & \diagup \\ & C\overset{\pi}{=}N & \\ & \diagup & \\ R & & \end{matrix}$$

the hydrazones,

$$\begin{matrix} R & & H \\ & \diagdown & \diagup \\ & C\overset{\pi}{=}N—N & \\ & \diagup & \diagdown \\ R & & C_6H_5, \end{matrix}$$

the compounds

$$\begin{matrix} R & \\ & \diagdown \\ & C\overset{\pi}{=}O, \\ & \diagup \\ R & \end{matrix}$$

where R is an alkyl or aryl group, a halogen atom, or the group CN, and the acids containing the carboxyl group:

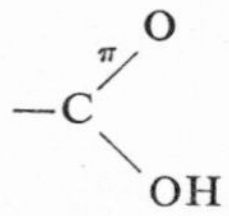

$$-C\overset{\pi}{\underset{OH}{\diagup}}\overset{O}{}$$

If the compound contains chains or rings of carbon atoms in the trigonal valence state, the π bonds overlap to form non-localised systems. Among the compounds containing non-localised π bonds are butadiene, benzene, and other aromatic compounds, the cyanuric compounds, and compounds of the type of triphenylmethyl, $(C_6H_5)_3C$, in which one p orbital of the carbon atom linked to the three phenyl groups is conjugated with the non-localised orbitals of the phenyl groups.

The tetrahedral valence state. The tetrahedral valence state is characteristic of carbon in the aliphatic organic compounds. Carbon is present in this state in diamond, and in the carbides SiC, BeC_2, derived from diamond. In a few compounds one of the orbitals of the tetrahedrally hybridised carbon atom is occupied by a lone electron pair. Examples are furnished by the anion in sodium triphenylmethyl, $Na^+[C(C_6H_5)_3]^-$, and by the remarkable compound dimethyl sulphonium-9-fluorenylidide:

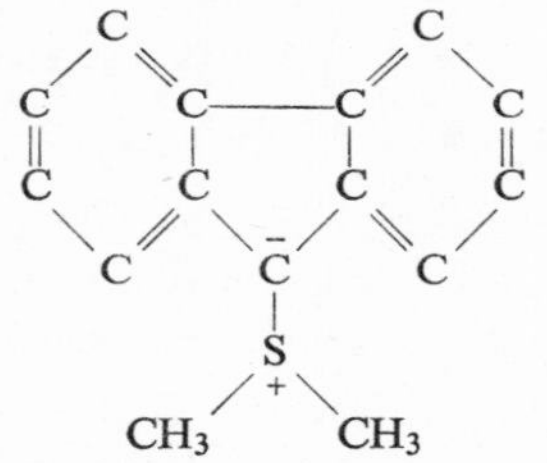

The classification of the compounds described in the following pages is based on the valence states of the carbon atom. In all its compounds the oxidation state of carbon is 4.

SECTION 1. CARBON COMPOUNDS WITH IONIC CHARACTER

There are no compounds containing the simple cation C^{4+}, but there are several classes of crystalline carbon compounds of the giant molecule type, in which the bonds have some ionic character. These compounds are composed of carbon and one other element, either metallic or non-metallic, and they may all be described generally as carbides. The different classes of compounds have different structures, and contain the carbon atom in different valence states. The classes are stated below, together with the pages on which the detailed descriptions are found.

The carbides may be grouped in the following classes:

(i) Carbides with ionic structures consisting of the acetylide ion $(C\overset{\pi}{\underset{\pi}{-}}C)^{2-}$ and the ion of an electropositive metal. The carbon atoms are digonally hybridised (p. 578).

(ii) Carbides with structures derived by the accommodation of atoms of other elements between the carbon layers of a graphitic lattice. The carbon atoms are trigonally hybridised (p. 591).

(iii) Graphitic fluorine compounds. The hexagonal rings are puckered. The carbon atoms are tetrahedrally hybridised (p. 593).

(iv) Carbides with structures related to the diamond lattice. The carbon atoms are tetrahedrally hybridised. To this class belong SiC, Be_2C, and possibly Al_4C_3 and $B_{12}C_3$ (p. 599).

19+A.T.I.C.

(v) Carbides with structures derived by the accommodation of carbon atoms in a metallic lattice. In many of these carbides the carbon atom is six co-ordinate, but its valence state is unknown. To this class belong TiC and the other carbides in Table 18.12 (p. 600).

SECTION 2. COMPOUNDS IN WHICH THE CARBON ATOM IS DIGONALLY HYBRIDISED

The following compounds are discussed in this section:

Acetylene	$H—C{\equiv}C—H$	Halogen cyanides	$F—C{\equiv}N$
Acetylides	$[:C{\equiv}C:]^{2-}$	Carbon monoxide	$:C{\equiv}O$
Cyanogen	$N{\equiv}C—C{\equiv}N$	Carbon dioxide	$O{=}C{=}O$
Cyanides	$R—C{\equiv}N$	Carbon disulphide	$S{=}C{=}S$
Isocyanides	$R—\overset{+}{N}{\equiv}\bar{C}$	Carbon diselenide	$Se{=}C{=}Se$
Isocyanates	$R—N{=}C{=}O$	Carbon oxysulphide	$O{=}C{=}S$
Thiocyanates	$R—S—C{\equiv}N$	Carbon oxyselenide	$O{=}C{=}Se$
Isothiocyanates	$R—N{=}C{=}S$		

Acetylene, C_2H_2, is a colourless gas with an ethereal odour. It condenses to a white solid, which sublimes at $-83.6°$. It is soluble in water, alcohol, and freely in acetone. Acetylene burns in oxygen with a highly exothermic reaction:

$$C_2H_2 + 2\tfrac{1}{2}O_2 = 2CO_2 + H_2O; \qquad \Delta H = -310.4 \text{ kcal.}$$

It undergoes a large number of additive reactions. It yields adducts with oxygen (by reaction with alkaline potassium permanganate solution), hydrogen, the halogens, hydrogen chloride, and hydrogen bromide, sulphuric acid, and ozone.

Homologues of acetylene are made by the action of alcohols, phenols, and alkyl or aryl halides on calcium acetylide:

$$CaC_2 + 2C_2H_5OH = C_2H_5C{\equiv}CC_2H_5 + Ca(OH)_2.$$

Diacetylides are obtained by the action of iodine on acetylene Grignard reagents:

$$2CH_3C{\equiv}CMgI + I_2 = CH_3 \cdot C{\equiv}C—C{\equiv}C \cdot CH_3 + 2MgI_2.$$

The unsaturated nature of the acetylene molecule is indicated by the triple bond between the two carbon atoms. The hydrogen atoms in acetylene are acidic ($K = 10^{-14}$) and are replaceable by metals; the product is an acetylide. The acidic nature of the hydrogen atom conforms to the generalisation that the greater the proportion of *s* to *p* in a hybrid carbon orbital, the more acidic is a hydrogen atom bonded to the carbon atom by that orbital. The $C{\equiv}C$ distance in diacetylene, $H—C{\equiv}C—C{\equiv}C—H$, is 1.21, but the C—C distance is diminished from the normal value 1.54 to 1.43. This suggests that the π bonds in the molecule are not localised, but extend over the whole chain of carbon atoms.

The acetylides and hydroacetylides are ionic compounds such as $(2Na^+)(C{\equiv}C)^{2-}$, or $Na^+(H—C{\equiv}C)^-$. On reaction with water (the reaction must be controlled for the alkali metals) they yield acetylene, provided that the metal exerts the same valency in the acetylide as it does in the hydroxide formed by hydrolysis. Acetylides and hydroacetylides are formed by all the metals of Group I. Other acetylides are those of the metals of sub-Group II N, BeC_2, MgC_2, CaC_2, SrC_2, BaC_2, those of the lanthanons,

LaC_2, CeC_2, PrC_2, NdC_2, and $Ce_2(C_2)_3$, and ThC_2, UC_2, VC_2, and $Al_2(C_2)_3$. Both cerium acetylide, $Ce_2(C_2)_3$, and aluminium acetylide, $Al_2(C_2)_3$, yield pure acetylene when treated with water. Both magnesium and aluminium yield not only the acetylides mentioned above, but also other carbides, Mg_2C_3 (p. 422) and Al_4C_3 (p. 534). Zinc,

Table 18.6. *Compounds of Carbon with Metals*

	Compound	Method of preparation	Crystal structure	Result of reaction with water
Methanides and similar compounds	Be_2C	(i) Heat elements at 1300° (ii) Heat BeO + C at 2000°	Antifluorite	Methane
	Mg_2C_3	(i) Methane or pentane on Mg metal at 750° (ii) C_2H_2 on metal at 600°	Hexagonal	Allylene
	$B_{12}C_3$	Heat B + C in electric furnace	NaCl	
	Al_4C_3	Heat Al + C above 1000°	C atoms 3·16 apart	Methane
	SiC	Heat Si + C	Near wurtzite	Inert
Interstitial carbides	TiC, etc., see Table 18.12, p. 600			
	Cr_3C_2	Heat Cr_2O_3 + C at 2000°	C—C distance 1·64	Inert
	Mn_3C	Heat Mn_3O_4 with C or CaC_2 to high temp.		Equal volumes of H_2 + CH_4
	Fe_3C			C + mixture of hydrocarbons
	Ni_3C			
	Co_3C			
Acetylides	$Na(C\frac{\pi}{\pi}C \cdot H)$ K,Rb,Cr	(i) Heat metal in C_2H_2 at 190° (ii) Pass C_2H_2 into a solution of metal in liquid NH_3		Acetylene
	Na_2C_2	Heat hydroacetylide		C_2H_2 if moderated; otherwise C + H_2
	CaC_2	Heat CaO + C	NaCl, tetragonal	C_2H_2
	BeC_2	Pass C_2H_2 over Be at 450°		C_2H_2
	MgC_2	(i) Pass C_2H_2 over Mg at 500° (ii) Pass C_2H_2 into $(C_2H_5)_2Mg$ in ether	Tetragonal	C_2H_2
	ZnC_2	C_2H_2 on $(C_2H_5)_2$ Zn in ligroin		Decomposes
	CdC_2			Inert
	$Hg_2C_2 \cdot H_2O$	Pass C_2H_2 into mercurous acetate solution		
	HgC_2	Pass C_2H_2 into an alkaline solution of K_2HgI_4		
	$Al_2(C_2)_3$	C_2H_2 over Al at 450–500°		Pure C_2H_2
	Cu_2C_2	C_2H_2 on ammonical CuCl		Dilute HCl or KCN gives C_2H_2
	Ag_2C_2	C_2H_2 on ammonical $AgNO_3$		Dilute HCl or KCN gives C_2H_2
	Au_2C_2	C_2H_2 on aqueous $Au_2S_2O_3$		
	YC_2, LaC_2 CeC_2 PrC_2 NdC_2, SmC_2 }	Heat oxide with C to 2000°		C_2H_2 + some methane
	$Ce_2(C_2)_3$			Pure C_2H_2
	UC_2	Heat oxide with C	CuC_2	Mixture of hydrocarbons†
	ThC_2		Tetragonal	Mixture of hydrocarbons†
	VC_2			

† In the reactions the metal changes from the divalent to the tetravalent state, and the hydrogen which is liberated by this change partially saturates the acetylene.

cadmium, and mercury form compounds of the type ZnC_2, but little about them has been reported. The acetylides of the transition metals, copper, silver, and gold are precipitated from aqueous solution. Cu_2C_2 and Ag_2C_2 yield acetylene on hydrolysis with warm KCN solution, or with HCl. (No thallous carbide appears to be known.) The modes of preparation and the properties of the acetylides are summarised in Table 18.6.

Crystalline calcium acetylide has a structure closely related to that of sodium chloride. In the calcium acetylide crystal the ions $(C\frac{\pi}{\pi}C)^{2-}$ occupy the positions of the Cl^- ions in sodium chloride. The ion $(C\frac{\pi}{\pi}C)^{2-}$ is not spherical, but is elongated along the C—C axis, and therefore the symmetry of the crystal is tetragonal and not cubic. This lattice structure suggests that the Ca—C bond is ionic. The sections through a NaCl crystal and a CaC_2 crystal are:

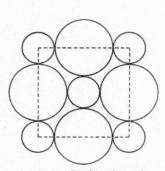

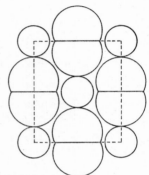

Fig. 18.1. Section through a crystal of sodium chloride, NaCl. The large circles represent Cl^- ions.

Fig. 18.2. Section through a crystal of calcium carbide, CaC_2. The ellipses represent $(C:C)^{2-}$ ions.

A slightly less symmetrical structure in an acetylide crystal is seen in that of thorium carbide. The $(C\frac{\pi}{\pi}C)^{2-}$ ions in a given layer lie in the direction of one of the diagonals across the horizontal section; in the neighbouring layers the ions lie in the direction of the other diagonal.

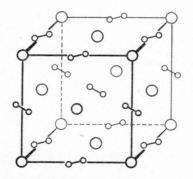

Fig. 18.3. Structure of thorium carbide, ThC_2.

Cyanogen, C_2N_2, is a colourless, extremely poisonous gas with the odour of bitter almonds. m.p. $-28°$, b.p. $-21°$. It is made by the following methods:

1. By heating the cyanides of silver, mercury, or gold:

$$Hg(CN)_2 = Hg + C_2N_2.$$

Paracyanogen, probably a polymer, is produced at the same time.

2. By mixing mercuric chloride with mercuric cyanide:

$$Hg(CN)_2 + HgCl_2 = Hg_2Cl_2 + C_2N_2.$$

3. By dropping concentrated potassium cyanide solution into a warm solution of 1 part of $CuSO_4,5H_2O$ in 2 parts of water:

$$CuSO_4 + 2KCN = Cu(CN)_2 + K_2SO_4,$$
$$2Cu(CN)_2 = 2CuCN + C_2N_2.$$

4. By warming cuprous cyanide with ferric chloride solution:

$$2CuCN + 2FeCl_3 = 2CuCl + 2FeCl_2 + C_2N_2.$$

Cyanogen is soluble in water (4·5 volumes in 1 of water at 20°) and in alcohol (23 volumes in 1 of water at 20°). It reacts like a halogen with aqueous potassium hydroxide:

$$C_2N_2 + 2KOH = KCNO + KCN + H_2O.$$

It is hydrolysed in acid solution to oxamide:

$$CN + 2H_2O = O:C \cdot NH_2$$
$$| \qquad \qquad |$$
$$CN \qquad \quad O:C \cdot NH_2$$

and on reduction it yields ethylene diamine. These two reactions establish the linkage of the two carbon atoms to one another. Cyanogen burns with a characteristic bluish red-edged flame, and a mixture of equal volumes of cyanogen and oxygen explodes when sparked.

The heat of formation of the molecule C_2N_2 from the elements in the standard state is $+71$ kcal, and from the atoms is -495 kcal; the heat of formation from atoms of the group $C\overset{\pi}{\equiv}N$ is -207 kcal. Cyanogen, however, is remarkably stable to heat. It is undecomposed by heat below 1000°, when it begins to dissociate into CN radicals which are so stable that they can be detected even in stella spectra. Electron diffraction shows that the molecule is linear. The distance N—C is 1·16 which is normal for a triple bond, but the distance C—C is only 1·37 which suggests that the system of π bonds is generalised.

Hydrogen cyanide, HCN, is a colourless, very volatile liquid, m.p. $-13\cdot4°$, b.p. $25\cdot6°$. It is strongly poisonous. It may be obtained:

(i) by heating ammonium formate with phosphorus pentoxide:

$$HCOONH_4 = HCN + 2H_2O,$$

(ii) by distilling potassium cyanide, or potassium ferrocyanide, with moderately concentrated sulphuric acid:

$$2K_4[Fe(CN)_6] + 3H_2SO_4 = 6HCN + FeK_2[Fe(CN)_6] + 3K_2SO_4,$$

(iii) by passing hydrogen sulphide through a tube containing mercuric cyanide warmed to 30°:

$$H_2S + Hg(CN)_2 = HgS + 2HCN.$$

The anhydrous acid is obtained (this is a dangerous preparation) by dropping cold 50% sulphuric acid on to lumps of potassium cyanide.

Hydrogen cyanide burns in air with a purple flame; a mixture with oxygen explodes. It dissolves readily in water to give a feebly acid solution; $K = 4.9 \times 10^{-10}$. The solution is slowly hydrolysed to ammonium formate.

The heat of formation of hydrogen cyanide from atoms is $+304$ kcal. Its dielectric constant is very high: 194·4 at the m.p. and 116 at 25°. The d.p.m. is 2·6 in benzene solution, and 3·0 in the vapour. In the crystalline state the molecules do not rotate, even at the m.p. (Some hydrides which exhibit molecular rotation in the crystal are H_2Se, HCl, and HBr above $-170°$, and AsH_3 above $-250°$.)

Hydrocyanic acid might be a tautomeric system:

$$H—C\overset{\pi}{\underset{\pi}{=}}N \rightleftharpoons H—\overset{+}{N}\overset{\pi}{\underset{\pi}{=}}\bar{C}.$$

(These are not canonical forms of a resonance structure, because the nuclei are not in the same relative positions.) Spectroscopic evidence indicates that HCN contains 99% of the form $H—C{\equiv}N$.

The ligand CN is present in many complex anions formed by transition metals, for example in the salts:

$K_2[M(CN)_4]$ where M is Ni^{II}, Pd^{II}, Pt^{II}
$K_4[M(CN)_6]$ where M is Mn^{II}, Fe^{II}, Co^{II}
$K_3[M(CN)_6]$ where M is Mn^{III}, Fe^{III}, Co^{III}, Ir^{III}
$K_2[M(CN)_6]$ where M is Os^{IV}, Ru^{IV}, Pt^{IV}
$K_5[M(CN)_8]$ where M is Mo^{III}
$K_4[M(CN)_8]$ where M is Mo^{IV}, W^{IV}
$K_3[M(CN)_8]$ where M is Mo^{V}, W^{V}.

Accurate X-ray measurements on $K_4[Mo(CN)_8]$, $K_4[Fe(CN)_6]$, and $K_3[Ag(CN)_4]$ indicate that the carbon atom in the ligand is directly attached to the atom of the transition metal.

The alkyl and aryl cyanides and isocyanides. The alkyl cyanides are made by the action of potassium cyanide in aqueous-alcoholic solution on the halogen derivative of the appropriate paraffin; the aryl cyanides are made by Sandmeyer's reaction. The alkyl and aryl isocyanides are made by the action of chloroform and aqueous potassium hydroxide solution on the appropriate amine; the alkyl isocyanides can also be made from the alkyl halides using silver cyanide instead of potassium cyanide. The cyanides and isocyanides behave differently on hydrolysis:

Cyanides $RCN + 2H_2O = RCOOH + NH_3$ catalysed by acids and by alkalis,
Isocyanides $RNC + 2H_2O = RNH_2 + HCOOH$ catalysed by acids only.

The isocyanides easily accept oxygen or sulphur to give $R \cdot N\overset{\pi}{=}C\overset{\pi}{=}O$ and $R \cdot N\overset{\pi}{=}C\overset{\pi}{=}S$.

It is clear that there are two well-characterised compounds, $H_3C—C\overset{\pi}{\underset{\pi}{=}}N$ and $H_3C—\overset{+}{N}\overset{\pi}{\underset{\pi}{=}}\bar{C}$, both containing a digonally hybridised carbon atom. Both display a characteristic Raman line, 2245cm^{-1} for the cyanide and 2180 cm^{-1} for the isocyanide. The d.p.m. of p-di-isocyanobenzene is zero, thus indicating that the group $C—N\overset{\pi}{\underset{\pi}{=}}C$ is linear. The metallic cyanides and isocyanides are indistinguishable, as the ion $[C\overset{\pi}{\underset{\pi}{=}}N]^-$ is common to both. The crystal of silver cyanide consists of chains:

$$Ag—C—N—Ag—C—N—Ag—C—N.$$

On thermodynamical grounds it is predicted that HCN is more stable than HNC, and that the alkyl cyanides are slightly more stable than the isocyanides. The alkyl isocyanides change into the cyanides on heating to about 200°. For a comparison of the structure of the alkyl cyanides and carbon monoxide, see p. 587.

Table 18.7.   *Certain Alkyl and Aryl Derivatives of Cyanogen*

	b.p. °C	d.p.m.	Heat of combustion of gas, kcal per mole
CH₃CN	81·6		312
C₂H₅CN	98	3·57†	471·5
C₆H₅CN	191	3·94†	
CH₃NC	59		325·7
C₂H₅NC	79	3·47‡	487·1
C₆H₅NC	166	3·53‡	
CH₃NCO	44		
C₂H₅NCO	60		
C₆H₅NCO	166		
CH₃SCN	132		
C₂H₅SCN	145		
CH₃NCS	118		
C₂H₅NCS	131		

† The positive end of the dipole is on the carbon atom.
‡ The positive end of the dipole is on the nitrogen atom.

Isocyanic acid and its derivatives.§ Isocyanic acid, $H—N\overset{\pi}{\underset{\pi}{=}}C—O$, is a liquid, m.p. $-86·8°$, b.p. $23·5°$, made by passing cyanuric acid (p. 688) through a hot tube. It reverts spontaneously to cyanuric acid. It dissolves in water to give an acid solution ($K = 12 \times 10^{-5}$), but it is hydrolysed in a short time to ammonia and carbon dioxide.

The alkali metal isocyanates are not decomposed below a red heat. They are made by oxidising the cyanides or ferrocyanides with lead monoxide or dioxide just below a red heat. The aqueous solutions are hydrolysed to carbonates and ammonia.

Certain alkyl and phenyl isocyanates are included in Table 18.7. They are readily hydrolysed by alkali to amines and carbon dioxide.

The hydrolysis of isocyanic acid and of its esters shows that the hydrogen atom or the alkyl group is linked to the nitrogen atom:

$$R—N—C—O + H_2O = RNH_2 + CO_2.$$

The Raman spectra of the acid, its esters, and the non-ionised silver and mercury derivatives, are alike, and differ from those of the potassium, tetramethyl ammonium, and plumbous salts; a similar relation is found for the ultraviolet spectra. By electron diffraction experiments the group N—C—O is linear, and the bond lengths suggest resonance between the forms:

$$R—N\overset{\pi}{=}C—O \qquad R—\overset{+}{N}\overset{\pi}{\underset{\pi}{=}}C—\overset{-}{O}.$$

The ion, which is probably a resonance hybrid of $N\overset{\pi}{\underset{\pi}{=}}C—\overset{-}{O}$ and $\overset{-}{N}\overset{\pi}{=}C\overset{}{\underset{\pi}{=}}O$, is also linear. It is isoelectronic with the azide ion (p. 686). Potassium azide and potassium cyanate are closely similar in many of their physical properties.

Thiocyanic acid, HNCS, and its derivatives. Thiocyanic acid is a gas at room temperature. If cooled with liquid air it becomes a white solid, m.p. $-110°$, but the liquid polymerises above $-90°$. The gas is obtained by the action of potassium hydrogen sulphate on potassium thiocyanate. In solution in water it is a strong acid, and the

§ All the covalent compounds of the general formula XCNO have the structure X—N—C—O. The normal cyanates, which would have the structure C—N—O—X, do not exist, and the name "cyanates" is often applied to the isocyanates.

alkali metal salts, which are very soluble, are strong electrolytes.† Ferric thiocyanate is red. The appearance of the red colour is used as a test for ferric ions and for thiocyanate ions. The acid is hydrolysed by 70% sulphuric acid:

$$H—N—C—S + H_2O = NH_3 + OCS.$$

The esters are included in Table 18.7. Both the normal and the isothiocyanate esters can be obtained; the isothiocyanate esters are the more stable. The chemical distinction between the two is seen in the reductions:

$$N\frac{\pi}{\pi}C—S—CH_3 + H_2 = HCN + HSCH_3$$

$$CH_3—N\frac{\pi}{\pi}C\frac{}{\pi}S + 3H_2 = CH_3NH_2 + CH_3SH.$$

The ion NCS⁻ is linear. Raman spectra indicate that it has the form $[N\frac{\pi}{\pi}C—\bar{S}]^-$ since there is a line for the triple link but no line for the double link. The esters exist in the two forms, $CH_3—N\frac{\pi}{}C\frac{}{\pi}S$ and $N\frac{\pi}{\pi}C—S—CH_3$. The Raman spectrum of the acid in carbon tetrachloride solution is similar to that of the ester $CH_3—N\frac{\pi}{}C\frac{}{\pi}S$, and hence the acid must be $H—N\frac{\pi}{}C\frac{}{\pi}S$. This structure is confirmed by the hydrolysis given above.

The cyanogen halides, or halogeno-nitriles, are colourless or white compounds. They are all strong lachrymators. Their properties are set out in Table 18.8. Their spectra are similar.

Table 18.8.‡   *The Cyanogen Halides*

	$Cl—C\frac{\pi}{\pi}N$	$Br—C\frac{\pi}{\pi}N$	$I—C\frac{\pi}{\pi}N$
b.p. °C	13	61·3	Sublimes at 146
m.p. °C	−6·9	51·3	146
Solubility in water	Fairly soluble	Soluble	Slightly soluble
Bond length X—C	1·67	1·79	1·96
Preparation	$Cl_2 + NaCN$ in presence of a little water and CCl_4 or, pass Cl_2 into aqueous HCN	$Br_2 + KCN$	$I_2 + KCN$
With KOH	Yields $KCl + KNCO + H_2O$		
With NH₃	Yields $H_2N \cdot CN$		
	Spontaneously polymerises to cyanuric chloride (p. 688)		

The absorption spectra give heats of dissociation corresponding to the linear structures $Cl—C\frac{\pi}{\pi}N$ and $F—C\frac{\pi}{\pi}N$, in which the halogen atom is directly linked to the carbon atom. The chemical reactions confirm this structure. Resonance is probable between the forms:

$$\overset{+}{Cl}\frac{\pi}{}C\frac{}{\pi}\bar{N} \qquad Cl—C\frac{\pi}{\pi}N.$$

Carbon monoxide, CO, is a colourless, odourless, but poisonous gas; m.p. −205·1°, b.p. −190°. It is made in very pure condition by the thermal decomposition of nickel

---

† Oxidation proceeds in acid solution:
$$2SCN^- = (SCN)_2 + 2e;$$
in alkaline solution:
$$SCN^- + 4H_2O = SO_4^{2-} + CN^- + 8H^+ + 6e$$
(SCN)₂ is *thiocyanogen*; there is no oxygen analogue.

‡ Fluorine cyanide has been described, but recent attempts to obtain it in macroscopic quantities have failed (E. E. Aynsley, R. E. Dodd, and R. Little, *Proc. Chem. Soc.*, 1959, 265). It has been detected spectroscopically among the products of the fluorination of cyanogen at low temperatures.

carbonyl at 200°. If calcium carbonate is heated with twice the stoichiometric amount of zinc at 700–750°, pure carbon monoxide is obtained. Barium carbonate does not act in this way. Carbon monoxide is ordinarily prepared by the reduction of carbon dioxide by carbon at 1000°, or by the dehydration of formic acid.

Carbon monoxide is sparingly soluble in water. It is absorbed in a solution of cuprous chloride in hydrochloric acid, and white crystals of the composition $CuCl,CO,H_2O$ can be crystallised from the solution. It is also absorbed by a solution of cuprous chloride in ammonia. Carbon monoxide is a poison as it combines with the haemoglobin of the blood to form a compound, carboxyhaemoglobin, which is not decomposed by oxygen. Haemoglobin which has reacted with carbon monoxide is incapable of fulfilling its function of oxygen carrier. Carbon monoxide burns in air with a blue flame. Its other reactions are summarised in Table 18.9.

Carbon monoxide is one of the ligands in certain complexes of platinum and palladium. The complexes may be neutral or anionic:

Carbon monoxide forms an important series of compounds with the transition metals, see Chapter 25.

Table 18.9. *Reactions of Carbon Monoxide*

Reagent	Conditions	Product
NaOH	160° under pressure	HCOONa
CsOH	350° 1 atm	HCOOCs (92% yield)
Cl_2	Sunlight or catalyst	$COCl_2$
HgF_2		COF_2
Ni	80°	$Ni(CO)_4$
Fe	200°	$Fe(CO)_5$
S	Vapour	COS
I_2O_5	90°	$I_2 + CO_2$
I_2	In solution pH 0–6	$CO_2 + HI$
	PdCl$_2$ as catalyst	
Ammoniacal AgNO$_3$	Room temperature	Ag
Cu$_2$Cl$_2$ in HCl	Room temperature	$CuCl,CO,2H_2O$
NaNH$_2$	Warmed	$NaCN + NH_3 + NaOH$
B_2H_6	100°	$OC \cdot BH_3$

The structure of carbon monoxide. The molecular formula is CO. The orbital structure is discussed below in terms of the valence bond theory and of the molecular orbital theory.

Valence bond theory. Both the carbon atom and the oxygen atom are digonally hybridised. One digonal orbital of the carbon atom combines with a digonal orbital of the O atom to form a σ bond linking the two atoms, and the second digonal orbital on each atom is occupied by a lone pair. Two of the p orbitals of each atom overlap and form two π bonds. The structure is:

$$:C\overset{\pi}{\underset{\pi}{=}}O:$$

This electron distribution requires a transference of one electron from the oxygen atom to the carbon atom, which would suggest the formal charge distribution $\bar{C}\ \overset{+}{O}$. The electronegativities of the elements (C 2·5, O 3·5), however, suggest a strong

19*

tendency towards the opposite distribution $\overset{+}{C}\,\overset{-}{O}$. The dipole moment of carbon monoxide ($0.10D$) indicates that these two opposing tendencies nearly neutralise one another.

Molecular orbital theory. The orbital structure of carbon monoxide according to the molecular orbital theory is best described with the aid of the cell-diagram which is closely similar to that of nitric oxide (p. 132). The cell-diagram for carbon monoxide (omitting the $\sigma 1s$ and σ^*1s orbitals) is:

Atomic orbitals	Molecular orbitals	Atomic orbitals
C	CO	O
$2p_z$ $\uparrow$ $2p_y$ $\uparrow$ $2p_x$ $\bigcirc$	$\pi 2p_y$ $\uparrow\downarrow$ $\uparrow\downarrow$ $\pi 2p_x$	$2p_x$ $\uparrow\downarrow$ $2p_y$ $\downarrow$ $2p_z$ $\downarrow$
	$\sigma 2p_z$ $\uparrow\downarrow$	
$2s$ $\uparrow\downarrow$	σ^*2s $\uparrow\downarrow$	$2s$ $\uparrow\downarrow$
	$\sigma 2s$ $\uparrow\downarrow$	

It is seen from the diagram that the effective bonding is one σ and two π bonds, and to this extent the structure is identical with that deduced from the valence bond theory. The displacement of negative charge from the oxygen atom to the carbon atom is also apparent, because whereas the oxygen atom originally had six valency electrons and the carbon atom four, in the carbon monoxide molecule the ten electrons are symmetrically distributed. The structure given by this theory, however, fails to account for the pronounced donor properties of carbon monoxide which indicate the presence of a lone electron pair on the carbon atom. Coulson has suggested a modification of the simple molecular orbital treatment which leads to the following cell-diagram:

Atomic orbitals	Molecular orbitals	Atomic orbitals
C	CO	O
Digonally hybridised orbitals		
$2p_z$ $\uparrow$ $2p_y$ $\uparrow$ $2p_x$ $\bigcirc$	$\pi 2p_y$ $\uparrow\downarrow$ $\uparrow\downarrow$ $\pi 2p_x$	$2p_x$ $\uparrow\downarrow$ $2p_y$ $\downarrow$ $2p_z$ $\downarrow$
	$\sigma 2p_z$ $\uparrow\downarrow$	
$2s$ $\uparrow\downarrow$		$2s$ $\uparrow\downarrow$ inert pair
Hybrid non-bonding lone pair $\uparrow\downarrow$		

He assumes that the atoms lie on the z axis. The $2s$ and the $2p_z$ orbitals of the carbon atom are hybridised to give two digonal hybrid orbitals along the z axis. The carbon hybrid orbital next to the oxygen atom, with the $2p_z$ orbital of the oxygen atom, forms the molecular orbital $\sigma 2p_z$. The hybrid orbital remote from the oxygen atom is occupied by a lone pair. The $\pi 2p_y$ and $\pi 2p_x$ orbitals are formed as before. The electrons in the oxygen atomic orbital $2s$ are unused, and behave as an inert pair. The structure may be written:

$$:C\overset{\pi}{\underset{\pi}{\equiv}}O,$$

which accords with the properties of carbon monoxide.

A corresponding structure is not permissible for the cyanides $R\!-\!C\overset{\pi}{\underset{\pi}{\equiv}}N$, and the isocyanides $R\!-\!N\overset{\pi}{\underset{\pi}{\equiv}}C$. Coulson's structure applied to an alkyl cyanide would assign an inert electron pair to the nitrogen atom, but this is not in accord with the donor properties of the alkyl cyanides; for example, the compounds $F_3B\cdot NC\cdot CH_3$ and $Cl_3B\cdot NC\cdot CH_3$ are easily formed and are stable (p. 504). Coulson's structure is inapplicable to the isocyanides in which the nitrogen atom exerts four bonds.

Carbon suboxide, C_3O_2, is a bad-smelling gas, b.p. $-6\cdot8°$. It is made by heating malonic acid with excess of P_2O_5 at 150–300°:

$$\underset{H}{\overset{H}{\diagdown}}C\underset{COOH}{\overset{COOH}{\diagup}} = O{=}C{=}C{=}C{=}O + 2H_2O.$$

It burns in air; the natures of the flame and of the products are governed by the conditions. It combines with water, hydrogen chloride, ammonia, and amines to form derivatives of malonic acid:

$$O{=}C{=}C{=}C{=}O + 2CH_3\cdot NH_2 = \underset{H}{\overset{H}{\diagdown}}C\underset{CO\cdot NHCH_3.}{\overset{CO\cdot NHCH_3}{\diagup}}$$

Electron diffraction experiments show that the molecule is linear, and the distances are C—O 1·20, C—C 1·30. The C—O distance is the normal ketone distance. The C—C distance, however, is short compared with the normal C=C distance, 1·33; it gives a bond order of 2·15 which indicates conjugation. The linear structure is supported by ultraviolet, Raman, and infrared spectra. The simplest formula which can be given to the molecule is

$$:\!\overset{..}{\underset{..}{O}}\overset{\pi}{\underset{\pi}{=}}C\overset{\pi}{\underset{\pi}{-}}C\overset{\pi}{\underset{\pi}{=}}\overset{..}{\underset{..}{O}}\!:$$

but there are no doubt other canonical forms such as

$$:\!\overset{..}{\underset{..}{\bar{O}}}\!-\!C\overset{\pi}{\underset{\pi}{\equiv}}C\!-\!C\overset{\pi}{\underset{\pi}{\equiv}}\overset{..}{\overset{+}{O}}\!:$$

Carbon monosulphide, CS. The radical CS, detected spectroscopically, is formed by the photolysis of carbon disulphide, or by the passage of an electric discharge through carbon disulphide vapour, or through a mixture of a paraffin and sulphur vapour. Its life is 10 min. at room temperature, and 3 min. at 100°. It is condensed at the b.p. of liquid nitrogen, but not at $-110°$.

The compounds in this Section remaining to be discussed are certain compounds of carbon of general formula CX_2 where X is an element of Group VI N. A list of these compounds with certain of their properties, is given in Table 18.10.

Table 18.10.　*Compounds CX_2 of Digonally Hybridised Carbon and the Elements of Group VI N*

	m.p. °C	b.p. °C	Solubility	Stability
CO_2		Sublimes -79	1·713 vol in 1 vol of water at 0°	Stable
CS_2	-109	46·3	0·204 gm in 100 c.c. water at 0°	Stable
CSe_2	-42	125	Insoluble in water	Decomposes slowly
[CTe_2	Could not be prepared by method analogous to CSe_2]			—
COS	$-138·8$	$-50·2$		Decomposes slowly
COSe	$-124·4$	$-21·7$		Very unstable
[COTe	has not been prepared]			
CSSe	-85	84·5	Yellow oily liquid insoluble in water: soluble in CS_2	Decomposes slowly
CSTe	-54	decomp. -54		Very unstable

Carbon dioxide, CO_2, is a colourless gas, easily compressed to a liquid below the critical temperature of 31°. The solid sublimes at $-79°$ under 1 atm.

Carbon dioxide is made by burning carbon in excess air at low temperatures, by the action of acids on carbonates, and by heating all carbonates except those of the alkali metals. It is liberated in certain fermentations and in many other reactions. It dissolves in water, and the solution probably contains the very weak acid $(HO)_2CO$. It is expelled from aqueous solution by boiling. Liquid carbon dioxide scarcely dissolves in water, but it is miscible with ether, pentane, and benzene. It is absorbed by alkalis to give carbonates; with sodamide it gives cyanamide

$$2NaNH_2 + CO_2 = NH_2CN + 2NaOH.$$

Carbon dioxide does not ordinarily support combustion, but Na, K, and Mg burn in it setting free carbon, and carbon at 1000° reduces it to carbon monoxide. It reacts with Grignard reagents to yield fatty acids. The molecule is linear. The C—O distance is 1·15 which is shorter than the ketone distance, 1·21. On the valence bond theory there are three canonical forms, excluding those in which the carbon octet is incomplete:

$$\ddot{\underset{..}{O}}\overset{\pi}{\underset{\pi}{-}}C{-}\ddot{\underset{..}{O}} \qquad \overset{-}{\ddot{\underset{..}{O}}}{-}C\overset{\pi}{\underset{\pi}{-}}\overset{+}{\ddot{O}} \qquad \overset{+}{\ddot{O}}\overset{\pi}{\underset{\pi}{-}}C{-}\overset{-}{\ddot{\underset{..}{O}}}$$

In all these forms the carbon atom is digonally hybridised; the neutral oxygen atom is trigonally hybridised, the $\overset{+}{O}$ atom is digonally hybridised, and the $\bar{O}$ atom is tetrahedrally hybridised. The resonance energy is 32 kcal per mole.

The di-imide $HN\overset{\pi}{-}C\underset{\pi}{-}NH$ corresponding to carbon dioxide does not exist, as the isomer cyanamide $H_2N{-}C\overset{\pi}{\underset{\pi}{-}}N$ is more stable. The diphenyl derivative $C(NC_6H_5)_2$ is known.

Carbon disulphide, CS_2, is a colourless mobile liquid (Table 18.10). It is made by the union of the elements at high temperature; the reaction starting from the solid elements is endothermic.

Carbon disulphide as ordinarily obtained has an unpleasant smell which can be temporarily removed by thorough purification. It is poisonous. It is miscible with absolute alcohol, with ether, with benzene, and with oils. It dissolves sulphur, white phosphorus, rubber, camphor, and resins. It burns readily in air; its ignition temperature is very low indeed. It forms explosive mixtures with air, oxygen and nitric oxide:

$$2CS_2 + 5O_2 = 2CO + 4SO_2.$$

Carbon disulphide is only very slightly soluble in water, but it dissolves in concentrated aqueous sodium hydroxide to give a mixture of sodium carbonate and sodium thiocarbonate, and in aqueous sodium sulphide solution to give a solution of sodium thiocarbonate Na_2CS_3. The free acid, H_2CS_3, an unstable yellow oil, is liberated by concentrated hydrochloric acid from crystals of ammonium thiocarbonate. With sodamide carbon disulphide gives sodium thiocyanate:

$$NaNH_2 + CS_2 = NaSCN + H_2S.$$

A deep red solution of ammonium thiocarbonate is formed when carbon disulphide stands in contact with concentrated ammonia solution for some days. Yellow crystals are deposited as the solution evaporates. If carbon disulphide is diluted with ethyl alcohol or ether, and dry ammonia is passed into the solution at room temperature, the two reactions occur:

$$2CS_2 + 4NH_3 = NH_4CS_2NH_2 + NH_4CNS + H_2S,$$
$$2CS_2 + 4NH_3 = (NH_4)_2CS_3 + NH_4CNS.$$

Carbon disulphide also undergoes the reactions described by the following equations:

$CS_2 + 4H_2 = CH_4 + 2H_2S.$ The vapour and H_2 are passed over Pt or Ni at 450°.
$CS_2 + 2H_2O = CO_2 + 2H_2S.$ The vapour and steam at 150°.
$CS_2 + 4K = C + 2K_2S.$ Red heat.
$CS_2 + 4Cu = C + 2Cu_2S.$ Red heat.
$CS_2 + 2H_2O + 6Cu = CH_4 + 2Cu_2S + 2CuO.$ Vapour and steam over red hot Cu.
$CS_2 + 2H_2S + 8Cu = CH_4 + 4Cu_2S.$ Vapour and H_2S over red hot Cu.
$CS_2 + 3Cl_2 = CCl_4 + S_2Cl_2.$ Cl_2 passed into boiling CS_2 containing a little iodine.
$CS_2 + 3SO_3 = COS + 4SO_2.$

Carbon disulphide is monomeric, and the orbital structure presumably corresponds to that of carbon dioxide. If this is the case the sulphur atom by its combination with the carbon atom is forced to exert π bonds. In SiS_2 with both elements in Period 3 no π bonds are exerted and the compound has a chain structure.

Carbon diselenide, CSe_2, is made in good yield by the interaction of CH_2Cl_2 and molten selenium at 550–600°. (CS_2, CSSe, CTe_2 cannot be made by analogous reactions.) Carbon diselenide is a yellow highly refracting liquid which does not wet glass. The vapour irritates the lungs and nose, and is a lachrymator. On keeping, carbon diselenide darkens in colour and polymerises. It is miscible with toluene, carbon disulphide, and carbon tetrachloride; it is sparingly soluble in methyl alcohol and in ethyl alcohol. It is insoluble in water. It dissolves white phosphorus.

Carbon diselenide reacts slowly with nitric acid and with sulphuric acid, but not with hydrochloric acid. It dissolves in aqueous potassium hydroxide and more readily in alcoholic potassium hydroxide. It reacts with chlorine to yield $SeCl_4$ and other products such as $(CCl_3)_2Se$.

Carbon oxysulphide, OCS, is a colourless, odourless gas. It is formed:

   (i) by reaction of carbon monoxide and sulphur vapour,
   (ii) by the action of sulphur dioxide on carbon at a red heat,
   (iii) by the action of sulphur trioxide and carbon disulphide:

$$3SO_3 + CS_2 = 4SO_2 + OCS,$$

(iv) by the hydrolysis of thiocyanic acid with 70% sulphuric acid:

$$HNCS + H_2O = NH_3 + OCS,$$

(v) by decomposing potassium ethyl thiocarbonate with dilute hydrochloric acid:

$$C_2H_5O \cdot CSOK + HCl = OCS + KCl + C_2H_5OH$$

The carbon oxysulphide produced in the last reaction is pure.

Carbon oxysulphide is decomposed by a hot platinum wire to sulphur and carbon monoxide. It is very inflammable, and it explodes feebly when mixed with oxygen and sparked. It is soluble in water (at 20°, 100 c.c. in 100 gm. of water at 1 atm). It is scarcely attacked by strong alkali, but dilute alkali gives:

$$OCS + 4KOH = K_2CO_3 + K_2S + 2H_2O,$$

and not potassium thiocarbonate. However, with an alcoholic solution of ammonia it gives ammonium thiocarbamate:

$$OCS + 2NH_3 = NH_4(C(NH_2)OS);$$

the reaction is reversed by hydrochloric acid.

The molecule is linear. The orbital structure corresponds to that of carbon dioxide. The relative importance of each canonical form is roughly

$$O \overset{\pi}{-} C \underset{\pi}{-} S \qquad \bar{O} - C \overset{\pi}{\underset{\pi}{-}} \overset{+}{S} \qquad \overset{+}{O} \overset{\pi}{\underset{\pi}{-}} C - \bar{S}$$

$$58\% \qquad\qquad 14\% \qquad\qquad 28\%$$

The resonance energy is 20 kcal per mole.

Carbon oxyselenide, OCSe, is prepared by passing carbonyl chloride over aluminium selenide at 219°. The rate of passage of carbonyl chloride is 1·75 litres per hour. The yield is 36%:

$$Al_2Se_3 + 3COCl_2 = 2AlCl_3 + 3OCSe.$$

It is decomposed by light, and by water. Its dipole moment is 0·59 debyes.

SECTION 3. COMPOUNDS IN WHICH THE CARBON ATOM IS TRIGONALLY HYBRIDISED

GRAPHITE

Graphite is a black crystalline substance with a metallic lustre. The crystals are soft and flaky, m.p. about 3800°K. Graphite is the stable allotrope of carbon at room temperature. Bridgman found experimentally that at 2000° and 30,000 kg/cm² graphite and diamond are stable in contact with one another, but at lower pressures diamond changes to graphite. The heat of transformation of graphite to diamond is 0·45 kcal at 25° and 1 atm. It may be calculated using this datum that equilibrium is attained between graphite and diamond at 300°K and 15,000 atm, and at 1500°K and 40,000 atm.

The heat of sublimation of graphite is a very important quantity in the calculation of heats of formation of carbon compounds from atoms. The experimental determination of the magnitude of this quantity, however, has been found very difficult. It is now generally accepted that the heat of dissociation of graphite to carbon atoms is 170·4 kcal per mole at 0°K. The vapour pressure of monatomic carbon above graphite at 2600°K is about 10^{-6} atm. Graphite forms an azeotropic mixture with maganous sulphide; the two substances sublime together at 1375°.

The crystal of graphite is a layer structure. Each layer consists of a hexagonal network of carbon atoms with the distance C—C 1·42. The layers are 3·35 apart, which is too great for the formation of chemical bonds. The layers must be held together by van der Waals forces. The interlayer binding energy has been calculated to be 3·99 kcal per mole. The electrical properties of graphite correspond to its layer structure. The magnetic susceptibility along the plane of the layers is $-0·5 \times 10^{-6}$, and at right angles to this plane is -22×10^{-6}. The resistivity of a single crystal is 10^{-4} ohms cm along the plane, and 2 to 3 ohms cm at right-angles to it. Graphite does not show supraconductivity. According to the valence bond theory each carbon atom in graphite is trigonally hybridised, and the atoms in the hexagons are linked by σ bonds. The fourth electron of each carbon atom is part of a generalised orbital system. The generalised orbitals are above and below the plane containing the carbon nuclei. The bond order is 1·33, which is used in conjunction with the bond length 1·42 to give one of the fixed points on the curve in Fig. 11.5.

Graphite is chemically inert, but the presence of an electron concentration above and below the carbon atoms in graphite makes possible the formation of various graphitic compounds in which atoms or molecules are held between the layers of carbon atoms. The intercalation is accompanied by the transfer of electrons from the conduction band in graphite to one of the atoms in the reagent, or vice versa. Graphite thus reacts with potassium, bromine, chlorine, and iodine monochloride, ferric chloride, mineral acids under certain conditions, strong oxidising agents, and fluorine to give highly peculiar products which are described in the following paragraphs.

Potassium-graphite "alloys". Liquid potassium wets graphite, and causes it to swell up. If the product is heated the excess potassium distils off, leaving a residue which is copper-coloured and pyrophoric, and has the composition C_8K. If the residue is heated somewhat more strongly some of the intercalated potassium is driven off, and a steel-blue product is obtained with composition $C_{16}K$. The potassium is loosely held, and may be completely removed from the graphitic "compound" by treatment with mercury.

X-ray examination shows that the potassium atoms are inserted between the graphitic layers of carbon atoms. In C_8K one potassium atom for every eight carbon atoms is inserted between every pair of carbon layers; in $C_{16}K$ one potassium atom for every eight carbon atoms is inserted between every other pair of carbon layers. Other spacings have been observed up to one layer of potassium atom for every five graphite layers, corresponding to the composition $C_{60}K$.

The presence of the potassium atoms reduces the magnetic susceptibility of graphite to about 6% of its original value, which suggests a diminution in the range of the non-localised π bonds in the graphite. The presence of the potassium atoms increases the conductance of powdered graphite up to that of copper powder. These effects indicate that the graphite-potassium system has the properties of a metal; electrons are free to move from layer to layer as well as in a given layer.

Graphite bromine compounds. If graphite is exposed to a saturated bromine vapour bromine is absorbed to form a solid of composition C_8Br. The bromine enters the graphite as atoms or ions, which are assumed to occupy the same positions as the potassium atoms in C_8K. The absorption of bromine by graphite increases the layer spacing from 3·4 to 7·05. All except about 13% of the bromine can be removed by a stream of inert gas, or by pumping at low pressure. The presence of the bromine has an effect similar to that of potassium in modifying the properties of graphite. The graphitic layer appears to be amphoteric; it can receive electrons from potassium atoms, or give them to bromine atoms. Neither the potassium nor the bromine compound shows supraconductivity.

Ferric chloride compounds. Ferric chloride is absorbed by graphite at 180°. Electron diffraction and X-ray diffraction experiments show that single layers of ferric chloride lie between successive graphitic layers. Three stages of compound formation can be observed if the ferric chloride is gradually removed. Stage I has composition about 1 $FeCl_3$ to 6–9 carbon atoms. Calculation shows that the largest proportion of $FeCl_3$ that could be accommodated between layers would be $FeCl_3 \cdot 6C$.

Exhaustive leaching leads to Stage II with the composition $FeCl_3 \cdot 12C$. The $FeCl_3$ here is very firmly bound. At 300° it may be removed by volatilisation to give Stage III. Above 410° it yields graphite.

The chlorides of many other transition elements in their higher oxidation states, and the chlorides of all Group III elements form graphitic compounds.

Graphitic salts. There is a class of salt of the general formula $(C_{24})^+, X^-, 2HX$, where X^- may be HSO_4^-, $HSeO_4^-$, ClO_4^-, NO_3^-, $H_2PO_4^-$, $H_2AsO_4^-$, or $\frac{1}{2}H_2P_2O_7^{2-}$. These salts may be obtained by suspending graphite in the appropriate acid in the presence of a small quantity of a strong oxidising agent. An analogous fluoride $(C_{24})^+$, HF_2^-, 4HF has been obtained by the oxidation of graphite in the presence of anhydrous HF.

The sulphuric acid compound is blue. It is difficult to prepare pure, as it parts with part of its sulphuric acid on washing with water; if it is washed with phosphoric acid the product still contains 0·32 gm of sulphuric acid per gm of graphite. If a graphitic salt be treated with a reducing agent, the acid content is reduced in discrete stages which are correlated with diminution in the interlayer distance. It is therefore deduced that at each stage one interstitial layer of acid molecules and ions is withdrawn.

Fig. 18.4 shows the relation of the layer spacing to the different compositions of graphitic sulphates. The sulphates do not show supraconductivity.

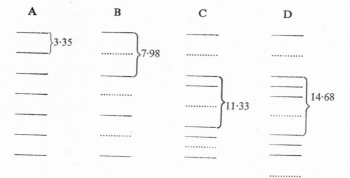

Fig. 18.4. Separation of graphite layers by ions HSO_4^- and molecules H_2SO_4 in graphite sulphate. Column A shows the undisturbed graphite layers spaced at 3·35. If a layer of HSO_4^- ions and H_2SO_4 molecules is inserted between every graphite layer (Column B) the spacing is increased to 7·98. If the pattern of spacing is 2 graphite layers to one acid layer the distance of spacing before the pattern is repeated is 11·33 (Column C). Column D shows the next more dilute arrangement.

Graphitic oxide. If graphite is treated with a mixture of concentrated H_2SO_4, concentrated HNO_3 and solid $KClO_3$ for several days, a product is obtained which is known as graphitic oxide (or hydroxide). This may be washed with water and dried over P_2O_5 at 70° in vacuo. As a result of this action the graphite loses its hydrophobic character, and its metallic lustre, and becomes greenish-brown in colour. The crystalline form is retained, but the interlayer distance increases from 3·4 to 6·2. It is not clear whether the substance is graphitic oxide with the composition (C_xO_y) or a hydroxide with the composition $C_x(OH)_z$.

When graphitic oxide is heated it decomposes almost explosively, yielding CO_2 and CO. It may be reduced to finely divided graphite by H_2S, $SnCl_2$ or hydroxylamine, but the bound oxygen is stable to HCl, HBr, HI, and NH_3 at 70°. There is evidence that the oxide has acidic properties. The amount of alkali neutralised by 1 gm of the oxide suggests the empirical formula C_6O_2OH. The dehydrated graphitic oxide may be methylated by diazomethane (in the process the spacing between the layers increases from 6·3 to 8·5), and it can be acetylated. It appears to be agreed that oxygen atoms are attached to both sides of each graphitic sheet; the distance between the sheet and the oxygen atoms is 1·4. It is probable that the carbon lattice has a hydroaromatic character, that the layers undulate, and that the C—C distance is 1·52. If this is the case, the constitution is similar to that of $(CF)_n$.

Graphitic oxide can absorb water (the interlayer distance expands to 11·0) and dioxan (the interlayer distance expands to 14·5). If the hydrated oxide is treated with dilute alkali, peptisation occurs and a colloidal solution of graphite is obtained; presumably peptisation takes place when both sides of each graphitic layer are covered with unimolecular layers of water molecules.

Graphitic fluorine compounds. Pure fluorine reacts with graphite at about 450°. The presence of hydrogen fluoride facilitates the reaction, and enables it to take place at room temperature. The reaction rate is proportional to the partial pressure of hydrogen fluoride.

In the presence of hydrogen fluoride at room temperature (or below 100°) the reaction product is $(C_4F)_n$. X-ray examination of the product shows that the graphite sheets are planar with intersheet distance 5·34. The fluorine atoms are found occupying trans-*para* positions in each sheet. The solid is unaffected by boiling alkali

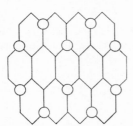

Fig. 18.5.   Layer of $(C_4F)_n$.

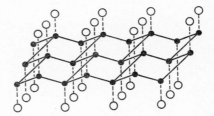

Fig. 18.6.   One layer of the chair ring structure of $(CF)_n$.

or dilute acids, including HI. The nature of the bonding is unknown, but it may be covalent.

At higher temperatures the reaction product is $(CF)_n$. This is obtained as a grey hydrophobic residue when graphite is treated with fluorine up to 500°, or when norite, a variety of carbon with the least well-developed crystal orientation, is heated with fluorine at 25 mm pressure and 280°. Both these reactions occur without ignition. The grey colour of $(CF)_n$ may be due to the incomplete conversion of the carbon to $(CF)_n$; it is claimed that $CF_{0.988}$ is white and transparent, and that its specific resistance is 10^5 times that of graphite.

$(CF)_n$ decomposes explosively when heated; the graphite derivative yields CF_4 and C_2F_6 in addition to free carbon; the norite derivative yields also C_2F_4.

$(CF)_n$ is insoluble in ordinary solvents. It is unattacked by acids and bases. It may be reduced by zinc dust and acetic acid to the original form of carbon. It does not react with hydrogen at 400°. It is decomposed by oxidising melts, and by heating with metallic sodium. Its adsorptive properties are considerably less than those of graphite; alkalis have a peptising effect on it, which suggests that the surface is acidic.

X-ray analysis shows that the intersheet distance in $(CF)_n$ is 6·9 to 8·17. The C—C distance is 1·54. Hence the graphitic nature of the original carbon has disappeared.

The sheets have become chair rings, in which each carbon atom is covalently bound to one fluorine atom. The fluorine atoms on alternate carbon atoms are above or below the plane of the ring as in Fig. 18.6.

ETHYLENE AND COMPOUNDS WHICH CONTAIN THE CARBONYL

GROUP $\overset{\displaystyle\diagdown}{\underset{\displaystyle\diagup}{C}}\overset{\pi}{=}O$

Ethylene,

$$\overset{\displaystyle H\diagdown \quad \diagup H}{\underset{\displaystyle H\diagup \quad \diagdown H}{C\overset{\pi}{=}C}}$$

is a colourless gas, m.p. $-169°$, b.p. $-104°$. The outstanding characteristic of ethylene is its property of combining with saturated molecules to form compounds in which the valence state of the carbon atom changes from trigonal to tetrahedral. In non-polar conditions the reaction does not take place. In the presence of a polar compound (the salts in the glass of the containing vessel are sufficient) the symmetry of the charge distribution in the ethylene molecule is disturbed, and addition takes place, thus:

$$\overset{\delta-}{H_2C}\overset{\pi}{=}\overset{\delta+}{CH_2}+\overset{+}{H}\overset{-}{Br} = H_3C\!-\!\overset{+}{CH_2}+\overset{-}{Br} = H_3C\!-\!CH_2Br.$$

Ethylene reacts with cuprous compounds, with palladium compounds, with silver nitrate, and with aluminium chloride dissolved in benzene, to form addition co-ordination compounds; the constitution of these compounds is uncertain.

The distance $C\overset{\pi}{=}C$ in ethylene is $1\cdot337$. Derivatives of ethylene of the form

$$\overset{\displaystyle R_1\diagdown \quad \diagup R_3}{\underset{\displaystyle R_2\diagup \quad \diagdown R_4}{C\overset{\pi}{=}C}}$$

are not optically active, and hence the molecule is planar. Ethylene derivatives of the forms:

$$\overset{\displaystyle H\diagdown \quad \diagup H}{\underset{\displaystyle CH_3\diagup \quad \diagdown CH_3}{C\overset{\pi}{=}C}} \qquad \overset{\displaystyle H\diagdown \quad \diagup CH_3}{\underset{\displaystyle CH_3\diagup \quad \diagdown H}{C\overset{\pi}{=}C}}$$

are geometrical isomers. The difference in energy content of the two forms is small when there is no interaction between the groups, and is of the order of one or two kcal per mole. The heat of activation of the change from one isomer to the other is large (30 to 40 kcal) and this is a measure of the energy required to break a π bond between the two carbon atoms.

Compounds of the type $\overset{\displaystyle X\diagdown}{\underset{\displaystyle X\diagup}{C}}\overset{\pi}{=}O$. There are numerous compounds of this type which include the aldehydes and ketones. X may represent not only H, or an alkyl or aryl radical, but also an electronegative atom or group such as OH, CN, or a halogen atom. The characteristic addition reactions of aldehydes and ketones are determined largely by the charge distribution of the C—O group, $(CH_3)_2\overset{\delta+}{C}$—$\overset{\delta-}{O}$. When X is an electronegative group the characteristic reactions of aldehydes and ketones are no longer observed, and the chemistry of such a molecule as Cl_2CO is concerned with the reactivity of the chlorine atoms. The physical properties of certain compounds of the general formula X_2CO, where X is an electronegative element are given in Table 18.11.

Table 18.11 *The carbonyl halides*

	m.p. °C	b.p. °C
COF_2	− 114	− 83
$COCl_2$	− 104	+ 8·2
$COBr_2$		64·5
COI_2		
$COClF$		
$CO(CN)_2$†	− 37·9	65·7

† The d.p.m. of $CO(CN)_2$ is 1·35 debyes.

Carbonyl fluoride, COF_2, is prepared (i) by burning fluorine in carbon monoxide, (ii) by the action of carbonyl chloride on antimony trifluoride in an autoclave, (iii) by passing carbon monoxide over AgF_2. Reaction (ii) also yields $COClF$.

Carbonyl fluoride is hydrolysed by water. It attacks glass, but not silica. With alcohol, or with primary or secondary amines, it reacts thus:

$$COF_2 + 2C_2H_5OH = CO(OC_2H_5)_2 + 2HF,$$
$$COF_2 + 2HN(CH_3)_2 = CO(N(CH_3)_2)_2 + 2HF.$$

Carbonyl chlorofluoride, $COClF$, is a by-product in reaction (ii) above. If it is treated with alcohol or with amines the chlorine atom is replaced thus:

$$COClF + C_2H_5OH = CO(OC_2H_5)F + HCl,$$
$$COClF + HN(CH_3)_2 = CON(CH_3)_2F + HCl.$$

Carbonyl chloride, $COCl_2$, is made by the direct action of carbon monoxide on chlorine, either in sunlight or in the presence of active charcoal. Carbonyl chloride reacts with water slowly to yield carbon dioxide and hydrochloric acid. With alcohol it yields ethyl chloroformate, $ClCOOC_2H_5$, or diethyl carbonate, $OC_2H_5 \cdot CO \cdot OC_2H_5$. With ammonia it yields urea. It is poisonous.

Its crystal structure has been shown to be tetragonal. The distance C—Cl is 1·74, and $C\overset{\pi}{—}O$ is 1·15; the angle ClCCl is 111·0°. Carbonyl chloride is covalent and does not undergo ionisation to $CO^{2+}(Cl^-)_2$ or $(COCl^+)Cl^-$.

Carbonyl bromide, $COBr_2$, is made (i) by a reaction between carbon monoxide and bromine vapour, or (ii) by dropping concentrated sulphuric acid on to carbon tetrabromide at 160°:

$$CBr_4 + H_2SO_4 = COBr_2 + SO_3 + 2HBr.$$

The oxyacids of carbon. Carbon does not form the acid $C(OH)_4$ or the ion $[CO^{4-}]$ which would be derived from it. The esters of this acid, however, are well characterised (p. 599).

The characteristic acid group containing a carbon atom is the carboxyl group, —COOH, and the simplest acid in which it is present is formic acid. The molecule of formic acid, in which the carbon atom is trigonally hybridised, is represented by two canonical forms in resonance:†

$$
\begin{array}{ccc}
& O\!-\!H & \\
H\!-\!C & & \\
& \overset{\pi}{}\!\!\diagdown O &
\end{array}
\qquad
\begin{array}{ccc}
& O\!-\!H & \\
H\!-\!\overset{+}{C} & & \\
& \diagdown O &
\end{array}
$$

At room temperature, however, 90% of formic acid molecules in the vapour are dimeric.

Electron diffraction and spectroscopic studies have been used to determine the bond angles and bond lengths of the monomeric and dimeric molecules. The dimensions are as follows:

$$
\begin{array}{c}
\overset{0\cdot96}{O\!-\!H} \\
\overset{1\cdot3}{\diagup} \quad\\
H\overset{1\cdot08}{-\!-}C \quad 123° \\
\overset{1\cdot23}{\diagdown} \\
O
\end{array}
\qquad\qquad
\begin{array}{c}
\xleftarrow{\;2\cdot73\;} \\
O \qquad O \\
\overset{1\cdot36}{\diagup}\;\;58° \;\; H \\
H\!-\!C\;\;\cdots\cdots\cdots\;\; C\!-\!H \\
\overset{1\cdot24}{\diagdown}\;\;63°\;\; H \\
O \qquad O
\end{array}
$$

It is clear that the hydrogen atom in the molecule RCOOH is attached to a particular oxygen atom, and that the symmetrical arrangement of the atomic nuclei:

$$
\begin{array}{c}
O \\
\diagup \quad\cdots \\
H\!-\!C \qquad H \\
\diagdown \quad\cdots \\
O
\end{array}
$$

cannot be accepted. The corresponding arrangement, however, is adopted in the ion:

$$
\begin{array}{c}
\overset{\pi}{\diagup} O \\
H\!-\!C \\
\diagdown O
\end{array}
\qquad\qquad
\begin{array}{c}
\diagup \overset{-}{O} \\
H\!-\!C \\
\overset{\pi}{\diagdown} O
\end{array}
$$

In sodium formate the C—O distance is 1·27.

Carbonic acid is hydroxy formic acid. The canonical forms of the acid are:

$$
\begin{array}{c}
\overset{\pi}{\diagup} O \\
H\!-\!O\!-\!C \\
\diagdown OH
\end{array}
\qquad\qquad
\begin{array}{c}
\diagup \overset{-}{O} \\
H\!-\!O\!-\!\overset{+}{C} \\
\diagdown OH
\end{array}
$$

and those of the carbonate ion are:

$$
\begin{array}{c}
\overset{\pi}{\diagup} O \\
\overset{-}{O}\!-\!C \\
\diagdown \underset{\cdot}{O}
\end{array}
\qquad
\begin{array}{c}
\diagup \overset{-}{O} \\
\overset{-}{O}\!-\!C \\
\overset{\pi}{\diagdown} O
\end{array}
\qquad
\begin{array}{c}
\diagup \overset{-}{O} \\
O\overset{\pi}{=}C \\
\diagdown O
\end{array}
$$

† The resonance is sometimes given as

$$
\begin{array}{c}
\overset{\pi}{\diagup} O \\
H\!-\!C \\
\diagdown O\!-\!H
\end{array}
\qquad\qquad
\begin{array}{c}
\diagup \overset{-}{O} \\
H\!-\!C \\
\overset{\pi}{\diagdown} \overset{+}{O}\!-\!H
\end{array}
$$

This is not possible because it would involve a change from tetrahedral to trigonal hybridisation for the oxygen atom of the OH group, and consequent movement of the hydrogen atom. The two structures would thus be tautomerides and not canonical forms in resonance.

The C—O distance in calcite is about 1·27; the bond angles are 120°. The resonance in the acid concerns the C—O bond only, and then only the change from the co-ionic to the covalent link. The resonance energy is so small that it fails to stabilise the otherwise unstable molecule, which is so easily decomposed that carbon dioxide is completely expelled when its aqueous solution is boiled. The acid is dibasic; K_1 is $4\cdot4 \times 10^{-7}$ at 25°, and K_2 is $4\cdot01 \times 10^{-11}$ at 18°.

The carbonates are well-characterised, but all except those of potassium, rubidium, and caesium are decomposed by heat, those of the heavy metals very easily, and those of sodium, lithium, and barium only slowly. The increased stability of the carbonate ion over that of the acid may be due to the more extensive resonance which is possible in the ion.

Benzene, is the typical example of a compound which contains trigonally hybridised carbon atoms which contribute p orbitals to a non-localised system of π bonds. Its structure is discussed on p. 171.

TRIPHENYLMETHYL AND ITS DERIVATIVES

Among the most interesting compounds containing the carbon atom in the trigonal valence state are triphenylmethyl, $C(C_6H_5)_3$, and its many derivatives. Triphenyl methyl is formed by the dissociation of hexaphenyl ethane $(C_6H_5)_3C—C(C_6H_5)_3$ when dissolved in benzene. Hexaphenyl ethane is colourless, and it would be expected to be inert. Its benzene solution, however, is yellow, and in the solution it reacts with air to form the peroxide, $(C_6H_5)_3C—O—O—C(C_6H_5)_3$, and with bromine to yield $(C_6H_5)_3CBr$. These properties are explained by the existence of the equilibrium represented by the equation:

$$(C_6H_5)_3C—C(C_6H_5)_3 = 2(C_6H_5)_3C; \quad \Delta H = +11 \text{ kcal.}$$

The percentage dissociation of the dimer can be measured experimentally by several different methods, and is found to be 2·8.[†] Much work has been done on triphenyl methyl and its derivatives, but space forbids any detailed account of these studies in this book. It has been concluded that the dissociation of the dimer hexaphenyl ethane, and similar compounds, is due to three effects:

(a) the weakening of the C—C bond linking the two triphenylmethyl groups,

(b) the stability of the radical $C(C_6H_5)_3$,

(c) the steric effect of three large groups round one carbon atom, which would hinder the recombination of two radicals.

The bond energy of the ethane C—C bond in hexaphenyl ethane has been measured; it is 44·6 kcal whereas the bond energy of the C—C bond in ethane is 83 kcal. The stabilisation of the triphenylmethyl radical in terms of the valence bond theory probably depends on the number of canonical forms which are comprised in its structure, and on the extent to which conjugation is possible in each of these forms. The relation between dissociation of the dimer into radicals and the extent of conjugation in the radical is set out below for three dimeric compounds. Each Kekulé form of the benzene ring is counted as a canonical form, but the Dewar structures are neglected.

† This value was found for a 0·03 molar solution in toluene at 20°.

Radical†	% dissocia-tion of dimer	Number of canonical forms in radical	Number of completely conjugated double bonds in radical
Triphenylmethyl	2·8	44	9 in 36 of the forms
Phenyldiphenylene methyl	0	29	9 in 27 of the forms
Triphenyldiphenylene ethyl	100	104	6 in diphenylene group, and 3 in each phenyl group in 104 forms

In terms of the theory of non-localised orbitals, the stability of the monomeric forms is explained in the formation of non-localised orbitals over the whole of a large molecule. Dipole moment evidence indicates that molecules of the triphenyl methyl type are planar. If the central carbon atom is trigonally hybridised in the xy plane, the central carbon atom contains one electron in the p_z orbital which is not included in the hybridised orbitals, $sp_x p_y$. The p_z orbital then overlaps the delocalised orbital systems of the aromatic rings. Each of these consists of two regions of maximum charge density lying parallel to, and above and below the plane of the nuclei in the ring.

In such compounds as triphenylmethyl the non-localised orbitals carry a deficiency of electrons. The orbital system of the molecule is able to tolerate a deficiency of one in the number of electrons required to occupy fully all the molecular orbitals in the system. The more extensive the resonance of the orbital system, the more readily is the deficiency tolerated, or, in other words, the more stable is the radical.

SECTION 4. COMPOUNDS IN WHICH THE CARBON ATOM IS TETRAHEDRALLY HYBRIDISED

Among the compounds of the tetrahedrally hybridised carbon atom are the bulk of the aliphatic organic compounds. In these compounds a tetrahedrally hybridised carbon atom is linked to other carbon atoms, or to hydrogen atoms, to halogen atoms, or to univalent groups such as OH, OCH_3, COOH, NH_2.

It is interesting to note that certain structures in which four identical groups are linked to one carbon atom are unstable and cannot be made. For example:

Stable compounds	Non-existent compounds
CH_4	$C(OH)_4$
$C(CH_3)_4$	$C(NH_2)_4$
$C(OCH_3)_4$	$C(COOH)_4$
CF_4	
CCl_4	

† The structural formulae of the radicals are:

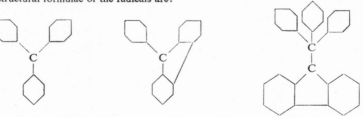

Triphenylmethyl   Phenyldiphenylene methyl   Triphenyldiphenylene ethyl

Although orthocarbonic acid, $C(OH)_4$, does not exist its esters are well-known, and may be obtained by the action of sodium alcoholates on chloropicrin, CCl_3NO_2. The ethyl ester, b.p. 158° and the propyl ester, b.p. 220°, are colourless oils with fragrant odours. They are hydrolysed by sodium hydroxide to yield sodium carbonate and the alcohol.

For reasons of space no account is given in this book of organic compounds in general. Carbon tetrafluoride and carbon tetrachloride and a few other halogen compounds of carbon are described under the halogens. The concluding pages of this section contain descriptions of diamond and of certain carbides.

Diamond. The crystal is a giant molecule; the distance C—C is 1·54. The co-ordination is 4:4. Each carbon atom is assumed to be tetrahedrally hybridised, and to exert four covalent bonds to different neighbours. The points of the crystal lattice at which the carbon atoms are found correspond to the positions of all the atoms (both Zn and S) in wurtzite (p. 347). The diamond lattice is not close-packed; an assembly of atoms in a close-packed cubic or hexagonal structure could not accommodate atoms of the same radius in the tetrahedral holes (p. 342).

Diamond has a very high refractive index (2·4), and it is the hardest substance yet discovered. It is chemically inert. It burns in oxygen at 700° to form carbon dioxide, and in fluorine at the same temperature to form carbon tetrafluoride. It is not attacked by acids, alkalis, or by fused potassium chlorate.

Silicon carbide or carborundum, SiC. The lattice of silicon carbide consists of carbon atoms at points corresponding to those occupied by atoms in a close-packed face-centred cubic or hexagonal structure, with silicon atoms at half the points corresponding to the positions of the tetrahedral holes. Carborundum exists in three forms which are different combinations of "layers" corresponding to the zinc blende and wurtzite structures. The forms are:

Carborundum   I   *aaa bb* ⎫ where *a* is a "zinc blende layer",
            II   *aaa bbb* ⎬
           III   *aa bb* ⎭ and *b* is a "wurtzite layer".

Carborundum is made by heating carbon with silicon or silica in an electric furnace. It is very hard, does not decompose below 2200°, and is attacked by chemical reagents only at high temperatures. It is oxidised by fused sodium hydroxide in contact with air:

$$2O_2 + SiC + 4NaOH = Na_2CO_3 + Na_2SiO_3 + 2H_2O.$$

Other carbides which are not acetylides, are beryllium methanide, Be_2C (p. 425), and aluminium carbide, Al_4C_3 (p. 534) both of which yield methane on treatment with water or dilute acids, and magnesium carbide, Mg_2C_3 (p. 442) which yields allylene on treatment with water. In the antifluorite structure of Be_2C the carbon atom is 8 co-ordinate.

Two other classes of carbides are discussed in the following paragraphs. These are: (i) the interstitial carbides, formed by transition metals which have atomic radii large enough to permit the accommodation of carbon atoms in the octahedral holes of the close-packed metallic lattice, and (ii) the carbides of Cr, Mn, Fe, Co, Ni, of which the atomic radii are too small to permit the formation of interstitial carbides; the structures of the second type of carbide are unknown.

The interstitial carbides. The crystals of certain transition metals are able to absorb carbon atoms to yield products of the composition MC or M_2C. It is found that whatever the crystal structure of the reacting metal, the carbide obtained has a sodium chloride structure. The metal atoms have cubic close-packing and the carbon atoms are in the octahedral holes. The relative sizes of the carbon atom and the metallic atoms are an important factor; the ratio of the radius of the metallic atom to that of the non-metallic must be $1:0.41-0.59$. This means that if a metal is to take part in this structure its atomic radius must be at least 1·3 and not more than 1·9†. A list of transition metals with atomic radii greater than 1·3 is given in Table 18.12 which also includes the melting point of the metal and that of the carbide derived from it, and the crystal lattice of the metal.

The interstitial carbides are made by heating carbon and the powdered metal at about 2200°. The product is in the form of a powder. It may be purified by compression into rods followed by sintering at some temperature not far below its melting point, when all impurities volatilise away. The carbides may also be made by heating a wire of the metal electrically in an atmosphere of methane at low pressure; if the pressure of methane is too high graphite is deposited on the surface of the metal. As a variation of this method a tungsten wire is used, and the gas phase is a mixture of methane and a volatile chloride of the metal which is to form the carbide. The metal and carbon are deposited on the tungsten, where they react to form the carbide; the tungsten is subsequently volatilised away.

Table 18.12. *The Interstitial Carbides*

Metal	Atomic radius for C.N. 6	For C.N. 12	m.p. °K	Carbide	m.p. °K	Hardness, Moh's scale	Crystal structure of metal
Ti	1·41	1·47	2073	TiC	3410	8–9	b.c.c. and hex. c.p.
Zr	1·54	1·60	2173	ZrC	3805	8–9	b.c.c. and hex. c.p.
Hf	1·53	1·59	1973	HfC	4160		b.c.c. and hex. c.p.
V		1·35	2000	VC	3023		.
				V_2C			
Nb	1·41	1·47	2773	NbC	3770		b.c.c.
Ta	1·41	1·47	3273	TaC	4150		b.c.c.
W	1·35	1·41	3643	$\begin{cases} W_2C \\ WC \end{cases}$	3130 3130	9–10	b.c.c. b.c.c.
Mo	1·34	1·40	2953	$\begin{cases} Mo_2C \\ MoC \end{cases}$	2600 2840		b.c.c. and hex. c.p. b.c.c. and hex. c.p.

C.N. represents co-ordination number

The existence of W_2C and WC, and of Mo_2C and MoC rests on good evidence; the compounds M_2C might be written $MC_{\frac{1}{2}}$ and it may be taken that the carbon atoms occupy only one-half of the octahedral holes.

Except in the cases of the carbides of tungsten and molybdenum all the carbides melt at higher temperatures than the metal from which they are formed. Carbon can be melted and vaporised in a crucible of tantalum carbide. The binary systems of certain pairs of interstitial carbides have been investigated. The system tantalum carbide–zirconium carbide contains a solid phase of composition 4TaC,ZrC which melts at 4215°K. This is the highest m.p. recorded for any substance.

The carbides of molybdenum and tungsten are somewhat more reactive chemically than the metals from which they are derived, but the other carbides are less reactive than the parent metals. Titanium carbide is insoluble in boiling potassium hydroxide solution, and is not attacked by hydrogen chloride or water at 600°. Vanadium

† This is on the assumption that the carbon atom is tetrahedrally hybridised with radius 0·771. If the atom is exerting one σ and two π bonds, as suggested by Pauling, its radius is 0·602, in which case the radius limits for the metal would be 1·0–1·67.

carbide is not attacked by chlorine or sulphur below a red heat, but it is slowly attacked by cold nitric acid. The carbides are most likely to be attacked by oxidising agents.

In physical properties the carbides are metallic. They are opaque, they have high electrical conductivities which are diminished by increase of temperature, they exhibit the phenomenon of supraconductivity, they are weakly paramagnetic, and the susceptibility varies but little with temperature.

The sodium chloride crystal structure of the carbides gives to each carbon atom the co-ordination number 6. The carbon atom cannot undergo octahedral, d^2sp^3, hybridisation. If, however, the atom is digonally hybridised and the two unhybridised p orbitals (at right-angles to one another and the linear axis) are also used for bond formation, a pseudo octahedral bond system is obtained. If the system is in resonance all the bonds are equivalent. This system can be occupied by eight electrons, and hence the bond order is 4/6. This represents a stronger bond than those in, say, tantalum metal in which, if the number of valence electrons is four, the bond order is 4/8. It is significant that the only elements to form the so-called interstitial compounds with metals are B, C, N, O, which are the elements which exert π bonds in other circumstances.

The carbides of certain transition metals with small atomic radii. The transition metals Cr, Mn, Fe, Co, Ni have the atomic radii given in Table 18.13.

Table 18.13.　*Atomic Radii of Transition Metals with Small Atomic Radii*

Metal	Cr	Mn	Fe	Co	Ni
Atomic radius for C.N. 12	1·29	1·37	1·26	1·25	1·25
Atomic radius for C.N. 6	1·24	1·31	1·21	1·20	1·20

C.N. represents co-ordination number

Except for manganese, the radii for C.N. 6 are too small to enable these metals to form interstitial carbides. The carbides of chromium, manganese, and iron are briefly considered below.

Chromium carbide, Cr_3C_2, is made by heating Cr_2O_3 and carbon in the electric furnace. It is inert, and resists attack by acids and alkalis. It appears to be in a class by itself. In the crystal each carbon atom is surrounded by six chromium atoms at the corners of a trigonal biprism containing it, and a given carbon atom is only 1·665 from two other carbon atoms. The arrangement of the carbon atoms may be regarded as a hydrocarbon chain stripped of the H atoms. Other examples of mutually bonded carbon atoms in a metallic structure are the metal acetylides, and the potassium graphite compounds.

Manganese carbide, Mn_3C, is formed when Mn_3O_4 is heated to a high temperature with either carbon or calcium acetylide. It reacts with water to give a gas consisting of 75% hydrogen, the remainder being chiefly methane and ethane.

Cementite, Fe_3C, is readily decomposed by water with the deposition of free carbon and the formation of ethane, ethylene, and more complex hydrocarbons. Ni_3C is much less stable than cementite. The existence of Co_3C is inferred only from the thermal analysis of the Co—C system.

SILICON

Silicon is obtained:

- (i) by reducing silica at a high temperature with one of the reducing agents carbon, magnesium, calcium carbide, or a mixture of aluminium and sulphur; the reaction with magnesium is violent,
- (ii) by reducing sodium fluorosilicate, Na_2SiF_6, silicon tetrafluoride, or silicon tetrachloride with Na, K, or Al,
- (iii) by passing a mixture of hydrogen and silicochloroform, $SiHCl_3$, over silica at 950°.

Silicon is not highly reactive. It combines with many elements at high temperatures and reacts with alkalis and with the halogens, but not with acids except hydrofluoric acid. Certain reactions of silicon are set out in Table 18.14.

Table 18.14.   Reactions of Silicon

Reagent	Conditions of reaction	Product
Oxygen	Ignition	SiO_2
Sulphur	Pass vapour over heated Si	SiS_2
F_2	Ignition occurs spontaneously	SiF_4
Cl_2	Pass over heated Si	$SiCl_4$
Br_2	Pass over heated Si	$SiBr_4$
I_2	Pass vapour over heated Si	SiI_4
HCl	Pass gas over Si at dull red heat	$SiHCl_3$
HBr	Pass gas over Si at dull red heat	$SiHBr_3$
HI	Pass gas mixed with iodine vapour over Si at dull red heat	$SiHI_3$
N_2	Heat to 1350°	Si_3N_4
NaOH	Dilute aqueous solution	Na_2SiO_3 and H_2
Mg	Heat mixture of Mg and Si in an atmosphere of H_2	MgSi

GENERAL CHEMISTRY OF SILICON

Silicon follows carbon in sub-Group IV N. The chemistry of silicon is best outlined by comparing it with the more familiar chemistry of carbon.

The valency shell of the silicon atom possesses d orbitals, but the p orbitals of this shell ($n=3$) do not take part in the formation of π bonds. The valency shell of the carbon atom ($n=2$) does not possess d orbitals, but its ability to form π bonds is responsible for much of the characteristic chemistry of carbon. These important differences in atomic constitution between the atoms of silicon and carbon account in considerable degree for the sharp difference in the chemical properties of these elements and their compounds. Some of these differences are:

(i) The silicon atom never assumes the digonal valence state, and hence there are no silicon compounds corresponding to CO_2, CS_2, and C_2H_2. It is true that substances with the formulae SiO_2 and SiS_2 are well-known, but these have giant molecules in which the silicon atoms are probably present in the tetrahedral valence state; the solid compounds SiO_2 and SiS_2 are quite unlike the gaseous compounds CO_2 and CS_2.

(ii) The silicon atom never assumes the trigonal valence state (p. 570), and hence there are no compounds corresponding to C_2H_4, Cl_2CO, benzene, and graphite. There are no sheet structures consisting solely of silicon atoms. The layers of silicon atoms in the interstitial calcium silicide are not planar but puckered, indicating that the atoms are tetrahedrally hybridised.

(iii) The acids characteristic of carbon, such as carbonic acid and the fatty acids exemplified, say, by acetic acid, CH_3COOH, have no counterparts among the oxygen compounds of silicon. The carbonate $CaCO_3$ and the silicate $CaSiO_3$ have parallel formulae, but whereas the carbonate ion is discrete, the SiO_3 group is a notional unit in an infinite chain structure of SiO_4 tetrahedra (p. 606).

(iv) There is no silicon radical corresponding to triphenylmethyl, $(C_6H_5)_3C$. $(C_6H_5)_3Si$—$Si(C_6H_5)_3$ is known, but it does not dissociate.

The bond energies of bonds between silicon atoms and certain other atoms are often very different from the bond energies of corresponding bonds exerted by carbon. A few numerical values of bond energies are given in kcal in Table 18.15.

Table 18.15. *Bond Energies (kcal) of certain Silicon and Carbon Bonds*

Si—Si 42·5	Si—H 75·1	Si—O 89·3	Si—F 127·9
C—C 83	C—H 99·3	C—O 80·2	C—F 121

From these values it follows that chains of silicon atoms are likely to be less common than chains of carbon atoms, and that the silicon hydrides are more open to chemical attack than the carbon hydrides. The very high reactivity of the silanes (p. 612) is in noticeable contrast to the inertness of the paraffins. The strength of the Si—O bond compared with that of the C—O bond is evident in the existence of the wide range of silicones which are without parallel among the carbon compounds.

The silicates are also without counterpart in the chemistry of the carbon compounds. The structural unit of the silicates is the group SiO_4 in which the oxygen atoms are close-packed. This group is different from the carbonate group $[CO_3^{2-}]$, in which the carbon atom is exerting one π bond, and from the sulphate group $[SO_4^{2-}]$ in which the sulphur atom is exerting two πd bonds. The absence of any form of double bonding in the SiO_4 group probably determines its highly characteristic properties.

COMPOUNDS IN WHICH THE OXIDATION STATE OF SILICON IS 2

Silicon monoxide, SiO. The only compound in which silicon is bivalent is silicon monoxide, SiO. This is an amorphous brown powder which is pyrophoric in air. In these properties it differs from carbon monoxide, but, like carbon monoxide, it is a strong reducing agent. It reduces steam at 410°, carbon dioxide at 500°, and sulphur dioxide at 800°. It reduces dolomite at 1350° to metal, and Ta_2O_5 and Nb_2O_5 to metal.

It is made by heating silicon with either silica or a silicate to 1450° in vacuo. The silicon sublimes as an oxide, and the condensate has the composition SiO. (The b.p. of silicon is about 2500°, and the b.p. of SiO_2 is 2590°.)

The existence of SiO in the solid state is not definitely established.† If amorphous

† No evidence for its existence is furnished by thermal analysis, *Ann. Reports.*, **54**, 1957, 107.

SiO is heated to 1000° for one hour in vacuo, it develops a f.c.c. lattice without loss of oxygen, but no such change occurs at 200°. At temperatures up to 1000° it changes to a mixture of amorphous silica and cristobalite. From the method of its preparation, and from its spectrum, there is evidence for the existence of SiO in the vapour state. By an effusion technique the partial pressure of SiO over a solid phase of Si and SiO_2 at 1050–1200° has been determined, and the heat of formation of gaseous SiO is calculated to be 26 kcal/mole at 1125°, and 23·3 at 25°.

Certain sub-compounds of silicon have been identified but they are probably polymers:

$(SiH)_n$ formed by reduction of tribromosilane with magnesium,

$(SiBr)_n$ formed by reduction of silicon tetrabromide with magnesium,

$(SiBr_2)_n$ formed by reduction of silicon tetrabromide with silicon at 1200°.

The dibromide gives dialkyls with Grignard reagents and hydrolyses to subsilicic acid $[Si(OH)_{2·2}]_n$.

COMPOUNDS IN WHICH THE OXIDATION STATE OF SILICON IS 4

SECTION 1. GIANT MOLECULE STRUCTURES IN WHICH THE BONDS HAVE BOTH IONIC AND COVALENT CHARACTER

Silicon carbide, carborundum, SiC, is described on p. 599.

Silicon nitride, Si_3N_4, is made by heating silicon in nitrogen to 1350°. The heat of formation at 25° is 143 kcal per mole. Silicon nitride has the phenacite structure, and is chemically very stable.

Silicon dioxide, or silica, SiO_2. Silica can be made in the laboratory by the hydrolysis of silicon tetrachloride or tetrafluoride with water. It is found as a mineral in three crystalline forms of which the transition temperatures and the specific gravities are given below:

$$\text{Quartz} \leftarrow 870° \rightarrow \text{Tridymite} \leftarrow 1470° \rightarrow \text{Cristobalite, m.p. } 1710°$$
$$2·65 \qquad\qquad 2·26 \qquad\qquad 2·32$$

Although the last two forms exist indefinitely at room temperature, at such a temperature they are metastable. Each of the above polymorphic forms of silica exists in two subsidiary forms with the following transition points:

α-β quartz	α-β tridymite	α-β cristobalite
573°	120–160°	200–275°

The α form is stable at low temperatures. In each case the α differs from the β form only by a slight alteration in the disposition of the SiO_2 tetrahedra; there is no difference in the way the tetrahedra are linked together.

Silica melts at 1710° and on cooling sets to a transparent glass. The glass has a very small coefficient of expansion, and hence withstands sudden big changes of temperature. It is chemically resistant, but it is attacked by alkalis or by hydrofluoric acid according to the equations:

$$SiO_2 + 2NaOH = Na_2SiO_3 + H_2O,$$
$$SiO_2 + 4HF = SiF_4 + 2H_2O,$$

and when heated with an alkali metal, an alkaline earth metal, or with aluminium it is reduced. When mixed with carbon and heated with certain other metals the silicide of the metal is produced. Silica glass is non-polar, and it is used for the construction of apparatus from which polar compounds or acid-base catalysts must be excluded. It is transparent to ultraviolet light. At 1200° silica glass slowly crystallises to cristobalite.

Crystals of quartz, tridymite, and cristobalite consist of three-dimensional networks of tetrahedra of SiO_4 joined so that each oxygen atom is common to two tetrahedra. The relation between cristobalite and tridymite corresponds to that between zinc blende and wurtzite, although neither cristobalite nor tridymite have close-packed structures. In zinc blende the S atoms of ZnS are cubic close-packed, and the Zn atoms occupy one half of the tetrahedral holes. In β-cristobalite the Si atoms are found at points which correspond to the positions of cubic close-packing, and the O atoms are at all the points corresponding to the positions of the tetrahedral holes. In wurtzite the S atoms are in hexagonal close-packing, and in tridymite the Si atoms are found at the corresponding positions. The O atoms are again at the positions of the tetrahedral holes.

In quartz the tetrahedra are so linked that they acquire a spiral formation, and the crystal is optically active.

THE SILICATES

The SiO_4 tetrahedron in the silicates. The fundamental chemical unit of a silicate is the tetrahedron:

$$
\begin{array}{c}
O \\
| \\
Si \\
\diagup\ |\ \diagdown \\
O\ \ O\ \ O
\end{array}
$$

If this unit is made up of free atoms of silicon and oxygen it must acquire four extra electrons in order that each atom may have an octet of electrons in its valency shell. These extra electrons have been donated by the atoms of the metals which are present in the silicate as cations. For the purpose of calculating the number of additional electrons accepted, which will determine the negative charge on the anion, it is assumed that the silicon atom is linked to each oxygen atom by one covalent bond. Each oxygen atom linked to the silicon atom then accepts one extra electron to complete its octet, and hence the tetrahedral unit as a whole carries four negative charges, and is written thus: $(SiO_4)^{4-}$.

In most silicates the SiO_4 tetrahedra are not discrete, but are parts of larger systems in which certain oxygen atoms are held in common by two tetrahedra. The simplest unit of this kind is the ion $(Si_2O_7)^{6-}$, which consists of two tetrahedra with one oxygen atom in common:

$$
\begin{array}{ccc}
O & & O \\
\diagdown & & \diagup \\
O\!-\!Si\!-\!O\!-\!Si\!-\!O \\
\diagup & & \diagdown \\
O & & O
\end{array}
$$

The oxygen atom held in common exerts two covalent bonds, and this bicovalency completes its electron octet. The remaining six oxygen atoms each accept one extra electron, and hence the anion as a whole carries six negative charges. By assigning one negative charge to every oxygen atom attached to one silicon atom only, the ionic valency of a structural unit may be calculated.

No silicon atom ever forms more than one Si—O—Si link to a second silicon atom; that is, tetrahedra are joined by corners only, and never by edges or faces. This is consonant with the tetrahedral hybridisation of the oxygen atoms. The bond angle Si—O—Si is 109°. If the two tetrahedra had an edge in common, the angle would be 71°.

The following classification of silicates based on possible arrangements of SiO_4 tetrahedra may be devised.

1. Silicates with discrete anions.

    (a) Orthosilicates Be_2SiO_4 (phenacite), and Mg_2SiO_4

    (b) Thortveitite $Sc_2(Si_2O_7)$

       Hemimorphite $Zn_3(Si_2O_7) \cdot Zn(OH)_2 \cdot H_2O$

    (c) Beryl $Be_3Al_2(Si_6O_{18})$

The anion in beryl consists of a ring of six tetrahedra (small black circles represent Si atoms):

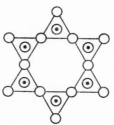

By the rule stated above, the negative charge on this anion is the number of oxygen atoms attached to one silicon only, which is 12. This negative charge is neutralised by $3Be^{2+}$ and $2Al^{3+}$.

2. Silicates with the anions as long chains. This class includes the pyroxenes, and the metasilicates such as diopside, $(Mg,Ca)SiO_3$.

The arrangement of the tetrahedra is:

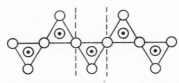

Such a structure may be continued indefinitely, and its formula must be referred to a unit in much the same way as a crystal structure is defined in terms of a unit cell. The unit between the dotted lines contains one Si atom, two oxygen atoms wholly within the unit, and two oxygen atoms shared by neighbouring units. The formula of the unit is $SiO_2 + O^{2-} = (SiO_3)^{2-}$.

It should be noted that although by the above notation calcium metasilicate is assigned a formula which appears to be analogous to that of calcium carbonate, there is no relation whatever between the two structures (for the carbonate structure, see p. 596).

3. Silicates with the anions as bands. This class includes the amphiboles and tremolite $Ca(OH)_2 \cdot CaMg_5(Si_4O_{11})_2$.

The tetrahedra are arranged as a long band:

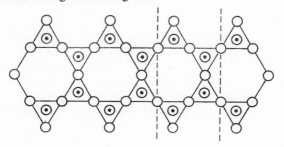

The anionic unit consists of four silicon atoms and nine oxygen atoms wholly within the unit, and four oxygen atoms shared between neighbouring units. In the unit there are six oxygen atoms each of which is attached to one silicon atom only. The unit is therefore written $(Si_4O_{11})^{6-}$.

4. Silicates with the anions as sheets, $(Si_2O_5)^{2-}$. The anion of composition $(Si_2O_5{}^{2-})_n$ represents a sheet of SiO_4 tetrahedra arranged in a pattern which is an infinite extension in two dimensions of the phenacite structure. There is no simple silicate based on this structure but it is part of the complex structure of kaolin, talc, and the micas.

5. Silicates with a three-dimensional framework. A three-dimensional network of SiO_4 tetrahedra gives a unit of zero valency, $(SiO_2)^0$. This network is in fact the structure of silica. Since the framework is electrically neutral it cannot be the anion of a salt. If, however, one of the silicon atoms in a crystal of silica is replaced by an aluminium atom, the particular SiO_4 tetrahedron affected has one electron less than before, because the atomic number of aluminium is one less than that of silicon. This loss of one electron can be imagined to be made good by the acceptance of one electron from a metallic atom which thus becomes a cation; the silicate structure then becomes an anion with a unit negative charge. If the silicate structure contains one atom of aluminium and m atoms of silicon, its formula is $(AlSi_mO_{2(1+m)})^{1-}$. If the replacement of silicon by aluminium had continued until the structure consisted of n atoms of aluminium and m atoms of silicon, the formula would be $(Al_nSi_mO_{2(n+m)})^{n-}$. If $n=1$ and $m=3$, the formula becomes $(AlSi_3O_8)^{1-}$, which is the anion of orthoclase, $K(AlSi_3O_8)$.

THE CRYSTAL STRUCTURE OF SILICATES

The crystallographic fundamental unit of the silicates is also the SiO_4 tetrahedron, but for the purpose of elucidating the structure of the crystals all the atoms are regarded as ions. The central ion of the tetrahedron is Si^{4+} and the ions at the apices are O^{2-}. The co-ordination number of the Si^{4+} ion is four and this is in accordance with the radius ratio of the Si^{4+}/O^{2-} in Table 12.2. The radius of the Si^{4+} ion (0·50) is so small that the O^{2-} ions in the tetrahedron are close-packed. The silicon ions and the metallic ions which make the structures electrically neutral are in the tetrahedral or octahedral holes.

The application of the above general statements to particular silicates is most simply illustrated by consideration of beryllium orthosilicate Be_2SiO_4 and magnesium orthosilicate Mg_2SiO_4. In the crystals of these silicates the oxygen ions are in hexagonal close-packing. The hexagonally close-packed lattice is shown in Fig. 12.4, p. 341. The unit cell contains 6 oxygen ions, 6 tetrahedral holes and 6 octahedral holes. The Si^{4+} ions occupy $1\frac{1}{2}$ tetrahedral holes per unit cell. The $SiO_4{}^{4-}$ ions are electrically neutralised by cations $2(Be^{2+})$ or $2(Mg^{2+})$. Table 12.7 shows that Be^{2+} ions may be accommodated in tetrahedral holes. Hence Be_2SiO_4 contains Be^{2+} ions in three tetrahedral holes per unit cell. $1\frac{1}{2}$ tetrahedral holes per unit cell are unoccupied. The Mg^{2+} ion $(r=0·71)$ is too large to occupy a tetrahedral hole, but it may occupy an octahedral hole. In Mg_2SiO_4 three octahedral holes per unit cell are occupied by Mg^{2+} ions.

The Na^+ ion and the Ca^{2+} ion are much too large to occupy an octahedral hole, and hence there can be no such silicate as Na_2SiO_4 or Ca_2SiO_4.

SUBSTITUTION IN THE CRYSTAL OF ONE ATOM FOR ANOTHER

The lattice structure of close-packed oxygen ions, with positive ions in the tetrahedral or octahedral holes, permits the substitution of one ion for another, provided there is no great difference in ionic radii. On account of this flexibility of constitution the structure of a silicate, although based on simple crystallographic principles, may not be revealed by a knowledge of its composition determined by chemical analysis.

There are two possible types of substitution in the lattice:

The replacement of one metallic cation by another. An example is furnished by olivine which may be regarded as magnesium orthosilicate in which about 10% of the Mg^{2+} ions have been replaced by Fe^{2+} ions. The composition may be written $(Mg,Fe)_2SiO_4$.

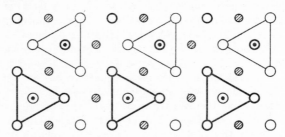

Fig. 18.7.   Plan of the structure of Mg_2SiO_4. Small black circles represent Si atoms, shaded circles Mg atoms, and open circles O atoms. Light and heavy lines are used to distinguish between SiO_4 tetrahedra at different heights.

This type of replacement is comparable to the substitution of one alkali metal for another in the alums.

The introduction of a metallic oxide, hydroxide, or fluoride into the lattice. The structure of a silicate is based on a close-packed array of oxygen ions. Such an array may be regarded as a series of layers stacked on top of one another. Any other compound having a structure based on close-packed oxygen ions can also be regarded as composed of the same layers arrayed in exactly the same way. A series of layers of certain metallic oxides or hydroxides can therefore be inserted between

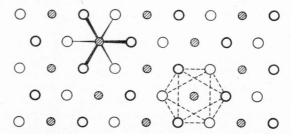

Fig. 18.8.   Plan of the structure of $Mg(OH)_2$. Shaded circles represent Mg atoms, and open circles O atoms. The relation of a Mg atom to its six nearest oxygen neighbours is indicated.

the oxygen ion layers of a silicate structure, without disturbing the relations of the atoms or ions in the separate substances.

A simple example is furnished by the relation of the chondrodite minerals to magnesium orthosilicate. The general formula for chondrodite is $(Mg_2SiO_4)_n$ $(Mg(OH)_2)_m$. Fig. 18.7 shows the structure of $MgSiO_4$ in plan, and Fig. 18.8 shows that of $Mg(OH)_2$ in plan. Two octahedral holes are indicated with Mg ions at the centres. Fig. 18.9 shows a plan of the structure of chondrodite. Comparison of

Fig. 18.9 with Fig. 18.7 shows how the structure of Mg_2SiO_4 has been modified by the insertion of a layer of Mg^{2+} ions and OH^- ions. Throughout the new structure the Si^{4+} ions are still in tetrahedral holes, and the Mg^{2+} ions are in octahedral holes. One octahedral hole is indicated, and it is seen that of the O^{2-} ions surrounding it, four are part of $(SiO_4)^{4-}$ tetrahedra, and the other two are part of OH^- ions.

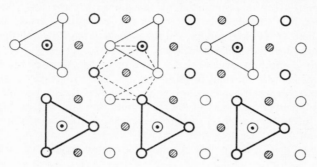

Fig. 18.9. Plan of the structure of chondrodite. One of the octahedral holes occupied by a Mg atom is indicated. (Figs. 18.7, 18.8, and 18.9, are based, with permission, on Figs. 188 and 189, pp. 574 and 575 of *Structural Inorganic Chemistry* by A. F. Wells, 2nd Edition, 1950, Oxford University Press.)

The modification of magnesium orthosilicate may be carried further by the replacement of some of the OH^- ions by F^- ions, thus giving $(Mg_2SiO_4)_n(Mg(OH)_2,F_2)_m$. It should be noted that although OH^- and F^- ions may replace O^{2-} in one of these composite structures, it is always the O^{2-} ion in the additional metallic oxide that is replaced, and never the O^{2-} ion in the $(SiO_4)^{4-}$ tetrahedra.†

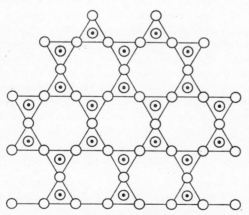

Fig. 18.10. Plan of the structure of the anion $(Si_2O_5)_n$ in kaolin.

Another example of a silicate which can be regarded as an interlocked array of SiO_4 tetrahedra and a metallic oxide structure is furnished by kaolin, $Al_2(OH)_4Si_2O_5$. Kaolin has a sheet structure. Sheets with the composition $(Si_2O_5)_n$ consist of units of

† Nevertheless Li_2MoO_4, Li_2WO_4, and Li_2BeF_4 are isomorphous with phenacite Be_2SiO_4, and NaF/BeF_2 serves as a model for CaO/SiO_2.

SiO_4 tetrahedra arranged in a pattern (Fig. 18.10) which is an infinite extension in two dimensions of the beryl structure. The SiO_4 tetrahedra in Fig. 18.10 may be imagined to be standing on a horizontal plane, placed corner to corner so that the inside edges form a series of hexagons. At each corner an oxygen atom is held in common by two tetrahedra. The apices of all the tetrahedra point upwards. The complete kaolin structure is obtained by imagining that the SiO_4 tetrahedra are standing on top of a gibbsite layer (p. 536), in such a way that certain oxygen atoms are common both to the SiO_4 groups and the gibbsite layer. Talc and the micas have structures constructed on similar principles.

Among other important structures are those of certain silicates which consist of chains or sheets made up of rings of six tetrahedra. These rings play a special part in silicate structure because their dimensions are such that the oxygen ion exactly fits into the central space of the ring. Talc has the composition $Mg_2(Si_2O_5)_2 \cdot Mg(OH)_2$. It is composed of sheets of rings of six tetrahedra, and the central oxygen in each sheet is furnished by an $(OH)^-$ ion from the $Mg(OH)_2$. Tremolite consists of chains of six-membered rings, and again in this example the central oxygen in each ring is an $(OH)^-$ ion.

The majority of the silicates, however, among the most familiar of which are beryl, the felspars, the zeolites, and the ultramarines, are based not on close-packed arrays of oxygen ions, but on more open structures.

The silicate anion of beryl is discrete, and contains the ring of six tetrahedra, but the ring is not filled by a central oxygen atom, and hence the crystal structure contains open channels. The cross-section of these channels is great enough to enable the crystal to occlude atoms of helium.

The felspars possess a macro-anionic structure made up of chains; each link in the chain is a ring of four tetrahedra. Typical formulae of felspars are $Na(AlSi_3O_8)$ and $Ca(Si_2Al_2O_8)$.

The zeolites, of which analcite, $Na(AlSi_2O_6),H_2O$, is an example, have still more open structures than the felspars. The oxygen tetrahedra are joined up to form four- and six-membered rings, and these are cross-linked to form a three-dimensional framework. Water, or an aqueous solution, may percolate through the channels in the framework, and hence the crystals take up or lose water very easily. The cation of a salt in solution may be exchanged for a cation in the crystal. For example, if analcite is treated with a solution of silver nitrate the sodium is replaced by silver. The process of changing one cation for another is sometimes known as *base exchange*.

Use is made of the principle of base exchange in softening water by use of the artificial zeolite "permutit". The constitution of permutit is $Na_6(Al_4(OH)_{12} \cdot Al_2Si_6O_{18})$.†

On treatment with a solution of calcium sulphate, the calcium is removed from the solution by the reaction:

$$Na_6(Al_6Si_6(OH)_{12}O_{18}) + 3CaSO_4 = 3Na_2SO_4 + Ca_3(Al_6Si_6(OH)_{12}O_{18}).$$

If the calcium zeolite is treated with a solution of sodium chloride the action goes in the reverse direction, and the original sodium zeolite is regenerated ready for use again.

Gases are also able to pass through the channels in zeolite crystals by a process which is a combination of diffusion and adsorption. For example, in mordenite with sodium cations the channels are of cross section 4·0 to 4·9 Å. This substance occludes nitrogen (molecular diameter 3·0 Å) and oxygen (molecular diameter 2·8 Å) rapidly, and methane and ethane (mol. cross section 4·0 Å) only slowly, but it does not occlude

†The discrepancy in the group written $Al_2Si_6O_{18}$ between the actual ratio $(Al + Si):O = 8:18$, and the theoretical ratio $8:16$, probably arises because in the artificial zeolite the anions are discrete or low polymers, and hence the ratio of $(Al + Si):O$ falls, because not all the oxygen atoms are linked to two silicon atoms.

hydrocarbons with greater cross section. If, however, the sodium cations in mordenite are replaced by calcium cations, the cross section of the channel is reduced to 3·8 Å, and methane and ethane are no longer absorbed. By choice of the appropriate zeolite and appropriate conditions it is possible to bring about a complete separation of gases which would otherwise be separable only by rigorous fractionation. For example, butane, b.p. 1° may be separated from iso-butane, b.p. −10°.†

GIANT MOLECULE COMPOUNDS OF SILICON WHICH CONTAIN SULPHUR

Ultramarines. This name is given to a group of substances used as pigments. The composition of the deep blue ultramarine is $Na_8(Al_6Si_6O_{24})S_2$. It will be observed that the group $Na_8(Al_6Si_6O_{24})$ represents completely linked tetrahedra, of which the central ion may be either Al^{3+} or Si^{4+}. The tetrahedra are built up into polyhedral basket-like units. The surface of the basket consists of eight six-membered rings and six four-membered rings.

The ultramarines differ from the substances previously discussed in this Chapter by the inclusion in the structural unit of negative ions, such as S^{2-}, Se^{2-}, Te^{2-}, Cl^-, or SO_4^{2-}. The sodium cations may be replaced by Li^+, Tl^+, Ca^{2+}, and Ag^+. The colour of the substance varies from colourless to yellow and blue to violet, according to the nature of the ions in the unit.

Silicon disulphide, SiS_2, is made by heating a mixture of the elements. It may be sublimed. It exists as colourless needles, unaffected by dry air, but hydrolysed by water to SiO_2 and H_2S.

The structure is a long chain of tetrahedra, the opposite edges being shared:

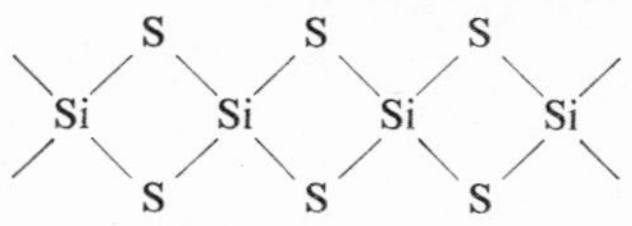

This arrangement of SiS_4 tetrahedra differs sharply from the arrangement of SiO_4 tetrahedra in silica or the silicates, in all of which the SiO_4 tetrahedra are linked together by corners held in common: edges of SiO_4 tetrahedra are never held in common. In SiS_2 both Si and S have d orbitals, and hence the Si—S—Si and the S—Si—S angles may approach 90° by something like planar hybridisation. The existence of thiosilicates is very doubtful; it may be stated with confidence that there is no chemistry of the group SiS_4 in any degree comparable with that of the group SiO_4.

SECTIONS 2 AND 3. DIGONAL AND TRIGONAL VALENCE STATES

Three oxygen compounds which in the monomeric form might be formulated to contain the silicon atom in the trigonal valence state are silicon oxalic acid, $(HOOSi—SiOOH)_n$, silicon meso-oxalic acid $(HOOSi—O—SiOOH)_n$, and ethyl metasilicate $((C_2H_5O)_2SiO)_n$, b.p. 233°. All these compounds, however, are polymerised. Silicon oxalic acid is made by the hydrolysis of Si_2Cl_6. It is a white solid, insoluble in water, with no acidic properties. It dissolves in alkali with the liberation of hydrogen. No salt or esters are known. Silicon meso-oxalic acid is made by the hydrolysis of Si_3Cl_8. Its properties resemble those of silicon oxalic acid. Ethyl metasilicate is obtained by the action of ethyl alcohol and a little water on silicon tetrachloride. There is no analogue of carbonyl chloride, Cl_2CO.

It is therefore concluded that the silicon atom adopts neither the digonal nor the trigonal valence state.

†For a complete discussion of the principles of the molecular sieve action of solids, see R. M. Barrer, *Quart. Rev.*, 3, 1949, No. 4.

SECTION 4. COMPOUNDS IN WHICH THE SILICON ATOM IS TETRAHEDRALLY HYBRIDISED

Crystalline silicon and the giant molecule compounds SiC, Si_3N_4, SiO_2, the silicates, and SiS_2, in all of which the silicon atom is probably present in the tetrahedral valence state, have already been described. The compounds described in this section are covalent compounds resembling in general character the corresponding carbon compounds.

Silicon hydrides. (Silanes). The hydrides are SiH_4, Si_2H_6, Si_3H_8, Si_4H_{10}. The first two compounds are gases at room temperature; the second two are liquids. The b.p. and m.p. are given in Table 18.16. Solid hydrides, said to be Si_5H_{12} and Si_6H_{14}, remain after fractionation, and another solid. $(SiH_2)_x$, is obtained by the treatment of the alloy CaSi with glacial acetic acid, or with an alcoholic solution of HCl.

Table 18.16. *Melting Points and Boiling Points of certain Hydrides of Silicon and of their Alkyl, Aryl, and Halogen Derivatives*

Compound	m.p. °C	b.p. °C
SiH_4	-185	$-111\cdot9$
Si_2H_6	$-132\cdot5$	$-14\cdot5$
Si_3H_8	-117	$+53$
S_4H_{10}	-90	$+109$
SiF_4	*ca.* -80	*ca.* -70
$SiCl_4$	-70	$-56\cdot8$
$SiBr_4$		$+153$
SiI_4	$+120\cdot5$	
$SiHF_3$	-110	$-80\cdot2$
$SiHCl_3$	-134	$+32$
$Si(CH_3)_4$	-99	$+27$
$Si(C_6H_5)_4$	$+238$	530
$Si(CH_3)_3Cl$		$+57\cdot3$
$Si(CH_3)_2Cl_2$		$+70$

When hydrochloric acid acts upon magnesium silicide a mixture of all the hydrides is obtained, those of lowest molecular weight being in the greatest proportion. The hydrides are separated by fractionation at low temperatures. Silane, SiH_4, is best made by treating magnesium silicide with ammonium bromide in liquid ammonia. The low b.p. of silane ($-112°$) permits it to volatilise from the solution. Pure silane may also be made by heating triethyl silicoformate (itself made by treating silicochloroform with sodium ethoxide) with sodium:

$$4SiH(OC_2H_5)_3 = SiH_4 + 3Si(OC_2H_5)_4,$$

or by treating silicon tetrachloride with lithium aluminium hydride.

The silicon hydrides are decomposed by heat at about 300°, and by exposure to ultraviolet light. They are spontaneously inflammable in air. They explode in contact with halogens at room temperature, but a mixture of SiH_3Br and SiH_2Br_2 is obtained by passing silane over solid bromine at $-80°$. A mixture of SiH_3Cl (silicochloroform) and SiH_2Cl_2 is obtained by treating silane with dry hydrogen chloride in the presence of aluminium chloride:

$$SiH_4 + HCl = SiH_3Cl + H_2.$$

The silicon hydrides are powerful reducing agents, as exemplified by the reactions:

$$SiH_4 + 2CuSO_4 = Cu_2Si + 2H_2SO_4,$$
$$SiH_4 + 4AgNO_3 = 4Ag + Si + 4HNO_3.$$

Water containing a trace of sodium hydroxide, but not pure water, decomposes them to hydrated silica and hydrogen:

$$Si_2H_6 + 2H_2O + 4NaOH = 2Na_2SiO_3 + 7H_2.$$

Ethane shows no tendency whatever to undergo this kind of reaction. Disilane and trisilane react vigorously with carbon tetrachloride and with chloroform thus:

$$Si_2H_6 + 2CCl_4 = 2SiCl_4 + 2C + 3H_2.$$

Disilane is soluble in benzene and in carbon disulphide.

Silicon alkyls and similar compounds. The silicon tetra-alkyls are best prepared by the action of Grignard reagents on silicon tetrachloride. The action goes more slowly as it proceeds. By regulating the proportions of the reagents, 1, 2, 3, or 4 halogens in the tetrachloride may be replaced, or mixed derivatives may be prepared. The last chlorine atom in the tetrachloride is replaced only at 100°. The tetra-alkyls, unlike the hydrides, are extremely stable. They are unaffected by air, water, or by concentrated potassium hydroxide, or concentrated sulphuric acid in the cold. They react slowly with the halogens, so that halogen atoms replace the hydrogen atoms in the carbon radical. The tetra-aryl derivatives are also stable. They are not attacked by hydrogen at 450° and 75 atm pressure. Bromine and phosphorus pentachloride react with them on heating to split off phenyl groups. Nitric acid reacts to give mononitro derivatives (i.e. each phenyl group is mononitrated); the nitro group has the properties of a nitro group in an organic compound.

Derivatives of silane with three alkyl groups in the molecule behave much like the tetra-alkyl derivatives. For example, $(C_2H_5)_3SiH$ is stable to air and to concentrated sulphuric acid. Fuming sulphuric acid converts it to the ether, $(C_2H_5)_3Si$—O—$Si(C_2H_5)_3$. Bromine reacts to replace the hydrogen atom by bromine, and lithium methyl gives $CH_3Si(C_2H_5)_3$ and lithium hydride. If, however, the molecule contains only one or two alkyl groups, the compound is almost as reactive as silane itself. CH_3SiH_3 explodes if shaken with mercury and oxygen; it is insoluble in water, but if alkali is present it a behaves like silane:

$$CH_3SiH_3 + 3H_2O = CH_3Si(OH)_3 + 3H_2.$$

The radicals $(C_2H_5)_3Si$— and $(C_6H_5)_3Si$— act as very weak amphoteric ions. There is good evidence for the existence of $LiSi(C_2H_5)_3$ and $LiSi(C_6H_5)_3$. $(C_2H_5)_3SiH$ and $(C_6H_5)_3SiH$ with potassamide in liquid ammonia react thus:

$$2(C_2H_5)_3SiH + KNH_2 = 2H_2 + [(C_2H_5)_3Si]_2NK;$$

the potassium salt can be obtained as colourless crystals. On the other hand $(C_2H_5)_3SiH$ and $(CH_3)_3SiH$ with oleum yield respectively $((C_2H_5)_3Si)_2SO_4$, b.p. 170°/12 mm, and $((CH_3)_3Si)_2,SO_4$, m.p. 57°.

SILICON HALIDES

Silicon tetrafluoride, SiF_4, is a gas which fumes strongly in moist air, and condenses to solid at −97° under 1 atm. It is made:

(i) by the action of fluorine on silicon; ignition is spontaneous,
(ii) by heating a mixture of CaF_2, SiO_2, and concentrated H_2SO_4, the essential reaction being:

$$4HF + SiO_2 = SiF_4 + 2H_2O,$$

(iii) as a variant of reaction (ii) a solution of silica in 70% HF solution may be dropped into excess of concentrated H_2SO_4; excess HF is retained as HSO_3F,

(iv) by heating $BaSiF_6$:

$$BaSiF_6 = BaF_2 + SiF_4.$$

The gas is collected over mercury; it does not attack glass if it is quite dry.

Silicon tetrafluoride is incombustible, and it extinguishes a burning taper. With water it is partially hydrolysed:

$$SiF_4 + 2H_2O = SiO_2 + 4HF,$$

$$SiF_4 + 2HF = H_2SiF_6.$$

Heated sodium and potassium burn in the gas:

$$4K + 2SiF_4 = K_2SiF_6 + 2KF + Si.$$

Its reactions with CaO and BaO take place with incandescence:

$$SiF_4 + 2CaO = 2CaF_2 + SiO_2.$$

Silicon tetrachloride, $SiCl_4$, is a colourless fuming liquid. It is made:

(i) by passing chlorine over heated amorphous silicon,
(ii) by passing chlorine over heated ferro-silicon,
(iii) by passing chlorine over a heated mixture of silica and magnesium powder,
(iv) by passing chlorine over a heated mixture of silica and carbon,
(v) by passing carbon tetrachloride vapour over heated silica.

Silicon tetrachloride is stable, but reacts violently with water. With ammonia it gives the di-imide $Si(NH)_2$ and NH_4Cl only.

Silicon tetrabromide is formed by methods corresponding to those used for making silicon tetrachloride.

Silicon tetraiodide is formed by passing iodine vapour over heated silicon.

The silicon hexahalides. Si_2F_6, a white solid, is made by warming Si_2Cl_6 with zinc fluoride. It is hydrolysed by moist air to silicon oxalic acid, an explosive white solid (p. 611).

Si_2Cl_6, a colourless liquid, is formed together with $SiCl_4$, when chlorine is passed over heated silicon, ferrosilicon, or Si_2I_6. It is best obtained by the action of chlorine on calcium silicide. If heated alone to 350° it yields Si and $SiCl_4$. The vapour ignites if heated in air. The liquid fumes in moist air to give silicon oxalic acid.

Si_2Br_6 is formed by the action of bromine on heated silicon, or on S_2I_6.

Si_2I_6 is formed by the action of silicon tetraiodide on finely divided silver at 280°:

$$2SiI_4 + 2Ag = 2AgI + I_3Si \cdot SiI_3.$$

The halogeno-silanes. There are a large number of derivatives of the silanes in which some hydrogen atoms of the original silane molecule have been replaced by halogen atoms. Two prominent members of this class of derivative are silicofluoroform and silicochloroform (mentioned on p. 612). Silicofluoroform is a combustible gas. It is formed by the action of stannic fluoride on silicochloroform:

$$4SiHCl_3 + 3SnF_4 = 4SiHF_3 + 3SnCl_4.$$

It decomposes on heating, and it reacts with water:

$$4SiHF_3 = 3SiF_4 + 2H_2 + Si, \qquad 2SiHF_3 + 2H_2O = SiO_2 + H_2SiF_6 + 2H_2.$$

The hydrolysis of the halogenosilanes. It may be imagined that the immediate effect of hydrolysis would be to replace a halogen atom by an OH group:

$$SiH_3Cl \rightarrow SiH_3OH$$
$$SiH_2Cl_2 \rightarrow SiH_2(OH)_2$$
$$SiHCl_3 \rightarrow SiH(OH)_3.$$

So great, however, is the tendency for the link Si—O—Si to be established that even the monohydroxy compound cannot be isolated; the product of the reaction of water on SiH_3Cl is siloxane, H_3Si—O—SiH_3 (p. 617). The diol might be expected to yield H_2SiO, analogous to formaldehyde. A product of this composition is indeed obtained, but it is polymerised, no doubt by the intermolecular elimination of water

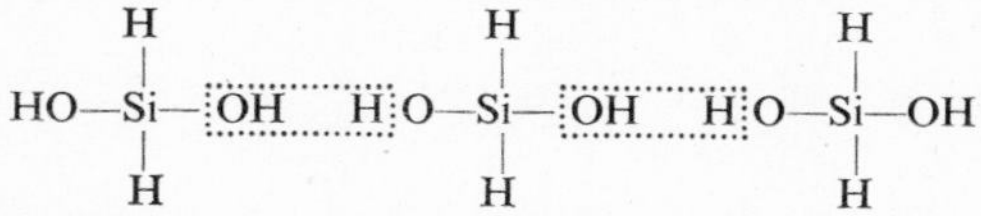

giving $H_2(OH)Si$—$(OSiH_2)_n$—$OSiH_2(OH)$. The formation of polymers of this kind indicates (i) the tendency to establish the link Si—O—Si, and (ii) the tendency of the silicon atom to avoid trigonal hybridisation.

Some interesting compounds are obtained by the hydrolysis of trihalogenosilanes. Ice-cold water on silicochloroform yields crystalline silicoformic anhydride, $[(HSiO)_2O]_n$. The stages of polymerisation can be imagined as:

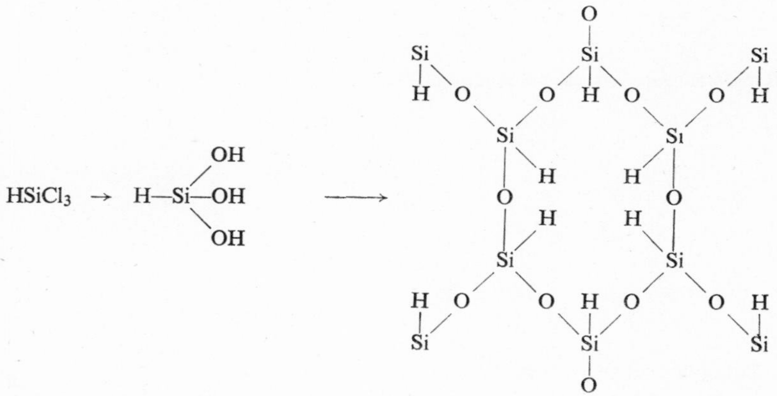

The final compound has a mica-like structure. It contains hydrogen atoms directly linked to silicon atoms, and it has some of the properties of silane. It acts as a powerful reducing agent because by so doing one hydrogen atom on each of two adjacent molecules is replaced by an oxygen atom held in common, and another Si—O—Si link is formed:

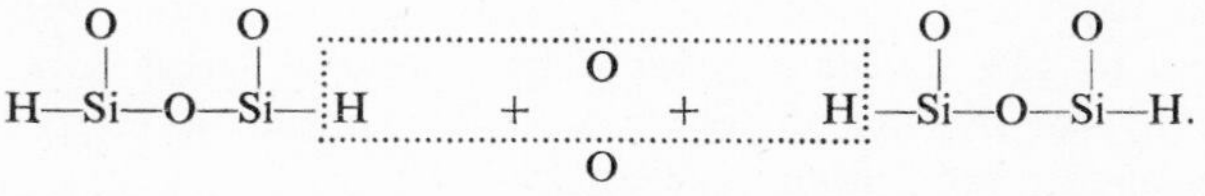

The same result is obtained by heating silicoformic anhydride at 507°, when hydrogen is directly evolved, and the oxide $(Si_2O_3)_n$ remains.

Silicones. The structure of silica (p. 604) is described as a three-dimensional configuration of silicon atoms linked by oxygen atoms. If certain of the oxygen atoms are imagined to be removed and replaced by alkyl or aryl groups, each linked to one silicon atom only, the resulting structure is that of a silicone. There are three types of silicone differentiated by their structures: three-dimensional silicones, ring silicones, and chain silicones. It is difficult to depict on paper the arrangement of SiO_4 tetrahedra in three dimensions. For clarity the structure of silica is represented here in two dimensions thus:

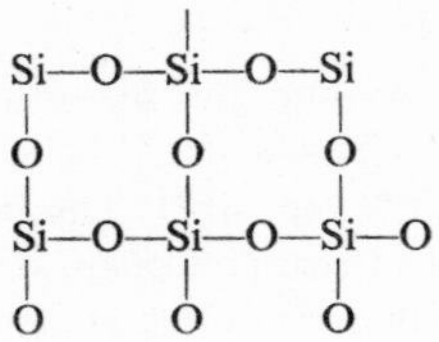

$$
\begin{array}{ccc}
 & | & \\
Si-O-Si-O-Si \\
| & | & | \\
O & O & O \\
| & | & | \\
Si-O-Si-O-Si-O \\
| & | & | \\
O & O & O \\
| & | & |
\end{array}
$$

and the three types of silicone are similarly represented thus:

(i) Three-dimensional silicones:

$$
\begin{array}{ccccc}
R & R & O & R \\
| & | & | & | \\
Si-O-Si-O-Si-O-Si-O-Si-O \\
| & | & | & | \\
 & & R & \\
O & O & & O \\
| & | & R & | \\
 & & | & \\
Si-O-Si-O-Si-O-Si \\
| & | & | & | \\
R & R & O & R \\
 & & |
\end{array}
$$

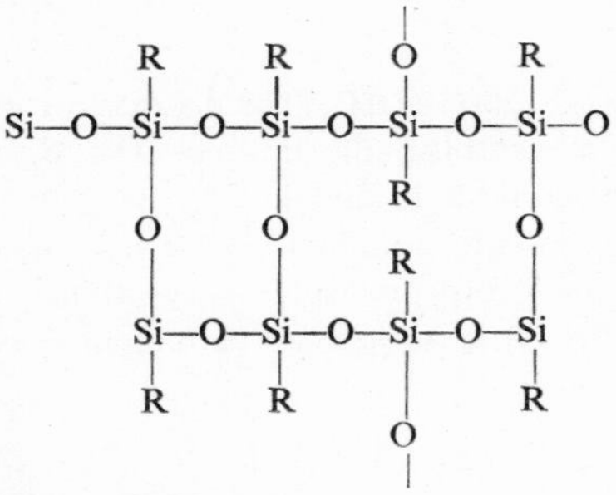

(ii) Ring structure, or planar silicones:

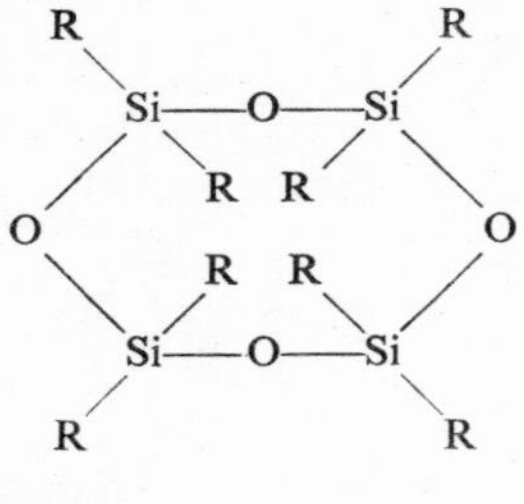

$$
\begin{array}{c}
R \qquad\qquad R \\
\diagdown \qquad\qquad \diagup \\
Si-O-Si \\
\diagup \quad R\ R\ \diagdown \\
O \qquad\qquad O \\
\diagdown \quad R\ R\ \diagup \\
Si-O-Si \\
\diagup \qquad\qquad \diagdown \\
R \qquad\qquad R
\end{array}
$$

(iii) Chain silicones or siloxanes:

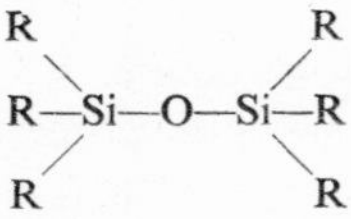

$$
\begin{array}{c}
R \qquad\qquad R \\
\diagdown \qquad\qquad \diagup \\
R-Si-O-Si-R \\
\diagup \qquad\qquad \diagdown \\
R \qquad\qquad R
\end{array}
$$

The silicones are formed, not directly from silica, but by the hydrolysis of the alkyl or aryl silicon halides. The effect of the hydrolysis illustrates the reluctance of the silicon atom to take up the trigonal valence state. Whereas dimethyl methylene dichloride on hydrolysis immediately loses water intramolecularly, and yields a trigonally hybridised carbon atom in acetone:

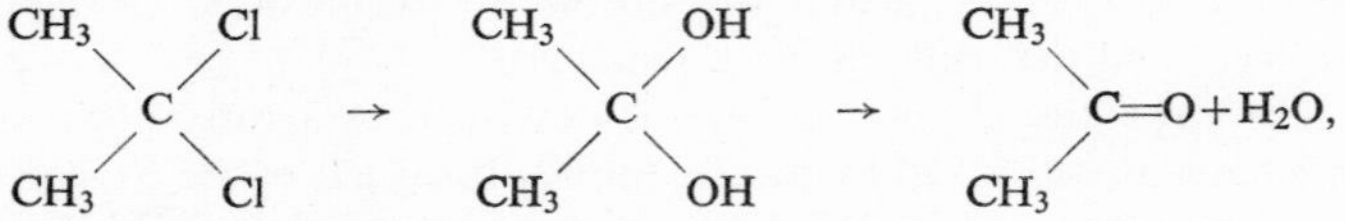

$$
\begin{array}{ccccc}
CH_3 \quad Cl & & CH_3 \quad OH & & CH_3 \\
\diagdown \quad \diagup & \rightarrow & \diagdown \quad \diagup & \rightarrow & \diagdown \\
C & & C & & C{=}O + H_2O, \\
\diagup \quad \diagdown & & \diagup \quad \diagdown & & \diagup \\
CH_3 \quad Cl & & CH_3 \quad OH & & CH_3
\end{array}
$$

the corresponding silicon compound yields silicones in which the silicon atom remains tetrahedrally hybridised. It is presumed that the first stage of the hydrolysis yields a silicon diol, although for alkyl derivatives this cannot be isolated:

$$
\begin{array}{ccc}
\mathrm{CH_3} \quad \mathrm{Cl} & & \mathrm{CH_3} \quad \mathrm{OH} \\
\diagdown \; \mathrm{Si} \; \diagup & \rightarrow & \diagdown \; \mathrm{Si} \; \diagup \\
\diagup \qquad \diagdown & & \diagup \qquad \diagdown \\
\mathrm{CH_3} \quad \mathrm{Cl} & & \mathrm{CH_3} \quad \mathrm{OH}
\end{array}
$$

$$
\begin{array}{ccc}
\mathrm{CH_3} & \mathrm{CH_3} & \mathrm{CH_3} \\
| & | & | \\
\mathrm{HO-Si-\,}[\mathrm{OH} & \mathrm{H}]\mathrm{O-Si-}[\mathrm{OH} & \mathrm{H}]\mathrm{O-Si-OH} \\
| & | & | \\
\mathrm{CH_3} & \mathrm{CH_3} & \mathrm{CH_3}
\end{array}
$$

The immediate elimination of water from the dimethyl silicon diol, as shown in the diagram, leads to polymerisation, and the final product is a mixture of linear molecules $\mathrm{HOSi(CH_3)_2 \cdot (O_2Si(CH_3)_2)_n \cdot Si(CH_3)_2OH}$, and of ring compounds formed by the elimination of water from the terminal groups of a chain. The tendency for this kind of polymerisation to occur is so great that even the silicon monols condense readily to give disiloxane. Disiloxane, $\mathrm{H_3Si-O-SiH_3}$, is a colourless, odourless, combustible gas, m.p. $-144°$, b.p. $-15\cdot2°$. It is made by the action of water on $\mathrm{SiH_3Br}$.

The hydrolysis of the trihalogeno organosilicon compounds produces three-dimensional silicones of type (i).

The silicones are used in industry. In general they are thermally stable, good electrical insulators, have a low volatility, and are water repellent. The three-dimensional silicones are rubbery, and retain their elastic properties to low temperatures. The two-dimensional silicones can be made with a range of viscosities depending on the chain length of the polymers. The viscosity is little affected by temperature. They are used in hydraulic systems and in electrical condensers.

In the preparation of a silicone for industrial use the degree of polymerisation must be controlled. This may be done in three ways:

(i) by the introduction, before hydrolysis, of $\mathrm{R_3SiCl}$ or of $\mathrm{SiCl_4}$; the former by leaving no OH group in the terminal position on hydrolysis reduces chain growth, and the latter produces a certain amount of cross-linking,

(ii) by controlled oxidation which increases the cross-linking by introducing —O— for each pair of alkyl or aryl groups removed,

(iii) by adding a small amount of concentrated $\mathrm{H_2SO_4}$, which opens up the Si—O—Si links to give $\mathrm{Si \cdot HSO_4}$ which undergoes hydrolysis, and if $\mathrm{Si(CH_3)_3}$ groups are present these terminate the chain. Cyclic silicones may be converted to linear silicones in this way.

The alkyl and aryl silicon halides. In these derivatives of the silanes the original hydrogen atoms of the silane molecule have been replaced, partly by halogen atoms and partly by alkyl or aryl groups. A few members of this class are included in Table 18.16. They are volatile and unpleasant-smelling substances.

Hydrolysis of the alkyl and aryl silicon halides; the silicols. The alkyl and aryl silicon halides undergo hydrolysis with water. The monohalogen derivatives yield simple silicols:

$$\mathrm{(CH_3)_3SiCl + H_2O = (CH_3)_3SiOH + HCl.}$$

The simple silicols distil without decomposition at the b.ps. Me $98\cdot6°$, Et $154°$, nPr $207°$. With sodium they slowly give $\mathrm{R_3SiONa}$ which is soluble in ether and aromatic hydrocarbons, and hence may be covalent. With acids they form esters which are very

20*

readily saponified by water. When allowed to stand over P_2O_5, water is eliminated intermolecularly, and a siloxane is obtained:

$$(CH_3)_3SiOH + HOSi(CH_3)_3 = (CH_3)_3Si—O—Si(CH_3)_3 + H_2O.$$

Hexaethyl disiloxane, b.p. 231°, is made by the action of phosphorus pentoxide on triethyl silicol, $(C_2H_5)_3SiOH$, or by the action of fuming sulphuric acid on triethyl silane.

The alkyl dihalogen derivatives on hydrolysis at once yield silicones (p. 615); the intermediate diol has not been prepared. The aryl dihalogen derivatives yield diols on hydrolysis, such as $(C_6H_5)_2Si(OH)_2$, m.p. 139°. This compound, however, yields silicone if heated above its melting point.

The products of hydrolysis of the alkyltrichlorosilanes vary with the nature of the alkyl group. It is of interest to note that the tert.-butyl derivative yields a compound:

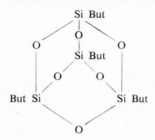

which is shown by X-ray analysis to be similar in structure to hexamethylene tetrammine, adamantane, and hexathioadamantane:

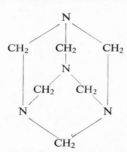
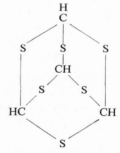

Hexamethylene tetrammine   Hexathioadamantane

Silylamines.† There is no primary or secondary silylamine, but the tertiary compound $(SiH_3)_3N$, has been prepared. Electron diffraction experiments have shown that the molecule of tertiary silylamine is planar. Hence the unhybridised p orbital of the nitrogen atom must be combined with the d orbitals of the silicon atoms to form non-localised πd bonds. This view of the structure is confirmed by the abnormally short distance Si—N in the molecule, and by its reluctance to act as an electron donor. Tertiary silylamine does not react with such a powerful acceptor as diborane, and it forms an adduct with boron trifluoride only in the temperature range $-40°$ to $-80°$.

At $-80°$ tertiary silylamine reacts with bromodiborane thus:

$$2(SiH_3)_3N + 2B_2H_5Br = 2(SiH_3)_2NBH_2 + 2SiH_3Br + B_2H_6.$$

The product when treated with diborane at low temperatures yields $(SiH_3)_2NB_2H_5$,

† The group silyl —SiH₃ corresponds to the methyl group —CH₃.

analogous to NN-dimethylamino borine (p. 520). This product polymerises. The silicon derivatives containing boron atoms are spontaneously inflammable in air.

Tetrasilylhydrazine, $(SiH_3)_2N \cdot N(SiH_3)_2$, like tertiary silylamine, also has negligible acceptor or donor properties.

SECTION 6. COMPOUNDS IN WHICH THE SILICON ATOM IS OCTAHEDRALLY HYBRIDISED

The silicon atom in the octahedral valence state is present in β-diketone complexes, and in the complex fluorosilicic anion, $[SiF_6{}^{2-}]$. The β-diketone complexes are cationic and not neutral, because the silicon atom must expel one valency electron before it can exert three covalent and three co-ionic bonds. The triacetylacetone derivative therefore has the structure:

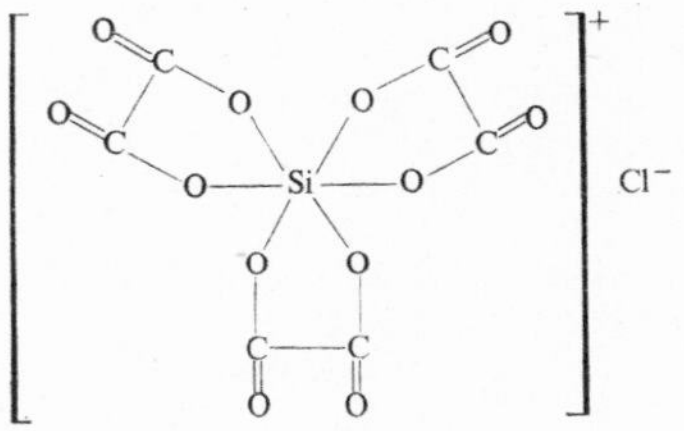

The compound is made by the action of silicon tetrachloride on acetylacetone in chloroform solution. The solid which separates has the formula $(A_3Si)Cl,HCl$.

Hydrofluorosilicic acid, H_2SiF_6, and the fluorosilicates. Pure hydrofluorosilicic acid has not been prepared; dry silicon tetrafluoride and hydrofluoric acid do not react. Hydrofluorosilicic acid is made in solution by the action of aqueous hydrofluoric acid on silica:

$$SiO_2 + 6HF = H_2SiF_6 + 2H_2O.$$

It is liberated when silicon tetrafluoride reacts with water:

$$3SiF_4 + 2H_2O = 2H_2SiF_6 + SiO_2.$$

A concentrated solution of the acid may be obtained, but on evaporation it decomposes:

$$H_2SiF_6 = SiF_4 + 2HF.$$

The di- or tetrahydrate can be crystallised from the aqueous solution.

Hydrofluorosilicic acid is a strong acid and it is as highly ionised in water as is sulphuric acid. It reacts with alkali thus:

$$2NaOH + H_2SiF_6 = Na_2SiF_6 + 2H_2O,$$
$$Na_2SiF_6 + 4NaOH = 6NaF + SiO_2 + 2H_2O.$$

The end-point, using phenolphthalein as indicator, is not reached until the second equation is complete.

Hydrofluorosilicic acid forms salts. Those of the highly electropositive metals, Na, K, Ba, are sparingly soluble, and those of the less highly electropositive metals Li, Ca, Sr are more soluble. The solubilities at 17–20° are, Na 0·65, K 0·12, Rb 0·16, Cs 0·027, Ba 0·027 gm per 100 gm of water. The anion $[SiF_6{}^{2-}]$ is octahedral.

No corresponding complex halides of the chloride, bromide, or iodide are known.

GERMANIUM

THE ELEMENT

Germanium is a greyish-white brittle metal which forms octahedral crystals with a diamond lattice. It is not highly reactive but is more reactive than silicon. Its chief reactions are set out in Table 18.17.

Table 18.17.   *Reactions of Germanium*

Reagent	Conditions	Reaction
Air	Cold	No action
	Red heat	Oxidised to GeO_2
Cl_2	At 100–180°	$GeCl_4$ formed (if the metal is finely divided, spontaneous ignition occurs)
HCl	Gas over warm metal	$GeHCl_3$ formed
	Dilute, or concentrated up to 90°	No action
H_2SO_4	Dilute	No action
	Concentrated	Dissolves
HNO_3	Concentrated	Dissolves
Water	Cold	No action
	Above 200°	Reacts
KOH	Dilute	No reaction except in the presence of H_2O_2†
	Fused	Oxidised with incandescence

† A solution of sodium hydroxide containing hydrogen peroxide is a good solvent for germanium.

GENERAL CHEMISTRY OF GERMANIUM

Germanium is less electronegative and more metallic than either carbon or silicon, but the germanium atom shows no tendency to lose its four valency electrons to form the ion Ge^{4+}. Germanium stands in sub-Group IV N between silicon, which forms only one ill-characterised bivalent compound SiO, and tin which forms a considerable range of bivalent stannous compounds. The bicovalent compounds of germanium are few only and are discussed on p. 621. They are all solids and there is no evidence that the germanium atom ever exerts two covalent bonds in a discrete molecule. In the majority of its compounds the germanium atom is quadrivalent.

One of the most characteristic properties of silicon is the strength of the Si—O—Si link which is revealed by the range and stability of the silicates, and by the strong tendency of the hydroxyl derivatives of silicon (produced by the hydrolysis of the halogenosilanes, p. 615) to condense to siloxanes and silicones. The link Ge—O is comparatively weak. The group GeO_4 can replace the group SiO_4 in certain silicates, but the chemistry of the germanates is not comparable with that of the silicates. Hydrolysis of the halogenogermanes yields GeO_2, and not compounds containing the link Ge—O—Ge. The link Ge—Ge has the same strength as the link Si—Si, 42·5 kcal. It is present in the unstable polygermanes, and in the more stable alkyl and aryl derivatives.

The orbital structures adopted by the germanium atom in its various types of compounds deserve brief discussion. The bicovalent germanium atom must retain the two electrons in the atomic 4s orbital as an inert pair; the two 4p electrons can then either be discarded to produce a Ge^{2+} ion, or hybridised to give a pair of hybrid orbitals which contain no *s* contribution. It is unlikely that the bicovalent germanium atom contains a lone pair in one of three trigonally hybridised orbitals, because there is evidence (see below) that the germanium atom is never trigonally hybridised.

Like silicon, germanium fails to form any compounds analogous to acetylene or to ethylene; on this evidence the atom of germanium cannot be digonally or trigonally hybridised. Hexaphenyl digermane does not dissociate into radicals, and hence there are no germanium compounds corresponding to triphenylmethyl. The compound $Ge_6(C_6H_5)_6$ (p. 625), if correctly formulated, requires the germanium atom to be trigonally hybridised, but it is surprising if germanium assumes the trigonal valence state in this one compound which has no analogues among the compounds of silicon or tin.

Germanium follows carbon and silicon in forming a large number of compounds in which the atom is in the tetrahedral valence state. It also adopts the octahedral valence state, in which it forms both neutral and anionic complexes, but no cationic complexes.

COMPOUNDS IN WHICH THE OXIDATION STATE OF GERMANIUM IS II

The compounds in which germanium is bivalent, the germanous compounds, are much more firmly characterised than the dubious silicon monoxide, but less stable than the stannous or plumbous compounds. The germanous compounds, which include GeNH GeO, GeS, the halides Gehal$_2$, and a few complexes of the type $Cs[GeCl_3]$, are all solids. Germanous sulphide has a distorted rocksalt structure, and germanous iodide a CdI_2 structure. In both these structures the metal atom is six co-ordinate, and its valence state in these compounds may well be octahedral. It seems probable that the germanium atom in the complex $Cs[GeCl_3]$ is in the tetrahedral valence state with a lone pair in one of the tetrahedral orbitals.

Germanium monoxide, GeO, is made:

 (i) by the action of water on $GeCl_2$,
 (ii) by reduction of an aqueous solution of germanium dioxide with hypophosphorous acid,
 (iii) by the action of water or ammonia on $GeHCl_3$,
 (iv) by reducing germanium dioxide with germanium or carbon monoxide at 900°,
 (v) by the action of carbon dioxide on germanium at 700–900°:

$$Ge + CO_2 = GeO + CO.$$

Germanous oxide is a black powder which decomposes at 500° to Ge and GeO_2. It is stable in cold air, but is readily oxidised by air if heated, and by most common oxidising agents. It is almost insoluble in water, and is scarcely attacked by acid or alkali.

The yellow hydrated form of the oxide is made by the action of alkali on $GeHCl_3$. The hydrated oxide is faintly acidic and gives rise to the germanites, but it is a weaker acid than acetic acid, although stronger than $Sn(OH)_2$ or $Pb(OH)_2$. It dissolves in warm alkali.

The ultraviolet spectrum of the vapour of germanous oxide indicates that the distance Ge—O is 1·65.

Germanous sulphide, GeS, is made by the reduction of germanic sulphide, GeS_2, with germanium, with hydrogen, or with a mixture of hydrogen and hydrogen sulphide, at high temperatures. Germanous sulphide is a red solid, m.p. 625°, which sublimes at 430°. On heating in air it is oxidised to GeO_2 and SO_2. It dissolves in hot alkalis to give a red solution. The amorphous form is easily soluble in dilute hydrochloric acid.

It is precipitated when hydrogen sulphide is passed into a slightly acid solution of a germanous compound; the precipitate is soluble in yellow ammonium sulphide.

The crystal lattice is a highly distorted rocksalt structure.

The germanous halides. The properties of the germanous halides are summarised in Table 18.18.

Table 18.18.   *Certain Properties of the Germanous Halides*

	GeF_2	$GeCl_2$	$GeBr_2$	GeI_2
Appearance	White powder	Pale yellow solid	Colourless solid	Pale yellow solid
Action of heat	Sublimes	Decomposes	Melts at 122°	Sublimes and decomposes
Decomposition temperature	300° to GeF_4 and Ge	450° to $GeCl_4$ and Ge	Above 122°	
Preparation	Pass GeF_4 over Ge at 250°	Pass $GeCl_4$ or $GeHCl_3$ over Ge at 430°		Allow HI to react with GeH_4

Germanous chloride reacts with oxygen at room temperature to yield GeO_2 and $GeCl_4$; it reacts with water to yield $Ge(OH)_2$, and with hydrogen chloride to yield $GeHCl_3$. X-ray analysis indicates that GeI_2 has the CdI_2 layer lattice. The distance Ge—I is 2·94. Germanous iodide reacts with liquid ammonia to yield germanous imide, GeNH, an insoluble yellow powder.

Complexes of the type $Cs[GeCl_3]$ have been made. They are hygroscopic and are hydrolysed by water. $Cs[GeI_3]$ is made by adding CsI to a solution of $Ge(OH)_2$ in HI. With NH_4I this gives $NH_4[GeI_3]$.

COMPOUNDS IN WHICH THE OXIDATION STATE OF GERMANIUM IS IV

SECTION 1. GIANT MOLECULE STRUCTURES IN WHICH THE BONDS HAVE BOTH IONIC AND COVALENT CHARACTER

Germanium nitride, Ge_3N_4 (p. 626), has the lattice structure of phenacite (Be_2SiO_4). The nitrogen ions are close-packed, and the germanium ions are in three-quarters of the tetrahedral holes. This structure is similar to that of silicon nitride (p. 604). *Germanium phosphide*, GeP, however, has the rocksalt structure.

Germanium dioxide, GeO_2, is made:

(i) by the oxidation of germanium,
(ii) by the action of nitric acid on germanic sulphide,
(iii) by the action of alkali on germanic chloride, $GeCl_4$.

Germanium dioxide occurs in two forms. One, m.p. 1086°, with the rutile lattice, is stable below 1033°, and the other, m.p. 1116°, with the quartz lattice is stable above 1033°. The form with the quartz lattice is said to be slightly soluble in water; the other form is insoluble. Germanium dioxide reacts violently with concentrated hydrofluoric acid solution (p. 626).

Germanium hydroxide, $Ge(OH)_4$, is soluble in hot water, and behaves as an extremely weak acid, $K = 2 \times 10^{-9}$. It separates from solution as a colloid. It cannot be isolated in the pure state, and it is perhaps to be regarded as a hydrated form of germanium dioxide. It is easily soluble in aqueous solutions of the hydroxides of the alkali metals to produce soluble germanates. The tetraethyl derivative of germanium hydroxide, $Ge(OC_2H_5)_4$, can be obtained by boiling germanic chloride with sodium ethylate in alcoholic solution. The group GeO_4 can replace the group SiO_4 in certain silicates; Be_2GeO_4 is isomorphous with Be_2SiO_4.

Germanium disulphide, GeS_2, is made (i) by the action of hydrogen sulphide on a strongly acid† solution of GeO_2, pH <2, (ii) by heating GeO_2 with sulphur or hydrogen sulphide at 800°, (iii) by acidifying a thiogermanate solution.

Germanium disulphide exists as white or amber coloured crystals. It melts above 800° to a dark liquid. It can be sublimed. Its solubility is 0·455 gm in 100 gm of water at 20°, but the solution rapidly hydrolyses with the evolution of hydrogen sulphide. Germanium disulphide dissolves in solutions of alkali sulphides, forming thiogermanates. The crystal structure of germanium disulphide is a three-dimensional tetrahedral structure of GeS_4 units, like that of silica, in which the angle S—Ge—S is 103°, and the distance Ge—S is 2·19.

SECTION 4.‡ COMPOUNDS IN WHICH THE GERMANIUM ATOM IS TETRAHEDRALLY HYBRIDISED

The compounds of germanium in which the atom is in the tetrahedral valence state include the germanium hydrides, the germanium alkyls and aryls, the germanium halides, and mixed derivatives of these compounds. Lists of these compounds, and certain of their properties, are given in Tables 18.19, 18.20, 18.21. The Ge—Ge link is present in each of the above types of compound, and it appears frequently in the aryl derivatives. There are no complex compounds in which a germanium atom is present in the tetrahedral valence state.

Table 18.19. *The Germanium Hydrides, Alkyls, and Aryls*

Compounds		m.p. °C	b.p. °C	Molecular constitution
Germanium hydrides	GeH_4 Ge_2H_6 Ge_3H_8	−165 −109 −106	− 90 + 29 +110	Monomeric§. The distance Ge—Ge is 2·41
Germanium alkyls	$Ge(CH_3)_4$ $Ge(C_2H_5)_4$ $Ge_2(C_2H_5)_6$	−88 −90 <−60	44 164 265	Monomeric in vapour Monomeric in vapour at 220°, and in benzene Monomeric in benzene
Germanium aryls	$Ge(C_6H_5)_4$ $Ge_2(C_6H_5)_6$ $Ge_3(C_6H_5)_8$	+233 340 247		Monomeric in benzene Monomeric in benzene
Ring compounds	$Ge_4(C_6H_5)_8$ $Ge_6(C_6H_5)_6$	294		Monomeric in benzene Monomeric in benzene
Mixed compounds	$GeH(C_2H_5)_3$ $GeH(C_6H_5)_3$	47	124·5	Monomeric in vapour (An unstable monotrope has m.p. 27°)

§ The term "monomeric" indicates that the constitution corresponds to the molecular formula given in the table.

† Hydrofluoric acid must not be used as it inhibits precipitation, probably by the formation of H_2GeF_6.

‡ Sections 2 and 3 are omitted as there are no compounds in which the germanium atom is present in the digonal or trigonal valence states.

Germanium hydrides. (Germanes). Germanium forms the gaseous hydrides GeH_4, Ge_2H_6, and Ge_3H_8, and the solid hydride $(GeH_2)_n$. A mixture of the gaseous hydrides is obtained:

(i) by the action of dilute hydrochloric acid on magnesium germanide, Mg_2Ge,
(ii) by the cathodic reduction of GeO_2 in concentrated H_2SO_4 using a lead cathode to make use of the overvoltage,
(iii) by the action of ammonium bromide in liquid ammonia on Mg_2Ge (much of the product is GeH_4).

GeH_4 is best made by the reduction of $GeCl_4$ with $LiAlH_4$ in ethereal solution.

The germanes are more easily decomposed by heat than are the silanes, but they are less reactive to oxygen or water. *Monogermane*, GeH_4, does not react with oxygen below 230°, or explode with it below 330°. It is not attacked by aqueous alkali. It reacts with sodium in liquid ammonia solution to give $NaGeH_3$. It also reacts with hydrogen iodide giving GeI_2 as the final product, and it liberates hydrogen on treatment with alkali.

Digermane, Ge_2H_6, is more reactive than monogermane.

The hydride $(GeH_2)_n$ is made by the action of hydrochloric acid on CaGe:

$$CaGe + 2HCl = CaCl_2 + GeH_2.$$

It is also formed when ammonia acts on GeH_2Cl_2 or on GeH_3Cl. It is a yellow solid. It reacts explosively with oxygen. On heating to about 200° it evolves hydrogen and the gaseous germanes. Alkalis convert it to sodium germanite Na_2GeO_2, with the evolution of hydrogen and monogermane. It reacts with bromine to yield $GeCl_4$ and HBr.

Germanium tetra-alkyls and tetra-aryls. The tetra-alkyls are made:

(i) by the action of a Grignard reagent on $GeCl_4$, but it is difficult to replace the last chlorine atom,
(ii) by the action of zinc alkyl on $GeCl_4$; this reaction works more satisfactorily than (i),
(iii) by heating germanium with an alkyl halide in the presence of copper.

The germanium tetra-alkyls are colourless, pleasant-smelling liquids. They are stable to air and water, in which they are insoluble. Germanium tetramethyl is oxidised by concentrated nitric acid in the cold; the tetra-ethyl compound is not attacked by hot fuming nitric acid, but it is attacked by a mixture of fuming nitric acid and concentrated sulphuric acid.

The tetra-aryl compounds are made by methods corresponding to those used for making the tetra-alkyl compounds. The Grignard reagent is used in toluene instead of ethereal solution.

$Ge(C_6H_5)_4$ volatilizes without decomposition. It is soluble in organic solvents, but not in water. It is not attacked by boiling alkalis. It reacts with a solution of sodium in liquid ammonia (p. 625).

Alkyl and aryl polygermanes. The link Ge—Ge is weak. In the polygermanes the link is easily broken, either by action with a halogen or with an alkali metal. In this germanium resembles silicon, but differs entirely from carbon.

$(C_2H_5)_3Ge$—$Ge(C_2H_5)_3$ is made by treating $(C_2H_5)_3GeBr$ with sodium for 12 hours at 210° (no solvent is used). It is a colourless, pleasant-smelling liquid. It is stable in air at least up to its boiling point. With bromine it gives $(C_2H_5)_3GeBr$, and with lithium in ethylamine solution it gives $(C_2H_5)_3GeLi$ (p. 625).

$(C_6H_5)_3Ge$—$Ge(C_6H_5)_3$, a solid, is made (i) by heating $(C_6H_5)_3GeBr$ with sodium in boiling xylene, or, (ii) by heating $GeCl_4$ with magnesium phenyl bromide for 60 hours.

It is soluble in benzene, from which it crystallises with three molecules of benzene of crystallisation, which it loses if exposed to air. No evidence of dissociation into the $(C_6H_5)_3Ge$ radical is given by the freezing point of its dilute benzene solution, by its magnetic properties, or by its chemical reactions.

$(C_6H_5)_3Ge—Ge(C_6H_5)_2—Ge(C_6H_5)_3$. The compound is made by the reaction:

$$2(C_6H_5)_3GeNa + (C_6H_5)_2GeCl_2 = 2NaCl + (C_6H_5)_3Ge—Ge(C_6H_5)_2—Ge(C_6H_5)_3$$

It dissolves in benzene, in which it is monomeric. It is stable to air and water. *Both* Ge—Ge links are broken when it reacts with bromine, the products of the reaction being $(C_6H_5)_2GeBr_2$ and $(C_6H_5)_3GeBr$, m.p. 247°.

$Ge_4(C_6H_5)_8$. If $(C_6H_5)_2GeCl_2$ is treated with sodium in xylene, the compound conjectured to be:

$$
\begin{array}{c}
\qquad C_6H_5\ \ C_6H_5 \\
\qquad |\qquad | \\
C_6H_5—Ge—Ge—C_6H_5 \\
\qquad |\qquad | \\
C_6H_5—Ge—Ge—C_6H_5 \\
\qquad |\qquad | \\
\qquad C_6H_5\ \ C_6H_5
\end{array}
$$

is obtained. Its molecular formula is deduced from the boiling point of its benzene solution. It reacts with sodium in liquid ammonia solution to give $Na_2Ge(C_6H_5)_2$.

$Ge_6(C_6H_5)_6$. This compound is made by the action of potassium on $(C_6H_5)GeCl_3$ in boiling xylene in the presence of carbon dioxide. (In argon or in nitrogen the reaction does not proceed. In oxygen, presumably damp, $(C_6H_5)GeO \cdot OH$ is formed.) The structure assigned to this compound is:

$$
\begin{array}{c}
\qquad\qquad C_6H_5 \\
\qquad\qquad |\\
C_6H_5\qquad Ge\qquad C_6H_5 \\
\ \ \diagdown\quad \diagup\ \diagdown\quad\diagup \\
\ \ \ Ge\qquad\qquad Ge \\
\quad |\qquad\qquad\qquad \| \\
\ \ \ Ge\qquad\qquad Ge \\
\ \ \diagup\quad \diagdown\ \diagup\quad\diagdown \\
C_6H_5\qquad Ge\qquad C_6H_5 \\
\qquad\qquad |\\
\qquad\qquad C_6H_5
\end{array}
$$

The compound is an amorphous white solid. It dissolves in benzene to give a yellow solution, in which it is monomeric. It resists oxidation. It adds on eight Br atoms per molecule, which shows that bromine, besides saturating the double bonds, breaks one of the Ge—Ge links.

Alkali metal derivatives of germane and of germanium alkyls and aryls. Germane and its alkyl and aryl derivatives react with the alkali metals under certain conditions to yield compounds of the type $NaGe(C_2H_5)_3$. If germane or tetraphenylgermane is added to a solution of sodium in liquid ammonia, the ammoniate $NaGeH_3,6NH_3$ or $NaGe(C_6H_5)_3,3NH_3$ crystallises from solution. The sodium derivative of germane, $NaGeH_3$, when heated above 100° evolves hydrogen and leaves a residue of sodium germanide. If $Ge_2(C_2H_5)_6$ is added to a solution of lithium or potassium in liquid ethylamine a yellow solution is obtained, which is presumed to contain $LiGe(C_2H_5)_3$ or $KGe(C_2H_5)_3$. The solution reacts with ethyl iodide to give $Ge(C_2H_5)_4$. If the original solution is evaporated, the lithium germanium triethyl reacts with the solvent to yield triethyl germane, thus:

$$LiGe(C_2H_5)_3 + NH_2C_2H_5 = (C_2H_5)_3GeH + LiNHC_2H_5.$$

Triethyl germane is a colourless liquid. It decolourises bromine, and it reacts with a solution of potassium in liquid ammonia, to evolve hydrogen.

In the above reactions the radical $(C_2H_5)_3Ge$ is behaving as an anion; in triethyl germanium bromide (p. 627) the same radical may be regarded as a cation. The radical is thus exhibiting the amphoteric character which is a property of the corresponding silicon radical (p. 613).

The germanium tetrahalides. The preparations and properties of the germanium tetrahalides are summarised in Table 18.20.

Table 18.20.   *The Preparations and Properties of the Germanium Tetrahalides*

	GeF$_4$	GeCl$_4$	GeBr$_4$	GeI$_4$
Appearance	Colourless gas	Fuming, colour-less liquid	Colourless liquid	Red crystals
m.p. °C	Solid sublimes	-49.5	26·1	144
b.p. °C		86·5	186·5	
Decomposition temperature, °C	Above 1000	950		Above 144
Preparation	Heat BaGeF$_6$ to 700° BaGeF$_6$= BaF$_2$+GeF$_4$	Pass chlorine over german-ium at 100–180°		(i) Allow iodine and germa-nium to react (ii) Treat GeCl$_4$ with KI
Distance Ge-hal		2·10 (electron diffraction)	2·32	2·57

All the germanium tetrahalides are hydrolysed by water to germanium dioxide and the halogen acid. In the case of germanium tetrafluoride the final product is fluorogermanic acid, H_2GeF_6:

$$GeF_4 + 2H_2O = GeO_2 + 4HF,$$
$$GeF_4 + 2HF = H_2GeF_6.$$

The trihydrate, $GeF_4,3H_2O$, can be crystallised from the solution obtained by dissolving germanium dioxide in concentrated hydrofluoric acid (p. 622). When heated the crystals melt, and hydrolysis occurs. Germanium tetrafluoride when dry does not attack glass.

The solubility of germanium tetrachloride in organic solvents indicates its covalent nature. It is insoluble in concentrated hydrochloric acid, and it is not attacked by concentrated sulphuric acid. The red colour of germanium tetraiodide fades with fall in temperature; it is orange at $-10°$, and pale yellow at $-185°$. Germanium tetraiodide is isomorphous with stannic iodide. The crystal structure consists of close-packed iodine ions. One-eighth of the tetrahedral holes are occupied by Ge ions, thus giving discrete GeI$_4$ molecules. Germanium tetraiodide reacts with liquid ammonia to yield germanium di-imide, $Ge(NH)_2$. This compound on heating to 150° yields germanam $(GeN)_2NH$, and at 350° yields the nitride Ge_3N_4.

The halogenogermanes. There is a large number of derivatives of the germanes in which some hydrogen atoms in the germane molecule are replaced by halogen atoms. Germanochloroform, $HGeCl_3$, a colourless liquid, is made: (i) by passing hydrogen chloride over warm germanium metal, (ii) by passing hydrogen chloride over germanium chloride at 40°, (iii) by passing hydrogen chloride over germanium sulphide at a low temperature. Germanochloroform is easily converted to germanous derivatives. Even at $-30°$ it decomposes to germanous chloride, $GeCl_2$, and hydrogen chloride. With water it hydrolyses to germanous oxide, GeO. This behaviour contrasts sharply with that of silicochloroform which with water gives polymerised silicoformic anhydride

(p. 615). If oxidised by air, germanochloroform yields water, $GeCl_4$ and also $GeCl_2$. Bromine and iodine oxidise it to $GeCl_2Br_2$ and $GeCl_3I$.

A mixture of GeH_2Cl_2 and GeH_3Cl is obtained when germane is heated with hydrogen chloride in the presence of aluminium chloride. These compounds decompose spontaneously even in the cold, and with water they give GeO, HCl, and H_2; with ammonia they give the solid hydride $(GeH_2)_n$. Germanium shows no tendency to form compounds corresponding to the siloxanes.

The alkyl and aryl germanium halides. There is a large range of germanium derivatives in which all four hydrogen atoms in germane have been replaced by alkyl or aryl groups and by halogen atoms. A few such derivatives are mentioned in Table 18.21.

Table 18.21. *The Alkyl and Aryl Germanium Halides*

$(CH_3)_3GeCl$	m.p. $-13°$, b.p. $115°$	$(C_6H_5)_3GeCl$	m.p. $111°$
$(C_2H_5)_3GeF$	b.p. $149°$	$(C_2H_5)_2GeCl_2$	m.p. $-38°$, b.p. $175°$
$(C_2H_5)_3GeCl$	$176°$		
$(C_2H_5)_3GeBr$	$139°$		
$(C_2H_5)_3GeI$	$157°$	$(C_2H_5)GeCl_3$	b.p. $144°$

The alkyl compounds are made:

(i) by the action of a limited amount of the appropriate Grignard reagent on a germanium tetrahalide,
(ii) by the action of bromine on a germanium tetra-alkyl,
(iii) by the action of a germanium tetra-alkyl on hydrogen bromide in the presence of aluminium bromide:

$$Ge(CH_3)_4 + HBr = (CH_3)_3GeBr + CH_4.$$

The aryl derivatives are made by corresponding methods.

SECTION 6. COMPOUNDS IN WHICH THE GERMANIUM ATOM IS OCTAHEDRALLY HYBRIDISED

Germanium in the octahedral valence state forms neutral complexes and complex anions. Neutral β-diketone complexes are formed when germanium tetrachloride acts on a β-diketone dissolved in chloroform. For example, acetylacetone yields the complex:

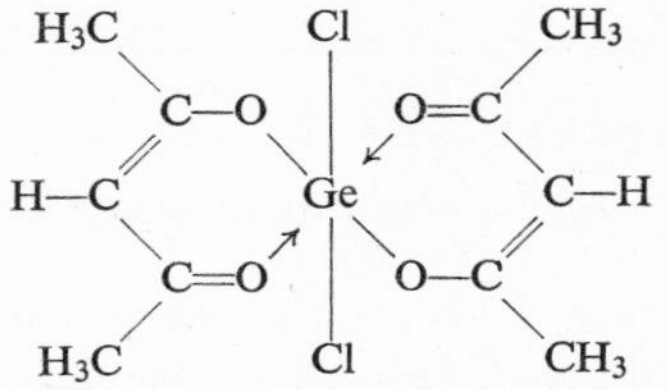

which is monomeric in solution in benzene and in chloroform. The complex is neutral, and not cationic like the silicon derivative of acetylacetone. When germanium tetrachloride reacts with cupric acetylacetone chloride, the product, $[A_3Ge]CuCl_2$, corresponds to the silicon derivative (p. 619).

Hydrofluorogermanic acid, H_2GeF_6, and the fluorogermanates. The acid is known only in solution. The potassium salt $K_2[GeF_6]$, m.p. $730°$, is decomposed by hydrochloric acid or by water. The caesium salt is isomorphous with potassium platinichloride, $K_2[PtCl_6]$.

The chlorogermanates. The caesium salt, $Cs_2[GeCl_6]$, is made by treating a mixture of germanium tetrachloride and caesium chloride with concentrated hydrochloric acid, and adding alcohol to the solution. Its crystal structure is similar to that of $(NH_4)_2[PtCl_6]$.

TIN

THE ELEMENT

Tin is a white metal which retains its lustre on exposure to air and moisture. It is not ductile and has a low tensile strength, but it is malleable and can be rolled into foil. Ordinary tin (white tin with a close-packed lattice) expands and crumbles when it changes into grey tin with a diamond lattice; grey tin is stable below 13·2° The change is slow and takes place most quickly at $-50°$

Table 18.22. *Reactions of Tin*

Reagent	Conditions	Product
Air	Cold	No action
	At 250°	A scum of SnO_2 forms on the surface
	White heat	SnO_2, formed with a white flame
Water	Cold	No action
Steam	High temperature	SnO_2 and H_2
Cl_2	Cold	$SnCl_4$
S	Heated	SnS or SnS_2
HCl	Dilute	Very little action
	Hot and concentrated	$SnCl_2$ and H_2
H_2SO_4	Dilute	No action
	Hot and concentrated	$SnSO_4$, SO_2, and H_2O
HNO_3	Dilute	$Sn(NO_3)_2$ and NH_4NO_3
	Concentrated with a trace of water	Metastannic acid $(H_2Sn_5O_{11})$ which on ignition gives SnO_2
Aqua regia		$SnCl_4$
NaOH	Boiling concentrated aqueous solution	No action

GENERAL CHEMISTRY OF TIN

The valency shell of the tin atom in the ground state has the electron configuration $5s^2$, $5p^2$.

Tin is present in its compounds either in the oxidation state 2 or the oxidation state 4. In this it resembles germanium, but the range of stannous (Sn^{II}) compounds is much greater than that of the germanous (Ge^{II}) compounds. Tin may be present as the stannous ion Sn^{2+} in stannous nitrate and stannous sulphate. The giant molecule compounds of Sn^{II} include the imide, the oxide, the hydroxide, the sulphide, and the halides. The stannous alkyls and aryls are well characterised although no hydride is known. Complex anions containing Sn^{II} are mentioned on p. 631.

The crystal and molecular structures of the stannous compounds are not simple. The molecules of the chloride, bromide, and iodide are not linear, the anion in K_2SnCl_4,H_2O has the $CdCl_2$ structure, the oxide (like PbO) has a pyramidal structure, and the sulphide has a distorted rock salt structure. These somewhat complex structures indicate that the simpler types of hybridisation are not responsible for the bonding in stannous compounds, and suggest that the $5s$ electron pair in the valency shell of the tin atom in the stannous state is inert (p. 487). The two covalent bonds exerted by the tin atom in the stannous state must be concerned with the two $5p$ electrons in the valence shell.

There are many compounds of tin in the oxidation state 4, in most of which the higher hybridisation states are adopted. There is no simple cation Sn^{4+}. The giant molecule compounds include SnO_2 and SnS_2.

There is no evidence for the existence of compounds containing a tin atom (Sn^{IV}) in the digonal valence state. Tin forms no compounds corresponding to ethylene or benzene, or to $Ge_6(C_6H_5)_6$, so it is probable that it does not adopt the trigonal valence state. If the compound $(C_6H_5)_3SnF$ is ionic (it is a high melting solid, whereas the parallel chloride, bromide, and iodide are liquid) the tin atom is in the trigonal valence state, but it is more probable that the tin atom is tetrahedrally hybridised and exerts four covalent bonds; the properties of the compound are determined by the high degree of ionic character of the bond Sn—F.

Tin forms numerous tetrahedral compounds, and a few tetrahedral complex anions. There are two chelate trigonal bipyramidal complexes of tin mentioned in Table 18.1 which are without parallel among the compounds of the other elements of the sub-Group. The octahedral complexes are neutral and anionic, and are non-chelate. There is no $Sn(C_6H_5)_3$ radical.

COMPOUNDS IN WHICH THE OXIDATION STATE OF TIN IS II

Stannous salts. Stannous nitrate $Sn(NO_3)_2$ and stannous sulphate $SnSO_4$ are known . The sulphate is made by boiling tin in copper sulphate solution acidified with sulphuric acid. The copper is filtered off:

$$CuSO_4 + Sn = SnSO_4 + Cu.$$

Stannous imide, SnNH, is a brown amorphous powder. It is obtained from the potassium derivative by the action of ammonium bromide in liquid ammonia:

$$KSnN + NH_4Br = SnNH + KBr + NH_3.$$

It undergoes the reactions:

$$NH_3 + SnNH + 2KNH_2 = K_2[Sn(NH_2)_4],$$
$$SnNH + 2NH_4CNS = Sn(CNS)_2 + 3NH_3,$$
$$SnNK + 3KNH_2 + I_2 = Sn(NK)_2 + 2KI + 2NH_3.$$

It loses ammonia at 340° to give Sn_3N_2.

Stannous oxide, SnO, is made by dehydrating precipitated stannous hydroxide (see below) at 100°. When free from water it exists as blue-black crystals or a brown powder. If heated in air it glows and forms stannic oxide, SnO_2. The crystal structure of stannous oxide is a layer structure. Each oxygen atom has four tin atoms arranged round it tetrahedrally; each tin atom has four oxygen atoms at the base of a tetragonal pyramid in the manner shown in the figure. The distance Sn—O is 2·21.

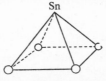

Fig. 18.11. Arrangement of atoms in stannous oxide, SnO.

Stannous hydroxide is precipitated when ammonia or an alkali is added to a solution of stannous chloride or sulphate. The precipitate is colloidal and has no definite composition. It is amphoteric; the acid and basic properties are about equal.

The precipitate dissolves in acids to yield solutions of stannous salts, and in alkalis to yield solutions of stannites which are very powerful reducing agents. The alkaline solution deposits stannous oxide on standing. Very concentrated alkalis cause stannous oxide to disproportionate to tin and the stannate:

$$2SnO + 2KOH = Sn + K_2SnO_3 + H_2O.$$

Stannous sulphide, SnS, is made from the elements. It melts at about 1000°, and boils at about 1100°, but above 265° it slowly changes to a mixture of stannic sulphide SnS_2, and tin. Hydrogen chloride (as gas or in solution) acts upon stannous sulphide to give hydrogen sulphide and stannous chloride. Stannous sulphide is precipitated when hydrogen sulphide acts on an acid solution of stannous chloride. The precipitate is insoluble in aqueous solutions of alkaline sulphides, but is soluble in a solution of ammonium polysulphide to give ammonium thiostannate, $(NH_4)_2SnS_3$. When the solution of ammonium thiostannate is acidified, stannic sulphide is precipitated.

The crystal of stannous sulphide has a distorted rocksalt lattice. The crystal structure of stannous sulphide thus resembles that of germanous sulphide, but differs from that of plumbous sulphide.

The stannous halides. Certain properties of the stannous halides are summarised in Table 18.23.

Table 18.23. *Preparation and Properties of the Stannous Halides*

	SnF_2	$SnCl_2$	$SnBr_2$	SnI_2
Appearance	White crystals	Transparent glass	Yellow solid	Red solid
b.p. °C		623	620	720
m.p. °C		246	216	316
Preparation	Dissolve metal or Sn(OH)$_2$ in HF	Pass HCl over heated tin		
Solubility in water, gm in 100 gm	Dissolves to a clear solution	Very soluble 270/15°	Soluble 85/0°	Much less soluble 0·99/20°
Distance Sn-hal		2·42	2·55	2·73

Anhydrous stannous chloride, besides being very soluble in water, is also soluble in acetone (55·4 gm in 100 gm at 18°), in ethyl acetate (4·46 gm in 100 gm at 18°), in alcohol and in ether. The fused chloride is an electrolyte; the vapour is to some extent associated. The dihydrate, $SnCl_2,2H_2O$ (tin salt), m.p. 40·5°, is made by dissolving tin in hydrochloric acid and crystallising the solution. The crystals lose acid on heating, and are hydrolysed in aqueous solution. If the proportion of water is large the oxychloride $(Sn(OH)Cl)_2,H_2O$ is precipitated. In the presence of air the hydrolysis may be accompanied by oxidation:

$$6SnCl_2 + 2H_2O + O_2 = 2SnCl_4 + 4Sn(OH)Cl.$$

If concentrated hydrochloric acid is added to the solution, the acids $HSnCl_3$ and H_2SnCl_4 are formed. The first acid can be crystallised as $HSnCl_3,3H_2O$; the salts of the second are known, $(NH_4)_2SnCl_4$ and K_2SnCl_4,H_2O. Stannous chloride in solution in hydrochloric acid is a powerful reducing agent. The reduction is probably brought about by the ion $[SnCl_4{}^{2-}]$, thus:

$$[SnCl_4{}^{2-}] + 2Fe^{3+} = SnCl_4 + 2Fe^{2+}.$$

The dihydrate of stannous iodide, $SnI_2,2H_2O$, crystallises on the addition of potassium iodide to a solution of stannous chloride. Stannous iodide dissolves in hydrogen iodide solution to form $HSnI_3$.

Electron diffraction analysis indicates that the molecules of the stannous halides are non-linear.

Stannous alkyls and aryls. Compounds of the types $Sn(CH_3)_2$ and $Sn(C_6H_5)_2$ are known both for tin and for lead, but not for germanium, silicon, or carbon. These compounds are liquids or solids, intensely coloured, unstable, and rapidly oxidised by air.

Tin diethyl, $Sn(C_2H_5)_2$, is a pale yellow oil. It is made:

   (i) by the action of ethyl magnesium bromide on stannous chloride,
   (ii) by the action of ethyl iodide on tin-sodium alloy,
   (iii) by reducing $Sn(C_2H_5)_2Cl_2$ with zinc,

but it has probably not been obtained pure.

It is insoluble in water, but soluble in organic solvents. It has a strong tendency to undergo reactions which yield stannic derivatives. It boils at about 150° with decomposition, yielding $Sn(C_2H_5)_4$ and tin. It is oxidised by air to $Sn(C_2H_5)_2O$; ethyl chloride converts it to $Sn(C_2H_5)_3Cl$; chlorine to $Sn(C_2H_5)_2Cl_2$.

Tin diphenyl, $Sn(C_6H_5)_2$, is a bright yellow powder, which melts at 130° to a red liquid. It is made by the action of magnesium phenyl bromide on stannous chloride in ether. Tin diphenyl dissolves in benzene or ether to give red solutions; the benzene solution turns yellow on dilution. It is not acted on by water, but it is so easily oxidised that it must be handled in an inert atmosphere and protected from bright light. It reacts with excess of phenyl magnesium bromide to give $(C_6H_5)_3Sn-Sn(C_6H_5)_3$. It is diamagnetic in the solid and in benzene solution. The freezing point of the freshly prepared benzene solution corresponds to the monomeric formula, but polymerisation takes place on standing. The d.p.m. is 1·10 debyes.

Complexes of tin in the stannous condition. The ions $[SnCl_3{}^-]$, $[SnI_3{}^-]$, and $[SnCl_4{}^{2-}]$ in the acids and salts mentioned on p. 630 are examples of non-chelate complex anions. The anion in the crystal of the salt K_2SnCl_4,H_2O has a chain structure in which the arrangement of atoms corresponds to that in the $CdCl_2$ layer; the co-ordination of the tin atom in this structure is 6. Stannous formate forms double salts with alkali metal formates, such as $2KHCO_2,Sn(HCO_2)_2$, which possibly contains the anion $[Sn(HCO_2)_4]^{2-}$.

COMPOUNDS IN WHICH THE OXIDATION STATE OF TIN IS IV

SECTION 1. GIANT MOLECULE STRUCTURES IN WHICH THE BONDS HAVE BOTH IONIC AND COVALENT CHARACTER

Two of the principal compounds in this Section are stannic oxide and stannic sulphide. Stannic oxide which crystallises with the rutile lattice is probably a stannic compound in which all the electrons in the valency shell of the tin atom are used in bond formation; stannic sulphide has the CdI_2 lattice, and is not clear whether four or only two of the valency electrons of the tin atom are used in bond formation.

Stannic oxide, SnO_2, occurs naturally as cassiterite which has the rutile structure.

Two other crystalline forms are known. Stannic oxide may be prepared in the laboratory by dissolving tin in nitric acid and heating the product.

Cassiterite, and the artificially prepared oxide after ignition, are quite insoluble in water, and are attacked only by hot concentrated acids and alkalis. With fused alkalis the oxide gives stannates; in the presence of sulphur, thiostannates.

Stannic hydroxide, $Sn(OH)_4$, is precipitated by the action of an acid on the solution of a stannate. It is thrown down in colloidal form and has not been characterised. It is amphoteric, and is a stronger acid than base.

Stannic sulphide, SnS_2, is made from the elements, or by precipitation of a stannic salt in solution with hydrogen sulphide. The form of stannic sulphide known as mosaic gold is made for use as a pigment by heating tin filings, ammonium chloride and sulphur:

$$2Sn + 6NH_4Cl + 2S = SnS_2 + (NH_4)_2SnCl_6 + 4NH_3 + 2H_2.$$

It is obtained as golden yellow scales. It is insoluble in acids except aqua regia, but is soluble in alkalis.

The precipitate obtained by the action of hydrogen sulphide on a stannic solution is soluble in alkaline sulphides to give thiostannates, which may be precipitated from solution by the addition of alcohol. Thiostannates are of two types: Na_2SnS_3 and Na_4SnS_4. They are hydrolysed by water, and decomposed by acids. Thioesters are known:

$$Sn(SCH_3)_4 \quad \text{b.p.} \quad 81°/0·001 \text{ mm} \quad \text{m.p. } 31°$$
$$Sn(SC_2H_5)_4 \quad \quad 105°/0·001 \text{ mm}$$

Stannic sulphide has a CdI_2 lattice.

SECTION 4.† COMPOUNDS IN WHICH THE TIN ATOM IS TETRAHEDRALLY HYBRIDISED

Tin closely resembles germanium in the types of compound formed by the atom in the tetrahedral valence state. The tin compounds of this Section include stannane, the stannic alkyls, aryls, and halides, and mixed derivatives of these compounds.

Stannane is the only hydride of tin. Although the polystannanes have not been prepared their alkyl and aryl derivatives are numerous, and it seems that chains of tin atoms are more stable than chains of germanium atoms. The only complexes in which a tin atom in the stannic condition is present in the tetrahedral valence state are salts of the type $Na[Sn(CH_3)_3]$.

Stannane, tin hydride, SnH_4, is made by the reduction of a stannic compound. The preparation may be carried out by the cathodic reduction of stannic sulphate in sulphuric acid, using a lead cathode to make use of the overpotential, but the yield is very small indeed. A better method is probably the reduction of stannic chloride by lithium aluminium hydride.

Stannane is a gas, b.p. $-52°$. It decomposes quickly at $+150°$, but it is stable for some days in a glass vessel at room temperature. It decomposes rapidly if brought into contact with tin, $CaCl_2$ or P_2O_5. It is unaffected by dilute acids or alkalis, but is absorbed by concentrated solutions of these substances. It reduces silver nitrate solution or mercuric chloride solution, but not solutions of ferric chloride or cupric sulphate.

† Sections 2 and 3 are omitted as there are no compounds in which the tin atom Sn^{IV} is present in the digonal or trigonal valence state.

STANNIC ALKYLS AND ARYLS

A list of certain alkyl and aryl derivatives of the stannanes is given in Table 18.24.

Table 18.24.   *Stannic Hydride and certain Stannic Alkyl and Aryl Compounds*

Compound		m.p. °C	b.p. °C	
Stannic hydride	SnH_4	-150	-52	
Stannic alkyls	$Sn(CH_3)_4$		78	
	$Sn(C_2H_5)_4$		175	
	$Sn_2(C_2H_5)_6$		160	Decomposes at 270°
	$Sn_2(CH_3)_6$	23		
	$SnH(CH_3)_3$		60	With HCl it gives $(CH_3)_3SnCl$, and with Na, $(CH_3)_3SnNa$
Stannic aryls	$Sn(C_6H_5)_4$	225		
	$Sn_2(C_6H_5)_6$	233		Decomposes at 250°
	$SnH(C_6H_5)_3$		173/6 mm	Colourless. Air oxidises it to $(C_6H_5)_6Sn_2$. With Na it gives $(C_6H_5)_3SnNa$

The alkyl and aryl derivatives of monostannane. The tin tetra-alkyls are made:

(i) by the action of a Grignard reagent on stannic chloride,
(ii) by the action of the zinc alkyl on tin dialkyl dichloride, for example:

$$Zn(C_2H_5)_2 + (C_2H_5)_2SnCl_2 = (C_2H_5)_4Sn + ZnCl_2,$$

(iii) by distilling the stannous alkyl, for example:

$$2Sn(C_2H_5)_2 = (C_2H_5)_4Sn + Sn,$$

(iv) by action of the alkyl halide on metallic tin, or on a tin-sodium alloy.

In methods (i) and (ii) some tin trialkyl monohalide is always formed. The quantity may be minimised by using excess of the Grignard reagent or the zinc alkyl. If ammonia is passed through the solution of the product in ether the monohalogen derivative is precipitated as the diammoniate, $(C_2H_5)_3SnCl,2NH_3$, and is so removed. The tin tetra-alkyls are colourless liquids, with a slight but pleasant smell. They are insoluble in water, but soluble in organic solvents. They neither polymerise, nor co-ordinate, nor disproportionate. They are stable to air and water, but by the action of halogens or halogen hydrides, alkyl groups are replaced by a halogen atom, as, for example, is shown by the equations:

$$Sn(C_2H_5)_4 + I_2 = Sn(C_2H_5)_3I + C_2H_5I,$$
$$Sn(C_2H_5)_4 + HCl = Sn(C_2H_5)_3Cl + C_2H_6.$$

Frequently two alkyl groups are removed at once; in mixed alkyls the lightest group is replaced by iodine.

The tin tetra-aryls are commonly made by the action of the appropriate Grignard reagent on stannic chloride.

The alkyl and aryl derivatives of distannane. Hexaethyl distannane is made by the action of sodium on $(C_2H_5)_3SnCl$ in ether or boiling xylene under pressure, or better in liquid ammonia. The product is purified by distillation at reduced pressure in an indifferent gas. Hexaethyl distannane is a colourless, low-melting solid with a penetrating and unpleasant smell. It is miscible with organic solvents. It distils unchanged. It is oxidised by air to the oxide, $(C_2H_5)_3Sn$—O—$Sn(C_2H_5)_3$. It reduces the halogens, or mercuric chloride or bromide, thus:

$$(C_2H_5)_3Sn\text{—}Sn(C_2H_5)_3 + Br_2 = 2(C_2H_5)_3SnBr,$$

and it reacts with sodium to give $(C_2H_5)_3SnNa$. With ethyl iodide it gives butane:

$$2C_2H_5I + (C_2H_5)_3Sn\text{—}Sn(C_2H_5)_3 = 2(C_2H_5)_3SnI + C_4H_{10},$$

but with methyl iodide it reacts differently:

$$CH_3I + (C_2H_5)_3Sn\text{—}Sn(C_2H_5)_3 = (C_2H_5)_3SnI + Sn(C_2H_5)_3CH_3.$$

Hexaphenyl distannane is made by heating stannous diphenyl:

$$3(C_6H_5)_2Sn = (C_6H_5)_3Sn\text{—}Sn(C_6H_5)_3 + Sn,$$

or by reducing triphenylchlorostannane with sodium in boiling xylene. It has no smell. It is stable to air, but it is a very powerful reducing agent. It reduces bromine in chloroform at $-30°$, and silver nitrate in alcohol to metal at $-75°$.

Attempts made to decide, by observations on the freezing points and boiling points of their solutions, whether the alkyl and aryl distannanes undergo any dissociation have led to contradictory results. Hexamethyl stannane and hexa-*o*-tolyl distannane are diamagnetic at temperatures between 25 and 80°. This is good evidence that these compounds do not dissociate into radicals in this range of temperature.

Alkyl derivatives of the higher polystannanes. Completely methylated chains of tin atoms up to Sn_5 are known:

$(CH_3)_3Sn$—$Sn(CH_3)_2$—$Sn(CH_3)_3$ is a colourless liquid, distilling at 100° in a high vacuum.

$(CH_3)_3Sn$—$Sn(CH_3)_2$—$Sn(CH_3)_2$—$Sn(CH_3)_3$ is a colourless viscid liquid, which is oxidised by air to a white solid. It is monomeric in benzene.

$(CH_3)_3Sn$—$Sn(CH_3)_2$—$Sn(CH_3)_2$—$Sn(CH_3)_2$—$Sn(CH_3)_3$ is a colourless oil, monomeric in benzene.

The aromatic analogues of these chain compounds have been reported.

Alkali metal derivatives of the tin alkyls and aryls. The alkali metal derivatives of the trialkyl stannanes such as $(CH_3)_3SnNa$ are more stable than those of the corresponding germanium compounds. They are made in solution in liquid ammonia by reactions illustrated by the equations:

$$(CH_3)_3SnCl + 2Na = (CH_3)_3SnNa + NaCl,$$
$$2(CH_3)_3SnH + 2Na = 2(CH_3)_3SnNa + H_2,$$
$$(CH_3)_3Sn\text{—}Sn(CH_3)_3 + 2Na = 2(CH_3)_3SnNa,$$
$$(CH_3)_3Sn\text{—}Sn(CH_3)_3 + NaNH_2 = (CH_3)_3SnNa + (CH_3)_3SnNH_2.$$

Sodium trimethyl tin separates from the solution as yellow crystals. The compounds $Na_2Sn(CH_3)_2$ and $Na(CH_3)_2Sn$—$Sn(CH_3)_2Na$ are also known.

Sodium triphenyl tin is an amorphous yellow powder which dissolves in liquid ammonia to give a yellow solution. The solution at $-33°$ is a good conductor. Sodium triphenyl tin is very reactive, and it is slowly oxidised by air to $Sn(C_6H_5)_4$, NaOH, and some $(C_6H_5)_6Sn_2$.

The tin tetrahalides. The preparations and properties of the tin tetrahalides are summarised in Table 18.25.

Table 18.25.   *The Preparations and Properties of the Tin Tetrahalides*

	SnF_4	$SnCl_4$	$SnBr_4$	SnI_4
Appearance	Colourless, hygroscopic solid	Colourless, volatile fuming liquid	White fuming crystalline solid	Yellow solid
m.p. °C		−33	30	143·5
b.p. °C	Sublimes at 705	114·1	293	343
Density	4·78	2·234	3·340	4·696
Solubility	Very soluble and is hydrolysed	Is hydrolysed		Is rapidly hydrolysed
Hydrates		$SnCl_4,5H_2O$	$SnBr_4,4H_2O$	
Preparation	Treat $SnCl_4$ with HF	Treat tin with Cl_2 in the cold	Treat tin with Br_2	Treat tin with I_2

Stannic fluoride is made by treating hydrogen fluoride with stannic chloride until no more hydrogen chloride is liberated. The residue has the composition $SnCl_4,SnF_4$. If this is heated to 220° the stannic chloride volatilises away, and pure stannic fluoride is left. The boiling point and the density of stannic fluoride compared with those of the other stannic halides indicate that the ionic character of stannic fluoride must be high.

Although stannic chloride slowly hydrolyses in aqueous solution, the hydrate 'butter'' of tin, $SnCl_4,5H_2O$, can be obtained by crystallisation. Hydrochloric acts on this compound at 0° to produce a hydrate of chlorostannic acid, $H_2SnCl_6,6H_2O$. Stannic chloride is an acceptor molecule. It combines directly with chlorides of alkali metals to form chlorostannates, such as Na_2SnCl_6, and it accepts electrons from donors containing an oxygen atom, such as alcohols, ethers, and aldehydes, ketones, acids, esters, and amides, to give $Sn(Cl_4)(OR)_2$. If any of the chlorine atoms in $SnCl_4$ is replaced by an alkyl group the accepting properties are much diminished; if two or more are replaced, the acceptor properties vanish. Clearly the reason is to be found in the electromeric effect:

$$\overset{Cl^{\delta-}}{\underset{Cl^{\delta-}}{\overset{|}{\underset{|}{\overset{\delta-}{Cl}-\overset{\delta+}{Sn}-\overset{\delta-}{Cl}}}}} \qquad \overset{CH_3^{\delta+}}{\underset{CH_3^{\delta+}}{\overset{|}{\underset{|}{\overset{\delta+}{CH_3}-\overset{\delta-}{Sn}-\overset{\delta+}{CH_3}}}}}$$

Stannic chloride also forms complexes with nitrogen compounds. Its reaction with ammonia proceeds beyond addition, and there is doubt whether the ammine $SnCl_4,2NH_3$ exists. Two molecules of pyridine add on to $SnCl_4$, and also to $AlkSnCl_3$ and to Alk_2SnCl_2, but only one molecule adds on to Alk_3SnCl and none to Alk_4Sn. Here again the influence of the alkyl group is clearly seen.

The crystal structure of stannic iodide is the same as that of germanium tetraiodide (p. 626). The tetrahedral configuration of the molecule of stannic iodide is found in the vapour of stannic iodide as well as in the crystal.

The alkyl and aryl tin halides. There is a large range of tin compounds derived from stannane by the replacement of hydrogen atoms by alkyl or aryl groups and by halogen atoms. A few such compounds are mentioned in Table 18.26. It is clear from the Table that the fluorine derivatives in all cases differ from the other halogen derivatives. The fluorine compounds are high melting solids which decompose below their boiling points; they are not usually soluble in organic solvents. The compounds of the other halogens are volatile, low melting liquids easily soluble in organic solvents.

The compound $Sn(CH_3)_3F$ is made (i) by the action of aqueous hydrofluoric acid on $Sn(CH_3)_3OH$, and (ii) by the action of potassium fluoride on a solution of the chloride $Sn(CH_3)_3Cl$. It is soluble in alcohol from which it can be recrystallised. It is without action on the eyes or lungs. The chloride, bromide, and iodide, by contrast, have repulsive smells and a violent action on the eyes and lungs. They are made (i) by the action of the appropriate halogen on tetramethyl stannane or on hexamethyl distannane, or (ii) by treating the methyl halide with metallic tin or sodium-tin alloy. Triphenyl fluorostannane is made by treating a hot dilute alcoholic solution of the chloride with potassium fluoride; triphenyl fluorostannane is precipitated quantitatively.

Table 18.26.   *The Alkyl and Aryl Tin Halides*

Compound	m.p. °C	b.p. °C	Compound	m.p. °C	b.p. °C
$Sn(CH_3)_3F$	*ca.* 360†		$Sn(C_6H_5)_2F_2$	360	
$Sn(CH_3)_3Cl$	37		$Sn(C_6H_5)_2Cl_2$	42	337
$Sn(CH_3)_3Br$	27	165	$Sn(C_6H_5)_2Br_2$	38	230
$Sn(CH_3)_3I$	3·4	170	$Sn(C_6H_5)_2I_2$	71	180
$Sn(C_6H_5)_3F$	357		$Sn(CH_3)F_3$		
$Sn(C_6H_5)_3Cl$	106	240	$Sn(CH_3)Cl_3$	43	
$Sn(C_6H_5)_3Br$	121	249	$Sn(CH_3)Br_3$	54	210
$Sn(C_6H_5)_3I$	121	253	$Sn(CH_3)I_3$	87	
$Sn(CH_3)_2F_2$			$Sn(C_6H_5)F_3$		
$Sn(CH_3)_2Cl_2$	85	220	$Sn(C_6H_5)Cl_3$		142
$Sn(CH_3)_2Br_2$	63	232	$Sn(C_6H_5)Br_3$		182
$Sn(CH_3)_2I_2$	45	240	$Sn(C_6H_5)I_3$		

† Decomposes at m.p.

SECTION 5. COMPOUNDS IN WHICH THE TIN ATOM IS EXHIBITING TRIGONAL BIPYRAMIDAL HYBRIDISATION

Two compounds of this class are known:

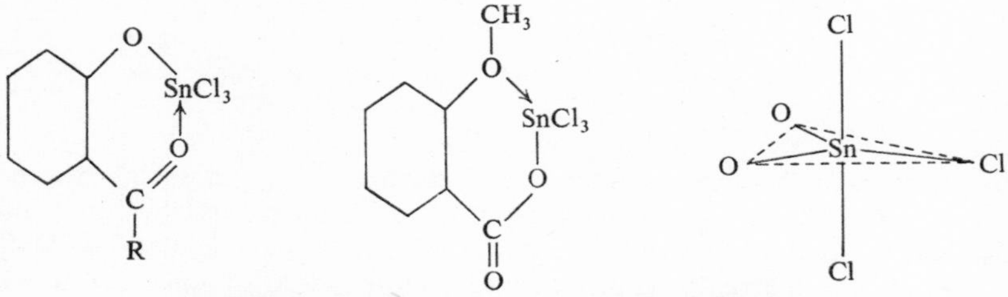

o-acetylphenol complex   methyl salicylate

The tin atom here is in the trigonal bipyramidal state, and the angle between the equatorial valence bonds enables the tin atom to complete the six-membered ring without strain. One chlorine atom is in the plane of the ring; the others are vertically above and below the tin atom, as shown in the diagram on the right of the formulae.

SECTION 6. COMPOUNDS IN WHICH THE TIN ATOM IS OCTAHEDRALLY HYBRIDISED

The only compounds in which the tin atom is octahedrally hybridised are neutral non-chelate complexes such as $SnCl_4,(C_2H_5OH)_2$, and non-chelate complex anions, such as those present in chlorostannic acid and its derivatives.

Neutral compounds of the general formula $SnCl_4,(RO)_2$ are numerous, and are formed by almost every type of organic compound containing oxygen.

The compounds in which tin is present in a complex anion may be regarded as derivatives of the hypothetical stannic acid which would have the constitution $H_2[Sn(OH)_6]$. The potassium salt is $K_2[Sn(OH)_6]$. It is isomorphous with $K_2[Pb(OH)_6]$, and with $K_2[Pt(OH)_6]$. Its lattice is similar to that of K_2PtCl_6, but it is distorted owing to the interaction of the hydroxyl groups. The stannates of the alkali metals lose water at about 150°, and undergo some constitutional change. After such dehydration the sodium salt is insoluble.

Derivatives of stannic acid are known in which the hydroxyl groups are replaced by atoms of fluorine, chlorine, bromine, or iodine, by alkoxy groups, such as OC_2H_5, or by alkyl groups. Chlorostannic acid, which may be isolated as $H_2SnCl_6,6H_2O$, m.p. 20°, is made by saturating a concentrated solution of stannic chloride with gaseous hydrogen chloride. Chlorostannic acid forms many stable salts. $(NH_4)_2SnCl_6$ is known as pink salt; it is not decomposed by boiling water. It has been found experimentally that the alkali metal chlorostannates have the antifluorite crystal structure (p. 348). The discrete anions $[SnCl_6^{2-}]$ are octahedral, and are situated at positions corresponding to the points on a face-centred cubic lattice. The K^+ ions are at the points corresponding to the eight tetrahedral holes.

Among the derivatives of stannic acid containing organic groups are $K_2[Sn(OC_2H_5)_6]$, $K_2[SnF_4(C_2H_5)_2]$, and $K_2[SnCl_5(C_2H_5)]$,Aq. $K_2[SnF_4(C_2H_5)_2]$ is obtained by the action of excess potassium fluoride on diethyl difluorostannane.

LEAD

THE ELEMENT

Lead is a soft grey metal which is bright and lustrous when freshly cut. It may be rolled and extruded through dies. If finely divided it is pyrophoric, but in the massive condition it is covered with a film of oxide or carbonate, and is so slowly attacked by air that it is used as a roofing material. It is only very slowly attacked by hydrochloric acid, and it is not attacked by sulphuric acid under 79% strength, but is quickly dissolved by nitric acid. Attack by nitric or sulphuric acids yields the plumbous salts.

Table 18.27. *Reactions of Lead*

Reagent	Conditions	Product
Air	Cold	Oxide or carbonate which arrests further action
	800°	PbO
Water	Oxygen free	No action
	Oxygen present	Pb(OH)$_2$
C		No action
N$_2$	Heated	No action
S		PbS
Cl$_2$		PbCl$_2$
HCl	Dilute or concentrated	PbCl$_2$ formed very slowly
H$_2$SO$_4$	Concentration above 79% and above 200°	PbSO$_4$
HNO$_3$	Dilute or concentrated	Pb(NO$_3$)$_2$

GENERAL CHEMISTRY OF LEAD

The valency shell of the lead atom in the ground state has the electron configuration $6s^2$, $6p^2$.

In the chemistry of lead the bivalent compounds in which the s electrons are inert are more familiar than the quadrivalent compounds in which all the electrons in the valency shell of the lead atom are used for bond formation. Lead in the bivalent (plumbous) condition forms salts such as $Pb(NO_3)_2$, an oxide PbO and a sulphide PbS, both of which are in the giant molecule class. It also forms covalent compounds such as $Pb(CH_3)_2$ and $Pb(C_2H_5S)_2$, and neutral, anionic, and cationic complexes.

There are no compounds in which the lead atom is in the digonal or trigonal valence state. The compounds in which the lead atom is tetrahedrally hybridised are lower in stability, and show a smaller range, than the corresponding compounds of tin. This difference between the chemistry of lead and tin continues a trend that is obvious in the sequence of elements carbon to tin. There is only one hydride of lead, PbH_4, and only two halogen compounds, PbF_4, $PbCl_4$; $PbBr_4$, and PbI_4 do not exist. There are, however, many alkyl and aryl derivatives of quadrivalent lead including compounds such as $Pb_2(C_6H_5)_6$, in which there is a Pb—Pb bond. This bond does not dissociate to give radicals such as $Pb(C_6H_5)_3$; the magnetic moment of $Pb_2(C_6H_5)_6$ in the solid state and in solution in benzene shows that its degree of dissociation is less than 0·01.

Lead does not imitate tin in adopting the trigonal bipyramidal valence state. The compounds containing lead in the octahedral valence state need no special comment. Lead is the only element of the sub-Group which undergoes dodecahedral hybridisation, as in the compound $K_3H[PbF_8]$.

COMPOUNDS IN WHICH THE OXIDATION STATE OF LEAD IS II

Plumbous salts. *Plumbous nitrate*, $Pb(NO_3)_2$, is made by dissolving lead, lead oxide, or lead carbonate in dilute nitric acid. It is very soluble in water (56·5 gm in 100 gm at 20°). It forms anhydrous crystals isomorphous with barium nitrate. It is precipitated from solution by concentrated nitric acid. When plumbous nitrate is heated it yields nitrogen dioxide and oxygen.

Plumbous sulphate, $PbSO_4$, occurs as the mineral anglesite, isomorphous with barytes and celestine. It is precipitated by sulphuric acid, or by a soluble sulphate, from a solution of a lead salt. It is sparingly soluble in water (0·04 gm per litre at 15°), and much less soluble in weak sulphuric acid (0·004 gm per litre in 0·5% acid at 15°). It dissolves in warm ammonium acetate solution ($BaSO_4$ is insoluble), probably because of the un-ionised nature of plumbous acetate. It dissolves in hot, concentrated sulphuric acid.

Plumbous chromate, $PbCrO_4$, is thrown down as a yellow precipitate when potassium chromate is added to a solution of lead nitrate. The precipitate is so insoluble in water that it is precipitated in the presence of ammonium acetate. When potassium dichromate is added to lead nitrate in aqueous solution the equilibrium is set up:

$$K_2Cr_2O_7 + H_2O + Pb(NO_3)_2 \rightleftharpoons 2KNO_3 + PbCrO_4 + H_2CrO_4.$$

If the acidity of the solution is reduced by the addition of ammonium acetate, the reaction proceeds to completion. Plumbous chromate is insoluble in dilute nitric acid but is soluble in the concentrated acid. Concentrated sodium hydroxide solution dissolves plumbous chromate, forming sodium plumbite:

$$PbCrO_4 + 4NaOH = Na_2PbO_2 + Na_2CrO_4 + 2H_2O.$$

Dilute sodium hydroxide solution reacts with plumbous chromate to give basic chromates which are used as pigments.

Plumbous oxide, litharge, PbO. If lead is heated in air a yellow powder is obtained called *massicot*; if this is fused it turns red, and the product is known as *litharge*. Plumbous oxide exists in two crystalline forms:

$$\alpha \longleftarrow \text{about } 500° \longrightarrow \beta$$

red	yellow
tetragonal	orthorhombic
stannous oxide structure	
solubility in water 25°	
0·0504 gm per litre	0·1065 gm per litre

Plumbous hydroxide is precipitated by the addition of alkali to a solution of plumbous nitrate. The precipitate has no definite composition, and at 145° it loses water to give plumbous oxide. Plumbous hydroxide is amphoteric, but is much less acidic than stannous hydroxide. The values of the acid and basic dissociation constants are: $K_a = 8 \times 10^{-12}$, $K_b = 1 \times 10^{-3}$. Plumbous hydroxide is slightly soluble in water, and the solution turns red litmus blue. It dissolves in acids to yield plumbous salts, and in excess of alkali to yield plumbites:

$$Pb(OH)_2 + 2KOH = K_2PbO_2 + 2H_2O,$$

but it does not dissolve in ammonia. *Magneto-plumbite*, $PbO,6Fe_2O_3$, consists of magnetite (Fe_3O_4 with the spinel structure) in which Pb^{2+} ions are intercalated.

Plumbous sulphide, PbS, m.p. about 1100°, can be made by burning lead in sulphur vapour. It is found as the mineral galena, which is blue-black and has metallic glance. It is precipitated as a black solid on passing hydrogen sulphide through a solution of lead chloride. PbS, PbSe, and PbTe all have undistorted rocksalt crystal structures, which indicates more ionic character in their crystals than in that of stannous sulphide. The double sulphide $PbSnS_2$ has the same structure as stannous sulphide.

The plumbous halides. Certain properties of the plumbous halides are summarised in Table 18.28.

Table 18.28. *Preparations and Properties of the Plumbous Halides*

	PbF_2	$PbCl_2$	$PbBr_2$	PbI_2
Appearance	Colourless crystals	White crystals	Colourless crystals	Yellow crystals
m.p. °C	835	498	373	400
b.p. °C	1290	956	916	950
Solubility in water, gm in 100 gm				
at 0°	}0·064 at 20°{	0·67	0·455	0·044
at 100°		3·2	4·71	0·41
Crystal structure	Fluorite	Peculiar	Peculiar	CdI_2
Preparation	An aqueous solution of the halogen acid, or its potassium salt, is added to an aqueous solution of plumbous nitrate			

Plumbous chloride and fluoride are hydrolysed by water to the basic salts Pb(OH)Cl and Pb(OH)F respectively. Plumbous chloride dissolves in concentrated hydrochloric acid to give H_2PbCl_4. Plumbous iodide dissolves in an aqueous solution of potassium iodide to yield the complex salt $KPbI_3$, but plumbous iodide is reprecipitated on dilution. The crystal structures of the plumbous halides are interesting. The fluoride has the fluorite structure, which indicates considerable ionic character in the bonds. The chloride and bromide have a peculiar structure in which each lead atom is surrounded by nine halogen neighbours. The iodide has the CdI_2 structure which suggests normal covalent linking.

The mixed halides PbFCl and PbFBr are known. They are insoluble in water, and have the SbOCl crystal structure (p. 757). The compounds MPb_2Cl_5 and MPb_2Br_5 are known, where M is K, Rb, or NH_4. They are interstitial compounds, and not complex salts; the structure consists of chains of $PbCl_2$ or $PbBr_2$ molecules, with the alkali metal atoms and one-fifth of the bromine or chlorine atoms present as ions.

The **plumbous mercaptans,** $Pb(SC_2H_5)_2$, m.p. 150°, and $Pb(SBut)_2$, m.p. 80°, are soluble in chloroform and in benzene. From the low melting points and solubility in organic solvents it is concluded that these compounds contain bicovalent lead.

Plumbous alkyls and aryls. These compounds are intensely coloured, unstable, and rapidly oxidised by air.

None of the plumbous alkyls has been isolated in a pure state. The red colour produced when methyl magnesium iodide is added to lead chloride is presumably due to $Pb(CH_3)_2$, but it fades at once, and the product actually obtained is a mixture of $Pb(CH_3)_4$ and lead. A red liquid has been produced by the electrolytic reduction of acetone with a lead cathode. The red colour may have been due to $Pb(CH(CH_3)_2)_2$. With bromine the red liquid yields lead di-*iso*-propyl dibromide.

Plumbous diphenyl is a dark red powder which gives a blood red solution in benzene or ether. From these solutions it is precipitated by alcohol. It is made by the action of phenyl magnesium iodide on plumbous chloride at 0°. It is fairly stable in the complete absence of air and light, but it is very easily oxidised by air, and it reduces silver nitrate to metal. It reacts additively with iodine to produce $Pb(C_6H_5)_2I_2$, and with excess Grignard reagent to yield tetra-aryls or hexa-aryls which are formed more readily than the corresponding compounds of tin.

Complexes of lead in the plumbous condition. Lead in the plumbous condition forms a number of complex compounds including non-chelate complex anions, and chelate neutral complexes and complex anions. The number of bonds made by ligands to the lead atom may be either four or six. Among the salts containing lead atoms in non-chelate anions are potassium formatoplumbite, $K_2[Pb(HCO_2)_4]$, and potassium chloroplumbite $K_2[PbCl_4]$. Potassium fluoroplumbite, obtained by the action of potassium fluoride on plumbous fluoride, is formulated $K_4[PbF_6]$. The corresponding rubidium and caesium compounds, however, have the perovskite structure, and are formulated $RbPbF_3$. The bisbenzoylacetonate complex has the structure:

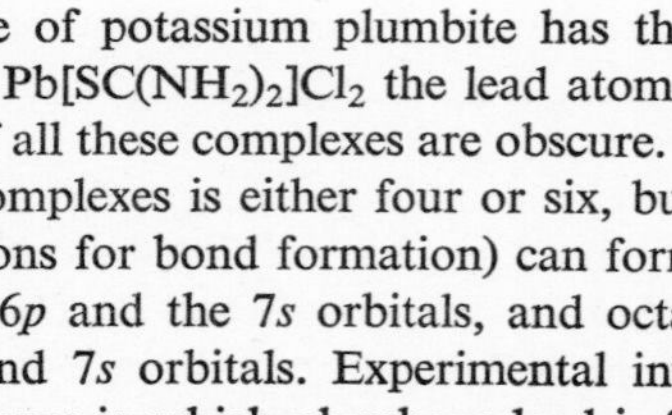

and the oxalate derivative of potassium plumbite has the formula $K_2[Pb(C_2O_4)_2]$. In the thiourea derivative $Pb[SC(NH_2)_2]_2Cl_2$ the lead atom appears to be trivalent.

The orbital structures of all these complexes are obscure. The co-ordination number of the lead atom in the complexes is either four or six, but the atom (since it is not using the pair of $6s$ electrons for bond formation) can form tetrahedral hybrids only by a combination of the $6p$ and the $7s$ orbitals, and octahedral hybrids only by a combination of $6p$, $6d$, and $7s$ orbitals. Experimental investigation has led to the conclusion that the complexes in which plumbous lead is four covalent are planar.

COMPOUNDS IN WHICH THE OXIDATION STATE OF LEAD IS IV

SECTION 1. GIANT MOLECULE STRUCTURES IN WHICH THE BONDS HAVE BOTH IONIC AND COVALENT CHARACTER

The number of lead compounds in this Section is small. The giant molecule compounds of lead always contain oxygen. Among them are lead dioxide, red lead, and compounds of the type PbP_2O_7, all of which are briefly discussed below. There is no lead sulphide PbS_2.

Lead dioxide, PbO_2, is made (i) by the oxidation of plumbous oxide by fusion with sodium chlorate and sodium nitrate, or (ii) by the oxidation of a plumbous salt in solution, either by sodium hypochlorite or by anodic oxidation. Lead dioxide can also be prepared by treating red lead with nitric acid, and collecting the insoluble lead dioxide by filtration.

Lead dioxide is dark brown or black, and has the rutile lattice. It is almost insoluble in water, but is slightly soluble in concentrated nitric acid or concentrated sulphuric acid. Lead dioxide is a strong oxidising agent. It liberates chlorine from warm concentrated hydrochloric acid, and reacts with sulphur dioxide to yield lead sulphate. If rubbed with sulphur it ignites and forms plumbous sulphide, PbS. In the presence of nitric acid it oxidises manganous sulphate to permanganic acid:

$$2MnSO_4 + 5PbO_2 + 6HNO_3 = 2HMnO_4 + 2PbSO_4 + 3Pb(NO_3)_2 + 2H_2O,$$

and in the presence of an alkali it oxidises chromic hydroxide to potassium chromate:

$$2Cr(OH)_3 + 10KOH + 3PbO_2 = 2K_2CrO_4 + 3K_2PbO_2 + 8H_2O.$$

There is no hydroxide $Pb(OH)_4$, but lead dioxide shows some tendency to be amphoteric. When heated with lime in air it yields calcium metaplumbate (p. 644), and when heated with phosphoric acid at 300° it yields PbP_2O_7.

Red lead, Pb_3O_4, is obtained when litharge is heated in air to 400°. No higher state of oxidation of lead can be reached by this process, as the red lead decomposes if heated to a higher temperature. The crystal structure of red lead consists of PbO_6 octahedra containing plumbic lead, and PbO_3 pyramids containing plumbous lead. Oxygen atoms are held in common by neighbouring octahedra, and by pyramids and octahedra. The dissociation pressure of red lead, 150 mm at 550°, is much less than that of lead dioxide.

SECTION 4.† COMPOUNDS IN WHICH THE LEAD ATOM IS TETRAHEDRALLY HYBRIDISED

Compounds in which the lead atom is tetrahedrally hybridised include plumbane, the alkyl and aryl lead compounds, which are surprisingly numerous and stable, and the plumbic halides and their derivatives.

Lead hydride, plumbane, PbH_4. Very small quantities of plumbane have been obtained by the electrolytic reduction of finely divided lead. This is prepared by sputtering a lead cathode in an atmosphere of hydrogen above the surface of the electrolyte. Sufficient plumbane is obtained to be condensed with liquid air and re-evaporated. It decomposes fairly rapidly at room temperature. The b.p. has been estimated to be −13°. Plumbane has not been fully examined. Higher plumbanes do not exist, but the alkyl and aryl derivatives of certain polyplumbanes are well-characterised.

Plumbic alkyls and aryls. A list of certain alkyl and aryl compounds of lead in the plumbic condition are given in Table 18.29. The *tetra-alkyl* compounds are made

† Sections 2 and 3 are omitted as there are no compounds in which the lead atom in oxidation state 4 is present in the digonal or trigonal valence state.

21 + A.T.I.C.

Table 18.29. *Plumbic Hydride, and certain Plumbic Alkyl and Aryl Compounds*

Compound	Formula	Appearance	m.p. °C	b.p. °C	Behaviour when heated
Plumbic hydride	PbH_4	Colourless gas		$c.a. -13$	Decomposes at room temperature
Plumbic tetramethyl	$Pb(CH_3)_4$	Colourless liquid	$-27\cdot5$	110	Can be distilled up to 145°: at higher temperatures the CH_3 or C_2H_5 radical is liberated
Plumbic tetraethyl	$Pb(C_2H_5)_4$	Colourless liquid		82/13 mm	
Plumbic hexamethyl	$Pb_2(C_2H_3)_6$		38		Decomposes to $Pb(CH_3)_4$ and Pb
Plumbic hexaethyl	$Pb_2(C_2H_5)_6$	Yellow oil	36	100/2 mm	
Plumbic hexacyclohexyl	$Pb_2(C_6H_{11})_6$	Bright yellow crystals			Blackens on heating to 195°
Plumbic tetraphenyl	$Pb(C_6H_5)_4$	White solid	225	240/15 mm	Above 270° gives lead and diphenyl
Plumbic hexaphenyl	$Pb_2(C_6H_5)_6$	Yellow crystals			

(i) by the action of zinc alkyl or a Grignard reagent on ammonium chloroplumbate, $(NH_4)_2PbCl_6$ (p. 644), (ii) by the action of the appropriate alkyl chloride on the metal or on plumbous chloride; the immediate product is $PbAlk_2$, which disproportionates on warming to the tetra-alkyl compound and metallic lead, (iii) by the action of the alkyl halide on an alloy of lead with 10% sodium in the presence of diethylaniline or pyridine as a catalyst (this is the method in use commercially).

The higher tetra-alkyls are volatile in steam. The compounds containing primary alkyl groups are stable to air, but those containing secondary groups are fairly easily oxidised, and those containing tertiary groups cannot be prepared pure. The tetra-alkyl compounds react readily with chlorine and with hydrogen chloride; gaseous hydrogen chloride at 90° reacts with $Pb(C_2H_5)_4$ to yield plumbous dichloride, and lead diethyl dichloride, $(C_2H_5)_2PbCl_2$. Lead tetraethyl is a cumulative poison; the poisoning is specific and differs from lead poisoning.

The *hexa-alkyl* compounds are made by the action of the appropriate Grignard reagent on plumbous chloride; for example, ethyl magnesium iodide and plumbous chloride react according to the equation:

$$2(C_2H_5)MgI + PbCl_2 = Pb(C_2H_5)_2 + MgCl_2 + MgI_2.$$

The plumbous diethyl at once disproportionates:

$$3Pb(C_2H_5)_2 = Pb_2(C_2H_5)_6 + Pb.$$

If the alkyl group in the lead hexa-alkyl is ethyl or some higher group the hexa-alkyl compound is stable at room temperature. The hexamethyl compound, however, breaks down at room temperature:

$$2Pb_2(CH_3)_6 = 3Pb(CH_3)_4 + Pb.$$

Lead hexa-alkyls can also be made by treating a lead sodium alloy with the appropriate alkyl iodide, keeping the temperature low. The hexa-alkyl compounds are easily oxidised, and react with chlorine and hydrogen chloride.

Lead tetraphenyl is made by the action of phenyl magnesium bromide on plumbous chloride; the plumbous diphenyl first formed disproportionates into lead tetraphenyl and metallic lead. Lead tetraphenyl is soluble in many organic solvents. It reacts with glacial acetic acid to give benzene and lead tetra-acetate.

Lead hexaphenyl is made from phenyl magnesium bromide and plumbous chloride. After evaporation of the ether the residue is extracted with benzene. The compound then separates as $(C_6H_5)_6Pb_2,C_6H_6$, but from alcohol it separates without solvent. Lead hexaphenyl is oxidised by potassium permanganate to $(C_6H_5)_3PbOH$.

Sodium lead triphenyl, $NaPb(C_6H_5)_3$, is made by the action of metallic sodium on lead triphenyl chloride in liquid ammonia. The solution thus obtained is pale yellow, but the crystals deposited from the solution are cream-coloured. Sodium lead triphenyl is stable at room temperature. It yields lead triphenylethyl when treated with ethyl iodide in liquid ammonia.

The lead tetrahalides. The only lead tetrahalide which has been obtained is lead tetrachloride, $PbCl_4$. It is a yellow volatile fuming liquid. It solidifies to a yellow crystalline solid, which melts at $-15°$. If warmed it explodes at $105°$. Lead tetrachloride is made by the action of concentrated sulphuric acid on ammonium chloroplumbate, $(NH_4)_2PbCl_6$. Lead tetrachloride reacts with a little water to give an unstable hydrate, but with more water it is hydrolysed to insoluble lead dioxide. Cold concentrated hydrochloric acid converts it to a crystalline hydrate of chloroplumbic acid.

The alkyl and aryl lead halides. Lead, like tin and germanium, forms a large number of compounds in which alkyl or aryl groups and halogen atoms are attached to a metal atom. A list of typical examples of these compounds is given in Table 18.30. The lead compounds are far less stable than the corresponding tin compounds.

The lead trialkyl monofluorides are salts. They are colourless, crystalline, and the most stable of the alkyl lead halides. They are more soluble in water than in benzene. They cannot be made by precipitating another halogen derivative with potassium fluoride (a method which is useful for making the corresponding tin compounds); they must be made from the trialkyl lead hydroxide and dilute hydrofluoric acid. The dust of these compounds is poisonous. The methyl and ethyl compounds have bad smells. This property is not found in derivatives containing higher alkyl groups, perhaps because of their lower volatility.

Table 18.30.   *The Alkyl and Aryl Lead Halides*

Compound	m.p. °C	Compound	m.p. °C
$Pb(CH_3)_3F$†		$Pb(CH_3)_2F_2$	
$Pb(CH_3)_3Cl$	Sublimes	$Pb(CH_3)_2Cl_2$	Sinters at 155
$Pb(CH_3)_3Br$	133	$Pb(CH_3)_2Br_2$	}Very unstable
$Pb(CH_3)_3I$	Sublimes	$Pb(CH_3)_2I_2$	
$Pb(C_6H_5)_3F$		$Pb(C_6H_5)_2F_2$	Below 300
$Pb(C_6H_5)_3Cl$	206	$Pb(C_6H_5)_2Cl_2$	Very unstable
$Pb(C_6H_5)_3Br$	106	$Pb(C_6H_5)_2Br_2$	
$Pb(C_6H_5)_3I$	Sinters at 142	$Pb(C_6H_5)_2I_2$	102

† Colourless crystals decomposing at 305°.

The lead trialkyl monochlorides are made by the action of the appropriate lead tetra-alkyl or lead hexa-alkyl on hydrogen chloride or on chlorine at about $-75°$. The lead trialkyl bromides and trialkyl iodides are made similarly. The bromides are colourless and the iodides are yellow. The chlorides have a repulsive smell, and a violent action on the eyes and the mucous membranes.

The lead triphenyl monohalides are made by the action of a halogen on lead tetraphenyl or lead hexaphenyl. The difficulty is to prevent the action going too far. The choice of solvent is important. Lead tetraphenyl in pyridine reacts with bromine to give lead triphenyl bromide, but in ether it gives lead diphenyl dibromide, $Pb(C_6H_5)_2Br_2$; lead hexaphenyl in aqueous alcohol or in pyridine gives, with iodine, lead triphenyl iodide, but in benzene it gives lead diphenyl di-iodide. Lead triphenyl bromide reacts with potassium fluoride to give $Pb(C_6H_5)_3F$, and with potassium iodide to give $Pb(C_6H_5)_3I$. The lead triphenyl halides react with sodium in liquid ammonia to yield sodium lead triphenyl $NaPb(C_6H_5)_3$.

The lead monoalkyl trihalides are yellow, extremely unstable substances. No lead monoaryl trihalide has been obtained.

SECTION 6. COMPOUNDS IN WHICH THE LEAD ATOM IS OCTAHEDRALLY HYBRIDISED

The complexes containing a lead atom in the octahedral valence state include salts with non-chelate anions such as $K_2[Pb(OH)_6]$ and $(NH_4)_2[PbCl_6]$, and salts with chelate anions, such as potassium sulphatoplumbate, $K_2[Pb(SO_4)_3]$.

The plumbic acids and their derivatives. The acid $H_2[Pb(OH)_6]$ is not known, but the alkali metal salts such as $Na_2[Pb(OH)_6]$ are stable. On heating they lose water to give metaplumbates:

$$Na_2[Pb(OH)_6] \xrightarrow{110°} Na_2PbO_3 + 3H_2O.$$

Among the metaplumbates are:

Na_2PbO_3, Ag_2PbO_3 black, $CuPbO_3$ black, $ZnPbO_3$ reddish-brown, $CaPbO_3$ white.

The potassium and sodium metaplumbates are formed when lead dioxide is added to potassium or sodium hydroxide fused in a silver dish. They are thermally more stable than lead dioxide. Sodium metaplumbate does not lose oxygen below 750°. Red lead may be plumbous metaplumbate.

Ammonium chloroplumbate $(NH_4)_2[PbCl_6]$, is a yellow crystalline substance, stable up to 225°. It is made by saturating a solution of plumbous chloride in hydrochloric acid with chlorine at 0°, and adding ammonium chloride. Ammonium chloroplumbate and the rubidium and caesium salts are isomorphous with $(NH_4)_2[PtCl_6]$, and have the antifluorite structure. These salts are hydrolysed by cold water to give lead dioxide.

SECTION 7. COMPOUNDS IN WHICH THE LEAD ATOM IS DODECAHEDRALLY HYBRIDISED

There are a few compounds of lead in which the lead atom is eight co-ordinate. It is possible that the lead atom in these compounds is in the dodecahedral valence state. The hybrid orbitals would be formed by the combination of the atomic orbitals sp^3d^4.

The fluoride $K_3H[PbF_8]$ is made by fusing lead dioxide with potassium hydrogen fluoride and crystallising the product from concentrated hydrofluoric acid. It can also be made by the action of hydrogen fluoride on potassium plumbate, or on lead tetra-acetate. It is very soluble in water which hydrolyses it.

Pyridine and ammonia complexes of diaryl lead dihalides. The compounds $(C_6H_5)_2PbCl_2,4pyr.$, $(C_6H_5)_2PbBr_2,4pyr.$, and $(C_6H_5)_2PbBr_2,4NH_3$, might possibly be neutral complexes of dodecahedral lead.

Lead tetra-acetate (plumbic acetate), $Pb(CH_3COO)_4$, is made by saturating hot glacial acetic acid with red lead; the lead tetra-acetate is only one-fortieth as soluble as plumbous acetate and is precipitated. Lead tetra-acetate is also made by oxidising plumbous acetate dissolved in acetic acid with chlorine. Similar derivatives are made from propionic acid, butyric acid, stearic acid, and benzoic acid. Lead tetra-acetate melts at 175° but at 190° it decomposes yielding plumbous acetate. With water lead tetra-acetate gives lead dioxide. It is an oxidising agent and converts glycol to formaldehyde, and acetone to dihydroxyacetone. In glacial acetic acid lead tetra-acetate has no measurable conductivity. If plumbous acetate and lead tetra-acetate are dissolved in acetic acid, radioactive lead atoms exchange between the two states; this is taken as evidence of the existence of the ion Pb^{4+}. It is difficult to see, however, why lead tetra-acetate should be ionic when there is no evidence for the existence of ionic compounds of Pb^{4+} in association with anions which are far more electronegative than the acetate ion. It is conjectured that the lead atoms in lead tetra-acetate are in the docecahedral valence state, and that each lead atom forms four covalent bonds and four co-ionic bonds with the oxygen atoms in four acetate groups, thus

$$Pb\left(\begin{array}{c} O \\ \diagup \diagdown \\   C \cdot CH_3 \\ \nwarrow \diagup\diagup \\ O \end{array}\right)_4$$

CHAPTER NINETEEN

SUB-GROUP V N

NITROGEN, PHOSPHORUS, ARSENIC, ANTIMONY, AND BISMUTH

The five elements in the sub-Group all have the electron configuration in the valency shell in the ground state:

$$
\begin{array}{cccc}
s & p & p & p \\
\uparrow\downarrow & \uparrow & \uparrow & \uparrow
\end{array}
$$

All the elements are moderately electronegative. None forms any simple anion. Only bismuth forms simple cations, X^{3+}, but even the bismuth salts containing this cation are very easily hydrolysed. The electronegativity of nitrogen is sufficient to enable it to form hydrogen bonds (p. 371).

The valency shell ($n=2$) of the nitrogen atom has no d orbitals, and hence the maximum number of bonds which can be exerted by the nitrogen atom is 4. This statement is also true for carbon, but whereas the four valency electrons in the carbon atom enable it to form four covalent links without further adjustments, the nitrogen atom in becoming quadrivalent needs to expel one electron, and thus forms cations such as (NH_4^+). Cations of this type are formed by all the sub-Group elements except bismuth. From their general chemical behaviour, it is concluded that the hydroxides of the tetramethyl ions $[X(CH_3)_4^+]$ where X may be nitrogen, phosphorus, arsenic, or antimony have roughly the same stability.

If the covalency of any of the elements is less than four, as in NH_3, at least two of the valency electrons must be unused for bond formation. This is a consideration which does not concern the lighter elements of previous Groups, for the atoms of elements in the first three Groups are electron deficient (p. 493) and the atoms of elements in Group IV have just the correct number of valency electrons to enable them to exert four covalencies. In the later Groups unused electron pairs are frequently present in atoms of elements which have taken part in the formation of molecules.

Table 19.1. *Examples of Types of Compound*

Compounds in which only 3 of the 5 valenc

Nature of unit formed	N	page	P	pa
Simple ionic compounds or compounds in which the bonds have ionic character				
Simple covalent compounds				
Non-chelate neutral complexes				
Non-chelate complex anions				
Chelate complex anions				

The place occupied by an unused electron pair of one of the atoms in the orbital system of a molecule is not altogether certain. There are two main possibilities:

(i) that the electron pair remains in the original atomic orbital which is not brought into the hybridisation system of the atom; the unused pair is then known as an *inert pair*;

(ii) that the original atomic orbital occupied by the unused electrons is brought into the hybridisation system, but one of the hybrid orbitals is occupied by a pair of electrons, both obtained from the original atom; the unused pair is then known as a *lone pair*.

There is no doubt that the $6s$ electrons in the bismuth atom remain inert throughout nearly all the chemical reactions of bismuth (p. 770), that there are certain compounds containing the antimony atom (p. 755) in which an inert pair is present, and that there are complexes of arsenic such as $[(CH_3)_2NH_2][AsCl_4]$ in which the inert pair must be present unless the valence state of the arsenic atom is assumed to be trigonal bipyramidal. The inert pair, however, is not present in the phosphorus atom in any of its compounds; the group PCl_4 is not anionic, and it is actually present as a cation in the ionic form of phosphorus pentachloride, $[PCl_4^+][PCl_6^-]$. If the phosphorus atom does not adopt the inert pair configuration it follows *a fortiori* that the nitrogen atom does not do so. There is, therefore, this significant difference between the orbital properties of the nitrogen and the phosphorus atoms on the one hand, and the orbital properties of the arsenic, antimony, and bismuth atoms on the other. In spite of this difference all the five elements form trivalent compounds which have been shown to be monomeric, for example:

$$NCl_3 \qquad PCl_3 \qquad AsCl_3 \qquad SbCl_3 \qquad BiCl_3.$$

It is therefore reasonable to assume that in these and other compounds of the general formula XA_3 the nitrogen and phosphorus atoms are tetrahedrally hybridised with one hybrid orbital occupied by a lone pair, and that the bismuth atom contains an inert pair so that its three bonding orbitals are constructed from the p atomic orbitals. Arsenic and antimony could adopt either of these possible structures.

An interesting comparison can be made between the structures of all the oxides and sulphides of the elements of the sub-Group. The formulae and structures of the oxides and sulphides are set out in Table 19.3.

The dissimilarity of these structures is remarkable. The nitrogen oxides consist of easily decomposed discrete molecules, and are the only compounds without ring structures. The oxides P_4O_6, As_4O_6, Sb_4O_6, and $(Bi_2O_3)_n$ all have similar cage structures,

rmed by Elements in Sub-Group V N.

ectrons of the element are active

As	page	Sb	page	Bi	page
		$(Sb_2O_3)_n$, Sb_2O_4, Sb_4O_{10}	755	$Bi(NO_3)_3$, $Bi_2(SO_4)_3$, $Bi(ClO_4)_3$	771
		Sb_2S_3	756	Bi_2O_3, Bi_2S_3, $BiOCl$	772
		$SbOCl$	757	BiF_3, BiI_3	773
		$Sb(OCOCH_3)_3$	758		
				BiH_3, $Bi(CH_3)_3$, $Bi(C_6H_5)_3$	774
		$(C_2H_5)_2O \cdot SbBr_3$		$CH_3CN \cdot BiCl_3$	773
		$Na[Sb(OH)_4]$, $Na[SbCl_4]$	758	$K[BiI_4]$, $H_3[BiF_6]$	775
		$K_2[SbCl_5]$, $K_3[SbCl_6]$			
		$K[Sbox_2]$, $K[Sb(SO_4)_2]$	759	$K[Biox_2]$, $K[Bi(SO_4)_2]$	775
				$K_5[Bi(OH)_5],4H_2O$	
		$K_3[Sbox_3]$		$(NH_4)_3[Biox_3]$	

Table 19.1. *Examples of Types of Compounds form[ed]*

Compounds in which all 5 valen[cies]

Section	State of atom of element — Hybridisation	Formal charge	Bonds	Nature of unit formed	N	page	[P]	pa[ge]
1				Giant molecules in which the bonds possess both ionic and covalent character	Li_3N Be_3N_2, Mg_3N_2, etc. Zn_3N_2, Cd_3N_2, Hg_3N_2 BN, AlN, GaN, InN Interstitial nitrides, TiN	654	Phosphides (Table 20.3)	7
2	Digonal				} See Table 19.5, p. 655		None	
3	Trigonal						None	
4	Tetrahedral	0	3σ one lone pair		NH_3, NR_3 $Zn(NH_2)_2$ $K_2[Mg(NH_2)_4]$, $K[Al(NH_2)_4]$ $H_2N\!\!>\!\!C\overset{\pi}{=}N—H$, $Si(NH_2)_4$ $P(NH_2)_3$, $HO—\overset{O}{\underset{O}{S}}—NH_2$, (ring structures) NF_3, NHF_2, NH_2F NCl_3, $NHCl_2$, NH_2Cl $NHBr_2$, NH_2Br $[NH_2OH$: no evidence$]$ H_2NNH_2 $[CH_3CN\!\!\overset{}{\longrightarrow}\!\!N—O]^+$ CH_3CN	689 694 688 695 700 703 666	P_4, PH_3, P_4O_6 P(hal)$_3$, $P(CF_3)_2Cl$, $P(CF_3)_2NH_2$, $P(NH_2)_3$ I_2PPI_2, P_2Cl_4 $[P_2H_4$: no evidence$]$	7 7 7 7 7 7
		-1	2σ two lone pairs		$[NH_2]^-$ $[NO_2]^{2-}$ (electron deficient) $CH_3—N—N\overset{\pi}{\underset{\pi}{=}}N$ $CH_3—N—C\overset{\pi}{\underset{\pi}{=}}O$ $R\cdot SO_2\cdot N{\leftarrow}S(CH_3)_2$	692 675 686 583		
		-2	1σ three lone pairs		Li_2NH	695		
		$+1$	4σ		Compounds in which NH_3 or its derivatives are electron donors $(CH_3)_3NO$ Infusible white precipitate $[NH_4]^+$, $[N(CH_3)_4]^+$	473 693	Compounds in which PH_3 or its derivatives are electron donors $(CH_3)_3PO$ POF_3, $POCl_3$, $POBr_3$ PSF_3, $PSCl_3$, $PSBr_3$ P_4O_{10}, $P_4O_6S_4$ $P_3N_3Cl_6$ The phosphorus oxy acids The phosphates $[PH_4]^+$, $[P(CH_3)_4]^+$ $[PCl_4]^+$, $[P(OH)_4]^+$	7 7 7 7 7 7 7 7
5	Trigonal Bipyramid	0	5σ		None		PF_5, PCl_5, PBr_5 PF_3Cl_2, PF_3Br_2	7
		-1	4σ one lone pair		None			
6	Octahedral			Neutral complexes	None			
		0	6σ	Complex anions	None		$K[PF_6]$, $[PCl_4^+][PCl_6^-]$	7

ctrons of the element are active

As	page	Sb	page	Bi	page
senides (Table 20.13)	738	Antimonides (Table 20.16)	759		
one		None		None	
one		None		None	
4, AsH$_3$, As(CH$_3$)$_3$ 4O$_6$, As$_4$S$_6$, As$_4$S$_4$	737 738 745	SbH$_3$, Sb(CH$_3$) Sb(C$_6$H$_5$)$_3$	760 761		
(OH)$_3$	748				
s(OCH$_3$)$_3$, As(CH$_3$CO$_2$)$_3$	748	Sb(OC$_2$H$_5$)$_3$	766		
				None	
(hal)$_3$, (CH$_3$)AsCl$_2$	744	Sb(hal)$_3$	763		
CH$_3$)$_2$As]$_2$, [(CH$_3$)$_2$As]$_2$O	741	[(CH$_3$)$_2$Sb]$_2$O, [(CH$_3$)$_2$Sb]$_2$	760		
				None	
				None	
npounds in which AsH$_3$ or its erivatives are electron donors					
3)$_3$AsO, (C$_6$H$_5$)$_3$AsO	743	(CH$_3$)$_3$SbO, (C$_6$H$_5$)$_3$SbO	766		
4O$_{10}$ and As$_4$S$_{10}$, no evidence]	746			None	
O$_4{}^{3-}$]	749				
(CH$_3$)$_4$]$^+$, [As(C$_6$H$_5$)$_4$]$^+$	743	[Sb(CH$_3$)$_4$]$^+$	764		
$_5$, CH$_3$AsCl$_4$	751	SbF$_5$, SbCl$_5$ (CH$_3$)$_3$SbCl$_2$	766	(C$_6$H$_5$)$_3$BiCl$_2$	775
I$_2$(CH$_3$)$_2$][AsCl$_4$] C$_6$H$_4$O$_2$)$_2$As],4H$_2$O	752 752				
		SbCl$_5$·O(CH$_3$)$_2$, SbACl$_4$	769	None	
AsF$_6$] C$_6$H$_4$O$_2$)$_3$As],5H$_2$O	752	M[SbX$_6$] X=OH, F, Cl K[((C$_6$H$_4$O$_2$)$_3$Sb] K$_2$[SbCl$_6$]	769	None	

Table 19.2.   *Properties of the Elements in Sub-Group V N*

	N	P	As	Sb	Bi
Atomic number	7	15	33	51	83
Electronic configuration	2, 5	2, 8, 5	2, 8, 18, 5	2, 8, 18, 18, 5	2, 8, 18, 32, 18, 5
Atomic weight	14·008	30·98	74·91	121·76	209·0
Density	0·8042 (at b.p.)	White 1·82 Red 2·20	Yellow 1·97 Grey 5·73	6·67	9·80
m.p. °C	−210	Red 590	Grey under pressure 817	630	271
b.p. °C	−196	280	615	1380	1560
Ionisation potential					
I	14·5	10·9	10·5	8·5	8·0
II	29·5	19·6	20·1	18	16·6
III	47·4	30·0	28·0	24·7	25·4
IV	77·0	51·0	49·9	44·0	45·1
V	97·4	65·0	62·5	55·5	55·7
Atomic radius (tetrahedral)	0·70	1·10	1·20	1·36	1·46
Ionic radius X^{3-}	1·71	2·12	2·22	2·45	
Pauling's crystal radius X^{5+}			0·47	0·62	0·74
Electronegativity	3·0	2·1	2·0	1·8	
Slater's atomic radius, r	0·56	0·92	1·01		
$(Z_{eff})_{mol}$	3·55	4·45	5·95	5·95	5·95
$(Z_{eff})_{mol}/r^2$	11·32	5·26	5·83		

except that in $(Bi_2O_3)_n$ the structure is slightly distorted and is not discrete. Sb_4O_6 and $(Bi_2O_3)_n$, however, exist in other isomorphic forms besides those mentioned here. The structure of P_4O_{10} is developed from that of P_4O_6; those of As_4O_{10} and Sb_4O_{10} are unknown.

The sulphides differ even in composition. The structure of As_4S_6 corresponds to that of As_4O_6; the structures of N_4S_4, P_4S_3, P_4S_5, and As_4S_4 are related to that of As_4S_6; the chain structures of $(Sb_2S_3)_n$ and $(Bi_2S_3)_n$ are related to the ring structure of N_2S_4. Of all the atoms mentioned in Table 19.1 only those of nitrogen and oxygen form π bonds. Hence the structures of the oxides of nitrogen (in which both atoms have this property) might be expected to differ from the structures of all the other compounds.

The tetrahedral group XO_4 (p. 783) is formed by phosphorus and by arsenic. It is absent from the chemistry of nitrogen because the formation of π bonds between the nitrogen and the oxygen atom makes possible the existence of the ion $[NO_3^-]$. It is also absent from the chemistry of antimony because the oxidised antimony atom tends to become 6 co-ordinate, and from the chemistry of bismuth because the oxidised bismuth atom tends to become 8 co-ordinate.

ELEMENTARY NITROGEN

Certain physical properties of nitrogen are included in Table 19.2. Nitrogen constitutes about 78% of the air. It may be isolated by fractional distillation of liquid air from which water and carbon dioxide have previously been removed. On a small scale nitrogen may be obtained by the thermal decomposition of the ammonium salt of an oxidising oxyacid; the hydrogen of the ammonium radical is oxidised to water, and the nitrogen is set free, for example:

$$(NH_4)_2Cr_2O_7 = Cr_2O_3 + 4H_2O + N_2.$$

Nitrogen is chemically inert at room temperature to all reagents except lithium. When heated it combines directly with oxygen, hydrogen, silicon, calcium acetylide, and the metals lithium, calcium, barium, magnesium, and aluminium, and with certain of the transition metals (p. 654).

Active nitrogen. If nitrogen at low pressure is subjected to the action of a condensed electric discharge a yellow glow is observed and a small proportion of the nitrogen is converted to an active variety. The glow and the activity persist a short time after the discharge has been discontinued.

Active nitrogen attacks phosphorus, arsenic, mercury, zinc, cadmium, and sodium to give nitrides, and sulphur compounds to give sulphur nitride. There is no complete explanation of the condition of active nitrogen. The active gas probably contains nitrogen atoms and metastable activated nitrogen molecules.

THE GENERAL CHEMISTRY OF NITROGEN

The valency shell of the nitrogen atom has the configuration

$2s$	$2p$	$2p$	$2p$
⇅	↑	↑	↑

In all its compounds the nitrogen atom is present in oxidation state 5. The nitrogen atom does not form the simple anion N^{3-}. There are no nitrides of the alkali metals other than lithium, and the nitrides of lithium and of the alkaline earth metals have giant molecule structures in which the bonding has covalent as well as ionic character. Certain nitrides are of the interstitial type (p. 654).

Nitrogen forms a very large number of compounds in which the atom is digonally or trigonally hybridised, and in which nitrogen and other atoms are linked by π bonds as well as σ bonds. Structures of this kind are present in the oxides of nitrogen, in the ions of the oxyacids of nitrogen, in the azides, the cyanides, and the cyanates.

The oxides of nitrogen, and the ions of the oxyacids of nitrogen are noteworthy in two ways.

(i) The same number of nitrogen and oxygen nuclei may enter into stable combination with varying numbers of electrons. For example, the three nuclei represented by NO_2 form the stable units NO_2^+, NO_2, NO_2^-, NO_2^{2-}. The existence of this series cannot be explained on the assumption that there is a common orbital structure which may be occupied by a number of electrons varying from 22 to 25, because the nitronium ion NO_2^+, is linear, whereas the nitrogen dioxide molecule, NO_2, and the nitrite ion NO_2^-, are triangular. Other isonucleic series are NO^+, NO, NO^-, and $N_2O_3^+$, N_2O_3.

(ii) When a group of three nuclei of any of the elements, C, N, O, S, is associated with 22 electrons the structure of the group is linear. Examples are N_3^-, N_2O, NO_2^+. It is probable that in all these groups the orbital structure is similar to that of carbon dioxide.

In compounds in which the nitrogen atom is exerting π bonds one, two, or three of the orbitals of the nitrogen atom may be occupied by lone electron pairs (p. 647).

The structures of all the nitrogen compounds so far mentioned are linear or branched. The nitrogen atom also takes part in ring structures in which the π bonds are non-localised and include all members of the ring (p. 687). A list of certain nitrogen

Table 19.3.   *The Structures of the Oxides and Sulphides of the Elements in Sub-Group V N*

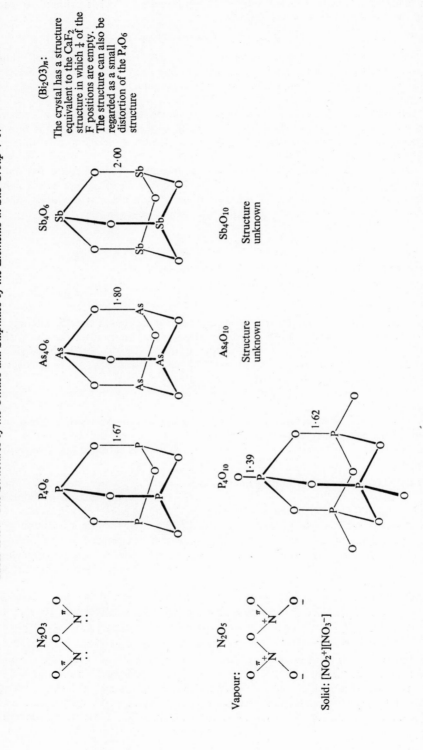

$(Bi_2O_3)_n$:

The crystal has a structure equivalent to the CaF_2 structure in which $\frac{1}{4}$ of the F positions are empty. **The structure can also be regarded as a small distortion of the P_4O_6 structure**

Sb_4O_6 2·00

As_4O_6 1·80

P_4O_6 1·67

P_4O_{10} 1·39   1·62

Sb_4O_{10}
Structure unknown

As_4O_{10}
Structure unknown

N_2O_3

N_2O_5

Vapour:

Solid: $[NO_2^+][NO_3^-]$

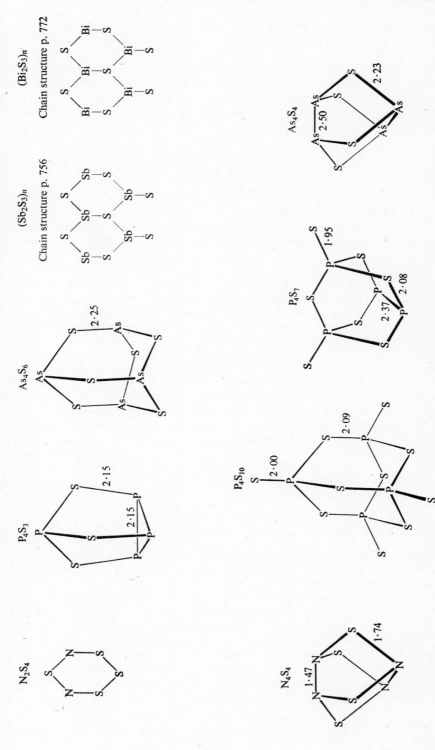

compounds in which π bonds are present is given in Table 19.5 under three headings which are explained in the Table. These compounds are discussed in Sections 2 and 3 of this Chapter.

The nitrogen atom undergoes tetrahedral hybridisation. This hybridisation is normal in the ammonium ion NH_4^+, and its derivatives, and in certain addition compounds such as $H_3N\rightarrow BH_3$. In numerous nitrogen compounds with the general formula NX_3 the nitrogen atom is deemed to be tetrahedrally hybridised, and one hybrid orbital is assumed to be occupied by a lone electron pair.

SECTION 1. NITROGEN COMPOUNDS CONSISTING OF GIANT MOLECULES IN WHICH THE BONDS HAVE BOTH IONIC AND COVALENT CHARACTER

THE NITRIDES

There are four types of nitrides.

(1) Covalent, volatile, compounds of nitrogen with hydrogen and with the electro-negative elements carbon, oxygen, sulphur, and the halogens. These nitrides are well characterised and familiar.

(2) Giant molecule compounds of nitrogen with the following elements of Groups I, II, III, and IV: Li†: Be, Mg, Ca, Sr, Ba, all having the anti-Mn_2O_3 structure: BN with the graphitic structure‡, and AlN, GaN, InN with the wurtzite structure: Si_3N_4, Ge_3N_4, Sn_3N_4 with the phenacite structure. The crystals of these nitrides are transparent and colourless, and have high melting points. With water they give ammonia and the metallic hydroxide.

(3) The nitrides of certain transition metals, such as Cu_3N, Zn_2N_2, Cd_3N_2, and Hg_3N_2. These are ill characterised, and the mercury compound is explosive.

(4) Interstitial nitrides formed by certain transition metals.

The first three types of nitrides are discussed under the element with which nitrogen is combined, the interstitial nitrides are discussed in the following paragraph.

The **interstitial nitrides** are formed by metals which crystallise with close-packed structures and have atomic radii sufficiently great to allow the inclusion of nitrogen atoms in the octahedral holes in the lattice. The structures of these nitrides resemble those of the carbides of metals in Groups IV, V, and VI (p. 599). The ranges of metallic radii permissible for the inclusion of a nitrogen atom in the octahedral holes of a face-centred cubic lattice are:

0·9 to 1·6 if the nitrogen atom is tetrahedrally hybridised,

1·17 to 1·75 if the nitrogen atom is exerting one σ bond and two π bonds.

Table 19.4 gives a list of the metals which form interstitial nitrides, the atomic radii of the metals, their melting points, and also the composition of the nitrides and their melting points. If the composition of the nitride is represented by MN, the N atoms are in all the octahedral holes, but in the cases of Mo_2N and W_2N only one-half of the holes are occupied, and in the cases of Mn_4N and Fe_4N only one-quarter.

The interstitial nitrides, like the corresponding borides and carbides, are difficult to fuse, hard, and inert. They may be made by heating the metal to 1100–1200° in a stream of nitrogen or ammonia, or by introducing a heated filament of platinum, carbon, or tungsten into a mixture of nitrogen and the vapour of the metallic halide. The filament is subsequently volatilised away by heating almost to the melting point of the nitride.

---

† Lithium is the only alkali metal which combines directly with molecular nitrogen.

‡ There is a cubic form of boron nitride known as *borazon* which has a zinc blende structure. It is hard enough to scratch diamond; diamond scratches it.

Table 19.4.   *The Interstitial Nitrides*

Metal	Atomic radius for C.N. 6	m.p. °K	Nitride	m.p. °K
Sc	1·75	1473	ScN	
La	1·75	1100	LaN	
Ce	1·75	913	CeN	
Pr	1·75	1213	PrN	
Ti	1·41	2073	TiN	3220
Zr	1·54	2173	ZrN	3255
V	1·30	1990	VN	2573
Nb	1·41	2223	NbN	2573
Ta	1·41	3273	TaN	3360
Mo	1·34	2890	Mo_2N	
W	1·35	3640	W_2N	
Mn	1·32	1573	Mn_4N	
Fe	1·21	1806	Fe_4N	

C.N. represents co-ordination number

SECTIONS 2 AND 3. NITROGEN COMPOUNDS CONTAINING THE NITROGEN ATOM IN THE DIGONAL OR TRIGONAL VALENCE STATE

A list of nitrogen compounds containing the nitrogen atom in the digonal or trigonal valence state is given in Table 19.5. As so many of these compounds are represented on the valence bond theory by resonance systems of canonical forms in which a nitrogen atom may be either digonally or trigonally hybridised, it is thought best to classify them for discussion on conventional chemical grounds, without reference to the valence states of the nitrogen atom. Under this classification are discussed (i) the oxides of nitrogen and the oxyacids of nitrogen, (ii) the azides and diazonium compounds, and the cyanides and isocyanides, (iii) ring compounds in which nitrogen atoms take part in a system of non-localised π bonds. The formulae and structures of the oxides and oxyacids of nitrogen are summarised in Table 19.6. In the following paragraphs these compounds are discussed in the order given in Table 19.6; the page references are given in the second column of Table 19.6.

Table 19.5.   *Examples of Compounds containing the Nitrogen Atom in the Digonal or Trigonal Valence State*

(1) *Structures of ions, molecules, or groups isoelectronic with the molecule of carbon dioxide. The central atom is always digonally hybridised; the terminal nitrogen atom may be digonally, trigonally, or tetrahedrally hybridised. All electrons are paired.*

Molecule or ion	Principal canonical forms	Canonical form with a terminal nitrogen atom in the trigonal valence state
Carbon dioxide molecule, CO_2†	$:\ddot{O}\overset{\pi}{=}C\underset{\pi}{=}\ddot{O}:$ $:\overset{+}{\underset{..}{O}}\overset{\pi}{\underset{\pi}{=}}C-\overset{-}{\underset{..}{\ddot{O}}}:$ $:\overset{-}{\underset{..}{\ddot{O}}}-C\overset{\pi}{\underset{\pi}{=}}\overset{+}{\underset{..}{O}}:$	

† The canonical forms of carbon dioxide are stated for comparison.

Table 19.5 (*continued*)

Molecule or ion	Principal canonical forms	Canonical form with a terminal nitrogen atom in the trigonal valence state
Azide ion, $[N_3]^-$	$\left[:\overset{-}{\ddot{N}}\overset{\pi}{=}\overset{+}{N}\overset{}{\underset{\pi}{=}}\overset{-}{\ddot{N}}: \right]^-$ $\left[:N\overset{\pi}{\underset{\pi}{=}}\overset{+}{N}-\overset{2-}{\ddot{N}}: \right]^-$ $\left[:\overset{2-}{\ddot{N}}-\overset{+}{N}\overset{\pi}{\underset{\pi}{=}}N: \right]^-$	$\left[:\overset{-}{\ddot{N}}\overset{\pi}{=}\overset{+}{N}\overset{}{\underset{\pi}{=}}\overset{-}{\ddot{N}}: \right]^-$
Methyl azide molecule, † CH_3N_3	$H_3C-\overset{-}{\ddot{N}}-\overset{+}{N}\overset{}{\underset{\pi}{=}}N:$ $H_3C-\overset{}{\ddot{N}}\overset{\pi}{=}\overset{+}{N}\overset{}{\underset{\pi}{=}}\overset{-}{\ddot{N}}:$	$H_3C-\overset{}{\ddot{N}}\overset{\pi}{=}\overset{+}{N}\overset{}{\underset{\pi}{=}}\overset{-}{\ddot{N}}:$
Nitronium ion, $[NO_2]^+$	$\left[:\ddot{O}\overset{\pi}{=}\overset{+}{N}\overset{}{\underset{\pi}{=}}\ddot{O}: \right]^+$ $\left[:\overset{+}{O}\overset{\pi}{\underset{\pi}{=}}\overset{+}{N}-\overset{-}{\ddot{O}}: \right]^+$ $\left[:\overset{-}{\ddot{O}}-\overset{+}{N}\overset{\pi}{\underset{\pi}{=}}\overset{+}{O}: \right]^+$	
Nitrous oxide molecule, † N_2O	$\overset{-}{\ddot{N}}\overset{\pi}{=}\overset{+}{N}\overset{}{\underset{\pi}{=}}\ddot{O}:$ $:N\overset{\pi}{\underset{\pi}{=}}\overset{+}{N}-\overset{-}{\ddot{O}}:$	$:\ddot{N}\overset{\pi}{=}\overset{+}{N}\overset{}{\underset{\pi}{=}}\ddot{O}:$
Isocyanate ion, $[NCO]^-$	$\left[:N\overset{\pi}{\underset{\pi}{=}}C-\overset{-}{\ddot{O}}: \right]^-$ $\left[:\overset{-}{\ddot{N}}\overset{}{\underset{\pi}{=}}C\overset{\pi}{=}\ddot{O}: \right]^-$ $\left[:\overset{2-}{\ddot{N}}-C\overset{\pi}{\underset{\pi}{=}}\overset{+}{O}: \right]^-$	$\left[:\ddot{N}\overset{}{\underset{\pi}{=}}C\overset{\pi}{=}\ddot{O}: \right]^-$
The group NCO in methyl isocyanate	$CH_3-\ddot{N}\overset{\pi}{=}C\overset{}{\underset{\pi}{=}}\ddot{O}:$ $CH_3-\overset{+}{\ddot{N}}\overset{\pi}{\underset{\pi}{=}}C-\overset{-}{O}$ $CH_3-\overset{-}{\ddot{N}}-C\overset{\pi}{\underset{\pi}{=}}\overset{+}{O}:$	$CH_3-\ddot{N}\overset{\pi}{=}C\overset{}{\underset{\pi}{=}}\ddot{O}:$

† The formulation of the third canonical form of nitrous oxide

$$:\overset{2-}{\underset{\cdot\cdot}{N}}-\overset{+}{N}\overset{\pi}{\underset{\pi}{=}}\overset{+}{O}: \quad \text{and of methyl azide} \quad H_3C-\overset{+}{N}\overset{\pi}{\underset{\pi}{=}}\overset{+}{N}-\overset{2-}{\underset{\cdot\cdot}{N}}:$$

would break Pauling's adjacent charge rule. This rule states that an electron transfer does not occur if it results in the presence of formal charges of the same sign on adjacent atoms in a molecule.

Table 19.5 (*continued*)

(2) *Structures of ions, molecules or groups, in addition to those included in Sub-table* (1), *which contain a nitrogen atom in the digonal valence state. All electrons are paired.*

Ion, molecule, or group	Principal canonical forms
The nitrosyl cation, $[NO]^+$	$\left[:\overset{2+}{N}\!-\!\overset{..}{\overset{-}{O}}:\right]^+ \left[:\overset{+}{N}\!\overset{\pi}{-}\overset{..}{O}:\right]^+ \left[:N\overset{\pi}{\underset{\pi}{-}}\overset{+}{O}:\right]^+ \left[\overset{-}{:}\!\overset{..}{N}\overset{\pi}{-}\overset{2+}{O}:\right]^+$
Cyanogen, $(CN)_2$	$:N\overset{\pi}{\underset{\pi}{-}}C\!-\!C\overset{\pi}{\underset{\pi}{-}}N:$
Cyanogen fluoride, FCN	$F\!-\!C\overset{\pi}{\underset{\pi}{-}}N:$
Cyanogen chloride, ClCN	$Cl\!-\!C\overset{\pi}{\underset{\pi}{-}}N:$
Hydrocyanic acid, HCN	$H\!-\!C\overset{\pi}{\underset{\pi}{-}}N:$ or $H\!-\!\overset{+}{N}\overset{\pi}{\underset{\pi}{-}}\overset{-}{C}:$
The group C—N in methyl cyanide	$CH_3\!-\!C\overset{\pi}{\underset{\pi}{-}}N:$
The group NC in methyl iso-cyanide	$CH_3\!-\!\overset{+}{N}\overset{\pi}{\underset{\pi}{-}}\overset{-}{C}:$
The nitrogen molecule, N_2	$:N\overset{\pi}{\underset{\pi}{-}}N:$
The diazonium ion, $[C_6H_5N_2]^+$	$\left[C_6H_5\!-\!\overset{+}{N}\overset{\pi}{\underset{\pi}{-}}N:\right]^+$

(3) *Structures of ions, molecules, or groups, in addition to those included in Sub-table* (1), *which contain a nitrogen atom in the trigonal valence state.* Certain of these structures are paramagnetic and hence contain unpaired electrons. It is probable that an unpaired electron is present in an atomic orbital either of a nitrogen atom or of an oxygen atom, as there are several structural units which consist only of oxygen atoms, and which contain one or more unpaired electrons (p. 791), and there are at least two nitrogen compounds, NF_2 and $[(CH_3C_6H_4)_3N][ClO_4]$, in which one of the orbitals on the nitrogen atom must contain an unpaired electron.

(a) *Structures containing one unpaired electron*

Ion, molecule, or group	Principal canonical forms
Nitric oxide gas† NO	$\overset{-}{:}\!\overset{.}{N}\overset{\pi}{-}\overset{+}{\overset{..}{O}}:$ $\overset{.}{\overset{+}{N}}\!-\!\overset{..}{\overset{-}{O}}:$
The ion, $[N_2O_2]^+$	$\left[:\overset{..}{O}\overset{\pi}{-}\overset{..}{N}\!-\!\overset{..}{N}\overset{\pi}{-}\overset{.}{O}:\right]^+$ $\left[:\overset{..}{O}\overset{\pi}{-}\overset{.}{\overset{..}{N}}\!-\!\overset{..}{N}\overset{\pi}{-}\overset{..}{O}:\right]^+$
The ion, $[N_2O_3]^+$	$\left[\begin{array}{c}\overset{-}{:\overset{.}{O}}\\ \diagdown\overset{+}{N}\!-\!N\overset{\pi}{-}\overset{+}{\overset{.}{O}}:\\ {}^{\pi}\diagup\\ :\overset{..}{O}\end{array}\right]^+$ and two others

† If the unpaired electron occupies the π bond another possible form is $:\overset{.}{N}\overset{\pi}{-}\overset{..}{\overset{.}{O}}.$

Table 19.5 (*continued*)

Ion, molecule, or group	Principal canonical forms
Nitrogen dioxide, NO_2	$\overset{\cdot\cdot}{N}$ ... N ... $\overset{+}{N}$ ... $\overset{+}{N}$ ... $\overset{2+}{N}$ (series of canonical forms)
Nitrogen difluoride, NF_2	$\overset{\cdot\cdot}{N}$ with F and F

(b) *Structures with all electrons paired*

Ion, molecule, or group	Principal canonical forms
Nitric oxide liquid, $(NO)_2$	$:\overset{\cdot\cdot}{O}\overset{\pi}{-}\overset{\cdot\cdot}{N}-\overset{\cdot\cdot}{N}\overset{\pi}{-}\overset{\cdot\cdot}{O}:$
The nitrosonium cation, $[NO]^+$	$\left[:\overset{2+}{N}-\overset{-}{\overset{\cdot\cdot}{O}}:\right]^+$ I $\left[:\overset{+}{N}\overset{\pi}{-}\overset{\cdot\cdot}{O}:\right]^+$ II $\left[:\overset{-}{N}\overset{2+}{-}\overset{\cdot\cdot}{O}:\right]^+$ III $\left[:N\overset{+}{\underset{\pi}{-}}\overset{\cdot\cdot}{O}:\right]^+$ IV
The nitrosyl anion, $[NO]^-$	$\left[:\overset{\cdot\cdot}{\overset{-}{N}}\overset{\pi}{-}\overset{\cdot\cdot}{O}:\right]^-$ $\left[:\overset{\cdot\cdot}{N}-\overset{\cdot\cdot}{\overset{-}{O}}:\right]^-$
Cationic complex nitroso compounds	$(CH_3)_3\overset{+}{N}-\overset{\cdot\cdot}{N}\overset{\pi}{-}\overset{\cdot\cdot}{O}:$
Covalent nitroso compounds	$F-\overset{\cdot\cdot}{N}\overset{\pi}{-}\overset{\cdot\cdot}{O}:$ (also Cl, Br, and SCN)
Dinitrogen trioxide, N_2O_3	$:\overset{\cdot\cdot}{O}$ and $:\overset{\cdot\cdot}{\overset{-}{O}}$ bonded to $\overset{+}{N}-\overset{\cdot\cdot}{N}\overset{\pi}{-}\overset{\cdot\cdot}{O}:$
Dinitrogen tetroxide, N_2O_4	$:O$ and $O:$ with $\overset{+}{N}-\overset{+}{N}$ (π bonds), and $:\overset{\cdot\cdot}{O}:$, $\overset{\cdot\cdot}{O}:$
Nitryl compounds	$F-\overset{+}{N}$ with $\overset{\cdot\cdot}{\overset{-}{O}}:$ and $\overset{\cdot\cdot}{O}:$ (π bond)
Nitrous acid, HNO_2	$H-\overset{+}{N}$ with $\overset{\cdot\cdot}{\overset{-}{O}}:$ and $\overset{\pi}{}\overset{\cdot\cdot}{O}:$ $\rightleftharpoons$ $:N$ with $\overset{\cdot\cdot}{O}H$ and $\overset{\pi}{}\overset{\cdot\cdot}{O}:$

Table 19.5 (*continued*)

Ion, molecule, or group	Principal canonical forms
The nitro group, NO_2	
The nitrite ion, $[NO_2]^-$	
Nitric acid, HNO_3	
The nitrate ion, $[NO_3]^-$	
Peroxynitrous acid, HNO_3	
Peroxynitric acid, HNO_4	
Hyponitrous acid, $H_2N_2O_2$	
The diazotate ion	
Dinitrogen difluoride, N_2F_2	
Guanidine	

(4) *Compounds of nitrogen containing non-localised π bonds.* These compounds include nitrogen ring compounds (p. 687), and probably $N(SiH_3)_3$, in which the nitrogen atom is trigonally hybridised and some form of non-localised πd bond must exist between the nitrogen atom and the silicon atoms.

THE OXIDES, OXYACIDS, AND OXYACID IONS OF NITROGEN

A list of these compounds and ions is given in Table 19.6, which includes references to the pages on which they are discussed in detail. The canonical forms of the compounds mentioned in Table 19.6 are set out in Table 19.5.

Table 19.6.   *The Molecules, Groups, and Ions, consisting of Oxygen and Nitrogen Atoms, and the oxyacids of Nitrogen*

Formula of molecule, group, or ion	Name	Page reference
N_2O	Nitrous oxide	661
NO	Nitric oxide	661
	Dimer N_2O_2	662
$-NO$	Nitroso group	663
NO^+	Nitrosonium ion	665
NO^-	Nitrosyl ion	663
$N_2O_2{}^+$		
NO_2	Nitrogen dioxide	669
	Dimer N_2O_4	671
$-NO_2$	Nitryl group	674
$NO_2{}^+$	Nitronium ion	675
$NO_2{}^-$	Nitrite ion	679
$NO_2{}^{2-}$	Nitroxylate ion	675
$-NO_2$	Nitro group	679
N_2O_3	Dinitrogen trioxide	675
$N_2O_3{}^+$		
N_2O_5	Dinitrogen pentoxide	676
NO_3	Nitrogen trioxide	677
	Dimer N_2O_6	677
$NO_3{}^-$	Nitrate ion	788
$H_2N_2O_2$	Hyponitrous acid	677
HNO_2	Nitrous acid	678
HNO_3	Nitric acid	680

Table 19.7.   *Properties of the Oxides of Nitrogen*

	N_2O	NO	NO_2	N_2O_4	N_2O_3	N_2O_5
Appearance	Colourless gas	Gas colourless; liquid and solid deep blue	Red brown gas	Colourless solid	Blue solid at m.p.	Colourless solid
m.p. °C	$-90\cdot8$	-164	$-11\cdot2$		-102	41
b.p. °C	$-88\cdot5$	-152	$21\cdot2$			Sublimes at $32\cdot5$
Critical point °C	$36\cdot5$	-96	158			
Critical pressure, atm	$71\cdot6$	64	100			
Solubility in water, Bunsen's co-efficient						
at 0°	$1\cdot3$	$0\cdot074$				
at 60°	$0\cdot1$	$0\cdot03$				
Dimensions of molecule	Length $2\cdot32$ N—N $1\cdot126$ N—O $1\cdot191$	N—O $1\cdot15$	N—O $1\cdot188$ $\widehat{ONO}$ 134°	N—N $1\cdot60$ N—O $1\cdot20$ $\widehat{ONO}$ 108° $\widehat{NNO}$ 126°		N—O (in $NO_2{}^+$) $1\cdot15$ N—O (in $NO_3{}^-$) $1\cdot24$

NITROUS OXIDE, N_2O

Nitrous oxide, N_2O, is formed by the decomposition of hyponitrous acid (p. 677):

$$H_2N_2O_2 = H_2O + N_2O,$$

but the reaction is quite irreversible. Nitrous oxide is usually made by gently heating ammonium nitrate. The reaction is exothermic. It begins at 185° and becomes violent at 250°. Nitrous oxide made in this way is contaminated with NO_2, NO, N_2, and O_2. Nitrous oxide can also be made:

 (i) by adding a concentrated solution of sodium nitrite to a warm solution of hydroxylamine sulphate:

$$[NH_3OH^+]_2[SO_4{}^{2-}] + 2NaNO_2 = 2N_2O + 4H_2O + Na_2SO_4,$$

 (ii) by reducing nitrous acid with an acidified stannous salt,

(iii) by warming sulphamic acid with concentrated nitric acid:

$$HSO_3NH_2 + HNO_3 = N_2O + H_2SO_4 + H_2O,$$

 (iv) by acidifying a solution of potassium nitrosohydroxylaminesulphonate:

$$2HCl + K_2SO_3NO \cdot NO = N_2O + H_2SO_4 + 2KCl.$$

Nitrous oxide has a slightly sweet taste. The aqueous solution is neutral, and its conductivity is identical with that of pure water. Nitrous oxide is resistant in the cold to the attacks of O_2, O_3, H_2, the halogens, the alkali metals, PH_3, H_2S, and aqua regia. It reacts with alkali metals at their boiling points to form nitrites and nitrogen. At high temperatures (300°) it is a strong oxidising agent towards organic compounds. It forms an explosive mixture with hydrogen. If mixed with two volumes of hydrogen and one volume of oxygen and exploded it is completely decomposed. If passed over heated sodamide it yields sodium azide (p. 685). It is used as a light general anaesthetic.

The absorption spectrum of gaseous nitrous oxide, and the X-ray analysis of the solid and liquid, show the molecule to be linear. The Raman spectrum and the infrared spectrum show the molecule to be unsymmetrical. Hence the molecule is N—N—O. The canonical forms are shown in Table 19.5. The length of the molecule predicted by Pauling's covalent atomic radii for the first form is 2·35; for the second form is 2·45. The observed length is 2·32. Solid nitrous oxide has the same crystal lattice as solid carbon dioxide; the two oxides dissolve in one another to form a continuous series of solid solutions.

NITRIC OXIDE, NO

Nitric oxide, NO, is usually made in the laboratory by the action of dilute nitric acid on metallic copper, but the gas made in this way contains varying quantities of NO_2, N_2, and N_2O:

$$3Cu + 8HNO_3 = 3Cu(NO_3)_2 + 4H_2O + 2NO.$$

It can also be made:

 (i) by the action of saturated ferrous sulphate solution on a mixture of concentrated sulphuric acid and powdered potassium nitrate:

$$6FeSO_4 + 2KNO_3 + 4H_2SO_4 = 3Fe_2(SO_4)_3 + 2NO + K_2SO_4 + 4H_2O;$$

the gas is about 98% pure,

 (ii) by the action of concentrated sulphuric acid on a solution either of potassium nitrate, or of potassium nitrite, in contact with metallic mercury:

$$2KNO_3 + 6Hg + 4H_2SO_4 = 2NO + 3Hg_2SO_4 + K_2SO_4 + 4H_2O;$$

the gas is about 99·7% pure.

Equations for other reactions in which nitric oxide is produced are:

(a) $2H_2SO_4 + 2KI + 2NaNO_2 = K_2SO_4 + Na_2SO_4 + 2HI + 2HNO_2$
$$2HI + 2HNO_2 = I_2 + 2NO + 2H_2O.$$

(b) $K_4Fe(CN)_6 + HNO_2 + HAc = K_3Fe(CN)_6 + KAc + NO + H_2O.$

(c) $FeSO_4, 7H_2O + 2NaNO_2 = Fe(NO_2)_2 + Na_2SO_4 + 7H_2O$
$$6Fe(NO_2)_2 = Fe_2O_3 + 2Fe_2O_3 \cdot N_2O_5 + 10NO.$$

(d) $H_3AsO_3 + 2HNO_2 = H_3AsO_4 + 2NO + H_2O.$

(e) $(NH_3OH)Cl + HNO_3 = 2NO + 2H_2O + HCl.$

(f) $2KNO_2 + 2Hg + 2H_2SO_4 = 2NO + Hg_2SO_4 + K_2SO_4 + 2H_2O.$

Nitric oxide is an endothermic compound, but it is very stable and does not begin to decompose until heated to 1000°.

The liquid or the compressed gas slowly changes into dinitrogen trioxide and nitrous oxide:

$$4NO = N_2O_3 + N_2O,$$

and a corresponding change takes place if nitric oxide remains in contact with water or with dilute alkali:

$$4NO + 2NaOH = 2NaNO_2 + N_2O + H_2O.$$

Burning phosphorus or carbon continue to burn in the gas, but feebly burning sulphur is extinguished. With oxygen nitric oxide gives NO_2, with chlorine ClNO, and with bromine BrNO or $NOBr_3$. The molecule of nitric oxide is a free radical which will combine with other free radicals such as methyl. Small quantities of nitric oxide inhibit reactions by terminating chains.

Nitric oxide is freely soluble in ferrous sulphate or ferrous chloride solution to give the brown nitrosyl compound $(Fe(NO))SO_4$. The chlorides of Co, Ni, Mn, Cr^{2+}, Cu^+ also absorb nitric oxide. It also dissolves in potassium sulphite solution to give $K_2[SO_3NO \cdot NO]$; the solution when acidified liberates nitrous oxide (p. 661). Nitric oxide is slowly oxidised by acidified potassium permanganate solution to nitric acid.

Nitric oxide is reduced by lithium aluminium hydride to hyponitrous acid, $H_2N_2O_2$, which can be isolated as the silver salt, by tin and hydrochloric acid to hydroxyl-aminium chloride (p. 702), and by an arsenite in alkaline solution to nitrous oxide.

Nitric oxide is monomeric as a gas, but dimeric in the liquid and crystalline states. The structures of the molecules in the three states are different. The paramagnetism of nitric oxide gas indicates that there is one unpaired electron in the molecule. On the valence bond theory, both the nitrogen atom and the oxygen atom are regarded as trigonally hybridised, and the molecule is represented by a resonance structure of the canonical forms, Table 19.5(3)(a).

The structure of the molecule in terms of the molecular orbital theory is described on p. 132. According to this theory the electron density of the molecule in the region between the atoms is approximately that of one σ bond and $1\frac{1}{2}$ π bonds. This conclusion may be translated into a valence bond structure by formulating the molecule $N\frac{\pi}{\pi}O$, and assuming that the eleventh electron occupies an antibonding orbital (compare the structure of the molecule O_2, p. 792). The d.p.m. of the molecule is 0.16 debyes.

In the gas phase at low temperature and high pressure the molecule NO becomes slightly associated to the dimer which is the principal form present in the liquid phase. The dimeric molecule is not linear. It is diamagnetic, and hence all the electrons are paired. On the valence bond theory the dimer can be drawn:

$$\overset{\cdot}{N}\!-\!\overset{\cdot}{N}$$
$$\underset{:O}{\overset{\pi}{\diagup}} \qquad \underset{O:}{\overset{\pi}{\diagdown}}$$

Magnetic susceptibility measurements indicate that the dimerisation is not quite complete; the degree of dissociation varies from 2·7% at the m.p. to 5% at the b.p.

Nitric oxide solidifies to monoclinic crystals. The values of the residual entropy, the magnetic susceptibility, and the heat of sublimation, indicate that the crystals consist of dimeric molecules. Molecular rearrangement appears to take place on crystallisation, as the structure of the dimeric molecule in the crystal is reported to be rectangular with the bond lengths:

$$
\begin{array}{c}
\overset{2\cdot38}{N \text{———} O} \\
1\cdot101 \;\; | \quad\quad | \\
O \text{———} N
\end{array}
$$

The high value of the longer N—O distance indicates that the crystal is ionic, and it has been suggested that two ionic forms:

$$
\begin{array}{ccc}
\overset{-}{\cdot\ddot{N}\cdot} \quad \overset{+}{\ddot{O}} & & \ddot{N} \quad \cdot\ddot{O}\cdot \\
\Big|\pi \quad\; \pi\Big|\pi & \text{and} & \pi\Big|\pi \quad\; \Big|\pi \\
\cdot\ddot{O}\cdot \quad\; \ddot{N} & & \ddot{O} \quad\; \cdot\ddot{N}\cdot \\
& & \overset{+}{}
\end{array}
$$

are in resonance.

THE NITROSO GROUP, NO

The nitroso group is present in many compounds. The group is always univalent, but it has different functions. It may be present as a covalent group, or as the cation NO^+, or as the anion NO^-. The following structures can be assigned to the group:

$$
\begin{array}{ccc}
\text{covalent} & \text{cation} & \text{anion} \\[4pt]
-\ddot{N}\overset{\pi}{-}\ddot{O}\colon & \left[\colon N\overset{\pi}{\underset{\pi}{-}}O\colon\right]^{+} & \left[\colon\ddot{N}\overset{\pi}{-}\ddot{O}\colon\right]^{-}
\end{array}
$$

The only derivatives containing the anion are the sodium, potassium, and barium salts NaNO, KNO, and $Ba(NO)_2$. These are made by the action of nitric oxide on the metals dissolved in liquid ammonia. On evaporation, the salts are obtained as white solids which vigorously react with water, or aqueous sodium hydroxide solution, to yield nitrous oxide and sodium hyponitrite in varying proportions:

$$NaNO + H_2O = NaOH + HNO,$$
$$2HNO \rightarrow H_2N_2O_2 \rightarrow N_2O + H_2O,$$
$$H_2N_2O_2 + 2NaOH = Na_2N_2O_2 + 2H_2O.$$

NaNO has been shown to be diamagnetic, and hence there are no unpaired electrons in the anion NO^-.

Derivatives of the nitroso group in which it may be present in the covalent state, or as a univalent cation, are numerous.

Covalent compounds of the type X—N=O. Nitrosyl fluoride, chloride, and bromide can be made by the direct combination of nitric oxide with the halogens. These compounds may be regarded as the acid halides of nitrous acid.

Nitrosyl fluoride is isoelectronic with ozone, O_3, and the nitrite ion NO_2^-, both of which have structures which are not linear, and have bond angles close to 115°. The long X—N bond lengths in nitrosyl chloride and nitrosyl bromide suggest ionic structures. The ionic structure, $Cl^-(NO^+)$, is also indicated by (i) the force constants calculated from the infrared spectrum of nitrosyl chloride, and (ii) the high value of the d.p.m.; on the assumption that nitrosyl chloride is wholly covalent the calculated d.p.m. is only 0·3, and that of nitrosyl bromide is only 0·45. On the other hand, the specific conductivity of nitrosyl chloride at $-10°$ is only $2\cdot7 \times 10^{-6}$ ohm^{-1} cm^{-1}.

Table 19.8.   *The Nitrosyl Halides*

	FNO	ClNO	BrNO
m.p. °C	− 132·5	− 64·5	− 55·5
b.p. °C	− 59·9	− 6·4	*ca.* 0
Bond length X—N	1·52	1·95†	2·14†
N—O	1·13	1·14	1·15
Bond angle	110·2°	116±2°	117±3°
D.p.m. (in CCl₄ solution)	1·81	1·83	1·87

The ionisation in liquid SO_2, or liquid N_2O_4, is also small: the specific conductivity of these solutions is of the same order as the specific conductivity of corresponding solutions of acetyl or benzoyl chloride. The conclusion must be accepted that nitrosyl chloride has both covalent and ionic character.

Nitrosyl fluoride, FNO, is formed:

  (i) by heating nitrosyl chloride with silver fluoride at 250° in a platinum vessel:

$$ClNO + AgF = FNO + AgCl,$$

  (ii) by allowing streams of nitric oxide and fluorine to mix in a copper tube,

  (iii) by heating nitrosonium fluoroborate with sodium fluoride,

$$NOBF_4 + NaF = FNO + NaBF_4.$$

Nitrosyl fluoride is a very reactive gas which can be prepared only in the complete absence of water. Si, red P, As, Sb, and Bi inflame in it, but it does not react with sulphur or iodine. It attacks glass. Nitrosyl fluoride, when slowly mixed with fluorine monoxide, reacts according to the equation:

$$FNO + OF_2 = O_2 + NF_3;$$

if the mixing is rapid there is explosion even at low temperatures.

Nitrosyl chloride, ClNO, is formed:

  (i) by the direct combination of nitric oxide and chlorine at 40–50° in the presence of animal charcoal,

  (ii) by the action of phosphorus pentachloride on potassium nitrite:

$$PCl_5 + KNO_2 = NOCl + POCl_3 + KCl,$$

  (iii) by the action of dinitrogen tetroxide on moist potassium chloride,

  (iv) by warming below 80° nitrosonium hydrogen sulphate with dry sodium chloride:

$$NOHSO_4 + NaCl = NaHSO_4 + ClNO.$$

Nitrosyl chloride is an orange-yellow gas which condenses to a ruby red liquid, which freezes to a red solid; at the temperature of liquid air the solid is lemon-yellow. Nitrosyl chloride is thermally stable up to 700°, at which temperature it begins to dissociate into chlorine and nitric oxide. It reacts as an acid chloride with water and alkalis:

$$ClNO + 2KOH = KCl + KNO_2 + H_2O.$$

A mixture of nitrosyl chloride and hydrogen explodes. Nitrosyl chloride converts mercury, zinc, and cadmium to chlorides with the evolution of nitric oxide. Arsenic

† The bond lengths predicted by Pauling's covalent atomic radii are 1·71 and 1·84.

and antimony burn in nitrosyl chloride, sulphur and selenium react to give chlorides, but gold, platinum, nickel, magnesium, and phosphorus do not react. Nitrosyl chloride forms compounds with many metallic chlorides (see below). It reacts with ozone to yield nitronium chloride, NO_2Cl. Nitrosyl chloride reacts with trimethylamine at low temperatures to give $[(CH_3)_3N—NO^+]Cl^-$; this reaction is evidence for the ionic character of nitrosyl chloride. Nitrosyl chloride is diamagnetic, both in the gaseous and liquid states.

NITROSYL CHLORIDE AS THE SOLVENT OF AN ACID-BASE SYSTEM

There is evidence (p. 663) that nitrosyl chloride is capable of ionisation to yield the ions NO^+ and Cl^-. Its dielectric constant (18.2 at $12°$ and 22.5 at $-27°$) although smaller than that of water (81 at $18°$) is equal to that of liquid ammonia (22 at $-34°$), and nitrosyl chloride acts as an ionising solvent for nitrosonium compounds. Nitrosonium compounds such as $NOHSO_4$, are to be regarded as acids in the nitrosyl chloride system, and chlorides of cations other than nitrosonium as bases.

The reaction:

$$(NO^+)(FeCl_4^-) + (CH_3)_4NCl = N(CH_3)_4 \cdot (FeCl_4) + NOCl$$

represents the neutralisation of an acid by a base to give a salt and the undissociated solvent. This reaction has been followed by conductometric titration. Nitrosyl chloride is analogous to water in that the cation is solvated. The self-dissociation of the two substances may be compared in the equations:

$$H_2O + H_2O = (H_3O)^+ + OH^-: \quad NOCl + NOCl = (ONClNO)^+ + Cl^-.$$

The solvated ion has the structure

$$\left[\begin{array}{ccc} & \overset{..}{N} & \overset{..}{N} \\ \underset{\pi}{\diagup} & & \underset{\pi}{\diagdown} \\ :\overset{..}{O}: & .\overset{.}{Cl}. & :\overset{..}{O}: \end{array} \right]^+$$

which is in resonance with the ionic forms

$$\left[:\overset{\pi}{O}\overset{..}{=}\overset{..}{N}—\overset{..}{Cl}: \right] \left[:N\overset{\pi}{\underset{\pi}{=}}\overset{..}{O}: \right]^+ \quad \text{and} \quad \left[:\overset{..}{O}\overset{\pi}{=}N: \right]^+ \left[:\overset{..}{Cl}—N\overset{\pi}{=}\overset{.}{O} \right].$$

This resonance is reminiscent of the dissociation of the hydronium ion:

$$\left[\begin{array}{c} H \\ \diagdown \\ \quad O—H \\ \diagup \\ H \end{array} \right]^+ \quad \rightleftharpoons \quad \begin{array}{c} H \\ \diagdown \\ \quad O + H^+; \\ \diagup \\ H \end{array}$$

if the hydrogen atoms are labelled the equation can be written in three different ways.

Nitrosyl bromide, NOBr, is obtained by passing nitric oxide into bromine at $-15°$; at higher temperatures nitrosyl tribromide, $NOBr_3$, is formed. Nitrosyl bromide is a dark brown liquid. It is far less stable than nitrosyl chloride, and at $0°$ is 7% dissociated. Nitrosyl iodide, NOI, does not exist, as the iodide ion is oxidised to iodine by the nitrosonium ion:

$$2NO^+ + 2I^- = I_2 + 2NO.$$

THE NITROSONIUM ION, NO^+

The properties of the nitrosonium ion may be correlated with a resonance structure consisting of the four canonical forms, Table 19.5 (3) (b).

The N—O distance in nitrosonium compounds is only slightly less than the distance in nitric oxide. Gerding and Houtgraaf have determined the N—O bond length in the compounds:

		Bond lengths predicted from
NO	1·15	Pauling's covalent atomic
NOCl	1·14	radii for comparison
(NO)AlCl$_4$	1·12	
(NO)ClO$_4$	1·11	$N\frac{\pi}{\pi}O$ 1·05
(NO)HSO$_4$	1·107	$N\frac{\pi}{}O$ 1·15
		N—O 1·36

It appears that in the salts (NO)ClO$_4$ and (NO)HSO$_4$, the structures N $^\pi$ O and N$\frac{\pi}{\pi}$O must be given considerable weight.

Chemical evidence for the description of the nitrosonium ion as a resonance structure in which the forms I and II (p. 658) are important is furnished by the ability of the ion to act as acceptor in acceptor-donor reactions. These reactions are carried out by the addition of the donor molecule to dinitrogen tetroxide. The dinitrogen tetroxide acts as an ionised compound:

$$(NO)^+(NO_3)^- + (CH_3)_3N = ((CH_3)_3N \cdot NO)^+(NO_3)^-.$$

The structure of the complex cation:

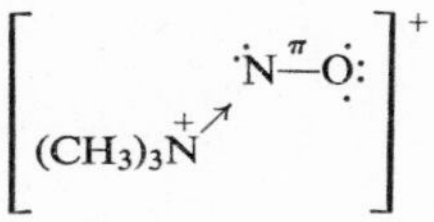

$$\left[\begin{array}{c} \overset{\pi}{N} \!\!-\!\! \overset{..}{O} : \\ (CH_3)_3\overset{+}{N} \nearrow \end{array} \right]^+$$

is based on form II of the nitrosonium ion. Acetonitrile forms the complex:

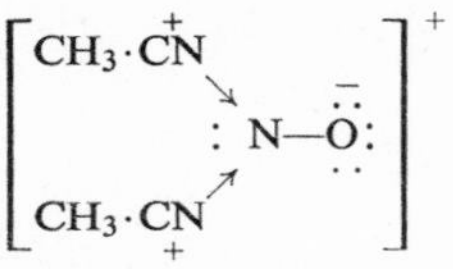

$$\left[\begin{array}{c} CH_3 \cdot \overset{+}{C}N \searrow \\ \quad\quad : N \!\!-\!\! \overset{..}{O} : \\ CH_3 \cdot CN \nearrow \\ \quad + \end{array} \right]^+$$

which is based on form I of the nitrosonium ion. There are many other compounds of these types, but they are stable only at low temperatures.

The nitrosonium ion is an oxidising agent, as is exemplified by the reactions:

$$NO^+ + Na = Na^+ + NO$$
$$NO^+ + NO_2^- = NO + NO_2$$
$$2NO^+ + 2I^- = I_2 + 2NO.$$

Certain nitrosonium salts in aqueous solution, for example nitrosonium hydrogen sulphate, react with nitric oxide under 20 atm pressure according to equations such as:

$$(NO)HSO_4 + NO = (N_2O_2)HSO_4.$$

Other nitrosonium salts in solution in sulphur dioxide also react with nitric oxide under pressure, thus:

$$NOSbCl_6 + NO = (N_2O_2)SbCl_6,$$
$$NOAlCl_4 + NO = (N_2O_2)AlCl_4.$$

Aluminium reacts directly with nitrosyl chloride to yield the same product:

$$Al + 4NOCl = (N_2O_2)AlCl_4 + 2NO.$$

Nitrosonium salts. Nitrous acid is amphoteric and may ionise as an acid to produce H^+ ions, or as a base to produce OH^- ions according to the equations:

$$H^+ + NO_2^- \rightleftharpoons HNO_2 \rightleftharpoons (NO^+) + (OH^-).$$

The nitrosonium ion may therefore be regarded as the cation of the weak base nitrous acid. Only strong acids react with this base to give salts. The first ionisation constant of sulphuric acid is great enough to permit the existence of $NOHSO_4$, but the second ionisation constant is not, and hence there is no $(NO)_2SO_4$. Selenic acid is twice as strong as sulphuric acid, and hence both $NOHSeO_4$ and $(NO)_2SeO_4$ are stable.

A list of compounds in which the NO^+ ion is present is given in Table 19.9. The nitrosonium ion in these compounds may be united to the anion of an oxyacid, as in nitrosonium hydrogen sulphate $NOHSO_4$, or to an anion containing a metal, as in $NOFeCl_4$. Compounds containing the NO^+ ion united to an oxyacid are probably true salts; there is some evidence that compounds of the other type may be in part covalent.

The nitrosonium salts are decomposed by water, and their reactions are studied in solvents such as nitrosyl chloride, nitromethane, or liquid sulphur dioxide. These solutions are conducting. If the anion is colourless the solution is colourless or yellow. Examination of the crystal structure of $NOBF_4$ and $NOClO_4$ shows that these compounds are isomorphous with NH_4BF_4, NH_4ClO_4, and $[H_3O]ClO_4$.

Table 19.9. *Compounds containing the Nitrosonium Ion*

Compounds in which the NO^+ ion is united to the anion of an oxyacid

$NOHSO_4$	$(NO)_2S_2O_7$†	$(NO)_2S_3O_{10}$	$(NO)(NO_2)S_3O_{10}$
$NOHSeO_4$	$(NO)_2SeO_4$	$NOHS_2O_3$ (unstable)	
$NOClO_4$	$NOReO_4$	$NOSO_3F$	$NOSO_2F$

Compounds in which the NO^+ ion is united to the anion of a chlorometallic acid

$NOBCl_4$	$NOAlCl_4$	$NOGaCl_4$	$NOInCl_4$	$NOTlCl_4$
$(NO)_2SnCl_6$‡	$(NO)_2PbCl_6$			
$NOSbCl_6$	$NOBiCl_4$			
$(NO)_2TiCl_6$	$NOUO_2Cl_3$	$NOMnCl_3$	$NOFeCl_4$	
$(NO)_2PdCl_4$	$(NO)_2PtCl_6$			
$NOCuCl_2$	$NOAuCl_4$	$NOZnCl_3$	$NOHgCl_3$	

Compounds in which the NO^+ ion is united to the anion of a fluorometallic acid§

$NOBF_4$	$(NO)_2GeF_6$	$NOPF_6$	$NOIF_6$
	$(NO)_2SnF_6$	$NOAsF_6$	
		$NOSbF_6$	
$(NO)_2TiF_6$	$NOVF_6$	$NOAuF_4$	

Compounds in which the NO^+ ion is united to the anion of a nitratometallic acid

$(NO)_2(Zn(NO_3)_4)$ and, possibly, $NO(UO_2(NO_3)_3)$.

Nitrosonium oxyacid salts. The nitrosonium salts of oxyacids are made by the action of nitric oxide, dinitrogen trioxide, or dinitrogen tetroxide, on an acid oxide or the concentrated solution of the acid concerned. The products are crystalline, often hygroscopic, and decompose if heated above 100°. An exception is nitrosonium disulphate which boils without decomposition at 360°. For lack of space examples

† Confirmed as ionic, m.p. 233°.
‡ Nearly insoluble in $NOCl$ and not solvated.
§ The compound $(NO)_2[Fe(CN)_6NO]$ is also known.

of this type of nitrosonium compound must be restricted to nitrosonium hydrogen sulphate, and nitrosonium disulphate.

Nitrosonium hydrogen sulphate, $NOHSO_4$, is formed during the chamber process for the manufacture of sulphuric acid. It is also formed by the action of dinitrogen tetroxide on chlorosulphonic acid. It is best prepared by passing sulphur dioxide into cooled fuming nitric acid:

$$SO_2 + HNO_3 = NOHSO_4.$$

The nitrosonium hydrogen sulphate separates as rhombic prisms, m.p. 73·5°. Nitrosonium hydrogen sulphate decomposes slowly if heated above its melting point, to yield nitrosonium disulphate (see below). It is violently decomposed by water. It dissolves in absolute nitric acid, and in concentrated sulphuric acid. With dry hydrogen chloride it forms nitrosyl chloride:

$$HCl + NOHSO_4 = ClNO + H_2SO_4.$$

Nitrosonium hydrogen sulphate reacts with alkalis quantitatively thus:

$$3NaOH + NOHSO_4 = NaNO_2 + Na_2SO_4 + 2H_2O,$$

with ammonia thus:

$$H_2O + 3NH_3 + NOHSO_4 = NH_4NO_2 + (NH_4)_2SO_4,$$
$$NH_4NO_2 = N_2 + 2H_2O,$$

and with ether thus:

$$(C_2H_5)_2O + NOHSO_4 = C_2H_5NO_2 + C_2H_5HSO_4.$$

Nitrosonium hydrogen sulphate, however, dissolves in absolute alcohol without reaction.

Nitrosonium disulphate, $(NO)_2S_2O_7$, is formed† by the thermal decomposition of nitrosonium hydrogen sulphate:

$$2NOHSO_4 = (NO)_2S_2O_7 + H_2O.$$

It is prepared by the action of nitric oxide on sulphur trioxide at 200°:

$$3SO_3 + 2NO = (NO)_2S_2O_7 + SO_2.$$

It consists of colourless crystals, m.p. 233°. It boils without decomposition at 360°. It is rapidly solvolysed by water, alcohols, or ammonia.

Nitrosonium chlorometallic salts are made by the action of nitrosyl chloride on the free metal, metal oxide, or metal chloride. The chlorides of aluminium, iron, and antimony behave as strong acids in nitrosyl chloride solution (p. 665).

Nitrosonium chloroantimonate, $NOSbCl_6$, is made by the action of nitrosyl chloride on antimony pentachloride. By double decomposition of this salt with the appropriate tetramethyl ammonium salt, other nitrosonium salts are made, such as the perchlorate, fluorophosphate, and the nitroprusside. The double decomposition is carried out in solution in liquid sulphur dioxide. Pure nitrosonium chloroantimonate is yellow. It readily sublimes. The conductivity of $NOSbCl_6$ in liquid sulphur dioxide has been examined, and it is found that at low temperatures ($-70°$ to $-40°$) it is of the same order as that of strong electrolytes such as $KSbCl_6$. From $-40°$ to $0°$, however, the conductivity of $NOSbCl_6$ remains roughly steady, while that of $KSbCl_6$ increases by about 30% of the value at $-40°$. This difference between $KSbCl_6$ and $NOSbCl_6$ indicates the existence of the equilibrium:

$$(NO^+)(SbCl_6{}^-) \rightleftharpoons SbCl_5,ClNO.$$

There is this evidence that $NOSbCl_6$ is not wholly ionic.

† See also the reaction of sulphur on dinitrogen pentoxide (p. 676).

Nitrosonium fluoroborate, $NOBF_4$, is made by passing dinitrogen trioxide in excess into a concentrated solution of fluoroboric acid (p. 527). Nitrosonium fluoroborate can be purified by sublimation in vacuo. It is hygroscopic and very soluble in water The solution decomposes, however, with the evolution of nitrous fumes. Nitrosonium fluoroborate crystallises from the solution as the monohydrate. It is nearly insoluble in nitrosyl chloride, by which it is not solvated. It converts methyl alcohol into methyl nitrite.

NITROGEN DIOXIDE AND DINITROGEN TETROXIDE

In the gaseous and liquid phases, these two substances exist in equilibrium:

$$N_2O_4 \rightleftharpoons 2NO_2. \quad \Delta H = 12 \text{ kcal for the forward reaction.}$$

The solid consists wholly of dinitrogen tetroxide, N_2O_4. The liquid consists of dinitrogen tetroxide with 0.7% of nitrogen dioxide. The gas is also a mixture of dinitrogen tetroxide and nitrogen dioxide in which the proportion of nitrogen dioxide increases with temperature:

Temperature °C	% by volume of NO_2 in the gas at equilibrium
27	33·3
50	57·1
100	94·2
154	100·0

At higher temperatures the nitrogen dioxide itself dissociates into nitric oxide and oxygen. The percentage by volume of nitric oxide in the equilibrium mixture is 2% at 222°, and 29.8% at 390°.

The mixture may be prepared:

(i) by heating lead nitrate and passing the gaseous product through a cooled tube on which the nitrogen dioxide condenses, while the oxygen passes on,

(ii) by heating nitrosonium hydrogen sulphate (p. 668) with dry potassium nitrate:

$$NOHSO_4 + KNO_3 = KHSO_4 + NO^+NO_3^- = KHSO_4 + N_2O_4,$$

(iii) by passing a dry mixture of 1 vol. of oxygen and 2 vol. of nitric oxide slowly through a cooled tube:

$$2NO + O_2 = 2NO_2,$$

(this reaction goes faster at lower temperatures),

(iv) by the action of concentrated nitric acid on copper:

$$Cu + 4HNO_3 = Cu(NO_3)_2 + 2NO_2 + 2H_2O.$$

At high temperatures the system (consisting wholly of nitrogen dioxide) acts as an oxidising agent, and yields the whole of its oxygen to such powerful reducing agents as brightly burning phosphorus or carbon, or strongly heated iron or copper. In these reactions nitrogen is set free. When the gaseous system mixed with excess of hydrogen is passed over red hot platinum sponge, ammonia is formed. At lower temperatures the reactions of the system are more complex. They have been interpreted by assigning certain chemical properties to nitrogen dioxide and others to dinitrogen tetroxide. The following are the principal reactions of the system. The equations are mere statements of the reagents and the products of each reaction; they do not indicate the course of the reactions.

Table 19.10(a). *Reactions ascribed to Nitrogen Dioxide,* NO_2

1. Oxidation of transition metals by the vapour, for example:

$$2Cu + NO_2 = Cu_2O + NO.$$

The cuprous oxide absorbs nitrogen dioxide. Iron, cobalt, and nickel behave similarly.
2. Oxidation of inorganic compounds, for example:

    (a) $CO + NO_2 = CO_2 + NO$ (room temperature),
    (b) $ONCl + NO_2 = O_2NCl + NO$,
    (c) $SO_2 + NO_2 = SO_3 + NO$,

(the product here is variously stated to be $2SO_3 \cdot NO$, or nitrosyl pyrosulphate, $O(SO_2 \cdot O \cdot NO)_2$),
3. Reaction with chlorine when passed through a hot tube:

$$Cl_2 + 2NO_2 = 2ClNO_2.$$

(Bromine reacts similarly. Neither fluorine nor iodine reacts with nitrogen dioxide at room temperature.)
4. Reaction with powerful oxidising agents, for example:

$$O_3 + 2NO_2 = N_2O_5 + O_2 \text{ (at } 25°),$$
$$ClNO_2 + 2NO_2 = ClNO + N_2O_5,$$
$$NO_3 + NO_2 = N_2O_5,$$
$$H_2O_2 + 2NO_2 = 2HNO_3.$$

5. Nitration of paraffins in the vapour phase:

$$C_2H_6 + 3NO_2 = C_2H_5NO_2 + H_2O + N_2O_3.$$

6. Addition to unsaturated compounds:
$$C_2H_4 + 2NO_2 = C_2H_4,2NO_2.$$

7. Decomposition:
$$2NO_2 = 2NO + O_2.$$

8. Reaction with nitric oxide:

$$NO_2 + NO = N_2O_3.$$

Table 19.10(b). *Reactions ascribed to Dinitrogen Tetroxide,* N_2O_4

1. Reactions with electropositive metals at $-10°$:
$$Na + N_2O_4 = NaNO_3 + NO,$$
$$Ag + N_2O_4 = AgNO_3 + NO,$$
$$Cu + N_2O_4 = CuNO_3 + NO.$$

2. Reactions with salts, for example:
$$KCl + N_2O_4 = KNO_3 + NOCl,$$
$$2KBr + 2N_2O_4 = 2KNO_3 + Br_2 + 2NO, \quad \text{(KI similarly)}$$
$$KN_3 + N_2O_4 = KNO_3 + N_2 + N_2O,$$
$$NaClO_3 + N_2O_4 = NaNO_3 + NO_2 + ClO_2,$$
$$2CH_3COONa + 2N_2O_4 = 2NaNO_3 + (CH_3CO)_2O + N_2O_3,$$
$$Na_2CO_3 + 2N_2O_4 = 2NaNO_3 + CO_2 + N_2O_3.$$

3. Reaction with anhydrous oxides and hydroxides, for example:
$$CaO + 2N_2O_4 = Ca(NO_3)_2 + N_2O_3,$$
$$NaOH + N_2O_4 = NaNO_3 + HONO. \quad \text{(NaNO}_3 \text{ is in 94\% yield).}$$

Table 19.10(b) (*continued*).

4. Reaction with water:

$$HOH + N_2O_4 = HNO_3 + HNO_2.$$

(A parallel reaction occurs with dilute aqueous sodium hydroxide.)

5. Reaction with concentrated sulphuric acid:

$$H_2SO_4 + N_2O_4 = NOHSO_4 + HNO_3.$$

6. Reactions with amines and ethers:

$$2C_5H_5N + NONO_3 = [(C_5H_5N)_2NO]NO_3.$$

Nitrogen dioxide, NO_2. The molecule of nitrogen dioxide is the only molecule or ion which contains 17 electrons. The paramagnetism of nitrogen dioxide shows that one of the electrons is unpaired. The molecule is non-linear. In terms of the valence bond theory it is a resonance structure of at least five canonical forms, Table 19.5 (3) (a). It is possible that the unpaired electron occupies a σ bond or a π bond, in which case many other canonical forms could be drawn in addition to those in the Table. In the canonical forms I, II, and III the unpaired electron is on the nitrogen atom; in forms IV and V it is on an oxygen atom. It may therefore be supposed that chemical attack on nitrogen dioxide takes place either at the nitrogen atom or at one of the oxygen atoms. Many reactions of nitrogen dioxide proceed by the formation of intermediate compounds by the addition of a radical either to the electron deficient nitrogen atom, thus:

$$X + NO_2 = XNO_2,$$

or to the electron deficient oxygen atom, thus:

$$X + NO_2 = XONO.$$

In general the nitro compound XNO_2 is stable, but the nitrite compound tends to break up:

$$XONO = XO + NO.$$

Reactions 1 and 2 in Table 19.10(a). can be thus interpreted.

The nitration of certain compounds by nitrogen dioxide can be explained if the molecule to be nitrated is assumed to react as if dissociated into two radicals, thus:

$$Cl_2 = Cl\cdot + Cl\cdot, \qquad Cl\cdot + NO_2 = ClNO_2,$$
$$C_2H_6 = C_2H_5\cdot + H\cdot, \qquad H\cdot + NO_2 = HNO_2$$
$$C_2H_5\cdot + NO_2 = C_2H_5NO_2,$$

$$C_2H_4 = \underset{\underset{CH_2\cdot,}{|}}{CH_2\cdot} \qquad \underset{\underset{CH_2\cdot}{|}}{CH_2\cdot} + NO_2 = \underset{\underset{CH_2\cdot}{|}}{CH_2NO_2}$$

It is found that the radical $CH_2NO_2.CH_2\cdot$ combines equally readily with nitrogen dioxide to form either a dinitro compound, or a nitro-nitrite compound, thus giving either

$$\underset{\underset{CH_2NO_2}{|}}{CH_2NO_2} \qquad \text{or} \qquad \underset{\underset{CH_2ONO.}{|}}{CH_2NO_2}$$

Dinitrogen tetroxide, N_2O_4, is colourless and diamagnetic.

There is no change in the Raman spectrum on melting, and no difference has been found between the infrared spectra of solid and gaseous N_2O_4.

The possible geometrical configurations of the molecule are:

I	II	III	IV
Planar	Non-planar		

The planar structure I is established. This structure, however, indicates no obvious route for the dissociation into $NO^+NO_3^-$, and the bonding arrangement:

contradicts Pauling's adjacent charge rule (p. 656).

Study of the temperature-dependence of the entropy indicates that free rotation is almost completely inhibited; the height of the barrier is about 10 kcal per mole.

The structure seems to be analogous to that of B_2Cl_4, which is planar, without free rotation, and has a long B—B bond (p. 503).

The oxalate ion $[C_2O_4^{2-}]$ is isoelectronic with N_2O_4. The resemblance extends beyond the structures and vibration frequencies to the chemical reactions of the two with concentrated H_2SO_4:

$$N_2O_4 \rightarrow NO^+NO_3^- \xrightarrow{2H^+} NO^+ + H_2NO_3^+ \xrightarrow{H^+} NO^+ + NO_2^+ + H_3O^+.$$
$$C_2O_4^{2-} \rightarrow CO\ CO_3^{2-} \xrightarrow{2H^+} CO + H_2CO_3 \xrightarrow{H^+} CO + CO_2 + H_3O^+.$$

The liquid system, $N_2O_4 \rightleftharpoons 2NO_2$, consists of dinitrogen tetroxide with about 0·7% of nitrogen dioxide. The liquid has a very low electric conductance (sp. cond. about 10^{-12} ohm^{-1} cm^{-1}) and a low dielectric constant (about 2·42). It is not an ionising solvent. Simple salts are not soluble in it. It dissolves a number of substances, including bromine and iodine, saturated hydrocarbons, aromatic hydrocarbons, halogeno- and nitro- compounds (aliphatic and aromatic), phenols and carboxylic acids. The carboxylic acids are associated in solution as they are in benzene. The liquid reacts with unsaturated hydrocarbons (p. 671), and it forms adducts with alcohols, ethers, amines, and other oxygen- and nitrogen-containing compounds (p. 671).

The reactions of dinitrogen tetroxide. In all its reactions liquid dinitrogen tetroxide behaves as though it were ionised

$$N_2O_4 \rightleftharpoons NO_3^- + NO^+.$$

For instance, the liberation of nitric oxide when liquid dinitrogen tetroxide reacts with metallic sodium (p. 670) is most simply formulated as an electron transfer from the sodium metal to the NO^+ ion. Although the reactions of dinitrogen tetroxide may thus be formulated, the liquid is not ionised to any measurable extent†. There is, however, experimental evidence of ionisation to an infinitesimal degree. If tetramethyl

---

† The following observations indicate that N_2O_4 is not ionised when pure:

(i) the molecular weight of N_2O_4 in glacial acetic acid is normal, and hence there is no dissociation,

(ii) pure liquid N_2O_4 is not decomposed when placed in an electrolytic cell between an iron cathode and a platinum anode at 230 volts, but when a crystal of sodium acetate is added to the liquid there is a rapid evolution of brown gas at the cathode.

ammonium nitrate, containing the isotope ^{15}N in the nitrate ion, is dissolved in liquid dinitrogen tetroxide containing the naturally abundant isotope ^{14}N, exchange of the isotopes occurs. This is explained by the reactions:

$$(CH_3)_4N^{15}NO_3 = (CH_3)_4N^+ + {^{15}NO_3}^-,$$
$$N_2O_4 \rightleftharpoons NO^+ + NO_3^-.$$

If the reactions of dinitrogen tetroxide are correctly interpreted as ionic, it is to be expected that they will proceed most readily if one or other of the nitrosonium or the nitrate ions is removed from the sphere of action.

Ionisation of dinitrogen tetroxide by removal of the nitrate ion. If dinitrogen tetroxide is dissolved in solvents which are strong proton donors, ionisation is promoted by the removal of the nitrate ions from the system. In sulphuric acid the reactions occur:

$$N_2O_4 \rightleftharpoons NO^+ + NO_3^-$$
$$H_2SO_4 + NO_3^- \rightleftharpoons HSO_4^- + HNO_3.$$

The nitric acid thus formed then itself acts as a proton acceptor to the sulphuric acid (p. 681):

$$HNO_3 + 2H_2SO_4 \rightleftharpoons NO_2^+ + H_3O^+ + 2HSO_4^-.$$

If less than 20% N_2O_4 is present the reaction proceeds wholly to the right, and ionisation of the dinitrogen tetroxide to NO^+ is complete. Other strong acids such as $H_2S_2O_7$, H_3PO_4, and $HClO_4$, also bring about the ionisation of dinitrogen tetroxide to NO^+.

The nitrate ion may also be removed from a solution by complex ion formation. Zinc nitrate dissolves in liquid dinitrogen tetroxide to give $(NO^+)_2(Zn(NO_3)_4{}^{2-})$. The nitrosonium uranyl nitrate is also known, $(NO^+)(UO_2(NO_3)_3{}^-)$.

Raman spectroscopy has shown that if dinitrogen tetroxide is dissolved in pure nitric acid, little or no NO_2 or N_2O_4 is present in solution; the N_2O_4 is present for the most part as NO^+ and NO_3^-.

Ionisation of dinitrogen tetroxide by the removal of the nitrosonium ion, NO^+. If amines, ethers or nitriles are dissolved in dinitrogen tetroxide, adducts are formed which have been assigned constitutions such as: $[(C_5H_5N)_2,NO^+]NO_3^-$ and $[(CH_3OCH_3)_2,NO^+]NO_3^-$. These compounds are analogous to the base-stabilised halogen nitrates $[(C_5H_5N)_2Cl^+]NO_3^-$ and $[(C_5H_5N)_2Br^+]NO_3^-$.

Reaction of dinitrogen tetroxide with metals. The metals Na, K, Zn, Ag, Pb, Hg react at low temperatures $(-10°)$ with dinitrogen tetroxide, thus:

$$Na + N_2O_4 = Na + NO_3^- + NO^+$$
$$= Na^+ + NO_3^- + NO.$$

The heat of activation for the reaction of dinitrogen tetroxide with zinc is 4500 calories, which is the same order as for the reactions of dilute mineral acids with zinc.

At higher temperature, partly by the decomposition of the nitrate formed as above, and partly by the direct attack of nitrogen dioxide on the metal, oxides of the metals are formed. Oxides are formed by the action of dinitrogen tetroxide on Mg, Mn, Fe, Co, Ni. The rate of solution of copper in liquid dinitrogen tetroxide is slow, and it is much increased by the addition of ether or of ethyl acetate to the reagents. No doubt these donor compounds increase the ionisation of dinitrogen tetroxide by the formation of such complexes as $[(C_2H_5OC_2H_5)_2NO^+]NO_3^-$. The attack on the copper then proceeds by electron transfer from the copper to the cation of the complex:

$$2[(C_2H_5OC_2H_5)_2NO^+]NO_3^- + Cu = Cu^{2+}(NO_3^-)_2 + 2NO + 4C_2H_5OC_2H_5.$$

Reaction of dinitrogen tetroxide with salts. Liquid and gaseous dinitrogen tetroxide reacts with many salts. The first step is an electron transfer from the anion of the salt to the ion NO^+, as a result of which the anion of the salt becomes a free atom or radical, X:

$$M^+X^- + NO^+NO_3^- = M^+ + NO_3^- + NO + X.$$

The radical may polymerise or undergo some further reaction to form a stable molecule. Particular reactions are:

(i) $K^+Cl^- + NO^+NO_3^- = K^+ + NO_3^- + NO + Cl,$†
$$NO + Cl = NOCl.$$

(ii) $K^+Br^- + NO^+NO_3^- = K^+ + NO_3^- + NO + Br,$‡
$$Br + Br = Br_2.$$

(iii) $K^+N_3^- + NO^+NO_3^- = K^+ + NO_3^- + NO + N_3,$
$$NO + N_3 = N_2 + N_2O.$$

(iv) $Na^+ClO_3^- + NO^+NO_3^- = Na^+ + NO_3^- + NO + ClO_3,$
$$NO + ClO_3 = O \cdot N \cdot O \cdot ClO_2,$$
$$= NO_2 + ClO_2.$$

(v) With certain sodium salts of oxyacids dinitrogen tetroxide liberates the acid anhydride and dinitrogen trioxide. The reactions may be formulated:

$$2CH_3CO.O^- + 2Na^+ + 2NO^-NO_3 = (CH_3CO)_2O + O + 2NO + 2NO_3^- + 2Na^+,$$
$$O + 2NO = N_2O_3.$$

The sodium salts of acetic acid, propionic acid, butyric acid, succinic acid and phthallic acid all give good yields of the corresponding acid anhydrides by the above reaction. By an analogous formulation the expulsion of carbon dioxide from a carbonate by dinitrogen tetroxide is represented by the equations:

$$CO_3^{2-} + 2Na^+ + 2NO^+NO_3^- = 2Na^+ + 2NO_3^- + CO_3 + 2NO,$$
$$CO_3 + 2NO = CO_2 + N_2O_3.$$

(vi) The primary reaction of dinitrogen tetroxide with dry oxides and hydroxides is:

$$Ca^{2+} + O^{2-} + 2NO^+NO_3^- = Ca^{2+} + 2NO_3^- + O + 2NO,$$
$$O + 2NO = N_2O_3.$$

Zinc oxide behaves similarly.

If dinitrogen tetroxide reacts with dry sodium hydroxide, sodium nitrate is produced in 94% yield:

$$Na^+ + OH^- + NO^+NO_3^- = Na^+ + NO_3^- + HONO.$$

(vii) Dinitrogen tetroxide reacts with water thus:

$$HOH + NO^+NO_3^- = H^+ + NO_3^- + HONO,$$

and hence when it reacts with a dilute solution of sodium hydroxide a mixture of sodium nitrate and nitrite is obtained.

THE NITRYL COMPOUNDS

The two compounds nitryl fluoride, FNO_2, m.p. $-166°$, b.p. $-72.4°$, and nitryl chloride, $ClNO_2$, m.p. $-147°$, b.p. $-15°$, are well-characterised. The highly reactive nitryl fluoride is formed at the temperature of liquid oxygen by the reaction:

$$4NO + F_2 = 2NO_2F + N_2.$$

† The action is almost quantitative; 2·5% of moisture is essential.
‡ Potassium iodide reacts similarly.

Nitryl chloride is formed by the reaction:

$$NOCl + O_3 = ClNO_2 + O_2.$$

It is also obtained when chlorosulphonic acid is added to an equimolar quantity of nitric acid as free as possible from water. Nitryl chloride is stable up to 100°.

There are two possible structures for a compound such as nitryl chloride: (i) it could be regarded as chloronitric acid, $Cl—NO_2$, or (ii) it could be regarded as nitrosonium hypochlorite $(NO)ClO$. The examples of nitrosonium salts in Table 19.9 show that nitrosonium hypochlorite is not likely to be stable.

Deductions from the infrared, the Raman, and the nuclear magnetic spectra of nitryl fluoride support the view that it is fluoronitric acid.

THE NITRONIUM ION, NO_2^+

The nitronium ion is present in pure nitric acid, in the solution of nitric acid in a strong acid (p. 681) and in the cation in certain salts of which the following are examples: $(NO_2)HS_2O_7$, $(NO_2)_2S_2O_7$, $(NO_2)_2S_3O_{10}$, $(NO_2)SO_3F$, $(NO_2)BF_4$, $(NO_2)PF_3$, $(NO_2)AsF_6$, $(NO_2)ClO_4$. Nitronium perchlorate has been shown by X-ray analysis to contain the ions NO_2^+ and ClO_4^-. Dinitrogen pentoxide (p. 676) in the solid state is nitronium nitrate, $NO_2^+NO_3^-$. Nitronium hydrogen sulphate, which is present in a mixture of nitric and sulphuric acids, cannot be obtained in the solid state, as it changes into nitronium hydrogen disulphate:

$$2NO_2HSO_4 = (NO_2)HS_2O_7 + HNO_3.$$

Nitronium salts are made by the action of dinitrogen pentoxide on the appropriate acid or acid anhydride in nitromethane solution, as for example, by the reaction:

$$NO_2^+NO_3^- + HClO_4 = HNO_3 + NO_2ClO_4.$$

The nitronium salts are hygroscopic, and are decomposed by water:

$$NO_2ClO_4 + H_2O = HNO_3 + HClO_4.$$

They undergo thermal decomposition at 100 to 150°, with the exception of $(NO_2)_2S_3O_{10}$ which boils at 200° without decomposition. The nitronium ion nitrates aromatic compounds, and esterifies alcohols to form nitrates. The nitronium ion is linear and symmetrical. It has 22 electrons, and is isoelectronic with the molecules, N_2O, FCN, BeF_2, and CO_2, and with the ions, NCO^- and N_3^-. There is little doubt that its structure is similar to that of the carbon dioxide molecule (p. 655). The distance N—O is 1·06 to 1·15. The ion has a characteristic Raman frequency of 1400 cm^{-1}.

THE NITROXYLATE ION, NO_2^{2-}

Sodium nitroxylate is said to be formed by the action of sodium nitrite on sodium in liquid ammonia. The nitroxylate ion seems to have been little examined. It is isoelectronic with the ion F_2O^+, and with the molecule ClO_2.

DINITROGEN TRIOXIDE, N_2O_3

Dinitrogen trioxide, N_2O_3, is a blue solid at the m.p., $-102°$. It is made by mixing nitric oxide and oxygen below $-100°$. Above $-20°$ the equilibrium is attained:

$$N_2O_3 \rightleftharpoons NO + NO_2.$$

At 25° and 1 atm, 10% of dinitrogen trioxide is present; at 100°, 1·2%.

A mixture of nitric oxide and nitrogen dioxide in the correct proportions to form dinitrogen trioxide is obtained by warming nitric acid with starch, or with arsenious oxide:

$$4H_2O + 4HNO_3 + As_4O_6 = 4H_3AsO_4 + 2N_2O_3.$$

The gaseous product of the reaction is red, but it condenses to a green liquid on cooling. Dinitrogen trioxide dissolves in alkalis to give nitrites. In water it gives a blue solution, which rapidly changes to nitric acid and nitric oxide.

Either of the structures ON—O—NO or ON—NO$_2$ would explain the ready thermal decomposition of dinitrogen trioxide. If ordinary ^{14}NO is mixed with ^{15}NO$_2$ there is a complete exchange of nitrogen atoms:

$$^{14}NO + {^{15}NO_2} = O^{14}N\text{—}O\text{—}^{15}NO = O^{14}NO + {^{15}NO},$$

which is in favour of the structure ON—O—NO.

DINITROGEN PENTOXIDE, N_2O_5

Dinitrogen pentoxide is made:

   (i) by the action of ozone on the lower oxides of nitrogen,
  (ii) by the action of chlorine on warm silver nitrate:

$$2AgNO_3 + 2Cl_2 = 2AgCl + 2NO_2Cl + O_2,$$
$$AgNO_3 + NO_2Cl = AgCl + NO_2{}^+NO_3{}^-,$$

  (iii) by the action of phosphoryl chloride on warm silver nitrate:

$$3AgNO_3 + POCl_3 = Ag_3PO_4 + 3NO_2Cl,$$
$$AgNO_3 + NO_2Cl = AgCl + NO_2{}^+NO_3{}^-,$$

  (iv) by distilling nitric acid with phosphorus pentoxide:

$$2HNO_3 + P_2O_5 = 2HPO_3 + N_2O_5.$$

The last method is used in laboratory practice. The mixture is distilled at a low temperature. The distillate crystallises if the receiver is maintained at $-80°$.

Dinitrogen pentoxide is a colourless solid, m.p. about 41°. It decomposes, even at 0°, to dinitrogen tetroxide and oxygen; the half life period at 0° is 10 days. The decomposition of dinitrogen pentoxide is a first-order reaction. The reaction remains first order down to pressures as low as 0·002 mm, although, according to the Lindemann theory of homogeneous gas reactions, the order should increase at low pressures. This anomaly is unexplained. Nitrogen dioxide has no influence on the thermal decomposition of dinitrogen pentoxide; nitric oxide and dinitrogen pentoxide react almost instantaneously to give nitrogen dioxide.

Dinitrogen pentoxide reacts with water exothermally to yield nitric acid. It converts iodine to iodine pentoxide, but it has no action in the cold and in the absence of catalysts on H$_2$, Cl$_2$, and Br$_2$. Warmed phosphorus and potassium burn in liquid dinitrogen pentoxide; charcoal burns only if previously ignited. Sulphur yields dinitrosonium disulphate, (NO)$_2$S$_2$O$_7$. For the action of dinitrogen pentoxide on acids, see p. 675. Anhydrous hydrogen peroxide converts dinitrogen pentoxide to monoperoxy nitric acid (p. 684).

The structure of the vapour is probably O$_2$N—O—NO$_2$, which would explain the action of dinitrogen pentoxide with nitric oxide. If the central oxygen atom is digonally hybridised the NON angle should be 180°, and the d.p.m. zero. The d.p.m. in carbon tetrachloride solution is 1·39 debyes, which indicates a bond angle of 145°. In the solid state the structure is NO$_2$$^+NO_3$$^-$. The N—O distance is 1·15 in NO$_2$$^+$, and 1·24 in

NO_3^-. The structure nitronium nitrate accords with the formulation of the reactions (ii) and (iii) above.

Nitrogen trioxide, NO_3, is a very unstable gas, detectable by its characteristic absorption spectrum. It has not been isolated.

It is made by treating the vapour of dinitrogen pentoxide with 7 to 8% of ozone. According to Lowry a blue gas is then formed which decomposes with luminescence at 100°. The solution in water has oxidising properties not due to a peroxide link, —O—O—. Nitrogen trioxide can be extracted from its aqueous solution with ether. On standing in water it goes to nitric acid and oxygen; alkali gives nitrate, nitrite, and oxygen. The structure of nitrogen trioxide is unknown.

Dinitrogen hexoxide, N_2O_6, is formed by the action of fluorine on nitric acid. It is probably the mixed anhydride of nitric acid and pernitric acid, O_2N—O—O—NO_2. It rapidly decomposes with loss of oxygen.

HYPONITROUS ACID, $H_2N_2O_2$

Both hyponitrous acid and its sodium salt are explosive. Hyponitrous acid may be made:

(i) by the action of nitrous acid on hydroxylamine:

$$HONO + H_2NOH = HON{=\!=}NOH + H_2O;$$

in practice an ethereal solution of amyl nitrite is used instead of nitrous acid, and to this solution is added a solution of sodium methylate and hydroxylamine in methyl alcohol; the yield is small,

(ii) by the oxidation of hydroxylamine with CuO, Ag_2O, or HgO:

$$2H_2NOH + O_2 = 2H_2O + H_2N_2O_2.$$

The yield by this method is also small.

The sodium salt may be made:

(i) by the reduction of sodium nitrate, or sodium nitrite, with sodium amalgam; crystals of sodium hyponitrite are deposited,

(ii) by warming sodium hydroxylamine N-sulphonate with sodium hydroxide:

$$HON{<}^{H}_{SO_3Na} + NaOH = HON + Na_2SO_3 + H_2O$$

$$2HON = H_2N_2O_2$$

$$H_2N_2O_2 + 2NaOH = Na_2N_2O_2 + 2H_2O.$$

(iii) by warming sodium hydroxylamine N-benzene sulphonate with sodium hydroxide.

If silver nitrate is added to the aqueous solution of sodium hyponitrite, the sparingly soluble, canary yellow silver salt is precipitated. If the precipitate is added to a dry ethereal solution of hydrogen chloride, silver chloride is precipitated, and hyponitrous acid is left in solution. The acid is deposited as leaflets on the evaporation of the ether in vacuo.

Crystalline hyponitrous acid is explosive when dry. In solution it is more stable, but it decomposes with the evolution of nitrous oxide:

$$H_2N_2O_2 = H_2O + N_2O.$$

Hyponitrous ester also decomposes on heating:

$$(CH_3CH_2)_2N_2O_2 = CH_3CH_2OH + CH_3CHO + N_2.$$

The liberation of the group N_2 on decomposition indicates the presence of the group $N{=}N$ in the molecule.

Sodium hyponitrite decomposes explosively at $260°$ according to the equation:

$$3Na_2N_2O_2 = 2NaNO_2 + 2Na_2O + 2N_2.$$

The hyponitrites are reducing agents. In acid solution they are oxidised by potassium permanganate to nitric acid; in alkaline solution to sodium nitrite. It is remarkable that neither the acid nor its salts or esters can be reduced. Hyponitrous acid is a weak dibasic acid. K_1 is 9×10^{-18}, and K_2 is 1×10^{-11} at $25°$. The acid and the normal barium salts are known.

The molecular formula of the acid is in accordance with the freezing point of its aqueous solution, and with the freezing point of the solution of its diethyl ester in benzene. The d.p.m. of the diethyl ester is zero, thus indicating that the molecule has the *trans* configuration

$$\begin{array}{c} C_2H_5ON \\ \| \\ NOC_2H_5. \end{array}$$

The orbital structure of the nitrogen atoms in sodium hyponitrite is the same as that in potassium diazotate, $C_6H_5{-}N{=}NOK$, which is also explosive. It has not been explained why neither hyponitrous acid nor its salts can be obtained by the action of nitrous oxide on water or on an alkali, nor why hyponitrous acid is so resistant to reduction, and in particular why it cannot be reduced to hydrazine.

NITROUS ACID, HNO_2

Nitrous acid is stable only in solution. The aqueous solution is obtained by dissolving dinitrogen trioxide in water, or by treating a solution of barium nitrite with the calculated quantity of sulphuric acid, and filtering off the precipitated barium sulphate.

There is spectroscopic evidence that nitrous acid can exist in the vapour phase. The infrared absorption spectrum of a mixture of H_2O, NO, and NO_2 shows bands which are present in nitrites, but not in the three substances mentioned.

Nitrous acid is a weak acid, $K = 4 \cdot 5 \times 10^{-4}$. It decomposes easily in water;

$$2HNO_2 = H_2O + N_2O_3 = H_2O + NO + NO_2$$
$$N_2O_4 + H_2O = HNO_3 + HNO_2.$$

Nitrous acid is both a reducing and an oxidising agent. It is oxidised quantitatively to nitric acid by potassium permanganate in acid solution, by hydrogen peroxide, and by silver bromate:

$$AgBrO_3 + 3HNO_2 = 3HNO_3 + AgBr.$$

(It reduces halogens to halide ions in suitable buffered solution.)

(a) It is reduced, mainly to nitric oxide, by ferrous salts, by potassium ferrocyanide, by metallic mercury in the presence of sulphuric acid, by hydrogen iodide, and by arsenious acid. The equations for these reactions are on p. 662.

(b) It is reduced, mainly to nitrous oxide or to nitrogen,
(i) by stannous salts in acid solution:

$$2Sn^{2+} + 2HNO_2 + 4H^+ = 2Sn^{4+} + N_2O + 3H_2O,$$

(ii) by hydrazoic acid:

$$N_3H + HNO_2 = N_2O + N_2 + H_2O, \dagger$$

(iii) by compounds containing the amino group:

$$C_2H_5NH_2 + HONO = C_2H_5OH + N_2 + H_2O,$$
$$NH_2SO_3H + HONO = H_2SO_4 + N_2 + H_2O,$$

(iv) by sulphides, which are largely oxidised to free sulphur; very little sulphate ion is produced.

(c) It is reduced (ultimately to hydroxylamine) by sulphur dioxide in the presence of sodium carbonate. The first stage is the conversion of nitrous acid into hydroxylamine disulphonic acid:

$$HONO \ + \ \begin{array}{c} [HSO_3]^- \\ [HSO_3]^- \end{array} \ = \ \left[HON \begin{array}{c} SO_3 \\ SO_3 \end{array} \right]^{2-} + H_2O.$$

The salts of nitrous acid include those of the alkali metals, the alkaline earth metals, silver, and cadmium. They are all soluble, and are easily decomposed by heat, those of cadmium and silver break down at 100° or less. There are no nitrites of polyvalent cations such as beryllium or aluminium.

The nitrite ion, NO_2^- contains 18 electrons, and is isoelectronic with ozone, and with FNO. By X-ray analysis the angle ONO is 115°, and the distance N—O is 1·24.

Nitrous acid forms well-characterised organic derivatives, which fall into two isomeric classes:

the nitrites $$R{-}O{-}N \overset{\pi}{\underset{}{\diagup}} O$$

and

the nitro compounds $$R{-}\overset{+}{N} \overset{\pi}{\diagup} \overset{O}{\underset{O^-}{}}$$

for example:

methyl nitrite   nitromethane

$$CH_3{-}O{-}N \overset{\pi}{\diagup} O \qquad CH_3{-}\overset{+}{N}(\overset{\pi}{\diagup}\alpha) \overset{O}{\underset{O^-}{}} \qquad \alpha = 135 \pm 5°$$

Gas, b.p. −12°, d.p.m. 2·27   Liquid, b.p. 101°, d.p.m. 3·19
Distances: C—O 1·44,   Distances: C—N 1·47,
   O—N 1·37, N=O 1·22   N—O 1·22

The alkyl nitrites are made by the action of an alcohol on the acid solution of sodium nitrite. They are volatile, pleasant-smelling compounds, liquid at room temperature. The nitro compounds are made by the action of silver nitrite on the alkyl iodide. The boiling points of the nitro compounds are about 100° higher than those of the corresponding nitrites. The di-electric constants of the nitro compounds are high (that of $C_2H_5NO_2$ is 37 at 25°, and that of $C_6H_5NO_2$ is 35) but the nitro compounds are not good ionising solvents. The d.p.m. of the NO_2 group is about 3.0×10^{-18}.

† Hydrazoic acid does not react with nitric acid, and hence this reaction may be used for destroying or estimating nitrites in the presence of nitrates.

The primary or secondary nitroparaffins behave as pseudo acids:

$$CH_3{-}\overset{+}{N}\overset{\displaystyle O}{\underset{\displaystyle O}{\Big\langle}} \;\rightleftharpoons\; CH_2{-}\overset{\pi}{\overset{+}{N}}\overset{\displaystyle \bar{O}}{\underset{\displaystyle O{-}H}{\Big\langle}} \;\rightleftharpoons\; CH_2{-}\overset{\pi}{\overset{+}{N}}\overset{\displaystyle \bar{O}}{\underset{\displaystyle O}{\Big\langle}} \;+H^+.$$

$K = 4{\cdot}1 \times 10^{-5}.$

Peroxymononitrous acid, HOONO, is known only in solution. It is made by the action of hydrogen peroxide on nitrous acid.

NITRIC ACID, HNO_3

Nitric acid is a colourless, fuming, liquid, m.p. $-41{\cdot}5°$, b.p. $86°$ with decomposition. The density at $15°$ is $1{\cdot}5241$. Nitric acid is prepared:

  (i) by distilling potassium nitrate with concentrated sulphuric acid,
  (ii) by the catalytic oxidation of ammonia:

$$4NH_3 + 5O_2 = 4NO + 6H_2O; \quad \Delta H = -304{\cdot}6 \text{ kcal.}$$

The cooled nitric oxide is allowed to react with excess of air to produce dinitrogen tetroxide which reacts with water:

$$N_2O_4 + 2H_2O = HNO_2 + H_3O^+ + NO_3^-$$
$$2HNO_2 = H_2O + NO + NO_2$$
$$2NO + O_2 = N_2O_4.$$

The product is an aqueous solution containing 50–60% nitric acid. Distillation of any aqueous solution of nitric acid yields ultimately the constant boiling point mixture containing 68% of the acid; distillation of this with concentrated sulphuric acid gives a solution containing 98% of the acid. The pure acid is obtained by crystallising the 98% acid at $-42°$.

The pure liquid nitric acid obtained by the fusion of the crystals is not made up of a single molecular species. The molecule of nitric acid, like that of water, is a proton donor and a proton acceptor. Ionisation occurs thus:

$$HO{-}\overset{+}{N}\overset{\displaystyle \bar{O}}{\underset{\displaystyle O}{\overset{}{\underset{\pi}{\Big\langle}}}} \;+\; HO{-}\overset{+}{N}\overset{\displaystyle \bar{O}}{\underset{\displaystyle O}{\overset{}{\underset{\pi}{\Big\langle}}}} \;\rightleftharpoons\; HO{-}\overset{+}{N}\overset{\displaystyle OH}{\underset{\displaystyle O}{\overset{}{\underset{\pi}{\Big\langle}}}} \;+NO_3^-. \tag{i}$$

The cation may then dissociate:

$$HO{-}\overset{+}{N}\overset{\displaystyle OH}{\underset{\displaystyle O}{\overset{}{\underset{\pi}{\Big\langle}}}} \;\rightleftharpoons\; NO_2^+ + H_2O. \tag{ii}$$

At $-40°$ the percentage dissociation of pure nitric acid ionised in this way is $3{\cdot}5$. If the pure acid is diluted, the increased concentration of water drives the equilibria to the left, and water molecules replace nitric acid molecules as proton acceptors. The cation $(HO)_2NO^+$ reacts thus:

$$HO{-}\overset{+}{N}\overset{\displaystyle OH}{\underset{\displaystyle O}{\overset{}{\underset{\pi}{\Big\langle}}}} \;+\; H_2O = H_3O^+ + HNO_3,$$

and the equilibrium becomes that of an acid in dilute aqueous solution:

$$HNO_3 + H_2O \rightleftharpoons H_3O^+ + NO_3^-. \tag{iii}$$

The trend of the above arguments is not affected if the free acid is hydrated

or if the NO_3^- ion is hydrated.

The proportions of the molecular and ionic species present in aqueous solutions of nitric acid have been deduced from measurements of the vapour pressure and the values of the van't Hoff coefficient i. Some results are given in Table 19.11.

Table 19.11. *Proportions of Molecular and Ionic Species present in Aqueous Solutions of Nitric Acid*

Concentration of nitric acid in aqueous solution, per cent by weight	Number of moles of each species formed from 100 moles of HNO_3 in aqueous solution			
	NO_2OH	$(H_3O^+)(NO_3^-)$	HNO_3, H_2O	H_2O
94·5	80	0·3	19	1
65	3	12	85	34

The following two properties of concentrated aqueous solutions of nitric acid can be explained by consideration of the above modes of ionisation.

(i) The minimum electrical conductance is displayed by the anhydrous acid mixed with 3% of water. This effect arises because ionisations (i) and (ii) of the pure acid are suppressed by the addition of water but if more water is added, ionisation (iii) is promoted. At some stage in the dilution the number of ions present would be a minimum.

(ii) The absorption band at 3015A in the ultraviolet spectrum, correlated with the presence of NO_3^- or $[NO_3, H_2O^-]$, is absent from 80–100% nitric acid, and a band at 2600 A correlated with the presence of $[ON(OH)_2^+]$ can be detected. This band is not found in the spectra of N_2O_5 in solution in the solvents acetic acid, acetic anhydride, or carbon tetrachloride. Hence it is not due to NO_2^+ or NO_3^-.

If pure nitric acid is added to another acid it will act as a proton donor if the second acid is the weaker:

$$HNO_3 + H_2O = H_3O^+ + NO_3^-,$$

and as a proton acceptor if the second acid is the stronger. Thus in perchloric acid solution:

$$HNO_3 + HClO_4 = (HO)_2NO^+ + ClO_4^-$$
$$= NO_2^+ + H_2O + ClO_4^-$$
$$H_2O + HClO_4 = H_3O^+ + ClO_4^-.$$

Corresponding reactions occur in sulphuric acid solution:

$$HNO_3 + H_2SO_4 = (HO)_2NO^+ + HSO_4^-$$
$$= NO_2^+ + H_2O + HSO_4^-$$
$$H_2O + H_2SO_4 = H_3O^+ + HSO_4^-.$$

22*

The structure of the nitric acid molecule. In the vapour the molecule is monomeric. The structure indicated by electron diffraction measurements is that of a planar molecule with the dimensions:

The structure of the crystal at $-42°$, by X-ray measurements is

Chemical properties of nitric acid. At room temperature the pure acid undergoes thermal dissociation thus:

$$2HNO_3 \rightleftharpoons H_2O + N_2O_5,$$
$$2N_2O_5 \rightleftharpoons 2N_2O_4 + O_2,$$

When the pure acid is heated the gases oxygen and nitrogen dioxide are driven off, and the residual water dilutes the acid until the maximum boiling point mixture is obtained.† Liquid nitric acid is miscible with water in all proportions, and the solution gives rise to two solid hydrates, $HNO_3,3H_2O$, m.p. $-18.5°$, and HNO_3,H_2O, m.p. $-37.7°$.

Nitric acid is a strong monobasic acid which reacts with hydroxides and carbonates to form salts. It is a strong oxidising agent, organic substances such as sawdust and turpentine burn in it. Many non-metals such as phosphorus, sulphur, and iodine are oxidised to their oxyacids. It oxidises tin to hydrated stannic oxide. It oxidises stannous chloride in hydrochloric acid solution to stannic chloride, and is itself reduced to hydroxylamine and ammonia.

Ferrous sulphate and also metallic mercury (both in the presence of strong sulphuric acid) reduce nitric acid nearly quantitatively to nitric oxide (for equations, see p. 661). A mixture of nitric acid and sulphuric acid (p. 681) contains the nitronium ion, which probably takes part in these oxidising reactions. It has been established that the nitration of aromatic compounds by a mixture of nitric acid and sulphuric acid is initiated by the addition of a nitronium ion to a carbon atom in the benzene ring.

Action of nitric acid on metals. Rhodium, tantalum, iridium, platinum, and gold, are not attacked either by dilute or by concentrated nitric acid. Chromium and iron are rendered passive by concentrated nitric acid (in which condition they are unattacked by other reagents, such as cupric sulphate solution, to which they are normally vulnerable); aluminium is attacked only very slowly by nitric acid in the cold. The remaining metals are more or less rapidly attacked by nitric acid. Tin, arsenic, antimony, molybdenum, and tungsten are converted to oxide; the other metals to nitrates. The nature of the reaction products, other than metallic oxides or nitrates, is governed by the nature of the metals, the temperature and the concentration of the acid. The reaction products may contain one or more of the substances nitrous acid, nitrogen dioxide, nitric oxide, nitrous oxide, nitrogen, hydroxylamine, or ammonia; molecular

---

† The maximum boiling point mixture boils at 121°. The composition is 68% nitric acid, and the specific gravity is 1·414.

hydrogen is produced only when magnesium, manganese, or zinc is treated with very dilute nitric acid. The metals which possess standard reduction–oxidation potentials greater than that of the reaction:

$$H_2 = 2H^+ + 2e$$

tend to yield products such as hydrogen, nitrogen, ammonia, hydroxylamine, or nitrous oxide when treated with nitric acid. Metals which have standard reduction–oxidation potentials less than that of hydrogen tend to liberate nitrogen dioxide or nitric oxide. For reference the standard potentials are set out in Table 19.12.

Table 19.12. *Standard Reduction–Oxidation Potentials of certain Metals at* 25° ($\frac{1}{2}H_2 = H^+ + e$: electrode potential $= 0.00$)

A Reactions	Standard electrode potential, volts	B Reactions	Standard electrode potential, volts
$Mg = Mg^{2+} + 2e$	2·4		
$Mn = Mn^{2+} + 2e$	1·1	$Bi = Bi^{3+} + 2e$	−0·23
$Zn = Zn^{2+} + 2e$	0·76	$Cu = Cu^+ + e$	−0·5
$Cr = Cr^{2+} + 2e$	0·6	$Ag = Ag^+ + e$	−0·8
$Fe = Fe^{2+} + 2e$	0·44	$Hg = Hg^{2+} + 2e$	−0·86
$Cd = Cd^{2+} + 2e$	0·4	$Au = Au^+ + e$	−1·5
$Sn = Sn^{2+} + 2e$	0·13	$Fe^{2+} = Fe^{3+} + e$	−0·74
$Pb = Pb^{2+} + 2e$	0·12		

It is reasonable to assume that the primary reaction of metals in column A of Table 19.12 with nitric acid is the transfer of electrons from the metal to hydroxonium ions. The hydrogen thus potentially released could then by secondary reactions reduce the nitric acid to nitrous acid, and ultimately to ammonia.

It has been established experimentally that the presence of nitrous acid has an important influence on the course of the reaction between nitric acid and a metal in column B of Table 19.12. It has been shown that copper is not attacked by nitric acid which contains either urea or hydrogen peroxide; these compounds destroy any nitrous acid as soon as it is formed. A specimen of copper rotated rapidly in nitric acid is scarcely attacked, because the movement of the copper prevents the accumulation of nitrous acid at its surface. If copper is allowed to remain in contact with pure nitric acid it is gradually attacked at first, and then with increasing rapidity as the concentration of nitrous acid in the solution increases. The rate of the reaction is related to the concentration of nitrous acid. Bismuth and silver behave in much the same way as copper. The effect of nitrous acid on the solution of magnesium and cadmium in nitric acid, however, is just the opposite; it inhibits the attack of nitric acid on these metals.

There are many ionic and molecular species in a mixture of nitric and nitrous acids, and it does not follow that nitrous acid itself is responsible for modifying the attack of nitric acid on certain metals. It might be hazarded that the nitrosonium ion liberated by the action of nitric acid on nitrous acid:

$$6HNO_3 + 6HNO_2 = 6(HO)_2N^+ + 6NO_3^-, \tag{19.1}$$

$$6(HO)_2N^+ = 6H_2O + 6NO^+ \tag{19.2}$$

might play an important part. It is known to be an electron acceptor, and the first stage in the reaction with copper might be:

$$6Cu + 6NO^+ = 6Cu^+ + 6NO. \tag{19.3}$$

If one-third of the nitric oxide so liberated is oxidised by nitric acid to nitrogen dioxide, and if this reacts with water to yield a mixture of nitric and nitrous acids, one-half of the nitrous acid used in equation (19.1) is restored:

$$2NO + 2HNO_3 = 2HNO_2 + 2NO_2, \tag{19.4}$$

$$2NO_2 + H_2O = HNO_2 + HNO_3. \tag{19.5}$$

The second half is regenerated by the oxidation of the cuprous ion to the cupric ion:

$$6CuNO_3 + 6HNO_3 = 6Cu(NO_3)_2 + 6H, \tag{19.6}$$

$$6H + 3HNO_3 = 3HNO_2 + 3H_2O. \tag{19.7}$$

The addition of all the equations (19.1) to (19.7) gives the well-known equation

$$3Cu + 8HNO_3 = 2NO + 3Cu(NO_3)_2 + 4H_2O. \tag{19.8}$$

The accuracy with which equation (19.8) applies to any particular experiment depends (on the above interpretation) on the proportion of liberated nitric oxide, as shown by equation (19.3), which is retained in the system by the reactions indicated by equations (19.4) and (19.5). If the proportion is more than one third, nitrous acid will accumulate in the solution.

The inhibiting effect of nitrous acid on the solution of magnesium and cadmium in nitric acid could also be explained by the intermediate action of the nitrosonium ion. If the initial stage of the reaction is:

$$Mg + 2NO^+ = Mg^{2+} + 2NO$$

and if the nitric oxide, instead of escaping as a gas, remains adsorbed on the surface of the metal, further reaction would be impeded.

The passivity of iron and chromium produced by immersion in concentrated nitric acid, and the slow rate of solution of aluminium in nitric acid, may be due to the formation of a monomolecular oxide layer on the metallic surface, or to the adsorption of nitric oxide or of nitrogen dioxide molecules on the surface. Any mechanism to account for the action of nitric acid on metals must, besides accounting for the effect of nitrous acid, also explain why the rate of solution of palladium in nitric acid is accelerated if air or oxygen is passed through the solution, and why cadmium, which is rapidly dissolved both by strong and dilute nitric acid, is unattacked by nitric acid of more than 83% concentration if the cadmium is in contact with platinum.

Peroxymononitric acid, $HOONO_2$, is an explosive crystalline compound which smells like hypochlorous acid. It is made by the action of anhydrous hydrogen peroxide on dinitrogen pentoxide.

HYDRAZOIC ACID, N_3H

Hydrazoic acid is a poisonous, highly explosive liquid with an offensive smell, m.p. $-80°$, b.p. $+37°$.

Hydrazoic acid is formed by the oxidation of hydrazine by such reagents as sodium nitrite, ethyl nitrite, or nitrogen chloride. The general reaction may be formulated:

$$3N_2H_4 + 5O = 2N_3H + 5H_2O.$$

The alkali metal azides may be obtained by one of the three following methods:

(i) By the interaction of the nitrate and the amide of the metal:

$$KNO_3 + 3KNH_2 = KN_3 + 3KOH + NH_3.$$

The action is sometimes carried out by adding the nitrate to the molten amide at 175°, but in these conditions it proceeds with almost explosive violence. It is also carried out in anhydrous ammonia solution at 90–100°. In these conditions the sodium compounds give a yield of 16%, the potassium compounds 75%, and the lead compounds 80%.

(ii) By the action of nitrous oxide on the metallic amide at 190°:

$$N\text{---}N\text{---}O + NH_2^- = (N\text{---}N\text{---}N)^- + H_2O. \tag{19.9}$$

If sodium azide is to be made, it is convenient to make sodamide by passing ammonia over sodium in a porcelain boat in a hard-glass tube at 150–250°. The current of ammonia is then replaced by a current of nitrous oxide, and the tube is maintained at 190°. The steam liberated in accordance with equation (19.9) reacts with some of the sodamide, and the gas that actually leaves the tube is ammonia:

$$NaNH_2 + H_2O = NaOH + NH_3.$$

The yield is 90%.

To obtain the free acid, the mixture of sodium azide and hydroxide is distilled with dilute sulphuric acid, and a solution of N_3H is collected. The solution may be fractionated, dehydrated over calcium chloride, and redistilled, but these operations are very dangerous.

(iii) By passing active nitrogen over a film of metallic sodium; the nitride is formed initially, but yields the azide almost at once.

Hydrazoic acid dissolves readily in water. It is a slightly stronger acid than acetic acid, $K = 2 \cdot 8 \times 10^{-5}$. The aqueous solution readily dissolves iron, zinc, and copper, with the formation of the azide, nitrogen, and ammonia:

$$Zn + 3HN_3 = Zn(N_3)_2 + N_2 + NH_3.$$

In solution hydrazoic acid is fairly stable, but in the presence of platinum black it reacts thus:

$$HN_3 + H_2O = H_2NOH + N_2.$$

Light decomposes it in the same way.

Hydrazoic acid can be both reduced and oxidised. Hydrogen in the presence of palladium reduces it to ammonia. Zinc and sulphuric acid with no catalyst reduce it to NH_3, N_2H_4, and N_2. The proportion of N_2H_4 to N_2 increases with rise in temperature. Hydrazoic acid is oxidised by the ceric ion (quantitatively):

$$2Ce^{4+} + 2N_3H = 2Ce^{3+} + 3N_2 + 2H^+,$$

by hypochlorous acid (quantitatively):

$$HOCl + HN_3 = ClN_3 + H_2O,$$
$$ClN_3 + HN_3 = HCl + 3N_2,$$

by nitrous acid (quantitatively under certain conditions):

$$HNO_2 + HN_3 = N_2 + N_2O + H_2O.$$

The acid may be titrated against sodium nitrite, ferric chloride being used as indicator ($Fe(N_3)_3$ is red; the colour is discharged by acids), or against iodine in the presence of thiosulphate, sulphide, or CS_2 as catalyst:

$$I_2 + 2HN_3 = 2HI + 3N_2.$$

Hydrazoic acid is oxidised by potassium permanganate, but not quantitatively.

The azides (hydrazides). The azides of the alkali metals and of the alkaline earth metals are ionic, those of the coinage and transition metals display both ionic and covalent character. The azides of the halogens and organic radicals are covalent. Azides possessing covalent character are dangerously explosive, but the azides of the alkali metals are not explosive, and decompose quietly when heated. Sodium azide is colourless and crystalline. When distilled with sulphuric acid it yields hydrazoic acid. When heated it decomposes quantitatively at 150–300° to sodium and nitrogen. Barium azide is used as a source of pure nitrogen. Sodium azide heated with metallic sodium yields sodium nitride (p. 416), if heated with sodium nitrate it yields sodium oxide, Na_2O, and nitrogen, and if heated with barium carbonate it yields barium cyanide.

The silver, lead, and mercurous azides are insoluble, and may be obtained by adding a soluble salt of the metal to a solution of sodium azide. Silver, lead, and mercurous azides explode violently when struck. Lead azide, $Pb(N_3)_2$ is used in the explosives industry as an initiator. It is preferred to mercury fulminate because it deteriorates less on storage if not in contact with carbon dioxide or hydrogen sulphide, and because the maximum velocity of detonation (4500 m/sec) is reached more quickly than with mercury fulminate.

The explosive covalent azide derivatives include the acid itself, organic derivatives, halide derivatives, and salts of transition metals which behave to some extent as covalent compounds, owing to the polarising properties of the cation.

Chlorine azide, ClN_3, a dangerous explosive gas, is formed when a mixture of sodium azide and sodium hypochlorite is acidified with boric acid or acetic acid. Bromine azide, BrN_3, a dangerous orange coloured liquid, is formed from bromine and sodium azide. It is hydrolysed by water to bromine and nitrogen. Iodine azide, IN_3, is a pale yellow explosive solid, and is obtained by the action of iodine on silver azide. $CN \cdot N_3$ is a solid, m.p. 40·3°.

Structure of hydrazoic acid and the azides. The N_3^- ion. X-ray analysis shows the ion N_3^- to be linear. The crystal structures of the azides of the following cations have been determined, and the N—N distances are: Na 1·15, K 1·16, NH_4 1·17, Ag 1·18, Sr 1·12. It is assumed that the two distances N—N in the ion are equal. According to the valence bond theory the ion consists of the canonical forms $:\overset{\_}{N}\overset{\pi}{=}\overset{+}{N}\overset{}{=}\overset{\_}{N}:$ and $:N\overset{+}{=}\overset{2-}{N}—\overset{}{N}:$ and $:\overset{2-}{N}—\overset{+}{N}\overset{\pi}{=}N:$ in resonance.

The covalent N_3 group. From the electron diffraction of methyl azide Pauling and Brockway found the dimensions of the molecule

$$N\text{——}N\text{——}N$$
$$\diagup$$
$$H_3C$$

to be: distances C—N 1·47, N—N 1·26, N—N (remote from C) 1·10; the angle CNN is $135 \pm 15°$. From the infrared spectrum of the acid Herzberg concluded that the distances, later confirmed by Eyster, in the molecule of the acid

$$N\text{——}N\text{——}N$$
$$\diagup$$
$$H$$

are: H—N 1·01, N—N 1·24, N—N (remote from H) 1·13; the angle HNN is 111°. According to the valence bond theory methyl azide has a resonance structure of the canonical forms $H_3C—\overset{\_}{\overset{}{N}}—\overset{+}{N}\overset{\pi}{=}N:$ and $H_3C—\overset{}{N}\overset{}{=}\overset{+}{N}\overset{\pi}{=}\overset{\_}{N}:$

The bond lengths, both in the ion and in the covalent group are short. The bond order of the N—N bond in the ion is 2, and the distance N—N is about 1·15, whereas the distance N=N predicted by Pauling is 1·28. In methyl azide the bond order of the N—N bond next to the methyl group is 1·5, and the bond order of the other N—N bond is 2·5. The bond lengths N—N respectively are 1·25 and 1·12, but the values predicted by Pauling would be about 1·38 and 1·22.

Certain compounds containing the group CN. Cyanogen, $N\frac{\pi}{\pi}C\!-\!C\frac{\pi}{\pi}N$, hydrogen cyanide $H\!-\!C\frac{\pi}{\pi}N$, the nitriles $X\!-\!C\frac{\pi}{\pi}N$, and the isonitriles $X\_\overset{+}{N}\frac{\pi}{\pi}\overset{-}{C}$, all contain nitrogen atoms exerting triple bonds. These compounds, which are also interesting on account of the parts played by the carbon atoms, are discussed on pp. 580 to 583.

COMPOUNDS OF NITROGEN CONTAINING NON-LOCALISED π BONDS

The nitrogen atom takes part in an orbital system of non-localised π bonds when it is a member of a ring containing also boron atoms, or carbon atoms, or possibly phosphorus atoms. Examples are given below. The formulae show only σ bonds and lone electron pairs; non-localised π bonds are omitted.

Pyridine

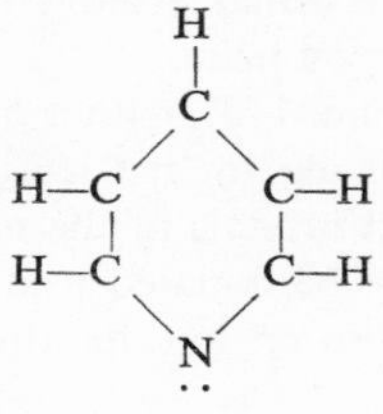

Quinoline

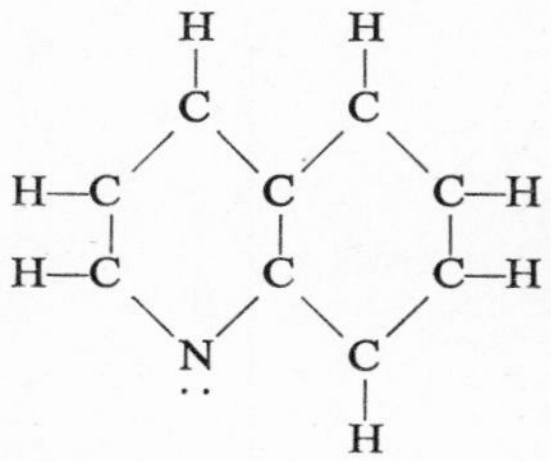

Cyanuric chloride

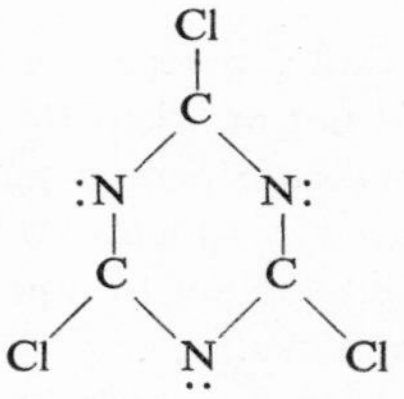

Boron nitride (p. 505)

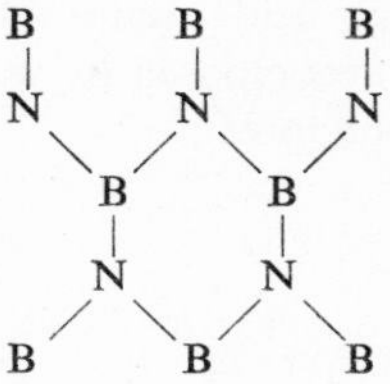

Borazole (p. 506)

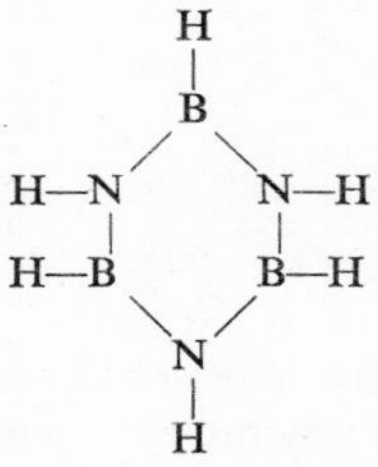

Phosphorus chloronitride
(p. 731)

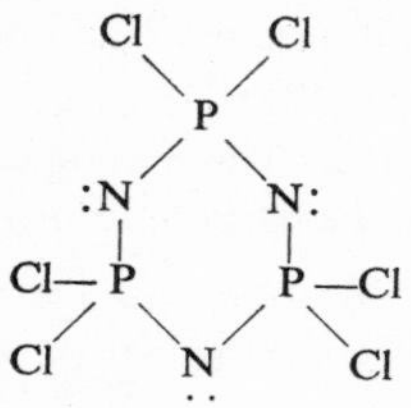

$$\begin{array}{ccc} Cl & & Cl \\ & \diagdown \; P \; \diagup & \\ :N & & N: \\ Cl-P & & P-Cl \\ Cl & N & Cl \end{array}$$

In pyridine and quinoline, in cyanuric chloride, in boron nitride, and in borazole, the nitrogen atoms are trigonally hybridised. One of the trigonal orbitals in pyridine or quinoline or similar compounds is occupied by a lone electron pair, but in boron nitride and in borazole all the trigonal orbitals of the nitrogen atoms are bonding orbitals occupied by shared electron pairs.

Pyridine. Pyridine is a liquid, b.p. 115°, with a pungent odour. It may be notionally derived from the benzene molecule by replacing one C—H group by a nitrogen atom; one of the trigonal hybrid orbitals of the nitrogen atom is occupied by a lone electron pair. The lone pair may be donated to a hydrogen ion, H+, which explains the miscibility of pyridine with water, and its ability to form stable crystalline salts of the ammonium chloride type:

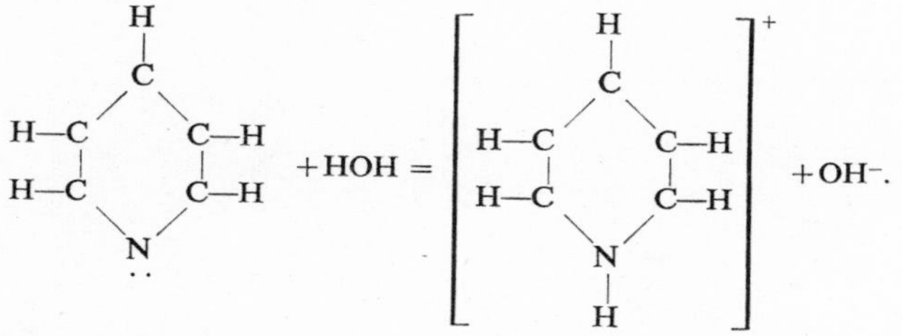

Otherwise, physically and chemically, pyridine resembles benzene. It is stable and resistant to chemical attack. It is not attacked by boiling nitric acid, or by aqueous solutions of chromic acid or potassium permanganate. With the halogens and with sulphuric acid it gives substitution products, but only with difficulty. Pyridine is reduced by anhydrous alcohol and sodium to piperidine, C_5NH_{11}, and by hydrogen iodide at 300° to pentane and ammonia.

The cyanuric compounds. Most nitriles, including chloronitrile, bromonitrile, and benzonitrile (but not hydrocyanic acid itself) polymerise to cyanuric compounds. Cyanuric chloride, m.p. 154°, is decomposed by water at 125° to give cyanuric acid, which might have either of the structures:

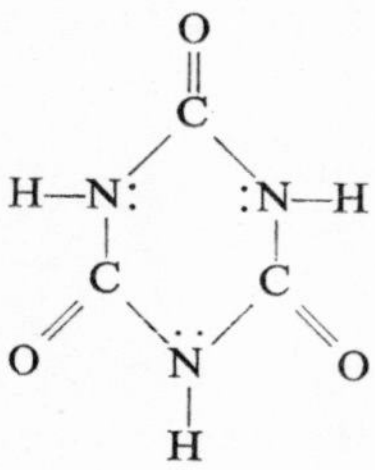

I

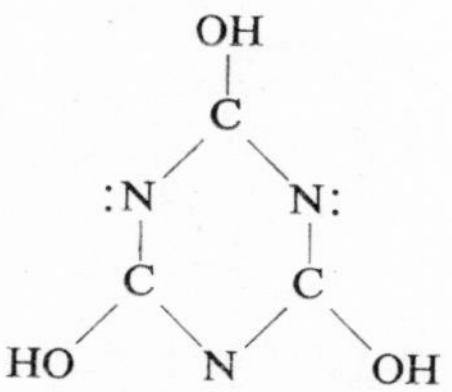

II

X-ray experiments on the solid are in accord with structure I, but esters of both forms are known. Structure II is a generalised π bond structure.

SECTION 4. COMPOUNDS IN WHICH THE NITROGEN ATOM
IS TETRAHEDRALLY HYBRIDISED

A tetrahedrally hybridised nitrogen atom exerting four σ bonds is present in the ammonium ion $[NH_4{}^+]$. A tetrahedrally hybridised nitrogen atom exerting three σ bonds and having the fourth hybrid orbital occupied by a lone pair is present in ammonia and in many other compounds. In the ions $[NO_2]^{2-}$ and $[Tol_3N]^+$ one of the hybrid orbitals on a tetrahedrally hybridised nitrogen atom is occupied by an unpaired electron.

AMMONIA

Ammonia exists as a colourless gas, a colourless liquid, or an ice-like solid. Pure ammonia is made by the reduction of sodium nitrate or sodium nitrite in hot aqueous solution containing sodium hydroxide, by metallic zinc, aluminium, or Devarda's alloy (Cu 50, Al 45, Zn 5):

$$NaNO_3 + 4Zn + 7NaOH = NH_3 + 4Na_2ZnO_2 + 2H_2O.$$

The reduction is quantitative, and by estimating the amount of ammonia produced, the concentration of nitrate or nitrite in the original solution may be determined.

Ammonia may be conveniently obtained either by heating a mixture of ammonium chloride and dry slaked lime, or by warming a concentrated aqueous solution of ammonia, sp. gr. 0·880. The ammonia is dried by passage over quicklime. Large quantities of ammonia are made industrially by the Haber process in which hydrogen and nitrogen combine directly in the presence of iron at a temperature of about 500°C and at pressures between 200 and 1000 atm.

Ammonia gas. Some of the physical properties of ammonia are given in Table 19.13. The heat of formation from atoms, and the heat of formation from molecular hydrogen and nitrogen are given by the equations:

$$N + 3H = NH_3; \quad \Delta H_a = -278 \cdot 7 \text{ kcal,}$$
$$\tfrac{1}{2}N_2 + 1\tfrac{1}{2}H_2 = NH_3; \quad \Delta H = -11 \cdot 0 \text{ kcal at } 20°.$$

Ammonia dissociates on heating. It is also partly decomposed by electric sparks, equilibrium being reached when 6% of ammonia is present with 94% of hydrogen and nitrogen; a mixture of nitrogen and hydrogen when sparked yields the same equilibrium mixture. Ammonia will not burn in air, but it will do so in oxygen. A mixture of ammonia and oxygen explodes to give steam and some oxides of nitrogen, but if the ammonia is first decomposed as far as possible by sparking, the products are steam and nitrogen only. In the presence of a heated platinum catalyst a mixture of ammonia and oxygen, or of ammonia and air, yields steam and nitric oxide. A mixture of ammonia and air containing 22% of ammonia explodes on ignition if the original pressure is 1 atm; higher pressures increase the range of composition of mixtures which explode.

Ammonia reduces many metallic oxides, such as lead monoxide and cupric oxide; the metal is formed together with steam, nitrogen, and a little nitric oxide. Under special conditions (p. 703) ammonia is oxidised to hydrazine. Chlorine, if not in excess, reacts with ammonia to yield nitrogen and ammonium chloride:

$$2NH_3 + 3Cl_2 = N_2 + 6HCl$$
$$6HCl + 6NH_3 = 6NH_4Cl.$$

Chlorine in excess yields nitrogen trichloride:

$$2NH_3 + 6Cl_2 = 2NCl_3 + 6HCl.$$

If ammonia is passed over carbon at 800–1000° hydrogen cyanide is formed. The yield is 25%. When ammonia is passed over a heated mixture of coke and sodium, sodium cyanide is formed. Ammonia reacts with potassium, sodium, and calcium to form amides (p. 694). It forms co-ordination compounds with many salts to give products such as $CaCl_2,8NH_3$ and $Cu(NH_3)_2SO_4$.

Structure of the ammonia molecule. Experimental evidence indicates that the molecule is pyramidal with the nitrogen atom at the apex. The angle HNH is 116°; the bond length NH is 0·94. The orbital structure of the molecule must be based either (i) on a valence state of the nitrogen atom in which the $2s$ electron pair is inert, and the three $2p$ orbitals are hybridised, or (ii) on the tetrahedral valence state of the nitrogen atom, one of the hybrid orbitals being occupied by a lone electron pair. An inert electron pair is found only in the atoms of heavy elements; there is no evidence of its presence in the atoms of carbon, oxygen, or phosphorus, in any state of combination. It is therefore reasonable to disregard alternative (i), and to suppose that the nitrogen atom in ammonia is tetrahedrally hybridised, and that the structure of the molecule is that shown in Fig. 19.1(a). If each hydrogen atom in the molecule

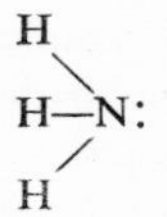

Fig. 19.1(a)   Fig. 19.1(b)

is identifiable, there are two structures, I and II (Fig. 19.1(b)), which are non-superposable, each structure being the mirror image of the other. The ammonia molecule is a resonance structure of these two forms, each of which is characterised by its own wave function, ψ_1 and ψ_2. Hence the structure possesses two energy levels, corresponding to the wave functions $\psi_1+\psi_2$ and $\psi_1-\psi_2$, the presence of which is shown in the vibration spectrum of ammonia. The spectrum arising through the existence of the two energy levels is known as the *inversion spectrum* of ammonia (p. 234).

Ammonia in aqueous solution. Ammonia is very soluble in water; 1 volume of water at 0° dissolves 1148 volumes of ammonia. All the ammonia is expelled from the solution on boiling. From the solution the crystalline hydrates NH_3,H_2O (or NH_4OH), m.p. −79°, and $2NH_3,H_2O$ (or $(NH_4)_2O$) m.p. −78·9°, have been obtained.

In aqueous solution the equilibrium is set up:

$$NH_3 + H_2O \rightleftharpoons NH_4OH \rightleftharpoons [NH_4]^+ + [OH^-]$$
$$46·2 \qquad\qquad 52·4 \qquad\qquad 1·4$$

The figures show, in molecular percentages, the proportions of ammonia and its two derivatives present in a decinormal solution of ammonia at 25°. The apparent dissociation constant of ammonium hydroxide, K_1, is given by:

$$K_1 = \frac{[NH_4^+][OH^-]}{[NH_4OH]+[NH_3]} = 1·8 \times 10^{-5}.$$

The true dissociation constant, K, is given by:

$$K = \frac{[NH_4^+][OH^-]}{[NH_4OH]} = 4 \times 10^{-5}.$$

Ammonium hydroxide is thus only a very weak base. The tetra-alkyl ammonium hydroxides, such as tetraethyl ammonium hydroxide, $(C_2H_5)_4NOH$, are strong bases. The dissociation constants at 18° for the four ethyl ammonium hydroxides are:

$$N(C_2H_5)H_3OH \qquad 6{\cdot}73 \times 10^{-4}$$
$$N(C_2H_5)_2H_2OH \qquad 10{\cdot}6 \times 10^{-4}$$
$$N(C_2H_5)_3HOH \qquad 7{\cdot}9 \times 10^{-4}$$
$$N(C_2H_5)_4OH \qquad 1{\cdot}0$$

If a derivative of the ammonium radical contains a hydrogen atom which is directly linked to the nitrogen atom, a hydrogen bond is established between this hydrogen atom and the OH^- ion, and the dissociation constant of the base is low. If no such hydrogen atom is present, as in the tetraethyl ammonium radical, the formation of a hydrogen bond is impossible and the dissociation constant of the base is high.

Liquid ammonia. The properties of ammonia, compared with those of the hydrides of the elements near to nitrogen in the periodic table, methane, water, and hydrogen fluoride, are given in Table 19.13. Methane is by far the most volatile of these compounds, because it is unassociated. The molecules of ammonia, water, and hydrogen fluoride contain atoms of electronegative elements which carry lone electron pairs, and consequently the molecules become linked by hydrogen bonds, and the liquids are associated.

Liquid ammonia dissolves the alkali metals and the alkaline earth metals to give blue solutions (p. 399). Liquid ammonia is a general solvent, but the solubilities of the compounds it dissolves vary greatly as they do in the case of water. All ammonium salts are very soluble, as they are acids in the liquid ammonia solvent system. Beryllium chloride is also very soluble, presumably because of the readiness with which the beryllium atom unites with donor molecules to give ions such as $[Be,4NH_3]^{2+}$. It is broadly true to say that metallic salts of the anions of monobasic acids, including NO_3, NO_2, CN, Br, I, are soluble in ammonia; fluorides, however, are for the most part insoluble. Metallic salts of the anions of polybasic acids, including SO_4, CO_3, PO_4, AsO_4, $(COO)_2$, S, are insoluble.

Metallic oxides and hydroxides are insoluble.

Table 19.13. *Physical Properties of Ammonia and of the Neighbouring Hydrides*

	CH$_4$	NH$_3$	H$_2$O	HF
M.p. °C	-184	-77	0	$-83{\cdot}7$
B.p. °C	-161	$-33{\cdot}4$	100	$19{\cdot}5$
Critical Point °C	$-82{\cdot}5$	$132{\cdot}5$	374	$230{\cdot}2$
Latent heat of fusion cal/gm	$14{\cdot}5$	$81{\cdot}5$	$79{\cdot}7$	$54{\cdot}7$
Viscosity, centipoises		$0{\cdot}255$/b.p. $0{\cdot}475/-70°$	$1{\cdot}798/0°$ $2{\cdot}549/-10°$	$0{\cdot}256/0°$ $0{\cdot}570/-50°$
Dielectric constant		22/b.p.	$81/18°$	$86{\cdot}3/0°$
Dipole moment		$1{\cdot}48$/b.p.	$1{\cdot}84/18°$	
Specific conductance ohm^{-1} cm^{-1}		$1{\cdot}97 \times 10^{-7}$ at $-38{\cdot}9°$		

Organic compounds containing electronegative atoms in the molecule (alcohols, phenols, ethers, esters, ketones, amines, nitrocompounds, sulphonic esters and certain alkyl halides) are readily soluble in liquid ammonia, but paraffins are insoluble, and benzene is only slightly soluble. The solubility of the alcohols and other compounds may be due to the formation of hydrogen bonds between the electronegative atoms (oxygen in the case of alcohol) and the nitrogen atoms of liquid ammonia. The paraffins and benzene would not be able to form such bonds.

Liquid ammonia is an ionising solvent. The ionisation of salts is less in liquid ammonia than in water, but owing to the lower viscosity of liquid ammonia the ionic mobilities are much greater. The ionisation of liquid ammonia:

$$2NH_3 \rightleftharpoons NH_4^+ + NH_2^-$$

is very slight. The ionic product $[NH_4^+] \times [NH_2^-] = 10^{-29\pm1}$ at $-40°$.

A substance which dissolves in liquid ammonia to produce NH_4^+ ions is an acid; a substance which produces NH_2^- ions is a base. Among the acids of the system are all ammonium salts, and also all compounds which are acids in water, because the ionisable hydrogen atoms of these compounds combine with NH_3 molecules to give NH_4^+ ions, just as they combine with water molecules to give OH_3^+. The amides of the alkali metals are bases. The reaction:

$$NH_4Cl + KNH_2 = KCl + 2NH_3$$
$$\quad\text{acid}\qquad\text{base}\qquad\text{salt}\qquad\text{solvent}$$

is analogous to the reaction in the water system:

$$OH_3Cl + KOH = KCl + 2H_2O.$$
$$\quad\text{acid}\qquad\text{base}\qquad\text{salt}\qquad\text{solvent}$$

Acids of the liquid ammonia system, like those of the water system, attack metals with the liberation of hydrogen. A solution of ammonium azide in liquid ammonia attacks the metals Li, Na, K, Mg, and Ca, to form metallic azides with the liberation of hydrogen:

$$2NH_4N_3 + 2Li = 2LiN_3 + H_2 + 2NH_3.$$

A solution of ammonium nitrite in liquid ammonia attacks the same metals; sodium and potassium yield the nitroxylates (p. 675) but the other metals form nitrates liberating hydrogen and ammonia. Ammonium salts also attack and dissolve the metals Mn, La, Ce, Fe, Co, Ni, Be.

There are three basic ions in the liquid ammonia system:

$$NH_2^- \qquad NH^{2-} \qquad N^{3-}$$

compared with two in the water system, OH^- and O^{2-}. Bismuth nitride, BiN, reacts with ammonium iodide in liquid ammonia, thus:

$$3NH_4I + BiN = BiI_3 + 4NH_3,$$

and this reaction is comparable to the reaction in the oxygen system:

$$6HI + Bi_2O_3 = 2BiI_3 + 3H_2O.$$

Bases in the liquid ammonia system produce ammonolysis, just as those in the water system produce hydrolysis. The reactions in liquid ammonia:

$$PbI_2 + 2KNH_2 = PbNH + 2KI + NH_3,$$
$$AgNO_3 + KNH_2 = AgNH_2 + KNO_3,$$

are comparable with the reactions in water:

$$PbI_2 + 2KOH = PbO + 2KI + H_2O,$$
$$AgNO_3 + KOH = AgOH + KNO_3.$$

Certain amides, like certain hydroxides, are amphoteric. Amides are more ready to become amphoteric in the ammonia system than are hydroxides in the water system. Not only zinc and aluminium form amphoteric amides, but also lithium, sodium, magnesium, calcium, strontium, barium, tin, and lead. If a little potassamide is added to sodium iodide dissolved in liquid ammonia, crystalline sodamide is precipitated. The precipitate dissolves on the addition of more potassamide to give potassium ammonosodiate $K[Na(NH_2)_2]$, in which the sodium is present in the complex anion.

The hydrides of certain non-metallic elements are usefully prepared by the action of ammonium bromide in liquid ammonia on the binary compound of the element with magnesium. For example:

$$4NH_4Br + Mg_2Ge = GeH_4 + 2MgBr_2 + 4NH_3,$$
$$4NH_4Br + Mg_2Si = SiH_4 + 2MgBr_2 + 4NH_3.$$

Ammonium salts. The ionic radius 1·48 is assigned to the ammonium ion. This value is the same as that assigned to the rubidium ion; ammonium salts are often isomorphous with the corresponding rubidium and potassium salts. Ammonium salts are soluble in water (the bitartrate, like that of potassium, is one of the least soluble), and they are nearly always anhydrous (the carbonate, oxalate, iodate, and periodate are hydrated like the potassium salts, and hence the water molecules are probably co-ordinated to the anions).

The crystal structures of ammonium salts which contain oxygen or fluorine are often profoundly affected by the presence of hydrogen bonds. For example, ammonium chloride, bromide, and iodide crystallise with close-packed structures. These salts are dimorphic; below 184·4°, 137·8°, and −17·6° respectively they have the CsCl (8:1) lattice, and above these temperatures the NaCl (6:1) lattice. Ammonium fluoride, however, is not dimorphic, and it crystallises with the open wurtzite structure. The nitrogen atoms are situated at points corresponding to the positions on a cubic face-centred lattice, and the fluorine atoms occupy one half of the tetrahedral holes. The hydrogen atoms lie between the nitrogen atoms and the fluorine atoms. The distance N—F is 2·66.

When ammonium fluoride is fused it yields ammonium hydrogen fluoride:

$$2NH_4F = NH_3 + NH_4HF_2.$$

In the crystal of NH_4HF_2 the fluorine atoms are linked in pairs by hydrogen bonds F—H—F. Each nitrogen atom is at the centre of four fluorine atoms arranged tetrahedrally, and each fluorine atom is bound to two nitrogen atoms. Hydrogen atoms lie between the nitrogen atoms and the fluorine atoms. A diagrammatic 2-dimensional representation of the relations of the atoms and bonds is shown below

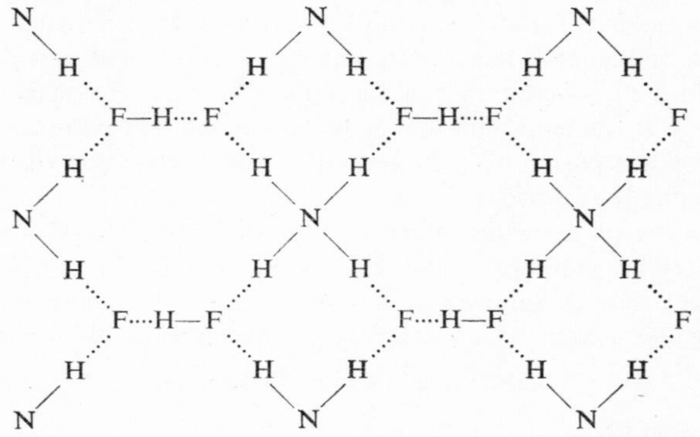

The open structure of crystalline hydrazinium fluoride $N_2H_6F_2$ and the distorted fluorite structure of $N_2H_6Cl_2$ furnish other examples of the influence of hydrogen bonds on the crystal structures of ammonium salts.

Pauling has suggested that dimorphism among ammonium salts containing the anions Cl^-, Br^-, I^-, NO_3^-, SO_4^{2-}, AsO_3^{3-}, $Cr_2O_7^{2-}$, $H_2PO_4^-$, may be due to rotation of NH_4^+ ions. The five polymorphs of ammonium nitrate may be dependent on the rotation of the NH_4^+ ions and the NO_3^- ions.

The alkyl and aryl derivatives of the ammonium ion. In a salt such as ammonium sulphate $(NH_4)_2SO_4$ any or all of the hydrogen atoms may be replaced by alkyl or aryl groups to give salts of the type $[N(CH_3)_4]_2SO_4$. The dissociation constants of the ethyl ammonium hydroxides are discussed on p. 691. The aryl ammonium hydroxides are even weaker bases, and the only salt of triphenylamine hydroxide is the perchlorate; the perchlorate ion is so resistant to distortion that it stabilises the cations of very weak bases.

The compound $[(CH_3C_6H_4)_3N][ClO_4]$ is of great interest because it contains a tetrahedrally hybridised nitrogen atom in which one orbital is occupied by an unpaired electron. The compound is crystalline and melts at 123°; at higher temperatures it explodes. It is made by adding tritolylamine to an ethereal solution of silver perchlorate and iodine. The ethereal solution is deep blue, and the salt is violet. The aqueous solution precipitates insoluble perchlorates.

The amides. The group $-NH_2$ is characteristic of the amides. The group is found covalently linked to non-metals in monochloramine, $ClNH_2$, and in the well-known organic amides, such as acetamide, CH_3CONH_2. It is also found linked to metals, as in sodamide, $NaNH_2$, and zinc diamide, $Zn(NH_2)_2$. In the ammonia acid-base system the group $-NH_2$ plays the same part as the group $-OH$ in the water acid-base system, but beyond this the similarity between the two groups is not close.

The alkali metal amides. The amides of lithium, sodium, and potassium are well-characterised. They are white crystalline solids, which melt at the following temperatures:

	Li	Na	K	Rb	Cs
m.p. °C	374	208	338	309	261
Conductivity (ohm^{-1} cm^{-1}) just above m.p.		0·593	0·389		

The fused compounds conduct electricity. During electrolysis the metal is liberated at the cathode, and a mixture of nitrogen and hydrogen (not hydrazine) at the anode.

The alkali metal amides can all be made by the action of liquid ammonia on the metal; the time required for the reaction diminishes with increasing atomic number (see Table 14.5). Sodamide is made more quickly if a slow stream of oxygen is passed through the solution of sodium in liquid ammonia at $-33°$ (see Table 14.6). Lithium amide, together with some lithium imide, and sodamide and potassamide are formed when dry ammonia is passed over the heated metals. Sodamide and potassamide can be made by heating the hydrides in ammonia gas.

The amides of the alkali metals (other than lithium which at 374° yields the imide, a colourless, crystalline, reactive substance) may be sublimed or distilled at fairly high temperatures, but they decompose at a dull red heat. The alkali metal amides are insoluble in organic solvents. They are violently decomposed by water:

$$NaNH_2 + H_2O = NaOH + NH_3;$$

caesium amide inflames.

Sodamide is oxidised by air to sodium nitrite; the mixture of sodium nitrite and sodamide is explosive. In the fused state sodamide and potassamide are reducing agents. They convert oxides and salts of heavy metals to the metal. The reaction is violent and sometimes explosive. On reduction with hydrogen at 150–300°, sodamide gives sodium hydride and ammonia:

$$NaNH_2 + H_2 = NaH + NH_3.$$

If warmed with carbon monoxide it gives sodium cyanide: -

$$NaNH_2 + CO = NaCN + H_2O.$$

With carbon dioxide it gives cyanamide:

$$2NaNH_2 + CO_2 = NH_2CN + 2NaOH,$$

but with carbon disulphide it gives sodium thiocyanate and hydrogen sulphide:

$$NaNH_2 + CS_2 = NaSCN + H_2S.$$

When fused with carbon, sodamide first yields cyanamide, and at higher temperatures, sodium cyanide. Sodamide reacts with nitrous oxide, and with sodium nitrate (p. 684), with fluorene (p. 413), and with magnesium (p. 438).

The amides of the metals other than the alkali metals. Beryllium does not form an amide. Magnesium, calcium, strontium, and barium form amides which are described in Chapter 15. Amides are also formed by zinc (p. 459), by cadmium (p. 467), and by nickel. The mercury compounds in which the bond Hg—N is present are discussed on p. 473.

The imides, for example lithium imide Li_2NH, contain the group $>NH$. Lithium, calcium, germanium, tin, and lead form imides. The imides of lithium and calcium are made by gently heating the metallic amides, but the amides of more electropositive metals decompose on heating directly to the metallic nitride, without the intermediate formation of the imide. The group $>NH$ can replace oxygen and sulphur atoms in the molecules of certain compounds. Lithium imide and lithium oxide are isomorphous; both have the antifluorite structure. The unstable thionyl imide, OSNH may be regarded as a derivative of sulphur dioxide, and the molecules of the compounds S_7NH and $S_4N_4H_4$ may be notionally derived by replacing S atoms in the puckered ring S_4 by NH groups.

HALOGEN DERIVATIVES OF AMMONIA

The compounds to be considered in the following paragraphs are the three fluorine derivatives of ammonia, NF_3, NHF_2, NH_2F, the three chlorine derivatives of ammonia, NCl_3, $NHCl_2$, NH_2Cl, the bromine compounds $NHBr_2$ and NH_2Br, and the iodine compounds NI_3 and NI_3,NH_3. In the discussion the compounds NF_2 and N_2F_2 are included with the three fluorine compounds mentioned above although they are not structurally related to ammonia.

Nitrogen trifluoride, NF_3, is a colourless gas; m.p. $-208\cdot5°$, b.p. $-119°$. Its heats of formation are:

$$\tfrac{1}{2}N_2 + 1\tfrac{1}{2}F_2 = NF_3; \quad \Delta H = -26\cdot5 \text{ kcal}$$
$$N + 3F = NF_3; \quad \Delta H_a = -188\cdot7 \text{ kcal}.$$

Nitrogen trifluoride is made by the electrolysis of fused ammonium hydrogen fluoride, $NH_4.HF_2$, at 125°. Three other compounds of nitrogen and fluorine are formed at the same time: NH_2F, NHF_2, and NF_2.

Nitrogen trifluoride is not explosive, and it is not chemically active. It is insoluble in water. It does not react with water, ammonia, alkalis, sulphuric acid, manganese dioxide, methane, or carbon monoxide, except at high temperatures. It does not react at all with acetylene, sulphur dioxide, or with glass or mercury. It explodes feebly if mixed with steam, giving hydrogen fluoride and oxides of nitrogen. A mixture with hydrogen explodes violently if ignited:

$$2NF_3 + 3H_2 = N_2 + 6HF.$$

The non-reactivity of nitrogen trifluoride is in accordance with its high negative heat of formation, and also with the lack of affinity of fluorine for oxygen. Although the first stage in the hydrolysis of nitrogen trifluoride might well be the formation of a hydrogen bond:

$$F_3N + H_2O = F_3N \cdots H—OH,$$

the reaction could not proceed in the manner suggested for the hydrolysis of nitrogen trichloride (p. 698) because hypofluorous acid, HFO, does not exist.

The results of electron diffraction experiments and microwave spectra indicate that the nitrogen trifluoride molecule has a pyramidal structure with the dimensions:

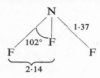

NH$_2$F and NHF$_2$ are products of the electrolysis of fused ammonium hydrogen fluoride. Little seems to be known about NH$_2$F. It is a gas; its sublimation point (1 atm) is $-77°$. NHF$_2$ is a gas with a fishy smell, m.p. about $-125°$, b.p. about $-70°$. It has not been obtained pure, and it is liable to explode spontaneously on keeping. It is soluble in water; it is stable both to water and to dilute sodium hydroxide solution.

Nitrogen difluoride, NF$_2$, is produced in small yield during the electrolysis of ammonium hydrogen fluoride. It has not been prepared pure. B.p. about $-125°$. Its relative density indicates a molecular weight of 54.

Dinitrogen difluoride, N$_2$F$_2$, has been prepared by the decomposition of fluorine nitrate, FNO$_3$ (p. 914). It is a colourless gas, and condenses to a colourless solid at about $-100°$. Electron diffraction experiments have shown that N$_2$F$_2$ is a mixture of the cis and trans forms of F—N=N—F, in which the distance F—N is 1·44, and the distance N=N is 1·25. The angle NNF is $115 \pm 5°$. Hence the structure is that of difluoryl hyponitrous acid, and not that of nitrous oxide in which an atom of oxygen is replaced by two fluorine atoms. On the other hand it seems as though NF$_2$ must be related to nitric oxide.

Chlorine derivatives of ammonia. There are three binary compounds of nitrogen and chlorine, and each of them can be prepared by passing chlorine into an ammonium chloride solution with the appropriate pH value as shown below:

Product	pH value of ammonium chloride solution
NH$_2$Cl	above 8·5
NHCl$_2$	4·5 to 5·0
NCl$_3$	below 4·5

The effect of the pH value on the nature of the product can be explained if the reactions which take place are analogous to those which have been demonstrated to take place when iodine acts upon aqueous ammonia solution (p. 699). The reactions would be:

$$Cl_2 + NH_4OH = NH_4Cl + HOCl \qquad (19.10)$$
$$HOCl + NH_3 = NH_4OCl \qquad (19.11)$$
$$NH_4OCl \rightleftharpoons NH_2Cl + H_2O \qquad (19.12)$$
$$2NH_2Cl \rightleftharpoons NHCl_2 + NH_3 \qquad (19.13)$$
$$3NHCl_2 \rightleftharpoons 2NCl_3 + NH_3 \qquad (19.14)$$

As the acidity of the solution is increased the concentration of free ammonia diminishes, and by the operation of equilibria (19.13) and (19.14) the disproportionation of monochloramine to dichloramine and nitrogen trichloride is promoted. This view of the reaction is confirmed by the formation of dichloramine when a solution of chloramine is acidified.

The three chlorine derivatives of ammonia all yield hypochlorous acid by reaction with water:

$$NH_2Cl + HOH = NH_3 + HClO,$$

and nitrogen and ammonium chloride by reaction with ammonia:

$$3NH_2Cl + 2NH_3 = N_2 + 3NH_4Cl.$$

In the case of chloramine it is possible to modify the conditions of the reaction, and to isolate hydrazine (p. 703) as an intermediate product.

Substituted nitrogen halides are known:

$(CH_3)_2NCl$; the distance N—Cl is 1·77
CH_3NCl_2; the distance N—Cl is 1·74

Chloramine-T is the sodium derivative of the chloramine of toluene-*p*-sulphonamide:

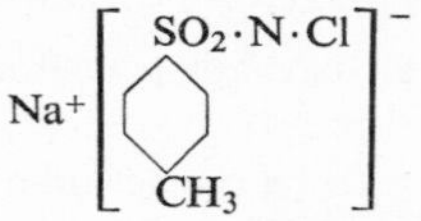

Nitrogen trichloride, NCl_3, is a pale yellow oily liquid, b.p. 71°; the crystals are rhombic, m.p. −27°. It has an irritating smell and attacks the eyes.

Its heats of formation are:

$$\tfrac{1}{2}N_2 + 1\tfrac{1}{2}Cl_2 = NCl_3; \quad \Delta H = +55\cdot4 \text{ kcal}$$
$$N + 3Cl = NCl_3; \quad \Delta H_a = -142\cdot8 \text{ kcal}.$$

It is insoluble in cold water, and is decomposed by hot water. It is soluble in benzene and carbon tetrachloride.

Nitrogen trichloride may be made:

(i) by the action of chlorine on an acid solution (pH less than 4·4) of ammonium chloride,

   or, by the electrolysis of ammonium chloride solution at 28°,

(ii) by the action of phosphorus pentachloride on nitrosyl chloride:

$$PCl_5 + ClNO = NCl_3 + POCl_3,$$

(iii) by the action of hypochlorous acid on ammonia, hydroxylamine, hydrazine, sodium azide, or urea:

$$NH_3 + 3HOCl = NCl_3 + 3H_2O.$$

Nitrogen trichloride is extremely unstable and it is dangerous to attempt to prepare it. It should be remembered that there is always a possibility of its being formed when chlorine or a hypochlorite comes into contact with an ammonia derivative. Nitrogen trichloride is decomposed by gentle heat, by exposure to light, and by contact with phosphorus, phosphine, fused potassium hydroxide, nitric oxide, and rubber, and with unsaturated organic compounds such as turpentine. The heats of formation of nitrogen trifluoride and nitrogen trichloride reveal that nitrogen trichloride is more ready than nitrogen trifluoride both to dissociate into *atoms*, and also to break down into *molecules* of its constituent elements. The relative stabilities of the chlorine and fluorine molecules as shown by the relative magnitudes of the bond energies of the chlorine and fluorine molecules, account at least in part for the differences in stability of nitrogen trifluoride and nitrogen trichloride.

Nitrogen trichloride is decomposed by water into ammonia and hypochlorous acid. It is supposed that the hydrolysis is initiated by the formation of a hydrogen bond, followed by the separation of a molecule of hypochlorous acid, thus:

$$
\begin{array}{ccc}
\text{Cl} & & \text{Cl} \\
| & & | \\
\text{Cl—N}+\text{HOH} = & \text{Cl—N}\cdots\text{H—O—H} \\
| & & | \\
\text{Cl} & & \text{Cl}
\end{array}
$$

$$
\begin{array}{c}
\text{Cl} \\
| \\
\text{Cl—N}\cdots\text{H}\,\vert\,\text{OH} = \text{Cl}_2\text{NH}+\text{ClOH.} \\
| \\
\text{Cl}
\end{array}
$$

By a repetition of this process the remaining chlorine atoms on the nitrogen atom are replaced by hydrogen atoms.

Nitrogen trichloride is quantitatively decomposed by ammonia:

$$NCl_3 + 4NH_3 = N_2 + 3NH_4Cl,$$

and hence it is not formed (except perhaps transitorily) when chlorine is passed into excess of aqueous ammonia solution.

Dichloramine, $NHCl_2$, is formed (i) by the action of chlorine on ammonium sulphate solution buffered to pH 4·5 to 5, and (ii) by the acidification of a solution of mono-chloramine. Dichloramine reacts with ammonia to liberate nitrogen:

$$3NHCl_2 + 7NH_3 = 2N_2 + 6NH_4Cl.$$

Monochloramine, NH_2Cl, is a gas which condenses to a yellow oil which at $-66°$ freezes to a colourless solid. It is made by the action of chlorine on ammonium sulphate solution, buffered to pH greater than 8·5, or by distilling in vacuo a solution consisting of ammonia and sodium hypochlorite in equimolar proportions:

$$NaOCl + NH_3 = NaOH + NH_2Cl.$$

The gas is dried by potassium carbonate and condensed in liquid air.

It is very slightly soluble in benzene, chloroform, and carbon tetrachloride. It decomposes thus:

$$3NH_2Cl = NH_4Cl + N_2 + 2HCl.$$

With ammonia, monochloramine gives hydrazine:

$$NH_2Cl + 2NH_3 = NH_2NH_2 + NH_4Cl,$$

and with hydrazine it yields nitrogen and ammonium chloride:

$$2NH_2Cl + NH_2NH_2 = 2NH_4Cl + N_2.$$

It is soluble in water, but the solution decomposes even at $0°$:

$$NH_2Cl + H_2O = NH_3 + HOCl.$$

With dilute alkalis it reacts thus:

$$3NH_2Cl + 3KOH = NH_3 + N_2 + 3KCl + 3H_2O.$$

No hydroxylamine is produced in the reaction with water or with alkali.

Bromine derivatives of ammonia. Nitrogen tribromide has not been prepared; NH_2Br and $NHBr_2$ have been made at $-50°$ by the action of bromine on an ethereal solution of ammonia, but they have not been isolated. The lack of affinity of nitrogen for bromine may be compared with the lack of affinity of oxygen for bromine. The reaction of sodium hypobromite on ammonia:

$$2NH_3 + 3NaOBr = 3NaBr + N_2 + 3H_2O,$$

under no conditions can be modified to yield a compound containing bromine and nitrogen.

If bromine reacts on ammonia at very low pressure (1–2 mm) at 100°, and the product is quickly cooled to $-95°$, a purple solid is obtained which is liable to decompose explosively if the temperature rises to $-70°$. The composition of the solid is $NBr_3,6NH_3$. It dissolves to give colourless solutions in liquid ammonia and in methyl and ethyl alcohol. These solutions become red at the temperature of liquid air.

Iodine derivatives of ammonia. A dark coloured precipitate is obtained when iodine is added to aqueous ammonia. The precipitate has the composition NI_3,NH_3, and is frequently referred to as nitrogen iodide. When dry it is very unstable and explodes when stroked with a feather.

It has been shown that the initial product of the action of iodine on aqueous ammonia is hypoiodous acid, which can be detected by the formation of a brown precipitate when a solution of manganous sulphate is added to the solution:

$$NH_4OH + I_2 = NH_4I + HOI.$$

Further addition of iodine gives a black precipitate of NH_3,NI_3. The course of the second stage of the reaction must follow the disproportionation of ammonium hypoiodite, thus:

$$3NH_4OI \rightleftharpoons NH_3,NI_3 + NH_3 + 3H_2O,$$

because, if excess of ammonia is added to the suspension of the black precipitate it dissolves without the liberation of nitrogen, which is explained by the reversal of the above reaction. If the nitrogen iodide had reacted in the normal way with the ammonia, nitrogen would have been liberated according to the equation:

$$NH_3,NI_3 + NH_3 = NH_3 + N_2 + 3HI.$$

The composition of nitrogen iodide is demonstrated by the reactions:

$$NH_3,NI_3 + 3Na_2SO_3 + 3H_2O = 3Na_2SO_4 + 2NH_3 + 3HI,$$
$$NH_3,NI_3 + 3Zn(C_2H_5)_2 = 3Zn(C_2H_5)I + NH_3 + N(C_2H_5)_3,$$

which can be carried out quantitatively.

Nitrogen iodide is a good oxidising agent. It converts sulphites to sulphates and arsenites to arsenates. One molecular weight is equal to six equivalents, in accordance with the equation:

$$NH_3,NI_3 + 3H_2O = 2NH_3 + 3HI + 3O.$$

Nitrogen iodide reacts with silver nitrate solution to yield an explosive black powder (Szuhay's salt):

$$AgNO_3 + NH_3,NI_3 = AgNH_2,NI_3 + HNO_3.$$

Pure nitrogen iodide, NI_3, is made by passing ammonia over potassium dibromo-iodide:

$$KIBr_2 \rightleftharpoons KBr + IBr,$$
$$3IBr + 4NH_3 = NI_3 + 3NH_4Br.$$

The product is washed with water to remove the potassium and ammonium bromides, and the nitrogen tri-iodide is left. It is an extremely explosive black solid. It is hydrolysed slowly by water, and rapidly by alkalis, thus:

$$NI_3 + 3KOH = NH_3 + 3KOI.$$

HYDROXYLAMINE, NH_2OH

At room temperature hydroxylamine exists as colourless, odourless, deliquescent crystals, m.p. 33°, b.p. 55–58°/22 mm.

It is prepared by the decomposition of hydroxylaminium salts (p. 701). A solution of sodium methoxide in methyl alcohol is added to a solution of hydroxylamium chloride in methyl alcohol:

$$[NH_3OH]Cl + CH_3ONa = NaCl + CH_3OH + NH_2OH.$$

The precipitated sodium chloride is filtered off, and the excess alcohol removed by distillation at 40 mm. The solution is cooled to $-18°$, and the hydroxylamine crystallises. Hydroxylamine may also be obtained by heating hydroxylaminium phosphate to 135° at 13 mm:

$$[NH_3OH]_3PO_4 = 3NH_2OH + H_3PO_4.$$

Hydroxylamine is poisonous. It readily dissolves in water or alcohol, but only slightly in ether or benzene. It is extremely unstable. Even at room temperature the solid, or the concentrated aqueous solution, slowly decomposes evolving nitrogen, nitrous oxide, and ammonia. The liquid explodes when heated at normal pressure, and the vapour explodes when warmed to 60–70° in contact with air.

In the absence of water, hydroxylamine is a very weak acid. The calcium salts $Ca(OH)(NH_2O)$ and $Ca(NH_2O)_2$ are known. They explode on heating. In aqueous solution hydroxylamine is a proton acceptor:

$$NH_2OH + HCl = HONH_3^+ + Cl^-,$$
$$NH_2OH + HOH \rightleftharpoons HONH_3^+ + OH^-,$$

but it is a weaker base than ammonia. It forms a series of co-ordination compounds. The compound $ZnCl_2,2NH_2OH$ yields hydroxylamine when distilled at 120°.

Hydroxylamine may act either as an oxidising agent or as a reducing agent. The reactions may perhaps be:

reducing $2HONH_2 = HON:NOH + 4H^+ + 4e,$
the hyponitrous acid decomposing almost at once to nitrous oxide and water,

oxidising $2e + HONH_2 + H_2O = NH_3 + 2OH^-.$

If these equations are correct the reducing actions should be favoured by the presence of bases, and the oxidising actions by the presence of acids, but in fact no such simple correlation can be made. Some of the important reactions are set out below.

Reducing action of hydroxylamine in alkaline solution. Hydroxylamine precipitates metallic gold from auric chloride, cuprous oxide from Fehling's solution, and metallic silver from ammoniacal solutions of silver salts. It reduces mercuric chloride first to mercurous chloride, and then to the metal. It also reduces sodium nitrite to sodium hyponitrite (p. 677). In all these reactions, the hyponitrous acid initially formed decomposes, and the final products are nitrous oxide and water, for example:

$$2NH_2OH + 4CuO = N_2O + 2Cu_2O + 3H_2O,$$
$$NH_2OH + ONOH = HON:NOH + H_2O = N_2O + 2H_2O.$$

Hydroxylamine reduces iodine to the iodide ion in the presence of sodium bicarbonate or sodium acetate:

$$4NaHCO_3 + 2I_2 + 2HONH_2 = 4NaI + N_2O + 5H_2O + 4CO_2.$$

Bromine and chlorine are attacked more readily, and some of the hydroxylamine is oxidised to the nitrate ion. Hydrogen peroxide and hydroxylamine undergo mutual reduction:

$$HONH_2 + H_2O_2 = NH_3 + O_2 + H_2O.$$

Reducing action of hydroxylamine in acid solution. Hydroxylaminium chloride in acid solution reduces ferric salts to ferrous salts, and nitric acid to nitric oxide:

$$(HONH_3)Cl + HNO_3 = 2NO + 2H_2O + HCl.$$

Oxidising action of hydroxylamine in alkaline solution. Hydroxylamine oxidises ferrous hydroxide to ferric hydroxide quantitatively:

$$2Fe(OH)_2 + HONH_2 + H_2O = 2Fe(OH)_3 + NH_3.$$

It also oxidises sodium arsenite to sodium arsenate:

$$NH_2OH + Na_3AsO_3 = Na_3AsO_4 + NH_3.$$

Oxidising action of hydroxylamine in acid solution. In strongly acid solution hydroxylaminium chloride oxidises hydriodic acid to iodine, stannous chloride to stannic chloride, sulphur dioxide to ammonium sulphate, and a solution of vanadium trioxide in sulphuric acid to vanadium tetroxide.

The density of hydroxylamine vapour indicates the molecular formula NH_3O. The liquid is probably associated. The molecule in the vapour has a plane of symmetry and either of the two forms $HONH_2$ or ONH_3 might be possible.

HYDROXYLAMINIUM SALTS

The hydroxylaminium salts of the mineral acids are $[NH_3OH]Cl$ m.p. 151°, $[NH_3OH]_2SO_4$ m.p. 170°, $[NH_3OH]NO_3$ m.p. 48°. The hydroxylaminium salts contain the cation $[NH_3OH]^+$, comparable with the ammonium ion $[NH_4]^+$. The salts are made by the reduction of nitric oxide, a nitrite, or a nitrate, or by the hydrolysis of the oximino group, $C=NOH$. The salt obtained in the first place is usually the chloride or the sulphate. It is noteworthy that hydroxylaminium salts are not formed by the hydrolysis of chloramine, NH_2Cl, which yields ammonia and hypochlorous acid (p. 698). Certain of the reactions leading to the formation of hydroxylaminium salts are discussed in the following paragraphs.

The electrolytic reduction of nitric acid. This is a convenient laboratory method for preparing hydroxylaminium sulphate. The electrolysis is carried out in a divided cell using lead electrodes. The electrolyte is 50% sulphuric acid; 50% nitric acid is added a drop at a time to the electrolyte in the cathode compartment. The reduction of the nitric acid may be summarised by the equation:

$$HNO_3 + 6H = NH_2OH + 2H_2O.$$

At the end of the electrolysis the cathode compartment contains an aqueous solution of hydroxylaminium sulphate and sulphuric acid. A solution of hydroxylaminium chloride may be obtained by adding the appropriate quantity of barium chloride solution, and filtering off the precipitated barium sulphate.

Reduction of sodium nitrite. If a solution of sodium nitrite is reduced by sulphur dioxide in the presence of sodium carbonate, the overall reaction occurs:

$$SO_2 + NaNO_2 + NaHSO_3 + 2H_2O = 2NaHSO_4 + HONH_2.$$

In practice the reaction is conducted in stages. The sulphur dioxide is slowly passed into a concentrated solution of sodium nitrite and sodium carbonate in the molar proportions 2:1. The temperature is maintained at $-2°$. It is probable under these conditions that the undissociated molecule of nitrous acid enters into reaction with two ions of sulphurous acid which are in the sulphonic form:

$$
HON{:}O \cdot + \begin{array}{c} H{:}-S{-}O \\ \\ H{:}-S{-}O \end{array} = \left[HO{-}N \right]^{2-} + H_2O.
$$

The solution is then warmed with a small quantity of dilute sulphuric acid, when hydroxylamine monosulphonate is formed:

$$
\left[HO{-}N \underset{SO_3}{\overset{SO_3}{\diagup}} \right]^{2-} + HOH = \left[HO{-}N \underset{SO_3}{\overset{H}{\diagup}} \right]^{-} + \left[O{-}S{-}O \right]^{-}
$$

The final stage requires the maintenance of the solution at 90–95° for two days, during which time slow hydrolysis occurs, and the second SO_3 group is replaced by hydrogen.

The solution is neutralised with sodium carbonate, evaporated, and as much as possible of the sodium sulphate is removed as $Na_2SO_4,10H_2O$. The filtrate deposits hydroxylaminium sulphate, $[HONH_3]_2SO_4$.

Reduction of nitric oxide. If nitric oxide is passed through a reacting mixture of granulated tin and concentrated hydrochloric acid, hydroxylaminium chloride is formed and remains in solution. When the tin is dissolved, the solution is treated with hydrogen sulphide to precipitate tin sulphide, filtered, and evaporated to dryness. The hydroxylaminium chloride is extracted with alcohol. It is precipitated from the alcoholic solution by ether.

Reduction of ethyl nitrate. If ethyl nitrate is added to a reacting mixture of granulated tin and concentrated hydrochloric acid, hydroxylaminium chloride is formed. This is isolated as in the previous method.

Acid hydrolysis of fulminic acid. Fulminic acid, $C{=}NOH$, yields hydroxylaminium chloride on boiling with hydrochloric acid:

$$ C{=}NOH + HCl + 2H_2O = [HONH_3]Cl + HCOOH. $$

Acid hydrolysis of hydroxamic acid. Hydroxylamine is obtained industrially as a by-product in the manufacture of acetic acid from ethane present in natural gas. Ethane is nitrated in the vapour phase by nitrogen dioxide. The nitroethane is treated with 80% sulphuric acid and yields hydroxamic acid:

$$ CH_3.CH_2.NO_2 = CH_3.C \underset{NOH}{\overset{OH}{\diagup}} $$

Hydroxamic acid by acid hydrolysis gives:

$$ HCl + H_2O + CH_3 \cdot C \cdot OH{:}NOH = CH_3COOH + [HONH_3]Cl. $$

The oxidising and reducing properties of the hydroxylaminium salts in aqueous solution are identical with those of hydroxylamine (p. 700), for in acid solution hydroxylamine forms a hydroxylaminium salt, and in alkaline solution free hydroxylamine is liberated from a hydroxylaminium salt.

HYDRAZINE, N_2H_4

Hydrazine, a poisonous, colourless liquid, m.p. $+1\cdot8$, b.p. $113\cdot5°$, is prepared by the restricted oxidation of ammonia. In Raschig's method the oxidising agent is sodium hypochlorite. The reactions are:

$$NH_3 + NaOCl = NH_2Cl + NaOH,$$
$$NH_2Cl + NH_3 = NH_2NH_2 + HCl.$$

The yield may be much reduced by the reaction:

$$2NH_2Cl + NH_2NH_2 = 2NH_4Cl + N_2,$$

which is catalysed by the presence of the merest trace of ferric or cupric ions. Such ions may be removed from the sphere of action, either by adsorption on colloids such as glue, gelatine, or peptised stannic acid, or by co-ordination with a reagent such as "Triton B" † to form an undissociated anionic complex.

In practice freshly prepared sodium hypochlorite solution is added to 20% aqueous ammonia solution containing a small quantity of a dilute solution (1%) of gelatine. The mixed solution is boiled for 30 minutes and then cooled. On acidification with dilute sulphuric acid hydrazinium sulphate $N_2H_4\cdot H_2SO_4$ crystallises out.

There are many variants of this method. It may be carried out at $160–180°$ at 50 atm pressure, when the reaction is complete in a few seconds. Urea may be used instead of ammonia. Chlorine, diluted with an inert gas, may be passed into anhydrous liquid ammonia, the ammonia being greatly in excess, or ammonia may be treated with fluoramine.

If hydrazine sulphate is distilled with concentrated potassium hydroxide solution in all-glass apparatus, a colourless, fuming liquid of composition N_2H_4,H_2O is obtained as the distillate. If this is distilled with its own weight of solid sodium hydroxide, anhydrous hydrazine comes over at $150°$. Another way of getting anhydrous hydrazine is to treat the hydrochloride with sodium methylate in methyl alcohol, filter off the sodium chloride, and distil under reduced pressure. The methyl alcohol distils over first:

$$N_2H_4HCl + CH_3ONa = N_2H_4 + NaCl + CH_3OH.$$

In contact with oxygen hydrazine is explosive.

Its dielectric constant at $22°$ is 53. It is a good ionising solvent. It is very hygroscopic, it fumes in air, and is very soluble in water and in alcohol. In aqueous solution it forms the hydrate N_2H_4,H_2O (see below).

When sparked it decomposes to ammonia and nitrogen. At $200–500°$ it decomposes to ammonia and nitrogen if in contact with silica, and to ammonia, nitrogen and hydrogen if in contact with platinum or tungsten. It is explosively attacked by oxygen, or by the halogens, to give nitrogen and water or a halogen hydride.‡

It dissolves lithium or sodium to give a blue solution (cf. liquid ammonia), but in a short time hydrogen is evolved, and the hydrazide, NH_2NHNa, remains. This explodes in contact with oxygen or moisture.

The high boiling point of hydrazine shows that the liquid is associated. In the vapour the N—N distance is $1\cdot47$ (electron diffraction). The d.p.m. is $1\cdot35\pm0\cdot15$. Consideration of the d.p.m. and the Raman spectrum, shows that the molecule is non-planar

---

† Triton B is disodium ethylenediamine tetra-acetate.

‡ Oxidising agents such as potassium perchlorate, hydrogen peroxide, and nitric acid, are capable of producing hydrazoic acid from hydrazine. The formation of hydrazoic acid by such reactions should be borne in mind.

and that the two NH_2 groups have no freedom of relative rotation. The Raman spectrum of $CH_3NH \cdot NHCH_3$ confirms this. The structure is

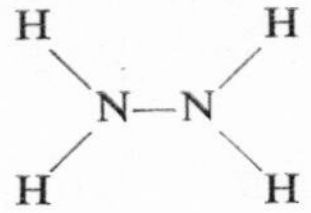

$$
\begin{array}{ccc}
H & & H \\
\diagdown & & \diagup \\
& N{-}N & \\
\diagup & & \diagdown \\
H & & H
\end{array}
$$

It is interesting to compare this with the structures of H_2O_2 and of ethane. In the three cases the atoms of C, N, or O appear to be tetrahedrally hybridised. In the case of the N atom one tetrahedral orbital is occupied by a lone pair, and in the case of the O atom two such orbitals are occupied by lone pairs.

Hydrazine hydrate, N_2H_4,H_2O **or** $(NH_2NH_3)OH$; m.p. $-51\cdot7°$, b.p. $120°$. Hydrazine hydrate is a fuming liquid. It attacks glass and porcelain. The explosive decomposition:

$$2N_2H_4,H_2O = 2NH_3 + N_2 + H_2 + 2H_2O$$

is catalysed by certain metals including nickel–chromium stainless steel. A mixture of hydrazine hydrate and a concentrated solution of hydrogen peroxide is ignited by the introduction of a copper catalyst. Hydrazine hydrate is a powerful reducing agent. It precipitates gold, silver, and platinum from their salts, and metallic mercury from a weakly acid (but not from a strongly acid) solution of mercuric chloride. It reduces iodates to iodides, ferric salts to ferrous salts, acid permanganate solution to the manganous salt, iodine (quantitatively in the presence of sodium bicarbonate) to iodide, ferricyanide in the presence of alkali quantitatively to ferrocyanide:

$$4K_3Fe(CN)_6 + 4KOH + N_2H_5OH = 4K_4Fe(CN)_6 + N_2 + 5H_2O.$$

It reduces an alkaline solution of cupric copper, when cold to cuprous oxide, and when hot to metallic copper. One of its reactions is an oxidising action resembling that of hydrogen peroxide:

$$H_2O + NH_2NH_2 + CHO \cdot COOH = 2NH_3 + (COOH)_2.$$

Hydrazine salts. Hydrazine is a monoacid base, K being about 1×10^{-6} (one-fifth that of ammonia). Its principal salts are the sulphate $N_2H_4 \cdot H_2SO_4$, and the chloride $N_2H_4 \cdot HCl$. The sulphate is not very soluble in water (about 28 gm per litre at room temperature) and crystallises well.

Hydrazine fluoride $N_2H_4 \cdot H_2F_2$ when dissolved in water yields the two ions $[N_2H_4 \cdot HF_2]^-$ and H_3O^+. In the crystal the units are $[N_2H_6]^{2+}$ ions and F^- ions, and the structure is very open because of the presence of long $N{-}H{-}F$ bonds.

CHAPTER TWENTY

SUB-GROUP V N CONTINUED. PHOSPHORUS, ARSENIC, ANTIMONY, AND BISMUTH

ELEMENTARY PHOSPHORUS

The allotropes of phosphorus. Phosphorus vapour consists of molecules P_4. It condenses to crystalline white phosphorus, which probably also consists of molecules P_4. White phosphorus is metastable. There are at least four forms which are more stable, to which white phosphorus changes under appropriate conditions (Table 20.1). Among these are violet phosphorus of which the molecular constitution is unknown, black phosphorus which has a giant molecule structure, and two other forms known as red phosphorus and scarlet phosphorus. The methods of preparation and certain properties of the allotropes are summarised in Table 20.1, and are further discussed in the following paragraphs.

White phosphorus is metastable with regard to the other allotropes. The heats of solution of the three allotropes in bromine show the differences in their energy content:

	Specific gravity	Heat of solution per gm atom in bromine
Black phosphorus	2·70	38·30 kcal
Violet phosphorus	2·34	42·50 kcal
White phosphorus	1·83	59·48 kcal

White phosphorus is poisonous, and chemically it is extremely active. Its principal reactions are mentioned in Table 20.2.

If cubic white phosphorus is cooled to $-76.9°$, or if it is subjected to a pressure of 12,000 atm, a hexagonal crystalline form is obtained. The cubic and hexagonal crystals of white phosphorus are probably polymorphs, in both of which the P_4 molecule is present.

Violet phosphorus, or α-metallic phosphorus, is chemically inert. In air it neither glows nor ignites, and it is not oxidised. There is no solvent for it and hence it is non-toxic. It is a non-conductor of electricity.

Black phosphorus, or β-metallic phosphorus, is chemically inert. It does not ignite at 400° in air. It conducts electricity.

Black phosphorus has a layer structure in which each atom forms three strong bonds with its nearest neighbours. The figure shows one layer idealised. The actual bond angles are 100° and not 90° as shown

If heated to 550° black phosphorus changes to the red variety.

Table 20.1. *The Allotropes of Phosphorus*

	White phosphorus	Violet phosphorus	Black phosphorus	Red phosphorus	Scarlet phosphorus
Appearance	White, translucent, waxy solid	Brilliant opaque violet crystals†	Black flaky solid	Reddish violet crystalline solid	
Crystal form m.p. °C b.p. °C	Cubic 44·1 287	Rhombohedral 592·5		592·5 (pressure 43·1 atm) 416 (sublimes)	
Sp. gr.	1·83	2·33	2·70	2·20	1·876
Solubility	Sparingly soluble in water. Soluble in benzene and in carbon disulphide	No solvent		Insoluble in water, ether, carbon disulphide, and in dilute alkali hydroxide solution	
Crystal structure	Molecular structure of P_4 units		Giant molecule layer structure		
Preparation	Condense phosphorus vapour under ordinary conditions	(i) Heat white phosphorus in a sealed tube at 530°, and condense the vapour on the upper part of the tube at 444° (ii) Dissolve white phosphorus in fused lead or bismuth and crystallise; dissolve away the metal with dilute nitric acid	Heat white phosphorus at 200° under a pressure of 12,000 atm	Heat white phosphorus in an atmosphere of nitrogen at 260°	Expose a solution of white phosphorus in carbon disulphide or phosphorus tribromide solution to sunlight

† Isomorphous with the corresponding crystal forms of As, Sb, Bi.

Red phosphorus is tasteless, smell-less, and non-toxic. It is chemically inert compared with white phosphorus; its principal reactions are mentioned in Table 20.2. Red phosphorus volatilises to molecules P_2. Red phosphorus sublimes at 416°, but volatilised red phosphorus condenses to white phosphorus. The volatilisation of red phosphorus proceeds irreversibly because the proportion of P_2 in equilibrium with P_4 is less than one part in 10^7.

It is probable that red phosphorus is a modification of violet phosphorus, since on prolonged heating the colour darkens to violet, and the sp. gr. rises to 2·34, and the m.p.'s of the two varieties are the same.

Table 20.2.   *Chemical Properties of White and Red Phosphorus*

Reactions of white phosphorus

Reagent	Reaction
Oxygen	At room temperature oxidation to P_2O_5 occurs spontaneously, accompanied by a green glow or phosphorescence. In dry air inflammation occurs at 50°. In moist air a liquid containing hypophosphoric acid, phosphorous acid, and phosphoric acid is obtained
Chlorine	PCl_5 and PCl_3 are formed with spontaneous inflammation
Bromine	PBr_5 and PBr_3 are formed with explosion
Iodine	Iodides of phosphorus are formed with inflammation. If water is added to a mixture of white phosphorus and iodine, PH_4I and H_3PO_4 are obtained
Sulphur	Fused sulphur and phosphorus react with explosive violence to yield a mixture of phosphorus sulphides
Concentrated HNO$_3$	Solution slowly occurs with the formation of H_3PO_4
KOH solution	A mixture of phosphine and hydrogen is evolved (p. 712)
CuSO$_4$ solution	In the hot the reaction occurs: $$3P + 3CuSO_4 + 6H_2O = Cu_3P + 2H_3PO_3 + 3H_2SO_4$$ In the cold the reaction occurs: $$2P + 5CuSO_4 + 8H_2O = 5Cu + 2H_3PO_4 + 5H_2SO_4$$
CaO	Phosphorus vapour passed over calcium oxide heated to low redness reacts thus: $$14P + 14CaO = 5Ca_2P_2 + 2Ca_2P_2O_7$$

Reactions of red phosphorus

Reagent	Reaction
Oxygen	There is no glow in air, but prolonged exposure produces H_3PO_4. Ignition in air does not occur below 240°
Chlorine	Combination with chlorine occurs only on heating
Bromine	Violent reaction occurs with bromine vapour, but with the liquid reaction proceeds quietly to yield PBr_3
Iodine	Combination occurs quietly on warming
Concentrated HNO$_3$	Solution takes place rapidly on heating
KOH solution	No reaction
Concentrated NaOH solution and H$_2$O$_2$	Hypophosphoric acid is obtained
Aluminium	Heated powdered aluminium reacts to yield AlP
Sulphur	Combination occurs on heating

Scarlet phosphorus is said to be obtained pure by heating PBr_3 with mercury at 240°:

$$2PBr_3 + 3Hg = 2P + 3HgBr_2.$$

It is probably another modification of violet phosphorus. It is oxidised only very slowly and is non-poisonous. It dissolves in alkali with the evolution of phosphine.

The phosphorus molecule. The molecular weight of phosphorus vapour below 700° corresponds to the molecule P_4. Electron diffraction experiments have established that each atom of the molecule is at the corner of a regular tetrahedron. The distance P—P is 2·21. Each phosphorus atom appears to be exerting three bonds at 60° to one another.

Above 700° the molecule begins to dissociate into molecules P_2; at 500° only about 1 in 10^7 molecules in the vapour are P_2, but at 1700° about 50% of the P_4 molecules are dissociated. At higher temperatures some phosphorus is present as single atoms. $P_4 = 2P_2$; $\Delta H = 30\cdot0$ kcal. $P_2 = 2P$; $\Delta H = 42\cdot2$ kcal. The bond energy P—P is 53 kcal.

Molecular weight determinations show that phosphorus is present as P_4 in its solutions in benzene and in carbon disulphide. The results of Raman spectra and X-ray experiments show that liquid phosphorus consists of P_4 molecules.

From the experimental evidence available it seems that the molecule P_4 is present in crystalline, liquid, and gaseous white phosphorus. The structure of the molecule P_2 is unknown. The phosphorus atom does not form simple π bonds, and hence it seems unlikely that P_2 is the analogue of the nitrogen molecule N≡N.

GENERAL CHEMISTRY OF PHOSPHORUS

The electron configuration of the valency shell $(n = 3)$ of the phosphorus atom is

$3s$	$3p$	$3p$	$3p$
⇅	↑	↑	↑

The penultimate shell $(n = 2)$ contains eight electrons. In all its compounds phosphorus is in the oxidation state 5.

There is no anion $[P^{3-}]$, but the metallic phosphides are giant molecule compounds in which the bonds possess some ionic character. An atom having a valency shell for which $n = 2$ can be bonded by a simple π bond to another atom (of the same or a different element) which also has a valency shell for which $n = 2$. This property explains the large number of unsaturated compounds of carbon and nitrogen. For phosphorus, with a valency shell for which $n = 3$, this type of bond is not possible, but the existence of d orbitals in the valency shell makes possible a type of double bond, the πd bond (p. 156) which cannot be exerted by the nitrogen atom. This sharp difference between the orbital properties of the nitrogen and phosphorus atoms is revealed in wide differences in the physical and chemical properties of these two elements and their compounds. Nitrogen is a gas with the molecule N≡N. Phosphorus is a solid with the molecule P_4, in which each phosphorus atom is linked to three other phosphorus atoms by σ bonds. The four phosphorus atoms are at the apices of a tetrahedron. Modified forms of this structure are present in P_4O_6, P_4O_{10}, P_4S_3, and P_4S_5. The oxides of phosphorus are solid bodies quite unlike the volatile oxides of nitrogen. The phosphorus atom, unlike the nitrogen atom, does not appear in molecules containing unpaired electrons.

The phosphorus atom in phosphine, like the nitrogen atom in ammonia, is in the tetrahedral valence state with one hybrid orbital occupied by a lone electron pair. The ammonium salts are more stable than the phosphonium salts because the N—H bond is stronger than the P—H bond, but ammonium hydroxide is a weaker base than phosphonium hydroxide because nitrogen (being more electronegative) forms stronger hydrogen bonds.

The oxyacids of phosphorus all contain the phosphorus atom in the tetrahedral valence state. The orthophosphate ion [PO_4^{3-}] contains πd bonds (p. 156); there is no ion corresponding to the nitrate ion [NO_3^-] because such an ion contains simple π bonds which the phosphorus atom does not exert. In the phosphorus chloronitrides $(PNCl_2)_3$ and $(PNCl_2)_4$ the phosphorus atom takes part in the formation of ring structures. The ring of the trimer contains non-localised π bonds, and hence is aromatic in character.

Since the valency shell for which $n = 3$ contains d orbitals, octahedral hybridisation is possible for the phosphorus atom. Phosphorus, however, forms only a few compounds, among them KPF_6, in which the phosphorus atom is present in the octahedral valence state.

COMPOUNDS IN WHICH THE OXIDATION STATE OF PHOSPHORUS IS V

SECTION 1. PHOSPHORUS COMPOUNDS CONSISTING OF GIANT MOLECULES IN WHICH THE BONDS HAVE BOTH COVALENT AND IONIC CHARACTER

The compounds included in this section are the metallic phosphides, and compounds of phosphorus with nitrogen. The oxides and sulphides of phosphorus consist of discrete molecules in which the phosphorus atom is in the tetrahedral valence state (p. 716).

The metallic phosphides. The crystal structures of the phosphides of certain metals in Groups I, II, and III are stated in Table 20.3.

Table 20.3. *The Crystal Structures of Certain Metallic Phosphides*

Li_3P	Na_3P	Be_3P_2	Mg_3P_2	Zn_3P_2	Cd_3P_2	AlP	GaP
A	A	B	B	C	C	Z	Z

The crystal structures are indicated as follows: *A*, Na_3P; *B*, anti-Mn_2O_3; *C*, Zn_3P_2; *Z*, zinc blende.

All the structures except the zinc blende structure have low degrees of symmetry, and cannot be simply described. The Na_3P structure resembles structures found in alloys, each atom of one element has eleven nearest neighbours consisting of atoms of the other element. The anti-Mn_2O_3 structure and the Zn_3P_2 structure can be regarded as examples of the fluorite structure from which the anions in certain positions are absent; both these structures must have considerable ionic character. AlP and GaP must be largely covalent. The phosphides of the rare earth metals, LaP and PrP have rocksalt structures.

The phosphides of the alkali metals and the alkaline earth metals are obtained by reducing the metallic phosphates with aluminium at high temperatures.

Phosphorus and nitrogen. There are at least three compounds consisting only of phosphorus and nitrogen. They may be represented as $(P_3N_5)_x$, $(P_2N_3)_y$, $(PN)_z$; they cannot be made by the direct union of the components; their structures and constitutions are unknown. No X-ray patterns have been obtained from them.

$(P_3N_5)_x$ is a white solid without taste or smell, and for which there is no solvent. It is made:

(i) by heating the addition compound $P_2S_5,6NH_3$ to redness in a current of ammonia,

(ii) by heating phospham $((PN_2H)_x$; see below) in vacuo:

$$3PHN_2 = NH_3 + P_3N_5.$$

Its reactions throw little light on its structure. When heated to 730° in vacuo, or in nitrogen, it gives $(PN)_z$. It inflames when heated in oxygen or chlorine; with chlorine at 700° it gives phosphorus chloronitrides, and with hydrogen it gives phosphorus and ammonia. It reacts with water, slowly at 100° and rapidly at 180°, to give ammonia and phosphoric acid. It is scarcely acted upon by nitric, sulphuric, or aqueous hydrochloric acid at the boiling point.

$(P_2N_3)_y$, a solid, is made by heating the imide $P_2(NH)_3$. It is stable up to 750°.

$(PN)_z$, a solid, is made by heating $(P_3N_5)_x$ to 750° in vacuo. Ammonia (but not nitrogen) converts it to $(P_3N_5)_x$ at 800°. It occurs in two forms. A red form (stable) is resistant to cold sulphuric acid, but not to hot. A yellow form is attacked by cold sulphuric acid.

Phospham, $(PN_2H)_x$, is made:

(i) by heating the product of the action of ammonia on phosphorus pentachloride (p. 735) in the absence of air:

$$PCl_5 + 4NH_3 = PN_2H + 2NH_4Cl + 3HCl,$$

(ii) by the action of the trimer phosphorus chloronitride on ammonia.

Phospham is a white powder. At a red heat it is only slowly oxidised by air. It is stable to dilute acids, water, and aqueous alkalis, but is decomposed with incandescence when fused with sodium hydroxide, to yield ammonia and sodium phosphate:

$$H_2O + PN_2H + 3NaOH = Na_3PO_4 + 2NH_3.$$

When heated in vacuo above 400° it yields pure $(P_3N_5)_x$ (see above). For possible structures for phospham and for $(P_3N_5)_x$, see p. 732.

SECTION 4. COMPOUNDS IN WHICH THE PHOSPHORUS ATOM IS TETRAHEDRALLY HYBRIDISED

Phosphorus forms hydrides and chlorides of the types PH_3, P_2H_4, and PCl_3, P_2Cl_4. The compounds PH_3, $P(CH_3)_3$, and PCl_3 have pyramidal structures:

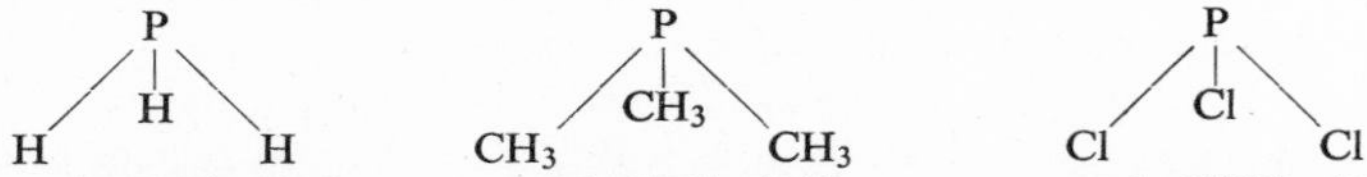

angle HPH = 100°   angle CPC = 100°   angle ClPCl = 102°

The structures of P_2H_4 and P_2Cl_4 are not known, but they are probably:

The phosphorus atom in all four compounds is 3 co-ordinate. On the assumption that the phosphorus atom in these compounds is tetrahedrally hybridised, and that one of the hybrid orbitals is occupied by a lone electron pair, the phosphorus atom is in the same state as it is in the molecule P_4, of which the structure is:

Another compound in which the phosphorus atom is in this state is phosphorus oxide, P_4O_6. The structure of the molecule is:

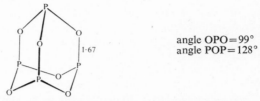

angle OPO=99°
angle POP=128°

and it can be notionally derived from that of the P_4 molecule by the insertion of an oxygen atom between each pair of adjacent phosphorus atoms in the P_4 tetrahedron. The structure of P_4O_{10} is:

The phosphorus atom is again tetrahedrally hybridised, but all the hybrid orbitals are used in forming links with oxygen atoms. The bond length P—O between a phosphorus atom and one of the four external oxygen atoms is only 1·39. The extreme shortness of this bond length suggests that a πd bond in addition to a σ bond is formed between the phosphorus atoms and the external oxygen atoms. (Pauling's covalent atomic radii predict the distances P—O 1·76, P═O 1·55, P≡O 1·43.)

The sulphides of phosphorus do not exactly correspond to the oxides (Table 19.3, p. 652), but their structures are notionally derived from the P_4 molecule by the insertion of sulphur atoms between pairs of phosphorus atoms.

Molecules of the general formula X_3P, in which the phosphorus atom is tetrahedrally hybridised and one of the hybrid orbitals is occupied by a lone pair, act as electron donors. The co-ordinating power of the phosphorus atom, however, is weaker than that of the nitrogen atom in corresponding circumstances. A few examples of co-ordination compounds formed by phosphorus compounds acting as donors are:

Donor molecule	Adduct	Notes
PH_3	$AlCl_3,PH_3$ $AlBr_3,PH_3$ AlI_3,PH_3	PH_3 reaches a dissociation pressure of 10 mm at +10°, 85°, and 93° respectively
	$TiCl_4,PH_3$ $2SnCl_4,3PH_3$ $2SnBr_4,3PH_3$	m.p. −33° formed at −110° m.p. +29°

Donor molecule	Adduct	Notes
PCl_3	$(Cl_3P)_2PtCl_2$	exists in cis and trans forms
$P(C_2H_5)_3$	$[Pt,4P(C_2H_5)_3]Cl_2$	
	$[Pt,2P(C_2H_5)_3,2NH_3]Cl_2$	exists in cis and trans forms
$P(OC_2H_5)_3$	$(P(OC_2H_5)_3)_2PtCl_2$	

The existence of the above compounds and their ease of formation support the assumption that the pair of non-bonding electrons in the phosphorus atom in molecules of the type X_3P is a lone pair and not an inert pair.

The phosphorus atom in the above co-ordination compounds is 4 co-ordinate. The 4 co-ordinate arrangement is found in many phosphorus compounds, including $POCl_3$, $PSCl_3$, the oxyacids, and in the phosphorus chloronitrides and their derivatives.

These different classes of phosphorus compounds, all containing the phosphorus atom in the tetrahedral valence state, are discussed in the following paragraphs in the order in which they are mentioned in this brief introduction.

PHOSPHORUS HYDRIDES AND THEIR DERIVATIVES

There are two hydrides of phosphorus:

$$PH_3 \quad \text{a gas} \quad \text{b.p.} -87.7° \quad \text{m.p.} -133°,$$
$$P_2H_4 \quad \text{a liquid} \quad \text{b.p.} +51.7° \quad \text{m.p.} -99°.$$

Both compounds are more volatile than the corresponding nitrogen compounds, no doubt because phosphorus does not form hydrogen bonds.

Phosphine, PH_3, is a colourless, poisonous gas with an unpleasant fishy smell; 10 parts per million breathed continuously cause death. It is made by the action of water or an acid on a metallic phosphide, by the thermal decomposition of an acid of which the molecule contains a P—H link, or by the decomposition of a phosphonium compound. The following are particular examples of these methods:

(i) White phosphorus is boiled with an alkaline hydroxide solution. The phosphine thus obtained is always contaminated with at least 50% of hydrogen, and with some P_2H_4. The principal reactions are:

$$4P + 3NaOH + 3H_2O = PH_3 + 3NaH_2PO_2$$
$$4P + 4NaOH + 4H_2O = 2H_2 + 4NaH_2PO_2$$
$$NaH_2PO_2 + 2NaOH = 2H_2 + Na_3PO_4.$$

(ii) Sulphuric acid is allowed to act on aluminium phosphide:†

$$2AlP + 3H_2SO_4 = Al_2(SO_4)_3 + 2PH_3.$$

(iii) Phosphorous acid is heated:

$$4H_3PO_3 = 3H_3PO_4 + PH_3.$$

(iv) Hypophosphorous acid or its salts are heated:

$$2H_3PO_2 = H_3PO_4 + PH_3.$$

---

† Hydrolysable phosphides, such as those of aluminium and silicon, liberate phosphine by the action of moisture. The presence of these substances in alloys, by design or as impurities, is therefore a matter of importance to the health of those who work such alloys, or who live and work in structures made of them.

(v) Phosphorus oxychloride is treated with water and excess of zinc dust (phosphorus trichloride does not react thus).

(vi) A solution of phosphonium iodide is treated with 30% potassium hydroxide solution:

$$KOH + PH_4I = PH_3 + KI + H_2O.$$

The gas obtained by any of the above methods is liable to contain hydrogen, and also P_2H_4 which renders it spontaneously inflammable. Pure phosphine is isolated by passing the crude gas through a tube immersed in a freezing mixture to liquefy the P_2H_4, and then through a tube immersed in liquid air to condense the phosphine.

Pure phosphine, if quite free from water vapour, ignites in the air in the cold, but pure phosphine containing a trace of moisture does not ignite in air below 150°. A mixture of pure phosphine and air or oxygen explodes when the pressure is reduced.

Phosphine is sparingly soluble in water, alcohol, or ether (0·26 vol dissolve in 1 vol of water at 17°). It is thermally decomposed at 440° (a wall reaction), or by sparking, to yield red phosphorus and hydrogen. It explodes with oxygen, with nitrous oxide, or with nitric oxide:

$$PH_3 + 4N_2O = H_3PO_4 + 4N_2.$$

With chlorine it reacts spontaneously:

$$PH_3 + 4Cl_2 = PCl_5 + 3HCl.$$

When phosphine is passed over heated copper, copper phosphide, and hydrogen are produced.

Phosphine is absorbed by a suspension of bleaching powder. It precipitates phosphides or metals from solutions of certain metallic salts. With silver nitrate solution the reactions occur:

$$PH_3 + 6AgNO_3 = Ag_3P,3AgNO_3 + 3HNO_3,$$
$$Ag_3P,3AgNO_3 + 3H_2O = 6Ag + 3HNO_3 + H_3PO_3.$$

Phosphine is oxidised by iodine in water to hypophosphorous acid, and it reacts with sodium triphenylmethyl (p. 410) to yield $NaPH_2$. The co-ordination compounds of phosphine are mentioned on p. 711.

From spectra the distance P—H in the phosphine molecule is 1·45, and the H—P—H angle is $98 \pm 5°$ or $93 \pm 2°$. This angle is more acute than that of ammonia, 116°. The barrier to inversion is about the same as for ammonia, but the frequency of inversion is only about 1/1000 that of ammonia.

Phosphonium compounds. The aqueous solution of phosphine is neutral, but in anhydrous conditions the gas acts as a very feeble base. It forms the phosphonium compounds, PH_4I, PH_4Br, PH_4Cl, all of which are decomposed by water into the halogen acid and phosphine.

The most stable of the three phosphonium compounds is phosphonium iodide. It is formed as white crystals when phosphine and hydrogen iodide are mixed at room temperature, but it dissociates again at 30°. It is most conveniently made by the action of water on a finely divided mixture of iodine and white phosphorus:

$$2P + I_2 + 4H_2O = PH_4I + H_3PO_4 + HI.$$

Iodine is added to a solution of white phosphorus in carbon disulphide under an atmosphere of carbon dioxide. The solvent is removed by distillation. Water is carefully dropped on to the residue, and the phosphonium iodide is isolated by sublimation. The atmosphere of carbon dioxide is preserved throughout the experiment.

Phosphonium chloride is produced as white crystals when phosphine and hydrogen chloride are cooled to $-35°$, or compressed to 18 atm at 15°.

23*

The alkyl and aryl phosphines. Derivatives of phosphine are known in which one or more hydrogen atoms in the phosphine molecule are replaced by alkyl or aryl groups. The boiling points of the simpler tertiary compounds are:

$$P(CH_3)_3, 37\cdot8°; \quad P(C_2H_5)_3, 128°; \quad P(C_6H_5)_3, \text{ above } 360° \text{ (m.p. } 80°).$$

The compounds are made by treating phosphine with the appropriate alcohol, or by treating phosphorus tribromide with the appropriate Grignard reagent. The alkyl derivatives are liable to catch fire in air, and are readily oxidised to the phosphine oxide, R_3PO. The structure of $P(CH_3)_3$ is shown by the infrared and Raman spectra to be pyramidal. The quaternary bases R_4POH are as strongly basic as the hydroxides of the alkali metals.

Phosphorus dihydride, P_2H_4, is a colourless, volatile, liquid. It is extracted from the other products of the action of water on crude calcium phosphide which contains Ca_2P_2:

$$Ca_2P_2 + 4H_2O = 2Ca(OH)_2 + P_2H_4.$$

The gases evolved in this reaction, after passage through a tube standing in cold water to remove water vapour, are led through a tube standing in a freezing mixture of ice and salt. The more volatile phosphine passes on; the less volatile P_2H_4 collects as liquid.

The vapour is unstable, and is spontaneously inflammable in air. The liquid decomposes on exposure to light, to give phosphine and red phosphorus:

$$3P_2H_4 = 4PH_3 + 2P.$$

Hydrogen chloride acting on the solid at $-125°$ brings about the same change. P_2H_4 exhibits no basic properties.

PHOSPHORUS TRIHALIDES

Phosphorus forms a compound of the type PX_3 with each of the halogens; there are also a few mixed halogen compounds of the type PX_2Y. The physical properties of all these compounds are set out in Table 20.4. The structures of the compounds have been examined by electron diffraction; all of them have pyramidal structures. The molecular dimensions are set out in the Table. The apical angles diminish from 104° for the fluoride to 98° for the iodide, although the radii of the halogen atoms increase from fluorine to iodine. It may be that the electronegative character of the fluorine atom causes polarisation along the bond P—F, which builds up the electron density

Table 20.4. *Phosphorus Trihalides*

	PF_3	PCl_3	PBr_3	PI_3	PF_2Cl	PF_2Br	$PFCl_2$	$PFBr_2$
b.p. °C	$-101\cdot1$	$+74\cdot7$	$+175\cdot3$	120°/15 mm	$-47\cdot3$	$-16\cdot1$	$-13\cdot85$	78·4
m.p. °C	$-151\cdot5$	$-93\cdot6$	-40	$+61$	$-164\cdot8$	$-133\cdot8$	$-144\cdot1$	-115
State at room temperature	Colourless gas	Colourless liquid	Colourless liquid	Dark red hexagonal crystals	Gas	Gas	Gas	Liquid
Structure	Pyramid	Pyramid	Pyramid	Pyramid				
Apical angle X—P—X	104°	102°	100°	98°				
Bond length P—X	1·52	2·00	2·23	2·47				

near the fluorine atom. The mutual repulsion among the charge clouds near the fluorine atoms may explain the large apical angle. The chemistry of the compounds is set out below.

Phosphorus trifluoride, PF_3, a colourless gas, is made:

(i) by the action of arsenic trifluoride on phosphorus trichloride:

$$PCl_3 + AsF_3 = PF_3 + AsCl_3,$$

(ii) by warming phosphorus tribromide with zinc fluoride:

$$2PBr_3 + 3ZnF_2 = 2PF_3 + 3ZnBr_2,$$

(iii) by heating copper phosphide with lead fluoride:

$$2Cu_3P + 3PbF_2 = 2PF_3 + 6Cu + 3Pb.$$

The gas is hydrolysed by water to hydrofluoric acid and phosphorous acid, but it does not fume in air. It does not attack glass except at high temperatures. It is decomposed by sparking:

$$5PF_3 = 3PF_5 + 2P.$$

A mixture of the gas and oxygen explodes when sparked:

$$2PF_3 + O_2 = 2POF_3,$$

but phosphorus trifluoride does not combine directly with sulphur.

Phosphorus trichloride, PCl_3, a colourless liquid, is made by passing a stream of dry chlorine over white or red phosphorus (not heated), and condensing the product in an ice-cold receiver. The apparatus is filled with carbon dioxide before the introduction of the phosphorus, and water is excluded by the use of calcium chloride tubes. The crude product is contaminated with chlorine, which is removed by standing the liquid over white phosphorus. Phosphorus trichloride is finally purified by distillation. Phosphorus trichloride can also be obtained by passing gaseous hydrogen chloride over phosphorous oxide P_4O_6:

$$6HCl + P_4O_6 = 2H_3PO_3 + 2PCl_3.$$

Phosphorus trichloride fumes in air and reacts violently with water (p. 722):

$$PCl_3 + 3H_2O = H_3PO_3 + 3HCl.$$

If phosphorus trichloride is treated with water in the presence of iodine it yields hypophosphoric acid (p. 723). If treated with ammonia at low temperatures phosphorus trichloride forms $PCl_3,5NH_3$, which on heating gives ultimately $(P_2N_5)_x$ (p. 710). Phosphorus trichloride behaves as an unsaturated compound, taking up chlorine to give PCl_5, oxygen to give $POCl_3$, and sulphur to give $PSCl_3$. It also acts as a reducing agent when treated with:

(i) sulphur trioxide:

$$PCl_3 + SO_3 = POCl_3 + SO_2,$$

(ii) hot concentrated sulphuric acid:

$$PCl_3 + 2H_2SO_4 = SO_3HCl + SO_2 + 2HCl + HPO_3,$$

(iii) sulphur chloride:

$$3PCl_3 + S_2Cl_2 = PCl_5 + 2PSCl_3.$$

When phosphorus trichloride is oxidised the 3 co-ordinate phosphorus atom becomes 4 co-ordinate, as in the compounds $[PCl_4^+][PCl_6^-]$, $POCl_3$, $PSCl_3$, or HPO_3.

The chlorine atoms in phosphorus trichloride can be successively replaced by fluorine by the action of AsF_3, SbF_3, or SbF_5, or by passing the vapour over heated calcium fluoride. The chlorine atoms can be replaced by iodine by the action of potassium iodide.

Phosphorus tribromide, PBr_3, a colourless liquid, is formed by the action of bromine on red phosphorus: the reaction is violent. It fumes in the air. If oxygen is passed into boiling phosphorus tribromide, combination to form $POBr_3$ takes place very easily, and an explosion may result. With excess bromine, phosphorus tribromide forms the yellow pentabromide.

If hydrolysed in the presence of iodine it yields hypophosphoric acid (p. 723).

Phosphorus tri-iodide, PI_3, a dark red solid, is made by the action of iodine on white phosphorus in carbon disulphide solution, or by the action of potassium iodide on phosphorus trichloride. It is hydrolysed by water to phosphorous acid.

Diphosphorus tetraiodide, P_2I_4, an orange red solid, m.p. 124°, is made by mixing carbon disulphide solutions of iodine and white phosphorus in the correct ratio, and evaporating. It is also formed by the action of iodine on phosphorus trichloride in warm glacial acetic acid solution:

$$2PCl_3 + 5I_2 = P_2I_4 + 6ICl.$$

It decomposes on heating. It is hydrolysed by water at 0° to hypophosphorous acid, H_3PO_2, phosphorous acid, and phosphoric acid. It is oxidised by alkaline hydrogen peroxide to hypophosphoric acid, $H_4P_2O_6$. This reaction indicates the structure:

Diphosphorus tetrachloride, P_2Cl_4, a colourless, oily, fuming liquid; m.p. $-28°$, b.p. 180°, is made:

(i) by striking an arc between zinc electrodes in phosphorus trichloride vapour,
(ii) by passing a silent discharge through a mixture of phosphorus trichloride vapour and hydrogen.

On standing, P_2Cl_4 decomposes to PCl_3 and P. It is oxidised by air, sometimes with inflammation.

THE OXIDES OF PHOSPHORUS

There are four oxides of phosphorus: P_4O_6, P_4O_{10}, $(PO_2)_n$, and P_2O_6. The structures of the first two are related to that of the phosphorus molecule P_4; those of the others are unknown.

Phosphorous oxide, P_4O_6, is a white solid, m.p. 23·8°, b.p. 174°. It has a smell of garlic and is very poisonous. It is made by passing a slow stream of air over burning phosphorus; the non-volatile P_4O_{10} is retained by a glass-wool filter.†

Liquid phosphorous oxide is a non-conductor. The vapour decomposes above 210° to $(PO_2)_n$ and elementary phosphorus. Phosphorous oxide in the cold takes up oxygen from the air to give P_4O_{10}, and it inflames if slightly warmed. With cold water it slowly gives phosphorous acid:

$$6H_2O + P_4O_6 = 4H_3PO_3.$$

† Free phosphorus is removed by dissolving the P_4O_6 in carbon disulphide, exposing to light to precipitate red phosphorus, and crystallising.

Phosphorous oxide reacts with chlorine and with bromine. With gaseous hydrogen chloride it gives phosphorus trichloride and phosphorous acid. It reacts with sulphur to form $P_4O_6S_4$ (p. 718). It inflames in contact with alcohol, but dissolves in ether, carbon disulphide, benzene, and chloroform.

The molecular weight of phosphorous oxide in solution in benzene, and in the vapour at low temperatures, corresponds to P_4O_6. The results of electron diffraction experiments indicate that the four phosphorus atoms in the molecule are at the corners of a tetrahedron; one oxygen atom is situated between each pair of phosphorus atoms (p. 711). The distance P—O is 1·65.

$(PO_2)_n$ is a solid, subliming at 180° in vacuo. It is made by heating phosphorous oxide† in a sealed tube to 440°:

$$nP_4O_6 = 3(PO_2)_n + nP.$$

It dissolves in water with evolution of heat to give a mixture of phosphorous acid and phosphoric acid in equal quantity; it does not give hypophosphoric acid. The vapour density at 1400° corresponds to the formula P_8O_{16}.

Phosphoric oxide, P_4O_{10}, is a white solid. It is made by burning phosphorus in excess of air or oxygen. The crude product may contain some P_4O_6. This can be removed by sublimation in a current of ozonised oxygen.

The solid is polymorphic. The hexagonal form is obtained when phosphorus is burnt. On heating, this form changes successively into two other forms of increasing density and diminishing volatility. Certain properties of the various forms of phosphoric oxide are set out below.

	Triple point	Specific gravity	Heat of volatilisation‡	Structure
Hexagonal	420°/360 cm	2·30	22·7 kcal/mole	Tetrahedral molecules as in vapour
Orthorhombic	562°/43·7 cm	2·72	36·4 kcal/mole	Sheets of interlocking rings of same type
Tetragonal	580°/55·5 cm	2·89	33·9 kcal/mole	Unknown
Metastable fused hexagonal			16·2 kcal/mole	
Stable liquid above 580°			18·7 kcal/mole	

Phosphoric oxide absorbs moisture giving first cyclotetraphosphoric acid and then the pyro- and ortho- phosphoric acids. All forms absorb water vapour at the same rate, but the hexagonal form is usually employed as a drying agent. It is more efficient than any other drying agent, and is as efficient at 90° as at 0°. Phosphoric oxide is used for making acid oxides by withdrawing the elements of water from the parent acid. For example:

$$H_2SO_4 - H_2O = SO_3,$$
$$2HNO_3 - H_2O = N_2O_5,$$
$$2HClO_4 - H_2O = Cl_2O_7.$$

On the addition of liquid water to phosphoric oxide the hexagonal form reacts violently, the orthorhombic very slowly even at 100°, and the tetragonal form produces a gel which slowly liquefies.

Phosphoric oxide is very stable, even at high temperatures. The formula P_4O_{10} (mol wt 142) is approximately in accordance with the experimental value of the

† If the product obtained by burning phosphorus in a limited supply of air (it consists of red phosphorus, P_4O_{10}, and P_4O_6) is heated in a sealed tube at 290°, a crystalline sublimate of $(PO_2)_n$ is obtained.

‡ The molecule of phosphoric oxide is P_4O_{10}.

molecular weight of the vapour (150) between 670° and 1100°. On evidence from electron diffraction the structure is similar to that of P_4O_6, with an extra oxygen atom on each phosphorus atom (p. 711).

P_2O_6. If a mixture of phosphoric oxide vapour and oxygen is sparked, a deep violet solid of high oxidising power is formed. This contains up to 5% of an oxide P_2O_6. If heated to 130° the solid is decolourised, and loses oxygen and oxidising power. Aqueous solutions of the solid oxidise potassium iodide to iodine, and the manganous ion to the permanganate ion. The reactions of P_2O_6 suggest that it is the anhydride of perdiphosphoric acid, and that its structure is:

$$\begin{array}{ccc} O & & O \\ \backslash & & \diagup \\ & P-O-O-P & \\ \diagup & & \backslash \\ O & & O \end{array}$$

Another possible structure would be the P_4O_{10} structure with peroxide groups in place of two of the oxygen atoms at the tetrahedron corners, but this would imply the existence of the oxide P_4O_{14} which has not been observed.

Sulphides of phosphorus. The formulae and certain properties of the three sulphides of phosphorus are set out in Table 20.5. All the sulphides are yellow and crystalline.

Table 20.5.   *Phosphorus Sulphides*

Formula	m.p. °C	b.p. °C	Solubility, gm per 100 gr CS_2	Rate of hydrolysis
P_4S_3	172	408	76·9	Slow
P_4S_{10}	290	530	0·22	Less slow
P_4S_7	305	523	0·029	Quick

These compounds can be made by warming the components together in the correct proportions, either alone or in solution in carbon disulphide, naphthalene, or xylene. Traces of iodine act catalytically. The phosphorus sulphides may be purified by recrystallisation from carbon disulphide, or by distillation in vacuo. They are hydrolysed by water to yield phosphoric acid, phosphorous acid, hypophosphorous acid, phosphine, and hydrogen sulphide. P_4S_{10} is used to replace an oxygen atom in an organic compound by sulphur; thio-alcohols and thio-ketones may be made in this way.

Each of the three sulphides is well-characterised. Molecular weight determinations indicate that there are four P atoms per molecule in solution and in the vapour. X-ray diffraction experiments have been carried out on P_4S_7 and P_4S_{10}, and electron diffraction experiments on P_4S_3, and the structures deduced are shown in Fig. 19.3.

Phosphorus oxysulphide, $P_4O_6S_4$, exists as colourless, deliquescent crystals, m.p. 102°. It is made by the direct combination of phosphorous oxide (P_4O_6) with sulphur. The reaction is violent. Phosphorus oxysulphide may be sublimed. It reacts with water to form hydrogen sulphide and probably cyclotetraphosphoric acid. The structure of phosphorus oxysulphide is probably that of P_4O_{10} in which each oxygen atom bound to one phosphorus atom only, is replaced by a sulphur atom. The P—S distance is very short (p. 711).

THE PHOSPHORYL HALIDES AND THE THIOPHOSPHORYL HALIDES

The general formula of the phosphoryl halides is POX_3, where X may be F, Cl, or Br, but not I. Mixed halogen compounds are known. The formulae of the compounds, and certain of their properties, are set out in Table 20.6.

Phosphorus forms no compound analogous to the nitrosyl compounds (p. 663) typified by Cl—N=O. It has been established experimentally that the chlorine atoms and the oxygen atom in $POCl_3$ occupy tetrahedral positions round the phosphorus atom. Hence the phosphorus atom is tetrahedrally hybridised. In phosphoryl fluoride and phosphoryl chloride the distances P—F, P—Cl, and P—O are very short. This effect is accounted for by the existence of a πd bond between the phosphorus atom and another atom:

$$
\begin{array}{c}
O \\
| \; \pi d \\
P \\
\diagdown | \diagdown \\
Cl \quad Cl \quad Cl
\end{array}
$$

Table 20.6   *Phosphorus Oxyhalides*

	POF_3	$POCl_3$	$POBr_3$	POF_2Cl	$POFCl_2$	POF_2Br	$POFBr_2$
b.p. °C	−40°	107	189·5	+ 3·1	52·9	30·5	110·1
m.p. °C	−39·45	+1·25	56	−96·4	−80·1	−84·8	−117·2
Apical angles	109·5°	106°	108°	106°	106°		
Distance P—O	1·55	1·45	1·41	1·55	1·55		
				P—F 1·51	P—F 1·51		
Distance P—X	1·51	2·02	2·06	P—Cl 2·02	P—Cl 2·02		

Table 20.7.   *Phosphorus Sulphur Halides*

	PSF_3	$PSCl_3$	$PSBr_3$	PSF_2Cl	$PSFCl_2$	PSF_2Br	$PSFBr_2$
b.p. °C	−52·9	125	decp. 175	+6·3	64·7	35·5	125·3
m.p. °C	−148·8	−36·2	+39	−155·2	−96·0	−136·9	−75·2
Apical angles	100°	101°	106°			106°	100°
Distance P—S	1·85	1·94	1·89			1·87	1·87
						P—F 1·45	P—F 1·50
Distance P—X	1·53	2·02	2·13			P—Br 2·14	P—Br 2·18

Phosphoryl fluoride, POF_3, is a colourless gas. It is made:

(i) by the action of water on phosphorus pentafluoride,
(ii) by treating phosphoryl chloride with zinc fluoride, or antimony trifluoride,
(iii) by the action of dry hydrogen fluoride on phosphoric oxide,
(iv) by heating a mixture of cryolite, $NaAlF_6$, and phosphoric oxide.

It fumes only slightly in air. When dry it does not attack glass. It is hydrolysed by water to HF and H_3PO_4.

Phosphoryl chloride, $POCl_3$, is a colourless fuming liquid. It is made:

(i) by the partial hydrolysis of phosphorus pentachloride by heating with oxalic acid, or with boric acid:

$$PCl_5 + (COOH)_2 = POCl_3 + CO + CO_2 + 2HCl,$$
$$3PCl_5 + 2H_3BO_3 = 3POCl_3 + B_2O_3 + 6HCl,$$

(ii) by heating a mixture of the pentachloride and the pentoxide:

$$P_2O_5 + 3PCl_5 = 5POCl_3,$$

(iii) by oxidising phosphorus trichloride with ozone, or with potassium chlorate:

$$PCl_3 + O_3 = POCl_3 + O_2,$$
$$3PCl_3 + KClO_3 = 3POCl_3 + KCl,$$

(iv) by heating calcium phosphate in a mixture of chlorine and carbon monoxide, at 300–350°:

$$Ca_3(PO_4)_2 + 6CO + 6Cl_2 = 3CaCl_2 + 2POCl_3 + 6CO_2.$$

Phosphoryl chloride dissolves slowly in water which hydrolyses it to phosphoric acid and hydrochloric acid. With water and excess of zinc dust it evolves phosphine; phosphorus trichloride does not undergo this reaction. Phosphoryl chloride is stable to heat.

Phosphoryl bromide, POBr$_3$, is a colourless crystalline solid. Its preparation and properties are analogous to those of phosphoryl chloride.

Thiophosphoryl fluoride, PSF$_3$, is a colourless gas. It is made:

(i) by heating thiophosphoryl chloride with arsenic trifluoride,

(ii) by heating phosphorus pentasulphide with lead fluoride:

$$P_2S_5 + 3PbF_2 = 2PSF_3 + 3PbS.$$

Thiophosphoryl fluoride is spontaneously inflammable in air. It is slowly hydrolysed by water. When heated strongly it dissociates into sulphur and phosphorus trifluoride which do not recombine on cooling.

Thiophosphoryl chloride, PSCl$_3$, is a colourless, fuming liquid. It is made:

(i) by the action of phosphorus trichloride on sulphur,

(ii) by the action of phosphorus pentachloride on the pentasulphide, or on hydrogen sulphide.

It is dimorphic in the solid state. It is hydrolysed by water:

$$PSCl_3 + 4H_2O = H_3PO_4 + H_2S + 3HCl.$$

Thiophosphoryl bromide, PSBr$_3$, is made by the action of bromine on a mixture of phosphorus and sulphur dissolved in carbon disulphide. It is only slowly hydrolysed by boiling water.

THE OXYACIDS OF PHOSPHORUS

The oxyacids of phosphorus may be grouped in three classes.

(i) Acids having molecules which contain one atom of phosphorus which is in the tetrahedral valence state. The acids in this class are orthophosphoric acid, H_3PO_4, phosphorous acid, H_3PO_3, and hypophosphorous acid, H_3PO_2. If the acids are written in the ionised form the formulae are:

The series may be continued, thus:

phosphonium iodide.

In all five compounds the valence state of the phosphorus atom is the same; oxidation of, say, phosphorous acid to phosphoric acid consists in the replacement of a hydrogen atom by an oxygen atom and not in any change in the state of the phosphorus atom.

(ii) Hypophosphoric acid, $H_4P_2O_6$, the molecule of which contains two phosphorus atoms directly linked to one another.

(iii) Di-, tri-, and cyclo-phosphoric acids which are discussed on p. 727.

It will be convenient to give accounts of the acids in the order hypophosphorous acid, phosphorous acid, hypophosphoric acid, and orthophosphoric acid; the polynuclear phosphoric acids can then be discussed immediately after orthophosphoric acid.

Hypophosphorous acid, H_3PO_2, is a solid, m.p. 27°. It is formed by the following methods:

(i) The oxidation of phosphine by iodine and water. The reaction is said to be quantitative:

$$PH_3 + 2I_2 + 2H_2O = H_3PO_2 + 4HI.$$

The hydriodic acid may be removed by evaporation.

(ii) The decomposition of barium hypophosphite with the calculated quantity of sulphuric acid. After filtering off the $BaSO_4$ the solution is evaporated at 130°, and cooled in a freezing mixture, when it crystallises. The barium hypophosphite is made by heating white phosphorus with barium hydroxide. Excess of barium hydroxide is removed by carbon dioxide, and the filtrate is evaporated until barium hypophosphite crystallises.

Hypophosphorous acid undergoes disproportionation when heated to 130°:

$$3H_3PO_2 = 2H_3PO_3 + PH_3,$$

and at 200° the phosphorous acid further disproportionates into phosphine and phosphoric acid.

Hypophosphorous acid can be reduced by dilute sulphuric acid and zinc to phosphine, but normally it is a strong reducing agent. It is used in the reduction of aromatic diazonium compounds to the parent aromatic compound, for example:

$$H_2O + C_6H_5N_2Cl + H_3PO_2 = H_3PO_3 + C_6H_6 + N_2 + HCl.$$

Hypophosphorous acid reduces solutions of the salts of Au, Ag, Pt, Hg, Bi, to metal, and precipitates an interstitial hydride of copper from the solution of a cupric salt:

$$3H_3PO_2 + 3H_2O + 2CuSO_4 = 2Cu,H + 3H_3PO_3 + 2H_2SO_4.$$

Hypophosphorous acid is monobasic. The acid and its salts (with the exception of the bismuth and thorium salts) are easily soluble in water, and the alkali metal salts are soluble in alcohol too. The rubidium and caesium salts are hygroscopic. They decompose at 140°. The salts when boiled with alkali evolve hydrogen:

$$NaH_2PO_2 + 2NaOH = 2H_2 + Na_3PO_4.$$

The monobasicity of hypophosphorous acid indicates that one hydrogen atom in the molecule is differentiated from the other two. The results of the determination of the crystal structure of the nickel salt $[Ni,2H_2O][H_2PO_2]_2$ show that the anion is tetrahedral. The structure assigned to the acid is:

$$H^+ \left[\begin{array}{c} H \qquad H \\ \diagdown \quad \diagup \\ P \\ \diagup \quad \diagdown_{\pi d} \\ O \qquad O \end{array} \right]^-$$

The presence of the two P—H bonds accounts for the powerful reducing properties of hypophosphorous acid.

Phosphorous acid, H₃PO₃, is a white, deliquescent crystalline compound, m.p. 73·6°. It is made by the addition of water to phosphorus trichloride. The reaction is violent, partly because of the heat liberated by the solution of the hydrogen chloride. The reaction can be moderated by adding the phosphorus trichloride to a saturated solution of hydrogen chloride; subsequently the solution is evaporated until the temperature reaches 180°; on cooling the phosphorous acid crystallises. The method may be varied by adding phosphorus trichloride to anhydrous oxalic acid:

$$3(COOH)_2 + PCl_3 = H_3PO_3 + 3CO + 3CO_2 + 3HCl.$$

Phosphorous acid when heated to 200° gives phosphoric acid and phosphine:

$$4H_3PO_3 = 3H_3PO_4 + PH_3.$$

It can be reduced to phosphine by treatment with zinc and dilute sulphuric acid, but it is normally a reducing agent, although neither so powerful nor so quick as hypophosphorous acid. It precipitates the heavy metals from solutions of their salts:

$$2AgNO_3 + H_3PO_3 = Ag_2HPO_3 + 2HNO_3,$$
$$Ag_2HPO_3 + H_2O = 2Ag + H_3PO_4,$$
$$2HgCl_2 + H_3PO_3 + H_2O = Hg_2Cl_2 + 2HCl + H_3PO_4.$$

It reduces copper sulphate only to the metal, and not to the hydride. It reduces iodine in neutral or weakly alkaline solution. It is oxidised by nitric acid, but only if nitrous acid is present. It reduces sulphur dioxide to sulphur:

$$SO_2 + 2H_3PO_3 = 2H_3PO_4 + S.$$

Phosphorous acid is very soluble in water. It is a dibasic acid, $K_1 = 0·031 - 0·021$, $K_2 = 1·5 \times 10^{-7}$. Only two types of salt are known, MH_2PO_3 and M_2HPO_3. When boiled with alkalis the salts do not lose hydrogen (cf. hypophosphites).

The dibasicity of phosphorous acid, and its reducing properties point to the structure:

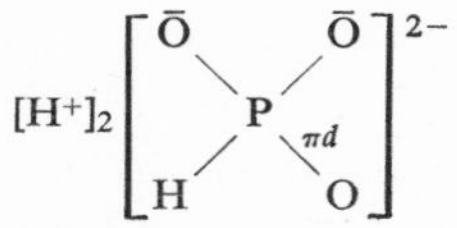

The ethyl derivative, b.p. 198°, corresponding to this structure is:

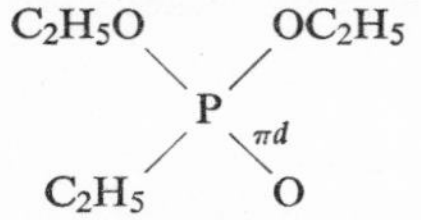

It is made by the esterification of ethyl phosphonic acid, $C_2H_5PO(OH)_2$. Phosphorus triethylate, $P(OC_2H_5)_3$, b.p. 156° has the same molecular formula as the above compound, but it is a derivative of phosphorus trichloride from which it is made by treatment with sodium ethylate in alcohol. In the presence of ethyl iodide it changes into diethyl phosphonic ester. The dialkyl esters of phosphorous acid are tautomeric:

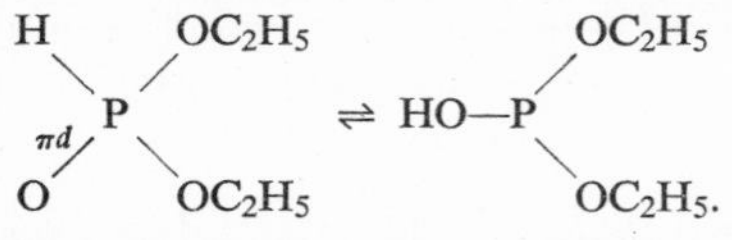

Hypophosphoric acid, $(OH)_4O_2P_2$, a crystalline compound, m.p. 70°, is obtained from the sodium salt. The sodium salt is made by the following methods:

(i) The oxidation of white phosphorus by moist air. The liquid which forms contains hypophosphoric acid, phosphorous acid, and phosphoric acid. If sodium acetate is added, the sparingly soluble disodium hypophosphate, $Na_2H_2P_2O_6, 6H_2O$, separates.

(ii) The oxidation of red phosphorus with concentrated sodium hydroxide and hydrogen peroxide.

(iii) The oxidation of P_2I_4 with concentrated sodium hydroxide solution and hydrogen peroxide.

(iv) The hydrolysis of phosphorus trichloride or tribromide in the presence of iodine: the solution is buffered with sodium acetate and sodium bicarbonate:

$$I_2 + 12NaHCO_3 + 2PCl_3 = (ONa)_4O_2P_2 + 2NaI + 6NaCl + 12CO_2 + 6H_2O.$$

To obtain the free acid, barium chloride is added to the solution of sodium hypophosphate. The very sparingly soluble barium salt is filtered off, and decomposed with sulphuric acid. The hydrate, $H_4P_2O_6,2H_2O$, is first obtained, m.p. 62°. If this stands in vacuo over P_2O_5 the anhydrous acid, m.p. 70°, is obtained.

Hypophosphoric acid decomposes on heating:

$$H_4P_2O_6 = H_3PO_3 + HPO_3.$$

It is hydrolysed in acid solution:

$$H_4P_2O_6 + H_2O = H_3PO_4 + H_3PO_3.$$

It is not a reducing agent. It is oxidised only by potassium permanganate or dichromate, and this perhaps only because preliminary hydrolysis has produced phosphorous acid. It is not reduced by zinc and dilute sulphuric acid to phosphine.

The hypophosphates (except for those of the alkali metals) are very sparingly soluble.

The formula, $H_4P_2O_6$, is established by determination of the molecular weight of the acid, the sodium salt, and the ester, $(C_2H_5)_4P_2O_6$. The acid is tetrabasic and forms the salts, $Ag_4P_2O_6$, $Pb_2P_2O_6$, and $Na_3HP_2O_6,9H_2O$, as well as the disodium salt mentioned above. The most acceptable structure is:

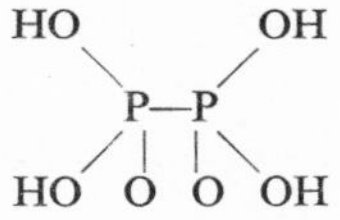

which is consistent with the Raman spectrum, with the symmetry of the hypophosphate anion deduced from X-ray experiments on diammonium hypophosphate, and with the absence of reducing properties of the acid.

THE PHOSPHORIC ACIDS

Classical work on the properties and constitutions of the phosphoric acids had led to the conclusion that there were three principal acids, orthophosphoric acid, H_3PO_4, pyrophosphoric acid, $H_4P_2O_7$, and metaphosphoric acid, HPO_3. Since about 1940 our knowledge of the properties of the metaphosphates has been extended by a number of studies, and something has been perceived of the variability and complexity of the constitutions of the substances previously described by this name. Much of the evidence on the constitution of the metaphosphates cannot be regarded as conclusive, but the deductions which can be made from it are consistent, and in accord with our knowledge of the silicates and other oxyacids. The classical nomenclature does not satisfactorily express the relations between the acids suggested by recent work. In the scheme below the structures of the acids are drawn, and the suggested new names are attached to them. There are two principal basic structures: (i) structures of unbranched chains composed of PO_4 tetrahedra, linked by oxygen atoms held in common, (ii) cyclic structures in which either three or four PO_4 tetrahedra are linked in the form of a ring, again by oxygen atoms held in common.

Structures of the phosphoric acids in the non-dissociated state.

Unbranched chains:

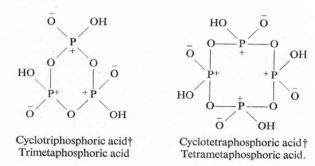

H_3PO_4

HO   OH

P

HO   O

Orthophosphoric
acid

$H_4P_2O_7$

OH   OH

HO—P—O—P—OH

O   O

Diphosphoric acid†
Pyrophosphoric acid

$H_5P_3O_{10}$

OH   OH   OH

HO—P—O—P—O—P—OH

O   O   O

Triphosphoric acid

The general formula for this series is $H_{4+n}P_{2+n}O_{7+3n}$. n is written 0 for diphosphoric acid, and -1 for orthophosphoric acid.‡

Cyclic structures:

Cyclotriphosphoric acid†
Trimetaphosphoric acid

Cyclotetraphosphoric acid†
Tetrametaphosphoric acid.

It is observed that certain regularities are present in the structures both of the chain and the cyclic acids:

(i) Each phosphorus atom is linked to one oxygen atom by a bond which is either a co-ionic bond or a πd bond.

(ii) One OH group on each phosphorus atom has the dissociation properties of a strong acid, $K=10^{-1}$ or 10^{-2}; any additional OH groups on the same phosphorus atom have dissociation properties of weak acids. This property shows up clearly in potentiometric titrations, and in the formation of such salts as $Na_2H_2P_2O_7$ and $Na_3H_2P_3O_{10}$.

(iii) Two adjacent tetrahedra are never bonded by more than one link, that is to say, tetrahedra may have corners in common, but not edges or faces.§

Chain polyphosphates differ from cyclopolyphosphates in that they:

(i) are less readily hydrolysed in alkaline solution, $pH>11$,
(ii) have a much stronger dispersive effect (p. 731),
(iii) inhibit the precipitation of calcite (p. 731).
(iv) form more stable anionic complexes with bi- and ter-valent metals (p. 730).

† The new name is above and the old name below.
‡ The general formula is also of significance in the discussion of the vanadic acids.
§ This is also true of phosphoric oxide, P_4O_{10}.

THE UNBRANCHED CHAIN PHOSPHORIC ACIDS AND THEIR SALTS

Orthophosphoric acid, H_3PO_4, exists as colourless, deliquescent, rhombic crystals, m.p. 42°. It is made by the following methods:

(i) Commercially, by treating calcium phosphate (bone-ash) with fairly strong sulphuric acid; after filtering off the calcium sulphate, the solution is evaporated and crystallised.

(ii) In the laboratory, by dissolving red phosphorus in nitric acid diluted with its own volume of water:

$$P_4 + 10HNO_3 + H_2O = 4H_3PO_4 + 5NO + 5NO_2.$$

When the reaction is over the solution is diluted with its own volume of water and evaporated until the temperature reaches 180°. The solution is then placed in a vacuum desiccator over concentrated sulphuric acid. The desiccator is cooled in a freezing mixture of ice and salt. Crystals of orthophosphoric acid are deposited.

Orthophosphoric acid is stable at room temperature, but the fused acid slowly changes to diphosphoric acid, which at higher temperatures changes to cyclotriphosphoric acid. Orthophosphoric acid is very soluble in water: 670 gm in 100 gm at 25°. Orthophosphoric acid is tribasic, but the first dissociation constant is much greater than the second or third. There is disagreement on the exact values of the constants, but they are approximately:

$$K_1 = 9 \times 10^{-3}, \qquad K_2 = 6 \times 10^{-8}, \qquad K_3 = 1 \times 10^{-12}.$$

The compound $[P(OH)_4][ClO_4]$ can be formed from orthophosphoric acid and perchloric acid; in this compound orthophosphoric acid acts as a base.

The orthophosphate ion, PO_4^{3-}. The orthophosphates. The primary, secondary, and tertiary orthophosphates of sodium are known: NaH_2PO_4, Na_2HPO_4, Na_3PO_4. The primary salt crystallises with one molecule of water of crystallisation, the others with twelve; at 34° the primary sodium salt becomes anhydrous. The solution of the tertiary salt is alkaline to litmus, the secondary is approximately neutral, and the primary is acid.

All primary orthophosphates are soluble in water, but of the secondary and tertiary orthophosphates, only those of the alkali metals (except lithium) and of ammonium are soluble in water. The metallic tertiary orthophosphates with the exception of those of titanium, zirconium, and thorium, ferric iron, aluminium, and chromium are soluble in acetic acid. The tertiary orthophosphates of ferric iron, aluminium, and chromium are soluble in dilute mineral acids, but those of titanium, zirconium, and thorium are not.

The orthophosphates are precipitated by three reactions which are important in analysis.

(1) An orthophosphate treated with excess of nitric acid and a solution of ammonium molybdate *in the cold* yields a yellow precipitate of ammonium phosphomolybdate:

$$(NH_4)_3(PMo_{12}O_{40}, 2HNO_3, H_2O).$$

(The corresponding precipitate from an arsenate is formed only on heating. Diphosphates and cyclotriphosphates show the reaction only if they have been partially converted to orthophosphate.)

(2) A neutral solution of an orthophosphate treated with a neutral solution of silver nitrate gives a yellow precipitate of Ag_3PO_4 soluble either in acid or ammonia.

(3) A solution of an orthophosphate boiled with a solution of magnesium chloride containing ammonia and ammonium chloride, gives a white precipitate of $MgNH_4PO_4,6H_2O$. This on heating yields the diphosphate:

$$2MgNH_4PO_4,6H_2O = Mg_2P_2O_7 + 13H_2O + 2NH_3.$$

By X-ray analysis the PO_4 ion has been shown to be tetrahedral. The P—O distances are:

$$1\cdot56 \text{ in } KH_2PO_4,$$
$$1\cdot54 \text{ in } BPO_4,$$
$$1\cdot61 \text{ in } Ag_3PO_4.$$

Pyrophosphoric or Diphosphoric acid, $H_4P_2O_7$, exists as white, granular crystals, m.p. 61°. It is made by the following methods:

(i) By heating orthophosphoric acid at 220°:

$$2H_3PO_4 = H_4P_2O_7 + H_2O.$$

(ii) From sodium diphosphate, which is obtained by heating secondary sodium orthophosphate above 240°:

$$2Na_2HPO_4 = Na_4P_2O_7 + H_2O.$$

The sodium diphosphate is dissolved in water, and by the addition of lead nitrate, lead diphosphate is precipitated. This can be decomposed by hydrogen sulphide to give the free acid.

(iii) By heating a mixture of orthophosphoric acid and phosphoryl chloride:

$$5H_3PO_4 + POCl_3 = 3H_4P_2O_7 + 3HCl.$$

The residue is cooled for some time in a vacuum desiccator at $-10°$. Crystals of $H_4P_2O_7$ separate.

If diphosphoric acid is boiled with water, or if the aqueous solution stands for some time, it takes up water to yield orthophosphoric acid.

In aqueous solution diphosphoric acid is tetrabasic. The dissociation constants are: $K_1 = 1\cdot4 \times 10^{-1}$, $K_2 = 1\cdot1 \times 10^{-2}$, $K_3 = 2\cdot9 \times 10^{-7}$, $K_4 = 3\cdot6 \times 10^{-9}$. The most familiar salts of diphosphoric acid are the acid salts such as $Na_2H_2P_2O_7$, and the salts formed by the complete replacement of hydrogen atoms in the acid, such as $Na_4P_2O_7$; the existence of salts such as $NaH_3P_2O_7$ and $Na_3HP_2O_7$ is doubtful. This distinction in stability is related to the values of the dissociation constants; the values of K_1 and K_2 are close to one another, and so are the values K_3 and K_4, but there is a gap between K_2 and K_3. Hence unless the conditions can be very carefully controlled, neutralisation of the acid replaces either two hydrogen atoms or four.

Tetrasodium diphosphate crystallises as the decahydrate, the diacid sodium salt is anhydrous, and the calcium salt, $Ca_2P_2O_7,4H_2O$ has four molecules of water of crystallisation. $Ag_4P_2O_7$ is formed as a white precipitate when silver nitrate acts on a solution of sodium diphosphate; $Ag_2H_2P_2O_7$ is soluble. Insoluble diphosphates of the heavy metals dissolve in alkali diphosphate solution, presumably to give complex salts. $Mg_2P_2O_7$ is formed by heating $MgNH_4PO_4$. The alkali metal diphosphates, unlike the free acid, are stable in aqueous solution.

Ethyl diphosphate can be made by the action of ethyl iodide on silver diphosphate:

$$Ag_4P_2O_7 + 4C_2H_5I = (C_2H_5)_4P_2O_7 + 4AgI,$$

or by the action of iodine on sodium diethyl phosphite, $(C_2H_5)_2PONa$. The mechanism of the second reaction must involve the tautomeric change mentioned on p. 722.

The higher polyphosphoric acids such as triphosphoric acid, $H_5P_3O_{10}$ and tetraphosphoric acid, $H_6P_4O_{13}$, have not been isolated, but the sodium salts of a few of them are known. Among such salts are sodium triphosphate, $Na_5P_3O_{10}$, and the hydrate, $Na_5P_3O_{10},6H_2O$.

Sodium triphosphate, $Na_5P_3O_{10}$, is made:

(i) by heating sodium cyclotriphosphate (p. 728), and sodium diphosphate at 600°:

$$Na_3P_3O_9 + 3Na_4P_2O_7 = 3Na_5P_3O_{10},$$

(ii) by heating an intimate mixture of primary and secondary sodium orthophosphate at 400°:

$$2Na_2HPO_4 + NaH_2PO_4 = Na_5P_3O_{10} + 2H_2O.$$

The intimate mixture is made by evaporating the common solution. Sodium triphosphate exists in two polymorphic forms. It decomposes if heated to 620°.

If the anhydrous salt is exposed to the atmosphere, or if its solution is crystallised, the crystalline hydrate, $Na_5P_3O_{10},6H_2O$, is obtained. If a concentrated solution of sodium cyclotriphosphate is mixed with excess of sodium hydroxide solution, crystals of the hexahydrate of sodium triphosphate slowly separate; acid hydrolysis of sodium cyclotriphosphate in the presence of a zinc salt yields sodium zinc triphosphate, $NaZn_2P_4O_{10},9H_2O$. The removal of water from sodium triphosphate by evaporation in vacuo below 100° gives a mixture of sodium orthophosphate and sodium diphosphate.

The molecular formula, $Na_5P_3O_{10}$, for sodium triphosphate is in agreement with the molecular weight determination based on the change of the transition point $Na_2SO_4, 10H_2O/Na_2SO_4$, when sodium triphosphate is added to the system. Arguments in favour of the chain structure of the anion are:

(i) electrometric titration curves of sodium triphosphate show that the corresponding acid has one strongly acidic hydrogen atom for each of three phosphorus atoms, and two much less strongly acidic hydrogen atoms,

(ii) the hydrolysis of sodium triphosphate gives sodium orthophosphate and sodium diphosphate,

(iii) no alternative formula retains the 4 co-ordinate phosphorus atom.

THE CYCLOPHOSPHORIC ACIDS AND THEIR SALTS

Sodium cyclotriphosphate, $Na_3P_3O_9$. The anion in this salt has the geometrical configuration shown in I. The distribution of formal charge in the anion might be that shown in II, which would make it possible for non-localised π bonds to be present in the ring. The phosphorus atoms are probably contributing d orbitals to the non-localised π bond structure:

Evidence for the formula of sodium cyclotriphosphate is based on (a) cryoscopic measurements, (b) measurement of ionic weight, (c) the hydrolysis:

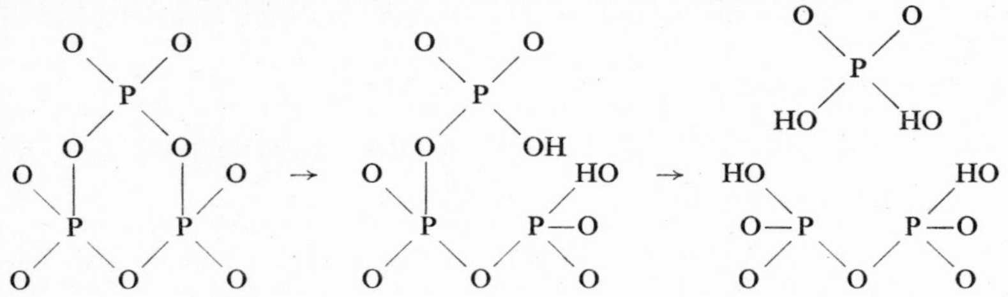

leading ultimately to a mixture of orthophosphoric acid and diphosphoric acid, (d) the presence of the cyclic ion, $P_3O_9^{3-}$ in the structure of strychnine "metaphosphate".

Sodium cyclotriphosphate exists in three polymorphic forms. All three forms are very soluble in water, and may be recrystallised as $Na_3P_3O_9,6H_2O$, or as the mono-hydrate if the crystallisation is carried out above 40°. Dehydration in vacuo at room temperature gives mostly the anhydrous salt, but at higher temperatures there is considerable conversion to NaH_2PO_4 and $Na_4P_2O_7$.

Cyclotriphosphoric acid. A compound of the empirical formula HPO_3 is made:

(i) by heating orthophosphoric acid or diphosphoric acid at 316°:

$$H_3PO_4 = HPO_3 + H_2O,$$
$$H_4P_2O_7 = 2HPO_3 + H_2O,$$

(ii) by heating secondary ammonium orthophosphate:

$$(NH_4)_2HPO_4 = HPO_3 + 2NH_3 + H_2O,$$

(iii) by the action of phosphoryl chloride on crystalline ortho- or di-phosphoric acid:

$$2H_3PO_4 + POCl_3 = 3HPO_3 + 3HCl,$$

(iv) by treating phosphoric oxide with water and ice, and keeping the temperature down to 0° during the hydrolysis.

The substance sets to a hard glass. At a white heat it volatilises, and the vapour is said to be associated. The constitution of this substance is not known.

A solution of what is probably cyclotriphosphoric acid is obtained by passing hydrogen sulphide into a solution of "lead metaphosphate". The acid thus made is two to three times a better conductor per atom of phosphorus than is the ortho acid into which it changes as the solution stands.

The salts of the acid (including those of Ca, Sr, Ba, Ag, Pb) are soluble in water.

Salts of cyclotetraphosphoric acid. Sodium cyclotetraphosphate, $Na_4P_4O_{12}$, is made by heating excess of phosphoric acid with cupric oxide or lead oxide to 350–400°; the cupric or lead cyclotetraphosphate so obtained is treated with sodium sulphide solution, and the sodium cyclotetraphosphate is crystallised. It is also obtained by hydro-lysing P_4O_{10} with $Na_2CO_3,10H_2O$ or with a cold suspension of $NaHCO_3$. The diagram shows the route of the controlled hydrolysis:

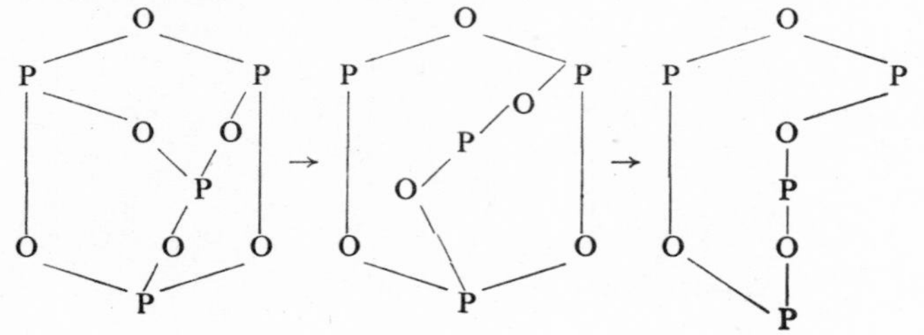

Sodium cyclotetraphosphate forms two well-defined hydrates, $4H_2O$ and $10H_2O$. It decomposes at 260–280° to give Maddrell's salt. Careful hydrolysis produces tetraphosphoric acid, and also orthophosphoric and higher members of the unbranched chain series.

The ionic weight of the ion P_4O_{12} has been determined by cryoscopic measurements. The crystal structure of the aluminium salt has been successfully worked out on the assumption that the constitution is $Al_4(P_4O_{12})_3$. It has been deduced from X-ray diffraction experiments on $(NH_4)_4P_4O_{12}$ that the anion is a puckered eight-membered ring of alternate oxygen and phosphorus atoms; eight further oxygen atoms are attached to the phosphorus atoms.

Sodium salts of phosphoric anions of high ionic weight. There are at least four fairly well characterised sodium salts containing phosphoric anions of high ionic weight: Graham's salt, Kurrol salt, and the two modifications of Maddrell's salt. At one time they were thought to be salts of polymeric forms of "metaphosphoric acid, $(HPO_3)_n$,". These substances can all be made from primary sodium phosphate by thermal changes carried out at regulated temperatures, as set out in Chart 20.1.

The Chart shows that at 150° primary sodium orthophosphate polymerises to secondary sodium diphosphate. Further heating at 230–300° produces three solid substances, (I) the stable sodium cyclotriphosphate with the definite constitution, $Na_3(P_3O_9)$, (II) Maddrell's salt h.t., and (III) Maddrell's salt, l.t. At 628° sodium cyclotriphosphate fuses to a melt which, if chilled, turns to a glass known as Graham's salt. If the glass is heated to 550° and seeded with a crystal of the product, Kurrol salt is formed, and this on annealing yields Maddrell's salt h.t.

Graham's salt is obtained as a glass by chilling the melt of sodium cyclotriphosphate. It is hygroscopic, easily soluble without limit in water, but not in alcohol. The glass liberates water on divitrification, and this water is thought to be present in the glass as OH groups attached to the terminal phosphorus atoms of a chain of PO_4 tetrahedra. The colloidal anions probably have ionic weight of 10,000 to 20,000. The dried glass dissolves in water with the behaviour of a colloidal gel.

Graham's salt has the property of combining with or adsorbing the cations of divalent metals such as calcium, and so inhibiting the precipitation of the metals as carbonates or as the salts of acids present in soaps. It is used for softening water.

Kurrol salt. When Graham's salt is annealed to 550° (especially if seeded with a crystal of the product) it is converted into an asbestos-like substance which gives a fibre X-ray pattern. It is insoluble in water, but swells to a gel.

It has been suggested that the fibrous character of Kurrol salt indicates that the anion possesses a chain structure, like that of calcium metasilicate.

Maddrell's salts are insoluble in water, and their anionic structure is uncertain.

It has been observed that the melt of sodium cyclotriphosphate, if very slowly cooled, yields the definite chemical compound $Na_3P_3O_9$. Graham's salt, Kurrol salt, and the Maddrell's salts, if annealed at 600°, also yield the same salt, but with the evolution of steam. It seems highly probable that the water in these compounds is constitutional, and that its presence is important for the changes that have just been described. Graham's salt is hygroscopic and takes up water from the atmosphere. If a small proportion of this water reacts with the cyclotriphosphate anions which were present in the melt of sodium cyclotriphosphate, the rings will be opened, and by polymerisation long unbranched chain anions may be formed. Such anions are almost certainly present in Kurrol salt, and may well be present in Maddrell's salts also. When these salts are annealed at 600° the process of polymerisation is reversed and water is lost.

The dehydration may be formulated in general terms, as follows. A phosphoric acid possesses one easily dissociable hydrogen atom per phosphorus atom, and therefore the formula of the most readily obtained sodium salt of the unbranched chain acid $H_{4+n}P_{2+n}O_{7+3n}$ is:

$$Na_{2+n}H_{(4+n)-(2+n)}P_{2+n}O_{7+3n}.$$

The equation for the dehydration of this salt is:

$$Na_{2+n}H_{(4+n)-(2+n)}P_{2+n}O_{7+3n} = Na_{2+n}P_{2+n}O_{6+3n} + H_2O.$$

If $n = 1, 4, 7$, etc., the right-hand side of the equation can be written $Na_3P_3O_9$, $2Na_3P_3O_9$, $3Na_3P_3O_9$, and so on. Thus the sodium salt of an unbranched chain phosphoric acid changes into sodium cyclotriphosphate with the elimination of a relatively small proportion of water.

The changes set out in Chart 20.1 are dependent on changes in the lengths of the phosphate anionic chains, and on the closing or opening of rings composed of three or four PO_4 tetrahedra.

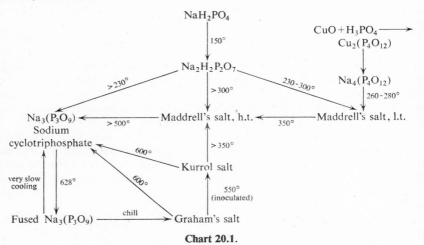

Chart 20.1.

Complex ion formation. If a solution of an alkali metal diphosphate or polyphosphate is added to a solution of a bi- or ter-valent metal salt, a precipitate is formed which redissolves in excess of the phosphate solution. The final solution must contain complex ions. This has been proved experimentally for the complex ions $(M''P_2O_7)^{2-}$ where M is Cd, Co, Cu, Pb, Mg, Ni, Zn, and for $(M'''P_2O_7)^-$ where M is Al or Fe. Calcium and strontium ions show the same power of forming complexes with certain phosphates. The calcium complexes of triphosphoric acid are sufficiently stable to permit the somewhat insoluble salts such as $CaCO_3$, CaC_2O_4,H_2O, and calcium soaps, to dissolve in sodium triphosphate. The complexes of cyclotri- and cyclotetra-phosphoric acids are less stable. The dissociation constant, K, of the dissociation:

$$(CaP_3O_{10})^{3-} \rightleftharpoons Ca^{2+} + (P_3O_{10})^{5-},$$

is given by:

$$K = \frac{[Ca^{2+}][(P_3O_{10})^{5-}]}{[(CaP_3O_{10})^{3-}]} = 3.9 \times 10^{-7} \text{ mol/litre.}$$

For the cyclotriphosphate ion,

$$K = 3.3 \times 10^{-4}.$$

For the cyclotetraphosphate ion,

$$K = 1.3 \times 10^{-5}.$$

When Kurrol or Maddrell's salts are used, complexes are produced in which Ca^{2+} ions are associated with 5–6 PO_3 groups, and the stability of the complex anions is the same as with the triphosphate.

Inhibition of crystallisation of calcium salts by the presence of chain phosphates. At concentrations 0·1 to 1·0% by wt, polyphosphates, but not cyclophosphates, exert a strong dispersive effect on suspensions of colloidal materials, such as clay. It is because of this property that sodium triphosphate is valuable as an addition to synthetic detergents. The presence in solution of Graham's salt or the sodium salt of a polyphosphate (but not the salt of a cyclophosphate) at concentrations as low as $1·5 \times 10^{-5}M$ (in terms of $NaPO_3$) inhibits the precipitation of calcite from a solution of $Ca(HCO_3)_2$ ($10^{-3}M$) by boiling, by the action of ammonia, or by the passage of a current of air. The same concentration also stabilises a supersaturated solution of calcium sulphate against crystallisation as the dihydrate. It is probable that the nuclei of calcite, or calcium sulphate dihydrate, initially formed, become coated with adsorbed polyphosphate ions, after which there is no further growth.

Peroxymonophosphoric acid, $HOOP(OH)_2O$, is known only in solution. It is made by the action of hydrogen peroxide on phosphorus pentoxide in acetonitrile solution at a low temperature. It is a powerful oxidising agent, and converts Mn^{2+} to MnO_4^-.

Peroxydiphosphoric acid, $((OH)_2PO_2)_2$, is made by the action of hydrogen peroxide on diphosphoric acid. The potassium salt is stable in the solid state. Its solution oxidises aniline to nitrosobenzene and nitrobenzene.

PHOSPHORUS CHLORONITRIDES

There is a group of compounds described by the general formula $(PNCl_2)_n$ known as the phosphorus chloronitrides. The monomer and the dimer of the group are unknown. The trimer and the tetramer are well-characterised solids:

$$P_3N_3Cl_6 \quad \text{m.p. } 114° \quad \text{b.p. } 127°/13 \text{ mm,}$$
$$P_4N_4Cl_8 \quad \quad 123·5° \quad \quad \quad 188°/13 \text{ mm.}$$

A mixture of the two compounds is obtained:

(i) by heating phosphorus pentachloride and ammonium chloride together, either in a sealed tube at 120°, or in solution in boiling tetrachloroethane (b.p. 146°),
(ii) by heating $(P_3N_5)_x$ in chlorine at 700°.

The trimer and the tetramer may be isolated by distillation of the mixture obtained in the above preparations, but only at the expense of polymerising much of the material.

It is convenient to discuss the structures of the two compounds before giving an account of their chemical properties. They are both soluble in benzene, and their molecular weights have been ascertained by freezing point methods in this solvent. The molecule of the trimer has been shown by electron diffraction to contain a plane hexagonal ring of alternate phosphorus and nitrogen atoms. The distance P—N in the ring is 1·65. A possible structure is:

in which each phosphorus atom is tetrahedrally hybridised, and each nitrogen atom is trigonally hybridised; one of the trigonal hybrids is occupied by a lone electron pair. One electron is contributed by each phosphorus atom and each nitrogen atom to a system of non-localised π orbitals obtained by combining one $2p$ orbital of each nitrogen atom and one $3d$ orbital of each phosphorus atom. Such an arrangement is satisfactory except that it requires some distortion of the tetrahedral bond angles around the phosphorus atom.

The attachment of the chlorine atoms in pairs to the phosphorus atoms, which is demanded by the orbital structure just outlined, is confirmed by two chemical experiments. Benzene reacts with $P_3N_3Cl_6$ in the presence of aluminium chloride (Friedel-Crafts reaction) thus:

$$
\begin{array}{c}
\text{Cl} \quad \text{Cl} \\
\diagdown \diagup \\
\text{P} \\
\diagup \diagdown \\
\text{N} \quad \text{N} \\
\text{Cl} \mid \quad \mid \text{Cl} \;+2C_6H_6 = \\
\diagdown \diagup \\
\text{P} \quad \text{P} \\
\diagup \diagdown \\
\text{Cl} \quad \text{N} \quad \text{Cl}
\end{array}
\qquad
\begin{array}{c}
\text{C}_6\text{H}_5 \quad \text{C}_6\text{H}_5 \\
\diagdown \diagup \\
\text{P} \\
\diagup \diagdown \\
\text{N} \quad \text{N} \\
\text{Cl} \mid \quad \mid \text{Cl} \;+2HCl. \\
\diagdown \diagup \\
\text{P} \quad \text{P} \\
\diagup \diagdown \\
\text{Cl} \quad \text{N} \quad \text{Cl}
\end{array}
$$

The product is hydrolysed by water to $(C_6H_5)_2PO\cdot OH$. Hence both the chlorine atoms must originally have been attached to the same phosphorus atom. Phenyl magnesium bromide at 115° also reacts with $P_3N_3Cl_6$ to produce diphenyl-P derivatives.

The molecule of the tetramer consists of a puckered eight-membered ring of alternate phosphorus and nitrogen atoms, which suggests that all the atoms are tetrahedrally hybridised.

Chemical properties of the trimer, $P_3N_3Cl_6$. The trimer in ethereal solution is hydrolysed by water to hydroxyl derivatives:

$$
\begin{array}{c}
\text{Cl} \quad \text{Cl} \\
\diagdown \diagup \\
\text{P} \\
\diagup \diagdown \\
\text{N} \quad \text{N} \\
\text{Cl} \mid \quad \mid \text{Cl} \;+2H_2O = \\
\diagdown \diagup \\
\text{P} \quad \text{P} \\
\diagup \diagdown \\
\text{Cl} \quad \text{N} \quad \text{Cl}
\end{array}
\qquad
\begin{array}{c}
\text{HO} \quad \text{OH} \\
\diagdown \diagup \\
\text{P} \\
\diagup \diagdown \\
\text{N} \quad \text{N} \\
\text{Cl} \mid \quad \mid \text{Cl} \;+2HCl. \\
\diagdown \diagup \\
\text{P} \quad \text{P} \\
\diagup \diagdown \\
\text{Cl} \quad \text{N} \quad \text{Cl}
\end{array}
$$

The silver derivative $P_3N_3O_6Ag_6$ is known. The trimer is hydrolysed in acid solution to orthophosphoric acid and ammonia. It reacts with ammonia to give products such as $P_3N_3Cl_4(NH_2)_2$. If the action is allowed to continue, all the chlorine atoms in the molecule are replaced by imino groups giving phospham:

$$
\begin{array}{c}
\text{Cl} \quad \text{Cl} \\
\diagdown \diagup \\
\text{P} \\
\diagup \diagdown \\
\text{N} \quad \text{N} \\
\text{Cl} \mid \quad \mid \text{Cl} \quad \rightarrow \\
\diagdown \diagup \\
\text{P} \quad \text{P} \\
\diagup \diagdown \\
\text{Cl} \quad \text{N} \quad \text{Cl}
\end{array}
\qquad
\begin{array}{c}
\text{N---H} \\
\parallel \\
\text{P} \\
\diagup \diagdown \\
\text{N} \quad \text{N} \\
\text{H} \mid \quad \mid \text{H} \\
\text{P} \quad \text{P} \\
\diagup \diagdown \\
\text{N} \quad \text{N} \quad \text{N}
\end{array}
$$

Phospham, when heated, gives $(P_3N_5)_x$ (p. 710). The apparent course of these changes suggests that $(P_3N_5)_x$ is a three-dimensional network of phosphorus and nitrogen atoms. Aniline, alcohols, and phenols also react with $P_3N_3Cl_6$ so that hydrogen chloride is eliminated, and compounds such as $P_3N_3(OC_6H_5)_6$ are produced. Lead fluoride fluorinates the trimer giving ultimately $P_3N_3F_6$, which, however, is obtainable only as the crystalline $P_3N_3F_6,2HF,2H_2O$, m.p. 32·5°. Some of the trimer is converted into derivatives of the tetramer, such as $P_4N_4Cl_4F_4$, and $P_4N_4Cl_2F_6$.

Chemical properties of the tetramer. The chlorine atoms in the tetramer possess the same reactivity as those in the trimer. In consequence the tetramer undergoes the reactions that have been described for the trimer. The tetraphenyl and the octaphenyl derivatives of the tetramer each exist in two isomeric forms.

At 250–300° the phosphorus chloronitrides are converted to a rubber-like substance. X-ray analysis shows that this substance is amorphous when not stretched, but when stretched it gives a crystalline pattern indicating that the structure consists of zig-zag chains.

The phosphorus fluoronitrides, $P_3N_3F_6$, m.p. 27°, b.p. 52°, and $P_4N_4F_8$, m.p. 30°, b.p. 90°, can be made by fluorinating the chlorides with solid potassium fluorosulphite, KSO_2F. They cannot be made by methods corresponding to those used for making the chloronitrides. They are stable up to 300°, but above this temperature they give colourless, liquid polymers.

SECTION 5. COMPOUNDS IN WHICH THE PHOSPHORUS ATOM IS IN THE TRIGONAL BIPYRAMIDAL VALENCE STATE

PHOSPHORUS PENTAHALIDES

Phosphorus forms compounds of the type PX_5 with fluorine, chlorine, and bromine, but not with iodine. There are also the mixed halides PF_3Cl_2 and PF_3Br_2. Electron diffraction has shown that the molecules of the fluorides and chlorides in the vapour state are trigonal bipyramids; in the compound PF_3Cl_2 the fluorine atoms are in the equatorial positions. This result indicates that the atomic orbitals of the phosphorus atom contributed to form molecular orbitals are the $3s$, the three $3p$ orbitals, and one of the $3d$ orbitals.

In the crystalline state, however, the pentachloride has an ionic structure, $(PCl_4)^+$ $(PCl_6)^-$, in which one phosphorus atom is tetrahedrally hybridised, and the other is octahedrally hybridised. The ionic character assigned to this compound is in accordance with its high dielectric constant, and with the conductivity of its solutions in nitrobenzene and in bromine. The pentabromide also has an ionic structure $(PBr_4)^+Br^-$. The difference in structure is in accordance with the stabilities of the PX_6 anions; $(PF_6)^-$ is well known and is decomposed only with difficulty, $(PCl_6)^-$ exists only in the solid form of PCl_5, and $(PBr_6)^-$ is unknown.

Phosphorus pentafluoride, PF_5, is a colourless gas. It is made:

(i) by heating a mixture of phosphoric oxide and calcium fluoride:

$$6P_2O_5 + 5CaF_2 = 2PF_5 + 5Ca(PO_3)_2,$$

(ii) by mixing arsenic trifluoride with phosphorus pentachloride in a freezing mixture:

$$3PCl_5 + 5AsF_3 = 3PF_5 + 5AsCl_3,$$

(iii) by heating phosphorus pentachloride with the fluoride of a divalent metal (Ca, Ba, Zn, Pb); if an ammonium or alkaline fluoride is used the complex $M(PF_6)$ is formed instead,

(iv) by warming phosphorus fluorobromide to 15°:

$$5PF_3Br_2 = 3PF_5 + 2PBr_5.$$

Phosphorus pentafluoride fumes in air and is decomposed by water:

$$PF_5 + H_2O = POF_3 + 2HF.$$

It does not attack glass when dry. With ammonia it gives solid $2PF_5,5NH_3$.

Table 20.8. *The Phosporus Pentahalides*

		PF$_5$	PCl$_5$	PBr$_5$	PF$_3$Cl$_2$	PF$_3$Br$_2$
	b.p. °C	−75	159 sublimes	Decomposes	+10	106
	m.p. °C	−83	160	Below 100	−8	−20
	State at room temperature	Colourless gas	White tetragonal crystals	Yellow rhombic crystals		
Vapour	Structure (Electron diffraction)	Trigonal bipyramidal	Trigonal bipyramidal		Trigonal bipyramidal	
Vapour	Bond length	P—F 1·57	P—Cl, polar, 2·11 P—Cl, equatorial, 2·04		P—Cl, polar, 2·05 P—F, equatorial, 1·59	
Liquid	Structure (Raman spectrum)		Trigonal bipyramid			
Solid	Structure (X-ray)		Ionic [PCl$_4$]$^+$[PCl$_6$]$^-$	Ionic [PBr$_4$]$^+$Br$^-$		
Solid	Bond length		Cation P—Cl, 1·98 Anion P—Cl, 2·06			

Phosphorus pentachloride, PCl₅, a solid, is described as white, or "pale greenish yellow". It is made:

(i) by burning phosphorus in excess of chlorine,

(ii) by dropping phosphorus trichloride into dry chlorine.

It sublimes without fusion. The vapour is dissociated into chlorine and phosphorus trichloride. The dissociation is complete at 300°. The vapour reacts with zinc, cadmium, gold, and platinum; presumably the attack is due to the presence of free chlorine:

$$PCl_5 + Zn = PCl_3 + ZnCl_2.$$

Phosphorus pentachloride is violently attacked by water, and is hydrolysed in two stages:

$$PCl_5 + H_2O = POCl_3 + 2HCl,$$
$$POCl_3 + 3H_2O = H_3PO_4 + 3HCl.$$

With sulphur or with liquid hydrogen sulphide it forms thiophosphoryl chloride, $PSCl_3$. It chlorinates arsenic to arsenic trichloride, and sulphur dioxide to thionyl chloride, $SOCl_2$.

At low temperatures phosphorus pentachloride reacts with ammonia to yield the ammine $PCl_5, 8NH_3$. With dry ammonia gas it yields $PCl_3(NH_2)_2$, from which phospham, and thence the nitride $(P_3N_5)_x$ are obtained (p. 710). When heated with ammonium chloride phosphorus pentachloride yields the chloronitrides (p. 731). The reactions of phosphorus pentachloride with the fluorides of divalent metals are mentioned on p. 733.

Phosphorus pentabromide, PBr₅, exists as yellow crystals, which undergo partial dissociation on melting. It is made by allowing phosphorus tribromide to react with bromine. With excess of bromine it forms a heptabromide, PBr_7, which is probably a polybromide $[PBr_4^+][Br_3^-]$.

SECTION 6. COMPOUNDS IN WHICH THE PHOSPHORUS ATOM IS OCTAHEDRALLY HYBRIDISED

The phosphorus atom has the co-ordination number 6 in only two instances; in $[PCl_4^+][PCl_6^-]$, and in the anion PF_6^-. The hexafluorophosphates are made: (i) by heating phosphorus pentachloride with excess of ammonium or potassium fluoride, or (ii) by adding potassium fluoride to a solution of phosphoric oxide in concentrated hydrofluoric acid. A 70–80% yield is obtained. If a divalent metal fluoride is used no PF_6^- is formed; all the phosphorus is evolved as PF_5.

HPF_6 is a strong acid. The salts are not hydrolysed by boiling aqueous alkali. On fusion with potash they first dissolve quietly and then react violently. They are slowly hydrolysed when heated with strong acids.

ARSENIC

Elementary arsenic is obtained:

(i) by heating arsenious oxide with charcoal in a crucible covered with an iron cone; the arsenic sublimes into the cone as a grey powder:

$$As_2O_3 + 3C = 2As + 3CO,$$

(ii) by heating arsenical pyrites:

$$FeAsS = FeS + As,$$

(iii) by heating arsenious sulphide with potassium cyanide:

$$As_2S_3 + 3KCN = 2As + 3KCNS.$$

Arsenic is purified by sublimation from charcoal powder.

Table 20.9.　*The Allotropes of Arsenic*

	Yellow arsenic	Black arsenic	Grey arsenic
Appearance			Grey metallic crystals
Crystal form			Rhombohedral
Crystal structure			Similar to that of metallic phosphorus
m.p. °C			816 (36 atm)
Sublimation p. °C			633
Sp. gr.	1·97	4·73	5·73
Solubility	Soluble in CS_2 (8 gm per 100 c.c. at 20°)	Insoluble in CS_2	Insoluble in CS_2
Stability	Metastable in all conditions. Changes to grey arsenic (i) on heating in the presence of I_2 or Br_2, (ii) when exposed to light even at −180°	At 360° it reverts to grey arsenic with evolution of heat	Stable
Preparation	(i) Cool arsenic vapour rapidly (ii) Evaporate the carbon disulphide solution in the dark	Heat grey arsenic in a glass tube in a current of hydrogen; black arsenic condenses on the cooler parts of the tube	

Table 20.10.　*Reactions of Grey Arsenic*

Reagent	Reaction
Oxygen	At room temperature, dry air has no effect on grey arsenic; moist air covers it with a dark grey film of As_4O_6. Air at 200° begins to oxidise grey arsenic, and at 250–300° the reaction is accompanied by phosphorescence. Arsenic, if ignited, burns in air to form As_4O_6 and a little As_4O_{10}. In oxygen, arsenic burns brilliantly
Fluorine	AsF_5 and AsF_3 are formed with inflammation
Chlorine	$AsCl_3$ is formed with inflammation
Bromine	Liquid bromine reacts with inflammation to give $AsBr_3$
Iodine	AsI_3 is formed on warming
Sulphur	On fusion, As_4S_{10} is formed
Carbon	No action
Nitrogen	No action
HCl	Attacks arsenic only in the presence of oxygen
HNO_3	Dilute nitric acid yields arsenious acid Hot concentrated nitric acid yields arsenic acid
H_2SO_4	Hot concentrated sulphuric acid yields As_4O_6
NaOH aq.	No action
NaOH fused	The reaction occurs: $As_4 + 12NaOH = 4Na_3AsO_3 + 6H_2$
$HgCl_2$	$AsCl_3$ is formed
Na (in liquid ammonia)	Na_3As is formed
Yellow ammonium sulphide	Arsenic dissolves

Arsenic is trimorphic; the three forms are described in Table 20.9. The yellow variety of arsenic is less stable than the corresponding white variety of phosphorus. It is rapidly oxidised by air at room temperature with a faint luminescence. The black variety is not well characterised; it is not oxidised by air at 80°. Grey arsenic is the stable and common form. It is isomorphous with black phosphorus, antimony, bismuth, and tellurium. It is insoluble in mercury. Its specific conductivity at 0° is $2\cdot56 \times 10^4$ ohm^{-1} cm^{-1}, about 1/25 that of copper.

The vapour of arsenic is colourless. The density shows the molecule to be As_4 up to 800°, when As_2 begins to appear. Dissociation is not complete until 1700°. Electron diffraction experiments show that the As_4 molecule is similar to the P_4 molecule. The distance As—As is $2\cdot44$.

The molecular weight of the yellow variety of arsenic dissolved in carbon disulphide corresponds to As_4. The heat of linkage As—As is 34 kcal, of As=As is $91\cdot3$ kcal.

GENERAL CHEMISTRY OF ARSENIC

The electron configuration of the valence shell ($n=4$) of the arsenic atom is:

$4s$	$4p$	$4p$	$4p$
⇅	↑	↑	↑

The penultimate shell ($n=3$) contains eighteen electrons. In all its compounds all the five valency electrons of arsenic are active.

There are no compounds which contain the simple ion As^{3-}. The arsenides are giant molecule compounds showing some ionic as well as covalent character, but even the arsenides of the alkali metals have the Na_3P structure which resembles that of an alloy rather than a salt.

There are no compounds in which the arsenic atom is in the digonal or trigonal valence state. In the large majority of arsenic compounds the arsenic atom is in the tetrahedral valence state. In the molecule of elementary arsenic, As_4, which structurally corresponds to the phosphorus molecule, P_4, the arsenic atom is in the tetrahedral valence state. The molecules As_4O_6, As_4O_{10}, As_4S_6, As_4S_4, may be regarded as modified forms of the As_4 structure. Such compounds as AsH_3, $As(CH_3)_3$, $AsCl_3$, in which the arsenic atom is 3 co-ordinate, are assumed to contain the tetrahedrally hybridised arsenic atom with a lone electron pair in one of the hybrid orbitals. The $4s$ electron pair in the arsenic atom may perhaps become inert in anions of the type $[AsCl_4]^-$, but otherwise there is no evidence in the chemistry of arsenic for the inert electron pair. The arsenic atom is 4 co-ordinate when it is present in a cation such as $[(C_6H_5)_4As^+]$. or when it acts as a donor in complexes such as $[(CH_3)_3As]_2SnI_4$. The 4 co-ordinate arsenic atom is also present in arsenic acid and in the arsenate ion. There are no arsenic compounds comparable with the phosphorus chloronitrides. The valence shell of the arsenic atom contains d orbitals, and hence the arsenic atom would be expected to adopt both the trigonal bipyramidal and the octahedral valence states. Examples of compounds containing the arsenic atom in these valence states are given on pp. 751–2.

The nucleus of the arsenic atom carries a higher positive charge than the nucleus of the phosphorus atom. The outermost atomic orbitals in the penultimate ($n=3$) shell of the arsenic atom are $3d$ orbitals containing ten electrons, whereas the outermost atomic orbitals in the penultimate shell ($n=2$) of the phosphorus atom are $2p$ orbitals containing six electrons. Although the difference between $(Z_{eff})_{mol}$ for phosphorus and $(Z_{eff})_{mol}$ for arsenic is $1\cdot5$ (Table 19.2), the difference between $(Z_{eff})_{mol}/r^2$ for phosphorus and for arsenic is only $0\cdot57$. The ionisation potentials of the valence electrons do not differ greatly, and the electronegativity of phosphorus ($2\cdot1$) differs little from that of arsenic (2·0). Nevertheless, one important difference not revealed by these figures is the unwillingness of arsenic to adopt the higher valence states, particularly when in combination with oxygen.

This property extends to other members of Period 4 and is especially noticeable in the case of bromine. Arsenic oxide is an oxidising agent and is thermally decomposed to arsenious oxide and oxygen above 500°, phosphoric oxide is not an oxidising agent, and the vapour can be heated to 1100° without change in the molecular weight. The arsenate ion is an oxidising agent (the phosphate ion is not), and although the arsenite ion is a reducing agent, arsenious acid is not (phosphorous acid is a powerful reducing agent). The structure of arsenious acid is probably $As(OH)_3$, whereas that of phosphorous acid is $HPO(OH)_2$ (p. 722). The only ion derived from arsenic acid which is stable in solution is the orthoarsenate ion, although sodium diarsenate, $Na_4As_2O_7$, and sodium meta-arsenate, $NaAsO_3$, can be prepared in the solid state, and the parent acids, $H_4As_4O_7$ and $HAsO_3$ can also be obtained. No cyclic arsenic acids have been reported.

The trigonal bipyramidal compounds of arsenic are few in type and number. There are no pentahalides except the pentafluoride, and there are no oxyhalides.

SECTION 1. ARSENIC COMPOUNDS CONSISTING OF GIANT MOLECULES IN WHICH THE BONDS HAVE BOTH COVALENT AND IONIC CHARACTER

The giant molecule compounds of arsenic are arsenides of the metals; the oxides, sulphides, and halides of arsenic have discrete molecules. The crystal structures of certain metallic arsenides are stated in Table 20.11.

Table 20.11.†   *The Crystal Structures of certain Metallic Arsenides*

Li_3As	Na_3As	K_3As	Mg_3As_2	Zn_3As_2	Cd_3As_2	$AlAs$
A	A	A	B	C	C	Z

GaAs	MnAs	FeAs	CoAs	NiAs	$PtAs_2$	$FeAs_2$
Z	N	N	N	N	Pyrites	Marcasite

The crystal structures are indicated as follows: A, Na_3P; B, anti-Mn_2O_3; C, Zn_3P_2; Z, zinc blende; N, NiAs.

SECTION 4. COMPOUNDS IN WHICH THE ARSENIC ATOM IS TETRA-HEDRALLY HYBRIDISED‡

ARSINE, ASH_3, AND ITS DERIVATIVES

The methods of preparation of arsine and its three methyl derivatives, and certain of the properties of these compounds, are summarised in Table 20.12. All the compounds are made by the reduction of arsenic compounds in a higher state of oxidation. They are themselves vigorous reducing agents, and the reducing action is intensified by each replacement of a hydrogen atom in the molecule of arsine by a methyl group. None of the compounds is basic, but trimethyl arsine gives rise to tetramethyl arsonium iodide,

† Compare Table 20.3, p. 709, and Table 20.16, p. 759.
‡ When the arsenic atom is 3 co-ordinate one of the four hybrid orbitals of the arsenic atom is assumed to be occupied by a lone electron pair.

Table 20.12. *Arsine, AsH$_3$, and its Methyl Derivatives*

	AsH$_3$	AsH$_2$CH$_3$	AsH(CH$_3$)$_2$	As(CH$_3$)$_3$
Appearance m.p. °C b.p. °C	Colourless gas −116·3 −62·4	Colourless liquid — +2	Colourless liquid — +36	Colourless liquid — +50
Preparation	(i) Reduce arsenic compounds with zinc and sulphuric acid (ii) Treat aluminium arsenide, or sodium arsenide, with water	(i) Reduce methyl arsonic acid with zinc and hydrochloric acid in the absence of oxygen: $3H_2 + CH_3As\!\!\begin{smallmatrix}O\\\nwarrow\end{smallmatrix}\!\!-\!OH=CH_3AsH_2+3H_2O$ $\quad\quad\overset{|}{OH}$ (ii) Treat NaAsH$_2$ with methyl chloride	(i) Reduce dimethyl arsinic acid, (CH$_3$)$_2$AsO·OH, with zinc and hydrochloric acid (ii) Reduce cacodyl oxide (p. 741)	(i) Treat sodium arsenide, Na$_3$As, with methyl iodide (ii) Treat arsenic trichloride with magnesium methyl iodide, or with zinc dimethyl
Solubility in water	Slight, 20 c.c. in 100 gm	Very slight		Slight
Action with air	Not attacked	Oxidised but not inflamed	Inflamed	Inflamed: (CH$_3$)$_3$AsO is formed
Action with oxidising agents	Silver nitrate gives metallic silver. Mercuric chloride gives black mercury arsenide, As$_2$Hg$_3$	Dry O$_2$ yields CH$_3$AsO. Moist O$_2$ yields CH$_3$AsO(OH)$_2$. I$_2$ yields CH$_3$AsI$_2$. S yields CH$_3$AsS	Oxidising agents convert it to cacodyl ((CH$_3$)$_2$As)$_2$, or to cacodyl oxide (CH$_3$)$_2$AsO, or to cacodyl chloride, or to dimethyl arsinic acid	Chlorine gives (CH$_3$)$_3$AsCl$_2$
Basic properties	None	Very weak		Feeble, but it combines with CH$_3$I to yield (CH$_3$)$_4$AsI
Donor properties				Strong; it forms e.g. [(CH$_3$)$_3$As]$_2$SnCl$_4$
Decomposition temperature °C	230	300		

$(CH_3)_4AsI$. In the following paragraphs arsine is described in some detail, and the methyl derivatives (Table 20.12) and the phenyl derivatives are mentioned briefly.

Arsine, AsH_3, is the only well-characterised hydride of arsenic. It is a poisonous, colourless gas with the odour of garlic. Certain of its properties are mentioned in Table 20.12. Arsine is prepared by the following methods:

(i) Excess of arsenic is slowly added to sodium dissolved in liquid ammonia, and the bright yellow solution of sodium arsenide so obtained is decomposed with ammonium bromide:

$$Na_3As + 3NH_4Br = (NH_4)_3As + 3NaBr,$$
$$= H_3As + 3NH_3 + 3NaBr.$$

(ii) Aluminium arsenide (made by the combination of the elements, intimately mixed and fired with an aluminium-barium peroxide primer) is treated with warm water:

$$AlAs + 3H_2O = Al(OH)_3 + AsH_3.$$

This method gives almost pure arsine.

(iii) Sodium arsenide is treated with water:

$$Na_3As + 3H_2O = 3NaOH + H_3As.$$

(iv) Zinc arsenide (prepared by heating the elements together in equivalent proportions) is treated with dilute hydrochloric acid:

$$Zn_3As_2 + 6HCl = 3ZnCl_2 + 2AsH_3.$$

(v) Sodium arsenite is heated with sodium formate (dried at 210°):

$$Na_3AsO_3 + 3HCOONa = 3Na_2CO_3 + AsH_3.$$

Arsine cannot be made by the direct union of molecular hydrogen and arsenic, but it is formed when zinc in contact with any material containing arsenic is acted upon with dilute sulphuric acid, or when a solution of an arsenic compound is electrolysed using a cathode of metallic mercury.[†] The formation of arsine by the action of nascent hydrogen on an arsenic compound is the basis of Marsh's test for arsenic.

Arsine decomposes into its elements on gentle heating and, if moist, on exposure to light. It is not oxidised by air, but it reduces many oxidising agents. It reduces dilute silver nitrate solution to metallic silver:

$$6AgNO_3 + 3H_2O + AsH_3 = H_3AsO_3 + 6Ag + 6HNO_3.$$

If concentrated silver nitrate solution is used, the initial product is the soluble complex, $Ag_3As,3AgNO_3$, which by a reaction in which the silver arsenide reduces the silver nitrate, yields metallic silver when treated with water:

$$Ag_3As,3AgNO_3 + 3H_2O = 6Ag + 3HNO_3 + H_3AsO_3.$$

Arsine reduces mercuric chloride to mercuric arsenide in three successive stages (Gutzeit's test): $AsH(HgCl)_2$, yellow; $As(HgCl)_3$, brown; As_2Hg_3, black. Arsine is not basic, and it forms no compounds analogous to the phosphonium compounds. Arsine reacts with sodium, potassium, or potassamide dissolved in liquid ammonia to give derivatives such as $NaAsH_2$.

Two solid arsenic hydrides are reported. One is made by the reduction of arsenious compounds, as for example, the reduction of an acidified solution of arsenious chloride by stannous chloride in ether:

$$2AsCl_3 + 2HCl + 4SnCl_2 = As_2H_2 + 4SnCl_4.$$

[†] A mercury cathode, with its high overpotential, must be used to ensure that arsenates are attacked. Potassium hydroxide solution acting on aluminium in contact with an arsenic compound liberates arsine (Fleitmann's test), except when the arsenic is present as arsenate.

The arsenic hydride is precipitated as a brown powder. The other solid arsenic hydride is made by the oxidation of arsine with stannic chloride:

$$4AsH_3 + 5SnCl_4 = As_4H_2 + 10HCl + 5SnCl_2.$$

The chemical individuality of these solid hydrides of arsenic awaits clear demonstration.

The methyl derivatives of arsine are described in Table 20.12. Trimethyl arsine is so readily oxidised in air to trimethyl arsine oxide that it must always be handled in an atmosphere of carbon dioxide or nitrogen. The Raman spectrum of trimethyl arsine indicates that the molecule has a pyramidal structure.

The phenyl derivatives of arsine are very reactive substances. Phenyl arsine, $C_6H_5AsH_2$ attacks the skin. It is oxidised by oxygen, by sulphur, and by the halogens, to give C_6H_5AsO, C_6H_5AsS, and $C_6H_5AsCl_2$ respectively. It reacts with iodine and phenyl magnesium bromide to give tetraphenyl arsine:

$$2C_6H_5AsH_2 + 3I_2 + 2C_6H_5MgBr = (C_6H_5)_2As—As(C_6H_5)_2 + MgBr_2 + MgI_2 + 4HI.$$

Diphenyl arsine resembles the dialkyl compound. Triphenyl arsine, m.p. 60°, b.p. about 360°, is more stable than the other two phenyl derivatives. It can be distilled unchanged. It has no basic properties, but it adds on alkyl (but not aryl) halides to form quaternary salts. With chlorine it gives $(C_6H_5)_3AsCl_2$ and with cyanogen chloride $(C_6H_5)_3AsCl·CN$. It can be nitrated, and the products may be reduced to amines without disturbing the C—As links.

The chemical relations of the methyl derivatives of arsine. Monomethyl arsine is formed by the reduction of methyl arsonic acid, and dimethyl arsine is formed by the reduction of dimethyl arsinic acid. The group $(CH_3)_2As—$ which is present in the dimethyl arsine derivatives, is known as the cacodyl group, although cacodyl itself is the dimer, $(CH_3)_2As—As(CH_3)_2$. The cacodyl group is of historic interest because it was the first group to be recognised to move as a unit from one compound to another in certain chemical reactions. The cacodyl compounds are:

> Cacodyl hydride (dimethyl arsine), $(CH_3)_2AsH$
> Cacodyl chloride, $(CH_3)_2AsCl$
> Cacodylic acid (dimethyl arsinic acid), $(CH_3)_2AsOOH$
> Cacodyl oxide, $(CH_3)_2AsOAs(CH_3)_2$
> Cacodyl, $(CH_3)_2As—As(CH_3)_2$.

The chemical relations of the methyl derivatives of arsine are set out in Chart 20.2.

Brief accounts of cacodyl and cacodyl oxide are given below; cacodylic acid and methyl arsonic acid are regarded as derivatives of arsenic acid, and they are discussed on p. 750.

Tetramethyl diarsine, cacodyl, $(CH_3)_2As—As(CH_3)_2$, is a very poisonous liquid, b.p. 170°, with a disagreeable smell. It is made:

(i) by heating dimethyl arsine chloride (cacodyl chloride) with zinc in an atmosphere of carbon dioxide,

(ii) by treating dimethyl arsine with dimethyl arsine chloride:

$$(CH_3)_2AsH + ClAs(CH_3)_2 = (CH_3)_2As—As(CH_3)_2 + HCl.$$

It is spontaneously inflammable in air, but is thermally stable up to 400°.

Cacodyl oxide, dimethyl arsine oxide, $(CH_3)_2As—O—As(CH_3)_2$, is a liquid, b.p. 150°, with a repulsive smell, very poisonous. It is made:

(i) by heating equal weights of arsenious oxide and potassium acetate:

$$As_4O_6 + 8CH_3·COOK = 2As_2(CH_3)_4O + 4K_2CO_3 + 4CO_2,$$

(ii) by oxidising cacodyl.

THE DIMETHYL SERIES

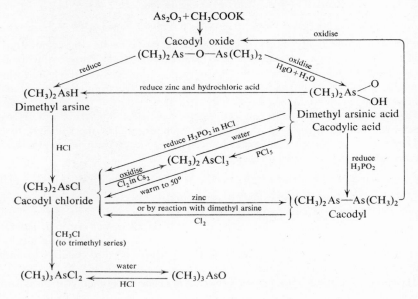

$$As_2O_3 + CH_3COOK$$

Cacodyl oxide

$(CH_3)_2As$—O—$As(CH_3)_2$

oxidise

reduce

oxidise
$HgO + H_2O$

$(CH_3)_2AsH$

Dimethyl arsine

reduce zinc and hydrochloric acid

$(CH_3)_2As$ ⟨ $\genfrac{}{}{0pt}{}{O}{OH}$

Dimethyl arsinic acid
Cacodylic acid

HCl

reduce H_3PO_2 in HCl

water

$(CH_3)_2AsCl_3$ ← PCl_5

oxidise
Cl_2 in Cs_2

warm to 50°

reduce
H_3PO_2

$(CH_3)_2AsCl$

Cacodyl chloride

zinc

or by reaction with dimethyl arsine

Cl_2

$(CH_3)_2As$—$As(CH_3)_2$

Cacodyl

CH_3Cl
(to trimethyl series)

$(CH_3)_3AsCl_2$ $\underset{HCl}{\overset{water}{\rightleftarrows}}$ $(CH_3)_3AsO$

THE MONOMETHYL SERIES

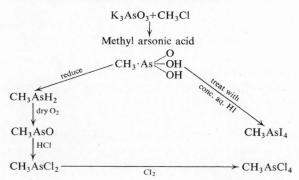

$$K_3AsO_3 + CH_3Cl$$

Methyl arsonic acid

$CH_3 \cdot As$ ⟨ $\genfrac{}{}{0pt}{}{O}{\genfrac{}{}{0pt}{}{OH}{OH}}$

reduce

treat with
conc. aq. HI

CH_3AsH_2

dry O_2

CH_3AsO

HCl

CH_3AsCl_2 —————Cl_2—————→ CH_3AsCl_4

CH_3AsI_4

THE TRIMETHYL SERIES

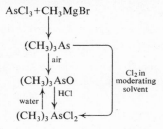

$$AsCl_3 + CH_3MgBr$$

$(CH_3)_3As$

air

Cl_2 in
moderating
solvent

$(CH_3)_3AsO$

water | HCl

$(CH_3)_3AsCl_2$

Chart 20.2. Chemical relations of the methyl derivatives of arsine.

It is insoluble in water. It is neutral. It is spontaneously inflammable in air if it contains cacodyl, but not otherwise. It is oxidised by mercuric oxide in the presence of water to cacodylic acid (dimethyl arsinic acid).

Methyl arsine oxide, $CH_3As=O$, is a solid, m.p. 95°, with an unpleasant smell. It is made:

    (i) by oxidising CH_3AsH_2 with dry oxygen,

    (ii) by the action of alkalis on the dihalogen derivatives.

Trimethyl arsine oxide, $(CH_3)_3As=O$, exists as deliquescent crystals. It is made by oxidation of the tertiary arsine with air.

Methyl dichloroarsine, CH_3AsCl_2, is a colourless, fuming liquid, m.p. $-42\cdot5°$, b.p. $132\cdot5°$. It is made by the action of hydrogen chloride on the oxide CH_3AsO. It is hydrolysed completely by water. It is extremely poisonous, attacking the lungs. The poison gas, Lewisite, is the chlorovinyl compound:

$$\begin{array}{ccc} Cl & & H \\ \diagdown & & \diagup \\ & C=C & \\ \diagup & & \diagdown \\ H & & AsCl_2 \end{array}$$

b.p. 190°. It is made by passing acetylene into arsenic trichloride.

Dimethyl chloroarsine, cacodyl chloride, $(CH_3)_2AsCl$, is a colourless liquid, b.p. 107°. It is made:

    (i) by the action of hydrogen chloride on secondary methyl arsine:

$$(CH_3)_2AsH + HCl = (CH_3)_2AsCl + H_2,$$

    (ii) by the action of chlorine on cacodyl,

    (iii) by the reduction of cacodylic acid with sodium hypophosphite in the presence of hydrochloric acid.

The poison gas blue cross is diphenyl chloroarsine, $(C_6H_5)_2AsCl$.

Tetra-alkyl and aryl arsonium salts. The *tetra-alkyl* arsonium salts are made from the tertiary arsines and the alkyl halide. The salts are crystalline, and neutral in solution. The free bases, made from the chloride and moist silver oxide, are like the alkalis, strongly basic, deliquescent solids. The solutions absorb carbon dioxide from the air. The salts are poisonous.

The *tetra-aryl* arsonium salts can only be made by the action of Grignard reagents on the arsine oxide:

$$(C_6H_5)_3AsO + MgBr(C_6H_5) = (C_6H_5)_4AsBr + MgO.$$

The quaternary salts are very stable and strong electrolytes. The chloride can be used for the quantitative estimation of Zn, Cd, Hg, or Sn, since the salts $((C_6H_5)_4As)_2MCl_4$ and $((C_6H_5)_4As)_2SnCl_6$ are insoluble in 1N to 3·5N sodium chloride solution. The salt $((C_6H_5)_4As)ReO_4$ is insoluble in water.

The cation $[(C_6H_5)_4As^+]$ has been shown to be tetrahedral by the X-ray analysis of tetraphenyl arsonium iodide; the distance C—As is 1·95.

Compounds formed by the addition of a donor molecule containing arsenic to an acceptor molecule.

Among these compounds are:

$H_3As \cdot BBr_3$

$(CH_3(C_6H_5)_2As)_2HgCl_2$, and the corresponding complexes formed by $ZnCl_2$ and $CdCl_2$

$((CH_3)_3As)_2SnI_4$

$((CH_3)_3As)_2PdCl_2$

$H(CH_3)_2As \cdot BH_3$ which loses hydrogen to yield the ring compound

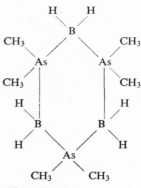

Table 20.13.   *The Arsenic Trihalides*

	AsF$_3$	AsCl$_3$	AsBr$_3$	AsI$_3$
Appearance	Colourless fuming liquid	Colourless fuming liquid	Colourless prismatic crystals	Red hexagonal and rhombo-hedral crystals
b.p. °C	60·4	130·2	221	394–414
m.p. °C	−8·5	−13	+31	140·7
Specific gravity at 0°C	2·666	2·205	3·66 (at 15°)	4·39 (at 15°)
D.p.m. in dioxane at 25°	—	3·11	2·90	1·83
Rate of Hydrolysis	Fast	Fast	Less fast	Slow
Structure	Molecule is pyramidal by the Raman spectrum	Molecule is pyramidal by the Raman spectrum	Molecule is pyramidal by X-ray analysis	

Arsenic trifluoride, AsF$_3$, is made by treating arsenious oxide with a mixture of powdered fluorspar and concentrated sulphuric acid:

$$As_4O_6 + 12HF = 4AsF_3 + 6H_2O.$$

It is hydrolysed by water, to arsenious oxide and hydrofluoric acid.

Arsenic trichloride, AsCl$_3$, is formed:

(i) by burning arsenic in chlorine (the reaction occurs spontaneously),

(ii) by heating arsenious oxide in chlorine:

$$11As_4O_6 + 12Cl_2 = 8AsCl_3 + 3(As_4O_{10}, 2As_4O_6),$$

(iii) by distilling a mixture of arsenious oxide, sodium chloride, and concentrated sulphuric acid; the distillate is freed from excess of chlorine by distillation over powdered arsenic,

(iv) by refluxing arsenious oxide with sulphur chloride, passing chlorine through the mixture, and distilling:

$$2As_4O_6 + 3S_2Cl_2 + 9Cl_2 = 8AsCl_3 + 6SO_2.$$

Arsenic trichloride is hydrolysed by water:

$$4AsCl_3 + 6H_2O = As_4O_6 + 12HCl.$$

The reaction is reversible, as is shown by reaction (iii) above. Arsenic trichloride is a good ionising solvent; the dielectric constant is 12·8 at 20°. Antimony pentachloride, a non-conducting liquid, becomes conducting when dissolved in arsenic trichloride. Arsenic trichloride reacts with arsine to give arsenic and hydrogen chloride.

Arsenic tribromide, AsBr$_3$, is made by treating arsenic with a solution of bromine in carbon disulphide.

Arsenic tri-iodide, AsI$_3$, is made:

(i) by treating arsenic with a solution of iodine in carbon disulphide,
(ii) by precipitating a solution of arsenious oxide in hot hydrochloric acid with potassium iodide:

$$AsCl_3 + 3KI = AsI_3 + 3KCl.$$

It is less readily hydrolysed than are the other arsenic halides, but it is unstable. The solid and its solutions are slowly oxidised by air.

THE OXIDES OF ARSENIC

Arsenious oxide, As$_4$O$_6$, exists in two crystalline forms and also as an amorphous glass. It is made by burning arsenic in air. The familiar form is a white solid consisting of octahedral crystals which are produced when the vapour condenses at room temperature, or when an aqueous or hydrochloric acid solution of arsenious oxide is allowed to crystallise†. The octahedral form sublimes freely above 135°. The m.p. is 275° under pressure, the b.p. is 465°. The octahedral form is metastable under ordinary conditions and tends to change into the monoclinic form (m.p. about 315°) with which it is in equilibrium at −13°. The change is very slow. It may be brought about by heating the octahedral form with water at 180° for about 40 hours. The monoclinic form is also obtained when the vapour is condensed above 250°, or by cooling a boiling saturated solution of the oxide in sodium arsenite solution.

Arsenious oxide is sparingly soluble in water and, as it is not easily wetted, it dissolves slowly. The solubility is 2% at 25° and 8·2% at 98°. The solution is weakly acid, and perhaps contains H$_3$AsO$_3$. Arsenious oxide forms arsenites with alkalis and with sodium carbonate, but with concentrated hydrochloric acid it gives arsenic trichloride. With concentrated sulphuric acid it gives arsenyl sulphate (AsO)$_2$SO$_4$, and with sulphur trioxide at 100° arsenious sulphate As$_2$(SO$_4$)$_3$.

Arsenious oxide is reduced to arsenic when heated with charcoal or potassium cyanide, or when treated with a mixture of hydrochloric acid and stannous chloride, or with hydrochloric acid and copper foil:

$$As_4O_6 + 12HCl + 12Cu = 4As + 12CuCl + 6H_2O.$$

If the reaction is carried out in a test tube the arsenic is deposited as a grey film on the copper foil. Se, Hg, Sb, Bi compounds also give grey deposits when thus treated. When the copper foil coated with arsenic is washed, dried, and heated in a tube open to the air a white sublimate of arsenious oxide is obtained on the cooler parts of the tube. If the same procedure is carried out on the deposits of the other metals no sublimate is obtained. These reactions are the basis of Reinsch's test for arsenic.

Arsenious oxide is, however, usually thought of as a reducing agent, and it is oxidised to arsenate by ozone, H$_2$O$_2$, halogens, hypochlorites, ferric chloride, nitric acid, and

† The crystallisation of a solution of 11 gm of As$_4$O$_6$ in 100 c.c. of 11% hydrochloric acid takes place with the emission of brilliant flashes of light. This phenomenon is not understood.

24*

potassium dichromate solution. The reduction of iodine is reversible unless the acidity of the solution is kept low, say, by the addition of potassium bicarbonate:

$$8KHCO_3 + As_4O_6 + 4I_2 = As_4O_{10} + 8KI + 8CO_2 + 4H_2O.$$

It seems, therefore, that the reducing properties are to be associated with the arsenite ion, rather than with the free acid. Arsenious oxide, or perhaps the arsenite ion, reduces Fehling's solution, precipitating cuprous oxide.

Arsenious oxide is highly poisonous, and is the more dangerous because the vapour has neither taste nor smell. The lethal dose for a man is about 0·1 gm. The recommended antidote is freshly prepared ferric hydroxide made by adding magnesia to a solution of ferric chloride. The ferric hydroxide is said to adsorb the arsenious oxide. Arsenious oxide is a very weak bactericide.

The molecular weight of arsenious oxide vapour corresponds to As_4O_6 up to 800°, and to As_2O_3 above 1800°. The molecular weight determined cryoscopically in nitrobenzene solution corresponds to As_4O_6. X-ray analysis shows that the structure of the molecule in the solid is similar to that of P_4O_6; the distance As—O is 1·80. Electron diffraction analysis shows that the molecules in the vapour have the same structure as in the As_4O_6 tetrahedron. The angle OAsO is $100 \pm 5°$, and the angle AsOAs is $126 \pm 3°$. These values are the same as those of the corresponding angles in the molecule P_4O_6. In the octahedral form of arsenious oxide the As_4O_6 groups are in positions corresponding to those of carbon atoms in a diamond lattice.

Arsenic oxide, As_4O_{10}, is a white deliquescent solid. The conversion of arsenious oxide to arsenic oxide by direct oxidation is not quantitative, even by treatment with oxygen under pressure. Arsenic oxide is best prepared by heating crystalline arsenic acid above 200°:

$$4(H_3AsO_4)_3, H_2O = 3As_4O_{10} + 22H_2O.$$

Arsenic oxide melts at a red heat, when it begins to decompose into arsenious oxide and oxygen. It is an oxidising agent (unlike P_4O_{10}). It liberates chlorine from hydrogen chloride. With phosphorus pentachloride it reacts according to the equation:

$$As_4O_{10} + 10PCl_5 = 10POCl_3 + 4AsCl_3 + 4Cl_2.$$

Arsenic oxide dissolves slowly in water to form arsenic acid. The vapour of arsenic oxide is wholly dissociated into arsenious oxide and oxygen. No investigation of the solid appears to have been made.

An oxide of arsenic, As_2O_4, is known. It is probably arsenious arsenate, $As[AsO_4]$ (compare Sb_2O_4, p. 755).

THE SULPHIDES OF ARSENIC

Arsenious sulphide, the mineral orpiment, As_4S_6, is a yellow solid, m.p. 320°, b.p. 707°. It sublimes below the m.p. It is obtained:

(i) as a sublimate, by heating arsenious oxide with sulphur,
(ii) as a yellow precipitate, by passing hydrogen sulphide into a solution of arsenious oxide in dilute hydrochloric acid:

$$4AsCl_3 + 6H_2S = As_4S_6 + 12HCl.$$

If the hydrogen sulphide is passed into a neutral solution of arsenious oxide, free from electrolytes, a yellow colloidal solution of arsenious sulphide is obtained.

Arsenious sulphide burns when heated in air to yield sulphur dioxide and arsenious oxide. It is oxidised by nitric acid, and converted by chlorine to arsenious chloride and sulphur chloride, S_2Cl_2. It dissolves easily in alkali, ammonia, or warm ammonium carbonate solution, to form a mixture of arsenite and thioarsenite:

$$As_4S_6 + 4NaOH = NaAsO_2 + 3NaAsS_2 + 2H_2O,$$

and in alkali sulphides to give thioarsenites only. On the acidification of these solutions, arsenious sulphide is reprecipitated quantitatively. Arsenious sulphide reacts with boiling sodium carbonate solution to yield a precipitate of the sulphide As_4S_4 (see below). When arsenious sulphide is fused with sodium carbonate, part of the arsenic sublimes, and the remainder is present in the residue as sodium arsenate and sodium thioarsenate. Arsenious sulphide dissolves in alkaline or ammonium polysulphides to form thioarsenates, such as $(NH_4)_3AsS_4$. It is almost insoluble in hot concentrated hydrochloric acid.

Electron diffraction shows the vapour of arsenious sulphide to consist of molecules As_4S_6, with a structure similar to that of As_4O_6.

As_4S_4, **the mineral realgar,** is a red or orange solid, m.p. 307°, b.p. 565°. At 267° it undergoes an allotropic change and turns black. Light converts it into a mixture of arsenious oxide and arsenious sulphide, and hence it turns yellow. It is made:

(i) by treating arsenious sulphide with boiling sodium carbonate solution; As_4S_4 is precipitated,
(ii) by heating arsenious sulphide in a sealed tube with sodium bicarbonate solution,
(iii) industrially, by heating iron pyrites and arsenical pyrites,
(iv) by fusing arsenious oxide with sulphur.

As_4S_4 is scarcely attacked by water. It inflames in chlorine. It is used in pyrotechny, as it violently inflames when heated with potassium nitrate.

It is insoluble in hot concentrated hydrochloric acid; it is oxidised by nitric acid. When warmed with alkaline hydroxides, or sulphides, it gives thioarsenites with the separation of elementary arsenic.

At 550° the molecular weight of the vapour corresponds to the formula As_4S_4. At about 1000° the molecular weight corresponds to As_2S_2. X-ray analysis shows that the geometrical configuration of the molecule is that of an 8-membered puckered ring. The distance As—S is 2·23 and As—As is 2·49. If the arsenic atoms are coupled in pairs this structure can be regarded as the As_4 molecule in which four sulphur bridges have been interposed:

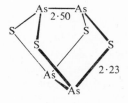

Arsenic pentasulphide, As_4S_{10}, is a yellow solid. It is made:

(i) by the fusion of arsenic with sulphur; the arsenic sulphide in the product is extracted with ammonia, and reprecipitated from the solution by hydrochloric acid,
(ii) by the action of a rapid stream of hydrogen sulphide on a strongly acid solution of sodium arsenate. (Under other conditions the arsenate is reduced to arsenite, and the arsenic is then precipitated as arsenious sulphide.)

Arsenic sulphide is stable in air up to 95°; at higher temperatures it dissociates to arsenious sulphide and sulphur. It is hydrolysed to arsenious acid and sulphur when boiled with water. It reacts with sodium hydroxide solution to produce a mixture of salts containing both oxygen and sulphur in the anion, as for example:

$$As_4S_{10} + 12NaOH = 2Na_3AsS_4 + 2Na_3AsO_3S + 6H_2O.$$

THE OXYACIDS OF ARSENIC

Arsenious acid, its salts and esters. Arsenious acid is known only in the aqueous solution of arsenious oxide. On recrystallisation the unhydrated oxide is obtained. The acid is weak. The dissociation constant of the hydrate, H_3AsO_3, is 8×10^{-10} at $25°$. The arsenite ion is a reducing agent, but the free acid is not. The structure of arsenious acid is therefore probably:

$$\overset{\displaystyle \cdot\cdot}{\underset{HO \quad OH \, OH}{As}}$$

and not, as it would be if it were analogous to phosphorous acid:

$$\underset{HO \qquad OH.}{\overset{H \qquad O}{As}}$$

Arsenious oxide dissolves in hot sodium hydroxide solution, and on evaporation sodium arsenite, Na_3AsO_3 or $NaAsO_2$, is obtained as a white amorphous powder. Sodium arsenite is soluble in water, by which it is hydrolysed. Sodium arsenite, when heated, disproportionates into sodium arsenate and sodium arsenide:

$$4Na_3AsO_3 = Na_3As + 3Na_3AsO_4.$$

Sodium arsenite is reduced by hydrogen sulphide in acid solution to yield As_4S_6.

Silver arsenite, Ag_3AsO_3, is formed as a yellow precipitate when a solution of sodium arsenite is added to silver nitrate solution; the precipitate is soluble in acetic acid (distinction from phosphate). Copper sulphate reacts with sodium arsenite to give Scheele's green $Cu_3(AsO_3)_2,2H_2O$. When this is boiled in sodium hydroxide solution, the arsenite ion reduces the cupric ion:

$$2Cu^{2+} + AsO_3^{3-} + 2OH^- = 2Cu^+ + AsO_4^{3-} + H_2O.$$

The arsenite ion is a reducing agent and it is readily oxidised by air or by iodine. The reaction:

$$AsO_3^{3-} + I_2 + H_2O = AsO_4^{3-} + 2HI,$$

must be carried out in alkaline or very weakly acid solution, so that the arsenite ion is not removed from the system as the non-reducing arsenious acid.

The methods of formation of the arsenic trihalides, which are formed reversibly from arsenious oxide and the halogen acid in aqueous solution, and of arsenious sulphate, $As_2(SO_4)_3$, which is made by the action of sulphur trioxide on arsenious oxide at $100°$, suggest that arsenious acid might be regarded as analogous to a trihydric alcohol. The hydrolysis of the acetate, $As(OCOCH_3)_3$ (m.p. $82°$, b.p. $165–170°$), by moist air to yield a mixture of arsenious acid and acetic acid supports this suggestion.

Arsenious acid nevertheless displays acidic properties in forming esters, $As(OR)_3$, which include those where R is:

	CH_3	C_2H_5	C_3H_7	C_4H_9	$iso\text{-}C_5H_{11}$
b.p. °C	129	166	217	263	288

The esters are made by treating the appropriate alcohol with $AsCl_3$, or, if the alcohol has a high molecular weight, by heating it with As_4O_6 in the presence of a hydrocarbon to reduce the partial pressure of water in the vapour phase, or, by treating the alkyl halide with silver arsenite.

Silver arsenite with methyl iodide gives $As(OCH_3)_3$; sodium arsenite with methyl iodide gives $CH_3 \cdot AsO \cdot (OCH_3)_2$, dimethyl methyl arsonate. The complete series of compounds is known:

$$As(OCH_3)_3, \quad CH_3AsO(OCH_3)_2, \quad (CH_3)_2AsO(OCH_3), \quad (CH_3)_3AsO,$$

and hence the formation of different esters from silver arsenite and sodium arsenite does not necessarily imply that arsenious acid is tautomeric.

Arsenic acid. Arsenic oxide is very soluble in water (230 gm in 100 gm of water at 20°), but the hydrates which separate from the solution are largely colloidal. The hydrate $3H_3AsO_4,H_2O$ is obtained by concentrating and crystallising the solution formed by the action of concentrated nitric acid on arsenious oxide:

$$As_4O_6 + 4HNO_3 = As_4O_{10} + 2N_2O_3 + 2H_2O.$$

The hydrated arsenic acid on warming loses water, yielding successively at 100°, H_3AsO_4, $H_4As_2O_7$, and at 200° $HAsO_3$. The dissociation constants of arsenic acid, H_3AsO_4 are:

$$K_1 = 5\cdot6\times 10^{-3}, \quad K_2 = 1\cdot7\times 10^{-7}, \quad K_3 = 3\cdot0\times 10^{-12}.$$

Arsenic acid has one strongly acid hydrogen atom per arsenic atom (compare phosphoric acid, p. 724).

Arsenic acid oxidises sulphur dioxide to sulphuric acid, and hot fuming hydrochloric acid to chlorine; arsenic trichloride is formed, perhaps with the pentachloride as an intermediate. In acid solution arsenic acid oxidises hydrogen iodide to iodine, itself being reduced to arsenious acid. Among the esters are $AsO(OCH_3)_3$, b.p. 214°, and $AsO(OC_2H_5)_3$, b.p. 237°.

The arsenates are generally isomorphous with the phosphates. Common sodium arsenate is $Na_2HAsO_4,12H_2O$. When it is heated it liberates water and yields sodium diarsenate:

$$2Na_2HAsO_4 = Na_4As_2O_7 + H_2O.$$

Sodium meta-arsenate is obtained by heating sodium dihydrogen orthoarsenate:

$$NaH_2AsO_4 = NaAsO_3 + H_2O.$$

In solution sodium diarsenate and sodium meta-arsenate at once produce the ortho-arsenate ion. The structure of the meta-arsenate ion is unknown. Silver arsenate Ag_3AsO_4, is obtained as a light chocolate brown precipitate when silver nitrate is added to an arsenate in strictly neutral solution; the precipitate is soluble in dilute nitric acid, and in ammonia solution. Lead arsenate, $PbHAsO_4$ and calcium arsenate $Ca_3(AsO_4)_2$ are used for controlling pests.

With a mixture of ammonium molybdate and concentrated nitric acid arsenates give a yellow precipitate of ammonium arsenomolybdate, but only on heating. They give with magnesia mixture a white crystalline precipitate of magnesium ammonium arsenate, $MgNH_4AsO_4,6H_2O$. On heating this gives magnesium diarsenate, $Mg_2As_2O_7$.

It is not known whether the structures of the arsenic acids are analogous to those of the phosphoric acids. The crystal structures of Ag_3AsO_4 and KH_2AsO_4 have been determined. In the silver salt the anion is a regular tetrahedron, the distance As—O is 1·75. In the potassium salt the tetrahedron is slightly distorted; the angles OAsO are 104° and 113°. The length of the hydrogen bond O—H····O is 2·54.

The thioarsenites and thioarsenates. The thioarsenites are formed by the solution of arsenious sulphide in solutions of the sulphides of the alkali metals, or of the alkaline earth metals. Neither the constitutions nor the formulae of the salts which result from crystallisation appear to be known with certainty.

A solution of ammonium thioarsenate is formed when arsenious sulphide is digested with ammonium polysulphide, $(NH_4)_2S_2$:

$$4(NH_4)_2S_2 + As_4S_6 = As_4S_{10} + 4(NH_4)_2S,$$
$$6(NH_4)_2S + As_4S_{10} = 4(NH_4)_3AsS_4.$$

On acidification of the solution a yellow precipitate is obtained which may be As_4S_{10}. Oxythioarsenates of the type Na_3AsO_3S are formed when arsenic sulphide dissolves in sodium hydroxide solution (see above). These salts are decomposed by acids to yield arsenic acid and free sulphur or arsenious sulphide.

The methyl derivatives of arsenic acid. There are two methyl derivatives of arsenic acid which are notionally derived by substituting a methyl group for one or two OH groups in the molecule of arsenic acid:

| Arsenic acid | Methyl arsonic acid | Dimethyl arsinic acid. |

Dimethyl arsinic acid, cacodylic acid, $(CH_3)_2AsOOH$, is a solid, m.p. 200°. It is made:

(i) by the action of water on the dialkyl trihalides, such as $(CH_3)_2AsCl_3$,

(ii) by the oxidation of cacodyl oxide by mercuric oxide in the presence of water.

Dimethyl arsinic acid is easily soluble in water, and it is extremely stable. The oxidising agents fuming nitric acid, aqua regia, and potassium permanganate have no action on it. The reducing agents hydrogen, ferrous sulphate, and sulphur dioxide have no action on it, but it is reduced by hypophosphorous acid and by stannous chloride. Dimethyl arsinic acid is amphoteric. It is a much weaker acid than methyl arsonic acid, $K_a = 7 \times 10^{-7}$; the salts are decomposed by carbon dioxide. The basic dissociation constant, $K_b = 5 \cdot 6 \times 10^{-13}$. A reaction of dimethyl arsinic acid is mentioned in Table 20.12.

Methyl arsonic acid, $CH_3AsO(OH)_2$, is a colourless crystalline solid. It is made:

(i) by the oxidation of methyl arsine, dichloromethyl arsine, or the oxide CH_3AsO,

(ii) by the action of methyl chloride on arsenious oxide:

$$As_4O_6 + 6H_2O + 4CH_3Cl = 4CH_3AsO(OH)_2 + 4HCl,$$

or on potassium arsenite:

$$K_3AsO_3 + CH_3Cl = CH_3AsO(OK)_2 + KCl.$$

Methyl arsonic acid is soluble in alcohol, and in water, but not in ether. The first and second dissociation constants of the acid differ considerably: $K_1 = 2 \cdot 46 \times 10^{-4}$, $K_2 = 5 \cdot 7 \times 10^{-9}$. When heated the acid loses water, thus:

$$2CH_3AsO(OH)_2 \xrightarrow{130°} CH_3 \cdot O \cdot OH \cdot As{-}O{-}As \cdot OH \cdot O \cdot CH_3 \xrightarrow{180°} 2CH_3OH + As_2O_3.$$

A further reaction of methyl arsonic acid is mentioned in Table 20.12.

Phenyl arsonic acid, $C_6H_5AsO(OH)_2$, is colourless and crystalline. It is made by the action of phenyl diazonium chloride on potassium arsenite. It is extremely stable towards reagents, but it is reduced by phosphorous acid to arsenobenzene,

$$C_6H_5As{=}AsC_6H_5.$$

SECTION 5. COMPOUNDS CONTAINING THE ARSENIC ATOM IN THE TRIGONAL BIPYRAMIDAL VALENCE STATE

Three types of arsenic compound are described in this Section: (i) arsenic pentafluoride, (ii) alkyl and aryl derivatives of a hypothetical arsenic pentachloride, (iii) certain compounds containing complex anions in which an arsenic atom is present, such as $[AsCl_4^-]$.

Arsenic pentafluoride, AsF_5, is a colourless gas, condensing to a yellow liquid at $-53°$. m.p. $-80°$. It is obtained by treating the trifluoride with antimony pentafluoride and bromine at a temperature below $55°$:

$$2SbF_5 + AsF_3 + Br_2 = 2SbF_4Br + AsF_5.$$

The arsenic pentafluoride is collected in a receiver cooled in liquid air. The density of the vapour indicates some dissociation.

Arsenic pentafluoride is the only arsenic halide in which the arsenic atom is in the trigonal bipyramidal valence state; there are no arsenic compounds corresponding to the range of phosphorus compounds in Table 20.8. (p.734)

Compounds of the general formula R_xAsCl_y, where $x + y = 5$. The formulae and certain properties of the methyl and phenyl derivatives of the hypothetical arsenic pentachloride are set out in Table 20.14. The ultimate members of the series are arsonium salts, for which it has been established that the four methyl or phenyl groups are tetrahedrally arranged round the arsenic atom. The structures of the other compounds are uncertain, but structures in which the arsenic atoms are pentacovalent seem more likely than ionic forms, such as $[CH_3AsCl_3]Cl$. Resonance between the two forms is not possible, as the change from tetracovalent to pentacovalent arsenic would require considerable movement of the chlorine atoms.

Table 20.14. *The Methyl and Phenyl Arsenic Chlorides*

CH_3AsCl_4	$(CH_3)_2AsCl_3$	$(CH_3)_3AsCl_2$	$[(CH_3)_4As]Cl$
Preparation: Pass Cl_2 into CH_3AsCl_2 in CS_2 at $-10°$	Preparation: Pass Cl_2 into $(CH_3)_2AsCl$ in CS_2	Preparation: Pass Cl_2 into $(CH_3)_3As$ in CS_2†	See p. 743
Decomposes at 0° to $AsCl_3$ and CH_3Cl	Decomposes at 50° to reagents. Water hydrolyses it to $(CH_3)_2AsO \cdot OH$	Decomposes to $(CH_3)_2AsCl$ and CH_3Cl. It is hydrolysed by water	
$C_6H_5AsCl_4$	$(C_6H_5)_2AsCl_3$	$(C_6H_5)_3AsCl_2$	$[(C_6H_5)_4As]Cl$
Yellow needles m.p. 45°	m.p. 191°	m.p. 204°	See p. 743
	All three compounds are prepared by methods similar to those used for the alkyl derivatives		
Fumes in air, is violently hydrolysed by water, converts acetic acid to chloracetic acid		Hydrolysed by water to $(C_6H_5)_3AsOHCl$, $(C_6H_5)_3As(OH)_2$, $(C_6H_5)_3AsO$	

† Also made (i) by the action of HCl on $(CH_3)_3AsO$ and (ii) by the action of CH_3Cl on $(CH_3)_2AsCl$.

The anions [Ashal₄]⁻. The following salts are known: [(CH₃)₂NH₂][AsCl₄], [(C₂H₅)₂NH₂][AsBr₄], and [Quin. H][AsCl₄]. The chlorides are colourless, and the bromide is pale yellow. The salts can be crystallised from the concentrated halogen acid concerned, but they are hydrolysed by water or alcohol. The ion [AsCl₄]⁻ contains ten valency electrons. Although the ion can be formulated as a trigonal bipyramid, one corner being occupied by a lone pair:

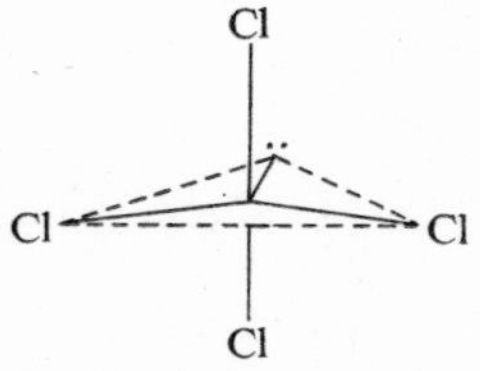

there is no experimental evidence for such a structure, and it is possible that one electron pair in the arsenic atom in anions such as [AsCl₄⁻] is truly inert.

There is also a complex acid prepared by the action of arsenic trioxide on catechol, $H[(C_6H_4O_2)_2As],4H_2O$. The anion of this acid could also be formulated in the same way as the chloroarsenate ion:

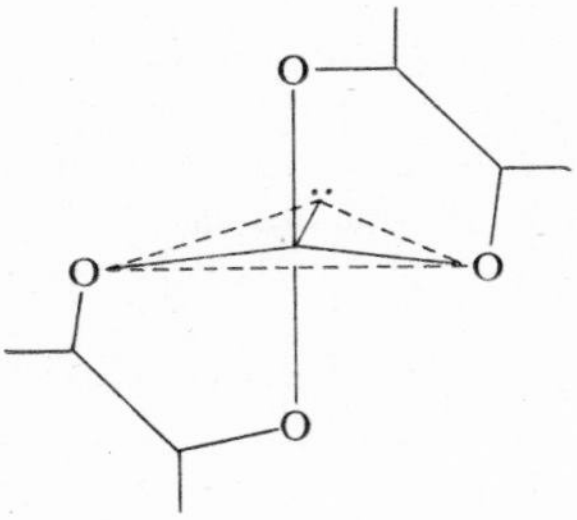

The ion has no plane of symmetry, and therefore should be optically active. If one of the water molecules in the acid is part of the anion, the structure could be written as octahedral with one lone pair.

A similar structure could be assigned to the ion [AsBr₅]²⁻, which is present in the salt [C₂H₅NH₃]₂[AsBr₅]. The ion [As₂Cl₉]³⁻ is known in the salt Cs₃As₂Cl₉.

SECTION 6. COMPOUNDS CONTAINING THE ARSENIC ATOM IN THE OCTAHEDRAL VALENCE STATE

Potassium hexafluoroarsenate, KAsF₆ has been reported. The catechol complex anion $[(C_6H_4O_2)_3As]^-$ has been obtained as the NH₄⁺, K⁺, and Ba²⁺ salts, and as the free acid $H[(C_6H_4O_2)_3As],5H_2O$. The anion is dissymmetric and the acid has been resolved. The salts are stable in water and in dilute alkali solution.

ANTIMONY

Elementary antimony is obtained:

(i) by heating stibnite, Sb₂S₃, with iron and a little salt:

$$Sb_2S_3 + 3Fe = 2Sb + 3FeS;$$

the antimony melts and collects below the slag,

(ii) by roasting stibnite in air:

$$2Sb_2S_3 + 9O_2 = 2Sb_2O_3 + 6SO_2,$$

and subsequently reducing the antimony oxide formed by heating to redness with charcoal and sodium carbonate:

$$Sb_2O_3 + 3C = 2Sb + 3CO,$$

(iii) by precipitating the metal by the addition of iron or zinc to a solution of antimonious chloride,

(iv) by reducing antimonic oxide by fusion with potassium cyanide, or by heating it in a current of hydrogen.

Antimony is trimorphic. The three forms are:

	Specific gravity	Solubility in CS_2	m.p.	b.p.
Yellow	—	Slight		
Black	5·3			
Metallic	6·67		630°	1325°

Yellow antimony corresponds to white phosphorus and yellow arsenic. It has been obtained by the action of oxygen on liquid stibine at $-90°$. At this temperature in the dark it changes into the black form. The black form may be obtained this way, or by the rapid cooling of antimony vapour. It may be pyrophoric. On warming it turns to the stable metallic form. This has metallic lustre, but it is brittle and not malleable, and has a specific conductivity of only $2·71 \times 10^4$ ohm^{-1} cm^{-1}, at 0°, which is about 1/25 that of copper. When a concentrated solution of antimony trichloride in hydrochloric

Table 20.15. *Reactions of Antimony (Metallic)*

Reagent	Result
Cold air	No effect
Heated air	Burns to Sb_2O_3
Oxygen	Burns brilliantly
Steam at a red heat	The steam is decomposed and Sb_4O_6 is formed
Dilute acids	No effect
Conc. HCl	Dissolves only in the presence of oxygen (the commercial metal dissolves in the absence of oxygen)
Conc. HNO_3	Oxides of nitrogen are evolved and a white powder of Sb_2O_5 (hydrated) remains
Aqua Regia	Dissolves to a solution of $SbCl_5$
Hot conc. H_2SO_4	Gives $Sb_2(SO_4)_3$
Cl_2	Ignites spontaneously
Br_2	Combines on heating
I_2	Combines on heating
S	Combines on heating
Calcium or sodium hypochlorite	Insoluble (cf. arsenic)
Conc. tartaric acid solution	Soluble to give $(SbO)_2C_4H_4O_6$
Yellow ammonium sulphide	Dissolves
Distilled with mercuric fluoride	SbF_3
Distilled with mercuric chloride	$SbCl_3$

acid is electrolysed using a high current density, the so-called "explosive antimony" is deposited on the platinum cathode. It looks like polished graphite. At about 200° this changes explosively to the metallic form; 2·4 kcal per gm atom are liberated. It has been suggested that explosive antimony is a gel of metallic antimony and antimony trichloride, and that the energy liberated is due to the crystallisation of the antimony.

The molecular weight of antimony vapour corresponds to $Sb_{2.96}$ at 1572°, $Sb_{2.68}$ at 1640°, and to Sb at 2070°. The structure of the molecule has not been determined. The vapour at high temperatures probably consists of a mixture of Sb_4 and Sb_2, and the Sb_4 molecules may be similar to the P_4 and As_4 molecules.

GENERAL CHEMISTRY OF ANTIMONY

The electron configuration of the valence shell ($n=5$) of the antimony atom is:

$5s$	$5p$	$5p$	$5p$
↑↓	↑	↑	↑

The penultimate shell ($n=4$) contains eighteen electrons.

The classification of the compounds of antimony in terms of the valence state of the antimony atom is less certain than the classification of the compounds of the lighter members of sub-Group V N, because the possibility of an inert electron pair in the valence shell of the antimony atom has to be considered. There is no need to postulate an inert electron pair in the atoms of nitrogen or phosphorus when in any state of combination, and in arsenic the inert pair is very rare. For bismuth the need for an orbital structure in which only three of the five valency electrons take part in hybridisation is clear and definite. In the case of antimony, however, it is difficult to decide whether in certain compounds the atom is tetrahedrally hybridised with one hybrid orbital occupied by a lone pair, or whether the atom contains an inert pair, and undergoes pyramidal hybridisation.

There are no simple compounds of trivalent antimony for which the postulation of an inert pair would be inescapable. There are, however, certain giant molecule structures, including Sb_2O_3, Sb_2S_3, and SbOCl, which are probably largely ionic, and there are the anionic complexes, such as $[SbCl_4]^-$, which are all reducing agents, and which clearly make use of only three of the valency electrons present in the isolated antimony atom. These two types of compounds are classified among those in which one electron pair of the antimony valence shell is inert. The evidence for such classification lies in the analogies between the compounds of antimony and bismuth, and between the antimonious and stannous compounds.

The effect of this classification is to make use for the first occasion when discussing the elements in sub-Group V N, of the Sections of Table 19.1 which contain compounds in which only three valency electrons of the element are active. Compounds with giant molecule structures which are comparable to corresponding compounds of nitrogen and phosphorus are classified in Section 1, since these compounds probably contain antimony atoms in which all the electrons in the valence shell are used in bond formation.

It is assumed that stibine and the antimony trihalides are analogous to the corresponding compounds of nitrogen, phosphorus, and arsenic, and they are assigned tetrahedral structures in which one orbital is occupied by a lone electron pair. The trialkyl and triaryl derivatives of stibine (p. 760), are highly reactive, but they are more sharply characterised than the dialkyl and diaryl compounds of tin, and it is proposed to accept them also as compounds of the antimony atom in the tetrahedral state.

COMPOUNDS IN WHICH ONLY 3 OF THE 5 VALENCY ELECTRONS OF ANTIMONY ARE ACTIVE

There are no simple ionic compounds in which the antimonious ion Sb^{3+} is present; the compounds discussed in the following paragraphs are giant molecule compounds in which the bonds have both covalent and ionic character.

Antimonious oxide, Sb_2O_3, is a white solid existing in two forms. The octahedral form, senarmonite, is stable up to 570°. The orthorhombic form, valentinite, is stable from 570° to the m.p. about 650°, b.p. 1560°. The structures of the two forms are different. The molecular weight of antimonious oxide in the vapour at 1560° corresponds to the formula Sb_4O_6. The octahedral form is made up of Sb_4O_6 groups, each occupying the position of a carbon atom in the diamond lattice. It is therefore probable that Sb_4O_6 in the vapour, and in the octahedral crystalline form, has an orbital structure corresponding to that of P_4O_6. If so, the antimony atom in the oxide in these forms is in the tetrahedral valence state.

The orthorhombic form, however, consists of long chains formed of puckered rings:

The angles of the structure are: $\alpha = 115°$, $\beta = 129°$. The three angles O—Sb—O at any given antimony atom are 79°, 92°, and 100°. Hence the chain is not constructed of regular tetrahedra, each with three shared corners, and this is evidence of the inert pair configuration for the antimony atom in this form of antimonious oxide.

The presence of the antimony atom in the tetrahedral valence state in the octahedral form of antimonious oxide would justify the inclusion of the oxide in Section 4 of Table 19.1. It is convenient, however, to discuss antimonious oxide with the other antimonious compounds in the present Section.

Antimonious oxide is made:

(i) by heating antimony or antimonious sulphide in air,
(ii) by hydrolysing antimony trichloride with sodium carbonate solution,
(iii) by digesting the oxychloride, SbOCl, with sodium carbonate solution,
(iv) by passing steam over red-hot antimony.

It becomes yellow on heating (the liquid is yellow), and pale buff on cooling. If heated in air it begins to combine with oxygen at 300° to give Sb_2O_4, but it is easily reduced to antimony by heating with hydrogen or carbon. It reacts with sulphur on heating to give Sb_2S_3. It is almost insoluble in water. It is soluble in hydrochloric acid to form $SbCl_3$, in tartaric acid to form $Sb_2(C_4H_4O_6)_3,6H_2O$, in hot concentrated sulphuric acid to yield crystalline $Sb_2(SO_4)_3$ on cooling, and in nitric acid to give $Sb(NO_3)_3$. It dissolves in sodium hydroxide solution to form sodium antimonite (see below). A solution of Sb_2O_3 in tartaric acid, neutralised by sodium carbonate, can be titrated against iodine:

$$Sb_2O_3 + 2H_2O + 2I_2 = 4HI + Sb_2O_5.$$

Antimony dioxide, Sb_2O_4, is a white solid. It is obtained as the ultimate product when metallic antimony, its oxides, or its sulphides, are heated in air between 300° and 900°. It is conveniently made by oxidising antimonious sulphide with nitric acid, and igniting the product in air at a dull red heat.

When heated it becomes yellow. It is infusible and non-volatile. If heated above 900°
it loses oxygen and forms antimonious oxide. It is easily reduced when heated with
carbon or hydrogen. It is insoluble in water, but it reddens blue litmus. It is resistant to
acids, but it dissolves in hydrochloric acid to give antimony trichloride if a reducing
agent, such as hydriodic acid, is present. With aqueous potassium hydroxide solution
it yields a mixture of potassium antimonite and antimonate. On fusion with potassium
hydroxide it gives $K_2Sb_2O_5$ which probably has the constitution $K_2(SbO)(SbO_4)$.
$K_2Sb_2O_5$ is sparingly soluble in cold water, but easily soluble in hot; the addition of
hydrochloric acid to its solution precipitates $K_2Sb_4O_9$.

The crystal structure of Sb_2O_4 is isomorphous with that of $SbTaO_4$, which has the
ionic structure $Sb^{III}Ta^VO_4$. Hence antimony dioxide has the corresponding structure
$Sb^{III}Sb^VO_4$, which is in agreement with the chemical reactions already mentioned.

Antimonious sulphide, stibnite, Sb_2S_3, consists of greyish-black, rhombic crystals.
It is made:

(i) by heating a mixture of antimony and sulphur, or a mixture of antimonious
oxide and sulphur,
(ii) by passing hydrogen sulphide through a solution of antimonious chloride in
dilute hydrochloric acid,
(iii) by heating a solution of antimonious chloride with an alkaline solution of
sodium thiosulphate:

$$2SbCl_3 + 6Na_2S_2O_3 = 6NaCl + Sb_2S_3 + 3Na_2S_3O_6.$$

In reactions (ii) and (iii) a red amorphous precipitate (specific gravity 4·28) is obtained. If this is dried, and heated at 200° in an atmosphere of carbon dioxide, it changes
to the black crystalline variety (specific gravity 4·65), and any free sulphur is expelled.

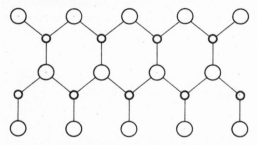

Fig. 20.1.   Chain of Sb_2S_3 units. The large circles
represent sulphur atoms.

A sol of antimonious sulphide can be made by adding a very dilute solution of
potassium antimonyl tartrate to an aqueous solution of hydrogen sulphide.

When antimonious sulphide is heated in air it yields antimonious oxide (p. 755).
It can be reduced by iron to the metal (p. 752). If heated in hydrogen the equilibrium
is set up:

$$Sb_2S_3 + 3H_2 \rightleftharpoons 3H_2S + 2Sb.$$

Antimonious sulphide is insoluble in water and in dilute acids. It dissolves in hot
concentrated hydrochloric acid (cf. As_2S_3). It dissolves in alkali metal sulphides in the
absence of air to give thioantimonites. It dissolves in hot concentrated solutions of
alkalis and alkali carbonates (but not in ammonium carbonate, cf. As_2S_3) to give a
mixture of antimonites and thioantimonites in a solution which, on dilution, yields a

red precipitate containing Sb_2O_3 and Sb_2S_3. If a mixture of antimonious sulphide and sulphur is treated with boiling sodium hydroxide solution, sodium thioantimonate, $Na_3SbS_4,9H_2O$ is obtained:

$$4Sb_2S_3 + 8S + 18NaOH = 5Na_3SbS_4 + 3Na[Sb(OH)_6].$$

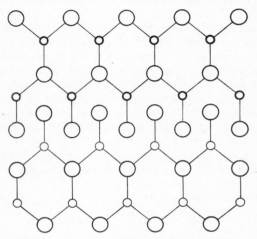

Fig. 20.2. A pair of Sb_2S_3 chains as they are present in the crystal of antimonious sulphide.

Antimonious sulphide possesses a giant molecule structure which extends infinitely in one dimension only. The structure consists of a pair of chains, shown separately in Fig. 20.1 and as they are associated in the crystal in Fig. 20.2.

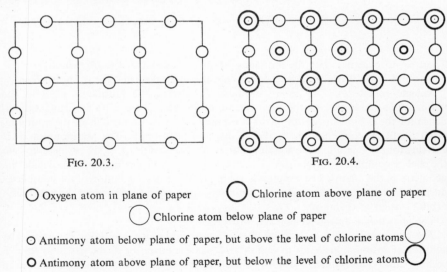

FIG. 20.3.   FIG. 20.4.

◎ Oxygen atom in plane of paper   ◯ Chlorine atom above plane of paper

◯ Chlorine atom below plane of paper

○ Antimony atom below plane of paper, but above the level of chlorine atoms ◯

○ Antimony atom above plane of paper, but below the level of chlorine atoms ◯

Antimonyl chloride, SbOCl. Antimonious chloride reacts with water to produce insoluble oxychlorides:

with little water $SbCl_3 + H_2O \rightleftharpoons SbOCl + 2HCl$

with more water $4SbCl_3 + 5H_2O \rightleftharpoons Sb_4O_5Cl_2 + 10HCl$

The precipitation of these compounds is inhibited if the solution of antimonious chloride is concentrated, or if alkali metal halides are present, probably owing to the formation of complexes.

Antimonyl chloride is crystalline, insoluble in alcohol or ether, but soluble in carbon disulphide, benzene, and chloroform. It dissolves readily in a dilute solution of hydrochloric acid.

Antimonyl chloride has a layer structure which may be pictured as follows: Fig. 20.3 shows a layer lattice of squares in which an oxygen atom is placed at the centre of each side. Chlorine atoms are now placed *above* the plane of the squares at square corners, and *below* the plane of the squares at square centres, Fig. 20.4. Antimony atoms are inserted *above* the plane of the squares vertically over the lower chlorine atoms, and *below* the plane of the squares vertically under the upper chlorine atoms. The antimony atoms are nearer than the chlorine atoms to the planes of the squares, and hence they are contained in the layer. Each antimony atom is surrounded by four oxygen atoms and four chlorine atoms in its own layer. When a series of layers are packed together, it is almost certain that there are significant forces between the antimony atoms in one layer and the chlorine atoms in the neighbouring layers.†

The structure of $Sb_4O_5Cl_2$ is uncertain.

Antimony triacetate, $Sb(OCOCH_3)_3$, probably contains the antimony atom in oxidation state III, with one electron pair inert.

THE ANTIMONIOUS COMPLEXES

Neutral complexes. The neutral complexes of antimony in the antimonious state are formed when the antimony atom accepts an electron pair from a donor molecule. Examples of such compounds are:

$$\begin{matrix} C_2H_5 \\ \diagdown \\ S \rightarrow SbCl_3, \\ \diagup \\ H \end{matrix} \qquad C_6H_5-\overset{\overset{\textstyle H}{|}}{C}=O \rightarrow SbCl_3, \qquad (C_2H_5)_2O \rightarrow SbBr_3$$

There is no evidence that the antimony atom is oxidised in the formation of these compounds, and therefore it is assumed that the inert electron pair is undisturbed.

Anionic complexes. The complex anions containing the antimony atom in the antimonious state can be either non-chelate or chelate. There is no experimental evidence for the orbital structures of the complexes; the valence orbitals of the antimony atom might be combinations of the $5p$, $6s$, and $5d$ orbitals. The antimony atom is exerting four covalent links in sodium antimonite, $Na[Sb(OH)_4]$, or six covalent links in the chelate complex $Na_3[Sb(C_2O_4)_3]$, but there is little evidence on which to decide the geometry of the anions. The complexes are reducing agents; oxidation of the complexes occurs when the inert electrons of the antimony atom are caused to enter the hybridised orbital system of the atom.

The non-chelate anionic complexes, $M[SbX_4]$.

The antimonites, such as $Na[Sb(OH)_4]$. Free antimonious acid does not exist. The solution of antimonious oxide in sodium hydroxide solution yields the sparingly soluble sodium antimonite, which crystallises from solution in octahedra with the constitution $Na(Sb(OH)_4),H_2O$. The ionic weight of the ion $(Sb(OH)_4)^-$ has been determined by

---

† Among the compounds with this crystal structure are:

SbOCl	BiOCl	LaOCl	PbFCl
SbOBr	BiOBr	LaOBr	PbFBr
SbOI	BiOI	LaOI	

the osmotic method. Potassium antimonite made by the solution of antimonious oxide in potassium hydroxide solution is much more soluble, and is said to be KSb_3O_5.

The antimonites are strongly hydrolysed by water. The solutions are reducing agents; silver nitrate is reduced to silver, and potassium chromate to chromite.

The esters of antimonious acid have the constitution $(RO)_3Sb$ (p. 766).

The complex halides. Some examples of these compounds are:

$$M[SbCl_4] \qquad M_2[SbCl_5] \qquad M_3[SbCl_6]$$
$$K[SbBr_3(NO_3)] \qquad K[SbBr_3(SCN)]$$
$$Na[SbI_3Br]$$

The chelate anionic complexes are exemplified by the following formulae of certain oxalato- and sulphato-complexes of antimonious antimony:

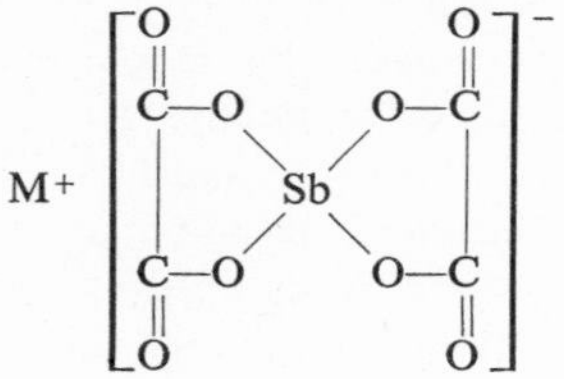

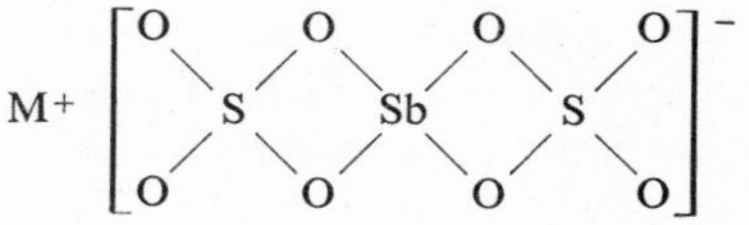

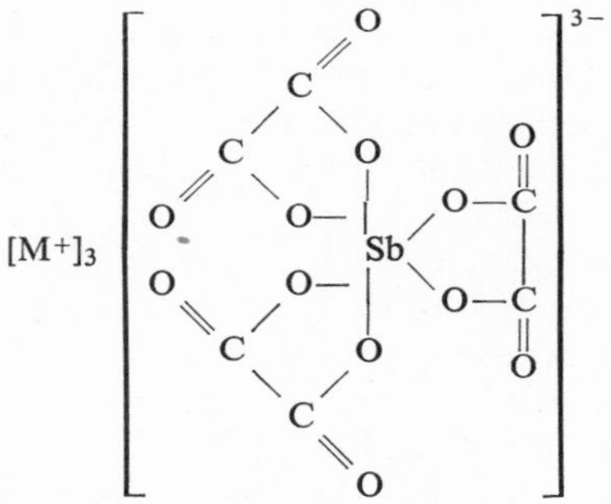

The oxygen atoms linked to the antimony atoms in the trioxalato complex are at the corners of a trigonal prism having the antimony atom at the centre.

COMPOUNDS IN WHICH ALL 5 VALANCY ELECTRONS OF ANTIMONY ARE ACTIVE

SECTION 1. ANTIMONY COMPOUNDS CONSISTING OF GIANT MOLECULES IN WHICH THE BONDS HAVE BOTH COVALENT AND IONIC CHARACTER

The giant molecule compounds of antimony are the antimonides of certain metals; the crystal structures are stated in Table 20.16.

Table 20.16. *The Crystal Structures of certain Metallic Antimonides*

Li_3Sb	Na_3Sb	K_3Sb	Mg_3Sb_2	AlSb	GaSb	CrSb	CoSb
A†	A	A	D	Z	Z	N	N

The crystal structures are indicated as follows:

A, Na_3P; D, anti-La_2O_3; Z, zinc blende; N, NiAs.

† The α form has structure A; the β form is cubic.

SECTION 4. COMPOUNDS IN WHICH THE ANTIMONY ATOM IS TETRAHEDRALLY HYBRIDISED

The compounds discussed in this Section include those in which the antimony atom is 3 co-ordinate, such as SbH_3, and those in which it is 4 co-ordinate, such as $C_6H_5SbO(OH)_2$. It is assumed that in the 3 co-ordinate compounds the antimony atom is tetrahedrally hybridised, and that one of the hybrid orbitals is occupied by a lone electron pair.

STIBINE AND ITS DERIVATIVES

Antimony hydride, stibine, SbH_3, is a poisonous gas, b.p. $-18°$, m.p. $-88°$, which condenses to a white solid. It has an unpleasant smell. Like phosphine and like arsine, stibine cannot be made by the direct union of the elements.

Stibine is obtained by the action of dilute sulphuric or hydrochloric acid on a Group II metal in the presence of antimony or a compound of antimony. The antimony is best introduced as an alloy of the Group II metal. The most satisfactory Group II metals for the purpose are magnesium and zinc. Calcium or barium may be used, but the yields of stibine are much smaller. Very little stibine is obtained by the action of acids on alloys of antimony with the alkali metals, or with aluminium (cf. Fleitmann's test for arsenic). The reduction of an antimony compound by hydrochloric acid acting on tin in contact with platinum produces metallic antimony.

The purest stibine is made by the action of hydrochloric acid on an alloy of magnesium and antimony in the proportions 2:1. The gas is washed with water, dried, and cooled in liquid air, which solidifies it. Pure gaseous stibine is evolved on warming, and may be collected over mercury.

Stibine is fairly soluble in water, and more soluble in carbon disulphide. It is endothermic and although fairly stable when dry, it decomposes into its elements when heated or sparked. It is attacked by air or oxygen to form water and antimony. It burns with a grey flame giving white fumes of antimonious oxide. It reacts with silver nitrate first to form a precipitate of Ag_3Sb:†

$$SbH_3 + 3AgNO_3 = Ag_3Sb + 3HNO_3.$$

This precipitate is then oxidised by excess of silver nitrate to metallic silver,

$$Ag_3Sb + 3AgNO_3 + 1\tfrac{1}{2}H_2O = 6Ag + \tfrac{1}{4}Sb_4O_6 + 3HNO_3,$$

with the precipitation of antimonious oxide, Sb_4O_6. These reactions are parallel to those of arsine, with the important practical difference that arsenic is finally present as the soluble As_4O_6, and antimony is finally present as the insoluble Sb_4O_6. If a mixture of arsine and stibine has been passed through dilute silver nitrate solution, the arsenic is present in solution, and the antimony in the precipitate.

THE ALKYL AND ARYL DERIVATIVES OF STIBINE

The primary and secondary derivatives, $RSbH_2$ and R_2SbH, are unknown.
The **trialkyl stibines** are prepared:

   (i) by the action of an alkyl iodide on a potassium antimony alloy (potassium antimonide),
  (ii) by the action of antimony trichloride on a zinc alkyl or the appropriate Grignard reagent,
 (iii) by the distillation of a trialkyl antimony dibromide, such as $(C_2H_5)_3SbBr_2$, with zinc.

† Arsine reacts with silver nitrate to yield the soluble complex $Ag_3As,3AgNO_3$.

Trimethyl stibine, $Sb(CH_3)_3$, b.p. 78·5°, and triethyl stibine, $Sb(C_2H_5)_3$, b.p. 158·5°, are colourless liquids, soluble in benzene, but insoluble in water, and unattacked by it. Both inflame spontaneously in air to give an oxide, R_3SbO. They react quantitatively with the halogens, sulphur, and selenium, to form addition compounds. They combine with alkyl halides to give quaternary halides. Trimethyl stibine combines with methyl iodide very rapidly. Triethyl stibine combines with ethyl iodide slowly in the cold, and very rapidly at 100°. Triethyl stibine reacts like a metal with acids:

$$(C_2H_5)_3Sb + 2HCl = (C_2H_5)_3SbCl_2 + H_2.$$

The chemical relationships of trimethyl stibine are summarised in Chart 20.3.

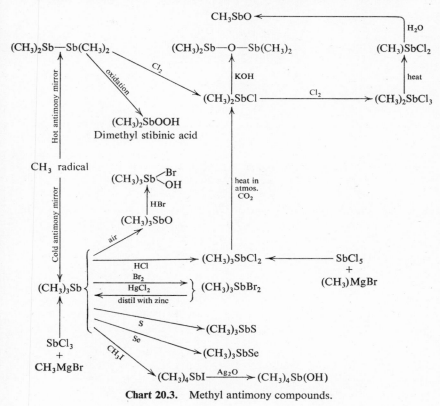

Chart 20.3. Methyl antimony compounds.

Triphenyl stibine, $(C_6H_5)_3Sb$, m.p. 48–50°, can be made:

  (i) by the action of phenyl magnesium bromide on antimony trichloride,
 (ii) by the action of sodium on a mixture of phenyl bromide and antimony trichloride,
(iii) by the reduction of triphenyl antimony dichloride, $(C_6H_5)_3SbCl_2$,
 (iv) by heating antimony phenyl oxide:

$$3(C_6H_5)SbO = (C_6H_5)_3Sb + Sb_2O_3.$$

Triphenyl stibine is stable to air, and does not combine with sulphur. It does not react as a metal when treated with hydrochloric acid, and it does not react with alkyl or aryl halides. Triphenyl stibine is a powerful reducing agent. It reduces cupric, thallic, and ferric chlorides to give $(C_6H_5)_3SbCl_2$, nitric acid to give $(C_6H_5)_3Sb(NO_3)_2$, and sulphuric acid to give $(C_6H_5)_3SbSO_4$. It reduces potassium permanganate in acid or alkaline solution, and hydrogen peroxide in neutral solution, to give $(C_6H_5)_3SbO$. With hot alkaline hydrogen peroxide it reacts thus:

$$NaOH + (C_6H_5)_3Sb + H_2O_2 = (C_6H_5)_2SbO \cdot ONa + C_6H_6 + H_2O,$$

and with mercuric chloride, thus:

$$HgCl_2 + (C_6H_5)_3Sb = C_6H_5HgCl + (C_6H_5)_2SbCl.$$

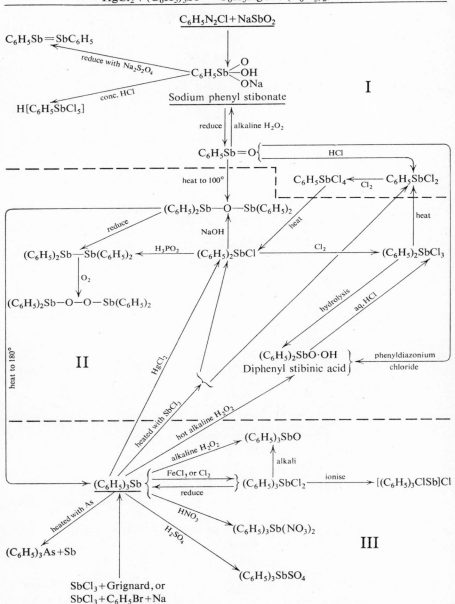

Chart. 20.4.   Phenyl antimony compounds. †

† The Roman numerals indicate the number of phenyl groups per antimony atom.

Triphenyl stibine can be nitrated, and the nitrobodies can be reduced without disturbing the Sb—C link.

The only mixed quaternary compounds are those of the type $(Alk_3Ar)SbX$. The chemical relationships of triphenyl stibine are summarised in Chart 20.4.

THE ANTIMONY TRIHALIDES

Certain properties of the antimony trihalides are set out in Table 20.17.

Table 20.17. Certain Properties of the Antimony Trihalides

	SbF_3	$SbCl_3$	$SbBr_3$	SbI_3
Appearance	Colourless octahedral crystals	White rhombic deliquescent crystals	White rhombic deliquescent crystals	Red mono-clinic plates†
m.p. °C	291	73	96	170
b.p. °C	318	223	288	410
Specific gravity at 25°	4·38	3·14	4·15	4·77
Molecular structure		Pyramidal‡	Pyramidal§	Pyramidal
Distance Sb—X		2·37	2·52	2·75

† Two other polymorphic forms are yellow.   ‡ By electron diffraction.
§ By electron diffraction and X-ray diffraction.

Antimony trifluoride, SbF_3, is made:

  (i) by dissolving antimonious oxide in aqueous hydrofluoric acid, and evaporating the solution,

 (ii) by distilling antimony with mercuric fluoride.

In aqueous solution antimony trifluoride is much less hydrolysed than the other antimony halides, but the solution has an acid reaction. When the aqueous solution is evaporated some hydrogen fluoride volatilises, and a basic antimony fluoride remains. A complex salt, K_2SbF_5, may be made by dissolving antimony trifluoride in hydrofluoric acid containing potassium fluoride in solution.

Antimony trichloride, $SbCl_3$, is made:

  (i) by heating antimony in chlorine (the chlorine not in excess),

 (ii) by heating antimony with mercuric chloride,

(iii) by dissolving stibnite in concentrated hydrochloric acid:

$$Sb_2S_3 + 6HCl = 2SbCl_3 + 3H_2S;$$

when the resultant solution is distilled, hydrochloric acid first comes over, and then antimony trichloride, which condenses in the receiver to a mass of white crystals (butter of antimony). Antimony trichloride is soluble in water and in certain organic solvents, such as ether, carbon disulphide, and chloroform. It forms addition compounds with aromatic hydrocarbons (not with paraffins) such as benzene, toluene, and mesitylene. The ratio of antimony trichloride molecules to hydrocarbon molecules is usually 1:1, but it may be 2:1. If the aqueous solution of antimony trichloride is considerably diluted the basic chlorides $SbOCl$ and $Sb_4O_5Cl_2$ are precipitated, but these compounds are not precipitated from a concentrated aqueous solution, or from solutions containing the chloride of an alkali metal. The presence of an alkali metal chloride in the solution also reduces the acidity of the solution. This behaviour indicates that the aqueous solution of antimony trichloride contains the complex salt $[SbO^+][SbCl_6^-]$, which is converted by the alkali metal chloride to, say, $Na[SbCl_6]$, and that both these complex salts are soluble. Antimony trichloride also forms the complex salts $NaSbCl_4$, K_2SbCl_5, and $BaSbCl_5$; with concentrated hydrochloric acid it forms the crystalline chloroantimonic acid, $HSb_2Cl_7,2H_2O$. An acidified aqueous solution of antimony trichloride reacts with hydrogen sulphide to precipitate antimonious sulphide, Sb_2S_3.

Fused antimony trichloride is a poor conductor of electricity, but potassium bromide dissociates when dissolved in it. The vapour density of antimony trichloride, and the boiling points of its ethereal solutions, correspond to the monomeric formula $SbCl_3$.

Antimony tribromide, SbBr₃, is made by the direct combination of the elements. In aqueous solution it is hydrolysed to $SbOBr$, and $Sb_4O_5Br_2$. It forms complex anions containing a high proportion of bromine. The potassium salts containing these anions are made by adding bromine and antimony tribromide to a solution of potassium bromide. $KSbBr_6$, $KSbBr_7$, and $KSbBr_9$ are known. These salts are black or violet-brown. They lose bromine easily when dry; in aqueous solution they are easily hydrolysed to antimonic oxide, Sb_4O_{10}. The constitutions of these salts are probably of the perbromide type:

$$K^+ \begin{bmatrix} Br & & Br \\ & \diagdown \diagup \\ Br-Sb-Br \\ & \diagup \diagdown \\ Br & & Br \end{bmatrix}^-$$

Antimony tribromide forms many complex salts, such as $K_3Sb_3Br_9(NO_3)_3$, $K_3Sb_3Br_9(SCN)_3$, and $NaSb_3Br_9(N_3)$. Dark red, almost black, crystals of the bromo-antimonic acid, $HSbBr_6,3H_2O$, can be obtained from a solution of antimony tribromide and bromine in concentrated hydrobromic acid. Antimony tribromide is monomeric in solution in benzene.

Antimony tri-iodide, SbI₃, is made by dissolving powdered antimony in a solution of iodine in carbon disulphide. When the solution is evaporated the antimony tri-iodide crystallises in red plates. The vapour of antimony tri-iodide is scarlet. In aqueous solution antimony tri-iodide hydrolyses to a yellow powder which is a mixture of $SbOI$ and $Sb_4O_5I_2$. Antimony tri-iodide forms many complex salts, such as $NaSbI_3Br$, K_2SbI_5,H_2O, and $3NH_4I,4SbI_3,9H_2O$.

Derivatives of stibonium hydroxide and their salts. Stibonium hydroxide, $[SbH_4]OH$, does not exist, but its derivatives are well-known. The tetra-alkyl stibonium hydroxides are made by the action of silver oxide on the quaternary halides. As bases they are as strong as the quaternary ammonium hydroxides. They are oils (except the methyl compound) easily soluble in water, but not soluble in ether. They form stable salts, including the chlorides, nitrates, sulphates, oxalates, and bicarbonates.

THE OXIDES OF ANTIMONY

Antimonious oxide, Sb₂O₃, in the octahedral crystalline form, contains antimony atoms in the tetrahedral valence state, and it might therefore be included in this Section. It is discussed on p. 755.

Antimonic oxide, Sb₄O₁₀, is a yellow powder. It is made:

  (i) by treating antimony with nitric acid and gently igniting the residue (above 440° it loses oxygen to give Sb_2O_4),

  (ii) by heating one of the precipitated hydrated forms; here again care is needed, or oxygen may be lost before all the water has been expelled.

Antimonic oxide is an oxidising agent. It is easily reduced when heated with carbon or hydrogen. It is almost insoluble in water, but it reddens damp litmus. With cold hydrochloric acid it forms $SbCl_5$, and this liberates iodine from potassium iodide quantitatively. Antimonic oxide is scarcely affected by either dilute or concentrated sulphuric acid, or by aqueous potassium hydroxide. It yields an antimonate when fused with potassium hydroxide.

Hydrated forms of antimonic oxide may be obtained (p. 767), but they are less well-defined even than the hydrates of arsenic oxide (p. 749). For the constitution of the antimonates, see p. 768.

THE SULPHIDES OF ANTIMONY

Antimonious sulphide is discussed on p. 756.

Antimonic sulphide, a red solid, is obtained:

(i) by direct combination of the elements,
(ii) by adding a saturated solution of hydrogen sulphide to a solution of anti-monic oxide in concentrated hydrochloric acid (15% of free HCl).
(iii) by the action of an acid on a thioantimonate (p. 768).

The formula of antimonic sulphide is usually assumed to be Sb_2S_5, but its chemical nature and constitution are not firmly established. The insoluble precipitates obtained as above dissolve in solutions of the hydroxides of the alkali metals, and of sodium carbonate (not ammonium carbonate) to form antimonates and thioantimonates. When they are treated with ammonia a yellow solution is obtained, and a residue of antimonious sulphide and sulphur is left. The precipitates dissolve in alkali metal sulphide solutions to form thioantimonates alone, and in hydrochloric acid to yield antimony trichloride and sulphur:

$$Sb_2S_5 + 6HCl = 2SbCl_3 + 3H_2S + 2S.$$

ANTIMONY ALKYL AND ARYL DERIVATIVES CONTAINING OXYGEN OR SULPHUR

The remaining paragraphs of this Section are briefly concerned with oxides and acid hydroxides in which an antimony atom is combined with alkyl or aryl groups. The relations of these compounds to one another and to other compounds of antimony are set out in Charts 20.3 and 20.4.

Phenyl stibonic acid, $C_6H_5SbO(OH)_2$, is an amorphous solid. It is made:

(i) by the oxidation of monophenyl antimony oxide with alkaline hydrogen peroxide,
(ii) by heating phenyl diazonium chloride with sodium antimonite (cf. phenyl arsonic acid).

The acid melts only with decomposition. It is insoluble in water, but is amphoteric. It dissolves in alkalis to give salts and in concentrated hydrochloric acid to give $H(C_6H_5SbCl_5)$. It easily becomes colloidal.

Diphenyl stibinic acid, $(C_6H_5)_2SbO \cdot OH$, is a solid, highly polymerised. It is made:

(i) from diphenyl antimony trichloride, $(C_6H_5)_2SbCl_3$, by hydrolysis:

$$(C_6H_5)_2SbCl_3 + 2HOH = (C_6H_5)_2SbO \cdot OH + 3HCl,$$

(ii) from monophenylantimony oxide and phenyl diazonium chloride:

$$H_2O + C_6H_5N_2Cl + C_6H_5SbO = (C_6H_5)_2SbOOH + N_2 + HCl,$$

(iii) by the action of hot alkaline H_2O_2 on triphenyl stibine.

Diphenyl stibinic acid dissolves in alkalis and in hot dilute (but not concentrated) hydrochloric acid. The aryl group can be nitrated without separation from the antimony.

Monophenyl antimony oxide, $(C_6H_5)SbO$, is an amorphous solid. It is made by the reduction of phenyl stibonic acid, $(C_6H_5)SbO(OH)_2$. It is insoluble in water or alkali, but is soluble in acids to form salts. (It is more basic than Sb_2O_3.) It sinters at 153–154°, and decomposes, thus:

$$4(C_6H_5)SbO = (C_6H_5)_2Sb\text{—}O\text{—}Sb(C_6H_5)_2 + \tfrac{1}{2}Sb_4O_6.$$

At 180–200° the thermal change continues, thus:

$$3(C_6H_5)_2Sb\text{—}O\text{—}Sb(C_6H_5)_2 = 4(C_6H_5)_3Sb + \tfrac{1}{2}Sb_4O_6.$$

The constitution of monophenyl antimony oxide is unknown. Like phenyl stibonic acid and diphenyl stibinic acid (which also contain the group SbO) it is amorphous, and must be highly polymerised. There is no evidence at all on the valence state of the antimony atom in this compound.

Diphenyl stibine oxide, $(C_6H_5)_2Sb\text{—}O\text{—}Sb(C_6H_5)_2$, is a solid, m.p. 78°. It is made by heating phenyl antimony oxide, or by treating diphenyl antimony chloride with sodium hydroxide.

Trimethyl antimony oxide, $(CH_3)_3SbO$, a neutral solid, is formed by the spontaneous oxidation of trimethyl stibine in air. It reacts with hydrogen bromide to give $(CH_3)_3Sb(OH)Br$, which loses water to give:

$$
\begin{array}{ccc}
 & \mathrm{Br} \quad \mathrm{Br} & \\
 & \diagup \qquad \diagdown & \\
(CH_3)_3Sb & & Sb(CH_3)_3. \\
 & \diagdown \qquad \diagup & \\
 & \mathrm{O} &
\end{array}
$$

Triphenyl antimony oxide, $(C_6H_5)_3SbO$, also a neutral solid, is made by the oxidation of triphenyl stibine with alkaline hydrogen peroxide. (The triaryl stibines are less easily oxidised than the trialkyl stibines.) It can also be made by the action of alkalis on triphenyl antimony dichloride. It is similar to trimethyl antimony oxide.

The esters of antimonious acid, such as $Sb(OC_2H_5)_3$, are formed by boiling antimonious oxide with the appropriate alcohol in conditions in which the partial pressure of water vapour is kept low. The esters are low boiling liquids.

Trimethyl antimony sulphide, $(CH_3)_3SbS$, is made by the direct addition of sulphur to trimethyl stibine. It is soluble in water, and precipitates metallic sulphides from solutions of metallic salts.

SECTION 5. COMPOUNDS IN WHICH THE ANTIMONY ATOM IS IN THE TRIGONAL BIPYRAMIDAL VALENCE STATE

Compounds containing the antimony atom in the trigonal bipyramidal valence state are antimony pentafluoride, SbF_5, m.p. $+7°$, b.p. 150°, and antimony pentachloride, $SbCl_5$, m.p. 5°, b.p. 140°, pentamethyl antimony $(CH_3)_5Sb$, b.p.1 27°, and pentaphenyl antimony $(C_6H_5)_5Sb$, m.p. 170°.

Antimony pentafluoride, a liquid, is made:

(i) by the addition of fluorine to antimony trifluoride,

(ii) by the action of hydrogen fluoride on antimony pentachloride at 30°.

Antimony pentafluoride is remarkably stable (the heat of formation is above 98 kcal). It dissolves in water with a hissing sound; crystals of composition $SbF_5,2H_2O$ separate from the solution. The aqueous solution of antimony pentafluoride is converted by alkalis to antimonates.

Antimony fluoride reacts with other fluorides to form salts, such as $KSbF_6$, which are discussed under "complex anions". Sulphur dissolves in antimony pentafluoride to form a dark blue solution from which SbF_5S can be obtained. Antimony pentafluoride reacts with iodine to produce two dark-coloured compounds, $Sb_2F_{10}I$ (m.p. 110–115°) and SbF_5I (m.p. 80°). Both compounds are easily decomposed by water. $Sb_2F_{10}I$ is stable to heat up to 240°.

Antimony pentafluoride is used in organic chemistry as a fluorinating agent to replace chlorine atoms by fluorine.

Antimony pentachloride, a fuming yellow oil, is made by the addition of chlorine to antimony trichloride. Pure liquid antimony pentachloride is a non-conductor, but it becomes conducting if dissolved in liquid sulphur dioxide, or in liquid arsenic trichloride.

Cold water converts antimony pentachloride to two hydrates, $SbCl_5,H_2O$ (soluble in chloroform) and $SbCl_5,4H_2O$ (insoluble in chloroform). Hot water decomposes it to hydrated antimonic oxide. Antimony pentachloride reacts with concentrated hydrochloric acid to yield a fairly stable crystalline chloroantimonic acid, $HSbCl_6,4\frac{1}{2}H_2O$, the salts of which are mentioned under "complexes". Antimony pentachloride loses chlorine easily. Ethylene reduces it to the trichloride. Sulphur or hydrogen sulphide converts it to $SbCl_3S$, and it reacts vigorously with carbon disulphide to give carbon tetrachloride, antimony trichloride, and sulphur. There are numerous addition compounds of antimony pentachloride not easily accounted for on valency theory: $SbCl_5,4H_2O$ already mentioned; $SbCl_5,3NH$, red, and $SbCl_5,4NH_3$, colourless; $SbCl_5,2ICl$ and $SbCl_5,3ICl$; $SbCl_5,2Cl_2$.

SECTION 6. COMPOUNDS IN WHICH THE ANTIMONY ATOM IS OCTAHEDRALLY HYBRIDISED

The antimony atom in the octahedral valence state is present in neutral complexes and in complex anions, both non-chelate and chelate.

NON-CHELATE COMPLEXES

Neutral complexes. Antimony pentachloride is an acceptor molecule. It forms 1:1 addition compounds with alcohols, ethers, aldehydes, nitriles, and esters, and a quinone complex, $2SbCl_5,C_6H_4O_2$, in which both oxygen atoms of the quinone molecule are co-ordinated to antimony atoms.

Complex anions. Salts which contain the octahedrally hybridised antimony atom in complex anions are of the types $M[Sb(OH)_6]$, $M[SbF_6]$, and $M[SbCl_6]$. The anions in the salts are octahedral. There are also hexabromoantimonates, $M[SbBr_6]$, but the anion in these compounds is probably a perbromide of trivalent antimony.

Antimonic acid and the antimonates. Hydrated forms of Sb_4O_{10} are obtained by treating antimony pentachloride with hot water, by treating the lower oxides with nitric acid, or by treating potassium antimonate with dilute nitric acid. It is difficult to know whether the substances so obtained are chemical individuals. The hydrolysis of antimony pentachloride (best in the presence of chlorine to prevent reduction) gives a colloidal form of antimonic acid, soluble both in acids and in alkalis. The electrical conductivity of potassium antimonate and the application of Ostwald's rule† show that antimonic acid is monobasic. It has been show by X-ray analysis that

---

† Ostwald's rule states that $\lambda_{1024} - \lambda_{32} = 10·8 \times$ basicity, where λ is the equivalent conductance of the potassium salt of the acid at 25°, and the subscripts indicate the number of litres of water in which one gram molecule of the potassium salt is dissolved.

the ions in the salts $Na[Sb(OH)_6]$, $Li[Sb(OH)_6]$, and $Ag[Sb(OH)_6]$ are arranged on a sodium chloride lattice, and that the OH groups are arranged octahedrally round the antimony atoms. Hence it follows that the hypothetical antimonic acid has the formula $H[Sb(OH)_6]$. Certain metal antimonates once called "pyroantimonates" and "meta-antimonates" must therefore be assigned formulae which include the anion $[Sb(OH)_6^-]$. In the following list the old formula is on the left and the new on the right:

Barium meta-antimonate	$Ba(SbO_3)_2,8H_2O$	$Ba[Sb(OH)_6]_2,2H_2O$
Sodium pyroantimonate	$Na_2H_2Sb_2O_7,5H_2O$	$Na[Sb(OH)_6]$
	$NaSbO_3,3H_2O$	$Na[Sb(OH)_6]$
	$LiSbO_3,3H_2O$	$Li[Sb(OH)_6]$
	$NaH_2SbO_4,2H_2O$	$Na[Sb(OH)_6]$

Potassium antimonate, $K[Sb(OH)_6],\frac{1}{2}H_2O$, is made:

(i) by heating a mixture of powdered antimony and potassium nitrate to a red heat, extracting the residue with warm water to remove excess of the nitrate, and then with boiling water to obtain the antimonate,

(ii) by oxidising potassium antimonite with potassium permanganate solution.

Potassium antimonate is slightly soluble in cold water, and more soluble in hot water. Sodium antimonate is less soluble than the potassium salt, and hence is precipitated when a solution of the potassium salt is added to a solution containing sodium ions. Lithium and ammonium antimonates are also insoluble.

The hexafluoroantimonates. Potassium hexafluoroantimonate, $K[SbF_6]$, is made by adding potassium fluoride to a solution of antimonic oxide in concentrated hydrofluoric acid. It is hydrolysed by water to $K[Sb(OH)_3F_3]$, and by a solution of potassium hydroxide to $K[Sb(OH)_6]$.

Diazonium hexafluoroantimonate is only slightly soluble in water and is not explosive. Nitrosonium hexafluoroantimonate, $NO[SbF_6]$, is made by the action of nitrosyl fluoride on antimony pentafluoride.

The salts K_2SbF_7,H_2O and $(NH_4)_2SbF_7,\frac{1}{2}H_2O$ have been isolated, but their structures are not known.

The hexachloroantimonates. Hexachloroantimonic acid, $H[SbCl_6],4\frac{1}{2}H_2O$, has been isolated. It is a strong acid. On long standing in aqueous solution it is hydrolysed to antimonic oxide and hydrochloric acid. The acid forms an interesting series of double salts with chlorides containing one of the cations Mg^{2+}, Fe^{3+}, or Cr^{3+}. The salts must be formulated $ClMg[SbCl_6]$, $Cl_2Fe[SbCl_6]$, and $Cl_2Cr[SbCl_6]$, because silver nitrate fails to precipitate six chlorine atoms per molecule.

Thioantimonates. The compounds $Na_3SbS_4,9H_2O$, K_3SbS_4, $(NH_4)_3SbS_4$, $Ba_3(SbS_4)_2$ are known.

The sodium salt is made by boiling Sb_2S_3 with sulphur and sodium hydroxide solution. On filtering (to remove the sparingly soluble Na_3SbO_4 which is formed as a by-product) and cooling it is obtained as large pale-yellow tetrahedral crystals.

On acidification of a solution of sodium thioantimonate a precipitate varying in colour from golden yellow to deep orange is obtained. Its composition is uncertain; it may be Sb_2S_5 or a mixture of Sb_2S_4 and sulphur:

$$2Na_3SbS_4 + 6HCl = Sb_2S_5 + 6NaCl + 3H_2S$$
$$\underbrace{}$$
$$Sb_2S_4 + S$$

CHELATE COMPLEXES

Among the neutral complexes formed by antimony in the octahedral valence state are the β-diketones, such as acetonyl antimony tetrachloride:

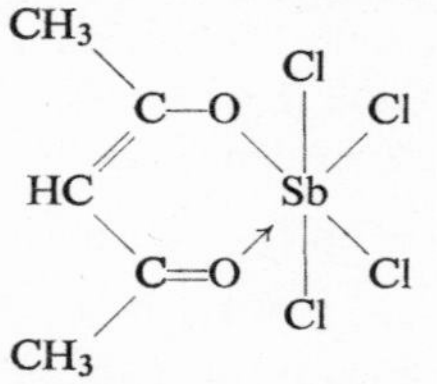

$$
\begin{array}{c}
CH_3 \\
\quad\diagdown \\
\qquad C-O \qquad Cl \\
HC \qquad\quad | \quad Cl \\
\qquad\diagup \qquad Sb \\
\qquad C=O \qquad Cl \\
\qquad\diagup \qquad Cl \\
CH_3
\end{array}
$$

The chelate complex anions of antimony in the octahedral valence state include the catechol compounds, such as I below.

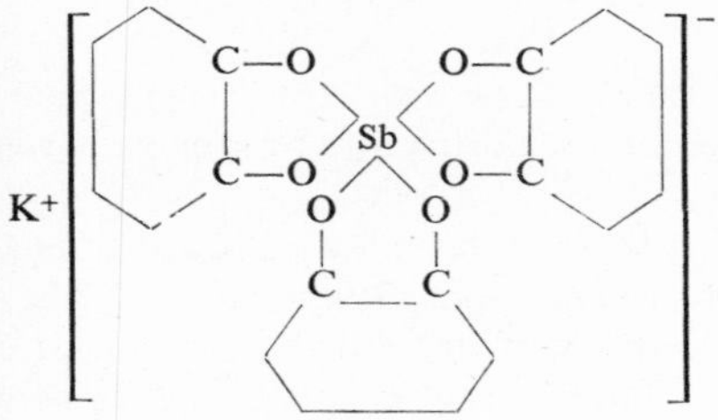

I

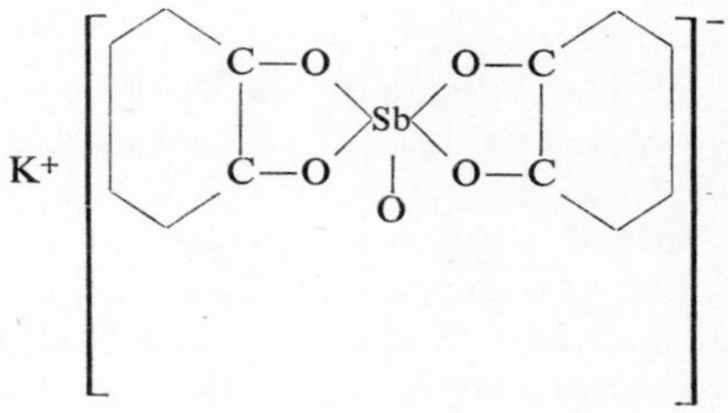

II

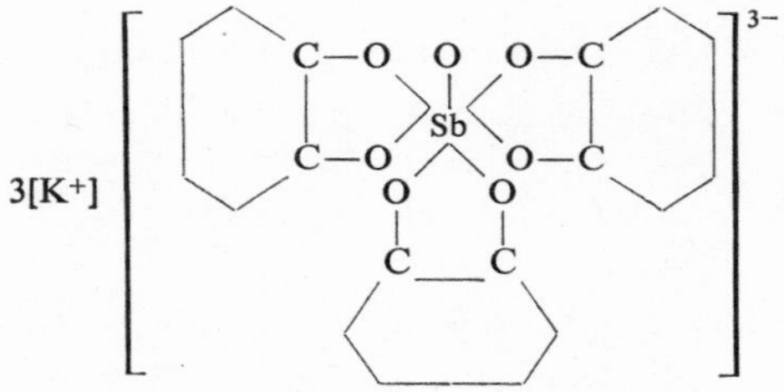

III

There are other catechol compounds in which the antimony atom has a co-ordination number of 5 or 7, as in II and III above.

The hexachloro- and hexabromo-antimonates, M_2Sbhal_6. The following salts containing the anion $[Sbhal_6]^{2-}$ are known: Rb_2SbCl_6, Rb_2SbBr_6, Cs_2SbCl_6, $(NH_4)_2SbBr_6$. The constitution of the anion needs discussion because the antimony atom appears to have seven valency electrons which are used to form six bonds. There is experimental evidence that the ion is diamagnetic, and it therefore contains no unpaired electron. The suggestion has been made by Pauling that the ion $[SbBr_6]^{2-}$ is a resonance structure of the two canonical forms:

$$[Sb^{III}Br_6]^{3-} \quad \text{and} \quad [Sb^{V}Br_6]^{-}.$$

The corresponding electron configurations of the valence shells of the antimony ions before octahedral hybridisation would be:

5s	5p	5p	5p	5d	5d	6s		5s	5p	5p	5p	5d	5d
⇅	↑	↑	↑	↑	↑	↑		↑	↑	↑	↑	↑	↑
inert													

X-ray analysis has shown that the salts Rb_2SbCl_6, Rb_2SbBr_6, and $(NH_4)_2SbBr_6$ have

25 + A.T.I.C.

the $K_2[PtCl_6]$ antifluorite lattice, which indicates that all the antimony atoms occupy similar positions.

The chemistry of salts containing the anion $[Sbhal_6]^{2-}$ is in agreement with the structure suggested by Pauling. If colourless solutions of antimony trichloride and antimony pentachloride in hydrochloric acid are mixed, a dark-brown solution is obtained. The intensity of the colour is proportional to the product of the concentrations $[SbCl_3] \times [SbCl_5]$, which is evidence for the equilibrium:

$$4HCl + SbCl_3 + SbCl_5 = H_3[SbCl_6] + H[SbCl_6].$$

Dark violet crystals of $Rb_2[SbCl_6]$ or of $Cs_2[SbCl_6]$ are precipitated when rubidium chloride or caesium chloride is added to the dark-brown solution. The violet crystals are stable in air, but in water they decompose to yield a mixture of Sb_2O_3 and Sb_2O_5.

BISMUTH

Elementary bismuth is obtained (i) by heating bismuth oxide with carbon using sodium carbonate as a flux, (ii) by the reduction of bismuth trichloride with hypophosphorous acid (p. 773).

Bismuth is a brittle white metal with a pinkish tinge. It has a low electrical conductivity, and is strongly diamagnetic. It is dimorphic. The vapour is a mixture of Bi and Bi_2 molecules. Bismuth is attacked only by oxidising acids, such as nitric acid, or hydrochloric acid in the presence of oxygen. It is attacked by steam at high temperature and by moist halogens. It burns in air with a blue flame.

GENERAL CHEMISTRY OF BISMUTH

The electron configuration of the valency shell of the bismuth atom in the ground state is:

$6s$	$6p$	$6p$	$6p$
⇅	↑	↑	↑

The penultimate shell ($n=5$) contains eighteen electrons, and the ante-penultimate shell ($n=4$) thirty-two electrons. The most remarkable feature of the chemistry of bismuth is the high stability of the inert electron pair, and hence the absence of compounds in which bismuth is in the oxidation state V. This, however, is in accordance with the trend of behaviour of metals in Period 6. Tables 17.1, 18.1, and 19.1 record that Tl^{III} forms many compounds, Pb^{IV} forms fewer compounds, and Bi^V none. The only compounds which might contain Bi^V are the pentafluoride, BiF_5, and the aryl compounds of general formula $(C_6H_5)_3BiX_2$, where X represents F, Cl, Br, I, CNO, NO_3, $\frac{1}{2}SO_4$, CO_2CH_3, $CO_2C_6H_5$, $\frac{1}{2}CO_3$, or OH. There are no corresponding alkyl compounds, which suggests that the phenyl groups in the aryl compounds may play a unique part in their structure, and that the bismuth atoms are not perhaps pentavalent after all. The bismuth atom is present in the bismuthous condition even in complex anions such as the hexachlorobismuthate ion $[BiCl_6^{3-}]$, and the bismuthate ion $[Bi(OH)_8^{5-}]$ (p. 772).

The orbital structures of molecules containing bismuth can only be conjectured. Little work has been done on the geometrical configurations of the molecules. $BiCl_3$ and $BiBr_3$ have pyramidal structures; $[BiCl_6^{3-}]$ is octahedral; $(C_6H_5)_3Bi$ must have an irregular structure, since the molecule has no elements of symmetry. In molecules of the type BX_3 the bonding orbitals are presumably hybrids of the three $6p$ orbitals. In the molecules or ions BiX_4, BiX_5, BiX_6, and so on, the bismuth atom presumably uses orbitals of the shell $n=7$ in the construction of bonding orbitals. As a provisional solution of the problem it is assumed that the bonding orbitals of the bismuth atoms in the simpler complexes are:

BiX_4 Combination of three $6p$ orbitals and the $7s$ orbital.
BiX_5 Combination of three $6p$ orbitals, the $7s$ orbital, and one $6d$ orbital.
BiX_6 Combination of three $6p$ orbitals, the $7s$ orbital, and two $6d$ orbitals.

The bismuth atom in which the $6s$ pair is inert forms ionic compounds, such as $Bi(NO_3)_3$ and $Bi_2(SO_4)_3$. These salts can be isolated as hydrates but they are very easily hydrolysed. Bismuth forms a considerable number of compounds of the giant molecule type, but the number of covalent bismuth compounds is small. Among such compounds are bismuthine BiH_3, and trimethyl bismuthine $Bi(CH_3)_3$, both of which are difficult to make and are very easily decomposed. These compounds differ sharply from ammonia and trimethylamine, the compounds of nitrogen to which they formally correspond. These two stable and well-known nitrogen compounds are assumed to contain a tetrahedrally hybridised nitrogen atom, one of the hybrid orbitals being occupied by a lone electron pair; no electrons in the valency shell of the nitrogen atom are inert.

Bismuth shows some resemblance to lanthanum in the crystal structures of the oxychlorides BiOCl and LaOCl (p. 758), and in the isomorphism of the double nitrates, and of the sulphates (see below).

COMPOUNDS IN WHICH ONLY 3 OF THE 5 VALENCY ELECTRONS OF BISMUTH ARE ACTIVE

COMPOUNDS CONTAINING THE CATION Bi^{3+}

The nitrate, sulphate, and the perchlorate of bismuth are well characterised. They are all hygroscopic and very easily hydrolysed to bismuthyl compounds.

Bismuth nitrate is made by dissolving bismuth oxide, or bismuth basic carbonate, in dilute nitric acid. When the solution is evaporated, deliquescent crystals separate having the constitution $Bi(NO_3)_3,5H_2O$. Bismuth nitrate is easily hydrolysed to the basic nitrate, $BiONO_3$.

Bismuth nitrate forms double nitrates of the formula $3M''(NO_3)_2,Bi(NO_3)_3,24H_2O$. M'' may be Zn, Cd, Co, or Ni. Bismuth may be replaced by lanthanum or by a rare earth metal. The whole series is isomorphous.

Bismuth sulphate, $Bi_2(SO_4)_3$, is made by dissolving bismuth trioxide in concentrated sulphuric acid. It can be heated fairly strongly without decomposition, but above $400°$ it breaks down to basic salts and bismuth oxide. The dihydrate and the heptahydrate are known. Bismuth sulphate is isomorphous with the sulphates of yttrium, lanthanum, and praseodymium.

GIANT MOLECULE COMPOUNDS IN WHICH THE BONDS HAVE BOTH COVALENT AND IONIC CHARACTER

The bismuthides. Sodium and potassium bismuthides, Na_3Bi and K_3Bi, have the sodium arsenide structure (p. 738); magnesium bismuthide Mg_3Bi_2, has the anti-La_2O_3 structure.

Bismuth trioxide, Bi_2O_3, is a pale yellow powder, m.p. $820°$. It is formed by heating the metal, the hydroxide, the basic carbonate, or the nitrate, to redness in air. It solidifies from the fused state to the α monoclinic form. At $704°$ the α modification changes to a tetragonal β form with a large evolution of heat. Bismuth trioxide sublimes at $1010°$ and is stable up to $1750°$.

A hydrated form of bismuth trioxide is formed as a white gelatinous precipitate on adding alkali hydroxide or ammonia to bismuth nitrate solution. It becomes crystalline on standing. Its formula has not been established, but it is conventionally written $Bi(OH)_3$. When heated to 100° the hydrated oxide loses water to form $BiO(OH)$, and subsequently Bi_2O_3. The hydrated oxide is insoluble in water. It is very slightly soluble (10^{-4} molar) in concentrated sodium hydroxide solution. It dissolves in acids to form bismuth salts.

Higher oxides of bismuth, and the bismuthates. Bismuth oxide can be made to take on additional oxygen when treated with oxidising agents such as chlorine, or air in the presence of alkalis. The substances so obtained lose oxygen very easily, and not one has been characterised as a chemical individual.

On fusing bismuth trioxide with KOH in air a brown mass of potassium bismuthate is obtained. This material is a strong oxidising agent, and it oxidises quantitatively a cold solution of a manganous salt in dilute nitric acid to a solution of permanganic acid. Use is made of this reaction in the detection and estimation of manganese. It was at one time thought that potassium bismuthate must be analogous to the phosphates, arsenates, and antimonates, K_3BiO_4, and consequently that the anion contains penta-valent bismuth. More recently the bismuthates are considered to be analogous to the ferrites and the chromites in which the metal in the anion is trivalent, but 8 co-ordinate. On this analogy potassium bismuthate should be formulated $K_5(Bi(OH)_8),4H_2O$, or $K_4(Bi(OH)_7,H_2O),3H_2O$.

Bismuth trisulphide, Bi_2S_3, is obtained as a grey crystalline solid by fusing together bismuth and sulphur. If hydrogen sulphide is passed into an acid solution of a bismuth salt, bismuth trisulphide is obtained as a very dark brown precipitate. The brown precipitate dissolves in nitric acid and in boiling concentrated hydrochloric acid, but not in alkalis or yellow ammonium sulphide. It dissolves in concentrated K_2S solution, or in K_2S melt, to yield the crystalline salt, potassium thiobismuthite, $KBiS_2$. Bismuth trisulphide is isomorphous with antimony trisulphide, and has a similar structure.

Table 20.18.   *The Bismuth Trihalides*

	BiF_3	$BiCl_3$	$BiBr_3$	BiI_3
Appearance	White powder	Deliquescent white crystals	Deliquescent golden yellow crystals; red liquid	Black or dark brown crystals
Crystal lattice	Fluorite	Pyramidal		
m.p. °C	(Infusible)	230	217	410
b.p. °C	(Non-volatile)	447	453	(Decomposes at 500°)
Solubility	Insoluble in water	Soluble in water (hydrolysed)	Soluble in water (hydrolysed)	Fairly soluble in water (not hydrolysed in the cold)
		Soluble in donating solvents	Soluble in donating solvents	Soluble in hydrocarbons

Bismuth trifluoride, BiF_3, is made by evaporating a solution of Bi_2O_3 in hydrofluoric acid. (Fluorine does not easily react with bismuth even when heated.) It is insoluble in water. It dissolves in concentrated hydrofluoric acid with the formation of complexes, such as $H_3(BiF_6)$. Bismuth trifluoride is infusible, and scarcely volatile at a red heat. It has the properties of a salt.

The crystal structure is that of fluorite, but additional fluorine ions are present at points corresponding to the positions of the octahedral holes.

Bismuth trichloride, $BiCl_3$, is made:

(i) by passing excess of chlorine over bismuth,
(ii) by distilling bismuth with mercuric chloride,
(iii) by dissolving bismuth in aqua regia, and evaporating the solution. Crystals of $BiCl_3,2H_2O$ are obtained, from which the anhydrous salt may be obtained by distillation.

Bismuth trichloride dissolves in water which hydrolyses it to BiOCl. It dissolves in alcohol and acetone, methyl cyanide, and nitrobenzene, presumably to form complexes of the type:

$$\begin{array}{ccc} CH_3 & & Cl \\ & \diagdown & \diagup \\ & CO \rightarrow Bi{-}Cl \\ & \diagup & \diagdown \\ CH_3 & & Cl \end{array}$$

It unites with ammonia to give ammines $BiCl_3,3NH_3$ (colourless and volatile) and $2BiCl_3,NH_3$ (red and decomposed by heating). Bismuth trichloride in solution in hydrochloric acid is reduced by hypophosphorous acid to give metallic bismuth in the form of a dull grey powder.

The density of bismuth trichloride vapour is normal. Bismuth trichloride is monomeric in solution in ether if the concentration is less than 1/10 molar; at higher concentrations association occurs.

Bismuth tribromide, $BiBr_3$, is made by warming bismuth with bromine. In general it is similar to the chloride. It is soluble in alcohol, acetone, and ether, and in xylene. With water it gives BiOBr.

Bismuth tri-iodide, BiI_3, is made:

(i) by warming bismuth with iodine,
(ii) by adding potassium iodide solution to a solution of bismuth trichloride,
(iii) by adding bismuth oxide to a solution of iodine in stannous chloride saturated with hydrogen chloride.

It is less soluble in water than bismuth chloride or bromide. It is hydrolysed to red BiOI only when its aqueous solution is boiled. It is soluble in benzene, toluene, xylene, and methylene iodide. It dissolves in hydriodic acid to form the acid $HBiI_4$, and in alkali metal iodides to form red salts such as $KBrI_4$.

The bismuthyl compounds. The action of water on the nitrate, sulphate, perchlorate, of bismuth, or on any of the bismuth trihalides, produces insoluble precipitates which are not hygroscopic (the perchlorate is an exception), and can be heated to a red heat before they decompose. The addition of ammonium carbonate to a solution of bismuth nitrate produces a white precipitate of $(BiO)_2CO_3$.

Brief accounts of some of these derivatives are as follows:

$BiONO_3$	White; it dissolves in warm fused tartaric acid.
$(BiO)_2SO_4$	Yellow.
$BiOClO_4,H_2O$	Or $4H_2O$. Hygroscopic.
$BiOF$	Crystalline and not hygroscopic.
$BiOCl$	Colourless; melts at a red heat; it is not attacked by cold alkali; hot concentrated alkalis give Bi_2O_3; it dissolves in warm fused tartaric acid.

BiOBr	Similar to BiOCl.
BiOI	Brick red; not attacked by boiling water.
$(BiO)_2CO_3,\frac{1}{2}H_2O$	It loses water at 100°, and carbon dioxide at higher temperatures.
$BiONO_2,\frac{1}{2}H_2O$	Crystalline, but decomposes at 60°; with alkali metal nitrites it forms yellow, readily hydrolysable complex salts of the general formula $M_3[Bi(NO_2)_6]$.

The bismuth oxyhalides have layer lattices of the form already described for antimony oxychloride (p. 757). In the bismuth oxyhalides there is no "bismuthyl group" in the crystal structure; the bismuth atoms are contained within an approximately close-packed array of oxygen and chlorine atoms. It is probable that the other so-called bismuthyl compounds have crystal lattices constructed on similar principles.

COVALENT BISMUTHOUS COMPOUNDS

Bismuthine, BiH₃, is made by dissolving an alloy Bi_2Mg_3 in hydrochloric acid, and freezing out by liquid air the bismuthine from the hydrogen evolved. The efficiency of the preparation in terms of bismuth dissolved is only 1 in 20,000. The quantities of bismuthine prepared have been small, and the knowledge of its chemistry is limited. By consideration of the boiling points of the hydrides of the other elements in Group V, that of bismuthine is judged to be about +20°, and so at room temperature bismuthine is an easily condensible gas. It is decomposed by gentle heating, by alkali, and by concentrated sulphuric acid. It reacts with silver nitrate solution, but not with hydrogen sulphide solution.

Bismuthine shows no tendency to form a cation $(BiH_4)^+$. Both alkyl and aryl derivatives of bismuthine have been prepared, but the primary and secondary derivatives $RBiH_2$ and R_2BiH are unknown.

Trimethyl bismuthine, $(CH_3)_3Bi$, is a colourless fuming liquid, b.p. 110°. It is made:

(i) by the action of a Grignard reagent on bismuth trichloride:

$$3CH_3MgBr + BiCl_3 = Bi(CH_3)_3 + 3MgBrCl,$$

(ii) by the remarkable reaction:

$$BiCl_3 + Al_4C_3 + 9HCl = Bi(CH_3)_3 + 4AlCl_3.$$

Bismuth trimethyl is active. On treatment with hydrogen chloride it yields methane:

$$Bi(CH_3)_3 + 3HCl = BiCl_3 + 3CH_4.$$

On solution in boiling alcohol and treatment with sulphur it yields ethane:

$$2Bi(CH_3)_3 + 3S = Bi_2S_3 + 3CH_3 \cdot CH_3.$$

On treatment with a cold ethereal solution of hydrogen sulphide it yields methane:

$$2Bi(CH_3)_3 + 3H_2S = Bi_2S_3 + 6CH_4.$$

On treatment with chlorine or bromine it yields methyl chloride or methyl bromide:

$$Bi(CH_3)_3 + Cl_2 = Bi(CH_3)_2Cl + CH_3Cl.$$

On treatment with methyl iodide at 200° it yields ethane:

$$(CH_3)_3Bi + 2CH_3I = CH_3BiI_2 + 2CH_3 \cdot CH_3.$$

In the last reaction trimethyl bismuthine behaves like a Grignard reagent or zinc alkyl.

Trimethyl bismuthine is spontaneously inflammable in air. It decomposes if heated above 150°. It is soluble in organic solvents. It is insoluble in water, by which it is attacked only on long boiling.

Triethyl bismuthine is similar to the trimethyl derivative, but it explodes when heated to 150°.

Triphenyl bismuthine, $(C_6H_5)_3Bi$, is a dimorphic colourless solid, m.p. 75–78°. It is made:

(i) by treating bismuth trichloride with a Grignard reagent:

$$BiCl_3 + 3C_6H_5MgBr = (C_6H_5)_3Bi + 3MgBrCl,$$

(ii) by treating bismuth trichloride with mercury diphenyl:

$$2BiCl_3 + 3Hg(C_6H_5)_2 = 2Bi(C_6H_5)_3 + 3HgCl_2,$$

(iii) by treating bismuth trichloride with phenyl diazonium chloride:

$$BiCl_3 + 3C_6H_5N_2Cl = (C_6H_5N_2)_3BiCl_6,$$

and decomposing the complex with copper in acetone solution:

$$3Cu + (C_6H_5N_2)_3BiCl_6 = Bi(C_6H_5)_3 + 3N_2 + 3CuCl_2,$$

(iv) by treating sodium-bismuth alloy with phenyl chloride:

$$BiNa_3 + 3C_6H_5Cl = Bi(C_6H_5)_3 + 3NaCl.$$

Triphenyl bismuthine is stable in air. Chlorine and bromine react with it additively to form dihalides; iodine does so only at $-80°$, and at room temperature the product breaks down to give $C_6H_5BiI_2$ and $(C_6H_5)_2BiI$. Triphenyl bismuthine is completely decomposed by warming with concentrated hydrochloric acid or with sulphuric acid:

$$Bi(C_6H_5)_3 + 3HCl = BiCl_3 + 3C_6H_6.$$

Triphenyl bismuthine is converted by nitric acid to the complex $(C_6H_4NO_2)_3Bi(NO_3)_2$. In the course of the reaction the phenyl group is nitrated, but it is not detached from the bismuth atom. The complex appears to contain a bismuth atom in the pentavalent state.

From X-ray analysis carried out on crystalline triphenyl bismuthine it has been found that the molecule has no elements of symmetry.

BISMUTH COMPLEXES

Trivalent bismuth acts as an acceptor, for example in the compounds $(CH_3)_3N{\rightarrow}BiCl_3$ and $(C_2H_5)_2O{\rightarrow}BiCl_3$. Bismuth forms complex halides of the types $MBiCl_4$ (including $NOBiCl_4$), M_2BiCl_5, MBi_2Cl_7, and M_3BiCl_6. The acid $HBi_2Cl_7,3H_2O$ is crystalline and stable at room temperature. It is made by dissolving bismuth trichloride in concentrated hydrochloric acid, and crystallising the solution at 0°. Bismuth is also present in the sulphato complex $M(Bi(SO_4)_2)$, and in the oxalato complexes $MBiOx_2$ and $(NH_4)_3$ $(BiOx_3)$. There are also a catechol chelate complex $M(BiCat_2)$, and a nitrite complex $M_3Bi(NO_2)_6$ with a crystal structure very like that of a cobaltinitrite.

PENTAVALENT BISMUTH COMPOUNDS

There are several compounds of general formula $(C_6H_5)_3BiX_2$. Of the four halogen compounds the fluoride is the most stable, and the iodide the least. The chloride and the bromide are made by direct addition. The fluoride is made by the action of potassium fluoride on the chloride in aqueous alcohol. It is a solid, m.p. 159°, easily soluble in ether and chloroform. The chloride and the bromide are similar with slightly lower melting points. All the compounds decompose on heating (the iodide below 0°) to give $(C_6H_5)_2BiX$ and C_6H_5X. The hydroxide $(C_6H_5)_3Bi(OH)_2$ is made by treating the chloride with silver oxide. Its general behaviour is that of an alcohol rather than a base. BiF_5, a giant molecule crystalline compound, is well characterised, but its orbital structure is uncertain.

CHAPTER TWENTY-ONE

SUB-GROUP VI N. OXYGEN, SULPHUR, SELENIUM, AND TELLURIUM

The atoms of these elements have six electrons in the s and p orbitals of the valency shells. In all compounds of oxygen and sulphur the s and the p orbitals of the valency shell are invariably part of the hybridised system; if any electron pair is non-bonding it is present as a lone pair. The s electrons in the valency shell are inert in one or two types of complex anions formed by selenium and tellurium, but among the compounds of these two elements those in which all the valency orbitals are hybridised are predominant. This behaviour of the four elements in Group VI is analogous to that of the corresponding elements in Group V N; bismuth is the only element in Group V N in which the s electron pair is nearly always inert, and bismuth corresponds to polonium in Group VI. From the little that is known about the polonium compounds (p. 891), it does not seem that they contain polonium in a state in which more than 4 valency electrons of the atom are active.

All the elements in Group VI N form simple anions $[X^{2-}]$ which are stable in association with cations of the alkali metals or alkaline earth metals, but the salts, alone or in solution, are increasingly easily oxidised to the free elements in the order Na_2S, Na_2Se, Na_2Te. All the elements combine with metals less electropositive than the alkaline earth metals to form crystalline compounds with giant molecule structures. Many oxides are regarded as close-packed structures of O^{2-} ions with the other element in the tetrahedral or octahedral holes (Table 21.3). The sulphides in general have less simple structures than the oxides, and the selenides and tellurides are more like alloys than are the oxides or sulphides.

All the elements form many covalent compounds. The nature of these compounds is determined by the orbital structures of the atoms of the element. Oxygen with a valency shell for which $n = 2$ has no d orbitals and hence cannot attain a higher state of hybridisation than the tetrahedral. In this state it forms such compounds as basic beryllium acetate (p. 809), a type of compound in which the part played by the central oxygen atom is not imitated by any other element.

Oxygen differs from the other elements in Group VI N in its ability to exert πp bonds. πp bonds exerted by an oxygen atom are accepted as part of the orbital structure of the oxygen molecule O_2, of the molecules of the oxides of nitrogen, of certain oxy-acid anions, and of aromatic ring structures containing oxygen atoms. Sulphur imitates oxygen to some extent in forming compounds which could be assigned structures which include πp bonds. Among such compounds are CS_2, COS, and the ions $[CS_3^{2-}]$ and $[SO_3S^{2-}]$. Selenium and tellurium also form one or two carbon compounds which may have structures corresponding to that of carbon dioxide (Table 18.10, p. 588), but these compounds are less stable than carbon disulphide. If the rule suggested on p. 573 that only members of Period 2 exert πp bonds is accepted, the π bonds in these compounds of carbon with sulphur, selenium, and tellurium must be πd bonds.

Oxygen is gaseous at room temperature; the molecule is diatomic. Sulphur is crystalline at room temperature, and the molecule is a puckered 8-membered ring in which there are no π bonds; the stable crystalline forms of selenium and tellurium at room temperature contain spiral chains of atoms. The vapour of sulphur at 800°, of selenium at 900°, and of tellurium at 1400° consist of diatomic molecules, but their structures are not known. The nitrides of oxygen are volatile and comparatively stable, and the molecules contain one or more πp bonds (Table 19.5, p. 655); the nitrides of sulphur (p. 853) are crystalline and decompose on slight shock. The nitrides of selenium (and tellurium) so far as is known are similar to the sulphur nitrides.

The part played by oxygen in the anions of the oxyacids, for example $[NO_3^-]$, $[SO_4^{2-}]$, $[SeO_4^{2-}]$, $[TeO_4^{2-}]$, $[SO_3S^{2-}]$, is not imitated by the heavier elements in the Group. There are no anions in which the functions of the oxygen atoms and the central atom are reversed; there is, for example, no ion $[OS_4^{2-}]$. The part played by the atoms of sulphur, selenium, and tellurium as the central atoms in the anions of their oxyacids is probably due to the presence of d orbitals in the valency shells of the atoms, which enable πd bonds to be formed between these atoms and the oxygen atoms. The bonds in the tetrahedral sulphate ion are:

and similar bonds are present in the sulphoxides:

and the sulphones:

and in sulphur dioxide and sulphur trioxide.

The silicates, in which the structural units are SiO_4 tetrahedra covalently linked to one another, occupy an intermediate position between the giant molecule oxides and discrete ions such as $[SO_4^{2-}]$. Sulphur, selenium, and tellurium form no compounds corresponding to the silicates.

Oxygen is present as a member of certain heterocyclic rings such as those of the metaborate ion and the cyclophosphate ion. In these and similar ions electron configurations are possible which permit the presence of non-localised π orbitals in the ring.

All the elements form compounds containing chains of the atoms of the elements; this property is shown most strongly by sulphur. Chains of oxygen atoms are present in the peroxides, and in the peroxyacids, but the maximum number of atoms in the oxygen chain is three, as in the unstable molecule of ozone, and in the ozonide ion. Chains of sulphur atoms are present in the sulphur molecule, S_8, in the persulphides, and in the polythionic acids. Selenium and tellurium form short chains, but there are

25*

Table 21.1. *Examples of Types of Compounds formed by the Elements in Sub-Group VI N*

Compounds in which only 4 of the 6 valency electrons of the element are active

O	page	S	page	Se	page	Te	page	Po	page
		S_2O_3	814	$K_2[SeCl_6]$, $K_2[SeBr_6]$		TeO	865	$Cs_2[PoBr_6]$	882
						$K[TeCl_5,H_2O]$, $K_2[TeCl_6]$	882	$(NH_4)_2[PoBr_6]$	891

Compounds in which all 6 valency electrons of the element are active

Section	State of atom			Nature of unit formed	O	page	S	page	Se	page	Te	page	Po	page
	Hybrid-isation	Formal charge	Bonds											
1				Giant molecules in which the bonds possess both ionic and covalent character	Na_2O, CaO, and the metal oxides in Tables 21.3 and 21.4	784	Na_2S, CaS, and the metal sulphides in Tables 21.17 and 21.18	815	Na_2Se, $CaSe$, and the metal selenides SeO_2, SeO_3	815 / 816	Na_2Te, $CaTe$, and the metal tellurides TeO_2, TeO_3	866		
2	Digonal	+1	1σ 2π 1 lone pair		$\overset{-}{:}\overset{+}{C}\!=\!\overset{\pi}{O}:$, $\overset{-}{O}\!-\!\overset{+}{C}\!\equiv\!O:$ $CH_3\!-\!N\!=\!C\!=\!O:$ $[N\!\equiv\!O:]^+$ $O_2(^3\Sigma)$, $[O_2^+]$	578 / 665 / 791	CS_2, CSO, $CH_3\!-\!N\!=\!C\!=\!S$	578	CSe_2, $CSeO$	866	$CTeS$	883		
3	Trigonal	0	1σ 1π 2 lone pairs		$:\!\ddot{O}\!=\!C\!=\!\ddot{O}:$ $CH_3\!-\!N\!=\!C\!=\!\ddot{O}:$ $[:\!\ddot{O}\!=\!\overset{+}{N}\!-\!\ddot{O}:]^+$ $O_2(^1\Delta)$ The compounds in Table 19.5 down to peroxynitric acid $(CH_3)_2CO$ CH_3CHO, $(CH_3)_2CHO$ [structure] $(C_2H_5)_2SO$, $(C_2H_5)_2SO_2$ H_2SO_4, and other oxyacids and their	578 / 655 / 596 / 836 / 841 / 844 / 589	$:\!\ddot{S}\!=\!C\!\overset{\pi d}{=}\!\ddot{S}:$ $CH_3\!-\!N\!=\!C\!=\!\ddot{S}:$ [structure]	578 / 589						

C.N.	Charge	Geometry	O (examples)	S	Se	Te	Po
4 Tetra-hedral	+1	2σ 1π 1 lone pair	[benzene-type C–C–O–P⁺ diagram] 790				PoH₂, PoCl₂, PoBr₂ 891
	0	2σ 1π† 1 lone pair	Boroxole, metaborate ion, Cyclic phosphate ion 509, 499, 727				
	0	2σ 2 lone pairs	H_2O, CH_3OH, $(CH_3)_2O$; XOX [X=F, Cl, Br], $[S_2O_7]^{2-}$, $[P_2O_7]^{4-}$; H_2O_2 and peroxyacids — 384, 801, 896, 846, 802	S_8, S_7NH, S_4N_4, S_4NH_4, H_2S, CH_3SH, $(C_2H_5)_2S$, $(C_2H_5O)_2S$, SCl_2, S_2X_2 [X=F, Cl, Br], H_2S_2 and polythionic acids, $CH_3S\cdot SCH_3$ — 853, 856	Se_4N_4 — 879; SeH_2, C_2H_5SeH, $(C_2H_5)_2Se$, $SeCl_2$, $SeBr_2$, Se_2Cl_2, Se_2Br_2, $CH_3Se\cdot SeCH_3$ — 868, 870, 871	TeH_2, C_2H_5TeH, $(C_2H_5)_2Te$, $TeCl_2$, $TeBr_2$ — 884, 885; $C_6H_5Te\cdot TeC_6H_5$ — 885	
		3σ 1πd 1 lone pair		$(C_2H_5)_2SO$, $(C_6H_5)_2SO$, X_2SO [X=F, Cl, Br], $[(R_3N)_2]SO]Cl$, $[SO_3^{2-}]$, $[(C_2H_5O)_2SO]$, $[O_2S\cdot SO_2^{2-}]$ — 836, 838, 819, 839, 840	$(C_6H_5)_2SeO$, X_2SeO [X=F, Cl, Br], $[SeO_3^{2-}]$, $(C_2H_5O)_2SeO$, $CH_3SeO\cdot OH$ — 873, 874, 876, 876	$(CH_3)_2TeO$ — 888; $[TeO_3^{2-}]$ — 889; $C_6H_5TeO\cdot OH$ — 889	
		4σ 2πd		$(C_2H_5)_2SO_2$, F_2SO_2, Cl_2SO_2, $(C_6H_5)XSO_2$ [X=F, Cl, Br], H_2SO_4, RSO_2OH, $Na_2S_2O_3$ — 841, 844, 844, 848, 846	$(C_6H_5)_2SeO_2$ — 877; H_2SeO_4, $RSeO_2OH$ — 877	$(CH_3)_2TeO_2$ — 889; K_2TeO_4 — 889	
	+1	3σ 1 lone pair	$[H_3O^+]$, $[(HgCl)_3O^+]$; $(CH_3)_2O\rightarrow B(CH_3)_3$; $[Be_4H_2O^{2+}]$ — 808, 496, 434	$[(CH_3)_3S^+I]$, $[SCl_3^+]Cl^-$, $(C_2H_5)_2S\rightarrow HgCl_2$ — 834, 825	$[(CH_3)_2Se^+]Cl^-$, $[SeCl_3^+]Cl^-$, $[C_2H_5Se(OH)_2]NO_3$ — 872, 873	$[(CH_3)_2TeICl$, $[TeCl_3]Cl$ — 886	PoCl₄
	+2	4σ	$(C_2H_5)_2O[In(CH_3)_3]_2$, Basic acetates, Crystalline oxides in which O is 4 co-ordinate Table 21.3 — 808, 809, 784				
	−1	1σ 3 lone pairs	$[OH^-]$, $[O_2^-]$, $[O_2^{2-}]$; O_3, $[O_3^-]$; Ions of oxyacids — 791, 787	$\overset{+\pi}{}\,S{-}C{-}\overset{..}{\underset{..}{S}}$: $[SH^-]$, $C_2H_5SO_2S$, $Na_2[SO_2S]$ — 578, 822	$[SeH^-]$ — 868		
5 Trigonal bipyra-midal	0	4σ 1 lone pair		SF_4 — 835	SeF_4, $(C_6H_5)_2SeCl_2$, $(C_6H_5)_2SeBr_2$ — 874, 879	$TeCl_4$ — 886	
6 Octa-hedral	0	6σ		SF_6, S_2F_{10}, SF_5OSF_5 — 852	SeF_6 — 879	$Te(OH)_6$, TeF_6, Te_2F_{10} — 890, 891	

† Non-localised.

no oxyacid anions based on chains of these atoms, although both selenium and tellurium can replace the central atom of sulphur in a polythionate ion.

Oxygen is the only element in the Group which is sufficiently electronegative to form hydrogen bonds. The physical properties of oxygen compounds which contain hydrogen therefore often differ considerably from those of the corresponding compounds of sulphur, selenium, and tellurium. The hydrogen bond is discussed on p. 371.

Examples of compounds formed by elements of Group VI N, classified according to the hybridisation of the element, are set out in Table 21.1. The chemical relations of certain compounds of sulphur, selenium, and tellurium are set out in Charts 21.1, 22.1, and 22.2. The Charts are similar in form so that the chemical relations of corresponding compounds of the three elements can be easily compared.

OXYGEN

OXYGEN: GENERAL CHEMISTRY

The electron configuration of the oxygen atom is:

1	2			
s	s	p	p	p
⇅	⇅	⇅	↑	↑

In chemical combination the atom may become ionised by the acceptance of two electrons to give O^{2-}, or it may adopt the digonal, trigonal, or tetrahedral valence states. In all its compounds all the valency orbitals of the oxygen atom are utilised; there is no evidence of the existence of an inert pair. The modes of chemical combination of the oxygen atom are set out and exemplified in Table 21.1.

The ionic state. The ion O^{2-} is present in the oxides of electropositive metals. It is also assumed to be present in a large number of metallic and non-metallic oxides which are regarded as structures of close-packed oxygen ions, with ions of the other element in the tetrahedral or octahedral holes. Many of these oxides form giant molecule structures. Examples are given in Tables 21.3–21.4. It is probable that the bonds in these molecules are not purely ionic, but are covalent with much ionic character. The chemistry of the ion O^{2-} is discussed in detail on p. 781.

The digonal and trigonal valence states. The oxygen atom adopts the digonal valence state only when exerting π bonds, and the trigonal valence state only when exerting either π or πd bonds. When exerting π bonds it is combined only with carbon or nitrogen, or with another oxygen atom (or with boron if the π bonds are non-localised). When exerting πd bonds it is combined with one of the elements Si, P, S, or Cl, all in Period 3.

The tetrahedral valence state. The chemistry of the oxygen atom in the tetrahedral valence state is particularly interesting on account of the stability of orbitals which contain lone electron pairs or even single electrons only. A list of ions and molecules consisting only of oxygen atoms is given in Table 21.6. Of the nine particles mentioned in the Table, three contain oxygen atoms in the tetrahedral valence state, and of these, two are electron deficient.

In the great majority of the compounds of oxygen in the tetrahedral valence state the oxygen atom controls the complete electron octet, either distributed in one σ bond and three lone pairs, or in two σ bonds and two lone pairs. In the peroxide ion, and in the hydroxyl ion $(OH)^-$, the oxygen atom is exerting one σ bond only, and it is in this condition in the sulphones, sulphoxides, and the ions of oxyacids if these are formulated with co-ionic bonds, thus:

$$
\begin{array}{ccc}
C_2H_5 & & \overset{-}{O} \\
& \diagdown \diagup & \\
& \overset{+}{S} & \\
& \diagup \diagdown & \\
C_2H_5 & & \overset{-}{O}
\end{array}
$$

Among compounds containing an oxygen atom exerting two σ bonds are water and the ethers (for other compounds see Table 21.1). Many of these compounds are electron donors, which form adducts such as $(CH_3)_2O \rightarrow BBr_3$; in the adduct the oxygen atom exerts three σ bonds, and one hybridised orbital is occupied by a lone pair. In a very few instances both lone pairs of the oxygen atom in the molecule of an ether may be donated, as in the indium compound:

$$
\begin{array}{ccc}
(CH_3)_3In & & In(CH_3)_3 \\
& \nwarrow \nearrow & \\
& O & \\
& \diagup \diagdown & \\
C_2H_5 & & C_2H_5
\end{array}
$$

The oxygen atoms in the ions $[H_3O]^+$ and $[(HgCl)_3O]^+$ are exerting three tetrahedral σ bonds, the fourth orbital being occupied by a lone pair. Finally there is the class of compound exemplified by basic beryllium acetate, and by the indium compound mentioned above, in which the oxygen atom carries two formal positive charges and exerts four tetrahedral covalent bonds. Certain oxides such as BeO and ZnO with zinc blende or wurtzite structures in which the co-ordination is 4:4, may also contain oxygen atoms in this condition.

SECTION 1. OXYGEN COMPOUNDS CONSISTING OF GIANT MOLECULES IN WHICH THE BONDS HAVE BOTH IONIC AND COVALENT CHARACTER

The monoxides, M_2O, of the alkali metals. The ion O^{2-} is most likely to occur in the basic oxides of the alkali metals. A summary of the preparations and properties of these oxides is given in Table 21.2. They can be made by the direct oxidation of the metal, but except in the case of lithium, the proportion of oxygen to metal must be controlled to prevent the formation of higher oxides. The monoxides of lithium and sodium are colourless, but potassium monoxide is yellow when hot, and the monoxides of rubidium and caesium† are highly coloured. All the monoxides except caesium have the anti-fluorite lattice; Cs_2O has the anti-$CdCl_2$ lattice. They may be reduced by hydrogen at about 150° to the hydrides.

Lithium monoxide is unaffected by heat alone, or by heat when in an atmosphere of oxygen; the other monoxides are converted to peroxides by disproportionation at 400°. Sodium monoxide is converted to the superoxide by heating with oxygen under high pressure, and the monoxides of the higher metals are converted to superoxides by heating with oxygen at atmospheric pressure. The monoxides dissolve in water to give the metallic hydroxides. This reaction is least violent for lithium monoxide and most violent for caesium monoxide. All the monoxides are soluble in the molten parent metal.

From the properties of the basic oxides of the alkali metals it is seen that the ion O^{2-} is not stable in aqueous solution; water converts it to the ion OH^-. The ion O^{2-} appears to be coloured, as the colour of the oxides deepens, especially on heating, with increasing atomic number of the metal. The ion is unstable to heat, as the basic oxides disproportionate to peroxides and the free metal at about 400°.

Oxides of other elements: Simple oxides. Oxygen combines to form giant molecules

† An oxide, Cs_3O m.p. 165° is reported. Its electrical conductivity is one-third that of the metal. The distance Cs—Cs is similar to that in the metal, and the distance Cs—O to that in Cs_2O.

Table 21.2. *Monoxides of the Alkali Metals*

	Li$_2$O	Na$_2$O	K$_2$O	Rb$_2$O	Cs$_2$O
Preparation	(i) Burn the metal in oxygen. Even at 12 atm and high temperatures no higher oxide is obtained (ii) Heat a mixture of lithium carbonate and carbon (iii) Heat lithium carbonate in hydrogen (iv) Heat lithium hydroxide at 780° (v) Heat lithium peroxide to 300° in vacuo	(i) Burn sodium very slowly in a limited supply of air, and distil off the excess sodium in vacuo (ii) Heat sodium carbonate with sodium (iii) Heat sodium hydroxide with sodium (iv) Heat sodium peroxide with sodium (v) Heat a mixture of sodium nitrate and sodium azide to 280°: $5NaN_3 + NaNO_3 = 3Na_2O + 8N_2$	Burn potassium very slowly in a limited supply of air, and distil off the excess potassium in vacuo		
State and Physical Properties	Colourless solid Antifluorite lattice m.p. above 1700°	Colourless solid Antifluorite lattice	White solid which turns yellow on heating Antifluorite lattice	Pale yellow solid, golden yellow at 200°, red at higher temperatures Antifluorite lattice	Orange-red solid, purple at 100°, nearly black at 250°, Anti-CdCl$_2$ layer lattice† (the only example of it) in which the Cs$^+$ ion is much polarised
Heat of formation $2M + \frac{1}{2}O_2 = M_2O$; ΔH	$-141\cdot2$ kcal	$-89\cdot96$ kcal	$-92\cdot1$ kcal	$-94\cdot9$ kcal	-100 kcal
Heat of reaction $M_2O(\text{solid}) + H_2O(\text{liq.}) = 2MOH$ (solid); ΔH	$-31\cdot2$ kcal	$-56\cdot5$ kcal	-75 kcal	-80 kcal	$-83\cdot2$ kcal
	Soluble in molten sodium	Soluble in molten sodium	Soluble in molten potassium	Soluble in molten rubidium	Soluble in molten caesium
Chemical Properties	Dissolves with reaction in water and in alcohol Does not undergo disproportionation at high temperature	Dissolves with violence in water, and quietly in alcohol Disproportionates at 400° to Na vapour and Na$_2$O$_2$ Reduced by hydrogen at 200° to NaH, and by CO at 300°: $2Na_2O + CO = Na_2CO_3 + 2Na$	Dissolves with violence in water Disproportionates	Dissolves almost explosively in water Disproportionates	Dissolves almost explosively in water Disproportionates at 360° to Cs vapour and Cs$_2$O$_2$ Reduced by hydrogen at 150° to CsH Combines with oxygen at 150° to give CsO$_2$ Reacts with moist CO$_2$ with inflammation With liquid ammonia gives a momentarily blue solution from which CsOH and CsNH$_2$ have been obtained F$_2$, Cl$_2$, I$_2$, have no action in the cold, but inflame at 200°

† *Ann. Reports Chem. Soc.,* 1956, 85.

with all elements except the inert gases and H, C, N, F, P, S, Cl, Br, I (Sb_4O_6 and As_4O_6 are molecular units). The crystal structures of the giant molecules may be three-dimensional, layer structures, or chain structures. It is conventional to regard all the atoms in these structures as ionised. The ionic radius of oxygen is 1·40. This value is greater than those of monatomic cations except Rb 1·48, Cs 1·69, Tl 1·44, and the ammonium ion 1·48. The crystals of a large number of oxides, therefore, are based on close-packed arrays of oxygen ions with the ions of the other element contained in octahedral or tetrahedral holes. The maximum radius of an ion to fit into a tetrahedral hole is $0·41 \times 1·40 = 0·57$, and the maximum radius to fit into an octahedral hole is $0·59 \times 1·40 = 0·83$.

Table 21.3 summarises the formulae and crystal structures of the more common simple metallic oxides. The structures in Rows 1 to 6, and Row 10 are described on p. 347. The corundum structure is the ilmenite structure in which all the metallic positions are occupied by M^{2+} ions of the same kind. The A rare earth structure contains the metallic ions in 7 co-ordination; six of the surrounding O^{2-} ions are at the apices of an octahedron, and the seventh is above one of the octahedron faces. The C rare earth structure may be regarded as a fluorite structure from which one quarter of the anions have been removed. The metallic ion is in 6 co-ordination. The six surrounding O^{2-} ions are situated at six of the eight corners of the fluorite cube (Fig. 12.14, p. 348).

The adoption of the rock-salt (6:6) structure by CaO, SrO, BaO, and CdO is interesting, as the ionic radii of the metal ions are too great for them to be present in the octahedral holes of a close-packed O^{2-} lattice.

Complex oxides. Table 21.4 summarises the formulae and crystal structures of certain complex oxides. The perovskite, ilmenite, and spinel structures are described on p. 349. Complex oxides contain two other elements besides oxygen in a composition unit of general formula $A_xB_yO_n$. There is a continuous transition from substances that are recognised as double oxides, such as $CuFe_2O_4$, through intermediate structures such as those of the silicates, to salts such as $BaSO_4$ or $CaCO_3$, in which the oxygen atoms are known to be closely associated with only one of the other two elements, so that a definite anion is present. Attempts to furnish a sharp definition of an ion in a solid oxide, however, have not been successful. Nevertheless it should be noted that any substance which can be proved to have one of the four structures mentioned in Table 21.3(a) is not a salt, but a complex oxide; $CaSnO_3$ and the corresponding compounds of Sr, Ba, Cd, and Pb, and the so-called titanates, $ATiO_3$, are not salts but complex oxides. (Similarly, there are no complex anions in the double fluorides $KMgF_3$ and $KZnF_3$.)

It is always assumed for the purpose of discussing the structures of oxides that the oxygen atoms are present as ions O^{2-}. It is probable, however, that in no case are the bonds in the crystals purely ionic. Indeed it is most likely that the concepts of ionic or localised covalent bonds in oxide crystals should be replaced by some generalised orbital picture, such as that postulated by the Bloch theory of metals.

The group XO_4, which is so prominent in inorganic chemistry and which has already been discussed on p. 574, needs special consideration. X covers a wide range of elements but it never represents a member of Period 2 (Li to F). This limitation suggests that d orbitals play some part in the bonding of the oxygen atoms to the X atom.

The group is found in combination with another element; AXO_4, A_2XO_4, and A_3XO_4, are common forms. It is interesting to enquire whether the substances thus generally represented are best regarded as entirely covalent, whether they contain two ions such as A^+ and XO_4^-, or whether each element is present as a separate ion. There is no doubt that examples of all these types of structure can be found.

Table 21.3. *Crystal Structures of Simple oxides*

(a) Infinite three-dimensional complexes

	Formula	Structure	Lattice of O²⁻ ions	Positions of metallic ions	Co-ordination numbers, M:O	Examples
1	MO	Rocksalt	f.c.c.	Octahedral holes	6:6	MgO, CaO, SrO, BaO, CdO, VO, MnO, FeO, CoO, NiO
2	M_2O	Antifluorite	b.c.c. (one-half cube centres)	Cube corners	4:8	Li_2O, Na_2O, K_2O, Rb_2O
3	MO_2	Fluorite	b.c.c. (cube corners)	One-half cube centres	8:4	ThO_2, CeO_2, ZnO_2 (at high temperatures), HfO_2
4	MO_2	Rutile	f.c.c.		6:3	GeO_2, SnO_2, PbO_2, TiO_2, VO_2, NbO_2, TeO_2, MnO_2, RuO_2, OsO_2, IrO_2
5	MO	Zinc blende	f.c.c.	One-half tetrahedral holes	4:4	BeO
6	MO	Wurtzite	Hexagonal c.p.	One-half tetrahedral holes	4:4	ZnO
7	M_2O_3	Corundum	Hexagonal c.p.	Two-thirds octahedral holes	6:4	$\alpha\text{-}Al_2O_3$, $\alpha\text{-}Fe_2O_3$, Cr_2O_3, Ti_2O_3, V_2O_3, $\alpha\text{-}Ga_2O_3$, Rh_2O_3
8	M_2O_3	Rare earth A	f.c.c. face centres only		7:6 and 4	La_2O_3, Ce_2O_3
9	M_2O_3	Rare earth C			6:4	Mn_2O_3, Se_2O_3, In_2O_3, Tl_2O_3
10	MO_3	Rhenium oxide		Octahedral holes at cube centres only	6:2	ReO_3
11	M_2O	Cuprite			2:4	Cu_2O, Ag_2O
12	MO_2	Silica structures			4:2	SiO_2, GeO_2

(b) Layer structures

Formula	Structure	Examples
M_2O	Anti-$CdCl_2$	Cs_2O
MO		SnO, PbO
MO_3		MoO_3

(c) Chain structures

	Examples
	Sb_2O_3

Table 21.4. *Crystal Structures of Complex Oxides*

Formula	Structure	Lattice of O^{2-} ions	Positions of metallic ions	Examples
ABO_3	Ilmenite	Hexagonal c.p.	Two-thirds of octahedral holes	$FeTiO_3$, $NiTiO_3$, $CoTiO_3$
AB_2O_4	Normal spinel	f.c.c.	For a unit cell of 32 O^{2-} ions, 8A in tetrahedral holes, 16B in octahedral holes	$FeAl_2O_4$, $ZnAl_2O_4$
$B(AB)O_4$	Inversed spinel	f.c.c.	For a unit cell of 32 O^{2-} ions 8B in tetrahedral holes 8B and 8A in octahedral holes	$Fe(MgFe)O_4$, $Mg(TiMg)O_4$, Fe_3O_4
ABO_3	Perovskite	f.c.c. face centres only	A at cube corners. B in octahedral holes at cube centres only	$CuTiO_3$, $SrTiO_3$, $SrSnO_3$, $SrZrO_3$, $SrHfO_3$, $BaCeO_3$

The co-ordination numbers with regard to oxygen of the elements in the group AXO_4 depend on the natures of the elements represented by A and X, as the following examples show:

Structure	Examples	Co-ordina-tion number of A	Co-ordina-tion number of X
Cristobalite	$BAsO_4$, BPO_4, $AlPO_4$	4	4
	$CrVO_4$, $ZnCrO_4$, $CdCrO_4$, $CuCrO_4$	6	4
	$CaSO_4$, $ZrSiO_4$, $CaWO_4$	8	4
	$BaSO_4$, $PbCrO_4$, $BaCrO_4$, $SrCrO_4$	12	4
	$SbTaO_4$, Sb_2O_4	6	6
Rutile	$AlSbO_4$, $FeSbO_4$, $FeTaO_4$	6	6

The cristobalite structure is wholly covalent. The crystals are infinite three-dimensional complexes of XO_4 tetrahedra linked together by oxygen atoms held in common. The bonding is accounted for if each oxygen atom exerts two covalent bonds, and each X atom, four bonds.

In aqueous solution at least, ions such as $(SO_4{}^{2-})$ and $(PO_4{}^{3-})$ exist as discrete tetrahedra. These ions are resonance structures which contain certain oxygen atoms linked to the X atoms by σ bonds, and others by σ and πd bonds. The bonding within such ions, which is wholly covalent, is discussed on p. 574.

In the solid state, if the co-ordination number of A is high, 12 for instance in the case of barium sulphate, it is probable that the crystal is composed of discrete A^+ and $XO_4{}^-$ ions. It is not possible to draw a hard and fast line between elements like sulphur and phosphorus which form discrete XO_4 ions, and those like silicon which never do so; the disulphate ion and the diphosphate ions:

show the beginnings of the silicate structure.

$FeTiO_3$ (p. 349) is an example of a structure in which the bonding is assumed to be completely ionic; the units are Fe^{2+}, Ti^{4+}, O^{2-}, and there is no unique relation of the Ti atom to the three oxygen atoms. There is some evidence to show that the co-ordination number of an element with regard to oxygen increases at high temperatures, for example:

	Li_2SO_4	Na_2SO_4	K_2SO_4	RB_2SO_4	Cs_2SO_4
High temperature C.N. for alkali metal	6	10	10	10	10
Low temperature C.N. for alkali metal	4	6	10	10	10
Transition temperature	575°	238°	588°	650°	660°

The three compounds Li_2SO_4, Li_2BeF_4, and Li_2MoO_4, possess the phenacite (C.N. 4) structure at low temperatures, and the spinel (C.N. 4 or 6) at high temperatures. The increase of co-ordination number might imply a change from covalent to ionic bonding in the group XO_4, or in the bonds A—O. No further correlations have been made. The influence of the electronegativity of X is obscure. Although magnesium and zinc have the same ionic radius and the same electronegativity, MgO has a rock-salt structure while ZnO has the wurtzite structure, and Mg_2SiO_4 has the olivine (in which the co-ordination number of Mg is 6) structure, while Zn_2SiO_4 has the phenacite (in which the co-ordination number of Zn is 4) structure.

SECTION 2. THE OXYGEN ATOM IN THE DIGONAL VALENCE STATE

The oxygen atom is present in the digonal valence state in the oxygen molecule ($^3\Sigma$ state), and in the anion O_2^+ (Table 21.6). The oxygen molecule is one of a number of structures which consist only of oxygen atoms, in most of which the oxygen atom is tetrahedrally hybridised. The oxygen molecule is therefore included among the structures discussed in Section 4. The oxygen atom in the digonal valence state is also present in certain compounds of oxygen with carbon and nitrogen which are included in Table 21.1, Section 2, and are discussed under carbon (p. 578), or nitrogen (p. 655).

SECTION 3. THE OXYGEN ATOM IN THE TRIGONAL VALENCE STATE

The oxygen atom is present in the trigonal valence state in the oxygen molecule ($^1\Delta$ state). Compounds containing the oxygen atom in the trigonal valence state are numerous (Table 21.1, Section 3) and include all the oxygen compounds containing

the carbonyl group $\diagdown C{=}O$. The carbonyl group undergoes many reactions which are

described in text-books of organic chemistry, and for lack of space must be omitted here. The sulphoxides and sulphones are discussed on pp. 836 and 841.

THE OXYACIDS

The ions of oxyacids are discussed in this Section, although they contain oxygen atoms in the tetrahedral valence state as well as in the trigonal valence state.

The oxyacids may be divided into three classes:

(1) Simple oxyacids formed by strongly electronegative elements: B, C, N, S, Cl, Si, P, V, Cr, Mn, As, Br, Se.
(2) Complex oxyacids formed from heavier and less electronegative elements: Sb, Te, I.
(3) Poly acids formed from V, Nb, Te, Mo, W, U.

There are, in addition, the diacids (pyroacids) from S, P, As, Sb, the monoperoxyacids from C, N, P, S, and the diperoxyacids from C, S, P, Cr.

The configurations of the ions of the oxyacids are stated in Table 21.5. In all these ions at least one oxygen atom exerts a π or a πd bond, but the valence state of the central atom can be varied from trigonal to octahedral. A structure in which the central atom is in the tetrahedral valence state and is also exerting πd bonds is stable and common. More complex structures are found in which the tetrahedra are linked corner to corner by holding one oxygen atom in common. If only two tetrahedra are thus linked the structure is that of a di-acid such as disulphuric acid, SO_3—O—SO_3, diphosphoric acid, PO_3—O—PO_3, or disilicic acid, SiO_3—O—SiO_3. If tetrahedra are linked by more than one corner, then rings, sheets, and three-dimensional systems are possible, as exemplified by the cyclic phosphoric acids (p. 724), and the silicates. A disc-like structure is obtained by filling the centre of a ring of six tetrahedra with another tetrahedron as in the isopolyacids (p. 1000). If a tetrahedron based on a different non-metal occupies the centre of the ring, a heteropoly acid is obtained (p. 999).

Table 21.5.   *The Configurations of Ions of certain Oxyacids*

Planar, trigonal	$(BO_2)_3^{3-}$	CO_3^{2-}	NO_3^-			
Non-linear						
Pyramidal				SO_3^{2-}	ClO_2^- ClO_3^-	BrO_3^- IO_3^-
Tetrahedral			PO_4^{3-} VO_4^{3-} AsO_4^{3-}	SO_4^{2-} CrO_4^{2-} SeO_4^{2-}	ClO_4^- MnO_4^-	
Octahedral					IO_6^{5-}	

The structures of the ions of the oxyacids formed by elements in Period 2. Of the elements in Period 2, boron, carbon, and nitrogen form oxyacid ions in which the central atom is trigonally hybridised. None of these elements forms an ion of the type XO_4.

The metaborate ion has a layer structure (a):

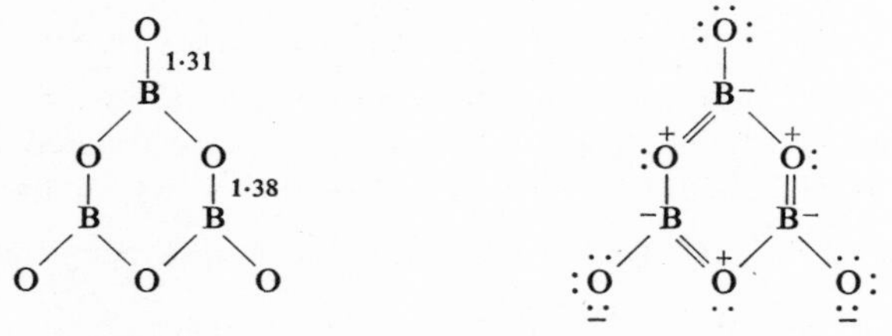

(a)   (b)

A formula with localised bonds (b) can be written, but no doubt the π bonds in the ring are non-localised as in benzene. The distance B—O, 1·31, for the length of the bond between a boron atom and an oxygen atom outside the ring, is exactly equal to Pauling's predicted length for B=O. This is probably fortuitous, and it should be noted that bond lengths between a non-metallic atom and an oxygen atom on the outside of a group are often very short (cf. P_4O_{10}, p. 711).

The carbonate ion is planar and symmetrical. The distance C—O in calcite is 1·27. It is a resonance structure of three canonical forms:

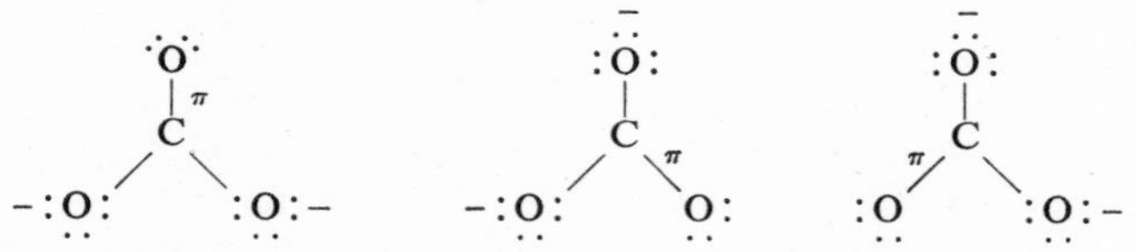

The nitrate ion also has a symmetrical planar structure in which the distance N—O is 1·21. The ion is diamagnetic. It has a resonance structure, and contains a nitrogen atom with unit formal positive charge:

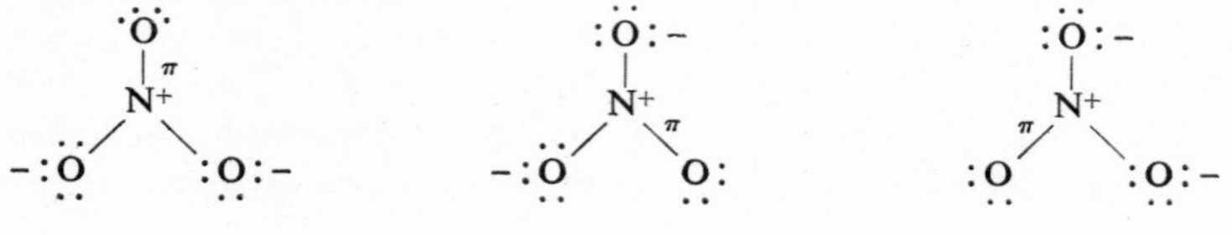

All these oxyacid ions in Period 2 are thus represented by structures in which:

(i) The negative ionic charge resides on one or more oxygen atoms.

(ii) The central atom is linked to at least one oxygen atom by a π bond.

(iii) All the molecular orbitals are constructed from s and p atomic orbitals only.

The structures of the ions of oxyacids formed by elements in Period 3. The ions of certain of the oxyacids formed by electronegative elements in Period 3, PO_4^{3-}, SO_4^{2-}, ClO_4^-, have the tetrahedral configuration. The bond lengths are:

	SiO_4	PO_4^{3-}	SO_4^{2-}	ClO_4^-
Bond length observed	1·61	1·56	1·50	1·50
Distances predicted by Pauling's cova- {X—O	1·91	1·84	1·78	1·73
lent atomic radii {X=O	1·62	1·55	1·50	1·44

The non-ionised group SiO_4 is included for comparison. The group SiO_4 never occurs as a discrete ion. The silicates (p. 605), consist of SiO_4 tetrahedra linked together by oxygen atoms held in common; the metallic ions are present in the tetrahedral or octahedral holes of the close-packed crystal structure (p. 607). Many other XO_4 groups which behave like SiO_4 are mentioned on p. 786.

The sulphate ion is a resonance structure based on the tetrahedral form:

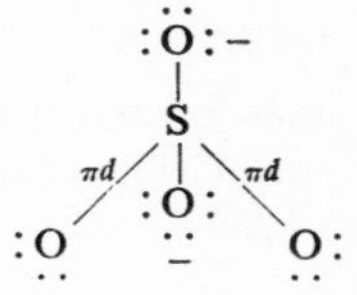

The orbital structure consists of four S—O σ bonds, on two of which π bonds are superposed. The orbitals from which the π bonds are constructed are a p orbital from the oxygen atom, and a hybrid π orbital from the sulphur atom (p. 156). The ions PO_4^{3-} and ClO_4^- are constructed on similar principles. One canonical form of each is shown below.

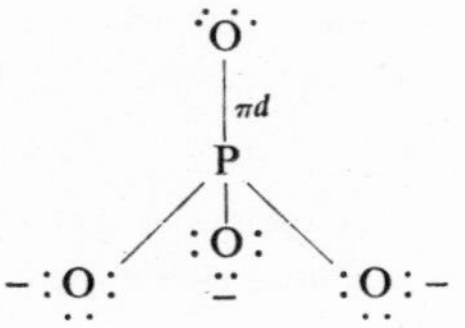

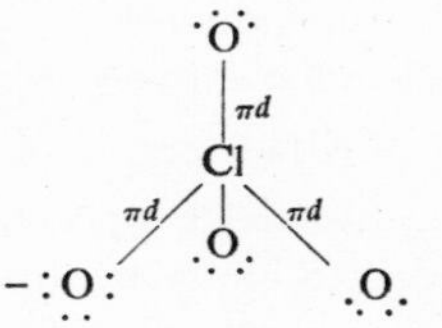

The ions PO_4^{3-}, SO_4^{2-}, ClO_4^-, are represented by structures in which:

(i) The negative ionic charge resides on one or more of the oxygen atoms.

(ii) The central atom is linked to at least one oxygen atom by a π bond.

(iii) The molecular orbitals include contributions from the s, p, and d orbitals of the central atom.

It is to be noted that the presence of a π bond in the group XO_3 or XO_4 appears to be necessary if the group is to exist as a discrete ion. A group such as CO_4 for which a structure containing a π bond cannot be formulated never exists as an ion although it may be present in well-characterised compounds. For example, the ester $C(OC_2H_5)_4$

is a well-known stable compound (p. 599), although the ion CO_4^{4-} does not exist. If it is admitted that a π bond must be present in the orbital structure of an oxyacid ion, the reason for the difference of configuration between the oxyacid ion XO_3 (where X is an element of Period 2) and YO_4 (where Y is an element of Period 3) is at once clear. An element X can exert only four bonds. If one is to be a π bond, the remainder must adopt a trigonal configuration; the tetrahedral configuration cannot be attained. An element Y can exert up to seven bonds, but it is in a highly stable state when exerting four σ tetrahedral bonds. The remaining three bonds can then be π bonds, of which one, two, and three are in use in PO_4, SO_4, and ClO_4 respectively.

In the compounds containing trigonally hybridised oxygen so far considered, the π bonds are assumed to be localised. Compounds are known in which a trigonally hybridised oxygen atom contributes to a non-localised π orbital system, but they are not common. Examples are furnished by the metaborate ion discussed above, boroxole (p. 509), the cyclic phosphates (p. 727), and by diphenyl ether if it is assumed to have a resonance structure:

A parallel structure cannot be assigned to *p*-dimethoxybenzene, however, although it has a closely similar bond angle (Table 21.10, p. 801).

SECTION 4. THE OXYGEN ATOM IN THE TETRAHEDRAL VALENCE STATE

Structures in which the oxygen atom is unicovalent. Among the structures in which the oxygen atom is present in the unicovalent state are those consisting only of tetrahedrally hybridised oxygen atoms (Table 21.6) which are described below. An oxygen atom in the unicovalent state is also present in the hydroxyl ion, (OH^-) and its alkyl derivatives such as $(C_2H_5O^-)$, and in the ions of the oxyacids, which are discussed on p. 787.

The hydroxyl ion (OH^-) is present to a small extent in liquid water and to a greater extent in alkaline aqueous solutions. In the solid state it is present in the hydroxides of the alkali metals. All the alkali metals form hydroxides of the general formula MOH. They are colourless and soluble in water to give strongly alkaline solutions from which the lithium and sodium hydroxides crystallise as hydrates, and the hydroxides of the other metals in the anhydrous state. Lithium hydroxide on heating at 780° loses water:

$$2\text{LiOH (cryst.)} = \text{Li}_2\text{O (cryst.)} + \text{H}_2\text{O (gas)}; \quad \Delta H = 146 \text{ kcal,}$$

but sodium hydroxide when heated dissociates into its elements and does not yield sodium oxide. Sodium hydroxide, however, yields sodium oxide when heated with sodium. The part played by the hydroxyl ion in forming hydrogen bridges is described on p. 373.

IONS AND MOLECULES CONSISTING OF OXYGEN ATOMS ONLY

The structures of the ions and molecules which contain oxygen atoms only are set out in Table 21.6.† The atom of oxygen (like the nitrogen atom) is able to form fairly stable molecules and ions in which one or two orbitals are occupied by a single electron. Structures containing an oxygen atom in this condition are marked in Table 21.6 by *.

†In considering these ions and molecules together a departure has had to be made from the classification based on valence states which is normally used throughout this book; it will be seen that digonal and trigonal structures, as well as tetrahedral structures, are included in Table 21.6.

All these electron deficient structures have in common the property of paramagnetism, which is related to the presence of unpaired electrons, but they appear to have no other common property. The oxygen molecule in the ground state, described in spectroscopic notation as $O_2(^3\Sigma_g^-)$ has the greatest bond energy and the shortest internuclear distance of all the states of the molecule (Table 21.7).

The O_4 molecule is thought to consist of two oxygen molecules held in association by the spins of their unpaired electrons. The structures of nitric oxide and nitrogen peroxide, which also contain electron-deficient atoms, are described on pp. 662 and 672.

Table 21.6. *Ions and Molecules formed of Oxygen Atoms only*

Particle	Hybridisation	Structure†	Internuclear distance
Oxide ion, O^{2-}		$(:\overset{..}{\underset{..}{O}}:)^{2-}$	
Oxygen molecule ($^3\Sigma$ state)	Digonal	$\overset{A}{\cdot} :O\underset{\pi}{\overset{\pi}{-}}O: \overset{A}{\cdot}$ *	1·21
Oxygen molecule ($^1\Delta$ state)	Trigonal	$\overset{..}{O}\overset{\pi}{-}\overset{..}{O}$	1·22
Ion $(O_2)^+$	Digonal	$(:O\underset{\pi}{\overset{\pi}{-}}O: \overset{A}{\cdot})^+$ *	1·23
Superoxide ion $(O_2)^-$	Tetrahedral	$(:\overset{..}{O}—\overset{..}{\underset{..}{O}}:)^-$ *	1·28
Peroxide ion $(O_2)^{2-}$	Tetrahedral	$(:\overset{..}{\underset{..}{O}}—\overset{..}{\underset{..}{O}}:)^{2-}$	1·49
Ozone O_3	Trigonal	$:\overset{..}{O}—\overset{..}{\underset{+}{O}}\overset{\pi}{—}\overset{..}{O}:$	1·28
Ozonide ion $(O_3)^-$	Tetrahedral	$(:\overset{..}{\underset{..}{O}}—\overset{..}{\underset{..}{O}}—\overset{..}{\underset{..}{O}}:)^-$ *	
O_4		Two oxygen molecules in association	

† According to the valence bond theory. A indicates anti-bonding orbital. * indicates the presence of one or more unpaired electrons.

Table 21.7. *Ground State and Excited States of the Oxygen Molecule*

Molecule	State	Bond energy in e.v.	Internuclear distance
$O_2(^3\Sigma_g^-)$	Ground	5·08	1·21
$O_2(^1\Delta_g^+)$	Excited	3·47	1·22
$O_2(^1\Delta)$	Excited	4·11	1·22
$O_2(^3\Sigma_u^-)$	Excited	0·97	1·60

Molecular oxygen is a colourless gas. The liquid and the solid are pale blue. It is made commercially by the distillation of liquid air, and on the bench scale by the thermal decomposition of compounds rich in oxygen, e.g.

$$2KClO_3 = 2KCl + 3O_2 \text{ (Manganese dioxide as catalyst.)}$$
$$2PbO_2 = 2PbO + O_2.$$

The physical properties of oxygen are as follows: m.p. $-219°$, b.p. $-183°$. One litre at 0° and 760 mm weighs 1·429 gr. 100 volumes of water at 8° dissolve 4 volumes. The magnetic susceptibility at 20° is $+106·2$ c.g.s. units. The solid exists in three modifications with transition points at $-230·6°$ and $-255·6°$.

Oxygen combines additively with the majority of metals and non-metals to form oxides. Oxygen is highly electronegative, and in these reactions it acquires electrons by forming either ionic or covalent bonds. The element which has combined with oxygen is said to be *oxidised.* The atoms of an element which is oxidised either yield up electrons to oxygen atoms as in the change:

$$2Ca + O_2 = 2Ca^{2+} + 2O^{2-},$$

or break mutual covalent bonds to form new bonds with oxygen atoms, as in the change:

$$-\overset{|}{\underset{|}{C}}-\overset{|}{\underset{|}{C}}-\text{(diamond)} + 2O_2 = 2(O\overset{\pi}{=}C\overset{\pi}{=}O).$$

Structure of the oxygen molecule, O_2. The structure of the oxygen molecule can be described in terms of the molecular theory and of the valence bond theory. The models furnished by both theories are molecules which contain unpaired electrons, and which therefore are paramagnetic.

The structure of the oxygen molecule according to the molecular orbital theory. The electronic configuration of the oxygen atom in the ground state is:

1	2			
s	*s*	*p*	*p*	*p*
⇅	⇅	⇅	↑	↑

The distribution of the twelve electrons originally in the valence shells of two oxygen atoms among the molecular orbitals of the molecule is shown in the cell diagram (see p. 129) below:

Atomic orbitals	Molecular orbitals	Atomic orbitals
O	O_2	O
	σ^*2p_z ○	
	π^*2p_y (↑) (↑) π^*2p_x	
$2p_z$ (↑) $2p_y$ (↑) $2p_x$ (↑↓)	$\pi 2p_y$ (↑↓) (↑↓) $\pi 2p_x$	$2p_x$ (↑↓) $2p_y$ (↓) $2p_z$ (↓)
	$\sigma 2p_z$ (↑↓)	
$2s$ (↑↓)	σ^*2s (↑↓)	$2s$ (↑↓)
	$\sigma 2s$ (↑↓)	

The electrons from the orbitals of the oxygen atoms shown in the lateral sections of the diagram are transferred to the molecular orbitals in the central section of the cell diagram, according to the aufbau principle. It is seen that when the bonding π orbitals are filled, two electrons remain for disposal. One of these is placed in each of the π^* anti-bonding orbitals. The spins of these electrons are unpaired, and hence the paramagnetism of the oxygen molecule is accounted for, and the molecule is in the $^3\Sigma$ state.

The two atoms are bound by the resultant bonding effect of the molecular orbitals:
(a) the $\sigma 2p_z$ orbital,
(b) the difference between the effect of the two completely occupied $\pi 2p$ bonding orbitals, and the effect of the two half-occupied $\pi^* 2p$ anti-bonding orbitals, which must be roughly equivalent to one π bonding orbital.

There is spectroscopic evidence of the oxygen molecule in the $^1\Delta$ state. This is diamagnetic, so all the electron spins in the molecule must be paired. The orbital distribution of the electrons is not clear. The $^1\Delta$ state is an excited state as is shown by the thermochemical equations:[†]

$$^3\Sigma \, O_2 = 2O; \quad \Delta H_a = +118 \cdot 2 \text{ kcal}$$
$$^1\Delta \, O_2 = 2O; \quad \Delta H_a = +96 \text{ kcal.}$$

The structure of the oxygen molecule according to the valence bond theory. Each oxygen atom is assumed to be digonally hybridised (sp_z). One of the digonal orbitals of one atom overlaps with a similar orbital from the other atom to form a σ bond; the two remaining digonal orbitals are occupied by lone pairs. Two π bonds are formed by the overlapping of corresponding p orbitals of the two atoms; each π orbital is occupied by an electron pair. At this stage the orbital configuration of the molecule is:

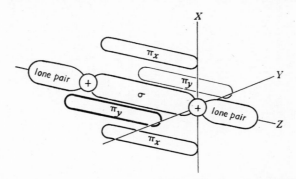

and each atom has one electron not yet placed in an interatomic orbital. So far only the bonding orbitals ($\psi_A + \psi_B$) formed by the combination of atomic orbitals have been considered. There are also three anti-bonding orbitals ($\psi_A - \psi_B$). It is reasonable to suppose that the three anti-bonding orbitals are hybridised, and that each of the two hybrids of least energy is occupied by one electron. The spins of these two electrons are unpaired.

In terms of the valence bond theory the oxygen molecule contains six bonding electrons, two anti-bonding electrons, and four non-bonding electrons. According to the molecular orbital theory the oxygen molecule contains eight bonding electrons, and four anti-bonding electrons. In both cases the resultant effect is four bonding electrons.

The ion [O—O]+. On both the molecular orbital and the valence bond theories the ion $(O_2)^+$ may be regarded as an O_2 molecule from which an electron occupying an anti-bonding orbital has been expelled, thus increasing the resultant bonding effect between

[†] It is sometimes stated that the $^1\Delta$ state is the double bond structure, O=O, but the term "double bond" has no meaning in molecular orbital language. If it is meant to indicate that the resultant bonding effect is that of one σ and one π bond, then the $^3\Sigma$ state is a double bond structure.

Table 21.8.   *The Superoxides.*

	NaO_2	KO_2	RbO_2	CsO_2
Normal physical state	Solid. Bright orange. Hygroscopic	Solid. Orange yellow. Hygroscopic. m.p. 380°	Solid. Orange yellow m.p. about 400°	Solid. Orange yellow m.p. about 500°
Preparation	(i) Heat sodium peroxide in oxygen at 500°, and 300 atm. Yield 92% (ii) Pass a rapid stream of oxygen through a solution of soda-mide in liquid ammonia	(i) Burn potassium in excess of air or oxygen (ii) Fuse potassium with potassium nitrate (iii) Allow potassium peroxide hydrate to decompose spontaneously: $3K_2O_2,H_2O = 2KO_2 + 4KOH + H_2O$ (iv) Heat potassium hydroxide in oxygen at 375° and 100 atm. Yield 70% (v) Allow cold air to react with liquid potassium amalgam; some Hg_2O is formed		(i) Heat caesium hydroxide in oxygen at 375° and 100 atm. Yield 95%
Reactions		(i) If heated in vacuo it loses oxygen and leaves K_2O_2. The dissociation pressure is 30 mm at 471° (ii) It reacts with water: $2KO_2 + 2H_2O = 2KOH + H_2O_2 + O_2$ (iii) It reacts with hydrogen at about 300°: $2KO_2 + H_2 = 2KOH + O_2$ (iv) It reacts with carbon monoxide below 100°: $2KO_2 + CO = K_2CO_3 + O_2$ (v) It reacts with carbon dioxide: $4KO_2 + 2CO_2 = 2K_2CO_3 + 3O_2$	Dissociation pressure is 30 mm at 600°	Dissociation pressure is 30 mm at 900°
Magnetic moment in Bohr magnetons	2·07	2·04		
Bond length O—O	1·33 ± 0·06	1·28 ± 0·07		
Crystal structure	Rocksalt; the O—O⁻ ions occupy the positions of the chlorine ions, but the orientation of the O—O axis is at random	Calcium carbide structure. The O—O axis is parallel to the tetragonal c axis	Calcium carbide structure	Calcium carbide structure
Heat of formation		− 133·7 kcal	− 137·6 kcal	− 141·46 kcal

the oxygen atoms. The state is $^2\Pi_g$, which indicates the presence of one unpaired electron in the ion.

The superoxide ion $(O—O)^-$ is present in crystals in association with the cations Na^+, K^+, Rb^+, Cs^+. The salts are coloured hygroscopic solids. Lithium superoxide has not been isolated. It is reported, however, that during the rapid oxidation of lithium in liquid ammonia solution at $-78°$ the solution turns bright lemon-yellow, and gives an absorption spectrum corresponding to that of sodium superoxide.

There is no definite evidence for the existence of superoxides of the alkaline earth metals, or of thallous superoxide. It has been calculated that the dissociation pressures of barium superoxide $Ba(O_2)_2$ at the following temperatures would be:

25°	100°	200°
32 atm	75 atm	2300 atm.

The paramagnetism of the alkali metal superoxides indicates the presence of *one* unpaired electron in the ion. According to the molecular orbital theory the structure of the ion would be similar to that of the oxygen molecule (cell diagram, p. 792) with one additional electron placed in one of the π^* anti-bonding orbitals. The ion would then possess only one unpaired electron which would account for the paramagnetism. The bond length O—O in the superoxide ion is shorter than that in the peroxide ion; this shortening must be due to the fact that one of the anti-bonding orbitals is only half occupied.

On the valence bond theory the structure might be six resonating canonical forms of which two are:

$$\left[\ddot{:}-\overset{..}{O}-\overset{..}{O}-\ddot{:} \right]^- \qquad \left[\ddot{:}-\overset{..}{O}-\overset{..}{O}-\ddot{:} \right]^-$$

The model used for the oxygen molecule on p. 793 cannot be used here, as the addition of one electron would result in the presence of *three* unpaired electrons (p. 135).

The peroxide ion, $O—O^{2-}$, contains two electrons more than the oxygen molecule. The structure on the *molecular orbital* theory is obtained by completing the occupation of the π^* anti-bonding orbitals in the cell diagram on p. 792. From this structure it may be deduced that the bond strength of the ion (roughly equivalent to that of one σ bond) is less than that of the oxygen molecule, that the bond length is greater, and that the ion is diamagnetic. All these deductions are valid.

According to the valence bond theory, the two oxygen atoms are tetrahedrally hybridised. One σ bond is formed by the overlapping of a hybridised orbital from each atom. The remaining three hybridised orbitals on each atom are occupied by unshared electron pairs, thus:

$$\left[\ddot{:}-\overset{..}{O}-\overset{..}{O}-\ddot{:} \right]^{2-}$$

The peroxide ion is present in crystals in association with the cations Li^+, Na^+, K^+, Rb^+, Cs^+, Ca^{2+}, Sr^{2+}, Ba^{2+}. The hydroxides of magnesium, zinc, and cadmium react with hydrogen peroxide to give mixtures in which the metallic peroxides are thought to be present, but the peroxides have not been isolated.

From an ice-cold solution of sodium peroxide the hydrate $Na_2O_2,8H_2O$ can be crystallised, thus showing that the ion $^-O—O^-$ is stable in ice-cold aqueous solution. Sodium peroxide treated with ice-cold 20% sulphuric acid yields a solution containing hydrogen peroxide; the ion $^-O—O^-$ has been converted to the weak acid H—O—O—H.

At normal temperatures, however, contact with water liberates oxygen from all the metallic peroxides.

The preparation and properties of the metallic peroxides are given in Table 21.9. Sodium peroxide may be taken as the typical representative of the alkali metal peroxides.

Sodium peroxide absorbs oxygen at 450° and 300 atm to give the superoxide, NaO_2. Potassium, rubidium, and caesium peroxides absorb oxygen more readily: lithium peroxide does not absorb oxygen at all. Sodium peroxide reacts with carbon monoxide:

$$Na_2O_2 + CO = Na_2CO_3; \quad \Delta H = -123\cdot3 \text{ kcal,}$$

and with carbon dioxide:

$$2Na_2O_2 + 2CO_2 = 2Na_2CO_3 + O_2; \quad \Delta H = -2 \times 55\cdot23 \text{ kcal.}$$

Table 21.9. *Metall*

Peroxide	Li_2O_2	Na_2O_2	K_2O_2	Rb_2O_2	Cs_2O_2
Normal physical state	Solid. White	Solid. Pale yellow	Solid. Orange yellow	Solid	Solid. Yellow; black if fused
m.p. °C		460†	490	600	400
Preparation	Heat Li_2O_2,H_2O_2, $3H_2O$, or dehydrate it over P_2O_5 [If heated in vacuo at 300° it gives pure Li_2O]	(i) Burn metal in air or oxygen (ii) Dispro-portionate Na_2O at 400°	(i) Burn metal in calculated quantity of air at 300° (ii) Heat excess potassium in nitrous oxide (iii) Heat KO_2 in vacuo (iv) Pass a slow current of O_2 through a solu-tion of K in liquid NH_3 at $-50°$		(i) Admit the theoretical quantity of O_2 into a glass vessel containin Cs in an alu-minium boat (ii) Dispro-portionate Cs_2O at 380°
Distance O—O	1·3				
Peroxide hydrates (Formulae, pre-paration, and reactions)	Li_2O_2,H_2O_2, $3H_2O$ Add H_2O_2 and alcohol to an aqueous solu-tion of LiOH Heated, see above With CO_2 gives the per-carbonate Li_2CO_4,H_2O	$Na_2O_2,8H_2O$ Crystallise a solution of Na_2O_2 in ice-cold water m.p. 30° with evolution of O_2 to give Na_2O With CO_2 gives Na_2CO_4, $8H_2O$	$3K_2O_2,H_2O$ Heated yields KO_2 and KOH		
Hydroperoxides		$NaOOH,\frac{1}{2}H_2O_2$ add con. HCl to an alcoholic sol-tion of Na_2O_2 Less stable than Na_2O_2			$CsOOH,H_2O_2$ add H_2O_2 and alcohol to $CsOI$ With CO_2 gives Cs_2CO_4,H_2O_2, H_2O

† Decomposes at the melting point.

With carbonyl chloride, however, it forms the percarbonate:

$$2Na_2O_2 + COCl_2 = 2NaCl + Na_2CO_4 + \tfrac{1}{2}O_2.$$

Sodium peroxide hydrate with either solid or liquid carbon dioxide yields a hydrate of sodium percarbonate, $Na_2CO_4,8H_2O$.

Fused sodium peroxide is a powerful oxidising agent. It is used for opening up for analysis insoluble silicates and native oxides, and it is more effective for this purpose than sodium carbonate. The reaction is carried out in a nickel crucible, since nickel is resistant to its attack. Chrome iron ore reacts with fused sodium peroxide thus:

$$2FeCr_2O_4 + 7Na_2O_2 = Fe_2O_3 + 4Na_2CrO_4 + 3Na_2O,$$

and iron pyrites thus:

$$2FeS_2 + 15Na_2O_2 = Fe_2O_3 + 4Na_2SO_4 + 11Na_2O.$$

roxides

MgO_2	CaO_2	SrO_2	BaO_2	ZnO_2	CdO_2
	Solid. White	Solid. White	Solid. White		
			450		
lixtures of gO and gO$_2$ have en made by e addition of $_2O_2$ to freshly •td. Mg(OH)$_2$, to an nereal solution diethyl agnesium]	(i) Dehydrate $CaO_2,8H_2O$ at 130° (ii) Add H_2O_2 to lime water above 40° [Cannot be made by heating Ca or CaO with oxygen] (iii) O_2 on sol. of Ca in liq. NH$_3$. Yield poor	Dehydrate $SrO_2,8H_2O$ at 130° Heat SrO at 400° under 100 atm of oxygen (iii) O_2 on soln. of Sr in liq. NH$_3$	Dehydrate $BaO_2,8H_2O$ at 130° Heat BaO in air or oxygen O_2 on soln. of Na in liq. NH$_3$	[Hydrated peroxides are made by the action of H_2O_2 on zinc hydroxide An ethereal solution of H_2O_2 on diethyl zinc or zinc amide yields a compound containing 86% of ZnO_2]	[Cadmium behaves similarly to zinc in the formation of indefinite peroxide compounds]
		1·31	1·47		
	$CaO_2,2H_2O$ $CaO_2,8H_2O$ (i) Add H_2O_2 to lime water below 40° (ii) Add Na_2O_2 to a solution of a calcium salt	$SrO_2,8H_2O$ Add H_2O_2 or Na_2O_2 to a solution of a strontium salt $SrO_2,8H_2O$ is only slightly soluble in water	$BaO_2,8H_2O$ Add H_2O_2 or Na_2O_2 to a solution of a barium salt		

Fused sodium peroxide converts metallic sodium to the monoxide. It oxidises many other metals, including silver and platinum, to oxides, and lower oxides to higher oxides. It is partially reduced to sodium if heated with charcoal:

$$3Na_2O_2 + 2C = 2Na_2CO_3 + 2Na.$$

Ozone is a gas, b.p. $-112\cdot3°$, m.p. $-249\cdot6°$. It is made by the action of atomic oxygen on molecular oxygen at low temperatures. At temperatures above $300°$ ozone immediately decomposes to oxygen, and at $100°$ the decomposition is quick. Three conditions are found in which ozone is produced without undergoing immediate decomposition:

(a) the passage of a silent electric discharge through oxygen,
(b) the exposure of oxygen to ultraviolet light,
(c) chemical reactions in which oxygen is evolved:

   (i) the decomposition of hydrogen peroxide,
   (ii) the action of fluorine on water,
   (iii) the thermal decomposition of periodic acid at $130°$,
   (iv) the electrolysis of moderately concentrated sulphuric acid at high current density.

Ozone is present in the atmosphere at the earth's surface to the extent of $0\cdot1$ to $1\cdot1$ parts per million. At about 25 km above the earth there is a layer of concentrated ozone equivalent to a layer 3 mm thick at atmospheric pressure. Ozone has a very strong absorption band beginning at $2,900\,\text{Å}$ which protects the earth from most of the sun's ultraviolet light.

Liquid and solid ozone are dark indigo blue. Ozone is paramagnetic. Ozone and oxygen form two liquid layers below $-158°$.

Ozone is an oxidising agent. In most of its actions it is reduced to molecular oxygen, but if the action can be carried on by molecular oxygen, then all the oxygen is used up. For example:

$$PbS + 4O_3 = PbSO_4 + 4O_2$$
$$2KI + H_2O + O_3 = 2KOH + I_2 + O_2,$$

but,

$$3SnCl_2 + 6HCl + O_3 = 3SnCl_4 + 3H_2O.$$

Ozone forms addition compounds with the ethylene link in organic compounds. Thus with ethylene:

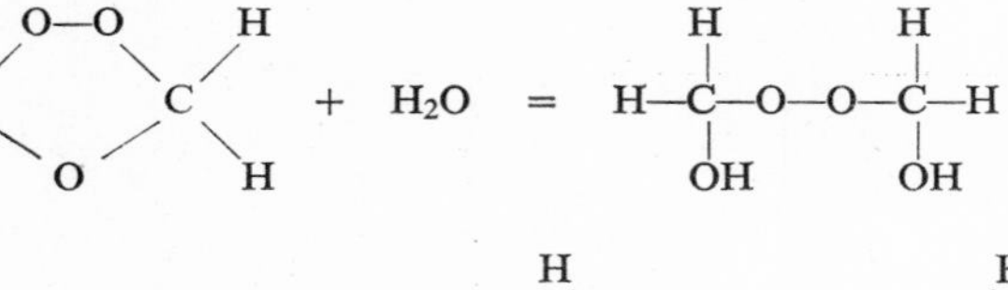

The product is an oil, b.p. $20°$ at 16 mm. It freezes to a glass at $-80°$. It explodes at room temperature, but is stable at $0°$. It hydrolyses thus:

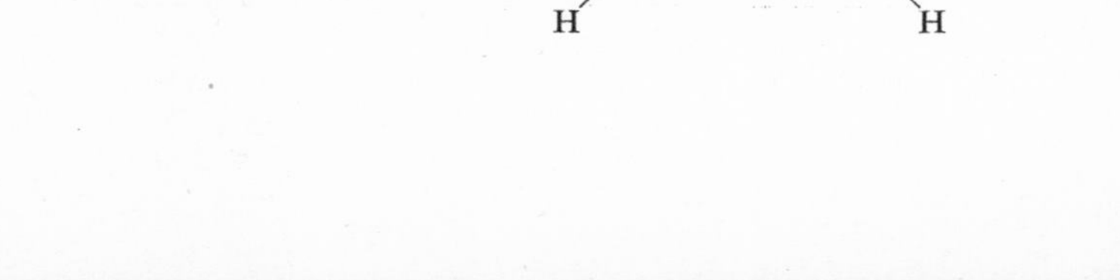

Structure of ozone. The following thermochemical data have been established:

$$2O_3 = 3O_2; \quad \Delta H = -68 \text{ kcal}$$
$$O+O = O_2; \quad \Delta H_a = -118\cdot2 \text{ kcal}$$
$$O+O+O = O_3; \quad \Delta H_a = -143\cdot6 \text{ kcal}$$
$$O+O_2 = O_3; \quad \Delta H = -25\cdot4 \text{ kcal}.$$

The heat evolved when one atom of oxygen combines with one molecule of oxygen is small. Ozone is always unstable with regard to oxygen. The bond energy O—O is 3·06 eV.

Absorption spectrum and electron diffraction experiments show that the molecule is not linear:

	Angle OOO	Distance O—O
Spectrum	122°	1·29
Electron diffraction	127±3°	1·26
Microwave	116·8±0·5°	

and hence the shape of the molecule is roughly:

The interbond angle suggests that the central oxygen atom is in the trigonal valence state, and the most probable structure is:

$$\begin{array}{c} \overset{+}{\overset{\cdot\cdot}{O}} \\ {:}O{:} \qquad {:}O{:} \end{array}$$

Several other canonical forms are possible, and resonance involving movement of charge would account for the strong absorption. Gaseous ozone is diamagnetic. Liquid ozone shows a very small degree of paramagnetism which is independent of temperature.

The ozonide ion, $(:\overset{\cdot\cdot}{O}—\overset{\cdot\cdot}{O}—\overset{\cdot\cdot}{O}:)^-$, is present in potassium ozonide, KO_3. This compound has been obtained in an impure condition in reddish-brown crystals containing about 90% of KO_3, and some KO_2, KOH, and KOH,H_2O. It is made by exposing dry powdered potassium hydroxide at -15 to $-10°$ to a stream of ozonised oxygen (6 to 8% O_3) flowing at about 300 c.c. per minute:

$$3KOH + 2O_3 = 2KO_3 + KOH,H_2O + \tfrac{1}{2}O_2.$$

By extraction with liquid ammonia at $-65°$ a red solution is obtained, which on evaporation yields the crystals. The ozonide slowly breaks down to yield the superoxide and free oxygen. At 50–60° it decomposes completely in 30 minutes.

Potassium ozonide reacts with water thus:

$$KO_3 + H_2O = K^+ + OH^- + O_2 + OH$$
$$2OH = H_2O + \tfrac{1}{2}O_2.$$

The magnetic moment is 1·67 Bohr magnetons, the molecular electrical conductivity in liquid ammonia at − 50° is 34 ohm⁻¹ cm⁻¹, and the distance O—O is about 1·38. It is claimed that X-ray diffraction shows that the lattices of KO_3 and KN_3 are similar. On the valence bond theory, however, it is impossible to formulate a linear arrangement of three oxygen atoms with a total of nineteen valency electrons. The structure of the ozonide ion corresponding to the structures already assigned to electron-deficient oxygen radicals would be:

$$\left(\begin{array}{c} \ddot{O} \\ \diagup \; \diagdown \\ :\!\ddot{O}. \qquad .\ddot{O}: \end{array} \right)^{-}$$

The O_4 molecule. The presence of O_4 molecules in diatomic oxygen was deduced by G. N. Lewis from a study of the magnetic susceptibility of solutions of liquid oxygen in liquid nitrogen. It was confirmed by other authors from the evidence of absorption spectra. There is enough O_4 present in air to be detected by absorption spectra. The spectra show that the two oxygen molecules cannot be linked by ordinary bonds. The heat of linkage is 0·13 kcal, whereas the structure,

$$\begin{array}{c} O—O \\ | \quad | \\ O—O \end{array}$$

gives a value of − 100·8.

O_4 probably consists of two ordinary $^3\Sigma$ O_2 molecules held together by the anti-parallel spins of the unpaired electrons. The molecule may have either coplanar rectangular configuration, or that of a tetragonal bisphenoid. The O_4 molecules have no more oxidising power than ordinary O_2 molecules. It is suggested that one form of crystalline oxygen may contain rotating O_4 molecules in a cubic close-packed arrangement.

SECTION 4. THE OXYGEN ATOM IN THE TETRAHEDRAL VALENCE STATE (CONTINUED)

Compounds in which the oxygen atom is bicovalent. The compounds in this class are very numerous, and include water,† the alcohols, the ethers, all the di- (or pyro-) acids and their derivatives, hydrogen peroxide, and all the peroxyacids. In all these compounds the oxygen atom is tetrahedrally hybridised, and two of the tetrahedral orbitals are occupied by lone electron pairs. The bond angles, if the tetrahedral arrangement is undistorted, should be 109·5°. The actual bond angles of certain typical compounds are given in Table 21.10.

The compounds may be classified by bond angles into three groups:

(i) *Bond angle 101·5 to 112°, average value close to 109·5°*:
H_2O, HOC_2H_5, $(CH_3)_2O$, H_2O_2, $(CH_3)_2O_2$, Hg_2O, $(S_2O_7)^{2-}$, $(S_2O_8)^{2-}$.

(ii) *Bond angle 117 to 124°*:
Ozone, and certain aromatic compounds, e.g. diphenyl ether.

(iii) *Bond angle 61·6 to 96°*:
Ethylene oxide and its derivatives. The bond angle here is decided by the geometry of the molecules. The COB bond angle in the glycerol derivative of boric acid (p. 499), and the bond angles in numerous chelate compounds is similarly decided.

† Water is discussed on p. 384.

Table 21.10. *Bond Angles in certain Compounds containing a Bicovalent Oxygen Atom*

Compound	Angle	Method	Distance O—X
Ethylene oxide, $\begin{array}{c}CH_2\\ \mid \quad \diagdown O\\ CH_2 \diagup \end{array}$	61·6°	M.W.	1·44
Trimethylene oxide, $\begin{array}{c}\quad CH_2\\ \diagup \qquad \diagdown\\ CH_2 \qquad\quad O\\ \diagdown \qquad \diagup\\ \quad CH_2\end{array}$	94·5°	E.D.	—
Mercury dimethylene oxide, $\begin{array}{c}\quad CH_2\\ \diagup \qquad \diagdown\\ Hg \qquad\quad O\\ \diagdown \qquad \diagup\\ \quad CH_2\end{array}$	96°	X-ray	—
Fluorine monoxide, F_2O	102°	Sp. and E.D.	$\begin{cases}1\cdot36\pm0\cdot10\\1\cdot41\pm0\cdot05\end{cases}$
Hydrogen-deutero oxide, HDO	104°	Sp.	1·01
Water, H_2O	104·8°	Sp.	0·955
Diethyl ether, $(C_2H_5)_2O$	108°	E.D.	1·43
Mercuric oxide, Hg_2O	109·8°	X-ray and N.D.	—
Chlorine monoxide, Cl_2O	111°	E.D.	$\begin{cases}1\cdot71\pm0\cdot02\\1\cdot68\pm0\cdot03\end{cases}$
Dimethyl ether, $(CH_3)_2O$	110°	D.M.	1·43
p-Dimethoxy benzene, $CH_3OC_6H_4OCH_3$	121°	X-ray	1·36
Di-p-bromophenyl ether, $(BrC_6H_4)_2O$	123°	X-ray	1·28
Diphenyl ether, $(C_6H_5)_2O$	124°	D.M.	—
H_2O_2	101·5°		0·97
Ozone, O_3	117°	See p. 798	—

M.W. = microwave, E.D. = electron diffraction, Sp. = infrared spectrum, N.D. = neutron diffraction, D.M. = dipole moment.

THE ETHERS, THE ALCOHOLS, AND HYDROGEN PEROXIDE

The properties of the oxygen atom in dimethyl ether, $(CH_3)_2O$, are typical of those of an oxygen atom exerting two σ bonds. The σ bonds are not easily broken; the ethers are non-reactive compared with many organic compounds. The oxygen atom, however, is ready to donate one of the lone pairs to some other molecule which contains an atom which may act as an acceptor. Many examples of acceptor molecules could be given, among them the trihalides of boron, aluminium, and gallium, and trimethyl gallium. Although the oxygen atom is known to exert four covalences, the ether molecule only rarely donates more than one electron pair. (Two electron pairs are donated in the etherate of ethyl dichloro boron, p. 808.)

The alcohols and water are more reactive than ether; this is due to the replacement of alkyl groups by hydrogen atoms. The hydrogen atom is replaceable by metals, and its presence also makes possible the changes:

$$H_2O + H_2O = (H_3O)^+ + (OH)^-, \quad \text{and}$$
$$C_2H_5OH + C_2H_5OH = ((C_2H_5)_2HO)^+ + (OH)^-.$$

26 + A.T.I.C.

Fluorine monoxide, F_2O, described on p. 914, is an exothermic compound in which metals burn brilliantly, and which explodes when warmed with non-metals. The monoxides of the other halogens show decreasing stability as the atomic weight of the halogen increases.

The anion of a pyroacid contains an oxygen atom linked by σ bonds to two atoms of an electronegative element which is commonly silicon, phosphorus, or sulphur. Examples are:

The pyrosilicate ion	$(O_3Si\!-\!O\!-\!SiO_3)^{6-}$
The pyrophosphate ion	$(O_3P\!-\!O\!-\!PO_3)^{2-}$
The pyrophosphite ion	$(O_2P\!-\!O\!-\!PO_2)^{1-}$
The pyrosulphate ion	$(O_3S\!-\!O\!-\!SO_3)^{2-}$
The pyrosulphite ion	$(O_2S\!-\!O\!-\!SO_2)^{2-}$.

Little is known about the properties of the central oxygen atom, and it is assumed that it is unreactive.

Hydrogen peroxide, H_2O_2; m.p. $-1.7°$, b.p. 68 mm $84°$, 26 mm $69.2°$, 760 mm (by extrapolation) about $150°$, but it decomposes explosively at $144°$. Heat of dissociation:

$$H_2O_{2_{liq.}} = H_2O_{liq.} + \tfrac{1}{2}O_{2_{gas}}; \quad \Delta H = -23.45 \text{ kcal.}$$

Dielectric constant, 89.2 at $0°$; d.p.m. 2.13 D.

The aqueous solution of hydrogen peroxide is obtained by the action of an acid on barium or sodium peroxide, or by the hydrolysis of perdisulphuric acid:

$$H_2S_2O_8 + 2H_2O = 2H_2SO_4 + H_2O_2.$$

The aqueous solution may be evaporated, and then distilled under reduced pressure to give 99% hydrogen peroxide. Crystalline hydrogen peroxide is obtained by cooling the concentrated (99%) aqueous solution.

Hydrogen peroxide is miscible in all proportions with water, and is fairly soluble in ether. The pure substance and its aqueous solution are both liable to decompose to water and oxygen. The decomposition is promoted by contact with rough surfaces, or finely divided metals. The aqueous solution may be stabilised by acids, glycine, acetanilide, and various organic compounds.

Pure hydrogen peroxide turns blue litmus red, $K = 0.5 \times 10^{-12}$, but a dilute aqueous solution is neutral. Concentrated solutions of hydrogen peroxide react with barium hydroxide, and liberate carbon dioxide from sodium carbonate.

Hydrogen peroxide reacts either as a reducing or as an oxidising agent, both in acid and in alkaline solution. The general equations for the four cases are given below; e represents an electron.

A. Hydrogen peroxide in *alkaline* solution,

    (i) acting as a *reducing* agent:

$$2OH^- + H_2O_2 = 2H_2O + O_2 + 2e,$$

    (ii) acting as an *oxidising* agent:

$$2OH^- + H_2O_2 + 2e = 2H_2O + 2O^{2-}.$$

B. Hydrogen peroxide in *acid* solution,

    (iii) acting as a *reducing* agent:

$$H_2O_2 = O_2 + 2H^+ + 2e,$$

    (iv) acting as an *oxidising* agent:

$$2H^+ + H_2O_2 + 2e = 2H_2O.$$

The equations for particular reducing and oxidising actions classified under the general equations, are given below:

A (i). Hydrogen peroxide acting as a *reducing agent* in *alkaline* solution:

$$2Fe(CN)_6^{3-} + H_2O_2 + 2OH^- = 2Fe(CN)_6^{4-} + 2H_2O + O_2.$$
$$2Fe^{3+} + H_2O_2 + 2OH^- = 2Fe^{2+} + 2H_2O + O_2.$$
$$2Ag^+ \dagger + H_2O_2 + 2OH^- = 2Ag + 2H_2O + O_2.$$
$$2Au^{3+} \ddagger + 3H_2O_2 + 6OH^- = 2Au + 6H_2O + 3O_2.$$
$$NaOCl + H_2O_2 = NaCl + H_2O + O_2.\S$$
$$KIO_4 + H_2O_2 = KIO_3 + H_2O + O_2.\|$$

A (ii). Hydrogen peroxide acting as an *oxidising agent* in *alkaline* solution:

$$Mn^{2+} + H_2O_2 + 2OH^- = Mn^{4+} + 2H_2O + 2O^{2-}.$$

B (iii). Hydrogen peroxide acting as a *reducing agent* in *acid* solution:

$$MnO_4^- + 2\tfrac{1}{2}H_2O_2 + 3H^+ = Mn^{2+} + 4H_2O + 2\tfrac{1}{2}O_2.$$
$$2Ce^{4+} + H_2O_2 = 2Ce^{3+} + O_2 + 2H^+.$$

B (iv). Hydrogen peroxide acting as an *oxidising agent* in *acid* solution:

$$2Fe(CN)_6^{4-} + H_2O_2 + 2H^+ = 2Fe(CN)_6^{3-} + 2H_2O.$$
$$2Fe^{2+} + H_2O_2 + 2H^+ = 2Fe^{3+} + 2H_2O.$$
$$SO_3^{2-} + \underbrace{O^{2-} + 2H^+} + H_2O_2 = SO_4^{2-} + 2H_2O.$$

$$H_2O$$

$$2NH_2OH + 6H_2O_2 = 2HNO_3 + 8H_2O.$$
$$Cr_2O_7^{2-} + 4H_2O_2 + 2H^+ = 2CrO_5 + 5H_2O.$$

It will be observed that in many of its familiar reactions hydrogen peroxide is a reducing agent. Whenever oxygen is evolved, as in the reactions with the ceric, permanganate, or hypochlorite ions, hydrogen peroxide is acting as a reducing agent. It has been shown, by using heavy oxygen as an indicator, that in these reactions the oxygen is wholly derived from the hydrogen peroxide; this is in accord with equations A (i) and B (iii).

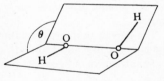

Fig. 21.1. Structure of H_2O_2.

If alternative reactions are possible between hydrogen peroxide and another reagent, then the reaction which occurs is that which results in the greatest decrease in the free energy of the system as a whole. The course of a reaction between hydrogen peroxide and another reagent is therefore determined by the nature of the reagent, by the stability of the final products, and the concentration, acidity, and temperature of the solution in which the reaction occurs.

The structure of hydrogen peroxide is shown in Fig. 21.1. The O—O bond length is

---

† Present as Ag_2O.
‡ Present as $KAuCl_4$.
§ Assuming hydrolysis of the sodium hypochlorite, this equation can be written:

$$OH^- + HOCl + H_2O_2 = Cl^- + 2H_2O + O_2.$$

‖ Assuming hydrolysis of the potassium periodate, the equation can be written:

$$OH^- + HIO_4 + H_2O_2 = IO_3^- + 2H_2O + O_2.$$

1·49. The OH bonds lie in two planes inclined at the dihedral angle θ. The values of θ obtained in several experiments are given in Table 21.11. The angle HOO is 102°.

Table 21.11.   *The Dihedral Angle in Hydrogen Peroxide*

Substance	Method of investigation	θ
$(NH_2)_2CO \cdot H_2O_2$	Crystallographic study	$106° \pm 2°$
Solid H_2O_2 at $-20°$	X-ray analysis	$94° \pm 1·5°$
H_2O_2	Spectroscopic	$80° \pm 20°$
F_5S—O—O—SF_5	Electron diffraction	$107° \pm 5°$
	Mean of extreme values $= 97°$	

There is a barrier to internal rotation in the molecule which is estimated from experimental data to have a value between 6 and 18 kcal per mole.

According to the molecular orbital theory, one σ bond between each oxygen atom and one hydrogen atom could be formed by the combination of the s orbital of the hydrogen atom, and the p orbital of an oxygen atom, which in the cell diagram on p. 792 is used to form an anti-bonding molecular orbital. The molecular structure of the hydrogen peroxide molecule would consist of one σ bond and two π bonds linking the oxygen atoms to one another, and one σ bond between each oxygen atom and a hydrogen atom. Since one of the two H—O bonds is formed from a p_x orbital and the other from a p_y orbital, the molecule should exhibit a dihedral angle of about 90°. The dihedral angle as experimentally determined is greater than this (see Table 21.11).

The effective electron charge in the two O—H σ bonds is about the same, and has about the same distribution, as the charge in the occupied anti-bonding orbitals in the O—O ion in crystal line BaO_2. Therefore, it may be deduced that the bond length in the ions and in the covalent structure would be nearly equal. This is confirmed by experimental data. The effective bonding between the two oxygen atoms on the assumption that the charge clouds of the two O—H σ bonds neutralize the bonding effect of the two π bonding orbitals is one σ bond. The energy of the bond O—O is 35 kcal per mole.

The barrier to internal rotation is accounted for on the molecular orbital theory by the presence of π and π^* bonds.

The structure of hydrogen peroxide on the valence bond theory would be:

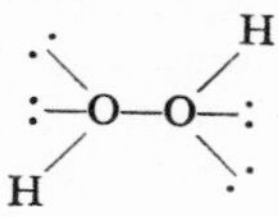

in which each oxygen atom is tetrahedrally hybridised and forms two σ bonds. The dihedral angle is determined not by the orientation of the bonds, but by the interaction of the charge clouds of the non-bonding orbitals. The calculation of the interaction energies shows that the equilibrium dihedral angle is about 100°.

Alkyl derivatives of hydrogen peroxide. The compounds C_2H_5OOH and $(C_2H_5)_2O_2$ are known. Diethyl peroxide, a colourless liquid, b.p. 63°, is made by heating hydrogen peroxide with diethyl sulphate in the presence of an alkali. Its reduction by zinc and acetic acid to ethyl alcohol supports the dihydroxyl structure for hydrogen peroxide. F_5S—O—O—SF_5 is mentioned on p. 853.

THE PEROXY ACIDS

The peroxyacids may be notionally derived by the action of an acid on hydrogen peroxide, thus:

$$O{-}S({=}O)({-}OH)({-}OH) + H{:}OOH = O{-}S({=}O)({-}OH){-}O{-}O{-}H.$$

Caro's acid, or peroxysulphuric acid

The reaction may be continued:

$$O{-}S({=}O)({-}OH){-}O{-}O{-}H + HO{-}S({=}O)({-}OH){-}O = O{-}S({=}O)({-}OH){-}O{-}O{-}S({=}O)({-}OH){-}O.$$

Peroxydisulphuric acid

The reactions expressed in this way are analogous to the formation of ethyl hydrogen sulphate from sulphuric acid and alcohol:

$$CH_3{-}CH_2{-}O{:}H + HO{:}S({=}O)({-}OH){-}O = CH_3{-}CH_2{-}O{-}S({=}O)({-}OH){-}O.$$

On this analogy the peroxyacids are esters of hydrogen peroxide.

There is much confusion in the accepted nomenclature of the peracids. The prefix *per* is used in perchloric acid, the name for $HClO_4$, and also in persulphuric acid, the name for $H_2S_2O_8$. The ambiguity is removed by using the prefix *peroxy*[†] when naming an acid derived from hydrogen peroxide. Some confusion remains, however, because the name *peroxydisulphuric* acid appears to be the only one available to describe the two acids:

$$O{-}S({=}O)({-}OH){-}O{-}O{-}S({=}O)({-}OH){-}O \quad \text{and} \quad O{-}S({=}O)({-}OH){-}O{-}S({=}O)({-}O{-}O{-}H){-}O$$

No attempt is made here to improve this nomenclature, but care will be taken to make clear precisely which acid is referred to in any discussion.

Table 21.12. *The Distribution in the Periodic Table of Elements which form Peroxyacids*

	Group 3	Group 4	Group 5	Group 6
Period 2	(B)	(C)	N	
3			P	S
4		Ti	V	Cr
5		Zr	Nb	Mo
6	Ce	Hf	Ta	W
		Th		

[†] *Inorganic Chemistry* by E. de Barry Barnett and C. L. Wilson, p. 44.

Peroxyacids or their salts are formed only by the more electronegative elements. The distribution in the periodic table of elements which give rise to peroxyacids is irregular (Table 21.12) and it is probable that further exploration of this field is desirable. For example, it would be interesting to know for certain that the normal elements in Groups IV, V, and VI in the Periods 4, 5, and 6, do not form peroxyacids.

The borates and carbonates of the alkali metals yield salts containing additional oxygen when treated with hydrogen peroxide, but it is not established whether the oxygen is present in a peroxy salt, or as hydrogen peroxide of crystallisation.† Of the

Table 21.13. *Peroxyacids formed by Elements of Low Atomic Number*

Acid	Formula	Physical state	Page reference
Perboric acid		Known only as the salt $NaBO_2,3H_2O,H_2O_2$	
Peroxymonocarbonic acid	$O\overset{\pi}{=}C$ with $O-OH$ and OH	Known only as salts of alkali metals	
Peroxymononitrous acid	$O\overset{\pi}{-}N-O-OH$	Known in solution	680
Peroxymononitric acid	$\overset{O}{\underset{HO}{>}}N-O-OH$	Crystalline	684
Peroxymonophosphoric acid	$\overset{HO}{\underset{HO}{>}}P\overset{O-OH}{\underset{O}{<}}$	Known only in solution	731
Peroxymonosulphuric acid	$\overset{HO}{\underset{O}{>}}S\overset{O-OH}{\underset{O}{<}}$	Crystalline solid, m.p. 45°	850
Peroxydicarbonic acid	$\overset{O}{\underset{HO}{>}}C-O-O-C\overset{O}{\underset{OH}{<}}$		
Peroxydiphosphoric acid	$HO-\overset{O}{\underset{OH}{P}}-O-O-\overset{O}{\underset{OH}{P}}-OH$	Known as the potassium salt	731
Peroxydisulphuric acid	$HO-\overset{O}{\underset{O}{S}}-O-O-\overset{O}{\underset{O}{S}}-OH$	Crystalline solid	850

† Nuclear magnetic resonance spectra at 90°K indicate that the crystalline perborates of the alkali metals are true perborates, but that the structure of sodium percarbonate is $2Na_2CO_3,3H_2O_2$. T. M. Connor and R. E. Richards, *J. Chem. Soc.*, 1958, 289.

other elements in Periods 2 and 3, nitrogen, phosphorus, and sulphur (in the highest states of oxidation) yield peroxyacids, or, if the acids cannot be isolated, their potassium salts. All except nitrogen yield both peroxyacids and peroxydiacids, which appear to possess structures analogous to those of the peroxysulphuric acids. Cerous and ceric hydroxides, and titanic acid, zirconic acid, and hafnic acid also yield peroxyacids.

There seems to be no structural reason why a peroxyacid should not be formed from any acid and hydrogen peroxide. The potassium peroxycarbonate KHC_2O_6 might be formulated as the peroxyacid of dicarbonic acid, thus:

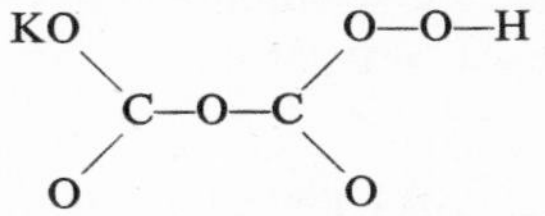

$$
\begin{array}{ccc}
KO & & O-O-H \\
\diagdown & & \diagup \\
& C-O-C & \\
\diagup & & \diagdown \\
O & & O
\end{array}
$$

and diphosphoric acid and disulphuric acid might be expected to form corresponding compounds.

The oxygen atoms in the group –O—O– in all the peroxy acids so far mentioned are either bicovalent or in the state found in the oxyacids (p. 788). All the OH groups, whether derived from the original oxyacid or from hydrogen peroxide, are acidic.

Table 21.14. *Peroxyacids formed by the Rare Earth and Transition Metals*

Acid	Formula	Physical state	Page reference
Group III. Rare earth metals Peroxymonocerous acid	$\begin{array}{c} HO \\ \diagdown \\ \quad Ce-O-OH \\ \diagup \\ HO \end{array}$		
Peroxymonoceric acid	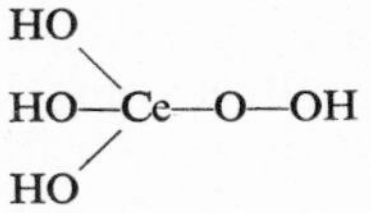 $\begin{array}{c} HO \\ \diagdown \\ HO-Ce-O-OH \\ \diagup \\ HO \end{array}$		
Sub-group IV T Peroxymonotitanic acid	$(HO)_3Ti-O-OH$	Yellow crystalline solid	963
Peroxymonozirconic acid	$(HO)_3Zr-O-OH$	Gelatinous	
Peroxymonohafnic acid	$(HO)_3Hf-O-OH$	Gelatinous	
Peroxythoric acid	$Th_2O_7, 4H_2O$		
Sub-group V T Peroxyvanadic acid	$H_4V_2O_{11}$		
Peroxyniobic acid	K_3NbO_8	Known only as the alkali metal salts	
Peroxytantalic acid	K_3TaO_8		
Sub-group VI T Red perchromic acid	$(K_3CrO_8)_n$	Known only as red alkali metal salts	992
Blue perchromic acid	$K_2Cr_2O_{12}$	Known only as blue alkali metal salts	993
Peroxymolybdic acid	$HOOMoO_2OH$	Yellow crystalline solid	1001
Peroxymolybdic acid	H_2MoO_8	Known only as red salts K_2MoO_8 and $Zn(NH_3)_4MoO_8$	1001
Peroxytungstic acid	$H_2W_2O_{11}$	Yellow solid	

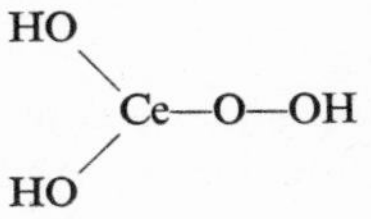

The transition elements in Group VI, chromium, molybdenum, and tungsten, form either peroxyacids or salts derived from them. The evidence available suggests that the structures of these compounds are different from those already discussed. It is probable that there is a peculiar structure common to the highly oxygenated chromium compounds:

$$(CH_3)_2O,CrO_5, \qquad (H_3N)_3CrO_4, \qquad [K^+]_3[(NC)_3CrO_4]^{3-},$$

and that this structure is also present in the red peroxychromium ion in the potassium salt K_3CrO_8, and in the blue peroxychromium ion in the potassium salt $K_2Cr_2O_{12}$. These compounds are discussed on p. 991.

SECTION 4. THE OXYGEN ATOM IN THE TETRAHEDRAL VALENCE STATE (CONTINUED)

Compounds in which the oxygen atom is tricovalent. The compounds in this class include the hydronium ion $[H_3O]^+$, and the trichloromercuri-oxonium ion $[(HgCl)_3O]^+$. There is evidence that the $[OH_3]^+$ ion possesses one threefold axis of symmetry, and that the bond angle is close to the tetrahedral value. Trichloromercuri-oxonium chloride has the pyramidal structure:

$$\left[\begin{array}{c} \ddot{O} \\ \diagup \mid \diagdown \\ Hg \quad Hg \quad Hg \\ \diagup \quad \mid \quad \diagdown \\ Cl \quad\quad Cl \quad\quad Cl \end{array} \right]^+ \quad Cl^-$$

in which the angle HgOHg is 175°.

The class also includes the numerous complexes containing water as a ligand, such as $(Be,4H_2O)^{2+}$, and the adducts formed by the union of donors such as diethyl ether with acceptors such as boron trimethyl, $(C_2H_5)_2O \rightarrow B(CH_3)_3$.

Compounds in which the oxygen atom is tetracovalent. The oxygen atom in these compounds is four co-ordinate like the nitrogen atom in the ammonium ion, or the carbon atom in methane. The class of compounds includes the chelate complexes formed by the action of many monobasic organic acids on beryllium hydroxide or carbonate, a few donor-acceptor compounds in which the oxygen atom in an ether donates both the lone pairs, as in the very unstable (m.p. below 0°) etherate of ethyl dichloroboron:

$$\begin{array}{c} Cl \\ \mid \\ C_2H_5-B \\ \mid \quad\nwarrow \qquad\qquad C_2H_5 \\ Cl \quad\quad\diagdown \\ \qquad\qquad O \\ Cl \quad\quad\diagup \\ \mid \quad\swarrow \qquad\qquad C_2H_5 \\ C_2H_5-B \\ \mid \\ Cl \end{array}$$

and in indium trimethyl etherate:

$$\begin{array}{c} C_2H_5 \\ \mid \\ (CH_3)_3In \leftarrow\!\!\!-O-\!\!\!\rightarrow In(CH_3)_3, \\ \mid \\ C_2H_5 \end{array}$$

and the oxides which have a wurtzite or zinc blende structure, such as BeO and ZnO.

Basic beryllium acetate, $Be_4O(CH_3COO)_6$, and similar compounds. Basic beryllium acetate is a typical example of a structure in which a central oxygen atom is linked to four atoms of a bivalent metal, which in turn are linked to six radicals of an organic acid; the structure might be described as a tetrahedral chelate complex of oxygen. The structure of basic beryllium acetate has been investigated by X-ray analysis. It is found that the centrally situated oxygen atom is tetrahedrally surrounded by four beryllium atoms, and each of the six edges of the tetrahedron thus formed consists of an acetate $(O \cdot CH_3 \cdot CO)$ group. In this arrangement each beryllium atom is tetrahedrally surrounded by four oxygen atoms, the centre one and three from acetate groups. All atoms (except hydrogen) in the molecule attain the octet, and the central oxygen atom and all the beryllium atoms exert four tetrahedral covalencies. In order to arrive at the correct distribution of valency electrons the central oxygen atom must carry two formal positive charges, and the four beryllium atoms must each carry two formal negative charges. There is no reason why the functions of the oxygen atoms in the bridges should differ, and the system must therefore be assumed to be in resonance.

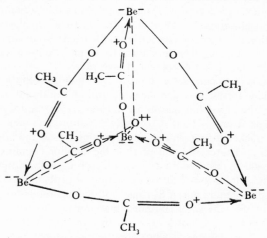

Fig. 21.2.   Structure of $Be_4O(CH_3COO)_6$.

A list of basic beryllium salts of certain organic acids is given in Table 21.15.

Table 21.15.   *Beryllium Complexes with certain Organic Acids*, $Be_4O(RCOO)_6$

Acid radical	m.p. of complex °C	b.p. of complex °C
Formate		sublimes
Acetate	285	330
Proprionate	134	340
n-Butyrate	26	239/19 mm
Benzoate	317	

These derivatives are crystalline, stable to heat, and soluble in non-donating solvents. They are monomeric in the vapour and in solution.

Basic beryllium acetate is made by treating beryllium hydroxide or carbonate with

26*

acetic acid, or by treating a solution of acetic acid in benzene with beryllium chloride in the presence of a very little water. It may be recrystallised from chloroform as tetrahedra. It is monomeric in the vapour, in benzene, and in acetic acid. It is insoluble in cold water, but dissolves in hot water; it is hydrolysed by boiling water and by dilute acids. It is insoluble in alcohol or ether, but it is soluble in other organic solvents.

There is a basic zinc acetate with the same constitution as the beryllium compound. It is made by distilling zinc acetate in a high vacuum. It is crystalline, m.p. 249–250°. It is at once hydrolysed by water or alcohol. Zinc benzoyl pyruvate (like the beryllium compound) has been resolved. There appear to be no corresponding derivatives of magnesium, but derivates of the zirconyl radical are known.

SULPHUR

At room temperature sulphur is a yellow solid which exists in several allotropic forms. The stable crystalline form at room temperature is rhombic sulphur, m.p. 112·8°. At 95·6° it changes to the monoclinic modification, m.p. 119·25°. Liquid sulphur boils at 444·6°. Various monotropic forms of crystalline sulphur can be obtained by controlling the method of crystallisation. There is also the well-known plastic sulphur which contains a proportion of a form of sulphur insoluble in carbon disulphide. All forms of sulphur are insoluble in water. The crystalline forms are soluble in carbon disulphide, disulphur dichloride, and in hot benzene and turpentine.

It is known that the molecule S_8† is the structural unit of both the rhombic and the monoclinic crystalline forms. It is also the structural unit of liquid sulphur, of sulphur vapour up to 800°, and of sulphur in solution in twenty-nine non-reacting solvents over a temperature range from $-75°$ (S_2Cl_2) to 277° (anthraquinone). The molecule S_8 has the form of a puckered ring; in the orthorhombic crystal the bond length is 2·12, and the angle 105°.‡ The crystal cell of rhombic sulphur contains sixteen of these molecules. Above 800° S_8 dissociates into S_2, which breaks down into single atoms at about 2000°. Plastic sulphur has a fibrous structure. It probably consists of molecular chains formed by the opening out of S_8 rings, and the recombination of the segments. The constitution of the variety of sulphur which appears to be insoluble in carbon disulphide is not known; it is not known whether the variety is in fact insoluble in carbon disulphide (in which case it would be the most stable variety) or whether its rate of solution is extremely slow.

Sulphur is chemically active. It combines directly with all elements except nitrogen, tellurium, iodine, gold, platinum, and iridium. It combines readily with hydrogen, oxygen, fluorine, chlorine, and bromine. It combines at high temperatures with the non-metals C, Si, P, As, Sb. It reacts in the cold with Li, Na, K, Cu, Ag, Hg, Be, Ca, Sr, Al, In, Tl, Ge, Sn, Pb, and Bi; all react fairly readily on heating. The transition metals, such as Cr, W, U, Fe, Co, Ni, react, not very readily, at high temperatures.

Sulphur is attacked by oxidising acids, according to such reactions as:

$$S + 2H_2SO_4 = 3SO_2 + 2H_2O,$$
$$S + 6HNO_3 = H_2SO_4 + 6NO_2 + 2H_2O.$$

It dissolves in alkalis to yield a mixture of sulphide and sulphite:

$$3S + 6KOH = 2K_2S + K_2SO_3 + 3H_2O.$$

It dissolves in alkali sulphides to form polysulphides, and in sodium sulphite to form sodium thiosulphate.

† See also S_7NH, p. 856.

‡ In the liquid each S atom is distant 2·05 from two nearest neighbours. The distance S–S in the vapour just above the b.p. is 2·07.

GENERAL CHEMISTRY OF SULPHUR

The electron configuration of the valency shell ($n=3$) of the sulphur atom in the ground state is:

3s	3p	3p	3p	3d	3d	3d	3d	3d
↑↓	↑↓	↑	↑					

There is no evidence from the chemistry of sulphur that the 3s electrons are ever inert. The inert pair is recognisable in certain complex anions of selenium, tellurium, and polonium, but there are no grounds for postulating its presence in any compound of sulphur.

The sulphur atom can accept two electrons to form the ion S^{2-} which is stable in the presence of ions of the alkali or alkaline earth metals. The sulphides of less electropositive metals have covalent character and form insoluble giant molecules in which the sulphur atoms are octahedrally or tetrahedrally hybridised.

The compounds containing digonally or trigonally hybridised sulphur atoms are interesting because many of them correspond in molecular formulae to oxygen compounds in which an oxygen atom is exerting πp bonds; for example, carbon disulphide CS_2 corresponds to carbon dioxide CO_2 (p. 588). There is no doubt, however, that the sulphur atom does not readily exert πp bonds. There are no sulphur analogues of the oxides of nitrogen all of which contain πp bonds (Table 19.5); the nitrogen sulphides are analogous to the oxides of phosphorus, arsenic, antimony, and bismuth (p. 853). The sulphur molecule S_8 does not contain double bonds, but consists of an eight-membered puckered ring. It is frequently found nevertheless that the sulphur atom in the higher valence states exerts πd bonds, and it is therefore possible that in the digonal and trigonal valence states the sulphur atom also exerts πd bonds. The structure of the carbon disulphide molecule could then be written in terms of the canonical forms:

$$S\overset{\pi d}{\underset{\pi d}{\rule{2em}{0.4pt}}}C\rule{2em}{0.4pt}S \qquad \overset{+}{S}\overset{\pi d}{\underset{\pi d}{\rule{2em}{0.4pt}}}C\rule{2em}{0.4pt}\overset{-}{S} \qquad \overset{-}{S}\rule{2em}{0.4pt}C\overset{\pi d}{\underset{\pi d}{\rule{2em}{0.4pt}}}\overset{+}{S}.$$

The use of the d orbitals in the sulphur atom requires promotion of electrons from the p orbitals they occupy in the ground state. For instance, if the canonical form $\overset{-}{S}\rule{2em}{0.4pt}C\overset{\pi d}{\underset{\pi d}{\rule{2em}{0.4pt}}}\overset{+}{S}$ of carbon disulphide is to be formed, the electron configuration in the valency shell of the sulphur atom $\overset{+}{S}$ (from which an electron has been transferred to the sulphur atom $\overset{-}{S}$) before digonal hybridisation would be:

$$\left[\begin{array}{cccccc} 3s & p & p & p & d & d \\ ↑↓ & ↑ & & & ↑ & ↑ \end{array}\right]^{+}$$

The molecules of sulphur dioxide and sulphur trioxide, both of which are non-linear, planar, and have the OSO angle $120 \pm 5°$, probably contain πd bonds linking a trigonally hybridised sulphur atom to oxygen atoms. The use of d orbitals in double bond formation is discussed on p. 776.

A large number of sulphur compounds contain the sulphur atom in the tetrahedral valence state. When a sulphur atom present in such a compound is bicovalent two of the tetrahedral orbitals are occupied by lone electron pairs, and if the sulphur atom is tricovalent one orbital is occupied by a lone pair. When the sulphur atom is quadrivalent no lone pair is present. The bond angles in those compounds which contain a sulphur atom in the tetrahedral valence state with two lone pairs (Table 21.19) are roughly:

C—S—H	105°		S—S—Se	103°
C—S—C	109°		S—S—Te	104°
S—S—C	104°		H—S—H	92°
S—S—S	106°		H—S—D	93°

812

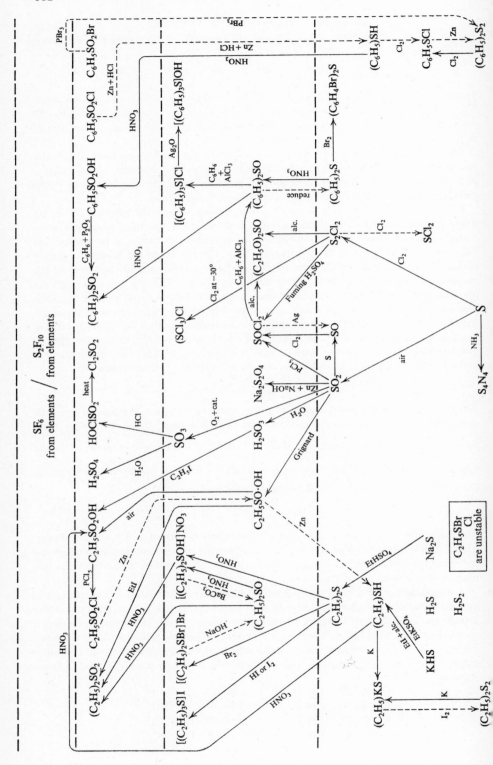

The very small values of the bond angle in hydrogen sulphide (and in HSD) may be accounted for by assuming that a contribution to the hybridisation is made by the *d* orbitals of the sulphur atom. Such a contribution would also account for the observed symmetry of the molecular electric field.

In some compounds the sulphur atom in the tetrahedral valence state with two lone pairs is a member of a conjugated ring, or a link between two conjugated rings. Examples are given below in structures I to VII. In six of these compounds the distance C—S is less than the distance predicted by Pauling's covalent atomic radii, 1·82.

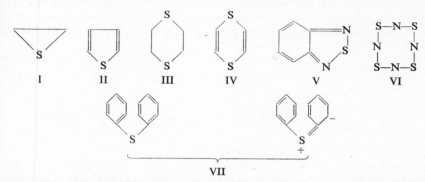

Fig. 21.3. Examples of ring and conjugated molecules containing a sulphur atom.

Table 21.16. *Bond Angles and Bond Lengths in the Molecules in Fig. 21.3*

Molecule	Structure	Angle	Distance C—S
C_2H_4S	I	CSC 65·8°	1·82
C_4H_4S	II	CSC 91°	1·74
$C_4H_6S_2$	III	CSC 99°	1·81
$C_4H_4S_2$	IV	CSC 101°	1·78
$C_6N_2H_4S$	V	NSN 102°	
N_4S_4	VI	NSN 102°	
$C_{12}H_{10}S$	VII		1·75

Among the compounds and ions which contain the sulphur atom in the tetrahedral valence state with one lone pair are the sulphoxides such as $(C_2H_5)SO$, the sulphite ion $[SO_3^{2-}]$, and the thionyl halides $SOCl_2$. The structures of these molecules and ions are pyramidal, and two of the possible canonical forms are:

$$C_2H_5 \diagdown \overset{+}{:S}-\overset{-}{O} \diagup C_2H_5 \qquad C_2H_5 \diagdown :S\overset{\pi d}{-}O \diagup C_2H_5$$

The sulphonium ion $[R_3S^+]$ is also pyramidal with one lone electron pair on the sulphur atom. The structure of the sulphonum ion thus corresponds to that of the ammonia molecule.

The sulphur atom in the tetrahedral valence state with no lone pair is present in the sulphones, such as $(C_2H_5)_2SO_2$, the sulphate ion $[SO_4^{2-}]$ and in the sulphuryl halides, SO_2Cl_2. The structures of these compounds are tetrahedral, but in the sulphuryl halides the tetrahedra are distorted. The sulphate ion is a typical example of an oxyacid anion in which πd bonds are present.

Many molecules contain sulphur atoms in long chains. $S_{100}Cl_2$ is known. In its ability to form chains sulphur differs from oxygen. The sulphur atom in a chain exerts two covalent bonds. It cannot exert three bonds unless it acquires a formal positive charge. As a member of a chain it is unlikely to do this, and hence sulphur chains are never branched.

The dihedral angle θ (p. 803), for the chain ASSB, where A and B may also be sulphur atoms, varies from 74° to 110°; in the molecule S_8 it is 99·3°. It has been observed that if θ is greater than 90°, as in S_8 or in the ion $(S_5O_6)^{2-}$, a sulphur atom added to the chain takes up a *cis* position; if θ is less than 90° as in $IC_2H_4 \cdot S \cdot S \cdot C_2H_4I$ or $(S_6)^{2-}$, the additional atom takes up a *trans* position. There appears to be no relation between the variations of the SSS valency angle and the variations of the dihedral angle.

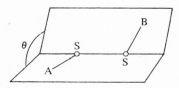

The sulphur atom adopts the octahedral valence state in such compounds as SF_6, in which each electron in the valency shell of the sulphur atom is present in a bonding orbital.

Tetrasulphur tetranitride and a number of other compounds with structures based on 8- or 6-membered rings containing both sulphur and nitrogen atoms are discussed on p. 833. The orbital structures of these compounds are uncertain.

Examples of the principal types of compounds formed by sulphur are included in Table 21.1, and the chemical reactions of many of them are summarised in Chart 21.1. The oxidation state of sulphur is 6 in all its compounds except possibly the sesquioxide S_2O_3.

Sulphur sesquioxide is the name given to a greenish-blue solid made by dissolving finely divided sulphur in anhydrous liquid sulphur trioxide. Its molecular weight and its structure are unknown, and it is doubtful whether its chemical individuality has been established.

SECTION 1. SULPHUR COMPOUNDS CONSISTING OF GIANT MOLECULES IN WHICH THE BONDS HAVE BOTH IONIC AND COVALENT CHARACTER

Sulphur is less electronegative than oxygen. Hence the bond M—S has less ionic character than the bond M—O, and the range of ionic sulphides is smaller than the number of ionic oxides. The sulphides of the alkali metals and of the alkaline earth metals are isomorphous with the corresponding oxides. Li_2S, Na_2S, K_2S, and Rb_2S crystallise with the antifluorite structure. MgS, CaS, SrS, and BaS crystallise with the rocksalt structure. Al_2S_3 is completely hydrolysed by water, and may be ionic.

The sulphide ion is colourless. Alkali metal sulphides (but not hydrogen sulphide) give a purple coloration with sodium nitroprusside, $Na_2[FeNO(CN)_5]$. A summary of the preparations and properties of the ionic sulphides is given in Table 21.17. For the sake of completeness BeS is included, but it is apparent from the Table that this compound is covalent.

The sulphides of metals other than those of the alkali metals, the alkaline earth metals, aluminium, and a few other metals which give rise to cations of low ionic charge, possess covalent giant molecule structures, which may consist of

Table 21.17. *The Monosulphides of the Alkali Metals and Alkaline Earth Metals*

Metallic sulphide	Li_2S	Na_2S	K_2S	Rb_2S	Cs_2S	BeS	MgS	CaS	SrS	BaS
Preparation	1. Burn excess metal in sulphur vapour and heat the product in vacuo. 2. Pass hydrogen over the heated sulphate. The hydrates $Na_2S,9H_2O$ and $K_2S,5H_2O$ may be obtained by saturating one volume of the aqueous solution of the metallic hydroxide with hydrogen sulphide, adding an equal volume of the hydroxide solution, and evaporating.					Burn the metal in sulphur vapour	1. Burn the metal in sulphur vapour. 2. Pass CS_2 over MgO or $MgSO_4$ at red heat	Reduce the sulphate with carbon at 1000°		
Crystal structure	Antifluorite lattice					Zinc blende lattice	Rocksalt lattice			
Behaviour with water	Soluble to give alkaline solutions					Insoluble	Completely hydrolysed	Sparingly soluble but hydrolysed on warming: $2MS + 2H_2O = M(OH)_2 + M(SH)_2$		

three-dimensional structures, layer structures, or chain structures. Examples are given in Table 21.18.

Table 21.18. *The Crystal Structures of Covalent Metallic Sulphides*

	Structure	Co-ordination numbers	Examples
Three dimensional	Nickel arsenide	6:6	FeS, CoS, NiS, VS
	Pyrites, or	6:6	FeS_2, CoS_2, NiS_2, MnS_2,
	marcasite		OsS_2, RuS_2
	Zinc blende ·	4:4	BeS, ZnS, CdS, HgS
	Wurtzite	4:4	ZnS, CdS, MnS
	Cooperite	4:4	PtS
Layer structures	Cadmium iodide	6:3	TiS_2, ZrS_2, SnS_2, PtS_2
	Molybdenum sulphide	6:3	MoS_2, WS_2
Chain structures			SiS_2, Sb_2S_3, Bi_2S_3

On the assumption that the valence bond theory applies to the covalent metallic sulphides, it is possible to assign valence states to the sulphur atoms in the different structures. On this assumption the sulphur atom in a sulphide with the nickel arsenide structure, such as FeS, is octahedrally hybridised. The iron atom, with eight electrons in its valency shell ($3d^64s^2$) is exerting eight bonds, six to sulphur atoms, and two to its nearest iron neighbours. In the pyrites and marcasite structures the bonding is complex, as the group S—S is a unit. In the zinc blende, the wurtzite, and in the two layer structures, the sulphur atoms are tetrahedrally hybridised; in the three-dimensional structure four bonds are exerted, and in the layer structure three bonds are exerted, while the fourth orbital is occupied by a lone pair. The chain structure of SiS_2 consists of SiS_4 tetrahedra with opposite edges shared. The sulphur atom here is tetrahedrally hybridised, and two orbitals are occupied by lone pairs. Since, however, several sulphides such as FeS_2 and PbS show metallic glance, and others such as cobalt sulphide have variable compositions like certain alloys, it is probable that all the crystalline sulphides should be regarded as metallic crystals possessing generalised systems of orbitals.

SECTION 2. COMPOUNDS IN WHICH THE SULPHUR ATOM IS DIGONALLY HYBRIDISED

This class of compound includes the two derivatives of carbon dioxide, carbon oxysulphide, OCS, and carbon disulphide, CS_2. These compounds are described on p. 588. The molecules are linear, and there is little doubt that they are resonance structures (p. 811) corresponding to that of carbon dioxide except that the π bonds are πd bonds instead of πp bonds. The second and third canonical forms (which probably make smaller contributions than the first form (p. 590)) contain a sulphur atom in the digonal state. $H\text{———}\overset{-}{\underset{\cdot\cdot}{\ddot{N}}}\text{———}C\overset{\pi d}{\underset{\pi d}{\text{———}}}\overset{+}{S}:$ and $CH_3\text{———}\overset{-}{\underset{\cdot\cdot}{\ddot{N}}}\text{———}C\overset{\pi d}{\underset{\pi d}{\text{———}}}\overset{+}{S}:$ are possible canonical forms for thiocyanic acid and its N-methyl ester (p. 583). The probability that the π bonds in these formulae are πd bonds is discussed on p. 778.

SECTION 3. COMPOUNDS IN WHICH THE SULPHUR ATOM IS TRIGONALLY HYBRIDISED

As shown in Table 21.1 the Section includes (i) certain canonical forms of carbon disulphide and of thiocyanic acid and its N-methyl ester, and the thiocarbonate ion, (ii) sulphur dioxide and its imide derivatives SONH and $S(NH)_2$, and (iii) sulphur trioxide. The compounds containing carbon are discussed in Chapter 18. The following paragraphs concern the oxides of sulphur and their derivatives.

Sulphur dioxide, SO_2, is a colourless gas, with a suffocating smell, m.p. $-75.5°$, b.p. $10.02°$, which at $15°$ may be condensed to a colourless heavy liquid by a pressure of 2.5 atmospheres. Critical point $157.2°$. Sulphur dioxide is made:

  (i) by the action of an acid on a sulphite,
  (ii) by burning sulphur, or certain metallic sulphides, in air,
  (iii) by the action of concentrated sulphuric acid on copper,
  (iv) by heating calcium sulphate (anhydrite) with carbon and clay at $1200°$:

$$2CaSO_4 + C = 2CaO + 2SO_2 + CO_2.$$

The calcium oxide combines with the clay to form calcium alumino-silicates.

Sulphur dioxide gas is readily soluble in water; at $15°$, 1 vol of water dissolves 45 vol of the gas, all of which is expelled by boiling. Sulphur dioxide is soluble in formic and acetic acids, and in acetone. It dissolves in alkalis to yield sulphites and bisulphites. Sulphur dioxide gas allows the metals K,† Sn, Fe, Mg to burn in it; it combines with zinc to give the hydrosulphite ZnS_2O_4; it reacts with carbon at $1100°$ to yield sulphur and carbon dioxide. Warmed lead dioxide and sodium peroxide become incandescent in the gas and yield the sulphates. In the presence of charcoal, it reacts with chlorine to yield sulphuryl chloride, SO_2Cl_2, and in the presence of platinum, it reacts with oxygen to yield sulphur trioxide. It reacts with phosphorus pentachloride to yield thionyl chloride (p. 838).

Sulphur dioxide oxidises moist hydrogen sulphide to sulphur:

$$2H_2S + SO_2 = 2H_2O + 3S.$$

In neutral or moderately acid solution sulphur dioxide reduces the soluble oxidising agents thus: permanganates to manganous salts, dichromates to chromic salts, iodates to hydriodic acid, chlorine and iodine to hydrochloric acid and hydriodic acid, ferric salts to ferrous salts, mercurous nitrate to metallic mercury. In all these reactions it is itself oxidised to sulphuric acid. In neutral, cooled, aqueous solution, sulphur dioxide reduces the insoluble oxidising agents manganese dioxide, ferric hydroxide, and cobaltic hydroxide, to manganous, ferrous, and cobaltous sulphates, and is itself oxidised to dithionic acid. In very strong acid solution sulphur dioxide oxidises ferrous chloride to ferric chloride, and stannous chloride to stannic chloride:

$$4FeCl_2 + SO_2 + 4HCl = 4FeCl_3 + 2H_2O + S$$
$$6SnCl_2 + 2SO_2 + 8HCl = 5SnCl_4 + 4H_2O + SnS_2.$$

Corresponding reactions occur with cuprous and mercurous salts.

If heated with water in the absence of air, sulphur dioxide disproportionates:

$$2SO_2 + SO_2 = S + 2SO_3; \qquad 2SO_3 + 2H_2O = 2H_2SO_4.$$

If oxygen is present no sulphur is deposited:

$$H_2O + SO_2 + O = H_2SO_4,$$

and the reaction proceeds in the cold.

† The reaction for K is: $4K + 3SO_2 = K_2SO_3 + K_2S_2O_3$; Sn and Fe give mixtures of oxides and sulphides.

Electron diffraction experiments on sulphur dioxide give the distance S—O $= 1.43$ (Pauling's covalent atomic radii predict for S—O 1.7, for S=O, 1.49), and the angle OSO, $120 \pm 5°$. The angle calculated from the spectrum is $121 \pm 5°$. There is a band in the absorption spectrum of sulphur dioxide which is similar to, but less intense than, a band in the ozone spectrum; this suggests a resonance structure with different charge distributions in different canonical forms. The magnitude of the bond angle OSO, $120°$, indicates that the sulphur atom is in the trigonal valence state. If one electron from the valency shell of the sulphur atom is transferred to one of the oxygen atoms, and another is promoted to a $3d$ orbital, the configuration of the sulphur atom in sulphur dioxide is:

$$\begin{bmatrix} 3s & 3p & 3p & 3p & 3d \\ \uparrow\downarrow & \uparrow & \uparrow & & \uparrow \end{bmatrix}^+$$

If in this state the sulphur atom is trigonally hybridised, one hybrid σ orbital is occupied by a lone pair, and a πd bond is formed with one of the oxygen atoms, then a resultant structure is obtained consisting of the two canonical forms:

Sulphur dioxide reacts with ethyl magnesium bromide in ethereal solution to give sulphinic acid:

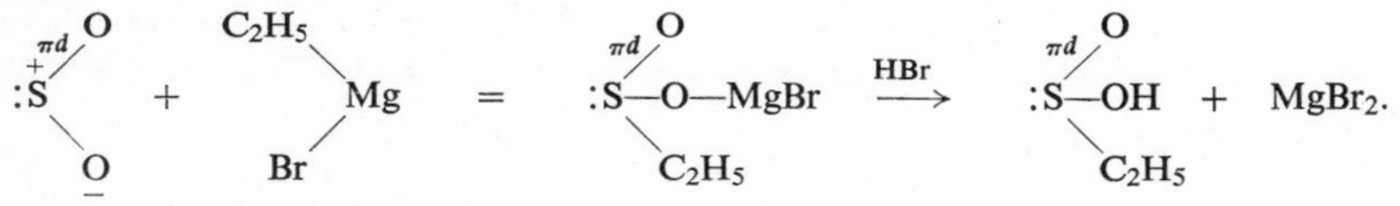

The reaction closely corresponds to the action of carbon dioxide on magnesium ethyl bromide, and it confirms the presence of double bonds in the molecule of sulphur dioxide.

Sulphur dioxide as solvent. Liquid sulphur dioxide is partially miscible with water. At $0°$ a crystalline hydrate, SO_2,H_2O separates from the solution. The hydrate decomposes at $12°$. At $22°$ 100 gm of sulphur dioxide dissolves 23 gm of water, and 100 gm of water dissolves 49.1 gm of sulphur dioxide. Sulphur dioxide is completely miscible with benzene, thionyl chloride, and thionyl acetate. Sulphur dioxide dissolves acetyl chloride and acetyl bromide, chlorine, bromine, iodine, phosphorus, and antimony pentachloride.

Inorganic compounds are in general not very soluble in liquid sulphur dioxide. Metallic oxides, hydroxides, and sulphides are frequently insoluble. Salts containing sulphur dioxide of crystallisation are known: $NaI,4SO_2$, $NaI,2SO_2$, $AlCl_3,SO_2$, $KCN,\frac{1}{2}SO_2$. The sulphites of barium and manganese are insoluble, and the other metallic sulphites are almost insoluble; the solubilities are of the order 0.02 to 0.05 gm per 100 gm of liquid sulphur dioxide. Tetramethyl ammonium sulphite is soluble in sulphur dioxide.

Liquid sulphur dioxide as an acid-base system. Liquid sulphur dioxide is a feeble conductor of electricity. The conductivities of water, liquid ammonia, and liquid sulphur dioxide at the m.p. are:

	Water	Liq. NH$_3$	Liq. SO$_2$
ohm^{-1} cm^{-1}	60×10^{-9}	5×10^{-9}	80×10^{-9}

The ionisation of sulphur dioxide is probably expressed by the equation:

$$2SO_2 \rightleftharpoons SO^{2+} + SO_3^{2-}.$$

The ionisation is promoted by the addition of ammonia or amines to liquid sulphur dioxide, as these compounds form adducts with the SO^{2+} ion, thus:

$$2R_3N + 2SO_2 = [(R_3N)_2SO^{2+}][SO_3^{2-}].$$

The product of the reaction is a base in the liquid sulphur dioxide acid-base system, and compounds such as $SOCl_2$ are acids. Neutralisation occurs thus:

$$SOCl_2 + [(R_3N)_2SO^{2+}][SO_3^{2-}] = [(R_3N)_2SO]Cl_2 + 2SO_2.$$

A metallic sulphite is also a base in the system. The neutralisation:

$$SOCl_2 + Cs_2SO_3 = 2CsCl + 2SO_2,$$

can be followed conductimetrically.

Aluminium sulphite, $Al_2(SO_3)_3$, made as a white precipitate by adding tetramethyl ammonium sulphite to aluminium chloride dissolved in liquid sulphur dioxide, behaves as an amphoteric substance.

From a knowledge of the solubilities of compounds in liquid sulphur dioxide, double decomposition reactions may be carried out. Thionyl bromide may be prepared by the reaction:

$$2KBr + SOCl_2 = 2KCl + SOBr_2.$$

The potassium chloride is precipitated, and after filtration the sulphur dioxide is evaporated.

From conductimetric experiments the presence of complexes in solution may be deduced, for example:

$$2K_3SbCl_6 + 3SOCl_2 = (SO)_3(SbCl_6)_2 + 6KCl.$$

The solubilities in sulphur dioxide of aluminium chloride and of the tetrachlorides of tin, titanium, and silicon, are all increased if thionyl chloride is added to the solution.

Disulphur monoxide, S_2O, has been obtained as a gas at low pressures:

(i) by the action of the electric discharge on sulphur dioxide, either alone or mixed with sulphur,
(ii) by the regulated combustion of sulphur in oxygen,
(iii) by the action of silver (and other metals which have a greater affinity for chlorine than for oxygen) on thionyl chloride.

The ultraviolet absorption spectrum of disulphur monoxide is characteristic at 2488–3396 Å. The gas is detected and its concentration determined spectroscopically. The molecule of disulphur monoxide has a limited life. At a pressure of about 1 mm in a clean dry vessel the gas is stable in the cold for several days, but if concentrated by pressure or freezing it polymerises, and if warmed to 100° it decomposes.

Disulphur monoxide reacts with metals to form sulphides, and with chlorine and bromine to form thionyl compounds. It gives a yellow solution in CCl_4. Disulphur monoxide is decomposed by water or by alcoholic potash to sulphurous acid and hydrogen sulphide (if aqueous alkali is used, thiosulphate is formed as well). It reduces nitric acid and nitrous acid to nitrogen. On cooling disulphur monoxide in liquid air an orange-red solid is obtained with the composition S_2O; on heating it decomposes to SO, SO_2, and S. It at once gives thiosulphuric acid with water, and with alkali a solution which reduces indigo, and may contain $Na_2S_2O_4$. The configuration of S_2O has been determined by microwave spectroscopy. The angle SSO is 118°, the distance S—S is 1·88, and the distance S—O is 1·46. It is possible that the orbital structure corresponds to that of sulphur dioxide.

Thionyl imide, OSNH. Thionyl imide is an unstable colourless gas, b.p. $-85°$. It is obtained by the action of thionyl chloride on gaseous ammonia. It polymerises, first to a yellow solid, and then to a brown solid, $(OSNH)_n$, which has been formulated as:

In the molecule of thionyl imide the group NH is playing the part of an oxygen atom in sulphur dioxide:

Sulphur di-imide, $S(NH)_2$, has not been obtained pure. The salt $S(NK)_2$ is made by treating $(BrSN)_x$ with ammonia and potassamide.

Sulphur trioxide, SO_3, is a colourless, trimorphic, crystalline solid, b.p. $44·52°$. It is made:

(i) by passing a mixture of sulphur dioxide and oxygen or air over heated ferric oxide, vanadium pentoxide, or platinum,

(ii) by heating ferric sulphate or ferrous sulphate:

$$Fe_2(SO_4)_3 = Fe_2O_3 + 3SO_3,$$
$$2FeSO_4 = Fe_2O_3 + SO_2 + SO_3,$$

(iii) by distilling fuming sulphuric acid:

$$H_2S_2O_7 = H_2SO_4 + SO_3,$$

(iv) by heating sodium hydrogen sulphate to $300°$:

$$2NaHSO_4 = Na_2S_2O_7 + H_2O,$$
$$Na_2S_2O_7 = Na_2SO_4 + SO_3.$$

The three allotropic forms are:

α	m.p.	16·8	"ice form" (orthorhombic form)
β		32·5	"asbestos form"
γ		62·6	colloidal form.

The vapour of sulphur trioxide just above its b.p. is probably polymerised. The liquid probably contains two forms, and this accounts for the unusual phenomena attending solidification, one of the most remarkable being that the vapour pressure of the solid just below the m.p. is greater than that of the liquid just above the m.p.

There are one or two chemical differences between the α and the β forms. In the reactions:

$$2SO_3 + CCl_4 = COCl_2 + S_2O_5Cl_2, \text{ and}$$
$$H_2O + SO_3 = H_2SO_4,$$

the β form is the less reactive. When the reaction:

$$2SO_3 + PCl_5 = POCl_3 + S_2O_5Cl_2,$$

is carried out with the α allotrope a certain amount of decomposition occurs, and SO_2 and Cl_2 are also liberated.

Sulphur trioxide is decomposed by passage through a red hot tube. It is entirely acidic. It reacts violently with water to give sulphuric acid. Above 100° it oxidises sulphur (to sulphur dioxide), hydrogen bromide, phosphorus, iron, and zinc. It forms adducts with tertiary organic amines:

$$R_3N + SO_3 = R_3NSO_3 \quad \text{perhaps}$$

and with other compounds containing donor atoms. It combines with hydrogen chloride to give chlorosulphonic acid, $ClHOSO_2$.

The vapour of sulphur trioxide is monomeric. The d.p.m. of the vapour between 80° and 160° is zero. The molecule is planar and symmetrical as indicated by the d.p.m. and the Raman spectrum.

is a conjectural structure which does not conflict with the data.

Sulphur tetroxide, SO_4. If an electric discharge is passed through a mixture of oxygen and sulphur dioxide, at a pressure of about 0·5 mm, the oxygen being in great excess, the product is a substance of composition SO_4. This can be solidified by liquid air. It melts at $+3°$ with evolution of oxygen, leaving a residue which is a liquid of composition S_2O_7. Sulphur tetroxide dissolves in concentrated H_2SO_4, in which its molecular weight corresponds to SO_4. It dissolves in water. The aqueous solution oxidises manganous salts to permanganate, and aniline to nitrobenzene, but more evidence is needed before it can be decided whether SO_4 is the anhydride of H_2SO_5 (compare Table 21.13, p. 806).

Sulphur heptoxide, S_2O_7, has been reported, but its chemical individuality is doubtful.

SECTION 4. COMPOUNDS IN WHICH THE SULPHUR ATOM IS TETRAHEDRALLY HYBRIDISED

When the sulphur atom is in the tetrahedral valence state the eight electrons in the valency shell of the combined sulphur atom can be disposed (i) in one σ bond and three lone pairs as in the ions $[HS^-]$ or $[SO_3S^{2-}]$, (ii) in two σ bonds and two lone pairs as in H_2S and a very large number of other compounds, some of which are included in Table 21.19, (iii) in three σ bonds and one lone pair as in the sulphonium ion $[(CH_3)_3S^+]$, or (iv) in four σ bonds as in the ion $[(CH_3)_4S^{2+}]$. When the sulphur atom is exerting one σ bond it acts as a substituent for an oxygen atom in certain anions; for example, $[SO_3S^{2-}]$, $[CS_3^{2-}]$, and $[SH^-]$ may be compared with $[SO_4^{2-}]$, $[CO_3^{2-}]$, and $[OH^-]$. When the sulphur atom is exerting two σ bonds it replaces an oxygen atom in such compounds as H_2O and H_2O_2, and when it is exerting three σ bonds it is equivalent to the oxygen atom in the hydroxonium ion $[H_3O^+]$. The sulphur atom, however, does not form a series of molecules and ions corresponding to those of oxygen included in Table 21.6, p. 791.

The valence state of the sulphur atom in tetrasulphur tetranitride and its derivatives may be tetrahedral, but it is not certain. These compounds are therefore discussed not in Section 4, but at the end of the Chapter, p. 853.

The hydrosulphides, MSH. The hydrosulphide ion SH^- is stabilised only by the ions of the alkali metals and the alkaline earth metals. Lithium hydrosulphide, however, is unstable. The hydrosulphides of the other alkali metals can be made by passing

Table 21.19. *Molecules in which a Sulphur Atom is Tetrahedrally Hybridised. Two Orbitals of the Atom form σ Bonds and two are occupied by Lone Pairs*

Molecule	Angle	Angle magnitude	Distance S—S
S_8	S—S—S	$107 \cdot 8 \pm 0 \cdot 5°$	$2 \cdot 037 \pm 0 \cdot 005$
H_2S_3, H_2S_4, H_2S_5			
CH_3—S—S—S—CH_3	S—S—S	$104 \pm 5°$	
CF_3—S—S—S—CF_3	S—S—S	$103 \cdot 8 \pm 3°$	$2 \cdot 065$
C_2H_4—S—S—S—C_2H_4	S—S—S	$113 \pm 2°$	$2 \cdot 05$
CH_3SO_2—S—SO_2CH_3	S—S—S	$104 \pm 3°$	
$C_6H_5SO_2$—S—$SO_2C_6H_5$	S—S—S	$106 \cdot 5 \pm 1°$	$2 \cdot 07$
BaS_3	S—S—S	$103°$	
BaS_4, H_2O	S—S—S	$104 \cdot 5 \pm 1°$	
CsS_6	S—S—S	$108 \cdot 8 \pm 2°$	
$BaS_4O_6, 2H_2O$	S—S—S	$103 \pm 2°$	
$BaS_5O_6, 2H_2O$	S—S—S	$107 \pm 3°$	
$BaSeS_4O_6, 2H_2O$	S—S—S	$103 \pm 2°$	$2 \cdot 13$
H—S—S—H	S—S—H		$2 \cdot 05$
HSH	H—S—H	$92 \cdot 2 \pm 0 \cdot 2°$	
HSD	H—S—D	$92 \cdot 3 \pm 0 \cdot 2°$	
CH_3SH	C—S—H	$99 \cdot 4 \pm 0 \cdot 5°$	
C_2H_5SH	C—S—H	$113 \pm 2°$	
C_6H_5SH	C—S—H		
CH_3SCH_3	C—S—C	$100 \pm 5°$	
CF_3SCF_3	C—S—C	$105 \cdot 6 \pm 3°$	
$C_6H_5SC_6H_5$	C—S—C	$113 \pm 3°$	
HOC_6H_4—S—C_6H_4OH	C—S—C	$112 \pm 1 \cdot 5°$	
$(p\text{-}CH_3C_6H_4)_2S$	C—S—C	$109 \pm 2°$	
$(p\text{-}BrC_6H_4)_2S$	C—S—C	$109 \cdot 5 \pm 1°$	
$(CH_3)_2S_2$	S—S—C	$107 \pm 3°$	$2 \cdot 04$
$(CF_3)_2S_2$	S—S—C	$105 \cdot 4 \pm 3°$	$2 \cdot 05$
$(p\text{-}BrC_6H_4)_2S_2$	S—S—C	$107 \pm 1°$	
$(CH_3)_2S_3$	S—S—C	$104 \pm 5°$	$2 \cdot 04$
$BaSeS_4O_6$	S—S—Se	$103 \pm 3°$	
$(p\text{-}CH_3C_6H_4SO_2S)_2Te$	S—S—Te	$103 \pm 3°$	$2 \cdot 11$
$(C_6H_5SO_2S)_2Te$	S—S—Te	$104 \pm 2°$	$2 \cdot 08$
$(NH_4)_2(S_2O_3)_2Te$	S—S—Te	$104°$	
$(CH_3SO_2S)_2Te$	S—S—Te	$105 \pm 3°$	$2 \cdot 14$
F—S—S—F	S—S—F		
C_6H_5S—SCl	S—S—Cl		
Cl—S—S—Cl	S—S—Cl	$104 \cdot 5 \pm 2 \cdot 5°$	$2 \cdot 07$
Br—S—S—Br	S—S—Br		
$Se(SCN)_2$	C—S—Se	$104 \pm 5°$	
C_6H_5SCl	C—S—Cl	$102 \pm 3°$	
S_4N_4	N—S—N	$104 \pm 1°$	
P_4S_7	P—S—P		
P_4S_3	P—S—P	$102 \pm 2°$	
P_4S_{10}	P—S—P	$109 \pm 1°$	
As_4S_6	As—S—As	$100 \pm 2°$	
As_4S_4	As—S—As	$102 \pm 3°$	
SCl_2	Cl—S—Cl	$100 \cdot 3°$	

hydrogen sulphide through a solution of the metal ethoxide in ethyl alcohol, or by the action of gaseous hydrogen sulphide on the metal. Sodium hydrosulphide is best made by the action of liquid hydrogen sulphide on the metal, as the use of the gas produces some sulphide.

The hydrosulphides of Na, K, Rb are isodimorphic. At low temperatures they exist as rhombohedral crystals. One explanation of this comparatively low degree of symmetry is that the proton in the HS^- ion rotates in a fixed plane about the sulphur nucleus; the anion is then planar like NO_3^- or CO_3^-. Above 200° the three hydrosulphides have the rocksalt structure; it would seem that all planes of rotation are possible, and hence the HS^- ion attains spherical symmetry. CsSH has the caesium chloride structure at all temperatures.

The hydrosulphides of the alkali metals and the alkaline earth metals are soluble in water.

HYDROGEN SULPHIDE AND ITS ALKYL AND ARYL DERIVATIVES

Hydrogen sulphide, H_2S, is a colourless gas with a characteristic smell, m.p. $-85\cdot5°$, b.p. $-60\cdot5°$, critical temperature $100\cdot4°$. The liquid is colourless, and the solid is transparent. Hydrogen sulphide is made:

   (i) by the action of dilute hydrochloric acid on ferrous sulphide,
  (ii) by passing hydrogen and sulphur vapour over pumice at 600°,
 (iii) by heating powdered stibnite with concentrated hydrochloric acid,
  (iv) by treating pure zinc sulphide or calcium sulphide with hydrochloric acid,
   (v) by heating to 60° a solution of magnesium hydrosulphide obtained by passing crude hydrogen sulphide through a suspension of magnesia in water.

Liquid hydrogen sulphide has a low dielectric constant ($8\cdot3$ at $-78\cdot6°$), and is a poor solvent for salts. At $-80°$ liquid hydrogen sulphide is miscible with carbon tetrachloride, monosulphur dichloride, and carbon disulphide.

The action for the synthesis of hydrogen sulphide:

$$H_2 + S \rightleftharpoons H_2S,$$

is reversible. The thermal decomposition of hydrogen sulphide is promoted if the gas is in contact with platinum. Tin and lead, however, when heated react with hydrogen sulphide to yield the metallic sulphides. A mixture of hydrogen sulphide and oxygen in the correct proportions explodes when ignited, but hydrogen sulphide normally burns in air or oxygen to yield sulphur or sulphur dioxide according to the temperature of the flame and the availability of oxygen. Chlorine and iodine react with hydrogen sulphide to liberate sulphur. In the presence of moisture hydrogen sulphide is also oxidised by sulphur dioxide thus:

$$SO_2 + 2H_2S = 2H_2O + 3S.$$

At 15° one volume of alcohol dissolves 9·54 volumes of hydrogen sulphide, and one volume of water dissolves 3·15 volumes. A solid crystalline hydrate is formed at low temperatures. The aqueous solution exposed to the air slowly deposits sulphur. Hydrogen sulphide may be completely expelled from its aqueous solution by boiling.

Hydrogen sulphide in aqueous solution is a very weak acid; the dissociation constants are: $K_1 = 9\cdot1 \times 10^{-8}$; $K_2 = 1\cdot2 \times 10^{-15}$. Hydrogen sulphide in extremely dilute aqueous solution may be estimated by titration against iodine solution, according to the equation:

$$H_2S + I_2 = 2HI + S.$$

Chlorine water in excess, however, converts hydrogen sulphide to sulphuric acid:

$$H_2S + 4H_2O + 4Cl_2 = H_2SO_4 + 8HCl.$$

Some further reducing actions of hydrogen sulphide on substances in aqueous solution are:

$$H_2SO_4 \text{ (conc.)} + H_2S = S + SO_2 + 2H_2O,$$

$$2FeCl_3 + H_2S = 2FeCl_2 + 2HCl + S,$$

$$2KMnO_4 + 3H_2SO_4 + 5H_2S = K_2SO_4 + 2MnSO_4 + 8H_2O + 5S,$$

$$K_2Cr_2O_7 + 4H_2SO_4 + 3H_2S = K_2SO_4 + Cr_2(SO_4)_3 + 7H_2O + 3S.$$

Hydrogen sulphide reduces moderately concentrated nitric acid to oxides of nitrogen and ammonia, and in the reaction is itself oxidised to sulphur and sulphuric acid. Hydrogen sulphide is absorbed by alkalis and by slaked lime to give sulphides and hydrosulphides.

The molecule of hydrogen sulphide is non-linear. The angle HSH is $92.2°$; the distance S—H is 1.34. At $25°$ the heat of formation in the gaseous state from atoms is 175 kcal. Hydrogen sulphide is not associated. Solid hydrogen sulphide is trimorphic with transition points at $-147°$ and $-170°$. The lower temperature is the point at which free rotation of the molecules ceases.

The mercaptans (thiols) and the thioethers. Either one of both of the hydrogen atoms in the molecule of hydrogen sulphide may be replaced by an alkyl or aryl group. The formulae and the boiling points of certain of the derivatives are given in Table 21.20; the boiling points of corresponding oxygen compounds are given for comparison. It will be noted that the thiols are more volatile than the corresponding alcohols; therefore the thiols are less associated.

Table 21.20. *Formulae and Boiling Points of certain Thiols and Thioethers,* $°C$

Thiols		Thioethers		For comparison	
HSH	-60	HSH	-60	H_2O	100
CH_3SH	$+6$	CH_3SCH_3	$+37$ (m.p. $-98°$)	CH_3OH	66
C_2H_5SH	36	$C_2H_5SC_2H_5$	92 (m.p. $-102°$)	C_2H_5OH	78
C_6H_5SH	169	$C_6H_5SC_6H_5$	296	$C_2H_5OC_2H_5$	35

The thiols and thioethers are only slightly soluble in water. The thiols are more acidic than the alcohols, which is an indication that the affinity of hydrogen for oxygen is greater than for sulphur, and hence the reaction occurs:

$$C_2H_5SH + H_2O \rightleftharpoons (C_2H_5S^-) + H_3O^+.$$

Phenyl *ortho* dimercaptan, $C_6H_4(SH)_2$, is nearly as strong an acid as acetic acid.

Ethyl mercaptan, C_2H_5SH, an offensive smelling liquid, may be taken as a typical alkyl mercaptan. It is made:

  (i) by treating ethyl alcohol with phosphorus pentasulphide:

$$10C_2H_5OH + P_4S_{10} = 10C_2H_5SH + P_4O_{10},$$

  (ii) by distilling a concentrated solution of ethyl potassium sulphate with potassium hydrogen sulphide:

$$C_2H_5KSO_4 + KSH = C_2H_5SH + K_2SO_4,$$

  (iii) by the action of ethyl iodide on potassium hydrogen sulphide in concentrated alcoholic, or aqueous, solution.

Ethyl mercaptan reacts with sodium or potassium yielding hydrogen and the mercaptide, KSC_2H_5, a white crystalline compound decomposed by water. When an alcoholic solution of ethyl mercaptan is warmed with mercuric oxide, the crystalline mercuric mercaptide is formed:

$$HgO + 2C_2H_5SH = C_2H_5S—Hg—SC_2H_5 + H_2O,$$

which on treatment with hydrogen chloride yields $C_2H_5S—Hg—Cl$. Nitric acid oxidises ethyl mercaptan to ethyl sulphonic acid:

$$C_2H_5SH + 3O = C_2H_5 \cdot OH \cdot SO_2,$$

but iodine or sulphuryl chloride convert sodium mercaptide to diethyl disulphide:

$$C_2H_5SNa + O + NaSC_2H_5 = Na_2O + C_2H_5—S—S—C_2H_5.$$

Similarly air oxidises ethyl mercaptan in ammoniacal solution. The mercaptans, in contrast to the thioethers, form few addition compounds. Examples are: $SbCl_3, C_2H_5SH$, $TiCl_4, C_2H_5SH$, and $TiCl_4, 2C_2H_5SH$.

Thiophenol, C_6H_5SH, an unpleasant smelling liquid, is made:

  (i) by treating phenol with phosphorus pentasulphide,
  (ii) by reducing benzenesulphonyl chloride with zinc and dilute hydrochloric acid:

$$C_6H_5SO_2Cl + 6H = C_6H_5HS + 2H_2O + HCl.$$

Its chemical properties resemble those of ethyl mercaptan.

The thioethers. Diethyl sulphide, $(C_2H_5)_2S$, is an inflammable liquid. As usually prepared it is offensive smelling, but it has no smell when pure. It is made:

  (i) by heating diethyl ether with phosphorus pentasulphide:

$$10(C_2H_5)_2O + P_4S_{10} = 10(C_2H_5)_2S + P_4O_{10},$$

  (ii) by distilling a concentrated solution of ethyl potassium sulphate with potassium sulphide:

$$2C_2H_5KSO_4 + K_2S = (C_2H_5)_2S + 2K_2SO_4,$$

  (iii) by the reduction of diethyl sulphoxide.

Diethyl sulphide is immiscible with water. The sulphur atom in the molecule is not displaceable by metals. Diethyl sulphide reacts with oxidising agents to yield diethyl sulphoxide (p. 836), or diethyl sulphone (p. 841). Diethyl sulphide reacts with iodine, with hydrogen iodide, or with ethyl iodide to yield triethyl sulphonium iodide:

$$2(C_2H_5)_2S + HI = [(C_2H_5)_3S]I + C_2H_5SH,$$
$$4(C_2H_5)_2S + I_2 = 2[(C_2H_5)_3S]I + (C_2H_5)_2S_2.$$

The thioethers react with many acceptor molecules to form additive compounds such as $(C_2H_5)_2SHgCl_2$. The most stable compounds of this kind are formed from the halides of the following metals:

Ni, Pd, Pt; Cu, Ag, Au; Zn, Cd, Hg; Al, Ti, Sn.

Copper, platinum, and palladium form chelate compounds of the type;

A thioether may form an adduct with an acceptor molecule by establishing a link to a carbon atom or a nitrogen atom. An example of a carbon atom thus linked is found in dimethyl sulphonium-9-fluorenylidide (p. 577), and an example of a nitrogen atom in sulphylimine:

$$CH_3 \cdot C_6H_4 - \overset{\overset{O}{|}}{\underset{\underset{O}{|}}{S}} - N \leftarrow S \overset{CH_3}{\underset{CH_3}{\diagdown}}$$

formed by the action of chloramine-T (p. 697) on dimethyl sulphide.

Diphenyl sulphide, $(C_6H_5)_2S$, a liquid smelling of leeks, is formed by the action of phosphorus pentasulphide on phenol. Its reactions are similar to those of diethyl sulphide. It reacts with bromine, however, to yield $(C_6H_4Br)_2S$, and not the additive compound $[(C_6H_5)_2SBr]Br$. It does not form an additive compound with methyl iodide (cf. p. 825).

The presence of the thioether grouping in a molecule sometimes modifies the properties of other groups. For example, the compound:

$$S \overset{C_6H_4OH}{\underset{C_6H_4OH}{\diagdown}}$$

is a much stronger acid than phenol, and a chlorine atom in the β position to sulphur in such a molecule as that of mustard gas:

$$S \overset{ClCH_2CH_2}{\underset{ClCH_2CH_2}{\diagup}}$$

is very non-reactive, although it confers vesicant properties on the substance.

The structures of several derivatives of diphenyl sulphide have been examined. The angle CSC varies from about $107°$ to $113°$. The two phenyl groups are not in the same plane. The angle between the normals to the rings is about $60°$.

Diethyl sulphoxylate, $(C_2H_5O)_2S$, is the only well-established derivative of the hypothetical sulphoxylic acid. It is a colourless liquid, b.p. $117°/33$ mm, made by decomposing diethyl thiosulphite with sodium ethylate:

$$(C_2H_5O)_2S_2 = (C_2H_5O)_2S + S;$$

the reaction is catalytic. Diethyl sulphoxylate has an unpleasant smell, it is insoluble in water. It is oxidised very easily by air, NO_2, $KMnO_4$, SeO_2, or $K_3Fe(CN)_6$ to diethyl sulphite:

$$\ddot{S} \overset{OC_2H_5}{\underset{OC_2H_5}{\diagup}} + O = \overset{\overset{O}{\diagdown}}{\underset{OC_2H_5}{\underset{\diagdown}{S}}} \overset{\pi d \diagup OC_2H_5}{}$$

but the oxidation does not proceed to the sulphate. Two other compounds are known which may be derivatives of sulphoxylic acid: cobaltous sulphoxylate, and thallous sulphoxylate, but the structures of these compounds are not certain.

THE HALOGEN COMPOUNDS OF SULPHUR

Sulphur difluoride, SF_2, may perhaps be produced by the thermal decomposition of S_2F_2, but its existence is uncertain.

Sulphur dichloride, SCl_2, a garnet red liquid, m.p. about $-70°$, b.p. $59°$, is made by the direct addition of chlorine to disulphur dichloride at room temperature in the presence of iodine trichloride or stannic chloride:

$$S_2Cl_2 + Cl_2 \rightleftharpoons 2SCl_2.$$

The reaction is reversible, and even at room temperature sulphur dichloride dissociates into chlorine and disulphur dichloride. Equilibrium diagram studies prove that SCl_2 appears at a maximum on a curve describing a metastable state; the curve describing the stable state indicates a peritectic change at the composition SCl_2 and at about $-83°$.

The molecular weight of sulphur dichloride in solution in liquid chlorine, in disulphur dichloride, and in various organic solvents is found to be about 105 (the formula weight of SCl_2 is 103). As determined by electron diffraction experiments the distance S—Cl is 2·00, and the angle ClSCl is $103 \pm 3°$.

Disulphur difluoride, S_2F_2, a colourless gas, m.p. $-105·5°$, b.p. $-99°$, is made by allowing argentous fluoride to react with molten sulphur. It is decomposed by water, and in this and other properties it resembles the corresponding chlorine compound. It is reactive and attacks glass.

Disulphur dichloride, S_2Cl_2, a golden-yellow liquid, m.p. $-80°$, b.p. 137°, is made by passing chlorine over fused sulphur, and distilling the crude product over sulphur to remove excess chlorine. It has an offensive smell. It dissolves sulphur, iodine, and certain organic compounds and metallic halides; it is miscible with benzene and ether. It unites with chlorine at room temperature to give monosulphur dichloride, and below $-30°$ to give the tetrachloride. Heated metals decompose disulphur dichloride to give the metallic sulphides and chlorides. It fumes in moist air, and is slowly decomposed by water to give hydrochloric acid, sulphurous acid, pentathionic acid, and sulphur; it is reduced to sulphur by hydrogen sulphide or by ammonia.†

The vapour density of disulphur dichloride is normal, and so is its molecular weight in solution in acetic acid or benzene. Electron diffraction experiments indicate that the molecule of disulphur dichloride,

has a non-planar structure with the angle SSCl 103°, and the distance S—S 2·05, and S—Cl 1·99. The d.p.m. in solution in benzene is 1·62.

Disulphur dibromide, S_2Br_2, a garnet red liquid, m.p. $-46°$, b.p. $57°/0·22$ mm, is made by heating sulphur with bromine in a sealed tube. It dissociates on warming, and is slowly decomposed by water to hydrobromic acid, sulphur dioxide, and sulphur. The molecular weight of disulphur dibromide in solution in bromine or in phosphorus oxychloride is normal.

Disulphur di-iodide does not exist. The compound SCl_4, which is very probably a sulphonium salt $[SCl_3^+]Cl^-$, and the compound SF_4 are discussed on p. 835.

Sulphur hexafluoride is described on p. 852.

Aliphatic and aromatic sulphur chlorides and bromides, R—S—hal. Tertiary butyl sulphur iodide, $(CH_3)_3C$—S—I can be made by the action of iodine on the mercury mercaptide:

$$((CH_3)_3CS)_2Hg + 2I_2 = 2(CH_3)_3CSI + HgI_2.$$

It soon decomposes in the cold, but it is remarkable as one of the few compounds in which iodine is directly linked to sulphur; the corresponding bromine and chlorine compounds are too unstable to be isolated.‡

---

† For an application of this reaction see p. 854.
‡ The trichloromethyl derivatives can be prepared and undergo the interesting reactions:
$$2CCl_3 \cdot SCl + H_2S = 2HCl + Cl_3C \cdot S \cdot S \cdot S \cdot CCl_3,$$
$$2CCl_3 \cdot SCl + H_2S_2 = 2HCl + Cl_3C \cdot S \cdot S \cdot S \cdot S \cdot CCl_3.$$

Phenyl sulphur chloride, C_6H_5SCl is a red oil b.p. 149°/12 mm, made:

(i) by the action of chlorine at a low temperature on phenyl mercaptan dissolved in carbon tetrachloride:

$$C_6H_5SH + Cl_2 = C_6H_5SCl + HCl,$$

(ii) by the action of chlorine on diphenyl disulphide:

$$C_6H_5S\!-\!SC_6H_5 + Cl_2 = 2C_6H_5SCl.$$

Phenyl sulphur chloride may be regarded as the acid chloride of phenyl sulphenic acid, C_6H_5SOH. By reduction with zinc it yields diphenyl disulphide, $C_6H_5SSC_6H_5$. The same product is obtained by action with a thiophenol:

$$C_6H_5SCl + HSC_6H_5 = C_6H_5SSC_6H_5 + HCl.$$

Phenyl sulphur chloride with ethylene yields $C_6H_5SCH_2CH_2Cl$, which has a vesicant action (chlorine in the β position to sulphur).

COMPOUNDS CONTAINING CHAINS OF TETRAHEDRALLY HYBRIDISED SULPHUR ATOMS

The molecule of a disulphur dihalide discussed in the preceding paragraphs contains a chain of two sulphur atoms. Other compounds containing chains of sulphur atoms may be divided into four classes:

(i) the hydrogen persulphides, $H\!-\!S_n\!-\!H$, sometimes known as the sulphanes,
(ii) the alkyl and aryl persulphides, such as $CH_3\!-\!S_n\!-\!CH_3$,
(iii) the metal polysulphides, such as CaS_n,
(iv) the salts of the polythionic acids, such as $Na_2[SO_3\!-\!S_n\!-\!SO_3]$, where n represents the number of sulphur atoms in the chain. In the compounds most frequently met with, n usually has a value between 1 and 5. In general the stability of the molecule or ion decreases as n increases. Compounds of the type S_nX_2, where X is H, Cl, Br, or CN, however, have been prepared in a pure state up to the value $n = 8$, and molecules with longer chains are known to exist in mixtures.

Hydrogen persulphides. If a solution of sulphur in aqueous sodium sulphide solution (the overall composition of the mixture being Na_4S_5) is run into cooled, concentrated hydrochloric acid, a pale yellow oil is obtained. The constitution of this oil is unknown (it may be H_2S_5, or a mixture, say, of H_2S_2 and H_2S_3 containing dissolved sulphur), but if it is distilled in quartz apparatus at a pressure of 2 mm two volatile fractions are obtained corresponding to H_2S_2 and H_2S_3. All the hydrogen polysulphides are so asily decomposed by alkali that glass apparatus cannot be used for handling them unless it has been treated with dry hydrogen chloride to remove surface alkali; the erying agent may be phosphorous pentoxide or calcium chloride treated with hydrogen chloride.

Hydrogen disulphide, H_2S_2, is a colourless liquid, m.p. $-89°$, b.p. 71°. It has a smell like that of hydrogen sulphide, but is lachrymatory. It is soluble in carbon disulphide, benzene, and ether. It dissolves sulphur, but does not react with it. The molecular weight is normal. Electron diffraction experiments show that the molecule has a chain structure,

$$\begin{array}{c} H \\ \diagdown \\ \quad S\!-\!S \\ \qquad\quad \diagdown \\ \qquad\qquad H \end{array}$$

The distance S—S is 2·05. The d.p.m. in benzene at 25° is 1·17. The Raman spectrum corresponds to that of hydrogen peroxide.

Hydrogen trisulphide, H_2S_3, is a colourless or pale yellow oil, m.p. $-52°$. Like hydrogen disulphide it is lachrymatory, it is soluble in the same solvents, and it dissolves sulphur. Hydrogen trisulphide is very sensitive to alkali. It readily loses sulphur on heating to form the disulphide, but the action is not reversible.

Hydrogen tetrasulphide, H_2S_4, and hydrogen pentasulphide, H_2S_5, are pale yellow oils. The pentasulphide is obtained by decomposing ammonium pentasulphide with anhydrous formic acid. It is unstable and cannot be distilled.

The alkyl and aryl polysulphides. The alkyl disulphides are made:

(i) by heating the appropriate mercury mercaptide, for example:

$$(CH_3S)_2Hg = CH_3—S—S—CH_3 + Hg,$$

(ii) by oxidising the appropriate sodium mercaptide with iodine or sulphuryl chloride (p. 843).

The alkyl disulphides are reduced to mercaptans, and are converted by alkali metals to the mercaptides, such as $NaCH_3S$. They are oxidised by nitric acid to disulphoxides, such as:

$$C_2H_5—S^{\pi d}O$$
$$|$$
$$C_2H_5—S^{\pi d}O$$

Electron diffraction experiments on dimethyl disulphide indicate the chain structure, $CH_3—S—S—CH_3$; the distance S—S is 2·02, C—S is 1·78, and the angle CSS is $107 \pm 3°$. The diphenyl and dibenzyl disulphides have been shown by X-ray analysis to have similar structures. The d.p.m. of diphenyl disulphide is 1·81.

The unbranched chain structure in dimethyl trisulphide is supported by the results of electron diffraction experiments, from which the distance C—S is 1·78, S—S is 2·04, and the angles CSS and SSS are $104 \pm 5°$. The dihedral angle between the S—CH_3 bonds and the S—S—S plane is 106°.

Metal polysulphides. Finely divided sulphur dissolves in the sulphides of the alkali metals, and in the sulphides of the alkaline earth metals. The Na_2S/S equilibrium diagram shows the presence of Na_2S, Na_2S_2, Na_2S_3, Na_2S_4, and Na_2S_5. Certain metal polysulphides are prepared by boiling a solution or suspension of the metal hydroxide with sulphur. Boiling milk of lime dissolves sulphur to give a reddish brown solution ($θέιον$ $ὥδορ$):

$$3Ca(OH)_2 + 12S = 2CaS_5 + CaS_2O_3 + 3H_2O.$$

If hydrogen sulphide is passed into concentrated ammonia solution (sp. gr. 0·880) in which powdered sulphur is suspended (air being absent) a deep red solution is formed which deposits yellow crystals of $(NH_4)_2S_5$.

The functions of the two sulphur atoms in the disulphide ion $S—S^{2-}$ are the same, because if ammonium disulphide made by dissolving radioactive sulphur in ammonium sulphide is decomposed by hydrochloric acid:

$$(NH_4)_2S_2 + 2HCl = H_2S + S + 2NH_4Cl,$$

radioactive sulphur is present, both in the hydrogen sulphide and in the sulphur set free. It has been shown experimentally that in the ion S_3^{2-} in barium trisulphide the angle SSS is 103°, and the distance S—S is 2·15.

THE POLYTHIONIC ACIDS

The polythionic acids are known only in solution, but they form crystalline salts. The general formula of these acids is $H_2S_nO_6$, where n may be any number from 2 to 6. The structures of the acids are:

Dithionic acid†

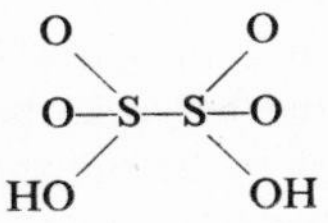

$$\begin{array}{ccc} O & & O \\ \diagdown & & \diagup \\ O-S-S-O \\ \diagup & & \diagdown \\ HO & & OH \end{array}$$

Trithionic aicd

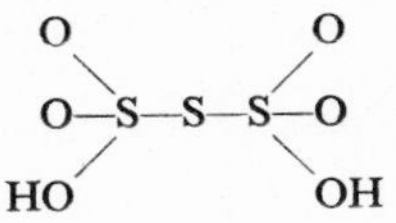

$$\begin{array}{ccc} O & & O \\ \diagdown & & \diagup \\ O-S-S-S-O \\ \diagup & & \diagdown \\ HO & & OH \end{array}$$ the analogue of disulphuric acid

Tetrathionic acid

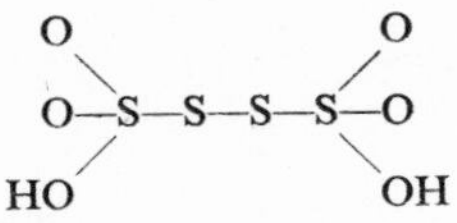

$$\begin{array}{ccc} O & & O \\ \diagdown & & \diagup \\ O-S-S-S-S-O \\ \diagup & & \diagdown \\ HO & & OH \end{array}$$

Pentathionic acid

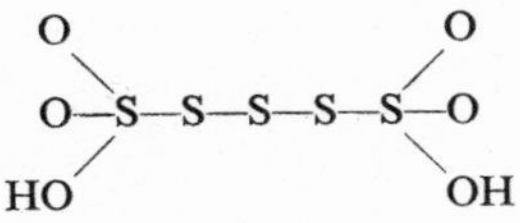

$$\begin{array}{ccc} O & & O \\ \diagdown & & \diagup \\ O-S-S-S-S-S-O \\ \diagup & & \diagdown \\ HO & & OH \end{array}$$

Hexathionic acid

$$\begin{array}{ccc} O & & O \\ \diagdown & & \diagup \\ O-S-S-S-S-S-S-O \\ \diagup & & \diagdown \\ HO & & OH \end{array}$$

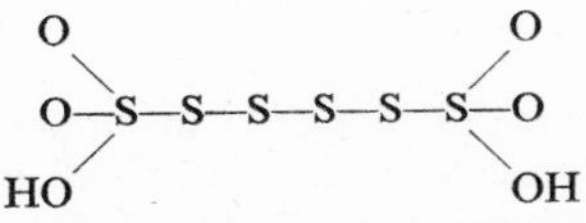

Certain properties of the sodium polythionates are summarised in Table 21.21 from which it may be noted that sodium dithionate does not react with sulphur, with sodium sulphite, or with sodium sulphide, and that sodium trithionate does not react with sodium sulphite.

Dithionic acid. Salts of dithionic acid are obtained by treating sulphurous acid or its derivatives with an oxidising agent maintained at a low concentration. This condition is most easily secured by using a solid insoluble oxidising agent such as manganese dioxide, ferric hydroxide, or cobaltic hydroxide. In these conditions the conversion of sulphurous acid to sulphuric acid is kept to a minimum. In practice sulphur dioxide is

†It is assumed that the S—O bonds in all the formulae of the acids are πd bonds (p. 779). The structure of the dithionic acid, for example, is

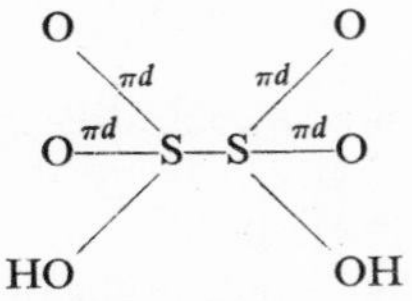

$$\begin{array}{ccc} O & & O \\ \diagdown{\scriptstyle \pi d} & & {\scriptstyle \pi d}\diagup \\ O \xrightarrow{\pi d} S-S \xrightarrow{\pi d} O \\ \diagup & & \diagdown \\ HO & & OH \end{array}$$

If the S—O bonds are written as co-ionic bonds, thus:

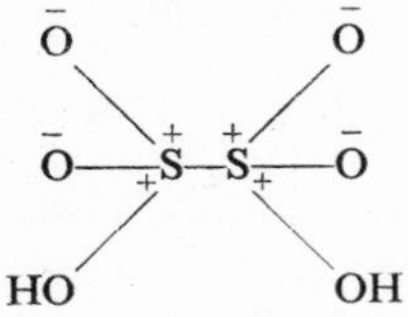

$$\begin{array}{ccc} \bar{O} & & \bar{O} \\ \diagdown & & \diagup \\ \bar{O}-\overset{+}{S}-\overset{+}{S}-\bar{O} \\ \diagup & & \diagdown \\ HO & & OH \end{array}$$

the structure is not in accordance with the adjacent charge rule (p. 656).

passed into a fine aqueous suspension of pyrolusite cooled in ice. It is probable that the following changes occur:

$$2MnO_2 + 3H_2SO_3 = Mn_2(SO_3)_3 + 3H_2O + O,$$
$$Mn_2(SO_3)_3 = Mn_2S_2O_6 + MnSO_3,$$
$$O + MnSO_3 = MnSO_4.$$

Addition of baryta water precipitates the manganese as $Mn(OH)_2$ and the sulphate ion as barium sulphate; passage of carbon dioxide precipitates excess baryta. After filtration the filtrate is evaporated to give colourless crystals of $BaS_2O_6,2H_2O$.

The essential reaction is the combination of two molecules of sulphurous acid, or of the sulphite ion, to give the dimerised ion $(S_2O_6^{2-})$. Two electrons are transferred to the oxidising agent:

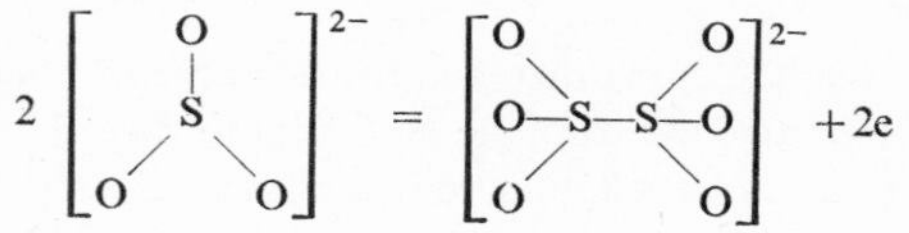

A dimerisation not involving oxidation occurs when barium ethyl thiosulphate spontaneously forms barium dithionate and diethyl disulphide:

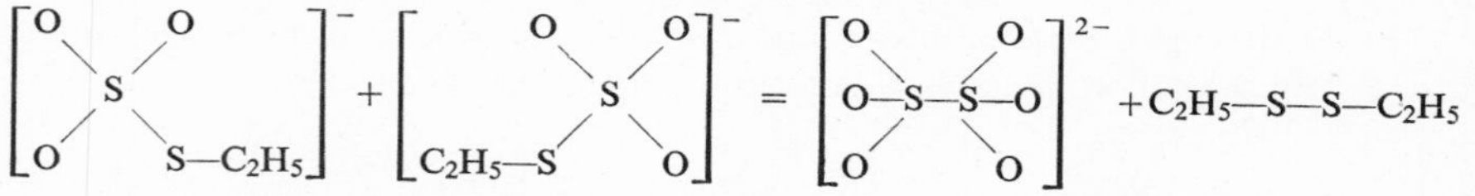

An aqueous solution of dithionic acid is obtained by adding dilute sulphuric acid to the solution of the barium salt. After filtration of the barium sulphate and

Table 21.21.   *Reactions of the Polythionic Acid Salts*

Reagent	Dithionates	Trithionates	Tetrathionates	Pentathionates	Hexathionates
Sulphur	No action	Forms tetra and and pentathionates	Forms pentathionates		
Sodium amalgam	Forms Na_2SO_3	Forms Na_2SO_3 and $Na_2S_2O_3$	Forms $Na_2S_2O_3$	Forms $Na_2S_4O_6$ and $Na_2S_2O_3$	
Sodium sulphite	No action	No action	Forms $Na_2S_3O_6$ and $Na_2S_2O_3$	Forms $Na_2S_4O_6$† and $Na_2S_2O_3$	Forms $Na_2S_5O_6$† and $Na_2S_2O_3$
Sodium sulphide	No action	Forms $Na_2S_2O_3$	Forms $Na_2S_2O_3$ and S	Forms $Na_2S_2O_3$ and S	
Decomposition in conc. aq. solution	Yields Na_2SO_4 and SO_2	Yields Na_2SO_4, SO_2 and S	Yields Na_2SO_4, SO_2 and S	Yields Na_2SO_4, SO_2 and S	Yields Na_2SO_4, SO_2 and S

† Ultimately the trithionate is formed.

concentration, evaporation is continued in a vacuum desiccator. When the solution attains sp. gr. 1·347 the acid decomposes thus:

$$H_2S_2O_6 = H_2SO_4 + SO_2.$$

The metal dithionates resist oxidation, even by concentrated nitric acid in the cold, and they are not decomposed by sulphides or sulphites. Reduction of sodium dithionate with sodium amalgam yields sodium sulphite. The metal dithionates are all soluble in water and are obtained by double decomposition of barium dithionate with the metallic sulphate, followed by filtration and crystallisation. The formulae of certain dithionates are given below:

$$Na_2S_2O_6 \qquad CaS_2O_6,4H_2O \qquad Al_2(S_2O_6)_3,18H_2O$$
$$K_2S_2O_6 \qquad ZnS_2O_6,6H_2O \qquad Cr_2(S_2O_6)_3,18H_2O \qquad PbS_2O_6,4H_2O.$$

The alkali metal and alkaline earth metal salts are stable in boiling aqueous solution. Other salts decompose to give the sulphate and sulphur dioxide.

Trithionic acid. The salts of trithionic acid are formed:

(i) by the action of sulphur dioxide on a thiosulphate:

$$2K_2S_2O_3 + 3SO_2 = 2K_2S_3O_6 + S,$$

(ii) by shaking a concentrated aqueous solution of potassium hydrogen sulphite with a solution of sulphur dichloride in light petroleum:

(iii) by treating an ice-cold saturated solution of sodium thiosulphate with hydrogen peroxide:

$$2Na_2S_2O_3 + 4H_2O_2 = Na_2S_3O_6 + Na_2SO_4 + 4H_2O.$$

The aqueous solution of trithionic acid decomposes on concentration:

$$H_2S_3O_6 = H_2SO_4 + SO_2 + S,$$

and the salts when heated decompose in the same way.

The silver, mercurous, and mercuric trithionates are insoluble; the trithionates of other metals are soluble. Sodium trithionate is reduced by sodium amalgam to sodium sulphite and sodium thiosulphate, and by sodium sulphide to sodium thiosulphate. Sodium trithionate is not reduced by sodium sulphite.

Tetrathionic acid. Sodium tetrathionate is formed in the reaction between iodine and sodium thiosulphate solution:

$$2Na_2S_2O_3 + I_2 = Na_2S_4O_6 + 2NaI.$$

Other mild oxidising agents have the same effect, but may give some sulphate.

Sodium tetrathionate in solution slowly decomposes:

$$Na_2S_4O_6 = Na_2SO_4 + SO_2 + 2S.$$

Sodium amalgam reduces sodium tetrathionate to sodium thiosulphate. Sodium sulphide reduces it to sodium thiosulphate and free sulphur:

Sodium sulphite reacts with sodium tetrathionate to form the trithionate:

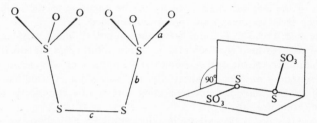

The aqueous solution of tetrathionic acid (obtained by decomposition of the lead salt with dilute sulphuric acid) can be concentrated by evaporation over sulphuric acid in a vacuum, but when a certain stage is reached, the acid decomposes:

$$H_2S_4O_6 = H_2SO_4 + SO_2 + 2S.$$

The structure of the ion as determined by X-ray analysis is shown in Fig. 21.4.

Fig. 21.4. Diagrammatic representation of the structure of the tetrathionate ion $(S_4O_6)^{2-}$. Distance $a = 1.4$, $b = 2.13$, $c = 2.02$. Angle $OSO = 111°$, $OSS = 108°$, $SSS = 103°$. The dihedral angle $= 90°$.

Pentathionic acid, $H_2S_5O_6$, is present in Wackenroder's solution, which is made by passing hydrogen sulphide into aqueous sulphur dioxide solution until all the sulphur dioxide is destroyed. Wackenroder's solution contains colloidal sulphur, and pentathionic and tetrathionic acids. On the addition of less than the equivalent quantity of potassium hydroxide and slow evaporation, monoclinic crystals of $K_2S_4O_6$, and rhombic crystals of $K_2S_5O_6,1\frac{1}{2}H_2O$ are deposited.

Sodium pentathionate is formed by the action of concentrated hydrochloric acid on sodium thiosulphate solution at $-10°$. The reaction is promoted by the presence of a little sodium arsenite.

It seems reasonable to suppose that part of the sodium thiosulphate decomposes in the way stated on p. 846:

$$Na_2S_2O_3 + 2HCl = 2NaCl + SO_2 + S + H_2O,$$

and that the sulphurous acid so formed combines with unchanged thiosulphuric acid (p. 832) to give trithionic acid which then reacts with the finely divided sulphur also produced by the first reaction.

The aqueous solution of the free acid may be obtained by the action of tartaric acid on the potassium salt. On concentrating, the acid decomposes:

$$H_2S_5O_6 = H_2SO_4 + SO_2 + 3S.$$

The potassium salt on heating decomposes similarly.

Potassium pentathionate is reduced by potassium amalgam to the tetrathionate, then to thiosulphate.

27 + A.T.I.C.

Sodium sulphide reduces sodium pentathionate to sodium thiosulphate and free sulphur:

$$S^{2-} + \left[\begin{array}{c} S \diagup S \diagdown S \diagup S \diagdown S \end{array} \text{...} \right]^{2-} = 2\left[\begin{array}{c} O \\ \| \\ O-S-S \\ \| \\ O \end{array}\right]^{2-} + 2S$$

and sodium sulphite reduces it to sodium thiosulphate and tetrathionate. The molecule of pentathionic acid contains a plane of symmetry passing through the middle sulphur atom of the sulphur chain, which may be regarded as the residue of an S_8 ring from which three sulphur atoms have been removed.

Hexathionic acid, $H_2S_6O_6$. Sodium or potassium hexathionate may be obtained by adding cooled concentrated hydrochloric acid to a solution of the alkali metal thiosulphate containing the nitrite or the arsenite. If the potassium salts are used, potassium hexathionate separates on concentration after the potassium chloride has crystallised; the potassium salt may also be made by adding potassium acetate to the solution prepared from the sodium salts.

The hexathionates slowly decompose in solution to give pentathionate and sulphur. They are converted to trithionate by the alkali metal sulphites.

THE SULPHONIUM COMPOUNDS

The sulphonium compounds have the general formula $[SX_3^+]A^-$. The sulphur atom in such a compound has expelled one electron and is exerting three covalent bonds; the fourth hybrid orbital is occupied by a lone pair. The sulphur atom acting as the donor in certain complexes, for example $(C_3H_5)_2S{\rightarrow}HgCl_2$, is in the same condition, except that it has disposed of the sixth valency electron by forming a co-ionic bond. The simplest types of sulphonium compounds are the alkyl and aryl sulphonium halides. The parent substance, $(SH_3)Cl$, which would correspond to $(NH_4)Cl$, has not been isolated.

The alkyl sulphonium halides are colourless, crystalline salts. The iodides are made:

(i) by the action of hydrogen iodide on a thioether:

$$2(C_2H_5)_2S + HI = [(C_2H_5)_3S]I + HSC_2H_5,$$

(ii) by the action of an alkyl iodide on a thioether,

(iii) by the action of iodine on a thioether:

$$4(C_2H_5)_2S + I_2 = 2[(C_2H_5)_3S]I + C_2H_5S—SC_2H_5,$$

(iv) by the action of sulphur or a metallic sulphide on ethyl iodide.

The sulphonium salts of other acids are prepared from the iodides. On distillation the alkyl sulphonium iodides break up into thioethers and the alkyl iodides. They form addition compounds with methyl iodide to yield $[S(C_2H_5)_3(CH_3)^{2+}](I^-)_2$. The change may be regarded as an oxidation of the sulphonium compound. The product is one of the few representatives of a class of compounds in which a sulphur atom is 4 co-ordinate in a cation.

The aryl sulphonium halides are made by the action of the diaryl sulphoxides, Ar_2SO, on aromatic hydrocarbons in the presence of aluminium chloride.

The sulphonium hydroxides, $(R_3S)OH$, are hygroscopic solids. They are made by the action of silver oxide on a sulphonium halide. They are strong bases. They absorb carbon dioxide from the air to give carbonates, they expel ammonia from ammonium salts, and cauterise the skin. They dissolve aluminium with the evolution of hydrogen.

Sulphonium compounds are known in which the alkyl groups in, say, the trimethyl sulphonium group are replaced by other groups or atoms. Among these compounds is **sulphur tetrachloride, SCl_4**, a yellow solid which melts at $-31°$ to a red liquid. It is made by the action of chlorine on disulphur dichloride below $-30°$. It is stable only in the presence of chlorine under pressure. The solid has a high dielectric constant, and it is almost certainly a salt, $[SCl_3^+][Cl^-]$. It forms addition compounds with the chlorides of many polyvalent elements, for example, Al, Tl, Sn, As, Sb, I, Fe. Certain of the addition compounds may be formulated as salts, for example, $[SCl_3^+][SbCl_6^-]$, $[SCl_3^+]_2[SnCl_6^{2-}]$, $[SCl_3^+][FeCl_4^-]$, $[SCl_3^+][AlCl_4^-]$, but the formulation of $SCl_4,TlCl_4$, $SCl_4,2ICl_3$, and $SCl_4,2AsF_3$ in this way is not satisfactory. The compound $SCl_4,SbCl_5$ has a low melting point ($125°$ in an atmosphere of chlorine), and it is soluble in organic solvents; these properties are not in accord with the ionic formulation of the compound.

If the sulphur atom in a sulphonium compound is linked to three different groups an optically active compound is obtained. For example, the compounds:

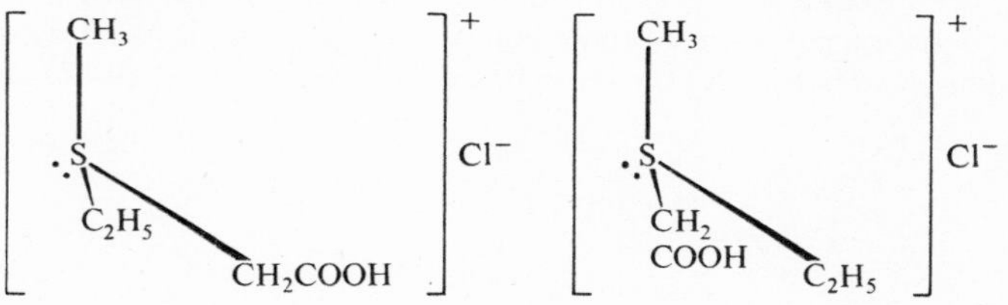

are optical isomers. The existence of these and other similar compounds indicates that the sulphonium group is not planar. Experimental evidence from Raman spectra shows that the ion $[(CH_3)_3S^+]$ is pyramidal in shape with the sulphur atom at the apex.

Sulphur tetrafluoride, SF_4, m.p. $-121°$, b.p. $-40\cdot4°$, is most conveniently made by the action of sulphur dichloride on sodium fluoride suspended in acetonitrile at $80°$:

$$3SCl_2 + 4NaF = SF_4 + S_2Cl_2 + 4NaCl.$$

It is a highly reactive substance, and is used as a fluorinating agent.

THE SULPHOXIDES, THE THIONYL COMPOUNDS, AND SULPHUROUS ACID

The compounds to be described in this section contain a sulphur atom linked to an oxygen atom and to two other atoms or groups; the oxygen atom is linked to no other atom than the sulphur atom. The compounds include:

Sulphoxides

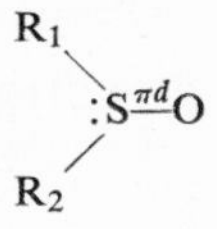

Thionyl halides

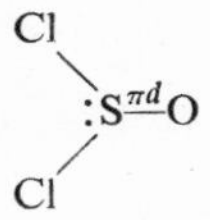

Sulphoxylic acid
$$\begin{array}{c} H \\ \diagdown \\ :S\overset{\pi d}{=}O \\ \diagup \\ HO \end{array}$$

and its derivatives
$$\begin{array}{c} C_2H_5 \\ \diagdown \\ :S\overset{\pi d}{=}O, \\ \diagup \\ OH \end{array} \qquad \begin{array}{c} C_2H_5 \\ \diagdown \\ :S\overset{\pi d}{=}O, \\ \diagup \\ C_2H_5O \end{array} \qquad Na^+ \left[\begin{array}{c} HOCH_2 \\ \diagdown \\ :S\overset{\pi d}{=}O \\ \diagup \\ O \\ \underline{} \end{array}\right]^-$$

Sulphurous acid
$$\begin{array}{c} HO \\ \diagdown \\ :S\overset{\pi d}{=}O \\ \diagup \\ HO \end{array} \qquad \text{and its derivatives}$$

Hydrosulphurous acid
$$\begin{array}{c} O \qquad\qquad O \\ \diagdown_{\pi d} \quad {}_{\pi d}\diagup \\ :S\!\!-\!\!S: \\ \diagup \qquad\qquad \diagdown \\ HO \qquad\qquad OH \end{array} \qquad \text{and its derivatives.}$$

The molecules of the compounds have a pyramidal structure with the sulphur atom at the apex. The distance S—O is short (about 1·46). The link between the sulphur atom and the unique oxygen atom in these compounds is a double bond consisting of one σ bond and one πd bond, and the hybridisation diagram of, say, Cl_2SO is:

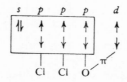

The sulphoxides are easily melted solids, or liquids.

	m.p.	b.p.	d.p.m. in benzene
$(CH_3)_2SO$	18·5°	192° extr.	
$(C_2H_5)_2SO$	4 to 6°	88–9°/15 mm	
But_2SO			3·90
$(C_6H_5)_2SO$		340° (decomposes)	4·00

The alkyl sulphoxides are made by the oxidation of the appropriate dialkyl sulphide with bromine, nitric acid, hydrogen peroxide, or dinitrogen tetroxide, followed by the hydrolysis of the product. The reaction proceeds by the formation of an intermediate sulphonium compound. The action of bromine on diethyl sulphide produces a yellow solid:

$$(C_2H_5)_2S + Br_2 = [(C_2H_5)_2SBr]Br.$$

This sulphonium bromide is soluble in water, which hydrolyses it to the sulphoxide:

$$[(C_2H_5)_2SBr]Br + H_2O = (C_2H_5)_2SO + 2HBr.$$

Nitric acid reacts with diethyl sulphide in a similar manner:

$$2(C_2H_5)_2S + 4HNO_3 = 2[(C_2H_5)_2SOH]NO_3 + N_2O_3 + H_2O.$$

The sulphonium nitrate is soluble in water, and is hydrolysed to the sulphoxide by a suspension of barium carbonate.

The alkyl sulphoxides are very soluble in water, and show weak basic properties, probably on account of the equilibrium:

$$(C_2H_5)_2SO + H_2O \rightleftharpoons [(C_2H_5)_2SOH]OH.$$

The sulphoxides (unlike the sulphones) may be reduced to sulphides. The alkyl sulphoxides on heating decompose with the formation of an aldehyde:

$$(C_6H_5CH_2)_2SO = C_6H_5CHO + C_6H_5CH_2SH.$$

They form 1:1 addition compounds with dinitrogen tetroxide. The aromatic sulphoxides are made by the action of sulphur dioxide, or of thionyl chloride, on an aromatic hydrocarbon in the presence of aluminium chloride.

Structure of the sulphoxides. The pyramidal nature of the sulphoxide molecule has been confirmed by many experiments; the angle XSO is roughly constant at about 105°; the XSX angles vary considerably. The presence of tetrahedral hybrid orbitals in diphenyl sulphoxide is supported by the observation that diphenyl sulphoxide can dissolve in diphenyl sulphone to form a continuous series of solid solutions which have the diphenyl sulphone crystal structure up to 90% of diphenyl sulphoxide. Hence one of the tetrahedral bonding orbitals of the sulphur atom in diphenyl sulphone can be replaced by a lone electron pair without disturbing the relative positions of the other atoms of the molecule.

The asymmetrical sulphoxides, such as:

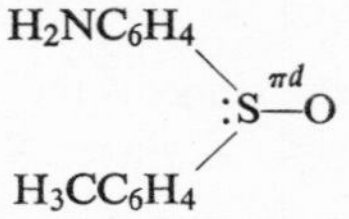

$$H_2NC_6H_4$$
$$\diagdown \ ^{\pi d}$$
$$:S—O$$
$$\diagup$$
$$H_3CC_6H_4$$

can be resolved into optical isomers. It has been shown that there are two optically active isomers of the dithiane derivative:

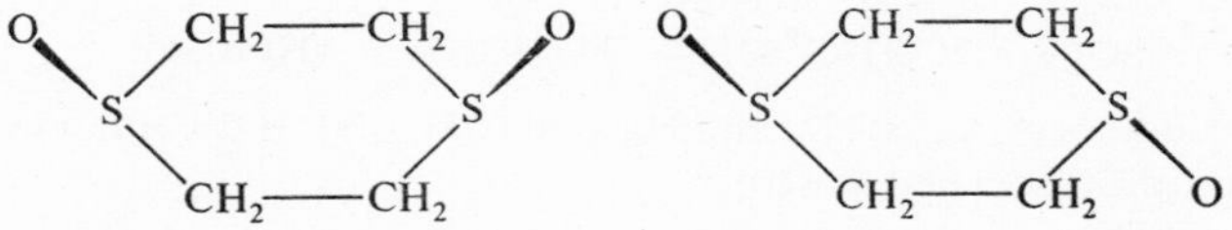

The dithiane isomers are stable for months in the cold. The existence of these optically active derivatives is evidence that the sulphur atom in the sulphoxides is not trigonally hybridised.

In diphenyl sulphoxide not only is the S—O bond shorter than the length computed from Pauling's atomic radii, but the C—S bond also shows 35–40% double bond character. Moreover the angle between the two benzene rings is 81·9°. No simple hybridisation diagram explains these facts, which should perhaps be interpreted in terms of generalised orbitals.

The thionyl halides. Certain properties of the thionyl halides are stated in Table 21.22. The molecular structures of the thionyl halides are pyramidal, the distance S—O is 1·45.

Thionyl fluoride, SOF$_2$, is a colourless gas. It is made by the action of antimony trifluoride on thionyl chloride:

$$3SOCl_2 + 2SbF_3 = 3SOF_2 + 2SbCl_3.$$

It fumes in air, but is less rapidly hydrolysed by water than is the chloride. The dry vapour attacks glass at 400°:

$$SiO_2 + 2SOF_2 = SiF_4 + 2SO_2,$$

Table 21.22.   *The Thionyl Halides*

Formula	m.p. °C	b.p. °C	Distances	Angle XSX	Angle XSO
SOF_2	− 110		S—F 1·6		
$SOCl_2$	− 99·5	+ 77	S—Cl 2·05	115°	106°
$SOBr_2$	− 49·5	59/40 mm 138/760 mm with decomp.	S—Br 2·27	97°	
SOFCl	− 139·5	+ 12·2			

but it does not attack iron, and, even at a white heat, it does not attack platinum. Up to 125° it does not attack Si, Mg, Ni, Cu, Zn, or Hg.

Thionyl chloride, $SOCl_2$, is a colourless fuming liquid. It is made:

(i) by the action of phosphorus pentachloride on sulphur dioxide:

$$PCl_5 + SO_2 = SOCl_2 + POCl_3,$$

(ii) by the action of fuming sulphuric acid on disulphur dichloride:

$$SO_3 + S_2Cl_2 = SOCl_2 + SO_2 + S;$$

if chlorine is passed through the reagents the overall action is:

$$SO_3 + S_2Cl_2 + 2Cl_2 = 3SOCl_2,$$

(iii) by the combination of chlorine monoxide and sulphur.

Thionyl chloride attacks water and organic compounds containing the hydroxyl group:

$$SOCl_2 + 2H_2O = (HO)_2SO + 2HCl,$$
$$SOCl_2 + 2C_6H_5COOH = 2C_6H_5COCl + (HO)_2SO.$$

It dissolves the iodides of Ag, Sb, Si, and Hg, and $(CH_3)_4NI$. It decomposes on heating, and it is two-thirds dissociated at 440°:

$$3SOCl_2 = SO_3 + S_2Cl_2 + 2Cl_2.$$

Liquid thionyl chloride tends to ionise thus:

$$SOCl_2 \rightleftharpoons SOCl^+ + Cl^-,$$

and it is the solvent of an acid-base system. The d.p.m. of thionyl chloride dissolved in benzene at 25° is 1·58.

The vapour density of thionyl chloride is normal at 150°, and its molecular weight when dissolved in benzene is also normal. The use of the isotope ^{36}S has proved that the reaction between sulphur trioxide and monosulphur dichloride takes place according to the structural equation:

Thionyl bromide, $SOBr_2$, is a red liquid, made by the action of gaseous hydrogen bromide on thionyl chloride:

$$2HBr + SOCl_2 = SOBr_2 + 2HCl.$$

It decomposes on heating.

Thionyl iodide does not exist. The mixed thionyl halide, SOClF is formed from $SOCl_2$, SbF_3, and $SbCl_5$. It slowly decomposes to a mixture of SOF_2 and $SOCl_2$.

Sulphurous acid, H_2SO_3, has not been isolated. The aqueous solution is obtained by the solution of sulphur dioxide in water. The apparent dissociation constants at 25° (assuming that all the unionised acid is present as H_2SO_3) are $K_1 = 0.013$, and $K_2 = 1 \times 10^{-7}$. Absorption spectra, however, suggest that the non-ionised part of the solute is unhydrated sulphur dioxide. The aqueous solution of sulphur dioxide reacts with magnesium to liberate hydrogen.

The alkali metal sulphites. Normal sodium sulphite, $Na_2SO_3,7H_2O$, and sodium metabisulphite, $Na_2S_2O_5$, can be obtained as colourless crystalline solids. Sodium bisulphite, $NaHSO_3$, is known in solution only.

Normal sulphites. The alkali metal sulphites are soluble; the sulphites of the other metals are insoluble. The alkli metal sulphites are alkaline in solution. They may be oxidised to sulphates. The oxidation is inhibited by the presence of stannous chloride, or of certain alcohols such as isopropyl or benzyl; it is promoted by the presence of the merest traces of copper or iron in solution. The action of the anti-catalysts may be due to their power of breaking a chain reaction, or to their interference with the catalytic effect of copper or iron. The normal sulphites are reduced by zinc and dilute hydrochloric acid to hydrogen sulphide. A solution of a sulphite with barium chloride gives a white precipitate of barium sulphite, soluble in dilute hydrochloric acid. An acidified solution of sodium sulphite has the reactions of sulphurous acid. Dry sodium sulphite breaks down on heating thus:

$$4Na_2SO_3 = Na_2S + 3Na_2SO_4.$$

Sodium sulphite solution dissolves sulphur to give $Na_2S_2O_3$, and selenium to give a mixture of Na_2SSeO_3 and Na_2SSeO_6. Silver sulphite reacts with ethyl iodide to give ethyl ethylsulphonate:

$$Ag_2SO_3 + 2C_2H_5I = C_2H_5SO_2 \cdot OC_2H_5 + 2AgI.$$

The ion SO_3^{2-} in the crystal of sodium sulphite has a pyramidal structure; the distance S—O is 1·39. The structure of the ion is:

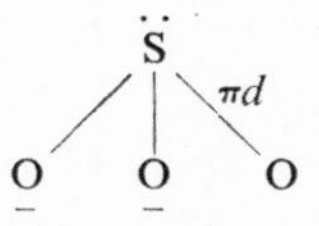

Bisulphites. The aqueous solutions of the alkali metal bisulphites are neutral because of the small value of the second dissociation constant of sulphurous acid. An aqueous solution of sodium bisulphite saturated with sulphur dioxide is reduced by zinc to a solution of sodium hydrosulphite, $Na_2S_2O_4$.

Sodium metabisulphite, $Na_2S_2O_5$, is made by saturating a solution of sodium hydroxide with sulphur dioxide, and evaporating it in an atmosphere of sulphur dioxide. X-ray analysis has shown that in the metabisulphite ion two oxygen atoms are linked to one sulphur atom, and three oxygen atoms to the other. The suggested orbital structure is:

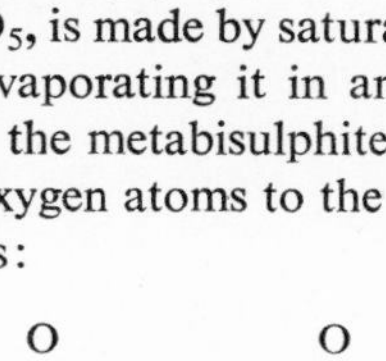

If this structure is correct one of the sulphur atoms has become oxidised during the preparation of the metabisulphite, and part of the sulphur dioxide used must have acted as an oxidising agent.

Complex sulphites. The transition metals of Groups 8, 9, 10, and 11, and manganese, zinc, cadmium, mercury, beryllium, and magnesium form complexes with the sulphite ion. The following are examples:

$$M'_2[Hg(SO_3)_2], \text{ where } M' = Na, K, Ag.$$
$$M''[Hg(SO_3)_2], \text{ where } M'' = Sr, Ba,$$

and also $(NO)_3[Co(SO_3)_3],4H_2O$.

The most general structure is:

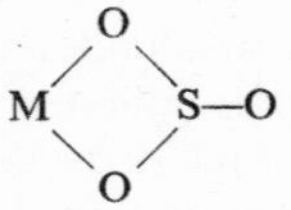

but in certain cases, e.g. in a cobalt pentammine sulphito complex the structure is probably:

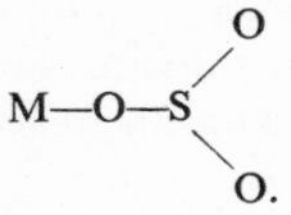

The mercury sulphito complex has the structure:

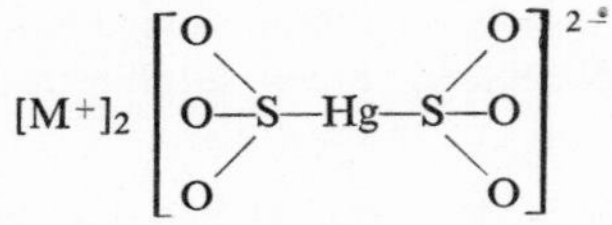

Diethyl sulphite, $(C_2H_5O)_2SO$, a liquid, b.p. 161°, made by treating ethyl alcohol with thionyl chloride, is isomeric with ethyl ethylsulphonate, mentioned on p. 839.

Sodium hydrosulphite, $Na_2S_2O_4$. The anhydrous salt, and the dihydrate, $Na_2S_2O_4,2H_2O$, are known, but the free parent acid does not exist. The sodium salt is made:

(i) by reducing sodium bisulphite saturated with sulphur dioxide, with zinc dust:

$$Zn + 2NaHSO_3 + SO_2 = ZnSO_3 + Na_2S_2O_4 + H_2O,$$

(ii) by shaking sodium amalgam with dry sulphur dioxide. The zinc salt, ZnS_2O_4, is made in solution by reducing sulphur dioxide in alcoholic solution with zinc dust.

Sodium hydrosulphite is a powerful reducing agent; it converts cupric or mercuric salts to the metal and is itself oxidised to sodium sulphite. In air it is oxidised to the sulphite. It is used in gas analysis to absorb oxygen.

It is unstable, both in the dry state and in solution. It decomposes in alkaline or neutral solution:

$$2Na_2S_2O_4 = Na_2S_2O_3 + Na_2S_2O_5,$$

in acid solution:

$$2H_2S_2O_4 = 3SO_2 + S + 2H_2O,$$

and when heated alone to about 200°:

$$2Na_2S_2O_4 = Na_2S_2O_3 + Na_2SO_3 + SO_2; \quad \Delta H = -20.8 \text{ kcal.}$$

It is diamagnetic. This, with the conductance and the freezing points of its solutions, shows that the anion has the formula $S_2O_4^{2-}$. Evidence from X-ray diffraction experiments indicates that the anion is planar, with the atomic arrangement:

$$\overset{-}{O}-\overset{\cdot\cdot}{\underset{|}{S}}\overset{\pi d}{-}O$$
$$\overset{-}{O}-\underset{\cdot\cdot}{S}\overset{\pi d}{-}O$$

THE SULPHONES, THE SULPHURYL HALIDES, THE SULPHONYL HALIDES AND SULPHURIC ACID

The compounds to be described in the following paragraphs contain a sulphur atom linked to *two* oxygen atoms and to two other atoms or groups; the two oxygen atoms are linked to no other atoms than the sulphur atom. A list of the formulae and certain molecular dimensions of the compounds are given in Table 21.23. The molecules of the compounds are tetrahedral. Each of the two unique oxygen atoms is linked to the sulphur atom by one σ bond and one πd bond.

Table 21.23.   *The Sulphones, the Sulphuryl Halides, and the Alkyl and Aryl Sulphuryl Halides*

	Formula	m.p. °C	b.p. °C	Distances		Angles		
				S—O	S—X	XSO	XSX	OSO
Sulphones	$(CH_3)_2SO_2$	109	238	1·43	1·85	105°	115±15°	125±15°
	$(C_2H_5)_2SO_2$	70	248					
	$(C_6H_5)_2SO_2$	76	379					
Sulphuryl halides	F_2SO_2	−120	−52	1·37	1·56	107°	92·8°	130°
	Cl_2SO_2	−46	+69·3	1·43	1·89	106·5°	111·2°	120°
	$ClFSO_2$	−124·7	+7·1					
Alkyl and aryl sulphuryl halides	CH_3FSO_2		124					
	$C_2H_5FSO_2$		135					
	$C_6H_5FSO_2$		207					
	$C_2H_5ClSO_2$		178					
	$C_6H_5ClSO_2$		252					

The **sulphones** have the general formula

where R is an alkyl or aryl group. They are colourless solids which distil without decomposition.

Diethyl sulphone is made:

(i) by oxidising diethyl sulphide or diethyl sulphoxide with fuming nitric acid or potassium permanganate,

(ii) by the action of ethyl iodide on sodium ethyl sulphinate (p. 818):

$$Na[C_2H_5SO_2] + C_2H_5I = (C_2H_5)_2SO_2 + NaI.$$

27*

Diethyl and dimethyl sulphones are very soluble in water. The aliphatic sulphones react with potassium hydroxide, thus:

$$(C_2H_5)_2SO_2 + KOH = C_2H_4 + KO \cdot C_2H_5 \cdot SO_2 + H_2O.$$

Disulphones are well known. The molecule of sulphonal, for example, has the structure:

Diphenyl sulphone is made:

(i) by the action of sulphur trioxide on benzene:

$$SO_3 + 2C_6H_6 = (C_6H_5)_2SO_2 + H_2O,$$

(ii) by heating phenyl sulphonic acid with benzene and phosphorus pentoxide:

$$C_6H_6 + C_6H_5 \cdot HO \cdot SO_2 = (C_6H_5)_2SO_2 + H_2O,$$

(iii) by the action of dichlorosulphonic acid on benzene in the presence of aluminium chloride:

$$2C_6H_6 + Cl_2SO_2 = (C_6H_5)_2SO_2 + 2HCl.$$

Diphenyl sulphone is very stable. It does not react with hydrochloric acid, and it is unchanged when heated with zinc dust to 380°, or with yellow phosphorus to 250°, but when heated with selenium it forms sulphur dioxide and diphenyl selenide.

In the molecule of a sulphone the two oxygen atoms and the two organic groups linked to the sulphur atom are situated at the apices of a distorted tetrahedron. The bond angles in dimethyl sulphone are given in Table 21.23. The very short bond length S—O indicates that the oxygen atoms are doubly bound to the sulphur atom. The hybridisation diagram for dimethyl sulphone is:

It is interesting to note that the distances C—S in certain sulphones are:

$$(CH_3)_2SO_2 \quad 1\cdot85; \qquad (p\text{-}BrC_6H_4)_2SO_2 \quad 1\cdot84; \qquad \beta\text{-}CH_3 \cdot C_4H_4SO_2 \quad 1\cdot74.$$

These values are approximately those of the single bond length (Table 11.5), and suggest that there is no conjugation between the phenyl groups, the d orbitals of the sulphur atom and the p orbitals of the oxygen atoms as there may be in the aryl sulphoxides (p. 837).

The sulphuryl halides have the general formula

$$
\begin{array}{ccc}
X & & O \\
 & \diagdown\!{\scriptstyle\pi d}\!\diagup & \\
 & S & \\
 & \diagup\!{\scriptstyle\pi d}\!\diagdown & \\
X & & O
\end{array}
$$

Sulphuryl fluoride, F_2SO_2, a colourless gas, is made:

(i) by burning fluorine in sulphur dioxide,
(ii) by heating barium fluorosulphonate:

$$Ba(SO_3F)_2 = F_2SO_2 + BaSO_4.$$

The most remarkable property of sulphuryl fluoride is its inertness. Water dissolves it sparingly but is without action on it up to 150°. It can be heated to a red heat without change, either alone, or with oxygen, or with sulphur or hydrogen chloride. It is also unaffected if heated with phosphorus or with arsenic to their boiling points, or with sodium up to its melting point. It is attacked, however, if heated with hydrogen, or if treated with ammonia or potassium hydroxide, and it is rapidly hydrolysed by alcoholic potash:

$$2KOH + F_2SO_2 = H_2SO_4 + 2KF.$$

The vapour density of sulphuryl fluoride is normal.

Sulphuryl chloride, Cl_2SO_2, a colourless liquid with a pungent smell, is made:

(i) by the combination of sulphur dioxide and chlorine at room temperature in the presence of camphor,
(ii) by heating chlorosulphonic acid with mercuric chloride as a catalyst:

$$
\begin{array}{ccccccc}
O & OH & HO & O & & Cl & O \\
\diagdown{\scriptstyle\pi d}\diagup & & \diagdown{\scriptstyle\pi d}\diagup & & & \diagdown{\scriptstyle\pi d}\diagup & \\
S & & S & & = \ H_2SO_4 \ + & S & \\
\diagup{\scriptstyle\pi d}\diagdown & & \diagup{\scriptstyle\pi d}\diagdown & & & \diagup{\scriptstyle\pi d}\diagdown & \\
O & Cl & Cl & O & & Cl & O
\end{array}
$$

Sulphuryl chloride can be distilled without decomposition, but it dissociates on further gentle heating, and the dissociation:

$$SO_2Cl_2 \rightleftharpoons SO_2 + Cl_2,$$

is about 90% at 100°. Sulphuryl chloride is a powerful solvent; it dissolves SO_2, I_2, As, $FeCl_3$, RbI, MgI_2, CdI_2, AsI_3, and SnI_4. It is very slowly hydrolysed by water. It reacts on heating with metal oxides to give chlorides and sulphides, and with metal sulphides to give chlorides. In organic chemistry sulphuryl chloride is used in the presence of aluminium chloride as a chlorinating agent. Sulphuryl chloride dissolved in dry benzene reacts with ammonia gas to give sulphamide, $SO_2(NH_2)_2$, a crystalline solid. The molecular weight of sulphuryl chloride dissolved in benzene is normal.

Sulphuryl chlorofluoride, $ClFSO_2$, is a gas with a pungent smell. It is hydrolysed at once by water, and it reacts rapidly with alkalis. It does not fume in air.

Neither sulphuryl bromide nor sulphuryl iodide are known.

The alkyl sulphonyl fluorides are volatile liquids with a pleasant smell. They are made by boiling the corresponding chlorides with a saturated aqueous solution of potassium fluoride:

$$C_2H_5SO_2Cl + KF = C_2H_5SO_2F + KCl.$$

They are chemically inert. They are hydrolysed only slowly by boiling water in which they are insoluble, they do not lose sulphur dioxide when treated with aluminium chloride, they react only slowly with amines, and not with pyridine in the cold.

The aryl sulphonyl fluorides are similarly made, and they are also inactive chemically.

The alkyl and aryl sulphonyl chlorides are colourless liquids or solids. They are made by the action of phosphorus pentachloride on the sodium salt of the sulphonic acid. The alkyl and aryl sulphonyl chlorides are much more reactive than the fluorides. They are readily hydrolysed by hot water in which they are only sparingly soluble; they react with pyridine in the cold, and they lose sulphur dioxide and yield the organic chloride when treated with aluminium chloride. They are readily reduced by zinc to the sulphinic acid, and then to the mercaptan:

$$C_6H_5\diagdown\!\!\!\diagup O \quad\quad\quad C_6H_5 \\ \quad\quad S \quad\quad \rightarrow \quad :S^{\pi d}O \quad \rightarrow \quad C_6H_5\!-\!S\!-\!H \\ Cl\diagup\;\diagdown O \quad\quad HO\diagup$$

The chlorine atom has the usual activity of a chlorine atom in an acid chloride.

The alkyl and aryl sulphonyl bromides are much less stable than the fluorides or chlorides. They are reduced by phosphorus tribromide (but not by the trichloride) to the disulphides:

$$2CH_3SO_2Br + 5PBr_3 = PBr_5 + 4POBr_3 + CH_3\!-\!S\!-\!S\!-\!CH_3.$$

Sulphuric acid, H_2SO_4. Evidence from equilibrium diagram and other studies indicates the existence of the following crystalline phases in the system H_2O,SO_3:

$H_2S_4O_{13}$	m.p. °C +4		H_2SO_4,H_2O	m.p. °C +9
$H_2S_3O_{10}$			$H_2SO_4,2H_2O$	−38·9
$H_2S_2O_7$	+36		$H_2SO_4,3H_2O$	−37
H_2SO_4	+10·36		$H_2SO_4,4H_2O$	−29
			$H_2SO_4,6H_2O$ peritectic pt. about −52	
			$H_2SO_4,8H_2O$ peritectic pt. about −62	

Of these crystalline phases the most familiar are sulphuric acid, H_2SO_4, and disulphuric acid, $H_2S_2O_7$.

Sulphuric acid, H_2SO_4, is a colourless oil, m.p. +10·36°, b.p. 320° with decomposition. With water it forms a constant boiling point mixture containing 98·33% H_2SO_4, and boiling at 330°.

Sulphuric acid is made commercially:

(i) by the interaction of sulphur dioxide, atmospheric oxygen, and steam in the presence of oxides of nitrogen; the initial reaction:

$$2SO_2 + N_2O_3 + O_2 + H_2O = 2(NO)(HSO_4),$$

is followed by two further reactions:

$$2(NO)(HSO_4) + H_2O = 2H_2SO_4 + N_2O_3,$$
$$2(NO(HSO_4) + 2H_2O + SO_2 = 3H_2SO_4 + 2NO,$$

(ii) by the solution of sulphur trioxide (made by the contact process, or by the reduction of anhydrite) in 98% sulphuric acid; water is added concurrently to keep the concentration of the acid constant.

Sulphuric acid is a vigorous chemical reagent. It has a great affinity for water, and it removes the elements of water from organic compounds such as alcohol and sucrose. When hot, it is an oxidising agent and it attacks copper, silver, lead, and mercury, which are unaffected by the cold dilute acid. Dilute sulphuric acid is not an oxidising agent. It is a good conductor of electricity, and it dissolves metals above hydrogen in the electrochemical series to give hydrogen and a metallic sulphate.

Just as it is impossible to obtain pure nitric acid wholly composed of molecules with the constitution HNO_3, so it is impossible to obtain sulphuric acid wholly composed of molecules H_2SO_4. Dissociation of the pure acid always occurs, thus:

$$2H_2SO_4 \rightleftharpoons HSO_4^- + H_3SO_4^+.$$

There is also decomposition:

$$H_2SO_4 = H_2O + SO_3;$$

the three molecules, H_2SO_4, H_2O, and SO_3, then interact:

$$H_2SO_4 + H_2O = (H_3O)^+ + (HSO_4)^-,$$
$$H_2SO_4 + SO_3 = H_2S_2O_7,$$
$$H_2SO_4 + H_2S_2O_7 = (HS_2O_7)^- + (H_3SO_4)^+.$$

The concentrations of the resulting ions of different kinds in liquid sulphuric acid at the m.p. are:

HSO_4^-, 0·013 molal; $H_3SO_4^+$, 0·013 molal; $HS_2O_7^-$, 0·0083 molal, H_3O^+, 0·0083 molal.

Sulphuric acid acts as a proton donor to the anions of weaker acids, such as water or nitric acid. If 0·1 molar proportion of water is added to pure sulphuric acid, 93% of it is present as the hydroxonium ion, owing to the setting up of the equilibria:

$$2H_2O \rightleftharpoons H_3O^+ + OH^-,$$
$$H_2SO_4 + OH^- \rightleftharpoons H_2O + HSO_4^-.$$

The donation of a proton to the nitrate ion in dinitrogen pentoxide, or dinitrogen tetroxide, leads to the ionisations:

$$N_2O_5 + 3H_2SO_4 \rightleftharpoons 2NO_2^+ + H_3O^+ + 3HSO_4^-,$$
$$N_2O_4 + 3H_2SO_4 \rightleftharpoons NO_2^+ + NO^+ + H_3O^+ + 3HSO_4^-.$$

The sulphates are familiar compounds, and it is not thought necessary to include any account of them in this chapter.

Complex sulphates. A few sulphates, such as the red form of rhodium sulphate, $Rh_2(SO_4)_3$, and the green amorphous form of chromic sulphate, $Cr_2(SO_4)_3$, when dissolved in water do not give an immediate precipitate with barium chloride. Such sulphates are probably complex, and should be written:

$$Rh[Rh(SO_4)_3] \quad \text{and} \quad Cr[Cr(SO_4)_3].$$

Other examples of complex sulphates are:

$$K_3[Ir(SO_4)_3],H_2O, \quad [en_2Co(SO_4)]Br, \quad [(NH_3)_4PtSO_4]Br_2.$$

In these complexes the central element is 6-co-ordinate, and the sulphate group forms two links with it. In the examples:

$$[(NH_3)_5CoSO_4]X \quad \text{and} \quad [(NH_3)_4PtBrSO_4]X_2,$$

the sulphate group is forming only one link with the central atom. Werner noticed that the change of valency of the sulphato group led to what he termed "ionisation isomerism". This is exemplified by the cobalt complexes:

$$[CoSO_4(NH_3)_5]Br, \text{ violet red, } \quad \text{and} \quad [CoBr(NH_3)_5]SO_4, \text{ violet.}$$

The well-characterised alkyl sulphates, $(CH_3)_2SO_4$, m.p. $-27°$, b.p. 186°, and $(C_2H_5)_2SO_4$, m.p. $-24°$, b.p. 208°, are made by the action of the appropriate alcohol on sulphur trioxide, or on chlorosulphonic acid.

Sodium disulphate (sodium pyrosulphate) $Na_2S_2O_7$. The parent acid is not known. The sodium salt is made by heating sodium hydrogen sulphate:

$$2NaHSO_4 = Na_2S_2O_7 + H_2O.$$

Further heating leads to decomposition:

$$Na_2S_2O_7 = Na_2SO_4 + SO_3.$$

Sodium disulphate is quickly hydrolysed by water to the acid sulphate, but it reacts with ammonia or an amine almost as quickly. Hence if sodium disulphate is added to aqueous ammonia it yields sulphamic acid, NH_2—SO_2—OH, and with a cold aqueous solution of trimethylamine it yields the compound $(CH_3)_3N^+$—SO_2—O^-. With phenol it yields the compound C_6H_5—O—SO_3Na. Potassium disulphate behaves similarly.

Pyrosulphuryl chloride, $S_2O_5Cl_2$, a colourless liquid, b.p. 152°, is made by heating sulphur trioxide with carbon tetrachloride:

$$CCl_4 + 2SO_3 = S_2O_5Cl_2 + COCl_2.$$

It is hydrolysed by water.

The thiosulphates. Free thiosulphuric acid is not known. **Sodium thiosulphate,** $Na_2S_2O_3$, which crystallises as the pentahydrate, is made:

(i) by heating sodium sulphite (alone or in aqueous solution) with sulphur,
(ii) by the oxidation of alkali metal and alkaline earth metal polysulphides:

$$2CaS_2 + 3O_2 = 2CaS_2O_3,$$
$$2Na_2S_5 + 3O_2 = 2Na_2S_2O_3 + 6S,$$

(iii) by the sulphonation of sodium hydrosulphide, either by N-pyridinium sulphonic acid in cold aqueous solution:

or, by potassium hydrogen sulphite:

$$4KHSO_3 + 2HSK = 3K_2S_2O_3 + 3H_2O,$$

(iv) by the action of alkalis on polythionates:

$$Na_2(O_3S\text{—}S\text{—}SO_3) + NaOH = Na_2S_2O_3 + NaHSO_4,$$

(v) by the decomposition of sodium hydrosulphite in alkaline or neutral solution.

The thiosulphates of the alkali metals and many divalent metals are very soluble. The solutions are stable in the cold and in the absence of air. Alkali metal thiosulphates in solution are oxidised by air, and other oxidising agents, to sulphate and free sulphur:

$$Na_2S_2O_3 + H_2O + Cl_2 = Na_2SO_4 + S + 2HCl.$$

and by iodine, quantitatively, to tetrathionate:

$$[O_3SS^{2-}] + I_2 + [SSO_3^{2-}] = [O_3SSSSO_3^{2-}] + 2[I^-].$$

Sodium thiosulphate in solution decomposes on the addition of acid:

$$Na_2S_2O_3 + 2HCl = 2NaCl + S + SO_2 + H_2O.$$

It has been claimed that if the reaction is carried out under strongly acid conditions there is no separation of sulphur for some hours, but the addition of alkali to the solution in this state does not re-form sodium thiosulphate. It appears that the strongly acid conditions stabilise, not the solution of thiosulphuric acid, but the colloidal solution of sulphur. Decomposition of the $[S_2O_3^{2-}]$ ion by the hydrogen ion in acid solution proceeds by the rapid reaction:

$$[S_2O_3^{2-}] + H^+ = [HSO_3^-] + S,$$

and a slow reaction:

$$5[S_2O_3^{2-}] + 6H^+ = 2[S_5O_6^{2-}] + 3H_2O.$$

The thiosulphate ion is tetrahedral. It is notionally derived by replacing one of the oxygen atoms in the sulphate ion by a sulphur atom:

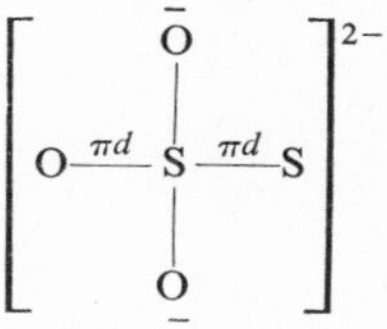

A distinction between the functions of the two sulphur atoms in the ion can be recognised in the following experiments.

(i) If ^{35}S is dissolved in sodium sulphite solution, and the silver salt is precipitated with silver nitrate, $Ag^{35}SSO_3$ is obtained. On boiling the silver salt decomposes:

$$H_2O + Ag_2^{35}SSO_3 = Ag_2^{35}S + H_2SO_4,$$

and all the labelled sulphur is present in the silver sulphide.

(ii) If S^{2-} ions of ^{35}S are introduced into sodium thiosulphate solution, exchange takes place with only half the sulphur in the thiosulphate ions.

(iii) If sodium thiosulphate made by adding ^{36}S to sodium sulphite is decomposed by hydrochloric acid, the labelled sulphur atoms are found only in the deposited sulphur thus:

$$Na_2S^{36}SO_3 + 2HCl = 2NaCl + {}^{36}S + SO_2 + H_2O.$$

Complex thiosulphates. The thiosulphate ion forms anionic complexes in which it exerts one covalent bond, or one covalent bond and one co-ionic bond. Each thiosulphate ion in the complex:

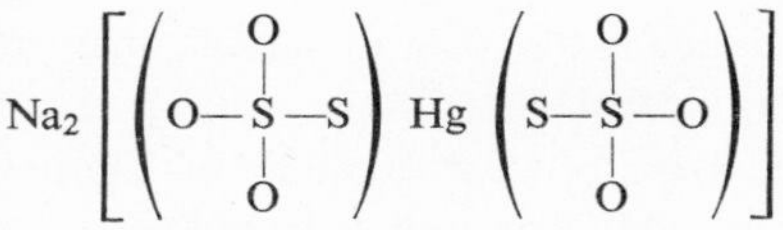

is linked by one covalent bond to the mercury atom.

The thiosulphate ion in the complex:

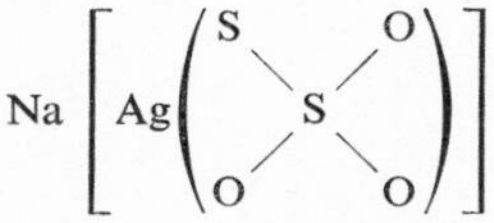

obtained by treating silver nitrate with sodium thiosulphate in excess, is linked by two bonds to the silver atom. Each thiosulphate ion in the complexes:

$$Na_3[Ag(S_2O_3)_2], 2H_2O \quad \text{and} \quad Na_3[Au(S_2O_3)_2].$$

is also linked by two bonds to the silver or gold atom.

On account of the stability of thiosulphate complexes many insoluble compounds of the heavy metals dissolve in an aqueous solution of sodium thiosulphate, for example silver chloride reacts thus:

$$AgCl + Na_2S_2O_3 = Na[AgS_2O_3] + NaCl.$$

In some cases a metal oxide dissolves with the production of an alkaline solution thus:

$$H_2O + Ag_2O + Na_2S_2O_3 = Na[AgS_2O_3] + 2NaOH.$$

From a solution of $Na[AgS_2O_3]$ the silver is precipitated by potassium iodide, but not by sodium chloride (the solubility product of AgI is 10^{-16}, of AgCl is 10^{-10}).

The sulphonic acids are notionally derived from sulphuric acid by the replacement of one OH group in the sulphuric acid molecule by an alkyl or aryl group, or by a halogen atom. For example, the relation of sulphuric acid to phenyl sulphonic acid may be shown thus:

The formulae of certain of the sulphonic acids and their esters are given in Table 21.24.

Table 21.24. *The Sulphonic Acids and Their Esters*

Compound	m.p. °C	b.p. °C
$C_2H_5SO_2 \cdot OH$		171/0·1 mm
$C_6H_5SO_2 \cdot OH$		
$FSO_2 \cdot OH$	−87·3	162·6
$FSO_2 \cdot OCH_3$		92
$FSO_2 \cdot OC_2H_5$		114
$FSO_2 \cdot OC_6H_5$		180
$ClSO_2 \cdot OH$	−80	151
$ClSO_2 \cdot OC_2H_5$		
$C_2H_5SO_2 \cdot OC_2H_5$		213

All the compounds mentioned in the table are liquids; many of them are lachrymatory.

The alkyl sulphonic acids are made:

(i) by oxidising mercaptans or alkyl sulphides with concentrated nitric acid,

(ii) by the action of ethyl iodide on sodium sulphite:

(iii) by the oxidation of ethyl sulphinic acid, $C_2H_5SO \cdot OH$.

Ethyl ethylsulphonate is made by the action of ethyl iodide on silver sulphite:

The **aryl sulphonic acids** are made by treatment of the aromatic hydrocarbons with oleum. They are liquids or low-melting solids which can be distilled under greatly reduced pressure. They are very soluble in water and their calcium and barium salts are also soluble. Potassium phenyl sulphonate hydrolyses in two ways:

(i) in alkaline solution: $C_6H_5SO_2OK + KOH = C_6H_5OH + K_2SO_3$,

(ii) in acid solution: $C_6H_5SO_2OH + H_2O = C_6H_6 + H_2SO_4$.

The potassium or sodium salts react with phosphorus pentachloride to give the corresponding acid chlorides.

Fluorosulphonic acid, $FSO_2 \cdot OH$, is a colourless, mobile liquid. The anhydrous acid is made by distilling a mixture of KHF_2 and oleum from a Jena glass flask. If pure it remains stable when heated up to 900°, but in the presence of sulphur it is completely decomposed at the b.p. to SO_3 and HF. With water the equilibrium is set up:

$$FSO_2 \cdot OH + H_2O \rightleftharpoons HF + H_2SO_4.$$

The alkali metal fluorosulphonates are formed from sulphur trioxide and the alkali metal fluoride:

$$SO_3 + KF = K[SO_3F].$$

They are stable, and can be crystallised from water which hydrolyses them only slowly. With ammonia they form sulphamates, $K[SO_3NH_2]$. KSO_3F is similar to $KClO_4$, $KMnO_4$, KPO_2F_2, and KBF_4. $NO[SO_3F]$ is formed together with $NO[HSO_4]$, when nitric oxide is passed into fluorosulphonic acid. $CsSO_3F$ has a Scheelite ($CaWO_4$) lattice.

Chlorosulphonic acid, $ClSO_2OH$, a colourless, fuming liquid, is made:

(i) by the action of phosphorus pentachloride on oleum,

(ii) by the combination of hydrogen chloride and sulphur trioxide, usually carried out by passing dry hydrogen chloride into fuming sulphuric acid, and distilling.

At 175° chlorosulphonic acid vapour decomposes thus:

$$2ClSO_2 \cdot OH = SO_2Cl_2 + H_2SO_4.$$

Chlorosulphonic acid is violently decomposed by water. It reacts violently with silver nitrate, forming nitrosonium hydrogen sulphate:

$$2ClSO_2 \cdot OH + 2AgNO_3 = 2NOHSO_4 + 2AgCl + O_2.$$

In general the salts of the acid are difficult to prepare, but the sodium salt may be made by the action of sodium chloride on the acid. The ammonium salt, $ClSO_2 \cdot ONH_4$ has been made. Chlorosulphonic acid is a powerful chlorinating and sulphonating agent. Ethyl chlorosulphonate can be made by the action of alcohol on sulphuryl chloride:

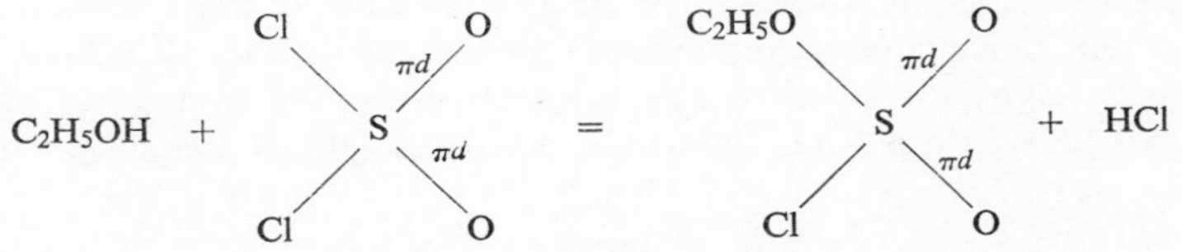

THE PEROXY SULPHURIC ACIDS

There are two peroxyacids of sulphur: peroxymonosulphuric acid, or Caro's acid, H_2SO_5, and peroxydisulphuric acid, $H_2S_2O_8$.

Peroxymonosulphuric acid, Caro's acid, H_2SO_5, exists as hygroscopic crystals, m.p. 45°. It is made:

(i) by the action of cooled chlorosulphonic acid on anhydrous hydrogen peroxide,
(ii) by the action of potassium or ammonium persulphate on ice-cold concentrated sulphuric acid:

$$HSO_3-O-O-SO_3H \quad = \quad HSO_3-O-O \quad + \quad H_2SO_4$$
$$H-OH \qquad\qquad\qquad H$$

It is stable in the air if pure. It is soluble in many aliphatic compounds, such as alcohol ether, and acetic acid, but the solutions are liable to explode; it explodes at once if mixed with aromatic compounds such as aniline, benzene, or phenol. It behaves in aqueous solution as a monobasic acid. It is slowly hydrolysed by water to sulphuric acid and hydrogen peroxide:

$$H-O-O \quad O \qquad\qquad\qquad\qquad HO \quad O$$
$$\diagdown \overset{\pi d}{\diagup} \qquad\qquad\qquad\qquad\qquad \diagdown \overset{\pi d}{\diagup}$$
$$S \quad + \quad HOH \quad = \quad H-O-O-H \quad + \quad S$$
$$\diagup \underset{\pi d}{\diagdown} \qquad\qquad\qquad\qquad\qquad \diagup \underset{\pi d}{\diagdown}$$
$$HO \quad O \qquad\qquad\qquad\qquad\qquad HO \quad O$$

The hydrolysis occurs least readily in dilute sulphuric acid; since it liberates H_2O_2 only slowly it can be used for oxidising sulphurous acid to dithionic acid (p. 830). Peroxymonosulphuric acid liberates iodine rapidly from potassium iodide, and reacts with hydrogen peroxide to yield oxygen.

No stable salt of peroxymonosulphuric acid is known.

Peroxydisulphuric acid, $H_2S_2O_8$, is a crystalline solid, m.p. 65°, with decomposition. It is made:

(i) by the action of chlorosulphonic acid on anhydrous hydrogen peroxide,
(ii) by the electrolysis of sulphuric acid, or of ammonium sulphate solution; the electrolyte must be kept cool, and the current density very high, 1–2 amp dcm^{-2}; the anode is of bright platinum, and the cathode is lead or graphite.

Peroxydisulphuric acid is more stable than Caro's acid. It is very hygroscopic. It is hydrolysed by sulphuric acid to Caro's acid, and ultimately to hydrogen peroxide. The three reactions are possible:

$$SO_3H-O-O-SO_3H + 2H_2O = H_2O_2 + 2H_2SO_4$$
$$SO_3H-O-O-SO_3H + H_2O = HOOSO_3H + H_2SO_4$$
$$2HOOSO_3H + 2H_2O = 2H_2SO_4 + 2H_2O + O_2.$$

It reacts with organic compounds and explodes with alcohol and ether.

The peroxydisulphates of the alkali metals and the alkaline earth metals (including barium) are soluble. The solubilities of the salts decrease in the order sodium, potassium, rubidium, caesium. Ammonium peroxydisulphate is more soluble than the potassium salt; thallium peroxydisulphate is less soluble than the caesium salt. Potassium peroxydisulphate is made by the action of fluorine on an aqueous solution of potassium hydrogen sulphate. Potassium peroxydisulphate decomposes if heated alone:

$$2K_2S_2O_8 = 2K_2SO_4 + 2SO_3 + O_2,$$

or in aqueous solution:

$$2K_2S_2O_8 + 2H_2O = 4KHSO_4 + O_2.$$

The peroxysulphates are powerful oxidising agents. In boiling aqueous solution in the presence of silver nitrate they convert chromium salts to dichromates, and manganous salts to permanganates. Silver nitrate also acts catalytically in promoting the oxidation of ammonia by ammonium peroxydisulphate:

$$3(NH_4)_2S_2O_8 + 8NH_3 = 6(NH_4)_2SO_4 + N_2,$$

or the decomposition of ammonium peroxydisulphate:

$$8(NH_4)_2S_2O_8 + 6H_2O = 7(NH_4)_2SO_4 + 9H_2SO_4 + 2HNO_3.$$

It has been suggested that the action of silver nitrate depends upon the transitory formation of the ion Ag^{3+}. In alkaline solution potassium peroxydisulphate converts magnesium, nickel, and lead salts to dioxides:

$$Mn(OH)_2 + K_2S_2O_8 = MnO_2 + 2KHSO_4.$$

Potassium peroxydisulphate oxidises silver nitrate in aqueous solution to a dark coloured oxide richer in oxygen than Ag_2O. The metals silver and zinc dissolve in an aqueous solution of potassium peroxydisulphate.

The reactions of peroxymonosulphuric acid and peroxydisulphuric acid with certain reducing and oxidising agents are summarised in Table 21.25; the behaviour of hydrogen peroxide with the same reagents is included for comparison.

Table 21.25. *Reactions of the Peroxysulphuric Acids with certain Reducing and Oxidising Agents*

Reagent	Result of reaction		
	with H_2SO_5	with $H_2S_2O_8$	with H_2O_2
HI	I_2 is liberated at at once	I_2 is liberated very slowly	I_2 is liberated slowly
KI buffered at 7·5 to 8·0 pH (Riesenfeld-Liebhafsky reagent)	I_2 is liberated	I_2 is liberated	O_2 is liberated
H_2O_2	O_2 is liberated	O_2 is liberated	No action
$KMnO_4 + dil.H_2SO_4$	No action	No action	O_2 is liberated
$K_2Cr_2O_7 + dil.H_2SO_4$	No action	No action	Blue CrO_5 is liberated
Titanium salts	No action	No action	Orange-red colour due to pertitanic acid is formed
Aniline	C_6H_5NO is formed	Aniline black is formed	No action

It has been shown by X-ray analysis of ammonium and caesium peroxydisulphates that the configuration of the ion is:

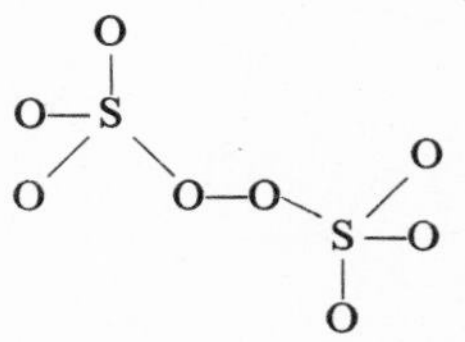

The angle SOO is 128°. The distance S—O is 1·50, and the distance O—O is 1·31; the oxygen atoms concerned are those in the peroxide link. The mid-point between the central oxygen atoms is a centre of symmetry.

SECTION 6. COMPOUNDS IN WHICH THE SULPHUR ATOM IS OCTAHEDRALLY HYBRIDISED

Sulphur hexafluoride, SF_6, is a colourless smell-less gas, remarkable for its chemical inertness. It is made by burning sulphur in fluorine. The pentafluoride, which is formed at the same time, is decomposed by passing the product through a tube heated to 400°:

$$2S_2F_{10} = 3SF_6 + SF_2.$$

The lower fluorides are removed from the hexafluoride by scrubbing with sodium hydroxide solution.

Sulphur hexafluoride condenses to a solid at $-63 \cdot 8°$ under one atmosphere; the solid melts at $-50 \cdot 7°$. The critical temperature is $+54°$. The solid is dimorphic, the transition point being $-178 \cdot 4°$. Sulphur hexafluoride is slightly soluble in water and in alcohol. It can be heated to 800° without decomposition. It is chemically inert; in the cold it is neither attacked by other elements, nor hydrolysed by water, acids, or bases. It is unaffected below a red heat by such reagents as the halogens, oxygen, boron, silicon, carbon, copper, magnesium, hydrogen chloride, or ammonia. Sodium does not react below its boiling point. Phosphorus and arsenic can be distilled in the gas. Fused potash, fused lead chromate, and glass at a low red heat do not attack it. Sulphur vapour or selenium vapour attack it at 400°. It is decomposed by hydrogen at 400°, and by sparking with hydrogen or oxygen.

Calculations based on the thermodynamic properties of sulphur hexafluoride indicate that it should be completely hydrolysed by water at 25°. Its inertness, therefore, is due to its very high energy of activation.

Sidgwick suggested that sulphur hexafluoride is inert because a sulphur atom exerting six covalent links to other atoms is covalently saturated, and therefore can neither donate nor accept any electrons. There are, however, other compounds containing fluorine and sulphur which are chemically inert. The alkyl and aryl sulphonyl fluorides, $RFSO_2$, are resistant to hydrolysis. Sulphuryl fluoride and thionyl fluoride are hydrolysed by alkalis, but they are not readily attacked by heated metals or non-metals.† The inactivity of sulphur hexafluoride is in accord with the increasing stability of the sulphur-halogen bond in the series S—I, S—Br, S—Cl, S—F.

The molecular weight of sulphur hexafluoride is normal. The configuration of the molecule is octahedral. The distance S—F is $1 \cdot 57$.

Sulphur pentafluoride, S_2F_{10}, a volatile liquid, m.p. $-92°$, b.p. $+29°$, is formed in small quantities when sulphur burns in fluorine. It is chemically inactive. The configuration of each SF_5 group in the molecule is octahedral. The two SF_5 groups are associated so that the equatorial planes are parallel, and the S—S bond is on the common axis, thus:

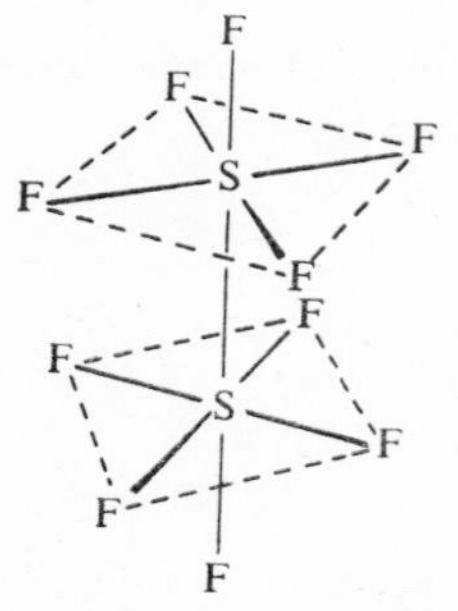

† Selenium hexafluoride (but not tellurium hexafluoride) is resistant to the attack of most other elements even when heated, but it is easily hydrolysed by aqueous alkali.

The equatorial fluorine atoms attached to different sulphur atoms are 45° out of phase. The distance S—F is 1·56, and S—S is 2·21.

Disulphur decafluorodioxide, F_5S—O—O—SF_5, has a structure similar to that of sulphur pentafluoride except that the two SF_5 groups are separated by the group —O—O—. The axes of the two SF_5 groups are not collinear; the angle SOO is 105°, and the dihedral angle is 107°. The distance O—O is 1·47.

THE NITRIDES OF SULPHUR

The bond between nitrogen and sulphur is a strong one, and an extensive chemistry is growing up of compounds with structures based on skeletons of nitrogen and sulphur atoms. The binary compounds of nitrogen and sulphur are S_2N_2, $(SN)_x$ into which S_2N_2 rapidly polymerises at room temperature, S_4N_4, and S_4N_2.†

The first two sulphur nitrides appear to be chain compounds; the remaining two are ring compounds, which, neglecting the details of the bonding, may be written:

$$\begin{matrix} S\!-\!N\!-\!S \\ | \quad\quad | \\ N \quad\quad N \\ | \quad\quad | \\ S\!-\!N\!-\!S \end{matrix}$$

Disulphur dinitride, S_2N_2, is a white, volatile solid. It is sensitive to shock, and above 35° it decomposes into its elements explosively. It is made by heating to 300° a stream of tetrasulphur tetranitride vapour, S_4N_4 (see below), at 0·1 mm pressure, and cooling the issuing gas strongly. S_2N_2 combines with ammonia to give S_2N_2,NH_3 which has been proved to be identical with the compound produced by the action of ammonia on S_4N_4. S_2N_2 can be sublimed from S_2N_2,NH_3 at room temperature. S_2N_2 is soluble in organic solvents. The molecular composition S_2N_2 has been established cryoscopically. At room temperature S_2N_2, if dry, polymerises to $(SN)_x$, if moist, to a mixture of $(SN)_x$ and S_4N_4. In an inert solvent in the presence of traces of alkali dimerisation to S_4N_4 is quantitative.

$(SN)_x$ exists as fibre-like crystals, with a metallic lustre, brass-coloured in bulk. In thin layers it is dark blue. It is made by the spontaneous polymerisation of S_2N_2 at room temperature. It is insoluble in organic solvents. It is a semi-conductor; at 25° the specific resistance is 0·013 ohm cm. The conductance rises with temperature. $(SN)_x$ is not explosive and is unaffected by shock or heat.

The molecule perhaps consists of long chains SNSNSNS····. The opportunities for resonance in such a chain would stabilise the molecule, and would account for the deep colour of the crystals. The semi-conductivity is no doubt to be explained in the same way as that of graphite.

Tetrasulphur dinitride, S_4N_2, is a dark red compound with an offensive smell, m.p. 23°. It is made by heating S_4N_4 with a solution of sulphur in carbon disulphide in an autoclave.

It is diamagnetic. The absorption spectrum suggests the atomic configuration given above.

Tetrasulphur tetranitride, S_4N_4, exists as yellow-orange crystals which darken on heating. The crystals are endothermic and explode on slight shock or on rapid heating to above 130°, but with care they can be melted (m.p. 178°) and distilled.

†Authoritative information on the nitrides of sulphur and their derivation is given by Margot Goehring, *Quart. Reviews*, X, 1956, 437.

Tetrasulphur tetranitride is made by the action of sulphur on anhydrous ammonia. If liquid ammonia is used the reaction is:

$$10S + 4NH_3 \rightleftharpoons S_4N_4 + 6H_2S.$$

The reaction is reversible, and it proceeds only if the hydrogen sulphide is precipitated as insoluble silver sulphide by the addition of silver iodide. A convenient variation of this method is the passage of dry ammonia into a solution of disulphur dichloride in benzene or ether. Some of the disulphur dichloride is reduced by the ammonia to sulphur:

$$3S_2Cl_2 + 8NH_3 = 6S + 6NH_4Cl + N_2,$$

which reacts with ammonia as above. The excess disulphur dichloride reacts with the hydrogen sulphide as it is formed, and so removes it:

$$2NH_3 + S_2Cl_2 + H_2S = 3S + 2NH_4Cl.$$

Tetrasulphur tetranitride is easily soluble in organic solvents such as benzene and carbon disulphide. It is not soluble in water which does not wet it. It undergoes numerous chemical reactions which are set out in Table 21.26.

Structure of S_4N_4. The formula S_4N_4 is decided by the f.p. of its solution in naphthalene, and by the b.p. of its solution in carbon disulphide. The d.p.m. in benzene at room temperature is 0·72.

The properties of specially prepared sulphur nitride, in which certain sulphur atoms were labelled by use of ^{35}S, gave no indication of differentiation between the sulphur atoms. K_α X-ray emission spectra show only one doublet. Hence the functions of all the sulphur atoms in the molecule are identical.[†]

Since decomposition of tetrasulphur tetranitride with alkali gives ammonia, and reduction with stannous chloride followed by decomposition with alkali also gives ammonia, there can be no N—N links in the molecule. (If the group N—N were present, direct decomposition would yield nitrogen, and reduction followed by decomposition would yield hydrazine, or one of its derivatives.)

Electron diffraction and infrared spectrum analysis show that the S—N bond lengths are 1·74, and that the angles are: SNN 110°, SNS 98°, NSN 76°. The distance S—S is 2·63, and the distance N—N is 1·47.[‡] Tetrasulphur tetranitride is diamagnetic. Two possible geometrical arrangements of the sulphur and nitrogen atoms which satisfy the above data are the puckered rings, A and B:

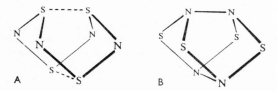

The nitrogen atoms in ring B are at the apices of a distorted tetrahedron. Some slight evidence in favour of B is furnished by the anion $(S_4N_4Al)^-$. If the structure of this anion suggested on p. 860 is correct, the aluminium atom must be surrounded tetrahedrally by the four nitrogen atoms.

[†] M. Goehring states (*loc. cit*, p. 439) that the position of the K_α doublet "corresponds to that which one would expect for a substance containing sulphur with the oxidation number $+3$". She proposes a reasonable structure for S_4N_4 of ten canonical forms, in which different sulphur atoms exert 2, 3, or 4 bonds.

[‡] *Tables of Interatomic Distances and Configurations in Molecules and Ions*, London Chemical Society, 1958, M76, where other values are also given.

An orbital structure for either of the models A or B in which each sulphur atom and each nitrogen atom exerts two covalent bonds, so that each sulphur atom controls

Table 21.26. *Reactions of Tetrasulphur Tetranitride*, S_4N_4

Reagent and conditions	Result
Heat rapidly to above 130°	Explodes
Heat to 300° at 0·1 mm	Disulphur dinitride, S_2N_2, which polymerises to $(SN)_x$
Water	No action
Dilute sodium hydroxide solution	$2S_4N_4 + 6NaOH + 9H_2O = Na_2S_2O_3 + 2Na_2S_3O_6 + 8NH_3$
Concentrated sodium hydroxide solution	$S_4N_4 + 6NaOH + 3H_2O = Na_2S_2O_3 + 2Na_2SO_3 + 4NH_3$
Stannous chloride in a mixture of benzene and alcohol	Tetrasulphur tetraimide: $\begin{array}{ccc} HN-S-NH \\ \mid \qquad \mid \\ S \qquad S \\ \mid \qquad \mid \\ HN-S-NH \end{array}$
$(C_2H_5)_2NH$	$(C_2H_5)_2N-S-N(C_2H_5)_2$
S_2Cl_2, or hydrogen chloride	$3S_4N_4 + 2S_2Cl_2 = 4(S_4N_3)Cl$, thiotrithiazyl chloride
S in CS_2 solution, heated in autoclave	S_4N_2 Tetrasulphur dinitride
Thionyl chloride	$S_3N_2O_2$ Trisulphur dinitrogen dioxide
AgF_2 in CCl_4	$S_4N_4F_4$
Chlorination	$S_3N_3Cl_3$
Bromination	$(BrSN)_x$
Ammonia	S_2N_2,NH_3 or, $(H-\overset{-}{N}-S-N{=}\overset{+}{S}-NH_2)$
Methyl alcohol	S_2N_2,CH_3OH (or, $H-\overset{-}{N}-S-N{=}\overset{+}{S}-OCH_3$)
Transition metals (Ni, Pd, Co) halides in alcoholic solution	$M(NS)_4$
Metal carbonyls in inert solvents (Ni, Co, Fe)	$M(NS)_4$
Cobalt carbonyl hydride	$Co(NS)_4$
Sulphur trioxide	$S_4N_4,2SO_3$ and $S_4N_4,4SO_3$
NO_2	$[NO]_2S_2O_7$

eight valency electrons, and each nitrogen atom controls seven valency electrons, is ruled out because it is in conflict with the diamagnetism of tetrasulphur tetranitride. Such a structure would be acceptable, however, if coupling between two nitrogen atoms nullifies the paramagnetic effect of the unpaired electrons in the nitrogen atoms.

It can be seen from Table 19.3, p. 652 that this model for the molecule of tetrasulphur tetranitride is similar to that put forward for the molecule of As_4S_4. These structures are related both to the 8-membered puckered ring of the elementary sulphur molecule S_8, and to the tetrahedral arrangement of the atoms of the Group V element which is present in the molecules P_4 and As_4. The orbital structure of the S_4N_4 molecule is quite uncertain. It is probably a resonance structure with a large number of canonical forms. The formulae in the following pages used to describe tetrasulphur tetranitride and its derivatives are intended to show only the geometrical configurations of the molecules; the positions of formal charges and double bonds are uncertain and therefore they are omitted.

Tetrasulphur tetraimide, $S_4N_4H_4$, crystallises as colourless needles, m.p. 152°. It is made by dissolving tetrasulphur tetranitride in a mixture of benzene and alcohol, and treating the solution with stannous chloride. It is soluble in acetone or pyridine, but in few other solvents. It is stable to air and moisture, and is only very slowly attacked by acids and alkalis unless these are very concentrated.

The molecular weight by elevation of the b.p. of acetone corresponds to $S_4N_4H_4$. Concentrated alkalis convert all the nitrogen to ammonia; tetrasulphur tetraimide cannot be converted to hydrazine or to nitrogen, and hence N—N bonds appear to be absent from the molecule.

It reacts with formaldehyde to give a compound $(CH_2OH)_4S_4N_4$, of which the molecular weight has been determined in benzene solution, and with phenyl isocyanate to give $(C_6H_5NH \cdot CO)_4S_4N_4$. The infrared spectrum shows NH frequencies, but no SH frequencies. The structural formulae of tetrasulphur tetraimide, and of its compound with formaldehyde and phenyl isocyanate are therefore:

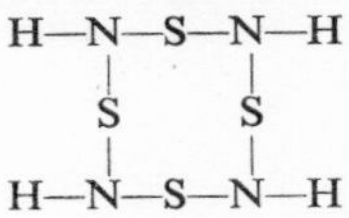

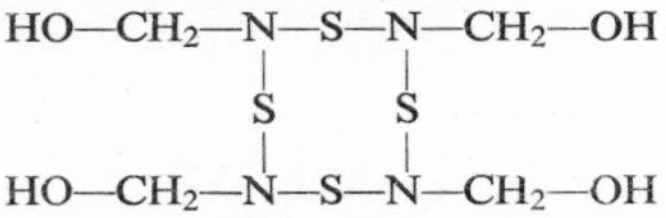

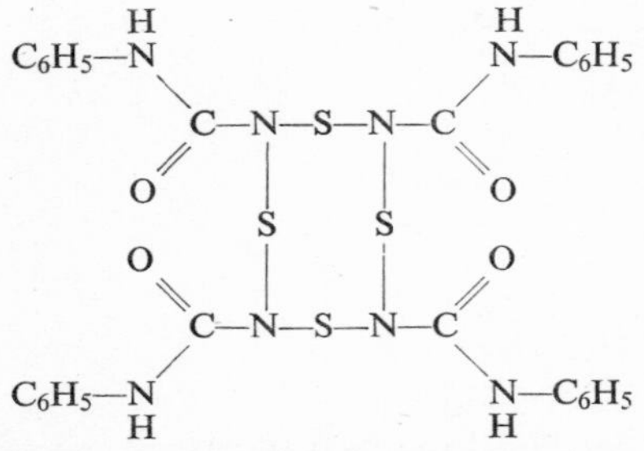

$S_4N_4H_4$ is easily oxidised back again to S_4N_4, for instance by chlorine. Other reactions of tetrasulphur tetraimide (p. 860) are the conversion of cuprous chloride to $(CuNS)_x$, and of lithium aluminium hydride to $Li(S_4N_4Al)$.

Heptasulphur monoimide, S_7NH, forms colourless crystals, m.p. 113·5°. The infrared spectrum shows NH bands. It is a by-product in the preparation of S_4N_4 by the reaction between disulphur dichloride and ammonia.

It reacts with mercuric mercury to give $Hg(S_7N)_2$, and with mercurous mercury to give $Hg_2(S_7N)_2$. The sodium derivative $Na(S_7N)$ has been reported. With formaldehyde it gives the stable hydroxy methyl derivative:

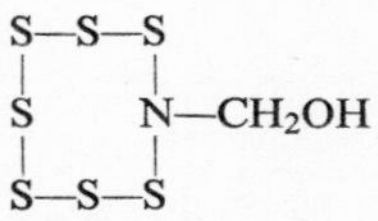

$$\begin{array}{ccc} S-S-S & & \\ | & | & \\ S & & N-CH_2OH \\ | & | & \\ S-S-S & & \end{array}$$

With acetyl chloride or benzoyl chloride it gives:

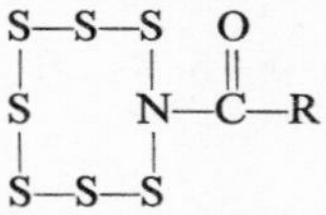

$$\begin{array}{cccc} S-S-S & & O & \\ | & | & \| & \\ S & & N-C-R \\ | & | & \\ S-S-S & & \end{array}$$

and with sulphur trioxide:

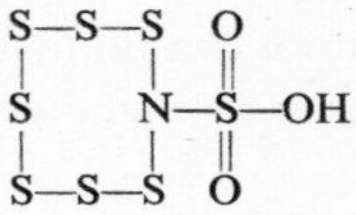

$$\begin{array}{cccc} S-S-S & & O & \\ | & | & \| & \\ S & & N-S-OH \\ | & | & \| & \\ S-S-S & & O & \end{array}$$

HALOGEN AND OXYGEN DERIVATIVES OF TETRASULPHUR TETRANITRIDE

$S_4N_4F_4$ consists of colourless needles. It is made by the action of argentic fluoride on tetrasulphur tetranitride in carbon tetrachloride solution at room temperature. Its d.p.m. is zero. It is quantitatively hydrolysed by warm dilute alkali thus:

$$S_4N_4F_4 + 12H_2O = 4NH_4F + 4H_2SO_3.$$

SN_2F_2. Fluorination of tetrasulphur tetranitride in boiling carbon tetrachloride gives a colourless gas, SN_2F_2, b.p. $-11°$, m.p. $-108°$. When hydrolysed it yields the same products as the tetrafluoride. The structures of these nitrogen sulphur fluorides are not known.

Trithiazyl chloride, $S_3N_3Cl_3$, is assumed to have the ring structure:

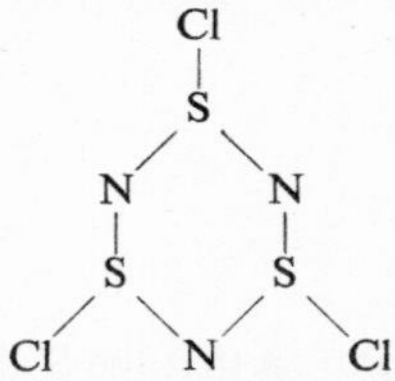

The chlorination of tetrasulphur tetranitride produces a yellow solid with a molecular weight corresponding to the formula, $S_3N_3Cl_3$. Concentrated hydrochloric acid reacts to break up the molecule:

$$6H_2O + S_3N_3Cl_3 = 3SO_2 + 3NH_4Cl,$$

but there are many reactions in which the ring structure is preserved. Sulphur trioxide reacts thus:

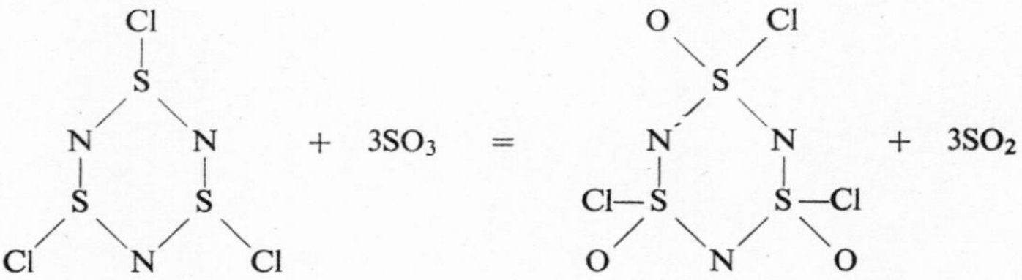

Sulphanuric
chloride

and tetrasulphur tetraimide thus:

$$
4 \quad
\begin{array}{c}
N \\
\text{Cl—S} \quad \text{S—Cl} \\
| \quad\quad | \\
N \quad\quad N \\
\text{S} \\
| \\
\text{Cl}
\end{array}
+ 3
\begin{array}{c}
\text{H—N—S—N—H} \\
| \quad\quad | \\
\text{S} \quad\quad \text{S} \\
| \quad\quad | \\
\text{H—N—S—N—H}
\end{array}
= 6
\begin{array}{c}
\text{N—S—N} \\
| \quad\quad | \\
\text{S} \quad\quad \text{S} \\
| \quad\quad | \\
\text{N—S—N}
\end{array}
+ \quad 12\text{HCl}
$$

Nitrogen dioxide gives $(NO)_2S_2O_7$, as it does with S_4N_4, and nitric oxide gives a dark green compound, S_3N_2Cl, of unknown constitution.

Thiotrithiazyl chloride, N_3S_4Cl, is a bright yellow, sternutatory powder which explodes on heating.

It is made by refluxing sulphur nitride with S_2Cl_2 in carbon tetrachloride:

$$3S_4N_4 + 2S_2Cl_2 = 4(N_3S_4)Cl.$$

It is quite insoluble in many organic solvents. It is a salt and by double decomposition it gives other salts: $(N_3S_4)^+(NO_3)^-$, crystalline, and $(N_3S_4)^+I^-$, and $(N_3S_4)^+(HSO_4)^-$. The structure of the ion $[N_3S_4]^+$ has not yet been established.

Trisulphur dinitrogen dioxide, $S_3N_2O_2$, consists of yellow crystals, not wetted by water, but easily soluble in organic solvents. It is made by the action between tetrasulphur tetranitride and thionyl chloride in the presence of sulphur dioxide. A little water hydrolyses it thus:

$$
2 \quad
\begin{array}{c}
\text{S} \\
N \quad\quad N \\
| \quad\quad | \\
\text{S} \quad\quad \text{S—O} \\
\text{O}
\end{array}
=
\begin{array}{c}
N \\
\text{S} \quad\quad \text{S} \\
N \quad\quad\quad N \\
\text{S} \quad\quad \text{S} \\
N
\end{array}
+ \quad 2SO_2
$$

By labelling with ^{35}S it has been shown that the S atom attached to two oxygen atoms is derived from $SOCl_2$ during the formation of the compound, and that this atom is present in the sulphur dioxide. Trisulphur dinitrogen dioxide is readily hydrolysed to ammonium trithionate, $(NH_4)_2S_3O_6$. It is oxidised by sulphur trioxide to $S_3N_2O_5$.

Trisulphur dinitrogen pentoxide, $S_3N_2O_5$, is a white solid. It may be prepared by the smooth oxidation of trisulphur dinitrogen dioxide by sulphur trioxide:

$$
\begin{array}{c}
\text{S} \\
N \quad\quad N \\
| \quad\quad | \\
\text{S} \quad\quad \text{S—O} \\
\text{O}
\end{array}
=
\begin{array}{c}
\text{S} \\
N \quad\quad N \\
O \quad\quad\quad O \\
\text{S} \quad\quad \text{S} \\
O \quad\quad\quad O \\
O
\end{array}
$$

It can also be prepared by the action of sulphur trioxide on tetrasulphur tetranitride.

Goehring gives the sequence ($*S = {}^{35}S$):

$$
\begin{array}{ccc}
\text{N—S—N} & & \text{S} \\
|\quad\quad| & \xrightarrow{+\overset{*}{S}O_3} & \diagup\;\diagdown \\
\text{S}\quad\quad\text{S} & & O_3\overset{*}{S}\text{—N}\quad\text{N—}\overset{*}{S}O_3 \\
|\quad\quad| & & |\quad\quad\quad| \\
\text{N—S—N} & & \text{S}\quad\quad\quad\text{S} \\
& & |\quad\quad\quad| \\
& & O_3\overset{*}{S}\text{—N}\quad\text{N—}\overset{*}{S}O_3 \\
& & \diagdown\;\diagup \\
& & \text{S}
\end{array}
$$

$\xrightarrow{+\overset{*}{S}O_3}$

$$
\begin{array}{c}
\text{S} \\
\diagup\;\diagdown \\
\text{N}\quad\quad\text{N} \\
|\quad\quad\quad| \\
O_2\overset{*}{S}\quad\quad\overset{*}{S}O_2 \\
\diagdown\;\diagup \\
\text{O}
\end{array}
\quad + \quad 2SO_2 + 2\overset{*}{S}O_2
$$

$2H_2O$ ↓ (to lower left, SO_2)

$$
\begin{array}{c}
H_2N\quad\quad NH_2 \\
|\quad\quad\quad| \\
O_2\overset{*}{S}*\quad\quad*SO_2 \\
\diagdown\;\diagup \\
\text{O}
\end{array}
$$

$2H_2O$ ↙ SO_2

$$
\begin{array}{c}
H_3N\quad\quad NH_2 \\
\overset{*}{H_2SO_4}\quad *SO_2 \\
\quad\quad| \\
\quad\quad HO
\end{array}
$$

$2H_2O$ ↓ (right branch)

$$
\begin{array}{c}
SO_2
\end{array}
$$

$$
\begin{array}{c}
HN\quad\quad NH_2 \\
\|\quad\quad\quad| \\
O_2\overset{*}{S}*\quad\quad*SO_3H
\end{array}
$$

$S_3N_2O_5$ can be sublimed. It is soluble in organic solvents. It is to be recognised as a derivative of disulphuric acid, $H_2S_2O_7$; two OH groups in the acid are replaced by the bridging group N_2S.

Derivatives of the eight-membered ring:

$$
\begin{array}{c}
\quad\quad O_2 \\
HN—\,S—NH \\
|\quad\quad\quad| \\
O_2S\quad\quad SO_2 \\
|\quad\quad\quad| \\
HN—S—NH \\
\quad\quad O_2
\end{array}
$$

are known, but the ring cannot be made by direct oxidation of S_4N_4.

THE METAL THIONITROSYLATES

Several metal thionitrosylates have been reported. All are solids. Their formulae and colours are set out in Table 21.27. For convenience of discussion the Table is divided into five sections.

Section I. The metal nitrosylates in this section are prepared by the action of disulphur dinitride ammoniate in liquid ammonia on a halide or nitrate of the metal in its lowest valency state. The disulphur dinitride ammoniate appears to act as though dissociated thus:

$$H_2N\text{—}\overset{+}{S}\!\!=\!\!N\text{—}S\text{—}\overset{-}{N}\text{—}H \;=\; H\text{—}\overset{-}{N}\text{—}\overset{+}{S}\!\!=\!\!N\text{—}H \;+\; S\!\!=\!\!N\text{—}H$$

The thionitrosylate is formed by the action of $S\!\!=\!\!N$—H; the di-imide of ortho-sulphurous acid acts as an oxidising agent, and it may raise the valency of the metal, thus:

$$2NH_4^+ + 2Cu^+ + HN\text{—}SNH \;=\; 2Cu^{2+} + 3NH_3 + SNH.$$

Section II. The metal thionitrosylates of Section II are made by treating cuprous chloride, silver nitrate, or mercuric chloride, with tetrasulphur tetraimide in pyridine solution. Little is known about these compounds. Doubtless they are polymerised;

Table 21.27.   *The Metal Thionitrosylates*

	Metal thionitrosylate	Colour	Remarks
Section I	$Pb(NS)_2$ $Tl(NS)_3$ $TlNS,5Tl(NS)_3$ $Ag(NS)_2$ $Cu(NS)_2$	Red Red-brown Ochre Red-brown Brown	Sensitive to heat and shock
Section II	$[Cu(NS)]_4$ $[Ag(NS)]_4$ $[Hg_2(NS)_2]_2$ $[Hg(NS)_2]_x$ $Cu(NS)_2Cl_2$	Brown-black Red-brown	For reaction with ethyl iodide, see below In solution monomeric and para-magnetic; diamagnetic in the solid
Section III	$Fe(NS)_4$ $Co(NS)_4$ $Ni(NS)_4$† $Pd(NS)_4$ $Pt(NS)_4$	Black Deep violet Deep violet Red Dark blue	Magnetic moment 2·94 Bohr. Mag. Magnetic moment 1·90 Bohr. Mag. Diamagnetic
Section IV	$Li(S_4N_4Al)$	White solid	Explosive
Section V	$[Na(NS)]_4$	Yellow solid	Burns in contact with traces of air or water

† It is reported that the correct formula of the nickel compound is $NiN_4S_4H_4$. (T. S. Piper, *Chem. and Ind.*, 1957, 1101.)

AgNS reacts with ethyl iodide to yield $S_4N_4(C_2H_5)_4$, and there is this evidence to show that the S_4N_4 ring is present.

Section III. The metal thionitrosylates of Section III are crystalline and stable. They are insoluble in water, but are soluble in organic solvents. Three methods are available for their preparation:

(a) A halide of the divalent metal is treated with an alcoholic solution of S_4N_4 in the presence of sodium dithionite, $Na_2S_2O_4$, as a reducing agent.
(b) The metallic carbonyl is treated with S_4N_4 in an inert solvent.
(c) The finely divided metal is treated with a solution of S_2N_2. This method gives a small yield only.

The platinum compound is made by treating chloroplatinic acid, H_2PtCl_6, with S_4N_4 in solution in hot dimethyl formamide.

Section IV. The compound, $Li(S_4N_4Al)$, is clearly different from the compounds previously discussed. It is made by a reaction between lithium aluminium hydride and tetrasulphur tetraimide:

$$Li(AlH_4) + S_4N_4H_4 = Li(S_4N_4Al) + 4H_2.$$

When dry the compound detonates if disturbed. On gentle hydrolysis the tetrasulphur tetraimide is formed again:

$$Li(S_4N_4Al) + 2H_2O = S_4N_4H_4 + LiAlO_2.$$

This reaction suggests that the S_4N_4 ring persists in $Li(S_4N_4Al)$ and the anion might have the structure:

$$\begin{bmatrix} S-N-S \\ | \quad | \quad | \\ N-Al-N \\ | \quad | \quad | \\ S-N-S \end{bmatrix}^{-}$$

Section V. The yellow sodium compound $[Na(NS)]_4$ is made by the action of tetra-sulphur tetraimide on sodium triphenylmethyl.

CHAPTER TWENTY-TWO

SUB-GROUP VI N (CONTINUED). SELENIUM, TELLURIUM AND POLONIUM

SELENIUM

THE ELEMENT

Selenium exists in two amorphous forms and in three crystalline forms.

Amorphous selenium. A red amorphous form is obtained as the immediate product when selenium is precipitated as the result of a chemical action in aqueous solution. Examples of such actions are the action of sulphur dioxide on selenous acid in aqueous solution, and the action of hydrochloric acid on potassium selenocyanide in aqueous solution. The sp. gr. of the red form is 4·26. It is a photoconductor. It is sparingly soluble in carbon disulphide, and readily soluble in selenium oxychloride. The red amorphous form turns black when boiled with water.

A black amorphous form, or vitreous selenium, is made by quenching molten selenium in cold water. It is an opaque, almost black, lustrous solid, but when powdered it is reddish at $-80°$, and quite red at the temperature of liquid nitrogen; sp. gr. 4·28. It softens at 50°, and if heated rapidly to 220° is liquid but viscous. Above 70° it changes to grey crystalline selenium.

The crystalline grey form is the stable form to which all other forms revert if maintained at 200°. The vapour condenses to this form if it is cooled above 200°. The m.p. of the grey form is 220°, and the sp. gr. is 4·80. The grey form is insoluble in carbon disulphide, but soluble in chloroform. Although the grey form is metallic in appearance, its electrical conductivity is only 2×10^{-6} ohm^{-1} cm^{-1}. The conductance is increased about 1000 times when selenium is exposed to light, but falls again when the exposure ceases. The crystals are hexagonal and are composed of continuous chains of selenium atoms arranged spirally round the parallel edges of a cube. Single crystals may be obtained by distilling pure selenium at 300° into glass tubes, sealing off, and heating to the b.p. of naphthalene for several months. Crystals 4 cm long have been obtained.

The two crystalline red forms, α and β, are produced by crystallising a solution of red amorphous selenium in carbon disulphide. The solution is orange red, and the crystals are red. They are monoclinic. The m.p. is about 150°, and the sp. gr. 4·47. The crystals are metastable and revert to the grey form.

The α selenium crystals contain a molecule which is an 8-membered ring similar to that of the sulphur molecule. The average value of the distance Se—Se is $2·34 \pm 0·02$, and the angle SeSeSe is $105·3 \pm 2·3°$. It is probable that the molecule of β selenium is also an 8-membered ring, but general agreement on the constitution of β selenium is still awaited.

Liquid selenium is brownish-red; sp. gr. 4·05. It boils at 685° to a dark red vapour.

The molecular weight of selenium in the vapour state and in solution has been measured. At 900° and somewhat higher temperatures the molecular weight corresponds to the formula Se_2, at 2000° it corresponds to Se, and at 200° to Se_6. Electron diffraction experiments indicate that the distance Se—Se in Se_2 is 2·19. The molecular weight of selenium in solution in carbon disulphide, liquid sulphur, diphenyl, and yellow phosphorus, corresponds to Se_8.

Chemical properties of selenium. Selenium is a reactive element which combines with hydrogen, chlorine, and the metals. It takes up hydrogen so readily that it is used for reducing hydroaromatic compounds to aromatic, and it is converted to SeH_2 when heated with a paraffin oil. When heated in air it burns with a blue flame to selenium dioxide, SeO_2, and it is oxidised by hot nitric acid to selenous acid, H_2SeO_3, but it is oxidised only with difficulty to compounds in which the selenium atom is 4 co-ordinate.

Chlorine converts selenium to Se_2Cl_2 or to $[SeCl_3]Cl$, according to the proportions in which the reagents are present. Hot silver nitrate solution reacts with selenium to yield silver selenide:

$$4AgNO_3 + 3Se + 3H_2O = 2Ag_2Se + H_2SeO_3 + 4HNO_3.$$

Selenium reacts directly with a Grignard reagent to give an alkyl selenium hydride. It combines vigorously with many metals, in particular with sodium to give Na_2Se, and with aluminium to give Al_2Se_3. It combines with potassium cyanide to give potassium selenocyanide, $KCNSe$. Selenium is little affected by dilute alkali, but it dissolves in concentrated alkali solutions, or in fused alkali according to the equation:

$$3Se + 6NaOH = 2Na_2Se + Na_2SeO_3 + 3H_2O.$$

Selenium dissolves in a solution of sodium sulphite, but is reprecipitated on dilution (p. 872).

THE GENERAL CHEMISTRY OF SELENIUM

The electron configuration of the valency shell ($n=4$) of the selenium atom in the ground state is:

$4s$	$4p$	$4p$	$4p$	$4d$	$4d$	$4d$	$4d$	$4d$
⇅	⇅	↑	↑					

The penultimate shell contains eighteen electrons which are never used in bond formation. The $4s$ electron pair is inert in the anions $[SeCl_6^{2-}]$ and $[SeBr_6^{2-}]$ (p. 865). The selenium atom accepts two electrons to form the ion $[Se^{2-}]$; the selenides of the alkali metals and of the transition metals are similar to the corresponding sulphides.

The general pattern of the chemistry of selenium follows that of sulphur, but the methods of preparation and the stabilities of selenium compounds often differ considerably from those of the sulphur compounds of corresponding types. This difference is not altogether to be expected, because the valence shells of both the sulphur and the selenium atoms contain d orbitals, and hence the double bonds exerted by either of the atoms are πd bonds; it is the exertion of πd bonds rather than πp bonds which differentiates the chemistry of sulphur from that of oxygen.

Compared with sulphur, selenium has an increased affinity for hydrogen and a diminished affinity for oxygen. In its diminished affinity for oxygen selenium is showing behaviour common to all the three elements at the end of Period 4, arsenic, selenium, and bromine; comment on the oxygen derivatives of arsenic is made on p. 738. A comparison of the different behaviour of corresponding compounds of sulphur and selenium on oxidation or reduction is made below. It is to be noted that the sulphur atom tends to become 4 co-ordinate when oxidised, whereas the selenium atom tends to become 3 co-ordinate. This contrast is apparent in Charts 21.1 (p. 812) and 22.1.

864

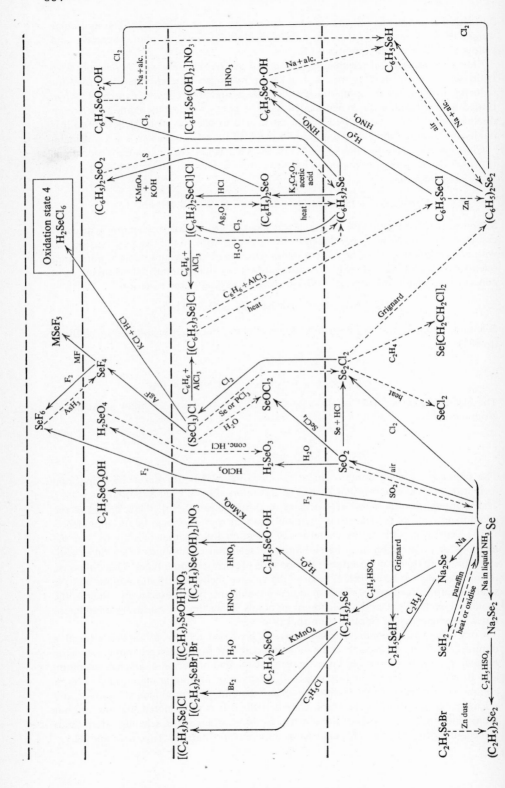

Table 22.1. *Comparison of the Effect of Oxidation and Reduction on certain Compounds of Sulphur and Selenium*

1. Sulphur in C_2H_5—S—S—C_2H_5 is oxidised by nitric acid to ethyl sulphonic acid, $C_2H_5SO_2 \cdot OH$; selenium in C_2H_5—Se—Se—C_2H_5 is oxidised by nitric acid only to the hydronitrate $[C_2H_5Se(OH)_2]NO_3$ which is a derivative of seleninic acid.
2. Sulphur is oxidised by nitric acid to H_2SO_4; selenium to H_2SeO_3.
3. H_2SO_4 when dehydrated with phosphorus pentoxide gives SO_3; H_2SeO_4 in the corresponding reaction gives $SeO_2 + O_2$.
4. A sulphate is not attacked by sulphur dioxide, but a selenate is reduced to selenium by sulphur dioxide in concentrated hydrochloric acid.
5. Ethyl iodide reacts with silver sulphite to give ethyl ethylsulphonate, $C_2H_5(C_2H_5O)SO_2$; ethyl iodide reacts with silver selenite to give diethyl selenite, $(C_2H_5O)_2SeO$.
6. The hydrolysis of diethyl sulphite gives sodium ethyl sulphonate, $NaC_2H_5SO_3$; the hydrolysis of diethyl selenite gives sodium selenite, Na_2SeO_3.
7. Sulphur forms a wide range of sulphones, but only two selenones are known (p. 877).

There is a marked contrast between the oxides of sulphur and those of selenium. Some of the differences are set out below:

	SO_2	SeO_2	SO_3	SeO_3
Appearance	Gas m.p. $-75 \cdot 5°$	Crystals m.p. 340°	White solid m.p. $16 \cdot 8°$	White solid m.p. 118°
Configuration of molecule	Planar	Chain	Planar	Pyramidal
Properties	A reducing agent	Easily reduced to selenium	Decomposes at a red heat	Decomposes above 180°

There is a greater difference between the two dioxides than there is between the two trioxides.

There are few examples of the selenium atom in the digonal and trigonal valence states, but there are many compounds in which it is tetrahedrally hybridised. These compounds include those which contain chains of selenium atoms, but selenium chains are not found so frequently as sulphur chains; polyselenides such as CH_3Se—$SeCH_3$ are known, but there are no compounds corresponding to the polythionic acids. There are, however, selenium derivatives of the polythionic acids (p. 872).

Selenium forms a number of compounds having molecules of the general formula SeX_4 (p. 872). Certain of these compounds are undoubtedly selenonium compounds, and should be formulated $[SX_3{}^+]X^-$, but certain others, including selenium diphenyl dibromide and dichloride, have trigonal bipyramidal structures.

The selenium atom is octahedrally hybridised in selenium hexafluoride SeF_6 which, like SF_6, is highly inert. Selenium nitride, Se_4N_4, is known and it appears to be comparable to S_4N_4.

COMPOUNDS IN WHICH ONLY 4 VALENCY ELECTRONS OF SELENIUM ARE ACTIVE

The only compounds of selenium in which the $4s$ electrons in the selenium atom are inert are the complex halides M_2SeCl_6 and M_2SeBr_6 (fluorine and iodine do not form such compounds).

Potassium hexachloroselenite, K_2SeCl_6, is made by adding a solution of potassium chloride in hydrochloric acid to a solution of selenium tetrachloride in hydrochloric acid. Anhydrous potassium hexachloroselenite crystallises when the solution is cooled

28 + A.T.I.C.

to 0°. The salt is hygroscopic and is hydrolysed by water. The ammonium and alkyl-amine salts are also known.

Potassium hexabromoselenite, K_2SeBr_6, a dark red salt, is made from selenium tetra-bromide by a reaction corresponding to that used for making the hexachloroselenite. Potassium hexabromoselenite readily loses bromine. The ammonium salt $(NH_4)_2SeBr_6$ is isomorphous with $(NH_4)_2PtBr_6$, which indicates that the ion $[SeBr_6{}^{2-}]$ is octahedral.

Hexabromoselenic acid, H_2SeBr_6, can be obtained as dark red crystals by adding selenium tetrabromide to concentrated hydrobromic acid.

It is probable that the six bonding orbitals of the selenium atom in these compounds are octahedral hybrids of the combination $4p^3 4d^2 5s$.

COMPOUNDS IN WHICH ALL 6 VALENCY ELECTRONS OF SELENIUM ARE ACTIVE

SECTION 1. SELENIUM COMPOUNDS CONSISTING OF GIANT MOLECULES IN WHICH THE BONDS HAVE BOTH IONIC AND COVALENT CHARACTER

The principal selenium compounds in this Section are the metal selenides. The selenides of the alkali metals are colourless and soluble. In solution they are oxidised by air to elementary selenium. Li_2Se, Na_2Se, and K_2Se have the antifluorite lattice. MgSe, CaSe, SrSe, and BaSe have the rock-salt lattice, but BeSe has the zinc blende lattice. ZnSe and HgSe also have the zinc blende structure, and CdSe has the wurtzite struc-ture. Cu_2Se and Ag_2Se are dimorphic; the structures of the low temperature forms are not known; the high temperature forms have defect lattices.

The oxides of selenium are the trioxide SeO_3 and the dioxide SeO_2; attempts to make SeO have failed, although TeO is well-characterised. The chemistry of selenium trioxide resembles that of sulphur trioxide, but the chemistry of selenium dioxide differs from that of sulphur dioxide. The structure of crystalline selenium dioxide consists of long chains which justifies its inclusion among giant molecule compounds. The structure of the group SeO_3 is pyramidal.

SELENIUM OXIDES

Selenium dioxide, SeO_2, exists as colourless crystals, m.p. 340° under pressure, sublima-tion point (1 atm), 315°.

Selenium dioxide is formed when selenium burns in air or oxygen, and it is made by heating selenous acid obtained by oxidising selenium with nitric acid.

The liquid and the vapour are yellow. Selenium dioxide absorbs water from the air, and it is very soluble in water, from which it crystallises as selenous acid. It dissolves in concentrated sulphuric acid, or in selenic acid, to give yellow solutions.

Selenium dioxide is very easily reduced to elementary selenium by sulphur dioxide, hydriodic acid, sulphur, and many other reducing agents. It is used as an oxidising agent in organic chemistry to oxidise the group $CH_2 \cdot CO$ to the group $CO \cdot CO$, thus:

$$CH_2(COOC_2H_5)_2 + SeO_2 = CO(COOC_2H_5)_2 + Se + H_2O,$$

and
$$CH_3 \cdot CH_2 \cdot C\overset{O}{\diagup}_{\diagdown R} + SeO_2 = CH_3 \cdot CO \cdot C\overset{O}{\diagup}_{\diagdown R} + Se + H_2O$$

R may be a hydrocarbon radical or hydrogen.

The property of selenium dioxide which enables it to oxidise certain organic compounds to ketone or aldehyde derivatives but no further, is remarkable. Chromium shows a similar property in Etard's reaction.

Ethylene and propylene also react with selenium dioxide thus:

$$2CH_2\!\!=\!\!CH_2 + 3SeO_2 = 2HC\!\!=\!\!O \cdot HC\!\!=\!\!O + 3Se + 2H_2O.$$

If, however, selenium dioxide in cold chloroform solution is added to an alkyl buta-diene (but not to butadiene itself) a quite different reaction occurs, and a cyclic sele-none is produced:

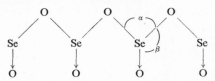

Selenium dioxide absorbs gaseous hydrogen fluoride to give a mobile fuming liquid which attacks glass only slightly (cf. $SeOF_2$, p. 874). On distillation a product is left with composition approximately $SeO_2,5HF$.

Selenium dioxide absorbs gaseous hydrogen chloride to give a mixture of $SeO_2,4HCl$ a yellow solid stable at $0°$, and $SeO_2,2HCl$ a yellow liquid stable up to $170°$ at which temperature it distils with some decomposition. The compound $SeO_2,2HCl$ is best made by passing hydrogen chloride over selenium dioxide at $30°$.

The density of the vapour corresponds to the molecular formula SeO_2; the distance Se—O is 1·61. In solution in $SeOCl_2$ the molecule is $(SeO_2)_3$. X-ray examination shows that the solid consists of chains of indefinite length:†

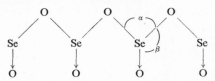

The distance Se—O in the chain is 1·79; outside, 1·73. The angles are:

Se—O—Se 125°; α, O—Se—O 90°; β, O—Se→O 90°.

The three bonds exerted by each selenium atom are not in the same plane.

Selenium trioxide, SeO_3, is a white deliquescent solid, m.p. 118°. There is no definite boiling point. Selenium trioxide cannot be made by the dehydration of selenic acid. The dehydration of selenic acid yields a mixture of selenium dioxide and oxygen, a reaction which when compared with the dehydration of sulphuric acid illustrates that the affinity of selenium for oxygen is less than that of sulphur for oxygen.

Selenium trioxide is made:

(i) by passing a glow discharge through a mixture of oxygen and selenium vapour at 4 mm,

(ii) by treating K_2SeO_4 with sulphur trioxide:

$$K_2SeO_4 + 3SO_3 = K_2S_3O_{10} + SeO_3.$$

Two liquid layers are formed; the upper is a solution of SeO_3 in SO_3. After separation, the SO_3 is vaporised off, leaving SeO_3.

Two crystalline forms of selenium trioxide have been obtained, one cubic, and the other as needles like asbestos. The cubic form is made by sublimation of the needles; it corresponds to α-SO_3. The needle form is probably a highly polymerised selenic acid. The liquid is colourless and highly refractive. It super-cools readily. When heated above 180° selenium trioxide dissociates to $SeO_2 + O_2$. It dissolves in water with the evolution of heat, but less violently than sulphur trioxide, to yield a solution of selenic acid, H_2SeO_4. The configuration of the molecule of selenium trioxide is pyramidal.

† Cf. thionyl imide (p. 820).

SECTION 2. COMPOUNDS IN WHICH THE SELENIUM ATOM IS DIGONALLY HYBRIDISED

Selenium forms the compounds CSe_2 (p. 589), $COSe$ (p. 590), and $CSSe$, which in composition are analogous to carbon disulphide and carbon oxysulphide. The selenium compounds, however, are very much less stable than the corresponding compounds of sulphur (Table 18.10, p. 588). There is no evidence on the structures of these selenium compounds, but it is assumed that they are analogous to the structure of carbon dioxide. If this is so, the selenium atoms must be exerting double bonds; the π bonds are probably πd bonds. The instability of the compounds is in accord with the considerable difference in energy between the carbon $2p$ atomic orbitals and the selenium $4d$ orbitals.

SECTION 3. THE SELENIUM ATOM AND THE TRIGONAL VALENCE STATE

The selenium compounds which might contain the selenium atom in the trigonal valence state are limited to certain canonical forms of carbon diselenide and other compounds mentioned in Section 2. The orbital structures of the two selenium oxides are not known, but it is clear that they do not contain the selenium atom in the trigonal valence state.

SECTION 4. COMPOUNDS IN WHICH THE SELENIUM ATOM IS TETRAHEDRALLY HYBRIDISED

The hydroselenides, MSeH, where M is an alkali metal, can be made by passing selenium hydride through a solution of the metal ethoxide in alcohol. The hydroselenides of sodium, potassium, and rubidium have rocksalt lattices; that of caesium has the caesium chloride lattice. The hydroselenides are decomposed by air and wat r.

SELENIUM HYDRIDE AND ITS ALKYL AND ARYL DERIVATIVES

Selenium hydride, SeH_2, is a colourless poisonous gas, b.p. $-41 \cdot 5°$, m.p. $-66°$. Its smell is more offensive than that of hydrogen sulphide. It is made:

(i) by the action of acids on aluminium selenide,
(ii) by heating selenium to 380° with a high boiling paraffin oil,
(iii) by heating a mixture of selenium and dry magnesium hydroxide to 225°.

Selenium hydride is inflammable in air. It decomposes into its elements slowly at room temperature and rapidly at 300°. It combines with ammonia gas to form solid $(NH_4)_2Se$.

Water dissolves three volumes at 0°. A solid hydrate exists, H_2Se,xH_2O, with a dissociation pressure of 432 mm at 2°. The dissociation constant,

$$K = \frac{[H][HSe]}{[H_2Se]} = 1 \cdot 3 \times 10^{-4},$$

and hence selenium hydride is a stronger acid than hydrogen sulphide. The aqueous solution is oxidised on exposure to air, and deposits selenium. The solution precipitates many metals as selenides.

The distance Se—H is $1 \cdot 6$. The angle H—Se—H is rather more than 90°. The heat of formation from atoms is $146 \cdot 3$ kcal per mole.

Ethyl selenium hydride, C_2H_5SeH, is a volatile liquid, with an extremely offensive smell, b.p. $53 \cdot 3°$. It is made:

(i) by the action of the Grignard reagent C_2H_5MgBr on selenium,
(ii) by distilling $C_2H_5SO_4H$ with alkaline $NaSeH$,
(iii) by the interaction of ethyl iodide and sodium selenide.

Ethyl selenium hydride is readily oxidisable (much more readily than ethyl hydrogen sulphide), and therefore all these reactions must be carried out in an atmosphere of hydrogen. Methods (ii) and (iii) correspond to the methods (ii) and (iii) used for preparing ethyl mercaptan (p. 824). Method (i) for preparing ethyl mercaptan is not available for preparing ethyl selenium hydride, as there is no P_4Se_{10}. Method (i) above applies to selenium, but not to sulphur.

Ethyl selenium hydride is immiscible with water, but it dissolves in aqueous alkali. It dissolves mercuric oxide, presumably to give the selenium compound corresponding to mercuric mercaptide, C_2H_5—Se—Hg—Se—C_2H_5.

Phenyl selenium hydride, C_6H_5SeH, a liquid, b.p. 183·6°, is made by reducing either diphenyl diselenide, C_6H_5Se—SeC_6H_5, or phenyl seleninic acid, $C_6H_5SeO_2H$, or phenyl selenonic acid, $C_6H_5SeO_3H$, with sodium and alcohol. Phenyl selenium hydride is only slightly soluble in water, but it is soluble in ether and in chloroform. It is rapidly oxidised by air to the diselenide, C_6H_5Se—SeC_6H_5; if a nitro group is present in the *o*- or *p*-position in the benzene ring the oxidation is more rapid.

Diethyl selenide, (diethyl selenoether), $(C_2H_5)_2Se$, an offensive smelling liquid, b.p. 108°, is made by the action of ethyl sulphuric acid on sodium selenide:

$$2C_2H_5HSO_4 + Na_2Se = Se(C_2H_5)_2 + 2NaHSO_4.$$

(Compare the preparation of thioethers, p. 825.)

Diethyl selenide is not so sensitive to oxidation as ethyl selenium hydride, but it is oxidised by potassium permanganate or potassium dichromate to diethyl selenoxide:

$$(C_2H_5)_2Se + O = (C_2H_5)_2SeO,$$

and by bromine or by nitric acid to selenonium compounds:

$$(C_2H_5)_2Se + Br_2 = [(C_2H_5)_2SeBr]Br,$$
$$(C_2H_5)_2Se + HNO_3 + O = [(C_2H_5)_2SeOH]NO_3,$$

but the oxidation proceeds no further, and neither selenones nor ethyl selenonic acid are produced. Compare Charts 21.1 and 22.1. Selenonium compounds are also formed by the action of an alkyl halide on diethyl selenide. Dimethyl selenide dissolved in acetone reacts with silver iodide in the presence of potassium iodide to give the addition compound $((CH_3)_2Se(AgI)_2)_n$; in this behaviour it resembles dimethyl sulphide.

Diaryl selenides. Diphenyl selenide, $(C_6H_5)_2Se$, is made by the action of selenium tetrabromide on mercury diphenyl:

$$SeBr_4 + 3(C_6H_5)_2Hg = (C_6H_5)_2Se + C_6H_5Br + 3C_6H_5HgBr,$$

or by heating diphenyl selenone with selenium:

$$(C_6H_5)_2SeO_2 + Se = (C_6H_5)_2Se + SeO_2.$$

Diphenyl selenide behaves as though unsaturated; it adds on bromine to give $(C_6H_5)_2SeBr_2$, and it is oxidised by a solution of potassium dichromate in acetic acid to diphenyl selenoxide $(C_6H_5)_2SeO$. Nitric acid, however, nitrates the phenyl groups without affecting the selenium atom. Diphenyl selenide does not form an addition compound with methyl iodide.

Unsymmetrical selenides are made from mercury diphenyl acting on a selenium aryl bromide:

$$\begin{array}{c} C_6H_5 \\ \diagdown \\ Hg + Se(C_6H_4CH_3)Br = HgBrC_6H_5 + Se(C_6H_4CH_3)C_6H_5 \\ \diagup \\ C_6H_5 \end{array}$$

or by the action of selenium diphenyl on a Grignard reagent:

$$\begin{array}{ccc}
C_6H_5 & & C_6H_5 \\
\diagdown & & \diagdown \\
Se + (C_6H_4CH_3)MgBr = & & Se + C_6H_5MgBr \\
\diagup & & \diagup \\
C_6H_5 & & C_6H_4CH_3
\end{array}$$

The phenyl selenium halides are more stable than the sulphur analogues. They are made:

(i) by the action of bromine on the selenocyanide in ether or carbon tetrachloride solution:

$$C_6H_5SeCN + Br_2 = C_6H_5SeBr + BrCN,$$

(ii) by the action of aluminium chloride on selenium dioxide dissolved in the appropriate hydrocarbon.

The monoselenohalides are reduced by zinc dust to the diselenides, and they react with bromine to give a selenonium compound, $[C_6H_5SeBr_2]Br$. Phenyl selenium chloride tends to disproportionate according to the equilibrium:

$$3C_6H_5SeCl \rightleftharpoons C_6H_5Se—SeC_6H_5 + [C_6H_5SeCl_2]Cl,$$

and its hydrolysis by water follows a similar course:

$$3C_6H_5SeCl + 2H_2O = C_6H_5Se—SeC_6H_5 + C_6H_5SeO \cdot OH + 3HCl.$$

THE HALIDES OF SELENIUM

For reference a complete list of the halides of selenium is given in Table 22.2. Detailed accounts of the tetrahalides and the hexafluoride are given on pp. 872 and 879. It is to be noted that there is no fluoride, SeF_2, that iodides of selenium are unknown, and that only in the fluoride SeF_6 is selenium hexavalent.

Table 22.2.   *The Halides of Selenium*

Compound	Physical state
$SeCl_2$	It exists only in the vapour state from $190°$ to $600°$
$SeBr_2$	It exists only in the vapour state from $200°$ to $500°$
Se_2F_2	
Se_2Cl_2	A yellow-brown, oily liquid, b.p. about $127°$
Se_2Br_2	A red liquid
SeF_4	A colourless liquid, m.p. $9·5°$, b.p. $106°$
$SeCl_4$	Colourless crystals, m.p. $305°$
$SeBr_4$	Yellow crystals
SeF_6	A colourless gas, m.p. of solid $-34·6°$, b.p. $-46·6°$

It is seen from Table 22.2 that the halides of selenium in which selenium is bivalent are less well-characterised than those in which its valency is higher.

Selenium dichloride, $SeCl_2$, exists only in equilibrium with chlorine when $SeCl_4$ or Se_2Cl_2 are maintained at a temperature between $190°$ and $600°$. *Selenium dibromide,* $SeBr_2$, is present when the mixed vapours of selenium and bromine are maintained between $250°$ and $500°$. On condensation only bromine, diselenium dibromide, and selenium tetrabromide, are found.

Diselenium dichloride, Se_2Cl_2, is a yellow-brown oily liquid. It is made:

(i) by the action of chlorine on selenium,

(ii) by the action of selenium tetrachloride on selenium,

(iii) by the reduction of selenium tetrachloride with phosphorus trichloride,

(iv) by passing gaseous hydrogen chloride into a hot solution of selenium and selenium dioxide in oleum:

$$SeO_2 + 3Se + 4HCl = 2Se_2Cl_2 + 2H_2O.$$

Diselenium dichloride is miscible with benzene and with ethylene dibromide. It is denser than water, with which it reacts to yield selenous acid and selenium:

$$2Se_2Cl_2 + 3H_2O = H_2SeO_3 + 3Se + 4HCl.$$

It dissolves selenium which, on concentration, separates in the grey form. It reacts with phenyl sulphinate in benzene to give $(C_6H_5SO_2)_2Se_2$, m.p. 80°, with ethylene to give selenium mustard gas, $Se(CH_2CH_2Cl)_2$, and with phenyl magnesium bromide to give $(C_6H_5)_2Se_2$. Chlorine and bromine oxidise it to $SeCl_4$ or $SeBr_3Cl$.

Diselenium dichloride is monomeric in solution in ethylene dibromide. The d.p.m. in benzene solution is 2·1. By analogy with S_2Cl_2 the structure would be:

$$Cl\!-\!\overset{..}{\underset{..}{Se}}\!-\!\overset{..}{\underset{..}{Se}}\!-\!Cl,$$

but

are also possible structures.

Diselenium dibromide, Se_2Br_2, is a red liquid, less stable than selenium dichloride, to which it is generally similar.

COMPOUNDS CONTAINING CHAINS OF TETRAHEDRALLY HYBRIDISED SELENIUM ATOMS

Molecules containing chains of selenium atoms appear to be less stable than the corresponding sulphur compounds (p. 828). It is doubtful whether hydrogen diselenide has been obtained. Se_2Cl_2 and Se_2Br_2 are discussed above. Certain alkyl and aryl di- and tri-selenides are known, including the following:

Diethyl diselenide is formed:

(i) by the action of sodium diselenide on ethyl hydrogen sulphate:

$$Na_2Se_2 + 2C_2H_5HSO_4 = (C_2H_5Se)_2 + 2NaHSO_4,$$

(ii) by the reduction of ethyl selenium bromide with zinc dust.

Diphenyl diselenide reacts additively with bromine to give $C_6H_5Br_2Se\!-\!SeBr_2C_6H_5$. The configurations of diphenyl diselenide and of dibenzyl diselenide have been established by X-ray analysis. These two compounds are isomorphous with the corresponding sulphur compounds. Mixed sulphide selenides are known.

† The d.p.m. of the corresponding toluene derivative is 2·29.

Metal polyselenides with compositions up to M_2Se_5 can be made by treating a metal with a solution of selenium in liquid ammonia.

The polyselenonic acids and the selenothionic acids. The polyselenonic acids appear to be much less stable than the polythionic acids, and only acids containing sulphur have been prepared. When selenium dissolves in potassium sulphite (particularly in the presence of the bisulphite) some $K_2SeS_2O_6$ is obtained. The same salt is formed by the action of selenium acetylacetone on potassium hydrogen sulphite:

$$(C_5H_7O_2Se)_2 + 4KHSO_3 = 2Se(SO_3)_2K_2 + 2C_5H_8O_2.$$

If sulphurous acid is used instead of the potassium salt a solution of selenotrithionic acid is obtained. Sodium selenopentathionate is formed by the action of selenium dioxide in acid solution on sodium thiosulphate:

$$SeO_2 + 4HCl + 4Na_2S_2O_3 = 4NaCl + Na_2S_4O_6 + Na_2SeS_4O_6 + 2H_2O.$$

The barium salt of the same acid, $BaSeS_4O_6, 2H_2O$ is known. In these compounds the selenium atom appears to occupy the central position.

COMPOUNDS OF THE TYPE SeX_4

Selenium forms a number of compounds of the general formula SeX_4 (Table 22.3), in which X may be a halogen atom, or an alkyl or aryl group, except that $SeAlk_4$ and $SeAr_4$ do not exist; all attempts to make them have failed. A compound SeX_4 might be assigned one of the three following orbital structures:

(i) it might be assumed that the $4s$ electron pair in the selenium atom is inert; the four bonding orbitals would then be hybrids constructed from the $4p$ and $4d$ orbitals, or from the $4p$ and $5s$ orbitals,

(ii) it might be assumed that the $4s$ electron pair is a lone pair occupying one of the five hybrid orbitals constructed by trigonal bipyramidal hybridisation of the orbitals $4s^14p^34d^1$,

(iii) it might be assumed that the $4s$ electron pair is a lone pair occupying one of the tetrahedral hybrid orbitals formed by hybridisation of the orbitals $4s^14p^3$; and that one of the electrons originally present in the valency shell of the selenium atom is transferred to an anion, thus giving a selenonium compound $[SeX_3^+]X^-$.

The $4s$ electron pair in the selenium atom is so rarely inert in its compounds that assumption (i) may be neglected. There is definite evidence that certain of the compounds SeX_4 have trigonal bipyramidal molecular structures, while others are selenonium compounds. Both the selenonium compounds and the trigonal bipyramidal compounds are described below, although according to the classification used in this book the trigonal bipyramidal compounds should be included under Section 5, p. 879.

The trigonal bipyramidal compounds. X-ray analysis indicates that selenium diphenyl dibromide and dichloride have a trigonal bipyramidal structure with the two halogen atoms in the polar positions. For selenium diphenyl dibromide:

Angle	Distance
C—Se—C $= 110 \pm 10°$	Se—C $= 1·91$
Br—Se—Br $= 180 \pm 3°$	Se—Br $= 2·50.$

For selenium diphenyl dichloride:

Cl—Se—Cl $= 180 \pm 5°$ Se—Cl $= 2·30.$

The d.p.m. in debyes of certain aromatic selenium dihalides are:

$(C_6H_5CH_2)_2SeI_2$	$(C_6H_5)_2SeCl_2$	$(C_6H_5)_2SeBr_2$
4·4	3·21	3·40

These values are much below that expected for a truly ionic compound, say, $[(C_6H_5)_2SeCl]Cl$, which would be about 10.

The selenonium compounds. The tri-alkyl and tri-aryl selenium halides are selenonium compounds. It is probable that selenium tetrachloride is also a selenonium compound $[SeCl_3]Cl$. It has been shown by X-ray analysis that in the unit cell of triphenyl selenium chloride the minimum distance $Se-Cl = 3\cdot60$. The bond therefore is ionic, and the constitution of the molecule is $[Se(C_6H_5)_3]Cl$. Selenium tetrachloride exists only in the solid state; the vapour from 190–600° consists of the dissociation products, Se_2Cl_2 and Cl_2. These properties suggest that the solid is $[SeCl_3]Cl$, which volatilises by decomposition. The compound $(C_6H_5)(CH_3)(CH_2COOH)SeBr$ has been resolved by means of the bromo-camphor sulphonate. The optical activity of this compound, however, does not enable distinctions to be made between the tetrahedral and the trigonal bipyramidal structures, as neither has a plane of symmetry.

Selenium hydronitrates, for example,

$$\left[\begin{array}{c} \quad\quad OH \\ C_6H_5-Se \\ \quad\quad OH \end{array}\right]^{+} NO_3^{-} \quad\text{and}\quad \left[\begin{array}{c} C_6H_5 \\ \quad\quad Se-OH \\ C_6H_5 \end{array}\right]^{+} NO_3^{-}$$

are made:

(i) by the action of nitric acid on a derivative of seleninic acid, for example, on phenyl, benzyl, methyl, or ethyl seleninic acid:

$$C_6H_5\cdot SeO\cdot OH + HNO_3 = [C_6H_5Se(OH)_2]NO_3,$$

(ii) by the oxidation of selenoethers with nitric acid,

(iii) by the action of nitric acid on a selenoxide.

The hydronitrates cannot be further oxidised, and illustrate the reluctance of selenium to go up to the 4 co-ordinate form. They are easily decomposed.

The selenium hydronitrates are usually formulated as selenonium compounds, but there appears to be no experimental evidence for doing so.

The selenium tetrahalides. Details of the preparations and properties of these compounds are given in Table 22.3. There is little evidence beyond the non-volatility of selenium tetrachloride to decide their structures. It is probable that SeF_4 is pyramidal and $SeCl_4$ is ionic, $[SeCl_3^+]Cl^-$. The addition compound $MSeF_5$ may have an octahedral structure in which one apex is occupied by a lone electron pair.

THE SELENOXIDES, THE SELENIUM OXYHALIDES, AND SELENOUS ACID

Diphenyl selenoxide, $(C_6H_5)_2SeO$, m.p. 114°, is made (i) by the oxidation of diphenyl selenide with potassium permanganate, potassium dichromate, or nitric acid, (ii) by heating selenium diphenyl dibromide with potassium hydroxide. Diphenyl selenoxide decomposes when heated in vacuo to 230° to diphenyl selenide and oxygen. It liberates iodine from potassium iodide. It is fairly soluble in hot water. In the aqueous solution the equilibrium is probably set up:

$$(C_6H_5)_2SeO + H_2O \rightleftharpoons [(C_6H_5)_2SeOH]OH,$$

because the solution with nitric acid gives $[(C_6H_5)_2SeOH]NO_3$, and with hydrochloric acid $[(C_6H_5)_2SeCl]Cl$. Diphenyl selenoxide is the only selenoxide which can be oxidised to a selenone:

$$(C_6H_5)_2SeO + O = (C_6H_5)_2SeO_2.$$

The oxidation is brought about by potassium permanganate in alkaline (but not in acid) solution. Unsymmetrical selenoxides have not been resolved.

28*

Table 22.3. *Selenium Compound.*

Compound	Preparation	State at room temperature	m.p.	b.p.
SeF$_4$	(i) Pass equal volumes of fluorine and nitrogen over selenium at 0° (ii) Treat silver fluoride with selenium tetrachloride at 50–60° (iii) Reduce selenium hexafluoride with arsine	Colourless liquid	9·5°	106°
SeCl$_4$	(i) Treat selenium with excess chlorine (ii) Treat selenium with chlorine under carbon tetrachloride (iii) Treat selenium dioxide with phosphorus pentachloride $SeO_2 + 2PCl_5 = SeCl_4 + 2POCl_3$ (iv) Treat selenium dioxide with concentrated hydrochloric acid	Colourless crystals (Red liquid)	305 ± 3° under pressure	Sublime 1 atm† at 196°
SeBr$_4$		Yellow crystals		Sublime
C$_6$H$_5$SeCl$_3$				
C$_6$H$_5$SeBr$_3$		Scarlet crystals	105°	
(CH$_3$)(C$_6$H$_5$)SeCl$_2$	Treat (CH$_3$)(C$_6$H$_5$)Se with chlorine	Yellow crystals	115°	
Alk$_3$Se hal	Treat the dialkyl selenoether with the alkyl halide	Solid		
Ar$_3$Se hal	Treat a mixture of (C$_6$H$_5$)$_2$Se hal$_2$ and benzene with aluminium chloride	Solid		

† The vapour contains no SeCl$_4$ molecules.

The selenium oxyhalides, SeOhal$_2$

SeOF$_2$	a liquid	m.p. 15°	b.p. 126°	
SeOCl$_2$	a liquid	8·5°	177°	
SeOBr$_2$	orange solid	42°	220° with decomposition	

Selenium oxyfluoride, SeOF$_2$, a colourless fuming liquid, is made:

(i) by treating selenium dioxide with fluorine diluted well with nitrogen; the product consists roughly of 80% SeOF$_2$ and 20% SeF$_4$,

(ii) by burning selenium in a stream of fluorine containing about 60% of oxygen,

(iii) by heating selenium oxychloride with silver fluoride at 140°.

of the Type SeX₄

Solubility	Reactions	Additive compounds
	1. Water yields hydrofluoric acid and selenous acid 2. Silicon reduces it to selenium and silicon tetrafluoride	It dissolves NaF, KF, RbF, CsF, TlF to form easily dissociable complexes with compositions approaching $MSeF_5$. It forms less stable complexes with LiF, AgF, and BaF_2. With pyridine and ether it yields $SeF_4,pyr,(C_2H_5)_2O$
Insoluble in carbon disulphide Soluble in phosphorus oxychloride	1. Dissociates at 190°: $2SeCl_4 \rightleftharpoons Se_2Cl_2 + 3Cl_2$ 2. Water yields first an oxychloride and then selenous acid 3. Phenyl magnesium bromide yields $(C_6H_5)_2SeCl_2$ 4. Benzene and aluminium chloride yield $(C_6H_5)_2Se$, $(C_6H_5)_2Se_2$, or $(C_6H_5)_3SeCl$ 5. Ammonia yields Se_4N_4 6. Selenium or PCl_3 reduces it to Se_2Cl_2	$SeCl_4,AuCl_3$ (perhaps $[SeCl_3][AuCl_4]$) $SeCl_4,SbCl_5$ (perhaps $[SeCl_3][SbCl_6]$)
	1. Dissociates at 70–80° to $Se_2Br_2 + Br_2$ 2. Water hydrolyses it to selenous acid and HBr	$SeBr_4,2SO_3$. m.p. 75°
	1. Loses chlorine only on fusion 2. Sodium hydroxide hydrolyses it to sodium phenyl seleninate $C_6H_5 \cdot SO \cdot ONa$ (more easily than the bromide)	
	1. Loses bromine easily to yield C_6H_5SeBr 2. Sodium hydroxide hydrolyses it to sodium phenyl seleninate	
Soluble in water, but with hydrolysis	1. Dissociates in carbon tetrachloride to $(C_6H_5)(CH_3)Se$ and chlorine 2. Dissociates on heating: $(C_6H_5)(CH_3)SeCl_2 \rightleftharpoons (C_6H_5)SeCl + (CH_3)Cl$ 3. Silver oxide hydrolyses it to $(C_6H_5)(CH_3)SeO$	
Soluble in water Insoluble in ether	1. Silver oxide yields Alk_3SeOH which is strongly basic	
Soluble in water, soluble in chloroform, perhaps as colloid	1. Dissociates on heating: $(C_6H_5)_3SeI \rightleftharpoons (C_6H_5)_2Se + C_6H_5I$	

After distillation in vacuo the selenium oxyfluoride does not attack dry glass, but if moist it violently attacks glass, silica, and silicon, forming selenium dioxide. The vapour of selenium oxyfluoride does not associate. The liquid is hydrolysed violently by water. It attacks phosphorus with inflammation. It gives coloured solids with KCl, KBr, and KI. It dissolves sulphur and selenium to give a brown and a green solution, but it scarcely dissolves tellurium.

Selenium oxychloride, $SeOCl_2$, a colourless liquid, is made by distilling $SeO_2,2HCl$ with phosphorus pentoxide. It can also be made by the action of selenium dioxide dissolved in carbon tetrachloride on selenium tetrachloride, or by the action of a little water on selenium tetrachloride. Selenium oxychloride is miscible with CCl_4, $CHCl_3$,

CS_2, C_6H_6, but not with paraffins. It is a powerful solvent which dissolves WO_3; a mixture of selenium oxychloride and sulphuric acid dissolves Nb_2O_5. It is hydrolysed by water to selenium dioxide and hydrochloric acid. It explodes violently if brought into contact with potassium, but it has scarcely any action on sodium. If treated with sodium ethoxide it yields ethyl selenite (below). Ammonia reacts with a dilute solution of selenium oxychloride in benzene to yield Se_4N_4.

Selenous acid, H_2SeO_3, exists as colourless, hygroscopic, hexagonal prisms. It is formed in solution by dissolving selenium dioxide in water. It is very soluble, but it forms no hydrates, and it separates from solution as the anhydrous H_2SeO_3. In dry air the crystals lose water to give selenium dioxide.

Selenous acid is a fairly strong acid; $K_1 = 4 \times 10^{-3}$, $K_2 = 10^{-8}$. It forms heteropoly acids with vanadic, molybdic, and uranic acids. There is some evidence that it is amphoteric as it reacts with excess of perchloric acid to yield a crystalline hygroscopic compound, soluble in nitromethane to give a conducting solution. The formula of the compound may be $[Se(OH)_3]^+[ClO_4]^-$.

The acid in solution is easily reduced to selenium, and oxidised to H_2SeO_4.

Selenites. Three types of selenites are known: normal K_2SeO_3; acid $KHSeO_3$; super acid salts such as $KH_3(SeO_3)_2$. The selenites of the alkali metals are soluble and stable to heat; the selenites of the alkaline earth metals are sparingly soluble, and may give selenides when heated. Crystalline $MgSeO_3$ has been prepared, but not the selenites of Ni, Co, or Zn. The Mg salt is isomorphous with Ni and Co sulphites. In acid solution, selenites are reduced to selenium; the reduction of a selenite in the presence of cupric sulphate in weakly acid solution leads to the formation of cuprous selenide.

Diethyl selenite, $(C_2H_5O)_2SeO$, a colourless liquid, b.p. 83° at 15 mm, is formed:

(i) by the action of selenium oxychloride on sodium ethylate:

$$SeOCl_2 + 2NaOC_2H_5 = SeO(OC_2H_5)_2 + 2NaCl,$$

(ii) by the action of ethyl iodide on silver selenite:

$$2C_2H_5I + Ag_2SeO_3 = 2AgI + SeO(OC_2H_5)_2.$$

Diethyl selenite is rapidly hydrolysed by water to ethyl alcohol and selenous acid. C_6H_5MgBr reduces it to selenium. With ammonia it yields selenium nitride.

It should be noted, by contrast, that ethyl iodide reacts with silver sulphite to give ethyl ethylsulphonate, and that diethyl sulphite is hydrolysed to sodium ethylsulphonate. These two reactions illustrate the ease with which compounds in which a sulphur atom is 3 co-ordinate are transformed to those in which a sulphur atom is 4 co-ordinate, and the reluctance of selenium compounds to undergo the corresponding change.

Seleninic acids. The general formula is

$$\overset{\displaystyle R}{\underset{\displaystyle HO}{\diagdown}}\!\!:Se\overset{\pi d}{=\!=\!=}O$$

The alkyl seleninic acids are hygroscopic solids. They are made:

(i) by the oxidation of alkyl diselenides (p. 871) with nitric acid,

(ii) by the action of hydrogen peroxide on the alkyl selenide (p. 869).

The alkyl seleninic acids are very soluble in water. They are amphoteric. With bases they give such salts as $CH_3 \cdot SeO \cdot ONa, 4H_2O$; with acids they form selenonium salts, just as ammonia forms ammonium salts:

$$CH_3SeO \cdot OH + HCl = (CH_3Se \cdot OH \cdot OH)Cl.$$

Compare:

$$NH_3 + HCl = (NH_4)Cl.$$

Phenyl seleninic acid, $C_6H_5SeO \cdot OH$, is a solid, m.p. 170°. It is made by oxidising diphenyl diselenide with nitric acid. The silver salt, $C_6H_5SeO \cdot OAg$, is prepared, and the free acid is released from it by the addition of hydrochloric acid. After filtering off the silver chloride, the filtrate is evaporated and the substance $[C_6H_5Se(OH)_2]OH$, m.p. 122° is obtained. At 130° this loses water, and gives phenyl seleninic acid, $C_6H_5SeO \cdot OH$.

Phenyl seleninic acid is reduced by zinc dust to the mercaptan, C_6H_5SeH; the silver salt is reduced by hydrogen sulphide to selenium. In the presence of water phenyl seleninic acid is in equilibrium with a selenonium compound. thus:

$$
C_6H_5\overset{+}{-}\underset{O^-}{\overset{\displaystyle OH}{Se:}} \quad + H_2O \rightleftharpoons \left[C_6H_5\overset{+}{-}\underset{OH}{\overset{\displaystyle OH}{Se:}} \right]^+ \quad [OH]^-
$$

Nitric acid reacts with methyl-, ethyl-, benzyl-, and phenyl-seleninic acid to give hydronitrates (p. 873), which are derived from the phenyl dihydroxy selenonium base.

THE SELENONES, SELENIC ACID AND ITS DERIVATIVES

Selenones. Only two are known (i) diphenyl selenone, $(C_6H_5)_2SeO_2$, and (ii) the selenone derived from methyl butadiene:

$$
\begin{array}{c}
CH_3-C-CH_2 \\
\quad\; \| \qquad\quad \diagdown \\
\quad\; \| \qquad\qquad SeO_2 \\
\quad\; \diagup \\
H-C-CH_2
\end{array}
\qquad \text{(the CH}_3 \text{ may be replaced by another alkyl group)}
$$

$(C_6H_5)_2SeO_2$ is a colourless crystalline compound, m.p. 155°, b.p. 270° at 9·5 mm. It is made by treating diphenyl selenoxide with neutral or alkaline permanganate solution (the selenoxide is not oxidised in acid solution, either by $K_2Cr_2O_7$ or by nitric acid).

At 300–400° it decomposes quietly into diphenyl selenide and oxygen. When heated with sulphur it is reduced to the selenide with the formation of SO_2. With HCl it forms the dichloride and liberates chlorine: but it liberates iodine from KI much more slowly than does the selenoxide.

Selenic acid, H_2SeO_4. The following crystalline phases are known in the system SeO_3, H_2O:

$H_2Se_2O_7$	H_2SeO_4, H_2O m.p. 26°
H_2SeO_4 m.p. 57°	$H_2SeO_4, 4H_2O$ m.p. −51·7°

Selenic acid exists as colourless hexagonal crystals which melt at 57° to a thick oily liquid. It is made by the vigorous oxidation of selenium, selenium dioxide, or selenous acid. The oxidising agent may be fluorine, chlorine, or bromine, chloric acid or potassium permanganate. Two methods are said to be satisfactory: (i) the oxidation of selenium dioxide with chloric acid at about 160°, and (ii) the oxidation of silver selenite with bromine:

$$
Ag_2SeO_3 + Br_2 + H_2O = H_2SeO_4 + 2AgBr.
$$

Selenic acid is hygroscopic. It evolves heat when mixed with water, and it chars organic matter. The crystalline acid may be obtained from the aqueous solution by evaporation at 210°, followed by further desiccation over sulphuric acid in vacuo, and finally by strong cooling. On treatment with phosphorus pentoxide selenic acid yields a mixture of selenium dioxide and oxygen.

Selenic acid is slightly stronger than sulphuric acid. It is a powerful and ready oxidising agent, and in this property it resembles nitric acid rather than sulphuric acid. Dilute selenic acid oxidises hydrogen iodide quantitatively. The concentrated acid attacks hydrochloric acid to liberate chlorine; in the reaction it is itself reduced quantitatively to selenous acid. The hot concentrated acid dissolves copper to form cupric selenate, and gold to form auric selenate. A mixture of selenic acid and hydrochloric acid behaves like *aqua regia* in dissolving gold and platinum. When iron is treated with selenic acid it receives a protective coating of selenium and is not dissolved. Selenic acid is reduced quantitatively to selenium by concentrated hydrochloric acid saturated with sulphur dioxide; the selenium may be filtered off, dried and weighed, and hence the original selenate may be estimated. The method may be used for estimating selenates in the presence of tellurates. Dilute selenic acid is also reduced to selenium by zinc dust.

The SeO_4 groups in crystalline selenic acid are tetrahedral. The selenium atom in each group is joined by four hydrogen bonds to selenium atoms in four neighbouring groups. The distance Se—O is 1·61.

The selenates are isomorphous with the corresponding sulphates, chromates, and manganates. They form alums and vitriols. The selenates are somewhat more soluble than the sulphates; at 25° one litre of water dissolves 0·002 gm of barium sulphate and 0·08 gm of barium selenate.

Very unstable acid esters of selenic acid, such as $C_2H_5 \cdot OSeO_2 \cdot OH$, are produced by the action of the acid on an alcohol. The sodium salts of the acid esters are isomorphous with those of the corresponding alkyl hydrogen sulphates. The normal esters are made by the action of an alkyl halide on silver selenate. $(C_2H_5)_2SeO_4$ decomposes explosively at 150°, but it may be distilled in vacuo.

Polyselenic acids. There is evidence for the existence of diselenates containing the anion $(SeO_3 \cdot O \cdot SeO_3)^{2-}$, and of salts containing the anion $(SO_3 \cdot O \cdot SeO_2 \cdot O \cdot SO_3)^{2-}$, derived by the replacement of the central sulphur atom in the trisulphate ion by a selenium atom.

These salts are made by treating dry finely powdered K_2SeO_4 with gaseous SO_3. A mixture of $K_2S_3O_{10}$ and $K_2SeS_2O_{10}$ is formed. X-ray analysis shows that these substances are probably isomorphous. If the product is heated to 150° it gives the mixture:

$$K_2SeSO_7 + K_2S_2O_7 + 2SO_3.$$

The two salts are also isomorphous. At 440° the selenium salt decomposes to yield potassium sulphate, selenium dioxide, and oxygen.

Selenosulphuric acid. There are no compounds of selenium which correspond in range and stability to the thiosulphates and their derivatives. Selenium dissolves in a solution of sodium sulphite but it is reprecipitated on dilution. The solution may contain sodium selenosulphate, Na_2SSeO_3, but neither this salt nor the parent acid have been isolated.

Ethyl selenonic acid, $C_2H_5SeO_3H$, is prepared by the oxidation of ethyl seleninic acid (p. 876) by potassium permanganate. None of the other methods corresponding to those for preparing ethyl sulphonic acid are available.

Phenyl selenonic acid, $C_6H_5SeO_3H$, exists as white crystals, m.p. 142°, which explode at 180°. It is made by heating benzene with selenic acid at 110°. The silver salt is obtained by treating an aqueous suspension of diphenyl diselenide with chlorine at 50°, and subsequently adding excess of silver oxide. Silver phenyl selenonate separates on concentration.

The silver salt is explosive. The free acid can be isolated by treating the silver salt with hydrogen sulphide; phenyl selenonic acid is not reduced by hydrogen sulphide.

Phenyl selenonic acid when heated yields a mixture of $(C_6H_5)_2Se$, $(C_6H_5)_2Se_2$, and selenium, with slight explosion. It oxidises cold concentrated hydrochloric acid.

The selenonic acids are slightly amphoteric and they combine with strong mineral acids, thus:

$$C_6H_5SeO_2OH + HCl = C_6H_5SeO(OH)_2Cl.$$

In this property they differ from the sulphonic acids.

SECTION 5. COMPOUNDS IN WHICH THE SELENIUM ATOM IS IN THE TRIGONAL BIPYRAMIDAL VALENCE STATE

Selenium compounds of the general formula SeX_4 are described on p. 872, where it is shown that there is experimental evidence for assigning trigonal bipyramidal structures to diphenyl selenium dichloride and diphenyl selenium dibromide. In these compounds the selenium atom is in the trigonal bipyramidal valence state, and one of the equatorial hybrid orbitals is occupied by a lone electron pair. Since other compounds of the formula SeX_4 are selenonium compounds, $[SeX_3^+]X^-$, it might be possible for all compounds of formula SeX_4 to exhibit the isomerism:

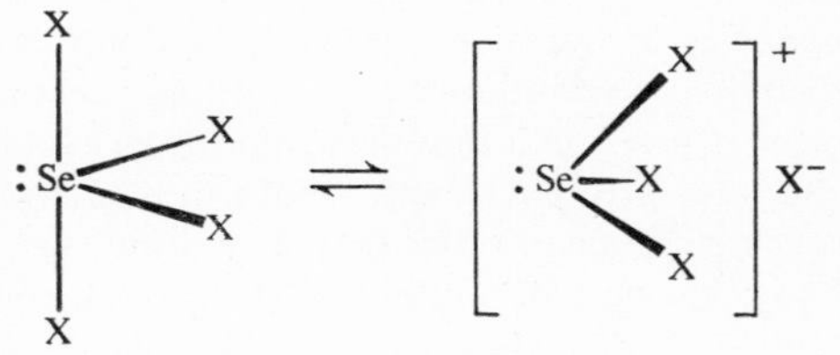

SECTION 6. COMPOUNDS IN WHICH THE SELENIUM ATOM IS OCTAHEDRALLY HYBRIDISED

Selenium hexafluoride, SeF_6, a colourless, very inert gas, m.p. $-34.6°$, sublimation point $-46.6°$, is made by the interaction of the elements in a copper tube at $300°$. If the selenium tetrafluoride which is also produced is condensed and returned to the reaction zone the yield of selenium hexafluoride is 90%.

Selenium hexafluoride reacts with pyrex glass at $700°$, but not at $500°$. It does not attack water. It reacts slowly with ammonia at $200°$, and more rapidly at $330°$ thus:

$$2NH_3 + SeF_6 = N_2 + Se + 6HF; \quad \Delta H = -116 \text{ kcal.}$$

It reacts slowly with mercury in the cold to give mercurous fluoride, Hg_2F_2. It reacts with sodium iodide in acetone solution to give selenium and iodine. It is reduced by arsine to selenium tetrafluoride. The vapour density of selenium hexafluoride shows it to be monomeric.

Selenium nitride, Se_4N_4, is an unstable orange coloured solid. It is made:

(i) by the action of ammonia on selenium tetrachloride; the product contains halogen,

(ii) by the action of dry ammonia on ethyl selenite dissolved in benzene:

$$6(C_2H_5)_2SeO_3 + 8NH_3 = Se_4N_4 + 12C_2H_5OH + 2Se + 2N_2 + 6H_2O,$$

(iii) by the action of dry ammonia on a dilute solution of $SeOCl_2$ in benzene.

Selenium nitride is very readily exploded by shock. The molecule has a puckered ring structure similar to that of sulphur nitride.

TELLURIUM

Tellurium exists in two crystalline forms, and in one amorphous form, but it is not certain whether these forms possess the same or different crystal lattices. One of the crystalline forms is metallic tellurium which has a bright lustre like antimony, but it is brittle and easily powdered. It conducts electricity, but its specific conductance is only 5 ohm^{-1} cm^{-1}. The m.p. is 450°; the sp. gr. 6·31.

If metallic tellurium is sublimed in vacuo and the vapour condensed at 400° trigonal crystals are obtained. The crystals are composed of spiral chains of tellurium atoms, and this form of tellurium therefore corresponds to the crystalline grey form of selenium (p. 862). Amorphous tellurium, sp. gr. 6·02, is made by reducing tellurous acid with sulphur dioxide.

Tellurium can be obtained by the electrolysis of a solution of tellurium dioxide in a mixture of sulphuric acid and hydrofluoric acid; if a lead cathode is used the deposit is coherent.

Liquid tellurium boils at 1390° to a golden yellow vapour. The vapour density corresponds to the molecular formula Te$_2$. Tellurium is insoluble in all solvents that do not react with it, and hence its molecular weight cannot be determined cryoscopically.

When heated in air or oxygen tellurium burns with a blue flame giving tellurium dioxide. Tellurium combines with many metals, including sodium and aluminium, to give tellurides. It dissolves in warm concentrated sulphuric acid to give a cherry red solution. Tellurium combines with fluorine with incandescence to give tellurium hexafluoride. With chlorine it gives tellurium tetrachloride or tellurium dichloride according to the proportions taken. It reacts with iodoform to yield tellurium tetraiodide. It is oxidised by hydrogen peroxide or other strong oxidising agents to orthotelluric acid, Te(OH)$_6$. With tetramethylene dibromide it yields the ring compound:

$$\begin{array}{ccc}
CH_2\!-\!CH_2 & & Br \\
| & & \diagup \\
& Te & \\
| & & \diagdown \\
CH_2\!-\!CH_2 & & Br
\end{array}$$

which is reduced by sulphur dioxide to:

$$\begin{array}{cc}
CH_2\!-\!CH_2 & \\
| & \diagdown \\
& Te. \\
| & \diagup \\
CH_2\!-\!CH_2 &
\end{array}$$

Tellurium reacts with methyl iodide to form dimethyl tellurium di-iodide (p. 886).

GENERAL CHEMISTRY OF TELLURIUM

The electron configuration of the valency shell of the tellurium atom in the ground state is:

$5s$	$5p$	$5p$	$5p$	$5d$	$5d$	$5d$	$5d$	$5d$
⇅	⇅	↑	↑					

The penultimate shell contains eighteen electrons, none of which is used in bond formation. The 5s electron pair is inert in tellurium monoxide, and in anions of the types [TeCl$_5$,H$_2$O$^-$] and [TeCl$_6{}^{2-}$], and perhaps in the anion [CH$_3$TeI$_4{}^-$].

The fall in affinity for oxygen which is noticeable in comparing compounds of selenium with the corresponding compounds of sulphur is not continued down the Group to tellurium. The stable oxyacid of tellurium is Te(OH)$_6$, whereas the oxyacid of selenium in the highest state of oxidation is H$_2$SeO$_4$. Two fluorides of hexavalent tellurium are known, TeF$_6$ and Te$_2$F$_{10}$, but selenium forms only the compound SeF$_6$.

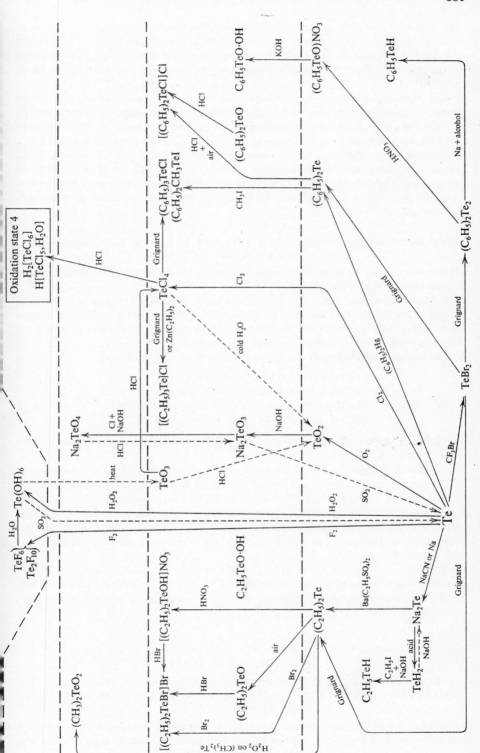

Chart. 22.2 Chemical relations of the compounds of tellurium

The effect of oxidation on compounds of sulphur, selenium, and tellurium is summarised in Chart 21.1 and Charts 22, 1 and 2. A strict comparison of the information in the charts is not possible because of the uncertainty of the constitutions of compounds of the type AX_4 where A represents an atom of one of the elements sulphur, selenium, or tellurium.

Tellurium shows less tendency than selenium to adopt the digonal or trigonal valence states. Compounds containing the tetrahedrally hybridised tellurium atom are common, but there are few compounds containing chains of tellurium atoms. A tellurium atom may replace the middle sulphur atom in the chain of sulphur atoms in the anion of a polythionic acid. Tellurium forms many compounds of the general formula TeX_4. These compounds may be telluronium compounds $[TeX_3^+]X^-$ or they may contain a tellurium atom in the trigonal bipyramidal valence state with one hybrid orbital occupied by a lone pair; the evidence for the orbital structures of particular compounds is discussed on p. 886.

COMPOUNDS IN WHICH ONLY 4 OF THE VALENCY ELECTRONS OF TELLURIUM ARE ACTIVE

The $5s$ electrons in the atom of tellurium are inert in the oxide TeO, and in the complex anions $[Tehal_5, H_2O^-]$ and $[Tehal_6{}^{2-}]$.

Tellurium monoxide, TeO, is an amorphous black powder. It is made by heating the mixed oxide $TeSO_3$. It is stable in air in the cold, but on heating in vacuo it disproportionates to Te and TeO_2. It dissolves in concentrated sulphuric acid to give a red solution from which tellurium separates on standing.

The halogenotellurous acids and their salts. The free acids are known:

$$H[TeF_5, H_2O], 4H_2O, \text{ crystalline}$$
$$H[TeCl_5, H_2O], 4H_2O, \text{ yellow needles,}$$
$$H[TeBr_5, H_2O], 4H_2O, \text{ orange crystals, m.p. } 20°,$$
$$H[TeI_5, H_2O], 7H_2O, \text{ black crystals, m.p. } 55°,$$

but salts are known only of the acids containing fluorine and chlorine. The acids readily lose halogen acid in the air.

The hexahalogenotellurites of the alkali metals, such as $K_2[TeCl_6]$, are well-known. The halogens may be chlorine, bromine, or iodine. $K_2[TeCl_6]$ is yellow, $K_2[TeBr_6]$ is orange, and $K_2[TeI_6]$ is black. The salts dissolve in a little water, but dilution causes hydrolysis and yields tellurium dioxide. The isomorphism of the bromine salts with K_2SeBr_6, K_2PbBr_6, K_2PtBr_6, K_2SnBr_6, and K_2SiF_6 indicates that the anions are octahedral, and suggests that the bonding orbitals of the tellurium atom are hybrids of the combination $5p^3 5d^2 6s$.

The anion of the salt $K[(CH_3)TeI_4]$ might contain a tellurium atom having five bonding orbitals formed from the combination $5p^3 5d^2$, the $5s$ electron pair being inert, or the tellurium atom might be octahedrally hybridised with one of the hybrid orbitals occupied by a lone pair (p. 888).

COMPOUNDS IN WHICH ALL 6 VALENCY ELECTRONS OF TELLURIUM ARE ACTIVE

SECTION 1. TELLURIUM COMPOUNDS CONSISTING OF GIANT MOLECULES IN WHICH THE BONDS HAVE BOTH IONIC AND COVALENT CHARACTER

The tellurides of the alkali metals are made by warming a mixture of the elements in an atmosphere of hydrogen; reaction occurs with incandescence. Sodium telluride may also be formed by treating a mixture of tellurium and zinc with boiling sodium hydroxide solution. Potassium telluride, K_2Te, is made by fusing tellurium with potassium cyanide.

The tellurides of the alkali metals are colourless. They are instantly decomposed by air. They are soluble in water, but the solutions are easily oxidised to red polytellurides. The alkali metal tellurides are strong reducing agents which reduce tellurites to metallic tellurium. Li_2Te, Na_2Te, and K_2Te have the antifluorite lattice. CaTe, SrTe, and BaTe have the rocksalt lattice. Among the other crystalline tellurides are BeTe (zinc blende), MgTe (wurtzite), ZnTe, CdTe, and HgTe (zinc blende); Ag_2Te (dimorphic) and Cu_2Te have more complex structures.

THE OXIDES OF TELLURIUM

There are two oxides of tellurium, TeO_2 and TeO_3. Their structures are not certain, but by analogy with the corresponding selenium oxides (p. 866), they are discussed in this Section.

Tellurium oxide, TeO_2, is a colourless crystalline compound, b.p. about 500°, which sublimes without melting. It is made by burning tellurium in oxygen. It is dimorphic. It separates from water, in which it is almost insoluble, as octahedra; if it is melted and subsequently cooled the crystals obtained are rhombic or monoclinic. Liquid tellurium dioxide is dark yellow. Tellurium dioxide can be distilled at a bright red heat without decomposition.

Tellurium dioxide is amphoteric. With hydrogen chloride it forms the compounds, $TeO_2,3HCl$ and $TeO_2,2HCl$, and with nitric acid the compound, $2TeO_2,HNO_3$. With concentrated perchloric acid it forms $2TeO_2,HClO_4$, which can be dried at 300°, but is at once hydrolysed by water. These compounds are reminiscent of those formed by selenium dioxide (p. 867) and selenous acid (p. 876), but the formulae of the selenium and tellurium compounds do not correspond. Tellurium dioxide dissolves in aqueous solutions of the alkali metal hydroxides (but not in aqueous ammonia solution) to give metal tellurites, M_2TeO_3; it dissolves in solutions of alkali metal carbonates only if the solutions are boiling.

The crystal structure of tellurium dioxide consists of branched chains of tellurium and oxygen atoms covalently linked.

Tellurium trioxide, TeO_3, an orange yellow powder, is made by heating telluric acid, H_6TeO_6. At a low red heat tellurium trioxide is decomposed to oxygen and tellurium dioxide. Tellurium trioxide is not very reactive towards acids and bases. It is not attacked by cold water, by cold hydrochloric acid or by hot nitric acid, or by moderately concentrated potassium hydroxide solution. It dissolves in hot water to give telluric acid, and in concentrated solutions of potassium hydroxide or potassium carbonate to give $K_2H_4TeO_6$. Tellurium trioxide is a strong oxidising agent; it oxidises hot concentrated hydrochloric acid liberating chlorine, being itself reduced to tellurium dioxide and tellurium tetrachloride. The specific gravity of tellurium trioxide is normally 5·075, but on prolonged heating it changes to a grey form which is denser (6·21) and much less reactive.

SECTIONS 2 AND 3. COMPOUNDS IN WHICH THE TELLURIUM ATOM IS DIGONALLY OR TRIGONALLY HYBRIDISED

Tellurium forms the very unstable compound CSTe which decomposes above −54°, but the other tellurium compounds analogous to those formed by sulphur or selenium with carbon in the digonal valence state (Table 18.10, p. 588) have not been prepared.

The difference in energy of the tellurium $5d$ orbitals and the carbon $2p$ orbitals is no doubt too great to permit stable bond formation between the atoms.

If the bond structure of CSTe includes the canonical form, $:\overset{\pi}{\underset{\pi}{S}}$—C—$\overset{..}{Te}:$ then the tellurium atom is present in the trigonal valence state. There is no other example of a compound which contains the tellurium atom in this valence state.

SECTION 4. COMPOUNDS IN WHICH THE TELLURIUM ATOM IS TETRAHEDRALLY HYBRIDISED

TELLURIUM HYDRIDE AND ITS ALKYL AND ARYL DERIVATIVES

Tellurium hydride, TeH$_2$, is a colourless, offensive-smelling gas, b.p. $-20°$, m.p. $-51 \cdot 2°$. It is made:

(i) by the action of an acid on aluminium telluride, Al_2Te_3,
(ii) by the electrolysis, at $-20°$, of dilute sulphuric acid or phosphoric acid, using a tellurium cathode.

Tellurium hydride condenses to a pale yellow liquid, which freezes to a colourless solid. The gas decomposes at room temperature. It burns in air to tellurium dioxide. It is fairly soluble in water, but the solution deposits tellurium. In the absence of air it reacts with sodium hydroxide to form sodium telluride. The first dissociation constant K_1 is $2 \cdot 3 \times 10^{-3}$. The heat of formation from atoms is $124 \cdot 6$ kcal per mole. The vapour density is normal.

Ethyl tellurium hydride, C_2H_5TeH, b.p. $90°$, is made by the action of tellurium hydride on an alcoholic solution of ethyl iodide containing sodium ethoxide:

$$TeH_2 + C_2H_5I = TeC_2H_5H + HI.$$

Phenyl tellurium hydride, C_6H_5TeH, is made by reducing diphenyl ditelluride with sodium and alcohol:

$$C_6H_5Te—TeC_6H_5 + H_2 = 2C_6H_5TeH.$$

Diethyl telluride, $(C_2H_5)_2Te$, b.p. $137 \cdot 5°$, a colourless and evil smelling liquid, is made:

(i) by the action of barium ethyl sulphate on potassium telluride,
(ii) by the action of ether vapour or alcohol vapour on aluminium telluride at high temperatures,
(iii) by the action of magnesium ethyl bromide on tellurium dibromide.

Diethyl telluride combines with chlorine and with bromine to form addition compounds such as $(C_2H_5)_2TeBr_2$. Air oxidises diethyl telluride to the telluroxide, $(C_2H_5)_2TeO$, and nitric acid converts it to the hydronitrate, $[(C_2H_5)_2TeOH]NO_3$.

Dimethyl telluride, $(CH_3)_2Te$, b.p. $82°$, undergoes reactions corresponding to those of the diethyl compound. In acetone solution it combines additively with many metallic salts. Silver iodide in the presence of saturated aqueous potassium iodide solution yields $(AgI)(Te(CH_3)_2)_2$, m.p. $73°$, or $(AgI)_2(Te(CH_3)_2)$, m.p. $137°$, according to the proportions taken. Mercuric bromide yields the compound $(CH_3)_2Te,HgBr_2$, m.p. $160°$. Dimethyl telluride forms a compound with cadmium iodide, but not with nickel bromide.

Diphenyl telluride, $(C_6H_5)_2Te$, b.p. $182°/16 \cdot 5$ mm, is made:

(i) by the action of tellurium on mercury diphenyl,
(ii) by the action of magnesium phenyl bromide on tellurium dibromide:

$$2Mg(C_6H_5)Br + TeBr_2 = Te(C_6H_5)_2 + 2MgBr_2.$$

If air is blown through an ethereal solution of diphenyl telluride in the presence of concentrated hydrochloric acid, the compound $(C_6H_5)_2TeCl_2$ is formed. Diphenyl telluride readily forms diphenyl methyl telluronium iodide by the addition of methyl iodide, but the corresponding reactions with ethyl iodide and other alkyl iodides take place only with difficulty.

Diphenyl ditelluride, $C_6H_5Te—TeC_6H_5$, is the only compound of its type known. It is made by the action of phenyl magnesium bromide on tellurium dibromide. It exists as blood red crystals, m.p. 53°. It is reduced by sodium and alcohol to phenyl tellurium hydride (p. 884). It is oxidised by nitric acid to the nitrate $C_6H_5TeO·NO_3$. The nitrate gives phenyltellurinic acid when treated with alkali.

THE HALIDES OF TELLURIUM

Tellurium forms a dichloride, $TeCl_2$, and a dibromide, $TeBr_2$. The structures of these compounds are uncertain, but it is probable that the tellurium atom is in the tetrahedral valence state, two of the hybrid orbitals being occupied by lone electron pairs. There is no compound TeI_2. Tellurium also forms the four tetrahalides mentioned in Table 22.4, and a hexafluoride and a pentafluoride (p. 891).

Tellurium dichloride, $TeCl_2$, is a black amorphous substance, m.p. 175°, b.p. 324°. It is made:

  (i) by the action of chlorine on tellurium in the correct proportions,
  (ii) by the action of carbon difluorochloride, CCl_2F_2, on tellurium at 500°.

Tellurium dichloride is soluble in ether. It is hygroscopic and it reacts with water to yield tellurous acid, tellurium, and hydrochloric acid. Acids and alkalis bring about similar decompositions. Tellurium dichloride is oxidised by oxygen to tellurium dioxide and tellurium tetrachloride. The spectrum of tellurium dichloride is characteristic, and the vapour density is normal.

Tellurium dibromide, $TeBr_2$, exists as blackish-green crystals, m.p. 210°, b.p. 339°; the vapour is violet. It is formed by the action of carbon trifluorobromide on tellurium:

$$2CF_3Br + Te = C_2F_6 + TeBr_2.$$

It is hydrolysed by water:

$$2TeBr_2 + 3H_2O = H_2TeO_3 + Te + 4HBr.$$

It reacts with ethyl magnesium bromide (p. 884), and with phenyl magnesium bromide (p. 884). It combines additively with bromine and with iodine giving respectively $TeBr_4$ and $TeBr_2I_2$. The vapour density of tellurium dibromide is normal; no dissociation occurs below 1000°. Electron diffraction experiments indicate that the angle BrTeBr is $98 \pm 3°$, and the distance Te—Br is 2·51.

COMPOUNDS CONTAINING CHAINS OF TETRAHEDRALLY HYBRIDISED TELLURIUM ATOMS

The tendency towards chain formation which is less for selenium than for sulphur, is less still for tellurium. The only organic compound containing a chain of tellurium atoms is diphenyl ditelluride (above), and there are no tellurium halides of the type Te_2hal_2. There are no polytelluronic acids, but salts are known of polythionic acids in which one sulphur atom is replaced by a tellurium atom. The salt $Na_2Te(S_2O_3)_2,2H_2O$ is prepared by dissolving tellurous oxide and sodium thiosulphate in a mixture of concentrated hydrochloric acid and glacial acetic acid at 0°. The salt is precipitated by the addition of alcohol. It is oxidised by iodine to tellurous acid and sodium tetrathionate. The potassium salt is made from the sodium salt by treatment with potassium acetate.

COMPOUNDS OF THE TYPE TeX₄

Like selenium (p. 872), tellurium forms a number of compounds of the type TeX_4. There are the four tellurium tetrahalides, and representatives at least of the derivatives $TeAlkHal_3$, $TeAlk_2Hal_2$, $TeAlk_3Hal$, and the corresponding aryl compounds; there are no compounds such as $Te(CH_3)_4$ and $Te(C_6H_5)_4$.

The structures of compounds with the general formula TeX_4, like those of the corresponding selenium compounds, are in doubt. It is possible to write them all as telluronium compounds, such as $[TeR_3^+][Hal^-]$, or $[TeR_2Hal^+][Hal^-]$. At least in the case of tellurium dimethyl di-iodide the telluronium compound exists as a dimer: $[(CH_3)_3Te^+][CH_3I_4Te^-]$. There is little direct evidence on the physical dimensions of

Table 22.4.   *Telluri*

Compound	Preparation	State	m.p.	b.
TeF₄	Heat TeF₆ to 200°	White needles		
TeCl₄	Treat tellurium (i) with chlorine (ii) with disulphur dichloride (iii) with arsenic trichloride	Hygroscopic white crystals (Orange red vapour)	225°	39
TeBr₄	Treat tellurium with bromine	Dark yellow or red crystals	380 ±6°	A) 4.
TeI₄	Treat tellurium with (i) iodine (ii) an alkyl iodide	Black crystals	259°	
CH₃TeBr₃ CH₃TeI₃		Yellow solid Chocolate solid		
(CH₃)₂TeBr₂ (CH₃)₂TeI₂ (C₆H₅)₂TeI₂	Treat tellurium dimethyl with bromine Treat tellurium with methyl iodide Treat tellurium diphenyl with iodine in ether			
(C₂H₅)₃TeCl	(i) Treat tellurium tetrachloride with zinc ethyl (ii) Treat tellurium diethyl with ethyl chloride		174°	
(C₂H₅)₃TeBr (CH₃)₃TeI	Treat β dimethyl tellurium di-iodide with potassium iodide	Colourless solid	162°	
(C₂H₅)₃TeI	Treat tellurium diethyl with ethyl iodide		92°	
(C₆H₅)₃TeI	(i) Treat diphenyl tellurium di-iodide with magnesium phenyl iodide (ii) Treat tellurium tetrachloride with magnesium phenyl iodide			
(C₆H₅)₂(CH₃)TeI	Treat tellurium diphenyl with methyl †iodide			

† Iodides of higher alkyl radicals do not react.

the molecules. The results of electron diffraction analysis on $TeCl_4$ indicate that the structure is a trigonal bipyramid with one equatorial position occupied by a lone pair:

Distance Te—Cl$=2·36$
Angle ClTeCl$=93 \pm 3°$

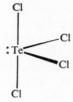

mpounds of the Type TeX$_4$

Solubility	Reactions	Additive compounds
	Rapidly hydrolysed	
luble in benzene, oluene, ethyl alco- ol. Insoluble in ther	Vapour density normal at 500°. Specific conductance 0·203 ohm^{-1} cm^{-1} at 316° 1. Cold water ppts. tellurium dioxide 2. Hot water gives a clear solution 3. Dissolves in hydrochloric acid to give H_2TeO_3, TeO_2, $HTeCl_5$, H_2TeCl_6 4. Phenyl magnesium bromide yields $Te(C_6H_5)_3Cl$	With dimethylaniline $((C_6H_5)(CH_3)_2N)_2TeCl_4 \rightarrow$ $((CH_3)_2NC_6H_4)_2TeCl_2$ $TeCl_4,3NH_3$ and $TeCl_4,6NH_3$ $TeCl_4,SO_3$ and $TeCl_4,2SO_3$ $TeCl_4,2(C_2H_5)_2O$ $TeCl_4, 2AlCl_3$
	1. Dissociates at 600° to tellurium dibromide and bromine 2. A little water gives a clear solution; more precipitates tellurium dioxide	Forms an addition compound with aniline $(H_2NC_6H_5)_2TeBr_4$
ghtly soluble in cetone, ethyl and ethyl alcohol. In- oluble in CCl$_4$, HCl$_3$, CS$_2$, ether, cetic acid	Dissociates at 100°	
oluble in ether or acetone to red solu- tions	{Hydrolysed by boiling water. Decomposed above 100°	
	Treated with C_6H_5MgI gives $(C_6H_5)_3TeI$	
oluble in ether, ut soluble in water r alcohol		
	Treated with Ag_2O gives a base $(C_6H_5)_2(CH_3)$ TeOH, which expels NH_3 from ammonium salts, and which forms a carbonate in solution	

Such a structure would be in accordance with $5s5p^35d$ hybridisation. The low d.p.m. of tellurium tetrachloride (2·57 debyes) is consistent with the trigonal bipyramidal structure. $TeCl_4$ forms many additive compounds with donating reagents (Table 22.4). The formation of the additive compound with dimethylamine might be explained by the octahedral hybridisation of the tellurium atom on the acceptance of an electron pair from the nitrogen atom, but the existence of the other compounds cannot be explained like this. Both $TeCl_4$ and TeI_4 react with phenyl magnesium bromide to give $Te(C_6H_5)_3Cl$ or $Te(C_6H_5)_3I$. These reactions suggest the telluronium structure for the tetrahalides $[TeCl_3{}^+][Cl^-]$ and $[TeI_3{}^+][Cl^-]$. Methyl tolyl phenyl telluronium iodide $[CH_3 \cdot C_6H_4CH_3 \cdot C_6H_5Te^+][I^-]$ has been resolved. The low d.p.m. of p-ditolyl tellurium dibromide $(C_6H_4CH_3)_2TeBr_2$ (3·21 debyes), and of p-ditolyl tellurium dichloride (2·98 debyes) suggests that the molecules of these compounds have trigonal bipyramidal structures.

The preparations and properties of certain tellurium compounds of the type TeX_4 are given in Table 22.4. The relations between the monomeric and dimeric forms of tellurium dimethyl di-iodide are discussed below.

Tellurium dimethyl di-iodide, $(CH_3)_2TeI_2$, exists in two forms. The α-form is made by the action of methyl iodide on tellurium. In solution this form yields a hydroxide $(CH_3)_2Te(OH)_2$, which reacts with hydriodic acid to form α dimethyl tellurium di-iodide again. If, however, the hydroxide is heated before treatment with hydriodic acid, a black form of dimethyl tellurium di-iodide is obtained, known as the β form. It has been shown that the effect of heat on the hydroxide is to eliminate water, and to bring about a migration of a methyl group and an oxygen atom to give trimethly tellurium methyl tellurinate, thus:

$$
\begin{array}{c} CH_3 \\ \diagdown \\ \quad Te-O \\ \diagup \\ CH_3 \end{array}
+
\begin{array}{c} CH_3 \\ \diagdown \\ \quad Te-O \\ \diagup \\ CH_3 \end{array}
=
\left[\begin{array}{c} CH_3 \\ \diagdown \\ CH_3-Te \\ \diagup \\ CH_3 \end{array} \right]^+
\left[\begin{array}{c} \quad O \\ \diagup \\ CH_3-Te \\ \diagdown \\ \quad O \end{array} \right]^-
$$

If the tellurinate is treated with one equivalent of hydriodic acid $(CH_3)_3TeI$ crystallises, and from the residue on evaporation, colourless $CH_3TeO—O—TeOCH_3$ is obtained; this compound is the anhydride of methyl tellurinic acid. If the anhydride is treated with hydriodic acid methyl tellurium tri-iodide is formed:

$$(CH_3)_2Te_2O_3 + 6HI = 2CH_3TeI_3 + 3H_2O,$$

which, on being mixed with trimethyl tellurium iodide, gives the β tellurium dimethyl di-iodide $[(CH_3)_3Te][CH_3TeI_4]$. If the β tellurium dimethyl di-iodide is treated with potassium iodide it yields a colourless precipitate of trimethyl tellurium iodide and, on evaporation of the red filtrate, the salt $K(CH_3TeI_4)$. The anion $(CH_3TeI_4{}^-)$ contains five co-ordinate tellurium.

THE TELLUROXIDES AND TELLUROUS ACID

The telluroxides have the general formula R_2TeO, where R represents an alkyl or aryl radical. The alkyl telluroxides are unstable oils. The telluroxides react with acids to give salts of the type $R_2Te(NO_3)_2$, and in water they probably are in equilibrium with the corresponding hydroxide, thus:

$$H_2O + R_2TeO \rightleftharpoons [R_2TeOH^+][OH^-].$$

Dimethyl telluroxide, $(CH_3)_2TeO$, is made by the atmospheric oxidation of dimethyl telluride, or by the action of silver oxide on dimethyl tellurium dichloride. Diethyl telluroxide is made by corresponding reactions.

Tellurous acid, H_2TeO_3. The compound H_2TeO_3 has not been isolated, but the tellurites of the alkali metals can be made by dissolving tellurium dioxide in solutions of the alkali hydroxides. The acid is weak, $K_1 = 0·6 \times 10^{-5}$.

The tellurites of the alkali metals are colourless, easily soluble, but the solutions decompose readily. The acid salts, such as $KHTeO_3$, react with water:

$$2KHTeO_3 = TeO_2 + K_2TeO_3 + H_2O.$$

In alkaline solution the salts are oxidised by air to the tellurates; in acid solution they are readily reduced to tellurium by sulphur dioxide, tin, zinc, copper, mercury, and by certain organic substances.

Salts of condensed acids are known: K_2TeO_5 up to $K_2Te_6O_{13}$. The ease of oxidation falls as the complexity increases. No tellurous esters are known.

Phenyl tellurinic acid, $C_6H_5TeO \cdot OH$, a white powder, m.p. 211°, is made by oxidising diphenyl ditelluride with nitric acid:

$$2HNO_3 + C_6H_5Te{-}TeC_6H_5 + 1\tfrac{1}{2}O_2 = 2(C_6H_5TeO)NO_3 + H_2O.$$

This nitrate on treatment with alkali gives phenyl tellurinic acid which is amphoteric. It is soluble in alkalis or acids. It is not soluble in organic solvents.

THE TELLURONES AND THE TELLURIC ACIDS

The **tellurones** of general formula R_2TeO_2, are represented by dimethyl tellurone, $(CH_3)_2TeO_2$, and cyclopentyl tellurone, $C_5H_{10}TeO_2,H_2O$. Dimethyl tellurone is a white powder insoluble in all solvents. It is made by the prolonged action of hydrogen peroxide on dimethyl telluride, $(CH_3)_2Te$. Cyclopentyl tellurone:

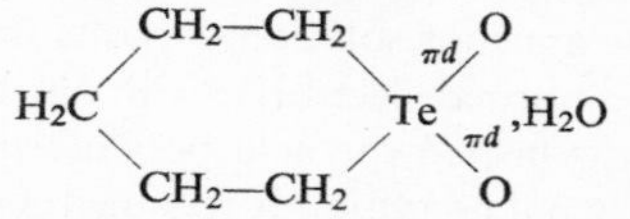

is a white, insoluble amorphous powder. It is made by the oxidation of cyclotelluropentane with hydrogen peroxide. It explodes on rapid heating, and decomposes violently on treatment with nitric or sulphuric acid. It is a strong oxidising agent, liberating chlorine from hydrochloric acid, and decolourising potassium permanganate solution.

The telluric acids. The simple telluric acid, H_2TeO_4, analogous to sulphuric acid and selenic acid, has not been isolated, although its salts are known. The stable acid derived from tellurium in its highest state of oxidation is orthotelluric acid, H_6TeO_6 in which the tellurium atom is in the octahedral valence state, and which is therefore described in Section 6.

Potassium tellurate, K_2TeO_4, is a stable compound. It is made:

(i) by fusing potassium tellurite with potassium nitrate,
(ii) by passing chlorine into an alkaline solution of potassium tellurite:

$$K_2TeO_3 + 2KOH + Cl_2 = K_2TeO_4 + 2KCl + H_2O.$$

Potassium tellurate is reduced to potassium tellurite by boiling hydrochloric acid:

$$K_2TeO_4 + 2HCl = K_2TeO_3 + Cl_2 + H_2O.$$

and to tellurium by sulphur dioxide. Potassium tellurate forms the hydrate $K_2TeO_4,5H_2O$ (which might be $K_2H_4TeO_6,3H_2O$). Barium tellurate is fairly soluble in water (compare sulphur and selenium, p. 878). Potassium tellurate has been shown by X-ray analysis to have the same structure as potassium selenate and potassium sulphate. The acid rubidium salts, $RbHTeO_4$, $RbHSeO_4$, $RbHSO_4$, form solid solutions. In general, however, the tellurates of the alkali metals are not isomorphous with the selenates and sulphates.

The potassium salts of polytelluric acids are known:

$$K_2Te_2O_7,4H_2O \text{ and } K_2Te_4O_{13},4H_2O.$$

SECTION 5. COMPOUNDS IN WHICH THE TELLURIUM ATOM IS IN THE TRIGONAL BIPYRAMIDAL VALENCE STATE

There are few compounds containing a tellurium atom in the trigonal bipyramidal valence state, and few in which the tellurium atom is 5 co-ordinate. The molecule of tellurium tetrachloride is said to have a trigonal bipyramidal configuration with a lone electron pair occupying one of the equatorial positions (p. 887), but most of the compounds TeX_4 are telluronium compounds.

SECTION 6. COMPOUNDS IN WHICH THE TELLURIUM ATOM IS OCTAHEDRALLY HYBRIDISED

The compounds in this Section are orthotelluric acid, $Te(OH)_6$, which is the most stable acid formed by tellurium in the highest oxidation state, and tellurium hexa-fluoride and tellurium pentafluoride.

Orthotelluric acid, H_6TeO_6, is a white crystalline compound. The crystals are dimorphic; one form is cubic and the other is monoclinic. It is made by oxidising tellurium with chromic acid in nitric acid, or with hydrogen peroxide. Tellurium is boiled with excess 30% hydrogen peroxide until the evolution of oxygen ceases. The solution is filtered, evaporated, and the orthotelluric acid is precipitated by the addition of nitric acid.

Orthotelluric acid is not hygroscopic. It is sparingly soluble in cold water, but easily soluble in hot. Below $10°$ the aqueous solution deposits the hydrate $H_6TeO_6,4H_2O$. In aqueous solution the acid is a normal electrolyte with one tellurium atom per molecule. When the aqueous solution is heated the acid polymerises and the solution becomes colloidal. On cooling the original condition is regained. Orthotelluric acid is insoluble in dilute nitric acid, in alcohol, and in acetone.

Orthotelluric acid is very weak. K_1 $(22°) = 1 \cdot 53 \times 10^{-8}$, K_2 $(18°) = 4 \cdot 7 \times 10^{-11}$; dissociation constants beyond the second are less than 10^{-15}. The acidity is increased by the addition to the solution of organic compounds with several OH groups per molecule. The explanation of the effect of polyhydric organic compounds on the acidity of boric acid (p. 500) is inapplicable to telluric acid. In the presence of glycerol, a solution of orthotelluric acid may be titrated against alkali using phenolphthalein as indicator.

When orthotelluric acid is heated it loses water, giving TeO_3, and later TeO_2 and oxygen. It is easily reduced to tellurium by sulphur dioxide, zinc, ferrous iron, or hydrazine.

X-ray analysis has shown that the OH groups are arranged octahedrally; the $Te(OH)_6$ molecules are held together by hydroxyl bonds.

Orthetellurates. Since the higher dissociation constants of orthotelluric acid are so small no alkali metal salts more basic than $Na_2H_4TeO_6$ are found. The silver salt, however, has the formula Ag_6TeO_6.

$Na_2H_4TeO_6$ is prepared by adding a slight excess of aqueous sodium hydroxide to H_6TeO_6, and keeping the mixture at $50°$ for several hours. $Na_2H_4TeO_6,2H_2O$ is made by mixing equal quantities of dilute solutions at $50°$. The dihydrate loses water below $50°$; at $165–170°$ the anhydrous salt decomposes, yielding water and the normal tellurate Na_2TeO_4.

Methyl orthotellurate, $(CH_3)_6TeO_6$, exists as white crystals, m.p. $86–87°$. It is made by the action of diazomethane on a solution of telluric acid in absolute alcohol. It is readily hydrolysed by water, acids, or alkalis.

Allotelluric acid, $(H_2TeO_4)_{11}$. If orthotelluric acid is heated in a sealed tube it melts at about $140°$ to a colourless syrupy mass, which contains a polymer of telluric acid:

$$11H_6TeO_6 \rightleftharpoons (H_2TeO_4)_{11} + 22H_2O.$$

The product dissolves in water, and the molecular weight of the polymer is indicated by the freezing point of the solution. The conductivity of the solution is three to four times that of the solution of orthotelluric acid. Addition of alcohol to the solution does not cause precipitation. On concentrating the solution, orthotelluric acid crystallises.

Tellurium hexafluoride, TeF$_6$, is a colourless gas with an unpleasant smell, sublimation point $-38\cdot9°$, m.p. $-37\cdot8°$. It is made by the combination of the elements at $-78°$. It is more reactive than selenium hexafluoride. It is slowly hydrolysed by water to orthotelluric acid. It reacts with tellurium below 200° to give a white solid which may be either TeF$_4$ or TeF$_2$.

Tellurium pentafluoride, Te$_2$F$_{10}$, is a colourless heavy liquid, b.p. 54°. It is prepared by the direct fluorination of tellurium in the presence of calcium fluoride. The yield is 20%. Tellurium pentafluoride is fairly stable and it resembles selenium pentafluoride.

Nitrogen telluride Te$_3$N$_4$ is said to be formed by the action of liquid ammonia on tellurium bromide.

POLONIUM (RADIUM F)

Polonium is formed by the radioactive decomposition of radium. Polonium is itself radioactive, and it emits an α particle to become radium G (radio lead). The half life is 138 days.

Because of the instability of the nucleus it has been difficult to accumulate large enough quantities of polonium to carry out experiments by normal chemical techniques, and so discover the chemical properties of polonium. The knowledge of the chemistry of polonium is based on two types of experiment:

  (i) experiments on milligram quantities of polonium,
  (ii) experiments on compounds of other elements carrying tracer quantities of polonium.

In the second method it is assumed that, if the tracer quantity of polonium accompanies the other element throughout a particular series of reactions then the chemical properties of polonium are similar to those of the other element, at least for this series of reactions.

Polonium metal is deposited when a silver plate is immersed in a slightly acid solution containing a polonium salt.

The metal is rapidly oxidised at 250–300° to give PoO$_2$. With bromine it gives PoBr$_4$. Treatment with dilute hydrochloric acid, followed by evaporation, gives PoCl$_4$. With hydrogen at 700° it gives PoH$_2$.

Polonium dihydride, PoH$_2$, is made by the action of hydrogen on the metal, and it is also formed when magnesium reacts with an acid solution containing polonium. Polonium dihydride is very unstable and decomposes even at $-180°$.

PoCl$_2$ is a ruby red solid, which sublimes with decomposition at 200°. It is made by the reduction of the tetrachloride with sulphur dioxide.

PoCl$_4$ is a yellow solid, m.p. about 300°. At 400° it volatilises to a purple brown vapour which becomes blue green at 500°. It is made by dissolving polonium metal in dilute hydrochloric acid, and evaporating the solution produced. It is reduced by sulphur dioxide to the dichloride.

PoBr$_4$ is a bright red solid, m.p. about 330°. It is made:

  (i) by the interaction of polonium and bromine,
  (ii) by dissolving the metal or oxide in aqueous hydrobromic acid.

If heated or reduced with H$_2$S it yields PoBr$_2$.

Other compounds which have been prepared are: PoCl$_2$Br$_2$. Cs$_2$[PoBr$_6$], Po$_2$S$_3$, (NH$_4$)$_2$[PoBr]$_6$.

Table 23.1. *Examples of Types of Compounds formed by Elements of Sub-Group VII N*

Section	Hybridisation	Formal charge	Bonds	F	page	Cl	page	Br	page	I	page
1			Compounds in which the bonds have ionic character	Metal fluorides	908	Metal chlorides	915	Metal bromides	925	Metal iodides	930
4	Tetra-hedral	+1	2σ 2 lone pairs							$(IO)_2SO_4$†	932
		0	1σ 3 lone pairs	HF, CH_3F, CH_2F_2, CHF_3, CF_4 F_2O KBF_4, K_2SiF_6 FNO_3, $FClO_2$, $FClO_4$ Fluorides of the other halogens	909 914 914 914 898	Al_2Cl_6 HCl, CH_3Cl Cl_2O $KOCl$, C_2H_5OCl ClF, ClI	539 917 918 920 898	HBr Br_2O $KOBr$ BrF, BrI	925 926 926 898	$[(C_6H_5)_2I]OH$ HI KOI $[I\,pyr^+]OCOCH_3$ ICl, IBr	931 930 936 931 899
		0	1 three-centre 3 lone pairs			$(BeCl_2)_n$	430				
		0	2σ $1\pi d$ 2 lone pairs			$KClO_2$	921			C_6H_5IO $(IO)_2SO_4$	931 932
		0	2σ $2\pi d$ 2 lone pairs			ClO_2‡	918				
		0	3σ $2\pi d$ 1 lone pair			$KClO_3$	922	$KBrO_3$	927	KIO_3 $C_6H_5IO_2$	938 931

No.	Geometry	Charge	Configuration	Cl compound	(p.)	Br compound	(p.)	I compound	(p.)
5		0	3σ, 3πd, 1 lone pair	ClO_3‡	919				
		0	4σ, 3πd	Cl_2O_7, $KClO_4$	920, 923			KIO_4	938
		+1	2σ, 2 lone pairs			$[BrF_2][AuF_4]$	902		
	Trigonal bipyramidal	+1	2σ, 3 lone pairs	$[Cl\,pyr_2]NO_3$		$[Br\,pyr_2]NO_3$		$[Ipyr_2]NO_3$	934
		0	3σ, 2 lone pairs	ClF_3	901	BrF_3	901	ICl_3, $C_6H_5ICl_2$, $I(NO_3)_3$, $I(IO_3)_3$, $I(OCOCH_3)_3$, $I(ClO_4)_3$, IPO_4	902, 933
		0	5σ, 2πd					Ag_3IO_5	938
		−1	2σ, 3 lone pairs	$[(CH_3)_4N][Cl_3]$	924	$KBrCl_2$	927	$KICl_2$, KI_3	932
6	Octahedral	0	5σ, 1 lone pair			BrF_5	903	IF_5, $MICl_4$	902
		0	5σ, 2πd					$H_2[H_3IO_6]$	938
7	sp^3d^3	0	7σ					$1F_7$	904

† In $(IO)_2SO_4$ the iodine atom may be in the trigonal valence state (p. 932).
‡ One non-bonding orbital is occupied by an unpaired electron.

CHAPTER TWENTY-THREE

SUB-GROUP VII N. FLUORINE, CHLORINE, BROMINE, AND IODINE

The properties of the elements in sub-Group VII N are given in Table 23.2. In the ground state the orbitals in the valency shells of the atoms of the elements are occupied thus:

$$
\begin{array}{cccc}
s & p & p & p \\
\text{1⌇} & \text{1⌇} & \text{1⌇} & \uparrow
\end{array}
$$

The orbital structures of the molecules of the halogens present certain problems. If it is assumed that the atoms in the halogen molecules are in the tetrahedral valence state, then the two atoms in the molecule are linked by one σ bond. Each fluorine atom in the molecule F_2, however, has such a large field at its periphery, as indi-

Table 23.2. *The Halogens*

	F	Cl	Br	I
Appearance	Yellow green gas	Green gas	Brown gas: red liquid: orange solid	Blue gas: grey solid: black liquid
m.p. °C	-223	-101	-7	$+114$
b.p. °C	-187	-34	$+59$	$+184$
Specific gravity of liquid	1·11	1·55	3·19	4·9 (solid)
Solubility, gm in 100 gm of water at 0°	(Reacts)	about 1·5	4·15	0·016
Hydrates		$6H_2O$	$10H_2O$	
Solubility in organic solvents	Freely soluble		Freely soluble	(Reacts)
Heat of dissociation to atoms, $X_2 = 2X$, kcal (gas phase)	$+37·6$	$+57·8$	$+45·5$	$+35·6$
Heat of dissociation of bond X—C, kcal	103·4	78·0	65·5	57·0
Heat of dissociation of bond X—H, kcal	132	102·7	87·3	70.5
Electronegativity	4·0	3·0	2·8	2·4
Effective nuclear charge, $(Z_{eff})_{mol}$	4·85	5·75	7·25	7·25
Slater's atomic radius, r	0·38	0·75	0·90	
$(Z_{eff})_{mol}/r^2$	28·85	10·22	8·95	
Bond length X—X	1·42	2·00	2·29	2·66
Pauling's covalent atomic radius	0·64	0·99	1·14	1·33
Radius of ion X^-	1·33	1·81	1·96	2·20

cated by the value of the expression $(Z_{eff})_{mol}/r^2$, that some distortion of the simple tetrahedral arrangement of the orbitals of the other atom might well be expected. The same effect might be expected to a lesser degree for the chlorine molecule. If the interatomic distances for F_2 and Cl_2 are calculated according to the method on p. 327, assuming that the atoms are in the tetrahedral valence state, the results obtained are smaller than the observed values:

	Distance F—F	Distance Cl—Cl
Calculated value	1·26	1·86
Observed value	1·42	2·00

A slightly better agreement is found if it is assumed that no hybridisation takes place, and that bonding occurs between p orbitals (with no s addition); the calculated distances, F—F 1·50 and Cl—Cl 2·15, however, are longer than the observed distances. It is assumed in this chapter that the bonds F—F and Cl—Cl are distorted tetrahedral bonds, in which the p orbital content is greater than it is in the simple sp^3 bond.

Examples of the types of compounds formed by the elements are set out in Table 23.1. The presence of the inert electron pair is not easy to detect in the types of compounds represented, and no reference is made to it in Table 23.1. It should be noted that the Table contains neither Section 2 nor Section 3. These Sections are omitted because no element in sub-Group VII N forms compounds in which it is present in the digonal or trigonal valence state.

Table 23.3.   *The Halogen Hydrides*

	HF	HCl	HBr	HI
Appearance	Colourless gas	Colourless gas	Colourless gas	Colourless gas
m.p. °C	−83·7	−114	−87	−51
b.p. °C	+19·5	−85	−67	−36
Heat of formation of gas, kcal $\frac{1}{2}X_2 + \frac{1}{2}H_2 = HX$	−64·2	−22·0	−8·66	+6·2
Solubility in water at 0°	Miscible	500 vols 42%	600 vols 68%	425 vols 70%
Composition and b.p. of maximum boiling point mixture	35% HF 120°	20% HCl 110°	48% HBr 125°	58% HI 127°

The valency shell of the fluorine atom ($n=2$) contains no d orbitals, and therefore it is complete when the atom accepts an additional electron, either in forming one covalent bond, or in becoming a univalent anion. The promotion of a valency electron in the fluorine atom to an orbital in the next higher shell ($n=3$) would require the absorption of so much energy that it may be disregarded, and therefore the chemistry of fluorine is limited to the reactions of the ion F^-, and of covalent compounds in which the fluorine atom is univalent. The valence shells of chlorine, bromine, and iodine contain d orbitals, and hence these elements form compounds containing πd bonds, such as ClO_2, $HClO_2$, $HClO_3$, $HBrO_3$, HIO_3. The chlorine atom does not form more than four σ bonds. Any valence electrons in the chlorine atom promoted to d orbitals are used either in the formation of πd bonds, or, in the case of the three chlorine compounds mentioned in Section 5 of Table 23.1, to form hybrid orbitals

Table 23.4. The Halogen Oxides

Formula	Appearance	Specific gravity of solid	m.p. °C	b.p. °C	Thermal stability	Stability	Structure
F_2O	Colourless gas: yellow-brown liquid	1·90 at m.p.	−224	−144·8	Decomposes slowly at 250°	Non-explosive	
F_2O_2	Brown gas, red liquid, yellow solid at −100°	1·90 at m.p.	−163·5	−57 (extr.)	Unstable above −100°		
Cl_2O	Brown gas: red-brown liquid	3·89	−11·6	+2	Decomposes at 100°	Explodes on heating or shock	
ClO_2	Orange yellow gas: red liquid: orange red crystals	3·09	−59	+11	Unstable at room temperature	Explodes on slight disturbance	
ClO_3	Red liquid: orange solid at −78°		+3·5		Decomposes at m.p.	Not highly explosive except when in contact with organic compounds	
Cl_2O_7	Oily colourless liquid: colourless solid		−91·5	83	Decomposes slowly at room temperature	Fairly stable but liable to explode on shock or distillation	
Br_2O	Brown liquid and solid		−17·5		Stable only below −40°		
$(BrO_2)_n$	Yellow solid				Stable only below −40°		
$(BrO_3)_n$	White solid				Stable below −80°		
$(I_2O_4)_n$	Yellow crystals	4·2	—	—	Decomposes at 130°	Explosive at 10°	
$(I_4O_9)_n$	Pale yellow solid		—	—	Decomposes at 75°		

occupied by lone pairs; they are not used to obtain a valence state in which 5 or 6 σ bonds are exerted by the chlorine atom. Bromine and iodine in the trigonal-bipyramidal and octahedral valence states form compounds in which the atoms exert five or six σ bonds. In certain compounds in which chlorine, bromine or iodine are in the higher valence states some of the hybrid orbitals of the halogen atom may be occupied by lone pairs. Among compounds of this type are those containing the so-called positive halogen ions. The halogens are too electronegative for a simple ion such as Cl^+ to be stable, but complex anions such as $Clpyr_2^+$ are well-characterised. The following salts of pyridine complexes have been prepared:

$[Clpyr_2]NO_3$	$[Ipyr]IO_3$
$[Brpyr_2]NO_3$	$[Ipyr]OCOCH_3$
$[Ipyr_2]NO_3$	$[Ipyr]OCOC_6H_5$
$[Brpyr_2]ClO_4$	$[Ipyr]_2C_2H_4(OCO)_2$ (succinate)
$[Ipyr_2]ClO_4$	$[Ipyr]_2C_6H_4(OCO)_2$ (phthalate).

In the ion $Xpyr_2^+$ the halogen atom X has 10 valency electrons and is in the trigonal-bipyramidal valence state; in the ion $Ipyr^+$ the iodine atom is in the tetrahedral valence state.

All the halogens form hydrides HX (Table 23.3). The two most electronegative halogens, fluorine and chlorine, take part in the formation of hydrogen bonds (p. 371).

The halogens combine with oxygen (Table 23.4), but all the halogen oxides are unstable, and it is difficult to investigate their physical and chemical properties. Only two oxides of fluorine, F_2O and F_2O_2, are known. The fluorine atom in fluorine monoxide, F_2O, is exerting one σ bond; the structure of F_2O_2 is unknown, but it is probably a peroxide. The absence of higher oxides of fluorine is in accordance with the assumption that the fluorine atom does not form double bonds. All the oxides of chlorine are explosive, and they undergo thermal decomposition at room temperature. Their molecular weights are known, however, and it is possible to make reasonable suggestions for the orbital structures of their molecules (p. 918). The oxides of bromine have a stable existence only at temperatures much below room temperature. The relatively small affinity of bromine for oxygen corresponds to a similar property shown by arsenic and selenium in the same Period. The oxyacid of bromine containing the highest proportion of oxygen is $HBrO_3$, whereas those of chlorine and iodine are $HClO_4$ and H_5IO_6. The oxides of iodine are all solids which are stable up to about $100°$. The formulae of the halogen oxides suggest that the molecular structures of the oxides of chlorine, bromine, and iodine do not correspond. The d orbitals of the chlorine atom probably play an important part in the structures of the chlorine oxide molecules, but it is not possible even to guess whether d orbitals (or orbitals of higher values of the l quantum number) are used in the molecular structures of the oxides of bromine and iodine.

The halogens form an extensive range of interhalogen compounds; in no other Group is there a comparable range of corresponding compounds. The interhalogen compounds are discussed together in the following paragraphs, since there are no grounds for classifying a particular compound under one halogen or the other. The formulae and certain properties of the interhalogen compounds are included in Table 23.5. It may be noted (i) that in no case is an atom of fluorine the central atom in the molecule of an interhalogen compound, (ii) that iodine is always the central atom in any interhalogen compounds in which it occurs, and (iii) that the heavier atom in an interhalogen compound is always present in the smaller atomic proportion.

29 + A.T.I.C.

THE INTERHALOGEN COMPOUNDS

Chlorine monofluoride, ClF, is an almost colourless gas which condenses to a yellow liquid, and a colourless solid. It has a characteristic odour. It is made by the action of chlorine on fluorine at room temperature; a trace of moisture must be present as catalyst:

$$\tfrac{1}{2}Cl_2 + \tfrac{1}{2}F_2 = ClF; \quad \Delta H = -15 \cdot 0 \text{ kcal.}$$

It reacts like fluorine, but more readily.

Bromine monofluoride, BrF, is a pale brown gas which condenses to a dark red liquid, and freezes to a yellow crystalline solid.

It is made by reaction between gaseous bromine and fluorine at $+50°$. It tends to disproportionate into the trifluoride or pentafluoride and free bromine, and has not been obtained pure. It is reactive.

Iodine monofluoride does not exist; in conditions which would be expected to lead to its formation IF_5 is obtained.

Iodine monochloride, ICl, consists of red transparent crystals which melt at $27 \cdot 2°$ to a brownish-red liquid.† It boils at about $100°$ to a red vapour with a choking smell, which attacks the nose and eyes and causes bad burns on the skin. Iodine monochloride attacks cork and rubber violently. In general physical character it is not unlike bromine. It dissolves in non-donating solvents such as CS_2, C_6H_{12}, and CCl_4, to give brown solutions; donating solvents such as acetic acid, ether, ethyl alcohol, or water, produce yellow solutions.

Iodine monochloride is made by adding iodine to liquid chlorine; the mixture is kept at $35°$ for 24 hours to ensure combination. It is formed in aqueous solution when hydrochloric acid reacts on a mixture of potassium iodide and potassium iodate:

$$6HCl + KIO_3 + 5KI = 6KCl + 3H_2O + 3I_2,$$
$$KIO_3 + 2I_2 + 6HCl = KCl + 5ICl + 3H_2O.$$

The reaction is quantitative, and the two stages can be observed by the appearance and disappearance of the red colour of the free iodine.

The heat of formation of iodine monochloride is:

$$\tfrac{1}{2}I_2(g) + \tfrac{1}{2}Cl_2(g) = ICl(s); \quad \Delta H = -3 \cdot 5 \text{ kcal,}$$

and the heat of formation from atoms is:

$$I + Cl = ICl; \quad \Delta H_a = -49 \cdot 6 \text{ kcal.}$$

The vapour is $0 \cdot 4\%$ dissociated at $25°$; $1 \cdot 6\%$ at $100°$. The d.p.m. is $0 \cdot 65$. The specific conductance of the liquid at $35°$ is $4 \cdot 6 \times 10^{-3}$ ohm^{-1} cm^{-1} which is 100 times greater than the conductivity of iodine. On electrolysis of the liquid, both iodine and chlorine are liberated at the anode, thus suggesting the dissociation‡:

$$2ICl = I^+ + [ClICl]^-.$$

Much of the chemistry of iodine monochloride depends on the possibility of this dissociation, although in aqueous solution the concentration of iodine cations is negligible. Liquid iodine monochloride is an ionising solvent in which the heavier alkali metal chlorides KCl, RbCl, CsCl, and NH_4Cl dissolve, but LiCl, NaCl, and $BaCl_2$ do not dissolve. The soluble alkali metal chlorides act as bases:

$$K^+ + Cl^- + I^+ + Cl^- = K^+ + [ICl_2^-],$$

and certain chlorides such as PCl_5, $SbCl_5$, $SnCl_4$, $TiCl_4$, VCl_4, and $AlCl_3$ act as acids:

$$I^+ + Cl^- + PCl_5 = I^+ + [PCl_6^-].$$

---

† A metastable form, m.p. $13 \cdot 9°$, is obtained if the liquid is suddenly chilled to $-5°$.
‡ The ion $[ICl_2]^-$ is discussed on p. 932.

In aqueous solution iodine monochloride reacts with hydrochloric acid to form the strong acid $HICl_2$:

$$H^+ + Cl^- + ICl = H^+ + [ICl_2^-].$$

It is evident that this acid is strong because the addition of $0.14N$ ICl to NHCl reduces the conductivity only by 0.7%. A neutral aqueous solution of iodine monochloride is hydrolysed thus:

$$5ICl + 3H_2O = HIO_3 + 2I_2 + 5HCl,$$

but this hydrolysis is arrested by the addition of $N/5$ hydrochloric acid, or of sodium chloride, presumably because both reagents convert the covalent ICl to the ion $[ICl_2]^-$. The acid aqueous solution of iodine monochloride is yellow with an absorption band at 3430Å. Iodine monochloride is not extracted from the acid aqueous solution by carbon tetrachloride, benzene, or nitrobenzene. These facts suggest that iodine mono-chloride in inert organic solvents is present as ICl which is brown, and in acid aqueous solution as the anion $[ICl_2]^-$ which gives a pale yellow colour to the solution. The ionised form of iodine monochloride is insoluble in inert organic solvents.

Iodine monochloride in the covalent state normally reacts as a chlorinating agent. For example, salicylic acid or phenol is chlorinated by reaction with iodine mono-chloride vapour. Elements usually react with liquid iodine monochloride to yield chlorides in which the element is present in its highest states of valency. In solution in nitrobenzene iodine monochloride iodinates both salicylic acid and phenol; if carbon tetrachloride is the solvent both chlorination and iodination occur, the iodination predominating. In nitrobenzene solution iodine monochloride attacks silver per-chlorate rapidly giving a precipitate of silver chloride; in carbon tetrachloride solution the attack is very slow.

The crystal structure of iodine monochloride is built up of two types of ICl molecule, one of bond length 2·37 and the other 2·44. These are arranged in puckered zig-zag chains, with strong interaction between the molecules in each chain. The distance between the chains corresponds to normal van der Waals forces. The orbital structure of the molecule ICl is uncertain. Studies of the crystal structures of the pyridine and dioxane addition compounds of ICl:

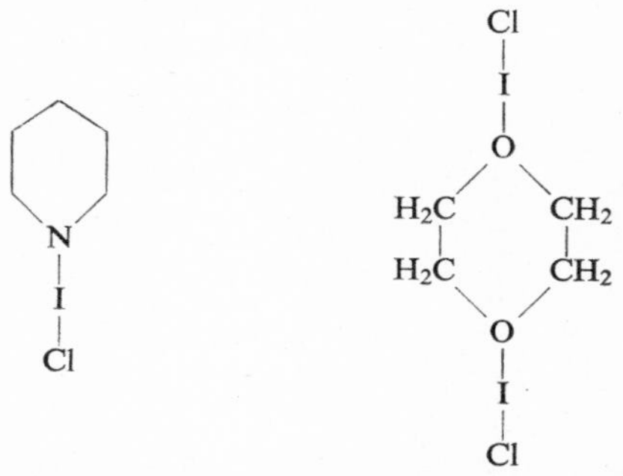

show that the I—N and I—O bonds are non-ionic. The iodine atom in these com-pounds may be in the trigonal bipyramidal valence state with the equatorial positions occupied by lone pairs.

Iodine monobromide, IBr, corresponds closely in formation and in properties to the monochloride. It is made by direct combination of the elements which form a con-tinuous series of solid solutions. It crystallises at 42° to a nearly black solid which boils at 116° to give a red, partially dissociated vapour. The vapour is more highly dissociated than that of ICl; at 25° the dissociation is 8%, and at 300°, 20%. In carbon

Table 23.5.   *The Interhalogen Compounds*

Compound	Appearance	m.p. °C	b.p. °C	Stability	Suggested structure
ClF	Colourless gas	−156	−101		$:\!\overset{..}{\underset{..}{Cl}}\!-\!\overset{..}{\underset{..}{F}}\!:$
BrF	Pale brown gas	−33	+20	Tends to dispropor-tionate to BrF_3 and Br_2	
(IF)†					
BrCl				Extremely unstable; only evidence for it is spectral	
ICl	Red crystals	27·2	*ca* 100	1·6% dissociated at 100°	
IBr	Black solid	42	116	About 15% dissoci-ated at 100°	
ClF₃	Colourless gas	−83	+12		
BrF₃	Yellow-green liquid	8·8	126		
(IF₃)†					
(BrCl₃)†					
ICl₃	Lemon-yellow crystals	101 under pressure		Dissociation is com-plete at 77°	
(IBr₃)†					
(ClF₅)†					
BrF₅	Colourless liquid	−61·3	41	Stable up to 460°	
IF₅	Colourless liquid	9·6	98 (extr)	Stable up to 400°	
IF₇	Colourless gas	45	5		

† Compounds represented by the formulae in brackets have not been prepared.

tetrachloride solution iodine monobromide is 9·5% dissociated. The heat of formation from atoms is given by:

$$I + Br = IBr; \quad \Delta H_a = -41 \cdot 5 \text{ kcal.}$$

Iodine monobromide is red in non-solvating solvents; yellow in solvating solvents. It always reacts as a brominating agent.

Chlorine trifluoride, ClF_3, is a colourless gas which condenses to a green liquid, and freezes to a white solid.

It is made by passing either chlorine or chlorine monofluoride mixed with excess fluorine through a nickel tube at 250°. The product is condensed with liquid air, and purified by distillation. The heat of formation is given by:

$$\tfrac{1}{2}Cl_2 + 1\tfrac{1}{2}F_2 = ClF_3; \quad \Delta H = -42 \pm 2 \text{ kcal.}$$

It reacts like fluorine but with greater vigour. Most elements are attacked explosively. It destroys glass or quartz, and inflames organic substances. Liquid ClF_3 reacts with water with a loud crack.

From microwave data the structure is planar and T-shaped,

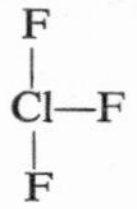

$$
\begin{array}{c}
F \\
| \\
Cl-F \\
| \\
F
\end{array}
$$

with two distances Cl—F 1·70 and one 1·60. This might indicate trigonal bipyramidal hybridisation, with F atoms occupying one equatorial position and two polar positions.

Bromine trifluoride, BrF_3, is a yellow-green liquid. It is made by mixing bromine vapour and fluorine in a stream of nitrogen; it is purified by distillation.

The specific conductance of the liquid at 20° is 8×10^{-3} ohm^{-1} cm^{-1}. This fairly high value, and the fact that the liquid obeys Ohm's law, indicate that bromine trifluoride is ionised, and the following reactions show that it is an ionising solvent which dissociates according to the equilibrium:

$$2BrF_3 \rightleftharpoons [BrF_2^+] + [BrF_4^-].$$

Bromine trifluoride reacts with many metals and metallic oxides to give compounds of which the following examples may be formulated:

$$[BrF_2^+][AuF_4^-] \quad [BrF_2^+][SbF_6^-] \quad [BrF_2^+][NbF_6^-] \quad [BrF_2^+][TaF_6^-]$$
$$[BrF_2^+][BiF_6^-] \quad [BrF_2^+]_2[TiF_6^-]$$
$$[BrF_2^+]_2[SnF_6^{2-}].$$

These compounds are acids in the bromine trifluoride system, as in every case the cation is the cation of the ionised solvent. The acids can be neutralised by a base of the system, which is a compound containing the anion $[BrF_4^-]$. The following reactions are examples of such neutralisations:

$$[BrF_2^+][SbF_6^-] + AgBrF_4 = 2BrF_3 + AgSbF_6$$
$$[BrF_2^+][AuF_4^-] + AgBrF_4 = 2BrF_3 + AgAuF_4$$
$$[BrF_2^+]_2[SnF_6^{2-}] + 2KBrF_4 = 4BrF_3 + K_2SnF_6.$$

A salt of the system, if placed in the solvent, undergoes solvolysis:

$$K_2TiF_6 + 4BrF_3 \rightleftharpoons [BrF_2^+]_2[TiF_6^-] + 2KBrF_4.$$

All the above reactions are in accord with the supposition that liquid bromine trifluoride is slightly ionised to $[BrF_2^+]$ and $[BrF_4^-]$ as water is ionised to H^+ and OH^-.

Bromine trifluoride is extremely reactive, and its reactions are somewhat similar to those of iodine pentabromide. It fluorinates and brominates the halides of carbon, thus: CCl_4 yields a mixture of derivatives in which Cl has been replaced by F; CBr_4 behaves similarly; CI_4 yields CF_4 and a mixture of fluorobromomethanes; C_6Cl_6 yields $C_6Br_2Cl_4F_6$.

BrF_3 dissolves many metals including silver, gold, niobium, and tantalum, to give compounds such as $[BrF_2][AuF_4]$ and $[BrF_2][TaF_6]$, which are acids in the bromine trifluoride system. BrF_3 reacts with metallic halides. The halides of K, Ag, Ba give $KBrF_4$, $AgBrF_4$, $Ba(BrF_4)_2$, but those of other metals give the metallic fluoride, as the tetrafluorobromates are unstable.

Bromine trifluoride reacts with a large number of oxides, both of metals and of the more electropositive of the non-metals, such as Si, As, I, to form fluorides, as exemplified by the equations:

$$3SiO_2 + 4BrF_3 = 3SiF_4 + 2Br_2 + 3O_2.$$
$$2WO_3 + 4BrF_3 = 2WF_6 + 2Br_2 + 3O_2.$$

It also acts with salts of oxyacids to form fluoroacids. Examples of such transformations are:

$$NaPO_3 \rightarrow NaPF_6, \quad Na_3PO_4 \rightarrow NaPF_6 + 2NaBrF_4,$$
$$\text{Borax} \rightarrow NaBF_4 \quad Ag_3AsO_4 \rightarrow AgAsF_6 + AgBrF_4.$$

It converts potassium salts of the oxyacids of sulphur to potassium fluorosulphonate or potassium fluorobromate, thus

$K_2S_2O_8$, $K_2S_2O_7$ yield KSO_3F only,
K_2SO_4, $K_2S_2O_5$, $K_2S_2O_3$ yield equal proportions of KSO_3F and $KBrF_4$,
K_2SO_3, $K_2S_2O_4$ yield $KBrF_4$ only.

With nitrosyl persulphate BrF_3 yields nitrosyl fluorosulphonate, $NOSO_3F$. It reacts with nitrogen peroxide and the oxide of an element which can form an anionic complex to yield a nitronium salt; with boric oxide, B_2O_3, for example, $(NO_2)(BF_4)$ is obtained, and with antimony pentoxide $(NO_2)(SbF_6)$. If $NOCl$ is used instead of NO_2, nitrosyl compounds are obtained such as $NOAuF_4$ and $NOPF_6$. A solution of sulphur trioxide in bromine trifluoride, however, reacts with a base such as silver fluorobromate to give a fluorosulphonate:

$$(BrF_2)(SO_3F) + AgBrF_4 = AgSO_3F + 2BrF_3.$$

The d.p.m. of bromine trifluoride vapour is in accord with a planar T-shaped molecule like that assigned to chlorine trifluoride.

Iodine trichloride consists of lemon yellow crystals which melt (under a dissociation pressure of 16 atmospheres) at 101° to a reddish brown liquid. The crystals are very volatile. The vapour density shows that dissociation is complete at 77°.

Iodine trichloride is made by the direct combination of the elements, *either*, by condensing chlorine on iodine at −80°, and, after some hours in a freezing mixture, evaporating off excess of chlorine, *or*, by passing chlorine over iodine until this is converted to ICl, and then raising the temperature to 100° and increasing the stream of chlorine. ICl_3 is obtained when the gaseous products of the reaction are condensed. It is also formed when I_2O_5 is heated with hydrogen chloride:

$$I_2O_5 + 10HCl = 2ICl_3 + 5H_2O + 2Cl_2.$$

The heat of formation from atoms is given by:

$$I + 3Cl = ICl_3; \quad \Delta H_a = -128 \cdot 2 \pm 2 \cdot 5 \text{ kcal},$$

and hence the average value for the formation of the bond I—Cl is $-42 \cdot 7 \pm 0 \cdot 8$ kcal.

Iodine trichloride unites with many metal chlorides to give tetrachloroiodides,

$MICl_4$, and with the fluorides of K, Rb, Cs to give polyhalides $MICl_3F$. It reacts with carbon disulphide thus:

$$3CS_2 + 4ICl_3 = CCl_4 + 2CSCl_2 + 2S_2Cl_2 + 2I_2.$$

It dissolves in water with extensive hydrolysis:

$$2ICl_3 + 3H_2O = ICl + HIO_3 + 5HCl,$$

but from concentrated solutions the unchanged substance can be precipitated by the addition of concentrated sulphuric acid. It can also be sublimed from the concentrated solution at 50° at a pressure of less than 200 mm. It dissolves in carbon tetrachloride, but its absorption spectrum when in this solvent is identical with the superposition of those of ICl and Cl_2.

X-ray analysis of the crystals of iodine trichloride has established that the molecule is dimeric

	Magnitudes of angles
α	96°
β	91°
γ	94°
δ	84°

The molecule is planar. Each iodine atom in the molecule controls 12 valency electrons. It may be conjectured that the iodine atoms are octahedrally hybridised, and that the polar orbitals are occupied by lone pairs.

Bromine pentafluoride, BrF_5, is a colourless fuming liquid. It is made by passing fluorine into bromine trifluoride at 100°, and heating the gaseous product to 200°. It is very stable to heat, but it reacts readily with most metals and non-metals, and with the chlorides, bromides, and iodides of the alkali metals. Liquid bromine penta-fluoride reacts explosively with water.

The configuration of the molecule of BrF_5 is similar to that of the molecule of IF_5.

Iodine pentafluoride, IF_5, is a colourless liquid. It is made:

(i) by the action of iodine on silver fluoride:

$$3I_2 + 5AgF = 5AgI + IF_5,$$

(ii) by the action of fluorine on heated iodine pentoxide:

$$5F_2 + I_2O_5 = 2\tfrac{1}{2}O_2 + 2IF_5,$$

(iii) by passing fluorine diluted with nitrogen over iodine in a quartz vessel; if any IF_7 is formed it is easily removed as it is highly volatile.

The specific conductance of iodine pentafluoride is 2×10^{-6} ohm^{-1} cm^{-1} at 20°. It is stable to heat up to 400°. The heat of formation at 18° is given by:

$$\tfrac{1}{2}I_2(s) + 2\tfrac{1}{2}F_2(g) = IF_5(l); \quad \Delta H = -204 \cdot 7 \text{ kcal}$$
$$\tfrac{1}{2}I_2(s) + 2\tfrac{1}{2}F_2(g) = IF_5(g); \quad \Delta H = -194 \cdot 6 \text{ kcal}.$$

Iodine pentafluoride is highly reactive. It fumes strongly in the air, and it reacts at once with water to form HF and I_2O_5. It attacks glass slowly in the cold and rapidly at 100° to give SiF_4 and I_2O_5. It reacts violently with organic compounds, usually causing them to carbonise and ignite. Its principal reactions may be grouped as follows:

(i) *with elements.* Metals such as silver, copper, mercury, and iron react with it slowly. Mercury yields a light brown solid, $Hg(IF_5)_2$, which changes to red on exposure to air. Sulphur, red phosphorus, silicon, bismuth, tungsten, and arsenic react at once usually with incandescence.

(ii) *with oxides.* I_2O_5, P_2O_5, V_2O_5, and CrO_3 dissolve freely in hot IF_5, and yield IOF_3, POF_3, VOF_3, and CrO_2F_2, respectively. WO_3, and MoO_3 also dissolve yielding substances with the compositions $WO_3,2IF_5$ and $2MoO_3,3IF_5$. As_2O_5 yields a white substance of indefinite composition; Sb_2O_5 yields $SbF_5,3IO_2F$. NO_2 yields IF_5NO_2, a cream-coloured crystalline solid which sublimes unchanged when gently heated. CO and SO_2 do not react.

(iii) *with carbon halides.* CCl_4 yields CCl_3F, ICl and ICl_3. CBr_4 yields a mixture of bromofluoromethanes. CI_4 yields CIF_3 (b.p. $-22\cdot5°$), and C_2I_4 yields C_2IF_5 (b.p. $13°$).

(iv) *with certain potassium salts.* Potassium periodate yields KIO_4,IF_5; potassium nitrate yields KIF_6; potassium fluoride also yields KIF_6. Iodine pentafluoride does not react with $NaCl$, KCl, $AgCl$, AgF or BaF_2.

Experiments on the infrared spectrum, the Raman spectrum, and the nuclear magnetic resonance of iodine pentafluoride suggest that the molecule has the form of a tetragonal pyramid. The hybridisation may be octahedral with a lone pair occupying one of the polar orbitals.

Iodine heptafluoride, IF_7, is a colourless gas, condensing to a colourless liquid, and a snow white solid. It is made by the combination of fluorine with warm iodine pentafluoride; there is no action in the cold. Fluorine is passed through liquid iodine pentafluoride at $90°$, and the vapours are passed through a platinum tube at $270°$. (The tube is attacked at $300°$.) The issuing gases are condensed, and the IF_7 is purified by distillation.

In the molecule IF_7 iodine is exerting its maximum covalency; there is no lone pair of electrons in the valency shell of the iodine atom. IF_7 is inert, but not as inert as SF_6 or NF_3. It reacts slowly with water. If the gas is blown through water, periodate ions and fluoride ions are formed in solution. At $350°$ in the presence of HgF_2 it fluorinates CCl_2F_2 to $CClF_3$. It does *not* react with alkali metal fluorides to form MIF_8.

The molecule has the form of pentagonal bipyramid with fluorine atoms at the corners. The hybridisation of the iodine atom is sp^3d^3.

FLUORINE

THE ELEMENT

Fluorine is prepared by the electrolysis of a mixture of potassium fluoride and pure anhydrous hydrogen fluoride. The equilibrium diagram for the system KF/HF is given in Fig. 23.1. The Figure also shows the partial pressure of hydrogen fluoride above the mixture at the temperature of the liquidus. In the electrolysis it is desirable to arrange (i) that the volatilisation of hydrogen fluoride is as low as possible, (ii) that the anode is not attacked by the fluorine, and (iii) that polarisation of the cell is reduced to a minimum. There are three conditions of temperature and composition of the electrolyte in which fluorine can be efficiently prepared. The procedures for electrolysis are usually referred to as low, medium, and high temperature processes. The conditions suitable for each of the three methods are shown by the shaded areas on the equilibrium diagram, Fig. 23.1, and are compared in Table 23.6.

The low temperature method was that originally employed by Moissan. Its disadvantages are the heavy loss of the platinum anode as K_2PtF_6, and the high proportion of hydrogen fluoride which contaminates the fluorine produced. Carbon can be used as the anodic material only if the proportion of KF in the electrolyte is high. If the composition of the electrolyte is less than 59% by weight of potassium fluoride, amorphous carbon is disintegrated by fluorine during the electrolysis; if the composition is less than $61\cdot7\%$ graphite is disintegrated. Hence amorphous carbon may be used as

Table 23.6. *Conditions for the Electrolytic Preparation of Fluorine*

	Low temperature	Medium temperature	High temperature
Working temperature	$-30°$	$100°$	$250°$
Composition of electrolyte (molar proportions)	KF,12HF	KF,2HF	KF,HF
Anode	Platinum iridium alloy	Amorphous carbon	Graphite
Cathode	Platinum iridium alloy	Mild steel	Silver
Containing vessel	Copper	Mild steel	Magnesium alloy
Insulator	Fluorspar	Teflon $(CF_2=CF_2)_n$	

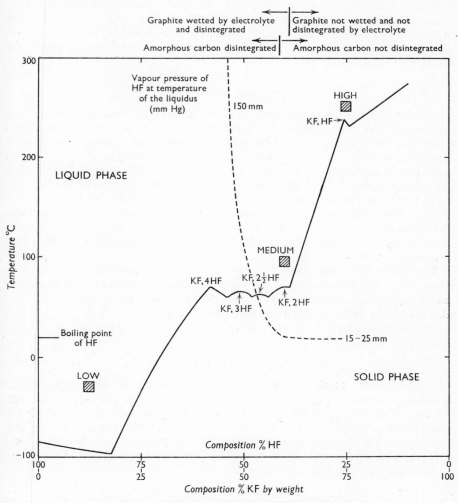

Fig. 23.1. Equilibrium diagram of the system KF/HF.

29*

the anode for the medium temperature process but the composition of the electrolyte must be carefully controlled by the addition of hydrogen fluoride as the electrolysis proceeds. Graphite is used as the anodic material for the high temperature process because amorphous carbon would be attacked at the high temperatures used; graphite is itself attacked if the temperature rises to 300°. The disintegration of the carbon anodes is due to the formation of graphitic fluorine compounds (p. 593). In all the electrolytic processes the electrolyte must be quite anhydrous; all water is removed by pre-electrolysis before the preparation of fluorine begins.

Fluorine is highly reactive. K, B, C, Si, P, As, Sb, S, Se, Te, Br, and I all ignite spontaneously in gaseous fluorine. Pb, Sn, and solder react with fluorine at room temperature. Ag, Mg, Zn, Al, Mn, Fe, Ni, take fire in the gas when gently warmed. Au and Pt are not attacked; copper exposed to fluorine is covered with a protective film of cupric fluoride, and so is not further attacked.

Up to 100° pure fluorine does not react with silica, hard glass, copper, nickel, monel metal, aluminium, magnesium, brass, or mild steel. Nickel and monel metal withstand corrosion up to 600°. If sintered alumina is exposed to fluorine a non-volatile layer of aluminium fluoride is formed on the surface, and up to 700° the metal is not further attacked. If, however, the fluorine contains hydrogen fluoride it attacks glass and silica, and the attack continues, as hydrogen fluoride is produced in the reaction:

$$SiO_2 + 4HF = SiF_4 + 2H_2O,$$
$$2H_2O + 2F_2 = 4HF + O_2.$$

Fluorine combines with the other halogens directly (p. 899). Fluorine does not combine directly with nitrogen or oxygen, but a mixture of fluorine and oxygen explodes when subjected to the silent electric discharge. Solid fluorine explodes with liquid hydrogen at $-252°$, but the two gases do not normally combine if mixed at room temperature, although sometimes they explode violently. There is little reaction if a mixture of fluorine and hydrogen in a magnesium vessel is exposed to ultraviolet light. It is probable that any reaction between fluorine and hydrogen is carried on through the combination of atoms released in a sequence of chain reactions, and that the chains are very easily broken. Fluorine reacts with nitric acid to give dinitrogen hexoxide (p. 677), or fluorine nitrate (p. 914), and with perchloric acid to give fluorine perchlorate (p. 914).

The internuclear distance in the fluorine molecule F_2 is 1·42 and the relative restoring force (that of HI is taken as unity) is 3·08 (from rotation vibration spectra). Symmetric and anti-symmetric molecules must be present in the gas as the spectrum shows lines due to rotation which are alternately weak and strong.

The orbital structure of the molecule F_2 is discussed on p. 895.

GENERAL CHEMISTRY OF FLUORINE

Fluorine is the most electronegative of the elements; its electronegativity on Pauling's scale is 4·0, and its effective nuclear charge is 4·85. The value of the term $(Z_{eff})_{mol}/r^2$ for fluorine is 28·85, which is a greater value than that found for any other element. Fluorine is therefore more ready than any other halogen to form ionic compounds. This is shown by a comparison of the crystal structures of certain metal fluorides with the structures of the chlorides of the same metals (Table 15.4, p. 421).

The electron configuration of the fluorine atom is

$1s$	$2s$	$2p$	$2p$	$2p$
⇅	⇅	⇅	⇅	↑

The quantum number n of the valence shell is 2. Hence the fluorine atom has no d orbitals to use in bond formation. The absence of d orbitals at once explains the absence of any oxides of fluorine corresponding to ClO_2, ClO_3, Cl_2O_7, and of any oxyacids corresponding to $HClO$, $HClO_2$, $HClO_3$, and $HClO_4$, all of which contain chlorine atoms linked to oxygen atoms by πd bonds. Fluorine atoms can often replace oxygen atoms in anions without great change of crystal structure. For example, there is an isomorphous series $[Cu(OH_2)_4]X$, where X is $[SiF_6{}^{2-}]$, $[SnF_6{}^{2-}]$, $[NbOF_5{}^{2-}]$, $[MoOF_5{}^{2-}]$, $[MoO_2F_4{}^{2-}]$, $[WO_2F_4{}^{2-}]$. In certain anions fluorine atoms appear to play the parts of oxygen atoms, as for example in the anion in K_2BeF_4, which resembles the sulphate ion in that they both have the tetrahedral configuration and the apices of the tetrahedrons are occupied by atoms of high electronegativity:

The $[BeF_4{}^{2-}]$ ion, however, differs from the $[SO_4{}^{2-}]$ ion in that (i) it contains no πd bonds, (ii) the *formal* negative charge resides on the central atom. From the values of $(Z_{eff})_{mol}$ for the atoms in the two ions (Table 4.4) it is evident, however, that the *actual* positions of the negative charges are roughly the same in both ions.

The valence shell of the fluorine atom contains p orbitals, but no d orbitals. Since the shell is completed by the formation of one σ bond with another atom, the fluorine atom has no opportunity of exerting πp bonds. Hence the chemistry of fluorine is much more restricted than that of oxygen or chlorine, because there are only two states in which the fluorine atom is present in combination. In one the fluorine atom is present in the ionic state as F^-, and in the other it is present in the tetrahedral valence state. In the tetrahedral valence state the fluorine atom exerts one σ bond; the remaining three hybrid orbitals are occupied by lone pairs. These properties of the fluorine atom are in accord with the absence of a series of fluorides of nitrogen corresponding to the oxides of nitrogen.

The radius of the fluorine atom is small and when the atom forms a covalent link it brings out the highest covalency of the other atom. This effect is seen by comparing the formulae of the highest chlorides and the highest fluorides of certain elements:

$$SCl_4, SF_6 : BrCl, BrF_5 : ICl_3, IF_5, IF_7 : NaAsCl_4, NaAsF_6.$$

In all its covalent compounds the fluorine atom exerts one σ bond; it never exerts co-ionic bonds or double bonds. Since fluorine is so highly electronegative it takes part in the formation of hydrogen bonds, and if hydrogen is present in any compound which also contains fluorine the physical and chemical properties of the compound may be modified by the presence of hydrogen bonds (p. 371).

Although fluorine is a very active element it forms several compounds with non-metals which are much more inert than the corresponding chlorine compounds. Among these inert compounds are aliphatic carbon compounds containing more than two fluorine atoms attached to the same carbon atom (p. 912), and the following fluorides or oxyfluorides: NF_3, PF_3 (PF_5 is active), SF_6, S_2F_{10}, CH_3FSO_2, SO_2F_2, SeF_6, and TeF_6.

SECTION 1. COMPOUNDS IN WHICH THE FLUORINE ATOM HAS IONIC CHARACTER

The fluorides. The monatomic fluoride ion, F^-, is stable and is present in the crystals of nearly all the metal fluorides and in their solutions. The crystal structures of the metal fluorides are predominantly ionic. Examples of cases in which the covalent contributions are important, however, are cuprous fluoride which has the zinc blende structure, beryllium fluoride which has a cristobalite lattice, and ammonium fluoride which has the wurtzite structure. The crystal structures of ammonium fluoride, ammonium hydrogen fluoride, and potassium hydrogen fluoride are determined by the presence of hydrogen bonds (p. 383). The following list gives the crystal structures of certain metal fluorides:

> Sodium chloride lattice. LiF, NaF, KF, RbF, CsF, AgF; TlF has a deformed sodium chloride lattice.
> Rutile lattice (the radius of the metal ion is 0·65 to 0·80). MgF_2, ZnF_2, FeF_2, CoF_2, NiF_2.
> Fluorite lattice (the radius of the metal ion is 0·97 to 1·35). CaF_2, SrF_2, BaF_2, CdF_2, HgF_2, PbF_2.
> ReO_3 lattice. AlF_3, ScF_3, CoF_3, RhF_3, PdF_3.
> Bismuth trifluoride has a modified fluorite lattice.

The fluoride ion is not found in any layer lattice.

Potassium fluoride is obtained by neutralising a solution of hydrofluoric acid with potassium hydroxide and evaporating the solution. Potassium hydrogen fluoride, KHF_2, is obtained by adding twice the equivalent proportion of hydrofluoric acid to potassium hydroxide and evaporating the solution. Potassium hydrogen fluoride is so stable that it can be dried by heating, but on strong ignition it decomposes to yield the normal salt:

$$KHF_2 = KF + HF.$$

The action is reversible, as both sodium and potassium fluorides are used for absorbing hydrogen fluoride. By contrast ammonium fluoride on heating yields the acid salt:

$$2NH_4F = NH_3 + NH_4HF_2.$$

Most fluorides, including silver fluoride, are soluble in water. Calcium fluoride is insoluble in water.

There is a sharp difference between the m.p.s of the metal fluorides in Period 3, and the m.p.s of the non-metal fluorides in the same Period. The m.p. (°C) are as follows:

NaF	MgF_2	AlF_3	SiF_4	PF_5	SF_6
980	1400	1040	−77	−83	−55

The high m.p.s of the metal fluorides indicate that the ions have attained high co-ordination numbers by forming giant molecules. The central atoms in the molecules of silicon tetrafluoride, phosphorous pentafluoride, and sulphur hexafluoride are all in their highest valency states; every electron in the valency shell is engaged in forming a covalent bond with a fluorine atom. Increase in co-ordination number by the formation of ionic crystals is therefore impossible, and the crystals of these compounds consist of simple molecules held together by van der Waals forces.

SECTION 4. COMPOUNDS IN WHICH THE FLUORINE ATOM IS TETRAHEDRALLY HYBRIDISED

Some of the principal compounds in which the fluorine atom is present in the tetrahedral valence state are hydrogen fluoride, fluorine monoxide (p. 914), complex anions such as BF_4^- and other anions mentioned on p. 907, and organic compounds containing fluorine.

Anhydrous hydrogen fluoride, HF, is made in the laboratory by the thermal decomposition of potassium hydrogen fluoride (p. 908). On a commercial scale hydrogen fluoride is made by the fractionation of a concentrated aqueous solution of hydrogen fluoride (p. 910). It is said that if hydrogen fluoride is quite free from water it does not attack glass or metals.

Hydrogen fluoride in the presence of a trace of moisture attacks glass to form silicon tetrafluoride:

$$4HF + SiO_2 = 2H_2O + SiF_4,$$

and it dissolves most metals

$$Fe + 2HF = FeF_2 + H_2.$$

It destroys organic compounds, but it does not attack the noble metals. Anhydrous hydrogen fluoride reacts with certain oxychlorides of sulphur, selenium, and phosphorus, including SO_2Cl_2, $SOCl_2$, HSO_3Cl, $SeOCl_2$, $POCl_3$, to yield the corresponding fluorides A solution of potassium nitrate in hydrogen fluoride attacks the transition metals, Cr, Mo, W, and Mn to give the oxyfluorides CrO_2F_2, $MoOF_4$, WOF_4, and MnO_3F.

Liquid hydrogen fluoride is a better solvent than water. The majority of the solutes which dissolve in other solvents in the cold dissolve in hydrogen fluoride. The solutions often have high conductivities. Solutions in hydrogen fluoride fall into a number of classes.

Hydrogen fluoride solutions of simple metal fluorides. Simple metal fluorides dissolve in hydrogen fluoride and ionise as they would in water:

$$NaF = Na^+ + F^-.$$

Fluorides of the alkali metals dissolve easily. The order of solubility is Li < Na < K < Rb < Cs, which is the same as for water. Ammonium, thallous, and argentous fluorides are also soluble. Fluorides of the alkaline earth metals are less soluble, and here again the solubility increases with atomic number. Except for aluminium fluoride, which is very soluble, the fluorides of the trivalent metals do not dissolve.

Hydrogen fluoride solutions of metal chlorides, bromides, iodides, cyanides, and azides. The acids from which these salts are derived are insoluble in hydrogen fluoride, and therefore when the salts are treated with hydrogen fluoride the parent acid is expelled:

$$NaCl + HF = Na^+ + HCl + F^-.$$

Hydrogen fluoride solutions of metal salts containing non-deformable anions of oxyacids. Salts of this kind dissolve and dissociate:

$$KClO_4 = K^+ + ClO_4^-,$$

but no further change occurs; the anions are so reluctant to take up H^+ ions that the hydrogen fluoride remains unionised. This class of metal salt includes the perchlorates, the periodates, and the fluoroborates, for example KBF_4.

Hydrogen fluoride solutions of metal salts containing deformable anions of oxyacids. Salts of this kind react with liquid hydrogen fluoride to yield oxonium ions. For example, nitrates form the nitronium ion:

$$KNO_3 + 2HF = K^+ + 2F^- + [H_2NO_3^+];$$

metal hydroxides behave in a corresponding manner.

$$KOH + 2HF = K^+ + 2F^- + [H_3O^+];$$

the reaction is often violent.

Sulphates and the salts of oxyacids derived from transition metals react to give oxyfluorides, for example:

$$K_2SO_4 + 4HF = 2K^+ + 3F^- + HSO_3F + H_3O^+,$$
$$K_2CrO_4 + 6HF = 2K^+ + 4F^- + 2H_3O^+ + CrO_2F_2.$$

Potassium permanganate yields manganese trioxyfluoride, MnO_3F. Potassium chlorate and barium chlorate yield chlorine dioxide.

Hydrogen fluoride solutions of organic compounds. The paraffins are insoluble in hydrogen fluoride. Benzene and anthracene dissolve to the extent of 2 or 3%. Ethylene and its derivatives are polymerised. Hydrogen fluoride is such a powerful proton donor that many organic compounds containing oxygen atoms or nitrogen atoms accept protons to form cations. Acetone, for example, ionises thus:

$$CH_3COCH_3 + HF = [CH_3COHCH_3^+] + F^-.$$

Many alcohols, phenols, aldehydes, ketones, carboxylic acids, nitriles, nitro-compounds, amines and amides react in a corresponding manner. Thioalcohols and thio-ethers react like the alcohols and ethers.

Above 80° at 1 atm. pressure, or at the b.p. and 20 mm pressure the vapour density of hydrogen fluoride corresponds to the monomeric formula HF; at 1 atm and at the b.p. the association factor is 3·45. Electron diffraction experiments show that the distance H–F in the monomeric molecule is $1·00 \pm 0·06$, and that the polymer consists of zig-zag chains:

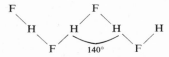

The distance F—F is 2·55, and the angle FHF is greater than 165°. The d.p.m. increases with decreasing pressure and increasing temperature, but the observed value is always less than the calculated value for the zig-zag model of H_4F_4. The low value of the d.p.m. could be explained by assuming that cyclic polymers exist, and that they are favoured by high pressures and low temperatures.

Liquid hydrogen fluoride is non-ionised as indicated by the low specific conductance, 1×10^{-7} ohm^{-1} cm^{-1}. Hence the molecule HF does not accept an H$^+$ ion to form [HFH$^+$]. Liquid hydrogen fluoride is associated.

At $-182°$ solid hydrogen fluoride consists of tetragonal crystals with four H_4F_4 molecules in a unit cell. The distance F–H–F is 2·7 and the angle FFF is 134°.

Aqueous hydrogen fluoride is made by distilling powdered fluorspar with 90% sulphuric acid in a lead retort and dissolving the gas evolved in water. The properties of an aqueous solution of hydrogen fluoride are given in Table 23.3. On solution in water hydrogen fluoride ionises:

$$HF = H^+ + F^-,$$

and the F$^-$ ion then forms a hydrogen bond with an undissociated hydrogen fluoride molecule:

$$F^- + HF = [FHF^-].$$

For the first reaction,

$$K = \frac{[H^+][F^-]}{HF} = 7·2 \times 10^{-4},$$

and for the second reaction,

$$K = \frac{[FHF^-]}{[F^-][HF]} = 5\cdot5.$$

Hence hydrogen fluoride, HF, is a weak acid, but H[FHF] is a strong acid.

An aqueous solution of hydrogen fluoride attacks glass. It reacts with boric acid to give fluoroboric acid.

ORGANIC COMPOUNDS CONTAINING FLUORINE

Fluorine forms three types of compound with carbon:

(i) interstitial compounds in which atoms of fluorine lie between the layers of carbon atoms in graphite; two of these compounds are the well-characterised $(C_4F)_n$ and $(CF)_n$,

(ii) derivatives of the aliphatic compounds in which fluorine atoms occupy one or more of the positions normally occupied by hydrogen atoms,

(iii) derivatives of the aromatic compounds in which fluorine atoms occupy one or more of the positions normally occupied by hydrogen atoms.

The behaviour of fluorine in organic reactions is largely governed by the great affinity of fluorine for carbon and for hydrogen. A fluorine atom bound to a carbon atom reacts with reluctance; a fluorine atom and a hydrogen atom bound to adjacent carbon atoms tend to separate from the organic compound as a molecule of hydrogen fluoride.

The **interstitial compounds** of fluorine and carbon are discussed on p. 593.

Aliphatic compounds in which only one fluorine atom is linked to a carbon atom. The simplest types of such compounds have the general formula $C_nH_{2n+1}F$. The lower members of the series are gases with b.p.s about 50° below those of the corresponding chloride:

	b.p. °C	
	X = F	X = Cl
CH_3X	-78	-24
C_2H_5X	-32	$+12\cdot5$
n-C_3H_7X	-3	$46\cdot5$
iso-C_3H_7X	-11	35
n-C_4H_9X	32 (746 mm)	$78\cdot5$

The first member of the series, methyl fluoride CH_3F, is made by heating tetramethyl ammonium fluoride:

$$(CH_3)_4NF = N(CH_3)_3 + CH_3F.$$

Compounds of this class do not differ much in chemical properties from the corresponding chlorine or bromine derivatives. They are hydrolysed quite easily, and more readily by acids than by alkalis. From C_5 upwards they readily lose hydrogen fluoride on heating and form olefines. Difluoroethane, CH_2FCH_2F, loses hydrogen fluoride spontaneously at 0° and is completely converted to glycol when passed through water.

In general the fluorine atom in compounds of the type under discussion is less reactive if the carbon atom to which it is attached carries another negative group. CH_2FCOOH and CH_2FCH_2OH are stable to water, but $CHFBrCOOH$ can nevertheless be hydrolysed to $CHOCOOH$. The most powerful inhibitor of the reactivity of a fluorine atom attached to a carbon atom is another fluorine atom. Its effect is so marked that compounds containing two fluorine atoms attached to a carbon atom can be treated as a separate class.

Aliphatic compounds in which two fluorine atoms are linked to a carbon atom. A typical compound is CH_3CHF_2, ethylidene difluoride, which resists hydrolysis (ethylidene dichloride is hydrolysed by aqueous potash). The two fluorine atoms are not only themselves unreactive, but they diminish the activity of other halogen atoms attached to the same carbon atom. CCl_2F_2 is more stable than CCl_2Br_2 or CCl_2H_2. The effect may extend to a neighbouring carbon atom. CH_2BrCH_2F is easily converted to glycol, but CH_2BrCHF_2 is so unreactive that the bromine atom is hydrolysed only by mercuric oxide and water at 150°. Magnesium has no action on the compound. The fluorine atoms in the group CF_2 may be so inert that their presence in the molecule is not revealed by the reactions of the compound. Thus, CHF_2CH_2OH is almost identical in properties with ethyl alcohol.

Certain physical effects are noticeable when fluorine atoms successively replace other atoms in the molecule of a methane derivative CX_4. The boiling point is raised, and the distance F—C is shortened, as is shown in Table 23.7.

Table 23.7.   *The Distance C–F in certain Derivatives of Methane*

One F atom		Two F atoms		Three F atoms		Four F atoms	
Compound	C–F	Compound	C–F	Compound	C–F	Compound	C–F
CH_3F	1·42	CH_2F_2	1·36	CHF_3	1·33	CF_4	1·32
CH_2FCl	1·40	CHF_2Cl	1·36	CF_3I	1·33		
$CHFCl_2$	1·41						
$CFCl_3$	1·40	CF_2Cl_2	1·35				

Aliphatic compounds in which three fluorine atoms per carbon atom are present. A typical compound is CHF_3. It is made by heating iodoform or bromoform first with excess of antimony trifluoride at 4 atmospheres pressure, and then treating the product with mercuric fluoride. The reactivity of fluoroform is less than that of $C_2H_2F_2$. It is unchanged by potassium iodide at 1150°, by nitric acid, alone or mixed with sulphuric acid, or by oxides of nitrogen. Silver nitrate has no action on it at 150°; manganese heptoxide has no action at 25°. The group CF_3 has the inertness commented on in the previous paragraph. CF_3CH_2R undergoes many changes in which the CF_3 group is undisturbed, for example:

$$CF_3COOC_2H_5 \rightarrow CF_3CONH_2 \rightarrow CF_3CN \rightarrow CF_3CH_2NH_2 \rightarrow CF_3CHN_2.†$$

On the other hand CF_3CH_2I does not react with magnesium to give a Grignard reagent, but yields instead MgIF and $CH_2=CF_2$.

The group CF_3 is also found in the compounds:

$$N(CF_3)_3, \quad CF_3I, \quad HgCF_3I, \quad Hg(CF_3)_2, \quad P(CF_3)_3, \quad and \quad As(CF_3)_3.$$

$N(CF_3)_3$ is one of the products of the fluorination of trimethylamine with cobaltic fluoride; it is inert and has no basic properties. CF_3I behaves as a positive iodine compound, and yields CF_3H (not CF_3OH) on hydrolysis.

Perfluorohydrocarbons. An organic compound in which all the hydrogen atoms have been replaced by fluorine atoms is known as a *perfluoro* compound. Perfluorohydrocarbons are made:

(i) by the action of fluorine on a hydrocarbon; the direct action is highly exothermic, and it is moderated by dissolving the hydrocarbon in carbon tetrachloride, or by diluting the hydrocarbon vapour with nitrogen,

† 1-trifluoro-2-diazoethane.

(ii) by passing the hydrocarbon vapour over cobaltic fluoride at 100–300°:

$$C_2H_6 + 12CoF_3 = C_2F_6 + 6HF + 12CoF_2,$$

the cobaltous fluoride is re-converted to cobaltic fluoride by treatment with fluorine at 300°,

(iii) by treating an organic halogen compound with one of the following reagents (which are in order of their effectiveness): antimony trifluoride alone, antimony trifluoride in the presence of bromine or antimony pentachloride, mercuric fluoride. Of the organic halogen compounds the chlorides are attacked with difficulty, the bromides readily, and the iodides often with violence. The conditions chosen are sometimes drastic; for example, C_2Cl_6 is converted into a mixture of $CCl_2F \cdot CCl_2F$ and $CClF_2 \cdot CCl_2F$ at 320° under a pressure of 60 atm using a mixture of antimony trifluoride and antimony pentachloride.

The properties of certain perfluorohydrocarbons are set out in Table 23.8.

Table 23.8.   *Properties of certain Perfluorohydrocarbons*

	CF_4	C_2F_6	C_2F_4
State	Gas	Gas	Gas
Solubility	Insoluble in CS_2, CCl_4, C_6H_6		
Limit of thermal stability	High temperature	Above 800°	
No reaction with	H_2 under sparking, H_2SO_4 up to 350°, Ag, Bi, Cu, Pb, As, S, Se, Fe, CaO, B_2O_3, CrO_3, KOH, KI	Conc. H_2SO_4, KOH, KI, PbO, SiO_2	Conc. H_2SO_4, NaOH
Reaction with	Na at red heat	Na at red heat	Na at red heat. Fuming sulphuric acid. Bromine water

The reactions of perfluoroethylene show that although the fluorine atoms are resistant to chemical attack, the carbon to carbon double bond retains the property of forming addition compounds with fuming sulphuric acid and with bromine. The information in Table 23.8 shows the remarkable inertness of the perfluorohydrocarbons.

Perfluoroethylene polymerises under pressure in contact with an aqueous solution of a persulphate to yield the polymer *teflon*. This is a hard non-conducting material which does not melt below 300°. It resists the attack of boiling aqua regia, and it is used in the medium temperature process for making fluorine.

Aromatic compounds containing fluorine atoms. Aromatic compounds with one or more fluorine atoms in the side-chain behave in the same manner as aliphatic compounds. Aromatic compounds in which a fluorine atom is attached to the nucleus are made by the decomposition of the diazonium borofluoride (which is not explosive) either by heat:

$$C_6H_5N_2BF_4 = C_6H_5F + N_2 + BF_3,$$

or by concentrated sulphuric acid. The reactions are quiet and smooth.

The fluorine atom is firmly bound to the carbon atom of the nucleus, but it reacts with alkalis and with alcoholic potassium hydroxide. Potassium hydroxide in methyl alcohol reacts with fluorobenzene to give methylphenyl ether. Fluorobenzene does not react with magnesium, but when it is heated with sodium in a sealed tube sodium fluoride is formed. A fluorine atom in the benzene ring is *ortho-* and *para*-directing.

Fluorine oxides. Fluorine monoxide, F_2O, is made by bubbling fluorine slowly through a 2% aqueous solution of sodium hydroxide. It is purified by fractional distillation. Fluorine monoxide is more poisonous than fluorine. It is not explosive, but it may explode if in contact with charcoal. At 250° it decomposes slowly, thus:

$$2F_2O = 2F_2 + O_2.$$

It dissolves in water (68 c.c. in 1 litre at 0°) but although the reaction

$$F_2O + H_2O(g) = O_2 + 2HF; \quad \Delta H = -74 \text{ kcal}$$

is highly exothermic, almost no reaction occurs. In the presence of alkali reaction takes place rapidly with the liberation of oxygen, but the course of the reaction is not clear. Fluorine monoxide attacks mercury in the cold, but many other metals only at high temperatures. Fluorine monoxide shows to some extent the inertness of fluorine compounds mentioned on p. 907.

Electron diffraction experiments indicate that the angle FOF in the molecule is 100°.

Fluorine dioxide, F_2O_2, is made by passing a silent electric discharge through a mixture of oxygen and fluorine at the temperature of liquid air. It decomposes at −100°. Its structure is unknown.

Anionic complexes containing fluorine. Salts containing the anionic complexes $[BeF_4^{2-}]$, $[BF_4^{-1}]$, $[PF_6^{-1}]$, $[AsF_6^{-1}]$, $[SbF_6^{-1}]$, $[SiF_6^{-2}]$, $[BrF_4^{-1}]$ have been prepared. Attempts to make fluoro ions centred on In, Tl, Th, Pb, Bi, Se, Te, Mo, W, U, I, and Mn have failed. In certain anions both oxygen and fluorine are linked to a third element (p. 960).

Fluorine nitrate, FNO_3, is a colourless explosive gas, b.p. −42°, m.p. −175°. It is made by the action of fluorine on concentrated nitric acid, or on solid potassium nitrate. It is a strong oxidising agent, oxidising potassium iodide to iodine:

$$FNO_3 + 2KI = KNO_3 + KF + I_2,$$

and manganous salts in the presence of silver ions to permanganates. It reacts with dilute alkalis to yield fluorine monoxide,

$$2FNO_3 + 2KOH = F_2O + 2KNO_3 + H_2O,$$

and with concentrated alkalis to liberate oxygen:

$$2FNO_3 + 4KOH = O_2 + 2KF + 2KNO_3 + 2H_2O.$$

The configuration of the molecule of fluorine nitrate is shown in the diagram:

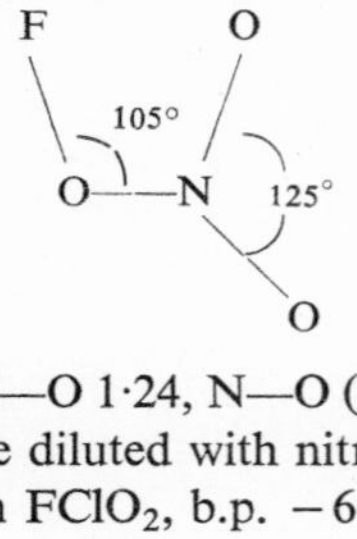

The dihedral angle is 90°.

The bond lengths are: O—F 1·42, N—O 1·24, N—O (O bonded to F) 1·39.

Fluorine chlorite, $FClO_2$. Fluorine diluted with nitrogen acts upon chlorine dioxide to give a compound of composition $FClO_2$, b.p. −6°, m.p. −115°. The gas fumes in the presence of water.

Fluorine perchlorate, $FClO_4$, is made by passing fluorine over cold concentrated aqueous perchloric acid. It is a colourless gas, b.p. −16°, m.p. −167·5°. It is extremely explosive.

CHLORINE

THE ELEMENT

Certain physical properties of chlorine are included in Table 23.2. Chlorine is prepared by the oxidation of a chloride by a chemical oxidising agent such as manganese dioxide, potassium permanganate, potassium dichromate or bleaching powder, or by the electrolysis of a metal chloride, either fused or in aqueous solution, in a divided cell. Chlorine combines directly with most metals, especially if heated, and if the chlorine is in excess the chloride produced contains the metal in its highest state of valency. P, As, Sb, and Hg react with dry chlorine; Cu, Zn, and Na do not react with dry chlorine, but they react spontaneously in the presence of moisture. Chlorine combines with hydrogen; the reaction is smooth in the presence of activated charcoal. Chlorine combines with the hydrogen in a hydrocarbon, and leaves a residue of carbon, but it reacts rapidly with hydrogen sulphide at all temperatures between 0° and 300° to yield monosulphur dichloride:

$$2Cl_2 + H_2S = 2HCl + SCl_2.$$

Excess of hydrogen sulphide may reduce the monosulphur dichloride to disulphur dichloride. Chlorine does not combine directly with oxygen or nitrogen. Chlorine reacts with water and with alkalis to produce oxyacids of chlorine or their salts.

GENERAL CHEMISTRY OF CHLORINE

The electron configuration of the valency shell ($n=3$) of the chlorine atom in the ground state is:

$$s \quad p \quad p \quad p \quad d \quad d \quad d \quad d \quad d$$
$$\uparrow\downarrow \quad \uparrow\downarrow \quad \uparrow\downarrow \quad \uparrow$$

The s and p orbitals are completely occupied when the atom becomes a univalent anion, or when it forms one σ bond. The chlorine atom is incapable of forming πp bonds. The valency shell contains d orbitals and by promotion of one of the p electrons a πd bond can be formed. The double bonds exerted by the chlorine atom in the oxides and oxyacids of chlorine are πd bonds.

The chlorine atom does not adopt the digonal or trigonal valence states. In combination it is usually in the tetrahedral valence state with 3, 2, 1, or 0 of the tetrahedral hybrid orbitals occupied by lone electron pairs. In chlorine dioxide and in chlorine trioxide one hybrid orbital is occupied by an unpaired electron. The covalently bound chlorine atom never has a co-ordination number greater than four, it does not adopt the octahedral valence state; it perhaps adopts the trigonal bipyramidal valence state in chlorine trifluoride and in the anion [Cl_3^-].

SECTION 1. COMPOUNDS IN WHICH THE CHLORINE ATOM HAS IONIC CHARACTER

The chlorides. The monatomic chloride anion Cl^- is stable and is present in the crystals of many metal chlorides and in their aqueous solutions. The alkali metal chlorides (except caesium chloride), silver chloride, and ammonium chloride above 184·3° crystallise with the rocksalt structure; caesium chloride, thallous chloride, and ammonium chloride below 184·3° crystallise with the caesium chloride structure; calcium chloride and strontium chloride crystallise with a slightly deformed rutile structure. Barium chloride and lead chloride crystallise with a structure in which each metal ion is surrounded by nine chloride ions, six at the apices of a trigonal prism, and three just outside the centres of the three prism faces.

The chlorides of the bivalent metals Mg, Zn, Cd, Mn, Fe, Co, and Ni crystallise with the cadmium chloride layer structure† (p. 352). In crystals of chromic chloride the chloride ions are in cubic close-packing and the chromic ions are in one third of the octahedral holes.

All the crystal structures so far mentioned are regarded as ionic; the chloride ions are close-packed and the metal ions are present in the octahedral holes. The crystals probably possess some covalent character, however, because lithium chloride is the only alkali metal chloride which crystallises with true close-packing in which the chloride ions are in mutual contact; in all the other alkali metal chloride crystals the metal ions are too large to be contained in the octahedral holes without forcing the chloride ions apart. The following chlorides form crystals in which the bonding is predominantly covalent. Cuprous chloride crystallises with the zinc blende structure. Mercuric chloride consists of discrete linear molecules; palladium chloride and cupric chloride have chain structures of indefinite length, thus:

$$\begin{array}{ccccccc} \text{Cl} & & \text{Cl} & & \text{Cl} & & \text{Cl} \\ \diagdown & \diagup & \diagdown & \diagup & \diagdown & \diagup & \\ & \text{Pd} & & \text{Pd} & & \text{Pd} & \\ \diagup & \diagdown & \diagup & \diagdown & \diagup & \diagdown & \\ \text{Cl} & & \text{Cl} & & \text{Cl} & & \text{Cl} \end{array}$$

Aluminium chloride and ferric chloride crystallise in layer structures, but the molecules in the vapour are dimeric, Al_2Cl_6 and Fe_2Cl_6. Arsenic trichloride and antimony trichloride form pyramidal molecules, which crystallise in layer structures so that each metal ion has six equidistant chloride neighbours.

Sidgwick‡ has pointed out that among 60 chlorides of 53 elements 31 have near the melting point specific conductances of 0·1 to 10 ohm^{-1} cm^{-1}, and 26 have conductivities of less than 2×10^{-6} ohm^{-1} cm^{-1}; only $BeCl_2$, $ZnCl_2$, and $HgCl_2$, with the respective conductivities 32×10^{-4}, 24×10^{-4}, and $0·82 \times 10^{-4}$, have values between 0·1 and 2×10^{-6} ohm^{-1} cm^{-1}. His conclusion that there is a sharp distinction between ionic and covalent chlorides, however, is not borne out by other considerations.

The chloride ion can be present in a giant molecule structure together with other anions, as for example in antimony oxychloride, SbOCl (p. 757).

The behaviour of chlorides with water may be summarised as follows:

(i) A chloride in which a chlorine atom is attached to a saturated carbon atom, for example CCl_4, C_2H_5Cl, is insoluble in water and is not attacked by it.

(ii) A chloride of a strongly electropositive metal such as sodium dissolves in water in the form of independent metal and chloride ions, but is not otherwise attacked by it.

(iii) A chloride of a moderately electropositive metal, or of a non-metal other than those mentioned in (iv), is attacked by water so that the chlorine atom is replaced by an OH group thus:

$$MgCl_2 + 2H_2O \rightleftharpoons Mg(OH)_2 + 2HCl,$$
$$SiCl_4 + 4H_2O = 4HCl + Si(OH)_4 = SiO_2 + 2H_2O + 4HCl,$$
$$CH_3COCl + H_2O = CH_3COOH + HCl.$$

(iv) A chloride of a highly electronegative element is attacked by water to yield hypochlorous acid and the hydride of the electronegative element:

$$NCl_3 + 3H_2O = NH_3 + 3HClO,$$
$$Cl_2 + H_2O = HCl + HClO.$$

† The chloride ions are in cubic close-packing, the crystals of the corresponding bromides and iodides have the cadmium iodide structure with the bromide or iodide ions in hexagonal close-packing .

‡N. V. Sidgwick, *Chemical Elements and Their Compounds*, Oxford University Press, 1950, vol. II, 1170.

This mode of attack depends on the initial formation of a hydrogen bond, for example $H—O—H\cdots NCl_3$.

(v) Beryllium chloride (which contains three centre bonds) is attacked by water to form the ions $[Be,4H_2O^{2+}]$ and Cl^-.

SECTION 4. COMPOUNDS IN WHICH THE CHLORINE ATOM IS TETRAHEDRALLY HYBRIDISED

The tetrahedral valence state is the predominant valence state adopted by the chlorine atom. In this state the chlorine atom most frequently uses one hybrid orbital for forming a covalent bond; the other three hybrid orbitals are occupied by lone pairs. Examples of chlorine atoms with this electronic arrangement are found in the molecules of hydrogen chloride HCl, carbon tetrachloride CCl_4, methyl chloride CH_3Cl, nitrogen trichloride NCl_3, and sulphur dichloride SCl_2. Most typical chlorides of this kind are described in the chapters on the other elements, but two important types of chloride have not been so described and they are discussed below.

Hydrogen chloride, HCl, is made commercially by the combination of hydrogen and chlorine. The very pure gas is made by the action of water on silicon tetrachloride. Hydrogen chloride is extremely stable to heat. Nernst has calculated the percentage dissociation at high temperatures:

Temperature, °K	500	1000	2000	3000
Percentage dissociation	$1·92 \times 10^{-8}$	0·00134	0·41	1·30

The d.p.m. of hydrogen chloride as a gas is 1·03, and in solution in benzene or carbon tetrachloride is 1·32. Stannic chloride dissolves in liquid hydrogen chloride to give a non-conducting solution, but most metal chlorides are insoluble in liquid hydrogen chloride. Hydrogen chloride is soluble both in water and in organic solvents. Its solubility in certain solvents is given below.

Solvent	Temperature, °C	Solubility in gm per litre
Hexane	25	6·20
Benzene	25	13·7
o-Nitrotoluene	25	18·0
Chloroform	0	10·0
Ether	20	220
Water	20	770

In the first four solvents Henry's law is obeyed, and hence the hydrogen chloride is covalent and unsolvated. In ether no doubt the oxonium ion is formed:

$$\left[\begin{array}{c} C_2H_5 \\ \diagdown \\ \diagup \\ C_2H_5 \end{array} O—H \right]^+ Cl^-$$

In dilute aqueous solution hydrogen chloride is present entirely as hydrated ions. The infrared absorption bands shown by liquid hydrogen chloride and its solutions in non-ionising solvents are not shown by its dilute aqueous solution. On the other hand in concentrated aqueous solution and in weaker ionising solvents (e.g. methyl alcohol) dis-ionisation occurs, and it takes place much more readily than it does in the case of an acid with a non-deformable anion, such as perchloric acid.

The chemical properties of hydrogen chloride are so familiar that there is no need to recount them in detail. Hydrogen chloride gas does not burn. It reacts with many metals when heated, liberating hydrogen and yielding the chloride of the metal in its lowest valency state. Hydrogen chloride is absorbed by phosphorus pentoxide, thus:

$$P_4O_{10} + 3HCl = POCl_3 + 3HPO_3.$$

Liquid hydrogen chloride is covalent. It does not conduct electricity, and most metals are unattacked by it; an exception is aluminium which is dissolved. Hydrogen chloride is avidly absorbed by water and in aqueous solution it is a strong monobasic acid. In aqueous solution it is a reducing agent, and it is oxidised to chlorine by powerful oxidising agents such as potassium permanganate.

THE OXIDES OF CHLORINE

A list of the oxides of chlorine and certain of their properties is given in Table 23.4. The valence states of the chlorine atom in the oxides of chlorine are uncertain. In chlorine monoxide, ClOCl, each chlorine atom is probably tetrahedrally hybridised and three of the hybrid orbitals are occupied by lone pairs. It is assumed that the chlorine atoms in chlorine dioxide and chlorine trioxide are also tetrahedrally hybridised, and that πd bonds are superposed on the two σ bonds in chlorine dioxide, and on the three σ bonds in chlorine trioxide. If these assumptions are made the chlorine atom in each of these oxides has one hybrid orbital occupied by an unpaired electron. On these assumptions the orbital structures of the molecules of the chlorine oxides can be written:

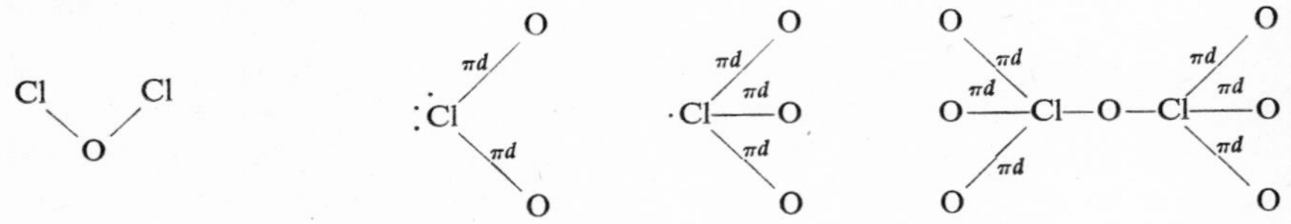

angle ClOCl = 111°   angle OClO = 118·5°   angle ClOCl = 128°
distance Cl–O = 1·70   distance Cl–O = 1·49

Chlorine resembles nitrogen in forming oxides having molecular structures in which unpaired electrons are present. Chlorine also resembles nitrogen (p. 651) in forming at least one atomic group, ClO_2, in which the same number of chlorine and oxygen nuclei may enter into stable combination with varying numbers of electrons. ClO_2 exists as the neutral chlorine dioxide, as the cation ClO_2^+, and as the anion ClO_2^-.

Chlorine monoxide, Cl_2O, is made by passing chlorine over cooled precipitated mercuric oxide:

$$2Cl_2 + 2HgO = HgO,HgCl_2 + Cl_2O,$$

or by distilling a fairly concentrated solution of hypochlorous acid at low pressure. Chlorine monoxide explodes readily but not violently on heating. It may be distilled in the absence of organic matter. It attacks the eyes and mucous membranes. It is a strong oxidising agent, and converts most metals into a mixture of oxides and chlorides. It is very soluble in water, with which it reacts to give hypochlorous acid of which it is the anhydride, and in carbon tetrachloride. It slowly attacks mercury. The composition of chlorine monoxide gas is given by its explosion on heating

$$2Cl_2O = 2Cl_2 + O_2,$$

and the subsequent absorption of the chlorine by potassium hydroxide.

Chlorine dioxide, ClO_2, is made by the action of chlorine on silver chlorate:

$$2AgClO_3 + Cl_2 = 2AgCl + 2ClO_2 + O_2,$$

or by the reduction of potassium chlorate either by disproportionation on treatment with sulphuric acid:

$$3KClO_3 + 3H_2SO_4 = HClO_4 + 3KHSO_4 + H_2O + 2ClO_2,$$

or by the action of oxalic acid:

$$2KClO_3 + 2C_2H_2O_4 = K_2C_2O_4 + 2H_2O + 2CO_2 + 2ClO_2.$$

Chlorine dioxide explodes violently on the smallest provocation. In solution in carbon tetrachloride, however, in the dark and in the absence of traces of chlorine monoxide, it is stable for a long time. Chlorine dioxide is extremely soluble in water. The hydrate $ClO_2,6H_2O$ is crystalline, yellow, and stable up to 18°. In the dark the aqueous solution is stable, and gaseous chlorine dioxide can be expelled from it by boiling. Chlorine dioxide is decomposed by light, when pure or when in aqueous solution, to a mixture of chlorine, oxygen, chlorine trioxide, and chlorine heptoxide.

Chlorine dioxide dissolves in potassium hydroxide solution according to the equation:

$$2ClO_2 + 2KOH = KClO_2 + KClO_3 + H_2O.$$

Chlorine dioxide reacts with hydrogen peroxide to yield chlorous acid, $HClO_2$, and with potassium permanganate solution to yield potassium chlorate, $KClO_3$, and a precipitate of manganese dioxide.

Chlorine dioxide is paramagnetic. The vapour density is normal, and no association occurs in the liquid state, or in solution in water or in carbon tetrachloride.

Chlorine trioxide, ClO_3, is made by the action of chlorine dioxide on ozone. When the mixed gases are cooled with ice, brown drops of a solution of chlorine dioxide in chlorine trioxide are formed. The chlorine dioxide is removed by distillation at low pressure.

Chlorine trioxide decomposes even at 0° to a mixture of other oxides of chlorine, and ultimately to chlorine and oxygen. If it is mixed with water vapour and cooled, it yields a mixture of chloric acid and perchloric acid:

$$2ClO_3 + H_2O = HClO_3 + HClO_4,$$

but an explosion occurs if it is added to liquid water.

If gaseous chlorine trioxide is decomposed by heating, the volume of the gas is doubled:

$$2ClO_3 = Cl_2 + 3O_2,$$

and hence in the gaseous state the molecules are monomeric. Liquid chlorine trioxide is diamagnetic, and hence the molecules are dimeric. The molecular weight of chlorine trioxide dissolved in carbon tetrachloride is 10% less than that of the dimeric form Cl_2O_6.

The molecular structures and the dimerisation of nitrogen dioxide and of chlorine trioxide show certain parallels illustrated by the equations:

It should be noted that the dimeric molecule Cl_2O_6 is incapable of resonance.

Chlorine heptoxide, Cl_2O_7, is made:

(i) by allowing a mixture of phosphorus pentoxide and anhydrous or highly concentrated perchloric acid to stand at $-10°$ for 24 hours; the product is distilled in vacuo;

(ii) by heating potassium perchlorate with chlorosulphonic acid $HOClSO_2$, under reduced pressure; a good yield is obtained, but the chlorine heptoxide is contaminated with sulphur compounds.

Chlorine heptoxide explodes when struck, or in contact with a flame. It has no action in the cold with sulphur, phosphorus, wood, or paper, but it explodes on contact with iodine. With water it gives perchloric acid of which it is the anhydride. The Raman spectrum of chlorine heptoxide indicates that the molecule consists of two ClO_3 groups linked by an oxygen atom.

THE OXYACIDS OF CHLORINE

The salts of four oxyacids of chlorine are known, but perchloric acid is the only one of the four acids which has been isolated. The other three acids, hypochlorous acid, chlorous acid, and chloric acid, are known in solution. The chlorine atoms in the anions of all the four acids are probably in the tetrahedral valence state. The anions are assigned the formulae:

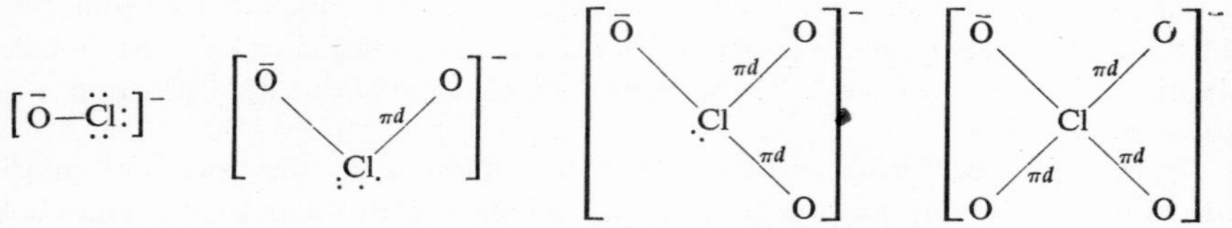

There is experimental evidence that the configuration of the chlorate anion is pyramidal, and that of the perchlorate ion is tetrahedral. All the four oxyacids and the anions except the perchlorate ion are oxidising agents.

Hypochlorous acid, HClO, is known only in solution. It is produced by the action of chlorine on water:

$$Cl_2 + H_2O \rightleftharpoons H^+ + Cl^- + HClO.$$

The action proceeds to completion in the presence of mercuric oxide which removes both H^+ ions and Cl^- ions from the solution, thus:

$$HgO + 2H^+ + 2Cl^- = HgCl_2 \text{ (covalent)} + H_2O.$$

The mercuric chloride is precipitated as the basic chloride, $HgO,HgCl_2$, which together with the excess of mercuric oxide is filtered off, and the filtrate is distilled.

The aqueous solution of hypochlorous acid is pale yellow. If a 25% aqueous solution of hypochlorous acid is distilled at a low pressure, pure chlorine monoxide is evolved:

$$2HClO = Cl_2O + H_2O;$$

if a more dilute solution is distilled the distillate is an aqueous solution of the acid. The volatility of hypochlorous acid from a dilute solution may be due to the evolution of chlorine monoxide which combines with water on cooling, or it may be due to the volatility of the undissociated acid in steam. The evolution of chlorine monoxide is unlikely, as the equilibrium constant,

$$K = \frac{[Cl_2O]}{[HClO]^2},$$

for a 5% solution of hypochlorous acid is only $9 \cdot 6 \times 10^{-4}$.

Hypochlorous acid is a very weak acid. Its dissociation constant at 25° is $3\cdot2 \times 10^{-8}$. Its salts are much hydrolysed in solution, and are decomposed by carbon dioxide. The aqueous solution dissolves magnesium with the liberation of hydrogen, but less electropositive metals such as iron and aluminium liberate a mixture of hydrogen and chlorine, and cobalt, nickel, and copper liberate a mixture of chlorine and oxygen.

Hypochlorous acid oxidises P, As, Sb, S, Se, and their hydrides, and it liberates chlorine from hydrochloric acid. It reacts with hydrogen peroxide to form hydrochloric acid, water, and oxygen. It liberates iodine from potassium iodide, and converts chromium salts to chromates, manganese salts to hydrated manganese dioxide, and lead salts to lead peroxide.

The hypochlorite ion is less easily reduced than the parent acid, but it slowly decomposes according to the equation:

$$2ClO^- = 2Cl^- + O_2.$$

Catalysts and rough surfaces assist the evolution of oxygen; among the materials used for this purpose are glass, platinum black, and the oxides of cobalt and nickel. If a hypochlorite solution is slightly acidified the liberated hypochlorous acid attacks the hypochlorite ion thus:

$$2HClO + ClO^- = ClO_3^- + 2H^+ + 2Cl^-.$$

Sodium hypochlorite solution is therefore often stabilised by the addition of a small quantity of sodium hydroxide.

An aqueous solution of hypochlorous acid may be differentiated from a solution of chlorine by shaking with metallic mercury; hypochlorous acid gives a light brown precipitate of basic mercuric chloride, $Hg(OH)Cl$, and chlorine gives a white precipitate of mercurous chloride.

It has been shown experimentally that hypochlorous acid is not associated in aqueous solution. The absorption spectrum of the aqueous solution of hypochlorous acid is similar to that of a solution of ethyl hypochlorite in ligroin, and is different from that of an aqueous solution of sodium hypochlorite.

The only metal hypochlorites which have been isolated are those of Na, K, Ca, Sr, Ba. Sodium hypochlorite forms two hydrates: $NaClO,7H_2O$, m.p. 19°, and $NaClO,5H_2O$, m.p. 45°.

Ethyl hypochlorite, C_2H_5OCl, is very unstable and explodes when brought into contact with a flame or exposed to bright light. It is formed by the action of chlorine on a cooled solution of ethyl alcohol in 10% aqueous sodium hydroxide solution. It decomposes to acetaldehyde:

$$C_2H_5OCl = CH_3CHO + HCl.$$

Chlorous acid, $HClO_2$, is known in solution only. The aqueous solution is obtained by treating barium chlorite with sulphuric acid:

$$Ba(ClO_2)_2 + H_2SO_4 = 2HClO_2 + BaSO_4,$$

and removing the insoluble barium sulphate by filtration. Barium chlorite is made by heating chlorine dioxide solution (p. 919) with hydrogen peroxide in the presence of barium peroxide:

$$2ClO_2 + H_2O_2 = 2HClO_2 + O_2,$$
$$BaO_2 + 2HClO_2 = Ba(ClO_2)_2 + H_2O_2.$$

A freshly prepared aqueous solution of chlorous acid is colourless but the chlorous acid soon decomposes to chlorine dioxide which colours the solution yellow. Chlorous acid is very weak, but many chlorites have been prepared, including those of the alkali metals, the alkaline earth metals, amines, and those of Cu^{2+}, Ag, Zn, Cd, Hg, Pb, Co, Ni. The chlorites form yellow crystals, and with the exception of those of lead and silver, they are very soluble in water and in alcohol. The solubility of silver chlorite in water at 0° is 0·17 gm/100 gm, and that of lead chlorite is 0·035 gm/100 gm. The metal chlorites disproportionate on heating, for example:

$$3NaClO_2 = NaCl + 2NaClO_3.$$

Sodium chlorite in solution reacts with chlorine liberating chlorine dioxide, and forming sodium chloride.

Chlorous acid and its salts are oxidising agents which liberate iodine from potassium iodide:

$$NaClO_2 + 4KI + 2H_2O = NaCl + 4KOH + 2I_2.$$

The chlorite ion, ClO_2^-, is non-linear. The angle OClO is 110° and the distance O–Cl is 1·6.

Chloric acid, $HClO_3$, is known in solution only. The aqueous solution is made by treating barium chlorate (see below) with sulphuric acid, filtering, and evaporating. The dilute aqueous solution may be heated to its boiling point, and the solution may be concentrated until its composition reaches $HClO_3,7H_2O$, without decomposing the chloric acid. If a dilute solution is allowed to stand, or if the concentration is carried too far, chloric acid decomposes according to the equation:

$$3HClO_3 = HClO_4 + 2O_2 + Cl_2 + H_2O.$$

The concentrated aqueous solution of chloric acid is a strong oxidising agent. It attacks organic substances, and dissolves certain metals to form the metal chlorides.

The chlorates. Sodium chlorate is made by the electrolysis of a solution of sodium chloride in a cell which permits the mixing of the chlorine liberated at the anode with the OH^- formed at the cathode. The reaction occurs:

$$Cl_2 + OH^- = HOCl + Cl^-,$$

and at the anode the hypochlorite ion is oxidised to the chlorate ion:

$$5OCl^- + 8H_2O - 16e = 3ClO_3^- + 2Cl^- + 2O_2 + 16H^+.$$

Some oxygen is also liberated at the anode by the discharge of hydroxyl ions:

$$4OH^- - 4e = 2H_2O + O_2.$$

The electrolysed solution is evaporated to precipitate the unchanged sodium chloride which is filtered off. Sodium chlorate is crystallised from the filtrate.

The metal chlorates are soluble. Barium chlorate is made by evaporating a mixed solution of sodium chlorate and barium chloride. The less soluble sodium chloride crystallises first, and when the hot filtered solution is evaporated, the hydrate, $Ba(ClO_3)_2,H_2O$, crystallises. Potassium chlorate is made by adding potassium chloride to sodium chlorate solution; potassium chlorate, which is slightly soluble, crystallises.

Potassium chlorate, when heated just above its m.p. 370°, is converted to a mixture of potassium chloride and potassium perchlorate:

$$4KClO_3 = KCl + 3KClO_4.$$

If manganese dioxide is present it promotes an alternative mode of decomposition:

$$2KClO_3 = 2KCl + 3O_2,$$

which takes place below the m.p. of potassium chlorate. Potassium chlorate forms explosive mixtures with sulphur, phosphorus, and charcoal. With concentrated hydrochloric acid it yields a mixture of chlorine and chlorine dioxide:

$$8KClO_3 + 24HCl = 8KCl + 9Cl_2 + 6ClO_2 + 12H_2O,$$

and with concentrated sulphuric acid a mixture of perchloric acid and chlorine dioxide (p. 919).

X-ray analysis of crystalline potassium chlorate indicates that the angle OClO is 106° and O–Cl is 1·48.

Perchloric acid, $HClO_4$, a colourless mobile liquid, m.p. $-112°$, b.p. 19° under 11 mm pressure, is made by treating potassium perchlorate with concentrated (90–92%) sulphuric acid and distilling under reduced pressure (10–20 mm). If perchloric acid is heated under atmospheric pressure it breaks up, often explosively, to steam, oxygen, and oxides of chlorine. Anhydrous perchloric acid oxidises organic substances, frequently with violence. The Raman spectrum of anhydrous perchloric acid indicates that the four oxygen atoms in the molecule are arranged tetrahedrally round the chlorine atom. Certain lines in the spectrum are identical with those of the spectrum of chlorine heptoxide. The spectrum is different from that of the ion ClO_4^-, and hence there is no dimer $[H_2ClO_4^+][ClO_4^-]$. When in contact with other acids, however, perchloric acid acts as an electron donor. It combines with hydrogen fluoride to form the rare cation $[H_2F^+]$.

Anhydrous perchloric acid is hygroscopic; it dissolves in water with a hissing sound to form hydrates with 1, 2, $2\frac{1}{2}$, 3, $3\frac{1}{2}$, molecules of water of crystallisation. An aqueous solution of perchloric acid may also be made by evaporating a solution of ammonium perchlorate in a mixture of concentrated hydrochloric acid and concentrated nitric acid.

The monohydrate $HClO_4,H_2O$ should be formulated $[H_3O^+][ClO_4^-]$. It is crystalline with the same lattice as ammonium perchlorate. It melts at 50° to a liquid ten times more viscous than the anhydrous acid. It can be heated nearly to its b.p. 110° without decomposition. Aqueous solutions of perchloric acid contain the ions $[H_3O^+]$ and $[ClO_4^-]$. Perchloric acid is the strongest of all acids. The perchlorate ion is not an oxidising agent except to very strong reducing agents such as titanous chloride, chromous chloride, sodium hydrosulphite, and alkaline ferrous hydroxide. It is not attacked by SO_2, H_2S, HCl, HI, or HNO_2. The metals iron and zinc dissolve in dilute aqueous solutions of perchloric acid to yield hydrogen; if the solution is concentrated, however, the volume of hydrogen liberated is less than the stoichiometric quantity. The perchlorate ion is tetrahedral, and is very resistant to deformation.

The perchlorates of the alkali metals and the alkaline earth metals are stable to heat; lithium perchlorate may be heated to 300° without decomposition, and potassium perchlorate to 400°. Ammonium perchlorate deflagrates with a yellow flame if heated to 200°:

$$2NH_4ClO_4 = N_2 + Cl_2 + 2O_2 + 4H_2O.$$

The anhydrous perchlorates of the alkali metals and some amines are dimorphic. Below the following temperatures the crystals are rhombic, and above these temperatures the forms are more symmetrical: Na 308°, K 300°, Rb 279°, Cs 219°, NH₄ 240°. The perchlorates of the alkali metals and the alkaline earth metals fall into two classes, those which are hydrated and very soluble, and those which are anhydrous and sparingly soluble:

very soluble perchlorates	less soluble perchlorates
Li, Na, Mg, Sr, Ba	K, Rb, Cs, amines

The solubilities of the above metal perchlorates in methyl alcohol and in ethyl alcohol follow the same trend. Silver perchlorate is extremely soluble in water, and also in glycerol, acetic acid, nitromethane, nitrobenzene, and chlorobenzene, and in the solvents mentioned in Table 23.9 below.

Table 23.9.   *Solubility of Silver Perchlorate in certain Solvents at 25°*

Solvent	Water	Aniline	Pyridine	Benzene	Toluene
Mol of silver perchlorate to 100 mol of solvent	48·2	2·42	10·0	2·03	44·8
Solid phase in equilibrium with the solution	$AgClO_4,H_2O$	$AgClO_4,6C_6H_5NH_2$	$AgClO_4,4pyr.$	$AgClO_4,C_6H_6$	$AgClO_4,C_7H_8$

From the solutions mentioned in Table 23.9 silver perchlorate crystallises with solvent of crystallisation. Dipole moment experiments show that silver perchlorate is present as ion-pairs in very dilute solution in benzene, but polymerisation occurs as the concentration increases. A solution of silver perchlorate in nitromethane has a high conductivity.

The methyl, ethyl, and propyl esters of perchloric acid have been made but they are highly explosive. Meyer and Spormann (1936) have said "that the explosions of the perchloric esters are louder and more destructive than those of any other compound".

SECTION 5. COMPOUNDS IN WHICH THE CHLORINE ATOM IS PRESENT IN THE TRIGONAL-BIPYRAMIDAL VALENCE STATE

The anion Cl—Cl—Cl⁻ is of the same type as the iodine dihalide anion (p. 932). A trihalide anion with a chlorine atom at the centre is much less stable than the anion with an iodine atom at the centre. The only salts reported are those containing large cations, for example $[(CH_3)_2SH^+][Cl_3^-]$ and $[(CH_3)_4N^+][Cl_3^-]$.

BROMINE

THE ELEMENT

Certain physical properties of bromine are included in Table 23.2. Bromine is a dark red liquid which readily volatilises to a choking, poisonous, brown vapour. It is chemically reactive. It combines spontaneously with P, As, and Sb, and with many other elements when warmed. The alkali metals burn or detonate in bromine. (Sodium in the massive state is said to be unattacked.) Gold is attacked, but not platinum. Silver is not attacked because it is quickly covered with a protective film of silver bromide. Bromine combines with hydrogen (p. 925). Bromine is a powerful oxidising agent. It dissolves in water, but the solution contains only small quantities of hypo-bromous acid and hydrobromic acid. Bromine is freely soluble in alcohol, chloroform, ether, and carbon disulphide.

Liquid bromine has a conductivity which is much less than that of the purest water. The distance Br–Br in the molecule Br_2, calculated from the spectrum and from electron diffraction experiments, is 2·27; the distance Br–Br in crystalline bromine is also 2·27.

GENERAL CHEMISTRY OF BROMINE

The electron configuration of the valency shell of the bromine atom is similar to that of the chlorine atom (p. 915), except that the quantum number n is 4. Bromine resembles chlorine both in its inability to form πp bonds, and in the possibility of the promotion of p electrons to d orbitals which enables the atom to form πd bonds. The bromine atom does not adopt the digonal or trigonal valence states. The co-ordination number of bromine sometimes exceeds four, as in the well-characterised BrF_5 (p. 903). The affinity of bromine for oxygen is less than that of chlorine or iodine; there is no oxyacid of bromine corresponding to $HClO_4$.

SECTION 1. BROMINE COMPOUNDS WITH IONIC CHARACTER

The monoatomic bromide ion, Br^-, is stable. The alkali metal bromides (except caesium bromide), silver bromide, and ammonium bromide above 137·8°, crystallise with the rocksalt structure; caesium bromide, thallous bromide, and ammonium bromide below 137·8°, crystallise with the caesium chloride structure. At low temperatures ammonium bromide has a tetragonal crystal form. Calcium bromide crystallises with a slightly deformed rutile lattice, but strontium bromide,† barium bromide, and lead bromide crystallise with the lead chloride structure (p. 640). The bromides of the bivalent metals Mg, Cd, Fe, Co, Ni, crystallise with the cadmium iodide layer lattice (see footnote p. 916). Chromic bromide has the same crystal structure as chromic chloride. Cuprous bromide has the zinc blende structure. Cupric bromide is isomorphous with cupric chloride and has a chain structure in which the atoms are coplanar. Mercuric bromide has a distorted cadmium iodide lattice; the mercuric ion is surrounded by six bromide ions but two are nearer to it than the other four; the structure stands between one of discrete molecules and one of a continuous uniform lattice. The crystal of aluminium bromide consists of close-packed layers of bromide ions with aluminium ions in adjacent tetrahedral holes. Arsenic tribromide and antimony tribromide have pyramidal molecules like those of the trichlorides. AgBr, TlBr, Hg_2Br_2, $HgBr_2$, $PbBr_2$, CuBr, and AuBr are sparingly soluble or insoluble in water.

The bromide ion reacts with water in the same manner as the chloride ion. Since hydrobromic acid is a weaker acid than hydrochloric acid, metal bromides are hydrolysed more readily than the corresponding chlorides.

SECTION 4. COMPOUNDS IN WHICH THE BROMINE ATOM IS TETRAHEDRALLY HYBRIDISED

Hydrogen bromide, HBr, is made:

(i) by adding bromine to a mixture of water and red phosphorus; sand should be present to moderate the reaction,
(ii) by the combination of bromine and hydrogen in the presence of platinised asbestos or charcoal at 200°,
(iii) by the action of bromine on benzene in the presence of aluminium powder.

Hydrogen bromide is best dried by exposure to calcium bromide.

Hydrogen bromide is stable to heat; its dissociation is as follows:

Temperature °K	1300	1381	1595
Percentage dissociation	0·5	0·73	1·08

These figures show that hydrogen bromide is slightly more dissociated than hydrogen chloride at the same temperature. The d.p.m. of hydrogen bromide as a gas is 0·78, and in solution in benzene or carbon tetrachloride is 1·00. Hydrogen bromide is soluble both in water and in organic solvents. Its solubility in a few solvents is given below:

Solvent	Temperature °C	Solubility in gm/litre
Benzene		small
Carbon tetrachloride	15	8
Ethyl alcohol		58
Water	25	1930

The chemical properties of hydrogen bromide are similar to those of hydrogen

† The structure of strontium bromide may be a distorted version of the lead chloride structure.

chloride. Bromine is liberated when chlorine is added to a solution of hydrogen bromide or a metal bromide. Hydrogen bromide inflames when mixed with fluorine. Hydrobromic acid is fairly easily oxidised to bromine by oxidising agents.

Bromine monoxide, Br_2O, a brown liquid, is made:

> (i) by passing bromine vapour over warm (50–100°) dry freshly-precipitated mercuric oxide; the gaseous product contains only 4% of bromine monoxide,
> (ii) by shaking a solution of bromine in carbon tetrachloride with mercuric oxide,
> (iii) by warming bromine dioxide in vacuo.

Bromine monoxide decomposes with the evolution of oxygen even just above its melting point. It dissolves in carbon tetrachloride to form a green solution which is stable below 0°; in the solution bromine monoxide is monomeric. Bromine monoxide is an oxidising agent; it converts iodine to iodine pentoxide.

The structure of bromine monoxide is unknown, but it is reasonable to suppose that it corresponds to the structure of chlorine monoxide.

Bromine dioxide, $(BrO_2)_n$, a yellow solid, is made by submitting a mixture of bromine and oxygen to an electric discharge at the temperature of liquid air. Any ozone formed and any excess bromine are removed by reducing the pressure and warming to $-30°$; bromine is more volatile than bromine dioxide.

Bromine dioxide is stable below $-40°$, but at 0° it decomposes vigorously to bromine and oxygen. It reacts with warm sodium hydroxide solution forming sodium hypobromite and sodium bromide in addition to sodium bromite and sodium bromate. When bromine dioxide is warmed in vacuo, bromine monoxide and a colourless solid, perhaps having the constitution Br_2O_7, are obtained. The volumes of oxygen and bromine liberated when bromine dioxide is allowed to decompose at 0° are in the ratio 2:1; hence the molecular formula of bromine dioxide is $(BrO_2)_n$.

$(BrO_3)_n$. This compound, an unstable white solid, is formed by the action of ozone on bromine at 0°; the ozone must be in heavy excess. The compound decomposes violently if warmed to 10°. It is stable at $-80°$, and if pure it remains stable up to $+10°$ in the presence of ozone. It is dimorphic with a transition temperature $-35 \pm 3°$. It dissolves in water to give a colourless solution, which is acidic and contains no bromine ions. It has been shown that the ratio of H^+ ions to bromine atoms is 1·33:1, and hence it is probable that the formula of the acid is $H_4Br_3O_{10}$. The solution liberates iodine when added to potassium iodide solution.

The empirical formula of the oxide BrO_3 is established by measuring the volumes of oxygen and bromine vapour which are liberated on decomposition. The structure is unknown.

Hypobromous acid, HBrO, can be obtained only in solution, and is always contaminated with its decomposition products, bromine and bromic acid. The solution is made (i) by the hydrolysis of bromine:

$$Br_2 + H_2O \rightleftharpoons H^+ + Br^- + HBrO,$$

using precipitated mercuric oxide to remove the H^+ and the Br^- ions; this process is less efficient than the corresponding process for the preparation of hypochlorous acid (p. 920), (ii) by the distillation of a mixture of bromine water and silver sulphate. The distillate is a dilute solution of hypobromous acid contaminated with bromine which can be removed by passing a stream of nitrogen through the solution.

Hypobromous acid is decomposed by rough surfaces with the liberation of oxygen; bromine (and not hydrobromic acid) is set free at the same time:

$$5HOBr = HBrO_3 + 2H_2O + 2Br_2.$$

This reaction differs from the corresponding reaction for hypochlorous acid (p. 920), because the reaction:

$$HBrO + Br^- + H^+ = Br_2 + H_2O,$$

takes place more readily than the corresponding reaction involving chlorine. In slightly acid solution hypobromous acid decomposes to form bromic acid, again with the liberation of bromine:

$$2HBrO + BrO^- = BrO_3^- + 2H^+ + 2Br^-,$$
$$HBrO + Br^- + H^+ = Br_2 + H_2O.$$

Bromic acid, $HBrO_3$, is known only in solution. A solution of the acid is obtained:

  (i) by shaking silver bromate with bromine water, and filtering off the precipitated silver bromide:

$$3H_2O + 5AgBrO_3 + 3Br_2 = 6HBrO_3 + 5AgBr,$$

 (ii) by treating barium bromate with dilute sulphuric acid, and removing the excess acid with baryta water, and filtering off the barium sulphate.

The aqueous solution of bromic acid may be concentrated up to 5% by evaporation on a water bath, and concentrated up to 50% by evaporation in a vacuum desiccator. An aqueous solution containing 50% of bromic acid corresponds to the composition $HBrO_3,7H_2O$. Attempts to concentrate the solution further cause the decomposition of the acid:

$$4HBrO_3 = 2Br_2 + 5O_2 + 2H_2O.$$

The aqueous solution of bromic acid is a strong oxidising agent. It oxidises sulphur dioxide to sulphuric acid, hydrogen sulphide to sulphur, and hydrogen bromide to bromine. In all these reactions bromic acid is reduced to bromine.

The bromates. Potassium bromate is made by dissolving a slight excess of bromine in hot concentrated potassium hydroxide solution:

$$3Br_2 + 6KOH = KBrO_3 + 5KBr + 3H_2O.$$

The potassium bromate is less soluble than potassium bromide, and it separates on cooling. Two variants of this reaction are described by the equations:

$$6KOCl + Br_2 = 2KBrO_3 + 4KCl + Cl_2, \text{ and}$$
$$3Cl_2 + KBr + 6KOH = KBrO_3 + 6KCl + 3H_2O.$$

The bromates of Na, K, Tl (ous), Ag, Hg (ous) are anhydrous; the bromates of Li, Ca, Sr, Ba, Zn and Pb have one molecule of water of crystallisation; those of Mg and Zn have six molecules of water of crystallisation. The bromates of Tl (ous), Ag, Ba, and Pb are sparingly soluble in water (of the order of 0·5 gm/100 gm at 20°), and those of the other metals mentioned above are fairly soluble (of the order of 50 gm/100 gm at 20°). The bromates are decomposed by heat, but the course of the reaction depends on the nature of the metal. Bromates of K, Hg (ous), and Ag give the metal bromide and oxygen; bromates of Mg, Zn, and Al give the metal oxide and bromine and oxygen; bromates of Pb and Cu give the metal bromide and oxide. Ammonium bromate and lead bromate are explosive.

The ion BrO_3^- has the same configuration as the chlorate ion; the angle OBrO is 108°.

SECTIONS 5 AND 6. COMPOUNDS IN WHICH THE BROMINE ATOM IS PRESENT IN THE TRIGONAL-BIPYRAMIDAL AND IN THE OCTAHEDRAL VALENCE STATES

Compounds of bromine classified in these Sections are not numerous. They include BrF_3 (p. 901), $KBrCl_2$, and $KBrF_4$.

IODINE

THE ELEMENT

The physical properties of iodine are included in Table 23.2. The deep blue of iodine vapour becomes violet when the vapour is mixed with air. Iodine is sparingly soluble in water, but freely soluble in organic solvents. The colours of the solutions differ.

> Violet solutions: Paraffins, many aliphatic halogen compounds, including halogen derivatives of ethylene, and aliphatic nitro compounds,
> Brown solutions: Water, alcohols,
> Red solutions: Concentrated hydrochloric acid, concentrated nitric acid, and aromatic compounds.

For the violet solution the main absorption band has a maximum in the same position as that of the vapour (5400 Å), Beer's law† is obeyed, and the value of the extinction coefficient is the same as that of the vapour. The brown solutions do not obey Beer's law. It has been suggested that the brown solutions contain iodine in a condition in which the molecule is polarised by co-ordination with the solvent molecules which act as electron donors. It has been shown by experiments on spectra that an equilibrium

$$I_2 + A \rightleftharpoons AI_2$$

is set up, where A is a molecule of an aromatic compound.

Iodine combines directly with many elements. It reacts with red or yellow phosphorus in the presence of water to yield hydrogen iodide and phosphorous acid. Mercury triturated with iodine yields mercurous iodide or mercuric iodide according to the proportions taken. Iodine reacts with gold to yield aurous iodide. It is said that sodium can be melted under iodine without reaction. Iodine and hydrogen are in reversible equilibrium with hydrogen iodide at high temperatures. Iodine combines with the other halogens to give IF_5, ICl and ICl_3, and IBr; the vigour of the reactions is in the order $F > Cl > Br$. Iodine reacts with potassium hydroxide solution to give potassium hypoiodite, which rapidly disproportionates to potassium iodate and potassium iodide.

Iodine is an oxidising agent, and it converts sulphurous acid to sulphuric acid, stannous chloride in hydrochloric acid solution to stannic chloride, arsenious oxide in the presence of potassium bicarbonate solution to arsenic acid, an aqueous solution of hydrogen sulphide (but not the dry gas) to sulphur, hydrogen peroxide in neutral solution to oxygen, and an aqueous solution of sodium thiosulphate to sodium tetrathionate:

$$I_2 + 2Na_2S_2O_3 = 2NaI + Na_2S_4O_6.$$

Iodine is itself oxidised to iodic acid by oxidising agents such as hypochlorites, chlorates, nitric acid, and persulphuric acid.

Iodine gives a blue colour with starch; the nature of the physical or chemical change which produces the colour has not been definitely established.

The molecular constitution of iodine vapour is I_2, which appears to be unchanged in solution. Dissociation of the molecules into atoms is just perceptible at 600° and is complete at 1000°. Solid iodine has a molecular lattice and is isomorphous with solid bromine. The conductivity of solid iodine falls with increasing temperature, and in this respect iodine shows metallic character.

---

†Beer's law (which relates to the absorption of light by solutions) states that $\log I/I_0 = - Elc$, where I_0 is the intensity of the incident light, I is the intensity of the transmitted light, l is the thickness of the solution, and c is the concentration in moles per litre. E, a constant, is the extinction coefficient which is dependent on the nature of the absorbent and the wave length of the light.

GENERAL CHEMISTRY OF IODINE

The electron configuration of the valency shell of the iodine atom is the same as that of the bromine atom except that the quantum number $n = 5$. Iodine, like bromine and chlorine, forms πd bonds but not πp bonds.

Iodine does not adopt the digonal valence state, and the only compound in which the iodine atom might be in the trigonal valence state is iodyl sulphate (p. 932), but iodine forms numerous compounds in which the atom adopts the tetrahedral valence state, several in which it adopts the trigonal bipyramidal valence state, and a few in which it adopts the octahedral valence state. In many of the tetrahedral and trigonal bipyramidal compounds some of the hybrid orbitals of the iodine atom are occupied by lone pairs.

The compounds of iodine with oxygen are interesting. The oxides are highly polymerised, and their compositions do not correspond to those of the oxides of bromine or of chlorine, Table 23.4; the orbital structures of the iodine oxides are unknown. The oxyacids of iodine, Table 23.11, follow the pattern of the oxyacids of chlorine (p. 920), except that there is no iodous acid HIO_2, and iodine forms anions of mesoperiodic acid, H_3IO_5, in which the iodine atom is 5 co-ordinate, and paraperiodic acid, H_5IO_6, in which it is 6 co-ordinate; there are no oxyacids in which a chlorine atom has a co-ordination number greater than 4. This distinction between iodine and chlorine corresponds to the similar distinction between tellurium and sulphur. In addition, however, to oxides and oxyacids, iodine forms the oxygen compounds iodosobenzene, C_6H_5IO, and iodoxybenzene, $C_6H_5IO_2$. These two compounds contain πd bonds, and in structure are analogous to the sulphoxides and sulphones respectively.

Although the iodine atom in the ground state is unicovalent, by promotion of p electrons to d orbitals the atom becomes multivalent. Trivalent iodine is present in

Table 23.10. *Salts of Polyhalide Anions*

Type of salt	Hybridisation	Configuration of anion	Cations represented by M
MI_3	Trigonal-bipyramidal	Linear. The central iodine atom is in the trigonal bipyramidal state with lone pairs in the equatorial positions.	Rb, Cs, NH_4†, and large complex cations, such as $Co(NH_3)_6{}^{2+}$ and $Ni(NH_3)_6{}^{2+}$. The hydrate KI_3, H_2O is stable at 25°, but the anhydrous salt is not.
$MICl_2$		Linear. As for MI_3.	Cs, $N(CH_3)_4$
$MIBr_2$			Cs
$MIBrCl$		Linear. As for MI_3.	Cs, NH_4.
$MICl_4$	Octahedral	Square planar. The iodine atom is in the octahedral valence state with lone pairs in the polar positions.	K, Rb, Cs. Cations of organic bases.
$MICl_3F$			Rb (m.p. 172°), Cs (m.p. 194°), $(CH_3)_4N$ (m.p. 270°) PyrH. (m.p. 190°).
MI_5		Planar. The arrangement of I atoms is V-shaped.	

† Phosphonium, arsonium stibonium, sulphonium, and iodonium cations also form polyhalides in this order of stability.

30 + A.T.I.C.

several important compounds including the iodonium compounds such as $[(C_6H_5)_2I]OH$, the iodine dichloride salts $K[ICl_2]$, the dipyridinoiodine salts $[Ipyr_2]NO_3$, phenyl iodine dichloride $C_6H_5ICl_2$, and the compounds IX_3, where X may be the chloride, nitrate, iodate, acetate, or perchlorate group.

Iodine shows more definitely than bromine the property of acting as the central atom in anions consisting of several halogen atoms. The salts which contain these polyhalide anions are stated in Table 23.10.

The concept of the inert electron pair which is found useful in assigning structures to certain tellurium compounds (p. 882), is not found to be necessary in assigning structures to the compounds of iodine described in this chapter.

SECTION 1. IODINE COMPOUNDS WITH IONIC CHARACTER

The iodides. The monatomic iodide ion, I^-, is stable. The crystal structures of the metal iodides are set out below.

Rocksalt	Alkali metal iodides (except CsI), NH_4I above $-17 \cdot 6°$.
CsCl	CsI, NH_4I below $-17 \cdot 6°$. (At low temperatures NH_4I has a tetragonal form.)
CdI_2	MgI_2, CaI_2, CdI_2, TiI_2, PbI_2, GeI_2, MnI_2, FeI_2, CoI_2, NiI_2, HgI_2 (distorted).
$PbCl_2$	BaI_2
BiI_3	AsI_3, SbI_3, BiI_3
Wurtzite	AgI
Zincblende	CuI
Discrete molecules	SnI_4, GeI_4, TiI_4.

Comparison of these crystal structures with those of the corresponding chlorides and bromides shows that the iodides have structures with less ionic character than the bromides.

Most iodides are soluble in water; AgI, TlI, PbI_2, and HgI_2 are insoluble or sparingly soluble.

SECTION 4. COMPOUNDS IN WHICH THE IODINE ATOM IS PRESENT IN THE TETRAHEDRAL VALENCE STATE

The iodine atom is tetrahedrally hybridised in the familiar compounds hydrogen iodide and ethyl iodide. The iodine atom in the tetrahedral valence state is also present in certain compounds which have no counterparts among the compounds of chlorine and bromine. These iodine compounds include diphenyliodonium hydroxide, iodosobenzene, iodoxybenzene, and iodyl sulphate. Hypoiodous acid, iodic acid, and metaperiodic acid (Table 23.11) contain the iodine atom in the tetrahedral valence state, but it is convenient to discuss them together with the other oxyacids of iodine on p. 936.

Hydrogen iodide, HI, is made:

(i) by heating potassium iodide with phosphoric acid (oxidising acids oxidise the liberated hydrogen iodide to iodine),

(ii) by dropping water on to a mixture of iodine and red phosphorus,

Hydrogen iodide is decomposed by light and is easily dissociated by heat. The effect of temperature on the dissociation is given by the data:

Temperature, °K	600	700	800
Percentage dissociation	19·1	22·2	24·9

Hydrogen iodide in aqueous solution is an acid. It is very easily oxidised, and is much used in the laboratory as a reducing agent. Most organic compounds if heated with saturated aqueous hydriodic acid at about 250° are reduced to saturated hydrocarbons. Heated potassium burns in hydrogen iodide, but burning sodium and magnesium are extinguished. Hydrogen iodide reacts with mercury forming mercurous and mercuric iodides. Hydrogen iodide reacts with the halogens other than iodine.

Many organic derivatives of hydrogen iodide, such as ethyl iodide and iodobenzene, are important compounds in organic chemistry. Accounts of these and similar substances will be found in text books of organic chemistry and it is not thought necessary to describe them here.

Complex cations formed by iodine. Iodine forms several salts (p. 897) containing the cations [Ipyr$^+$] and [Ipyr$_2^+$]. The cation [Ipyr$^+$] is usually present in association with anions of organic acids. The iodine atom in the cation is probably in the tetrahedral valence state with three hybrid orbitals occupied by lone pairs. The cation [Ipyr$_2^+$] is discussed on p. 934.

Diphenyliodonium hydroxide, [$(C_6H_5)_2$I]OH, is made by shaking a mixture of iodoso-benzene and iodoxybenzene with freshly precipitated silver oxide:

$$C_6H_5IO + C_6H_5IO_2 + AgOH = [(C_6H_5)_2I]OH + AgIO_3.$$

Diphenyliodonium hydroxide is strongly basic. The iodide is known. The hybridisation diagram is:

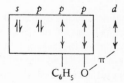

Iodosobenzene, C_6H_5IO, is a yellow solid which explodes at 210°. It is made by the action of very dilute sodium hydroxide solution on phenyl iodine dichloride. It is soluble in warm water and in alcohol. It is an oxidising agent and liberates iodine from potassium iodide in acid solution:

$$C_6H_5IO + 2HI = C_6H_5I + H_2O + I_2.$$

It behaves as a base when treated with an acid:

$$C_6H_5IO + 2CH_3COOH = C_6H_5I(CH_3COO)_2 + H_2O.$$

When treated with steam it disproportionates thus:

$$2C_6H_5IO = C_6H_5IO_2 + C_6H_5I,$$

to give iodoxybenzene which is non-volatile, and iodobenzene which is volatile in steam.

The hybridisation diagram is

The orbital structure of iodosobenzene is analogous to that of the sulphoxides (p. 836).

Iodoxybenzene, $C_6H_5IO_2$, is obtained as colourless needles by crystallisation of the aqueous solution which remains after iodosobenzene has been treated with steam.

Iodoxybenzene explodes at 230°. It is an oxidising agent but has no basic properties. The hybridisation diagram is probably

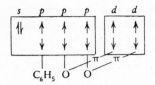

This orbital structure corresponds to that of a sulphone (p. 842).

Iodyl sulphate (iodous sulphate), $[IO^+]_2SO_4$, a white crystalline substance, is made by heating iodine pentoxide with concentrated sulphuric acid. It reacts with benzene derivatives containing a substituent which is *ortho-para*-directing to yield the *para* iodonium salt $[(C_6H_5)_2I]X$, but if the substituent is *meta*-directing the *meta* iodoso-benzene derivative is obtained.

The constitution of the iodyl ion $[IO^+]$, can only be conjectured. The electron configuration of the valency shell of the iodine atom after the expulsion of one electron would be:

$$\begin{array}{cccc} s & p & p & p \\ \uparrow\downarrow & \uparrow\downarrow & \uparrow & \uparrow \end{array}$$

If the assumption that only elements in Period 2 exert πp bonds is maintained then in the iodyl ion the iodine atom is trigonally hybridised and is exerting one σ bond and one πd bond thus:

If iodyl sulphate is covalent the hybridisation diagram must be drawn to correspond with that of iodosobenzene, thus:

SECTION 5. COMPOUNDS IN WHICH THE IODINE ATOM IS IN THE TRIGONAL BIPYRAMIDAL VALENCE STATE

This section includes the trihalide anions present in salts of the general formula MIX_2 (Table 23.10), certain compounds of trivalent iodine (p. 933), and silver meta-periodate (p. 938). The iodine atom in the cation $[Ipyr_2^+]$ is probably in the trigonal-bipyramidal valence state, three of the hybrid orbitals being occupied by lone pairs.

The trihalide anions. The general formula of the trihalide anions is $[IXY^-]$, where X and Y represent atoms of iodine, bromine, or chlorine. The iodide ion, I^-, in the presence of molecules of halogen is in equilibrium with the ion IXY^- thus:

$$I^- + XY \rightleftharpoons IXY^-.$$

The values of the equilibrium constant,

$$K = \frac{[IXY^-]}{[I^-][XY]},$$

in water near 25° for certain of the ions represented by [IXY⁻] are:

I_3^-	725	$IBrCl^-$	43·5
IBr_2^-	370	I_2Br^-	11·0
ICl_2^-	167	I_2Cl^-	2·1

The values of the corresponding equilibrum constants for the less stable bromine and chlorine compounds are added for comparison:

$BrBrBr^-$	17·8
$ClClCl^-$	0·01
$BrClCl^-$	—
$BrBrCl^-$	1·14

K is greater:

    (i) when X and Y represent atoms of the same element,
    (ii) the lower the atomic numbers of X and Y,
    (iii) the closer the atomic numbers of X and Y.

The trihalide ions form stable salts only in association with large cations. Rubidium, caesium, and ammonium readily form crystalline anhydrous tri-iodides, but KI_3 is stable only below 15°, and at 25° the stable solids are the hydrates KI_3,H_2O and $KI_3,2H_2O$, which at 70° break up liberating iodine. Lithium and sodium do not form tri-iodides. There is little evidence for the existence of tri-iodides of metals other than those in Group 1. Tri-iodides are soluble in benzene, phenyl cyanide, and nitrobenzene. If mixtures of the simple iodides and iodine are crystallised from phenyl cyanide (but not from methyl cyanide or from benzyl cyanide) the following crystalline products are obtained (B indicates one molecule of phenyl cyanide):

$HI_3,4B$	m.p. 97°	$NaI_3,2B$	m.p. 67°
$KI_3,4B$	m.p. 92·5°	$KI_3,2B$	m.p. 58°

The trihalide anions are linear; the length of the ion is between 3·8 and 4·8.

    The hybridisation diagram of the iodine dichloride ion is:

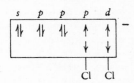

The chlorine atoms are probably at the polar positions of a trigonal bipyramid with the iodine atom at the centre.

    Trivalent compounds of iodine. Iodine forms many diverse compounds of the general formula IX_3. Phenyl iodine dichloride, $C_6H_5ICl_2$, has a T-shaped structure. The dimeric form of iodine trichloride is planar, and each group ICl_3 is T-shaped. These structures could be explained by assuming that the trivalent iodine atom is in the trigonal bipyramidal valence state, with two of the equatorial hybrid orbitals occupied by lone pairs.

    Iodobenzene dichloride, $C_6H_5ICl_2$, is obtained as yellow crystals when dry chlorine is passed into iodobenzene dissolved in chloroform. Very dilute sodium hydroxide solution slowly decomposes it to iodosobenzene, C_6H_5IO.

An X-ray analysis of iodobenzene dichloride has been made. The group Cl—I—Cl has been found to be linear, and to be at approximately 90° to the plane of the benzene ring. These results are in accord with the trigonal bipyramidal structure, thus:

$$
\begin{array}{c}
\mathrm{Cl} \\
|
\end{array}
$$

Iodine trinitrate, $I(NO_3)_3$, is made by oxidising iodine with cold concentrated nitric acid. It is a yellow unstable powder. On warming it decomposes to iodine, iodic acid, and oxides of nitrogen.

Iodine tri-iodate, $I(IO_3)_3$. It has been suggested that the oxide I_4O_9 (p. 936) is iodine tri-iodate.

Iodine triacetate, $I(OCOCH_3)_3$, is made by oxidising iodine in acetic anhydride solution with nitric acid, or in acetic acid solution with chlorine monoxide. It forms colourless crystals, stable in the cold, but decomposing at 100° and exploding at slightly higher temperatures. The acetic anhydride solution of iodine triacetate conducts electricity. During electrolysis iodine is deposited at the cathode. Iodine mono-, di-, and tri-chloroacetates, and iodine trifluoroacetate are known.

Iodine perchlorate, $I(ClO_4)_3,2H_2O$, is made by dissolving iodine in cold anhydrous perchloric acid and treating the solution with ozone:

$$I_2 + 6HClO_4 + O_3 = 2I(ClO_4)_3 + 3H_2O.$$

The salt separates as the dihydrate $I(ClO_4)_3,2H_2O$. It is easily decomposed by water.

Iodine phosphate, IPO_4, is made by adding nitric acid to iodine and orthophosphoric acid dissolved in acetic anhydride.

The cation, $[Ipyr_2^+]$, forms salts by association with the nitrate and perchlorate ions. Dipyridine iodine nitrate is obtained by treating a solution of silver nitrate in pyridine with iodine:

$$[Agpyr_2]NO_3 + I_2 = [Ipyr_2]NO_3 + AgI.$$

When a solution of dipyridine iodine nitrate in an organic solvent is electrolysed, iodine is liberated at the cathode. Dipyridine iodine perchlorate is obtained by treating a solution of mercurous perchlorate in pyridine with iodine. The nitrate and the perchlorate are stable at room temperature, but they decompose if warmed. They are hydrolysed by water. The first stage is probably the formation of hypoiodous acid, thus:

$$[Ipyr_2]NO_3 + H_2O = IOH + HNO_3 + 2C_5H_5N,$$

followed by the immediate disproportionation of the hypoiodous acid:

$$5IOH = HIO_3 + 2I_2 + 2H_2O.$$

The nitric acid and the iodic acid then combine with the pyridine.

The cation $[Ipyr_2^+]$ can be assigned the hybridisation diagram:

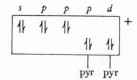

SECTION 6. COMPOUNDS IN WHICH THE IODINE ATOM IS OCTAHEDRALLY HYBRIDISED

Among compounds in this section are salts of the anions $[ICl_4^-]$ and $[ICl_3F^-]$ (Table 23.10), and paraperiodic acid, H_5IO_6 (p. 938).

The iodotetrachlorides, $MICl_4$, are stable when the ion ICl_4^- is associated with large cations such as the alkylammonium, pyridinium, quinolinium, and the diazonium ions, and the metal ions Cs^+, Rb^+, and K^+. $KICl_4$, however, loses ICl_3 when exposed to the atmosphere. The iodotetrachlorides of organic bases are golden yellow, and are fairly soluble in water. They melt sharply with decomposition. Smaller univalent cations, and divalent cations are associated with ICl_4^- in crystalline hydrates: $HICl_4,4H_2O$, $LiICl_4,4H_2O$, $NaICl_4,2H_2O$, $Ca(ICl_4)_2,8H_2O$; Ca may be replaced by Be, Mg, Sr, Ba, Zn, Mn, Co, and Ni.

The unstable acid $HICl_4,4H_2O$ is obtained by passing chlorine into a suspension of iodine in concentrated hydrochloric acid at $0°$. Certain of the bands of its absorption spectrum are identical with those of the alkali metal iodotetrachlorides. The crystal structure of $KICl_4$ has been determined. The anion is planar, and the four chlorine atoms are at the corners of a square with the iodine atom at the centre. This geometrical arrangement could be explained by assuming that the iodine atom is octahedrally hybridised, and that the two polar positions are occupied by lone electron pairs.

MI_5, MI_7, and MI_9. Potassium and other alkali metals of higher atomic number, and strong organic bases, form salts of these types. An X-ray analysis of crystalline $N(CH_3)_4I_5$ has been made. The configuration of the anion I_5^- was found to be planar, but not square. The dimensions of the anion are:

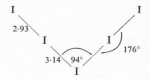

The orbital structures of the iodine atoms in the ion are uncertain.

THE OXIDES OF IODINE

The formulae and certain properties of the oxides of iodine are included in Table 23.4.

The three iodine oxides are solids which when heated decompose without melting. They are non-volatile and they are insoluble in any solvent with which they do not react, and hence their molecular weights cannot be determined. Their orbital structures are unknown. Some authorities regard I_2O_4 as iodyl iodate $[IO][IO_3]$, and I_4O_9 as iodine tri-iodate $I(IO_3)_3$, but there is neither physical nor chemical evidence for these suppositions. Brief accounts of the three iodine oxides are given below.

$(I_2O_4)_n$ is made by heating iodic acid with concentrated sulphuric acid for a long time. The product is washed with water, alcohol, and ether; the residue is I_2O_4. The yield is 30%. I_2O_4 is scarcely soluble in cold water, but it reacts with hot water to yield iodic acid and iodine:

$$5I_2O_4 + 4H_2O = 8HIO_3 + I_2.$$

I_2O_4 dissolves slowly in potassium hydroxide solution to give a mixture of potassium iodide and potassium iodate:

$$3I_2O_4 + 6KOH = KI + 5KIO_3 + 3H_2O,$$

and in hydrochloric acid to yield chlorine and iodine monochloride:

$$I_2O_4 + 8HCl = 3Cl_2 + 2ICl + 4H_2O.$$

When heated with sulphur trioxide or oleum it is partly oxidised to $I_2O_4,3SO_3$, a pale yellow hygroscopic substance stable up to 135°, and partly to iodine pentoxide.

$(I_4O_9)_n$ is made:

(i) by the action of ozonised oxygen on iodine at room temperature, or on its solution in chloroform, carbon tetrachloride, or nitrobenzene,

(ii) by warming powdered iodic acid with orthophosphoric acid; on standing, oxygen is evolved and I_4O_9 separates:

$$8HIO_3 = 2I_4O_9 + 4H_2O + O_2.$$

I_4O_9 is very hygroscopic. If exposed to moisture it deliquesces, turning red or brown, and ultimately decomposes to iodic acid and iodine. It has been suggested that the constitution of I_4O_9 is $I(IO_3)_3$, and that the first stage in the hydrolysis is:

$$I(IO_3)_3 + 3H_2O = I(OH)_3 + 3HIO_3.$$

Iodine pentoxide, I_2O_5, is made:

(i) by oxidising iodine with nitric acid or nitrogen pentoxide; iodine is heated with fuming nitric acid under a reflux condenser at 70–80°:

$$I_2 + 2\tfrac{1}{2}O_2 = I_2O_5; \quad \Delta H = -48 \text{ kcal.}$$

(ii) by the dehydration of iodic acid at 195°.

At a pressure of 100 atm and at 250° iodine is directly oxidised by oxygen to iodine pentoxide.

Iodine pentoxide reacts with water to yield iodic acid:

$$I_2O_5 + H_2O = 2HIO_3; \quad \Delta H = -4\cdot2 \text{ kcal.}$$

Iodine pentoxide dissolves in nitric acid from which it may be recrystallised without chemical change if the concentration of the nitric acid is more than 50%. Iodine pentoxide is a strong oxidising agent. With organic substances it sometimes detonates. It converts carbon monoxide slowly but completely to carbon dioxide (Ditte's reaction), but the reaction is quantitative only in the complete absence of water. Nitric oxide reduces iodine pentoxide, slowly at 80° and quickly at 120°, giving iodine and higher oxides of nitrogen.

THE OXYACIDS OF IODINE AND THEIR SALTS

The formulae and probable structures of five of the oxyacids of iodine are given in Table 23.11. In addition to the oxyacids mentioned in the Table the isopolyacids $H_4I_2O_9$ and $H_8I_2O_{11}$, and heteropoly acids such as $H_5IO_6,6MoO_3$ are also known (p. 999).

In the first three acids in the Table the iodine atom is in the tetrahedral valence state. In the two remaining acids the iodine atom is in the trigonal bipyramidal and the octahedral valence states respectively. The acids are so closely related and so readily interconvertible that it is more convenient to consider them together than to discuss them in the appropriate Sections of this Chapter.

Hypoiodous acid, HIO, is known only in dilute aqueous solution, which can be prepared by shaking an aqueous suspension of iodine and mercuric oxide. Hypoiodous acid is a much weaker acid than either hypochlorous acid or hypobromous acid. The dissociation constants

$$K = \frac{[H^+][OX^-]}{[HOX]}$$

for the three acids are:

HClO	HBrO	HIO
3×10^{-8}	2×10^{-9}	$4\cdot5 \times 10^{-13}$

Table 23.11. *The Oxyacids of Iodine*

Acid	Formula	Notes	Structure
Hypoiodous	HIO	Known only in dilute solution	
Iodic	HIO_3	It is the most stable of the oxyacids of iodine, and is produced by the hydrolysis of oxides of iodine or by the reduction of the higher oxyacids. It can be obtained as colourless anhydrous crystals	
Metaperiodic	HIO_4	Colourless crystals which sublime at 110°	
(Mesoperiodic)	(H_3IO_5)	The acid is not known. The only salt is Ag_3IO_5	
Paraperiodic	H_5IO_6	Colourless, deliquescent crystals which melt at 122°, and decompose at 138°	

Hypoiodous acid also acts as a weak base;

$$K = \frac{[OH^-][I^+]}{[HOI]} = 3 \times 10^{-10}.$$

Hypoiodous acid disproportionates to iodic acid and iodine much more readily than either hypochlorous acid or hypobromous acid undergo the corresponding disproportionations. Free hypoiodous acid in aqueous solution is mostly converted to iodic acid in 15 minutes, and one third of the potassium hypoiodite in aqueous solution is changed to potassium iodate in about 1 hour; the half-life of sodium hypochlorite in aqueous solution is about 3 years.

Iodic acid, HIO₃, a colourless solid, is made by dissolving iodine pentoxide in the smallest possible volume of warm water. On cooling, rhombic crystals of iodic acid are deposited. When iodic acid is heated it decomposes; at 110° HI_3O_8 is formed and at 195° this compound decomposes to iodine pentoxide and steam.

Iodic acid is very soluble in water; the solution first reddens and then bleaches litmus. The solid acid inflames when heated with sulphur, phosphorus, or organic matter, and its solution oxidises sulphur dioxide, hydrogen sulphide, and hydriodic acid with the liberation of iodine.

30*

X-ray analysis shows that the molecule of iodic acid has a pyramidal configuration. The distance I–O is $1\cdot85$; the angle OIO is $98\pm3°$. In the crystal the trigonal pyramids are so arranged that each iodine atom is surrounded by six oxygen atoms situated at the apices of an octahedron. The octahedron is much distorted because the distances I–O for the oxygen atoms which are not part of the pyramid are $2\cdot45$, $2\cdot70$, and $2\cdot95$. Each IO_3 group is linked to two other IO_3 groups by hydrogen bonds, and hence the lattice may be regarded as a chain structure reminiscent of the chain of bicarbonate ions in potassium bicarbonate (p. 371).

The iodates. The alkali metal and alkaline earth metal iodates can be made by the action of iodine on the metal hydroxide:

$$3I_2 + 6OH^- = IO_3^- + 5I^- + 3H_2O.$$

Barium iodate is sparingly soluble, and hence is easily made by this method.

Potassium iodate, KIO_3, can be made:

  (i) by the action of iodine on potassium hydroxide,
  (ii) by double decomposition between barium iodate and potassium sulphate,
  (iii) by the direct action of oxygen on potassium iodide at 100 atm pressure,
  (iv) by the action of iodine on potassium chlorate in slightly acid solution:

$$5KClO_3 + 3I_2 + 3H_2O = 3(KIO_3,HIO_3) + 2KCl + 3HCl.$$

The acid salt KIO_3,HIO_3 is sparingly soluble and crystallises from the solution.

The normal iodates of most metals are soluble, but those of Ag, Tl (ous), Cu (ic), Ba, and Pb are sparingly soluble. Lithium forms a normal iodate only, but the other alkali metals form acid iodates, MIO_3,HIO_3. Alkali metal iodates do not detonate when brought into contact with carbon or sulphur, but the mixtures explode when heated. The iodates are oxidising agents in aqueous solution. The metal iodates decompose when heated; the mode of decomposition is determined by the electro-negativity of the metal. The iodates of the most electropositive metals and silver on heating to 500° give the metal iodide and liberate oxygen; the iodates of less electro-positive metals decompose to the metal oxide, liberating iodine. Sodium iodate has intermediate properties. When heated it liberates iodine and leaves a residue of sodium iodide and sodium oxide. Ammonium iodate decomposes completely when heated, thus:

$$2NH_4IO_3 = N_2 + I_2 + O_2 + 4H_2O.$$

The iodate ion, IO_3^-, has a pyramidal structure. Experimental evidence has been obtained showing that in the crystal of sodium iodate the group IO_3 is a discrete ion, and is not part of a perovskite structure.

The periodic acids. Metaperiodic acid, HIO_4, can be obtained by heating paraperiodic acid in vacuo at 100°. Its sodium and silver salts are known. The distance I–O in sodium metaperiodate has been found to be $1\cdot79$. The ion IO_4^- has a tetrahedral configuration.

Mesoperiodic acid, H_3IO_5, has not been prepared. The only salt reported is silver mesoperiodate, Ag_3IO_5, which is obtained as a black precipitate by adding sodium paraperiodate to boiling silver nitrate solution.

Paraperiodic acid, H_5IO_6, is prepared by the action of chlorine or bromine on silver mesoperiodate:

$$4Ag_3IO_5 + 6Cl_2 + 10H_2O = 4H_5IO_6 + 12AgCl + 3O_2.$$

The silver chloride is filtered off and colourless crystals of the acid separate from the filtrate. The acid is deliquescent and very soluble in water. If heated it decomposes at 138° to iodine pentoxide, oxygen and water.

Paraperiodic acid usually behaves as a dibasic acid. The first three dissociation constants are:

$$K_1 = 2\cdot3 \times 10^{-2} \qquad K_2 = 10^{-6} \qquad K_3 = 2\cdot5 \times 10^{-13}.$$

Paraperiodic acid is a powerful oxidising agent.

Potassium paraperiodate, $K_2H_3IO_6$, is made by the anodic oxidation of potassium iodate dissolved in normal potassium hydroxide solution using platinum electrodes. Sodium paraperiodate is made by passing chlorine into a solution of iodine in boiling sodium hydroxide solution:

$$3NaOH + NaIO_3 + Cl_2 = Na_2H_3IO_6 + 2NaCl.$$

The sodium paraperiodate crystallises from the hot liquid. The alkali metal paraperiodates are oxidising agents. They are reduced by sodium sulphite to the metal iodates and ultimately to the metal iodides. They react with iodine to give the metal iodate or iodide according to the pH of the solution. They are reduced by hydrogen peroxide in acid, neutral, or alkaline solution.

Silver paraperiodate is obtained as a greenish-yellow precipitate by adding a solution of silver nitrate in dilute nitric acid to sodium paraperiodate solution. The precipitate can be converted to the silver salts of other periodic acids by the treatments indicated in the diagram:

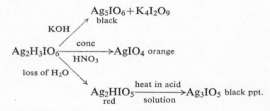

The group IO_6 is octahedral. Three of the hydrogen atoms associated with the group IO_6 take part in the formation of hydrogen bonds, and hence the basicity of paraperiodic acid is only two. The distance I—O is 1·93.

CHAPTER TWENTY-FOUR

THE TRANSITION ELEMENTS

The transition elements are metals of high melting point and well-marked metallic glance. In this chapter, the properties of the elements are set out in tables at the heads of the sections dealing with the transition elements in each Periodic Group. The atomic structures of the transition elements are characterised by the presence of d orbitals in the penultimate electron shell which are capable of taking part in bond formation; penultimate d orbitals with this property are never found in atoms of normal elements.†
The penultimate d orbitals of the isolated atoms of the transition metals are not completely occupied by electrons, and in accordance with Hund's rule and the Jahn Teller effect (p. 953) it would be predicted that the atoms would have resultant spin and thus resultant magnetic moment; hence the crystalline metal should show paramagnetism. In general, this is found to be the case, but in many instances the paramagnetism is weaker than would be expected because of the effect of the crystal field (see Kramers' theorem, p. 953). The only metals which are strongly paramagnetic are Cr, Mn, Fe, Co, Ni, Y, and Pd, and of these, Fe, Co, and Ni are ferromagnetic below a certain temperature. Cu, Zr, Ag, and Au show no paramagnetism and are weakly diamagnetic.

Paramagnetism is also a property of metallic compounds in which unpaired spins of d electrons have not been eliminated as the result of combination. The property of ferromagnetism, which is characteristic of the metals of the iron group, is also related to unpaired spins of d electrons in the metal atoms. Because the magnetic properties of the transition metals are of importance, the principles underlying paramagnetism and ferromagnetism are discussed in the next two sections of this chapter.

PARAMAGNETISM

If $I =$ intensity of magnetisation of a substance (magnetic moment per unit volume),

$$I = \chi H, \quad \text{where } \chi \text{ is the susceptibility.}$$

† The activity of the penultimate d orbitals in atoms of transition metals necessitates a departure from the classification of compounds, based on hybridisation, used hitherto in this book. The number of active electrons in the valency shell of a normal element is either the Group number or, if the s electron pair of the valency shell is inert, two less than this number; there is no further variation. In the transition elements the number of electrons in the penultimate and outermost shells of the atom which can be active varies more extensively, and the variation takes place unit by unit, and not in jumps of two. Ruthenium, for example (Table 24.27) may use in forming different types of compounds, 2, 3, 4, 5, 6, 7, or 8 of its eight valency electrons. The number of electrons in the atom of a transition metal which are active in bond formation in a particular compound is the oxidation state of the metal. The classification in this chapter of the types of compounds formed by a transition metal is based on the oxidation states of the metal; the compounds of any given oxidation state are then sub-divided into ionic compounds, giant molecules, and complexes. It so happens that in sub-Groups VI T, VII T, and in Group X, compounds of the metals in oxidation state I are known, and Section 1 of the tables corresponds to oxidation state I. In the other sub-Groups or Groups of the transition metals, oxidation state II is the lowest in which the metals are present in their compounds. In the tables referring to these sub-Groups or Groups (and in the text of the chapter) the Sections are given the same numbers as the oxidation states with which they are concerned, and hence there is no Section 1.

An expression for I may be developed in exactly the same manner as the expression derived for the electric moment per unit volume of a dielectric (p. 305).

$$I = nH\left(\alpha + \frac{\mu^2}{3kT}\right)$$

where μ is the permanent magnetic moment of each atom, α is the induced moment, and k is the Boltzmann constant. The expression is usually written in the form

$$\chi_M = N\left(\alpha + \frac{\mu^2}{3kT}\right),$$

where χ_M is the molar susceptibility and N is Avogadro's constant. If χ_M is positive, the substance is paramagnetic; if χ_M is negative the substance is diamagnetic (p. 98).

The expression for χ_M may be developed from quantum mechanical principles as follows:

The potential energy of an atom with magnetic moment in a field H is $-\mu_B M g H$ (p. 101) where M is the magnetic quantum number, and μ_B is the Bohr magneton. The value of M varies with the orientation of the particular atom considered. If a system of N atoms is assumed to behave as a gas to which the Maxwell–Boltzmann distribution law is applicable, then the number of atoms with a particular value of M is

$$N e^{M g \mu_B H / kT},$$

and the total magnetic moment, $\mathcal{M}$, of the system containing N particles is

$$\mathcal{M} = \frac{N \sum\limits_{M=-J}^{M=J} M g \mu_B e^{M g \mu_B H / kT}}{\sum\limits_{M=-J}^{M=J} e^{M g \mu_B H / kT}}.$$

if x is small e^x may be written as $(1+x)$ and, therefore, if $M g \mu_B H / kT$ is small,

$$\mathcal{M} = \frac{N g \mu_B \sum\limits_{M=-J}^{M=J} M(1 + M g \mu_B H / kT)}{\sum\limits_{M=-J}^{M=J} (1 + M g \mu_B H / kT)}.$$

Since

$$\sum_{M=-J}^{M=J} M = 0,$$

and since there are $(2J+1)$ values of M,

$$\mathcal{M} = \frac{N g^2 \mu_B^2 H}{kT} \frac{(J^2 + (J-1)^2 + \cdots + J^2)}{2J+1}$$

The expression in the bracket can be written approximately as $(2J+1)J(J+1)/3$.[†]
Therefore,

$$\mathcal{M} = \frac{N g^2 \mu_B^2 H J(J+1)}{3kT},$$

[†] See J. H. Van Vleck, *Electric and Magnetic Susceptibilities*, Oxford University Press, New York, 1932, p. 152.

and

$$\chi_M = \frac{Ng^2\mu_B{}^2 J(J+1)}{3kT}.$$

For a given substance, $Ng^2\mu_B{}^2 J(J+1)/3k$ is a constant; it is sometimes referred to as the *Curie constant* and written as C.

Thus

$$\chi_M = \frac{C}{T}.$$

This is known as the *Curie Law*.

According to the Curie law the paramagnetic moment of a substance is inversely proportional to the absolute temperature. Experiment has shown that this law is approximately true for those paramagnetic substances which consist of ions which are reasonably free from the influence of their neighbours. The magnetic susceptibilities of gases and liquids are independent of the direction of the applied field and it would therefore be expected that the Curie law would apply to gases and liquids but not to crystalline substances whose susceptibilities are in general dependent on the field direction. This is found to be so except where the internal crystalline fields are completely symmetrical; therefore the study of the temperature dependence of paramagnetic solids provides useful information as to the symmetry of crystalline fields. It is found, however, with certain ferromagnetic materials (Fe, Co, Ni, some alloys, some oxides of ferromagnetic metals, Ga, and a few compounds of the rare earths), that below a certain temperature characteristic of each particular ferromagnetic substance, the susceptibility becomes infinite, showing that the substance is spontaneously magnetised below this temperature. The Curie law has been modified by Weiss to explain these observations. In its modified form it is known as the *Curie-Weiss law*. It may be derived classically by the following argument.

It is supposed that the paramagnetic atom is subjected to an internal magnetic field as well as to the external field.[†]

If X is the total field,

$$X = H + \nu\rho n\bar{m},$$

where ν is a constant,

ρ is the density of the paramagnetic substance,

n is the number of atoms per unit volume of the paramagnetic sbustance,

$\bar{m}$ is the average magnetic moment of an atom in the field.

The average value of the magnetic moment per atom, parallel to the field (by analogy with the expression for the average value of the dipole moment of a molecule, parallel to the field (p. 305)), is given by the expression:

$$\bar{m} = \frac{\mu^2 X}{3kT},$$

where k is the Boltzmann constant.

Hence,

$$3\frac{\bar{m}}{\mu} = \frac{\mu H}{kT} + \frac{\mu\nu\rho n\bar{m}}{kT}$$

$$T\frac{\bar{m}}{\mu} = \frac{\mu H}{3k} + \frac{\bar{m}}{\mu}\left(\frac{\nu\rho n\mu^2}{3k}\right). \qquad (24.1)$$

Therefore

$$\frac{\bar{m}}{\mu} = \frac{\mu H}{3k}\left(\frac{1}{T - \nu\rho n\mu^2/3k}\right).$$

[†] In the calculation the induced magnetic moment, which is small, is neglected.

The term $v\rho n\mu^2/3k$ has the dimensions of temperature and is generally written as θ. Thus,

$$\frac{\bar{m}}{\mu} = \frac{\mu H}{3k}\left(\frac{1}{T-\theta}\right)$$

and

$$\chi_M = \frac{N\mu^2}{3k}\left(\frac{1}{T-\theta}\right) = \frac{C}{T-\theta}.$$

This is the *Curie–Weiss law* and θ is known as the *Curie point*. By measuring the susceptibility at different temperatures, C and θ may be determined. Equation (24.1) shows that when $H=0$ there is residual magnetism.

According to the simple theory outlined above, the paramagnetic Curie point (the temperature to which the substance must be cooled in order to lose its paramagnetism) is the same as the ferromagnetic Curie point (the temperature to which the ferromagnetic substance must be heated in order to lose its ferromagnetism). In practice it is found that they differ by $10°$–$15°$. The Curie point usually determined is the temperature at which the susceptibility of a paramagnetic substance becomes infinite. Experimentally observed Curie points in $°C$ are: iron, 770; cobalt, 1130; nickel 358; gadolinium, 16.

FERROMAGNETISM

In the absence of an external magnetic field, the crystal of a ferromagnetic substance, if it has not been previously magnetised, shows zero magnetic moment. In the presence of an external field a large magnetic moment is shown, much greater than that due to paramagnetism. As the field increases, the moment also increases till it reaches a saturation value which may persist when the field is removed.

A direct determination of the gyromagnetic ratio of iron has been made by measuring the angular momentum imparted to an iron rod as a result of magnetisation, and vice versa. The Landé g factor so determined is approximately 2, which shows that ferromagnetism like paramagnetism is mainly due to electron spin. It differs, however, from paramagnetism in that a small field of the order of 0.01 oersted is sufficient to saturate a ferromagnetic material, while a much greater field would be necessary to produce a saturation magnetic moment in a paramagnetic substance, and even so the resultant moment would be small. It has also been shown that the process of magnetisation of a ferromagnetic material is a discontinuous one and proceeds in a series of macroscopic steps. Consideration of these observations led Weiss to put forward the *domain theory* of ferromagnetism. This theory supposes that a ferromagnetic crystal contains a number of domains in each of which the condition of minimum energy requires that the spins of the electrons should be parallel to each other; each domain therefore has a resultant magnetic moment. In the absence of an external field, the domains are orientated so that the energy of the crystal is a minimum, in which condition the overall magnetic moment of the crystal is zero. When an external field is applied, the domains are gradually turned so that when saturation is attained, all the spins are aligned parallel to the field. It is found in practice that certain directions in the crystal are directions of "easy magnetisation", others are by contrast directions of "hard magnetisation". In recent years improved techniques have made it possible to photograph domain structures in ferromagnetic materials. For instance, Plate 23 shows magnetic domains in a thin film of nickel–iron. The magnetisation resulting from the application of a weak field to a ferromagnetic substance has been shown to be due to changes of size and shape of the domain boundaries (Plate 24), while the magnetisation resulting from the application of a strong field is due to rotation of whole domains so that their resultant magnetic moment is aligned with the field.

Since the domain structure is stable at temperatures below the Curie point and unstable at temperatures above it, it is reasonable to suppose that at the Curie point the energy of an electron in the internal field of the domain is approximately equal to the thermal energy. If this is so,

$$\mu_B H = \tfrac{3}{2} k T$$

where μ_B is the Bohr magneton, k the Boltzmann constant and T the absolute temperature. If the appropriate values are inserted into the equation, however, the value found for H is many times greater (by a factor of the order of 10^4) than the field which would be expected from purely dipole-dipole interaction; it therefore seems probable that the forces holding the domain together are electrostatic rather than magnetic in origin. It is the usual practice to describe these forces as quantum mechanical exchange forces, but their nature is not understood.

Spin wave theories of ferromagnetism. Bloch's theory of ferromagnetism is concerned with the magnetisation inside a domain. According to this theory, coupled spins are regarded as coupled harmonic oscillators, equivalent to superposed simple harmonic waves. The energy is quantised, and therefore the system has zero point energy. The ground state corresponds to the state at $0°K$ with all spins parallel. At any temperature other than absolute zero the energy state is an excited one. It might be expected that the first excited state would consist of one reversed spin and the rest parallel, but satisfactory eigenfunctions for the energy are not obtained unless a linear combination is made of wave functions each of which contains a spin reversal at a different lattice site. This is equivalent to a non-localised spin reversal. Since the spins are subject to the internal magnetic field, they all precess about the direction of this field, and a non-localised spin reversal may be described as a phase difference between successive precessing spins. Such a phase difference is equivalent to a simple harmonic wave passing through the lattice. The possible values of the phase difference depend on the boundary conditions and thus on the size of the particular crystal. As the phase difference is increased, more energy is required to do work against the forces which tend to align all the spins parallel. At $0°K$ all the spins precess in phase, with the Larmor frequency, and at this temperature the number of spins per lattice site would be integral but this would not be so at other temperatures. It has been found experimentally that in general the number of spins per lattice site is not integral for ferromagnetic materials.

The wave passing through the crystal is often known as the *spin defect* or *spin deviation*. Bloch showed that on the basis of his theory, if the number of spin defects is small compared with the total number of spins, the deviation of the spontaneous magnetic moment set up in a domain at temperature T from the spontaneous magnetic moment at $T=0$ is proportional to $T^{3/2}$. Experiment shows that this relationship holds reasonably well at temperatures considerably lower than the Curie point, although the constant of proportionality does not work out as the theory would predict. Interaction between the spins would introduce anharmonicity, but this effect is thought to be small and is neglected in the theory.

Heisenberg developed a spin wave theory of ferromagnetism based solely on the exchange interaction between the spins of electrons which are situated on adjacent atoms. He neglected all exchange integrals except those between nearest neighbours. For the sake of simplicity he assumed that the electrons were attached to particular atoms and were not free to move through the crystal. He supported Bloch's conclusion that the spin deviation is not localised but is propagated as a wave through the crystal.

He derived an expression for the relation between susceptibility and the applied field and obtained reasonably good agreement with experimental results.

Although an atom with $S = \frac{1}{2}$ cannot receive two spin deviations at the same time, the proximity of two spin deviations lowers the energy, and there appears to be an attraction between them. For $S = \frac{1}{2}$, attraction between spin deviations can lead to the formation of "spin complexes". By treating the spin deviation as a wave packet Bethe developed equations for the Curie temperature appropriate to all spin values and to several lattices, but the equations are very cumbersome, and it is customary in simple spin wave theory to neglect the interaction between the spin deviations.

Although theory allows for an infinite number of spin deviation frequencies, the selection rules for magnetic dipole radiation allow only one frequency in ferromagnetic resonance absorption, that which is symmetric in all the spins of the different atoms. The only spin deviation wave which satisfies this condition is the one with zero wave number; therefore the frequency of the wave absorbed in ferromagnetic resonance is the Larmor frequency with no spin deviation. This is of course an ideal condition; it is modified by spin-spin relaxation (p. 260) which is due to dipole interaction (*not* to spin deviation). Anharmonic perturbations are set up which may induce transitions between states of the harmonic oscillators. This effect is much influenced by the boundary conditions, that is the finite size of the crystal. It is thought to be responsible for the irregular distribution of metallic ions in spinels, for example the distribution of Ni^{2+} and Fe^{3+} in the octahedral sites in $Ni^{2+}Fe_2^{3+}O_4$. Resonance experiments on ferromagnetic substances are not easy to carry out because the internal field of the crystal is so large compared with the applied field; therefore these experiments have been rather disappointing in the light which they are able to shed on the mechanism of ferromagnetism. It has not been found possible to account satisfactorily for the observed large deviations of the g values from 2, and the abnormal widths of the resonance lines.

The conditions for ferromagnetism may be summarised thus:

(1) The atoms concerned must have a number of unpaired electrons. By Hund's rule these occupy separate orbitals and have parallel spins. The electron density at the nucleus must be low. The atoms must therefore have incomplete shells of d or f electrons; these are found in the transition elements.

(2) The energy bands must be narrow since the atoms must not be so close to each other that there is appreciable electron cloud overlap as this would lead to covalent bonding with opposite spins.

(3) The exchange integral must be positive. Since the exchange forces are probably electrostatic in origin, this condition implies that the interaction between the nuclei together with that between the electrons is greater than the interaction between the electrons and the nuclei. Heisenberg has shown that this is so for atoms with high atomic number. Where there is a large electron cloud overlap as in the covalent bond, the interactions between the electrons and nuclei predominate and the exchange integral is negative.

(4) The atoms must not be too far apart or the exchange integral will be too small, and the exchange energy will not be great enough to stabilise the system.

The conditions are summarised by the diagram in Fig. 24.1. Here the exchange integral is plotted against R, the ratio of the interatomic distance in the crystal to the radius of the d orbital. It can be seen that for a certain value of R the exchange integral has a maximum positive value; the value for iron lies in this region. It might be expected that manganese would be more ferromagnetic than iron since it has five unpaired electrons in d orbitals while iron has four, but manganese is not ferromagnetic; the manganese atoms are too close together and therefore there is too much electron overlap. Though many compounds of manganese are antiferromagnetic (below), some are ferromagnetic; in these the manganese atoms are pushed further apart. Similarly the Heusler alloys show ferromagnetism although they are composed of non-ferromagnetic atoms. If the value of R is diminished by compression, substances which belong to the right-hand side of the curve show increased magnetism, while those which belong to the left-hand side show diminished magnetism.

When there are few occupied d orbitals, there is a large d orbital overlap; as the d shell is gradually filled up the effective nuclear charge increases, and the radius of the d orbital contracts, but although cobalt and nickel have greater effective nuclear charges than has iron, they lie too far to the right on the curve of Fig. 24.1 to show the maximum exchange integral.

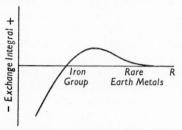

Fig. 24.1. Exchange integral plotted against the ratio of the interatomic distance in the crystal to the radius of the d orbital.

The simple spin wave theory of ferromagnetism does not take into account delocalisation of electrons in the energy band model of metals but it gives a reasonably good agreement with experiment, as for example Bloch's $T^{3/2}$ relation. Moreover, there is no firm theoretical or experimental ground for assuming that the exchange integral must be positive, but such a relation as shown in Fig. 24.1 seems to fit the facts. Another theory has been put forward by Zener in which he postulates that the exchange integral is always negative and that the required lowering of the energy is provided by a spin coupling between the electrons of the incomplete d shell and the conduction electrons in the metal. His theory has no firmer foundation than that of Heisenberg, but it has led to the identification of so-called *antiferromagnetic* substances, the crystals of which are composed of two interpenetrating sub-lattices with opposed spins. Such a system would have a negative exchange integral. It has been possible to identify this arrangement in crystals such as MnO by means of neutron diffraction, but Zener's hypothesis concerning ferromagnetism is very difficult to establish experimentally and it has not been confirmed. Theoretical treatment of antiferromagnetism shows that there must be antiferromagnetic spin deviation waves but that they require more energy to excite them than the spin deviation waves of ferromagnetism. The reason for this concerns the effect of a deviation on the precession of opposite spins since one will be advanced and the other retarded. An antiferromagnetic substance has a Curie temperature above which it is paramagnetic and below which resonance absorption dies out abruptly.

Ferrimagnetic substances have unequal moments in the two sub-lattices, therefore the resultant magnetic moment is not zero even when the two sub-lattices are aligned antiparallel.

THE VALENCE ORBITALS OF THE TRANSITION ELEMENTS

The valency system of an element in the first transition series consists of the orbitals:

penultimate shell	outermost shell
3d	4s 4p 4d 4f

In the ground state the 4s orbital is filled by one electron pair, and the 3d orbital is occupied by from 1 to 10 electrons according to the atomic number of the element;

the $4p$, $4d$, and $4f$ orbitals are unoccupied. The transition element of lowest atomic number, scandium, has the electron configuration in the ground state

$1s$	$2s$	$2p$	$3s$	$3p$	$3d$	$4s$
2	2	6	2	6	1	2

The electron configuration of titanium, the next following element in the first transition series (Sc to Zn), is obtained by adding one electron to the $3d$ shell of the scandium atom. The configurations of the succeeding elements are obtained by the further addition of electrons to the $3d$ shell in accordance with the aufbau principle (p. 64), so that when the zinc atom is reached the $3d$ shell contains 10 electrons. (The electron configuration of each transition metal is stated at the head of the Table of compounds of each sub-Group.) The atom may enter into chemical combination without using any of the d orbitals in the penultimate shell, or by using any number of them.

The elements in the transition series form simple cations. The maximum cationic valencies are found to be

Sc	Ti	V	Cr	Mn	Fe	Co	Ni	Cu
3	4	3	3	3	3	3	2	2

These valencies are attained by the expulsion from the atom of the s electrons in the outermost shell, and in certain cases by the expulsion also of one or two electrons from the penultimate d orbitals. The tendency to release electrons is measured by the standard electrode potentials of the metals. The magnitudes of the standard electrode potentials are given in Table 24.1.

Table 24.1. *Standard Electrode Potentials (volts) of the Transition Metals of Period 4*

Sc	Ti	V	Cr/Cr^{2+}	Mn/Mn^{2+}	Fe/Fe^{2+}	Co/Co^{2+}	Ni/Ni^{2+}	Cu/Cu^{2+}	Zn/Zn^{2+}
			0·56	1·10	0·44	0·28	0·28	−0·34	0·76

Sc	Ti^{2+}/Ti^{3+}	V^{2+}/V^{3+}	Cr^{2+}/Cr^{3+}	Mn^{2+}/Mn^{3+}	Fe^{2+}/Fe^{3+}	Co^{2+}/Co^{3+}
	−0·37	+0·2	+0·4	−1·5	−0·74	−1·8

The greater the positive value of the normal electrode potential the greater the tendency of the atom to ionise. Hence the tendency to form a divalent ion is greatest for manganese, and the tendency to form a trivalent ion is greatest for chromium.

In the formation of cations two, three, or in the case of titanium, four, electrons only may be expelled by an atom, but larger numbers of electrons are used by an atom in the formation of covalencies. The covalency of a transition metal is not easy to define, especially when the metal is present as the acceptor atom at the centre of a complex cation or anion. It is more satisfactory to describe the mode of combination of the atom by its oxidation state.

The term oxidation state is defined on p. 487 as the number of its own valence electrons which a given atom is using to establish ionic or covalent bonds in a particular compound. Among elements of the Normal sub-Groups the oxidation state is either the total number of valence electrons or, when the inert pair effect is observed, this number less two. Only s and p orbitals are concerned, as the penultimate d orbitals in the atom of a Normal element are not used for valency purposes. In an atom of a transition metal, any electrons occupying d orbitals in the penultimate shell are also valence electrons, and the term oxidation state refers to these electrons as well as to the s and p electrons in the outermost shell. The maximum oxidation states attained by the metals Sc to Cu are:

Sc	Ti	V	Cr	Mn	Fe	Co	Ni	Cu
3	4	5	6	7	6	4	2	2

The structures of many compounds of the transition metals, especially those in which the metal is present in a complex ion, may be explained in terms of the valence bond theory by assuming that certain of the orbitals in the valence shell are hybridised. The most frequent forms of hybridisation are sp^3 (tetrahedral), d^2sp^3 (octahedral), and dsp^2 (tetragonal planar). In addition, one, two, or three of the penultimate d orbitals may be used in forming πd bonds. In certain of the orbital structures some of the penultimate d orbitals are occupied by unpaired electrons; in $[Cr(H_2O)_6]Cl_3$, for example, three d orbitals are occupied by unpaired electrons, and in $K_3[Fe(CN)_6]$ one d orbital is so occupied.

The unpaired electrons possess a resultant spin, as a result of which the compound is paramagnetic. If there are n unpaired electrons with parallel spins, the resultant spin quantum number S is $n/2$, and if μ is the paramagnetic moment,

$$\mu = \frac{h}{2\pi}\sqrt{\left[\frac{n}{2}\left(\frac{n}{2}+1\right)\right]\frac{\epsilon g}{2m_0 c}} \quad \text{(pp. 90 and 101).}$$

Since the numerical value of g is 2 for spin,

$$\mu = \sqrt{(n(n+2))} \quad \text{Bohr magnetons.}$$

The correlation between μ and n is set out in Table 24.2.

Table 24.2. *Correlation between the Number of Unpaired Electrons in a Molecule and the Calculated Spin Moment*

Number of unpaired electrons, n	Calculated spin moment, μ
0	0·00
1	1·73
2	2·83
3	3·87
4	4·90
5	5·92

Pauling has compiled a table of the magnetic moments of cations formed by the first two members of Period 4 and the transition metals in that Period, showing that the agreement between observed and calculated spin moments is excellent as far as iron, but for the last four members of the transition series the observed moment is too big. The experiments were made on aqueous solutions of the cations; the same relation holds for salts of these ions in the solid state.

Much work has been done on the magnetic properties of the complexes of the transition metals. The results of the study of compounds of Sc, Ti, and Cr indicate that the hybridisation diagrams (for example those on p. 949) can be drawn in a straightforward manner showing that the $3d$, $4s$, and $4p$ orbitals are used in bond formation, and that the inactive d orbitals in the cation contain exactly the number of unpaired electrons to give the observed magnetic moment. For the elements Cr, Mn, Fe, and Co, however, the straightforward application of the normal procedure does

Table 24.3. *Magnetic Moments of Ions of Metals of Period 4 in Aqueous Solution*

Ion	Number of 3d electrons	Number of unpaired electrons	Calculated spin moment, Bohr magnetons	Observed moment Bohr magnetons
K^+, Ca^{2+}, Sc^{3+}, Ti^{4+}	0	0	0·00	0·00
V^{4+}	1	1	1·73	1·7
V^{3+}	2	2	2·83	2·4
V^{2+}, Cr^{3+}	3	3	3·88	3·8
Cr^{2+}, Mn^{3+}	4	4	4·90	4·8
Mn^{2+}, Fe^{3+}	5	5	5·92	5·9
Fe^{2+}	6	4	4·90	5·3
Co^{2+}	7	3	3·88	5·1
Ni^{2+}	8	2	2·83	3·2
Cu^{2+}	9	1	1·73	2·0
Cu^+, Zn^{2+}	10	0	0·00	0·00

not always yield the correct results. For example, the observed magnetic moment of $(NH_4)_3[Fe^{III}F_6]$ is 5·9, indicating the presence of 5 unpaired electrons. The orbital diagram of the anion constructed according to the usual procedure, shown in Fig. 24.2, indicates a magnetic moment of 1·73. Similarly from the orbital diagram for the

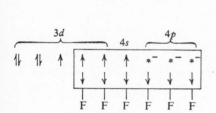

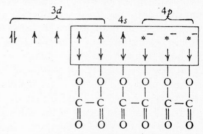

Fig. 24.2. Orbital diagram for the anion $[Fe^{III}F_6]^{3-}$.

Fig. 24.3. Orbital diagram for the anion $[Mn(C_2O_4)_3]^{3-}$.

anion in $K_3[Mn(C_2O_4)_3],3H_2O$ (assuming that the water is present as water of crystallisation), Fig. 24.3, μ would be predicted as 2·83, but the observed value is 4·90. Some of the complexes which show anomalous magnetic moments are given in Table 24.4.

Table 24.4. *Anomalous Magnetic Moments*

Complex	μ observed	μ calculated, assuming all electrons in the metal valency orbitals are contained in the 9 orbitals of the diagram
$K_3[Mn(C_2O_4)_3],3H_2O$	4·9	2·83
$(NH_4)_3[FeF_6]$	5·9	1·73
$(NH_4)_2[FeF_5H_2O]$	5·9	1·73
$[Fe^{II}(H_2O)_6][NH_4SO_4]_2$	5·3	0·00
$K_3[Co^{III}F_6]$	5·3	0·00
$[Co^{II}(H_2O)_6][NH_4SO_4]_2$	5·1	—
$[Mn^{II}Cl_2,2(CH_2)_6N_4,2H_2O]$	5·9	1·73

Various attempts have been made to solve the problem:

(i) Huggins suggested that the hybridisation system includes the $4d$ orbitals. Such a system, however, would be unstable and this suggestion has not been regarded as satisfactory.

(ii) Pauling suggested that the bonding in the complexes is ionic; the electron configuration of the iron atom in $(NH_4)_3[FeF_6]$ would then be

$$\left\{ \begin{matrix} d & d & d & d & d & s & p & p & p \\ \uparrow & \uparrow & \uparrow & \uparrow & \uparrow & \cdot & \cdot & \cdot & \cdot \end{matrix} \right\}^{3+} \quad [F^-]_6$$

There is no hybridisation, and the $3d$ orbitals are occupied by 5 unpaired electrons.

(iii) Griffith and Orgel † have suggested that the structures of these complexes must be explained in terms of the ligand-field theory. This theory, which was devised to explain certain properties of the spectra of transition-metal complexes, is described in the following paragraphs.

THE LIGAND-FIELD THEORY

Certain characteristic features observed in the spectra of complexes of the transition metals have been ascribed to the separation of the d orbitals of the central atom into two sets, due to the splitting of the formerly degenerate energy into two distinct values. In the simpler cases it is possible to identify an observed band with a transition between the two energy levels contained in the d shell, but this simple picture is in general modified by other factors. The study of spectra, however, has confirmed the supposition that the splitting of the d orbital energy is due to the electric field exerted by lone pairs of electrons in the ligands. The ligand-field theory has been developed in order to explain quantitatively the modification of the properties of the d orbitals; the theory has been found to be very valuable in the interpretation of many properties of transition metal complexes not previously understood.

The ligand-field theory was expressed by its authors in terms of the molecular orbital theory. It is therefore first discussed in terms of this theory, and afterwards it is translated into terms of the valence bond theory.

Consider a complex consisting of ligands attached to a central atom. The ligand is either an ion or a molecule with at least one orbital occupied by a lone electron pair. The electrostatic field set up by the lone electron pair on a ligand is the *ligand field*. The ligand fields act predominantly along the bonding directions in the complex which are known from stereochemistry, and hence the d atomic orbitals of the central atom fall into two classes: (i) those (denoted by the symbol e_g) whose wave functions lie mainly along the axes x, y, and z; these are the $d_{x^2-y^2}$ and d_{z^2} orbitals, and (ii) those (denoted by the symbol t_{2g}) whose wave functions lie mainly along the diagonals between the axes; these are the d_{xy}, d_{yz}, and d_{xz} orbitals. In the absence of the ligand field all five atomic d orbitals are degenerate; the effect of the ligand field is to give different energy values to each of the two classes. It may be shown that for tetrahedral complexes the t_{2g} orbitals‡ have the higher energy and the e_g orbitals the lower; for octahedral complexes the reverse is the case.

It can be shown that the formation of molecular orbitals by itself distinguishes between the functions of the t_{2g} and the e_g orbitals. In an octahedral complex the six *ligand orbitals* (one from each ligand) which are to be used with orbitals of the central atom for forming six molecular orbitals, may be combined together (in terms of the molecular orbital theory) to form six new orbitals of predetermined symmetry. Of these, one is to have the properties of an s atomic orbital, three are to have the

† J. S. Griffith and L. E. Orgel, *Quart. Rev.* **XI**, 1957, 381. L. E. Orgel, *Introduction to Transition Metal Chemistry* (Methuen, 1960).

‡ Other nomenclatures are used. e_g orbitals may be referred to as $d\epsilon$ or $d\gamma$, t_{2g} orbitals as γ_5 or γ_3.

properties of a *p* atomic orbital, and two are to have the properties of a *d* atomic orbital. A diagram could be constructed (Fig. 24.4) showing how bonding and antibonding molecular orbitals might be formed when the symmetry orbitals of the ligands overlap with the atomic orbitals of the central atom.† The energy levels of the diagram are conjectural.

It is seen from the diagram that the two e_g $3d$ orbitals of the central atom have combined with ligand orbitals to form two e_g type molecular orbitals with energies less than the original value, and two e_g type molecular orbitals of energies greater than the original value. The three t_{2g} orbitals have symmetry unsuitable for combination

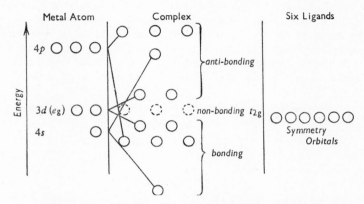

Fig. 24.4. Orbital arrangement for an octahedral complex in the absence of the ligand field.

and are unaffected; their energies are unchanged. It is found from spectroscopic observations, however, that the energy values of all four e_g type molecular orbitals are higher than the energy values of the original e_g atomic d orbitals.

The argument so far has considered only the effect of molecular orbital formation, and it has taken no account of the effect of the ligand field, which increases the energy of the $3d$ e_g orbitals. The energy levels in the diagram thus become modified, and the new values might be illustrated diagrammatically in Fig. 24.5.

Arrangement of electrons in the molecular orbitals. High and low spin complexes.‡ The positions taken up by the electrons in a complex are such as to make the energy of the whole a minimum. This may be brought about in two ways, both of which tend to reduce the energy but which, under certain circumstances, are not compatible with each other. The two ways of arranging the electrons are:

(a) by Hund's rule (p. 66), as many electrons as possible should have parallel spins,

---

† There are two ways of regarding the formation of a complex such as $K_3[Fe(CN)_6]$ from its constituent atoms:

(i) The 3 electrons from the potassium atoms are transferred to the iron *atom* with the result that the iron orbitals that are to be used for bonding (two $3d$, one $4s$, and three $4p$) are each occupied by one electron: covalent bonds are then formed by the overlapping of these orbitals with those of six CN radicals.

(ii) The 3 electrons from the potassium atoms and the three ionisable electrons from the iron atom are transferred to the six CN radicals to give six CN^- ions. Molecular orbitals are formed between the iron atom and the six CN^- ions, using the same orbitals as before. In this case, however, the bonds are co-ionic because each electron pair occupying a molecular orbital is furnished by a CN^- ion.

‡ The term *complex* in this context is used in the ordinary chemical sense in which it refers to an association of acceptor and donor molecules or ions; its use in this sense has no connection with its use in the theory of ferromagnetism.

(b) by the "aufbau principle" (p. 129), the electrons should fill up the molecular orbitals in order of increasing energy.

As to whether (a) or (b) is the dominating principle in minimising the energy depends on the strength of the ligand field. The strength of the ligand field is indicated by the value of Δ, the separation in energy between the t_{2g} and the e_g atomic orbitals of the central atom of the complex.

The magnitude of Δ depends on:

(i) The magnitude of the charge on the central atom.

(ii) The nature of the ligand. The ligands can be arranged empirically in a sequence so that their effect on Δ for a given metal is in the order: $I < Br < Cl < F < H_2O < C_2O_4 < pyridine < NH_3 < ethylene\ diamine < NO_2^- < CN^-$.

(iii) The degree of overlap of the orbitals of the central atom with those of the ligands. The energy of an e_g molecular orbital is higher the greater the overlap of the $3d$ atomic orbitals of the central atom and the ligand orbitals. This overlap is greater the smaller the value of the effective nuclear charge on the ligand atom.

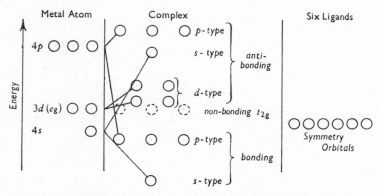

Fig. 24.5. Orbital arrangement for an octahedral complex in the presence of the ligand field.

In calculation of the energy of the molecular orbitals of different complexes different effective nuclear charges on the central atoms of the *ligands* should be allowed for. A change of ligand causes a change in the value of the screening constant (p. 136) of the central atom of the complex since there is a redistribution of charge surrounding it, and so its effective nuclear charge is modified. A decrease of effective nuclear charge on the central atom leads to a spreading of the wave function in the complex, and thus to a greater overlap and to a greater energy splitting between the two sets of d orbitals. A decrease of effective nuclear charge on the central atom of the complex therefore increases the strength of the ligand field.

If there are only one, two, or three electrons in d-type molecular orbitals of the complex, it is possible to fulfil conditions (a) and (b) simultaneously. Where there are more than three but less than eight electrons in the d-type molecular orbitals, the following rules are a reliable guide, though they may be modified by other factors:

(i) When Δ is large, the electrons fill up the orbitals of lowest energy; such an arrangement is known as a *low spin complex*.

(ii) When Δ is small, the electrons arrange themselves with parallel spins, and when there are no more vacant orbitals they then fill up from the lowest energy orbital; such an arrangement is known as a *high spin complex*.

If there are eight or nine electrons the first six are accommodated in the t_{2g} orbitals for both strong and weak fields; subsequent electrons go into the e_g orbitals, with parallel spins for the 7th and 8th.

These conclusions are summarised in Table 24.5.

Table 24.5. *The Effect of Ligand Field Strength on d Electron Arrangements in Octahedral Complexes*

Number of electrons in *d* orbitals	Arrangement in weak ligand field High spin complexes†					Arrangement in strong ligand field Low spin complexes‡				
	t_{2g}			e_g		t_{2g}			e_g	
1	↑			—		↑			—	
2	↑	↑		—		↑	↑		—	
3	↑	↑	↑	—		↑	↑	↑	—	
4	↑	↑	↑	↑		↑↓	↑	↑	—	
5	↑	↑	↑	↑	↑	↑↓	↑↓	↑	—	
6	↑↓	↑	↑	↑	↑	↑↓	↑↓	↑↓	—	
7	↑↓	↑↓	↑	↑	↑	↑↓	↑↓	↑↓	↑	
8	↑↓	↑↓	↑↓	↑	↑	↑↓	↑↓	↑↓	↑	↑
9	↑↓	↑↓	↑↓	↑↓	↑	↑↓	↑↓	↑↓	↑↓	↑

High spin complexes and low spin complexes may be distinguished by measurements which depend on the resultant magnetic moment of the ion concerned. This moment may include a contribution from orbital motion. When the molecular *d*-type orbitals are less than half full, the magnetic moment is predominantly one of spin only. Also, if the ligand field is very strong, it may quench the orbital magnetic moment completely, and in these cases measurement of the magnetic susceptibility of an ion gives the number of unpaired electrons correctly. There is, however, a very considerable orbital magnetic moment in ions such as Fe^{2+}, Ni^{2+}, Cu^{2+}, and in general it must be allowed for; it is particularly prominent in octahedral complexes. In many tetrahedral complexes the magnetic moment is almost entirely a spin moment, but when the effective nuclear charge of the central atom in the complex is large, there is a large spin-orbit coupling, and the resultant magnetic moment is much greater than that which would arise from spin alone.

The spin-orbit coupling is usually described by a factor λ, which has a positive value for an ion with a *d* shell which is less than half full, and a negative value when it is more than half full. In the one case the spin and orbital moments reinforce each other, in the other case they are opposed.

Whether the electron spins in the central atom of a complex ion are parallel or not may be predicted by means of *Kramers' theorem*. The theorem states that when an atom containing an odd number of electrons is subjected to an electric field the degeneracy (multiplicity) is always even. A further guide is found in the *Jahn Teller effect*, which may be described by the statement that any system having a degenerate ground state distorts itself so as to remove the degeneracy as far as possible. This is a more generalised statement of Hund's rule. The effect described by the Kramers' theorem, however, normally over-rides the Jahn Teller effect in cases where the field is strong.

† Also known as spin-free complexes.
‡ Also known as spin-paired complexes. The orbital diagrams used in this book (p. 163) do not indicate the energy levels of d-type orbitals.

If the number of electrons in the central atom of a complex ion is even, the ligand field causes all the electrons with parallel spins to pair up, so that all the electrons are spin paired, and the total orbit+spin degeneracy is a singlet in the ground state. Hence the ion possesses no spin magnetic moment, and shows no paramagnetic resonance. If the number of electrons in the ion is odd, one must remain unpaired, and must have a magnetic moment. In a magnetic field the energy of the unpaired electron is different from that of an electron pair. Transitions may take place between the energy levels of the paired and unpaired electron, and thus the ion shows paramagnetic resonance.

The resultant spin may be determined from observation of the multiplicity. If the multiplicity is 2 as in the case of one odd electron with all the others paired, since

$$\text{multiplicity} = 2S+1,$$
$$S = \tfrac{1}{2}.$$

If the multiplicity is 4, then $S=\tfrac{3}{2}$.

Where there is spin-orbit coupling, the value of g in the simple equation of paramagnetic resonance

$$h\nu = g\beta H \quad \text{(p. 258)}$$

is somewhat modified. When $\lambda=0$, g has the value for spin only, approximately 2. Various formulae have been derived empirically to account for the observed values of g. A simple relation which works reasonably well is

$$g = 2{\cdot}0023 - \left(\frac{8\lambda}{\Delta}\right),$$

where $\lambda=$ spin-orbit coupling, and Δ is the energy separation between the t_{2g} and e_g classes of d orbitals.

Δ is measured from the shift of absorption bands, and g may be calculated from the known values of ν, H, h, and μ. It is necessary that μ should be determined independently. The value of λ may thus be calculated and the ratio $\lambda_{\text{complex}}/\lambda_{\text{uncomplexed metal}}$ is an indication of the part played in the molecular orbital by the central atom of the complex.

The ligand-field theory and the valence bond theory. The inclusion of the ligand-field concept in the valence bond theory offers no difficulty when it is remembered that the valence bond theory accepts the basic principle that the linear combination of two atomic orbitals (one from each of two atoms) produces two interatomic orbitals, one of lower energy value than that of the original atomic orbital, and one of higher energy value. Interatomic orbitals of lower energy value than that of the original atomic orbital are normally bonding orbitals, and those of higher energy value are normally anti-bonding orbitals. The valence bond theory regards anti-bonding orbitals as unoccupied in non-excited states of the molecule. The ligand field by increasing the energy of an interatomic orbital raises it to an excited state, and in terms of the valence bond theory the orbital may be regarded as occupied, even though it is anti-bonding. If antibonding orbitals are considered to be part of the interatomic orbital structure of the complex, for an octahedral complex the orbitals connected with the central atom available for occupation by electrons would be

d	d	d	d	d	s	p	p	p	A	A	A	A	A	A

where the bracketed orbitals are bonding orbitals in the hybridised system, and the orbitals A represent the corresponding antibonding orbitals. If two of the antibonding orbitals have the properties of d orbitals, and if the spectral shifts discussed in the previous paragraph are referred to electron transfers between the t_{2g} orbitals and the antibonding orbitals, all the arguments presented in terms of the molecular orbital theory may be applied.

This method of using the ligand-field theory in terms of the valence bond theory will be applied in describing the complexes of particular metals.

The ionic radii and atomic radii of the transition elements. For successive metals in a transition series the real nuclear charge increases by unity, but the screening constant increases only by the value appropriate to a d electron in a penultimate shell. This value is less than unity. Hence the effective nuclear charge increases along the series, and consequently the atomic radii, and the ionic radii for successive ions of the same ionic valency, decrease along the series. The screening power of a d electron is greater for an atom than for the corresponding ion, and hence the diminution of atomic radius with increasing atomic number is less marked than that of the ionic radius.

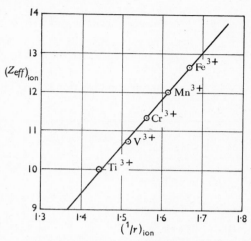

Fig. 24.6. $(Z_{eff})_{ion}$ plotted against $(1/r)_{ion}$ for the cations M^{3+} of the first transition series.

If $(Z_{eff})_{ion}$ is calculated† for the cations M^{3+} formed by the metals of the first transition series, and plotted against the reciprocal of the experimentally observed values of the ionic radii,‡ a linear relation is shown, Fig. 24.6.

SUB-GROUP III T. SCANDIUM, YTTRIUM, LANTHANUM

This sub-Group contains the metals, scandium, yttrium, and lanthanum. Certain properties of the metals are set out in Table 24.6, and examples of the types of compounds they form in Table 24.7. Lanthanum is the prototype of the lanthanons which are discussed on p. 1124. The chemistry of yttrium is similar to that of scandium, and need not be described. The group of three elements displays a fall in basicity with increasing atomic number. This is shown in the crystal structures of the fluorides: scandium fluoride has the ReO_3 structure, yttrium fluoride has a modified fluorite structure, and lanthanum fluoride has the tysonite structure.

Table 24.6. *Properties of the Metals in sub-Group III T*

	Sc	Y	La
Atomic number	21	39	57
m.p. °C	1400	1500	920
b.p. °C	2500	3000	4200
Specific gravity	3·0	4·6	6·15
Ionic radius, M^{3+}	0·81	0·93	1·06
Atomic radius (12 co-ordination)	1·66	1·82	1·87

† $(Z_{eff})_{ion}$ is the effective nuclear charge acting on an electron in the outermost orbital of the ion; this may be calculated by means of Slater's rules (p. 136).

‡ V. M. Goldschmidt, "Geochemische Verteilungsgesetze der Elemente", *Skrifter det Norske Videnskaps-Akad. Oslo, I. Matem-Naturvid Klasse*, 1926. Also *Trans. Faraday Soc.*, **25**, 1929, 253.

Table 24.7. *Examples of Compounds formed by the Elements in sub-Group III T*

$$\overbrace{}^{n-1} \quad \overbrace{}^{n}$$

Valency system of atom d d d d d s p p p

The values of n are: Sc 4, Y 5, La 6.

$$\overbrace{}^{n-1} \quad \overbrace{}^{n}$$

Normal prehybridisation electron configuration d d d d d s p p p

Oxidation state	Nature of unit	Hybridisation	Sc	Yt	La
	Interstitial compounds		ScN		LaN
	Simple ionic compounds		$Sc(NO_3)_3$, $Sc_2(SO_4)_3$		$La(ClO_4)_3$
III	Giant molecule compounds		Sc_2O_3, ScOOH, ScF_3		La_2O_3, $LaO \cdot OH$
	Neutral complexes	Octahedral	ScA_3		
	Complex anions	Tetrahedral	$K[ScF_4]$		
		Trigonal bipyramidal	$K_2[ScF_5]$		
		Octahedral	$K_3[ScF_6]$		

SCANDIUM

The valency system of the scandium atom in the ground state has the electron configuration

$$3d \quad 4s$$
$$\uparrow \quad \downarrow\uparrow$$

The three electrons are readily expelled from the atom, and in all the scandium compounds except the neutral complex ScA_3 and the complex anions $[ScF_4^-]$, $[ScF_5^{2-}]$, and $[ScF_6^{3-}]$, the scandium atom appears to be exerting ionic bonds, or at least bonds which possess much ionic character.

Scandium metal is obtained by the electrolysis of fused scandium chloride. It is dimorphic and crystallises with the close-packed hexagonal structure or the close-packed cubic structure. It is easily oxidised. When heated in nitrogen it yields the interstitial nitride ScN. The nitride is decomposed by water with the liberation of ammonia.

Scandium oxide, Sc_2O_3, a white powder, has the Mn_2O_3 structure (p. 783). It is more basic than aluminium oxide, but less basic than calcium oxide. It absorbs carbon dioxide from the air. Scandium hydroxide is thrown down as a gelatinous precipitate on the addition of an alkali to a solution of scandium chloride. The lattice of scandium hydroxide is similar to that of γ-AlO·OH.

Scandium fluoride is insoluble. The crystals have the ReO_3 structure. The other halides of scandium are soluble in water, and scandium chloride is soluble in alcohol.

Scandium sulphate and nitrate are soluble; the carbonate, oxalate, and phosphate are insoluble. Scandium nitrate and scandium carbonate easily decompose to scandium oxide on heating; scandium sulphate on heating also yields the oxide but less readily.

Scandium (like zirconium and thorium) forms a thiosulphate which is easily hydrolysed to an insoluble basic salt $Sc(OH)S_2O_3$; the thiosulphates of yttrium and lanthanum are soluble and not easily hydrolysed, and hence these metals may be separated from scandium.

The scandium atom, by accepting additional electrons in the valency system, may assume the tetrahedral, trigonal bipyramidal, or octahedral valence states. The orbital diagrams of certain complexes of the scandium atom are given below. These orbital diagrams (and all those later in the book) are drawn without subdividing the d-type orbital elections into the energy levels indicated by the ligand-field theory (p. 951).

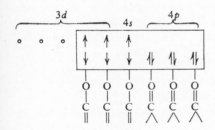

Fig. 24.7. Structural formula and orbital diagram for scandium triacetyl-acetonate.

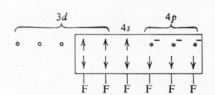

Fig. 24.8. Orbital diagram for the anion $[ScF_6]^{3-}$, octahedral.

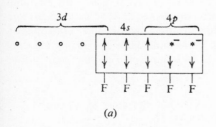

(*a*)

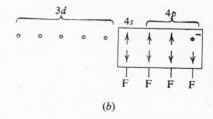

(*b*)

Fig. 24.9. (*a*) Orbital diagram for the anion $[ScF_5]^{2-}$, trigonal bipyramidal. (*b*) Orbital diagram for the anion $[ScF_4]^-$, tetrahedral.

SUB-GROUP IV T. TITANIUM, ZIRCONIUM, HAFNIUM

Table 24.8. *Properties of Metals in sub-Group IV T*

	Ti	Zr	Hf
Atomic number	22	40	72
m.p. °C	1680	1850	2000
b.p. °C	3300	4400	5100
Specific gravity	4·5	6·5	13·1
Ionic radius, M^{4+}	0·68	0·80	—
Atomic radius			
(12 co-ordination)	1·47	1·60	1·59
Crystal structure	Hexagonal, above 880° cubic	Hexagonal, above 865° cubic	

The three elements are chemically similar and it is convenient first to give an account of the chemistry of titanium, and to follow it with a short comparative account of the other elements. Certain properties of the metals are set out in Table 24.8, and examples of types of compounds they form in Table 24.9.

TITANIUM

Titanium is a ductile and malleable metal, but it loses these properties if contaminated with oxide. The crystal structure is close-packed hexagonal at room temperature; at about 880° it changes to the cubic structure.

Titanium when heated burns in fluorine to give TiF_4, in oxygen to form Ti_2O_3, and in nitrogen to form the interstitial nitride TiN (p. 654). Titanium dissolves in hydrochloric acid and in sulphuric acid, but nitric acid converts it to the insoluble "metatitanic acid" H_2TiO_3,nH_2O. Titanium combines with carbon at high temperatures to form the interstitial carbide TiC (p. 599), and, if cooled in hydrogen from a high temperature, yields a hydride of composition approaching TiH_2.

SECTION 2. COMPOUNDS CONTAINING A TITANIUM ATOM IN OXIDATION STATE II

All the compounds containing a titanium atom in oxidation state II are solids, and are very readily oxidised by air.

Titanium monoxide, TiO, consists of yellow crystals (the colour may be due to contamination with iron). It is made by heating titanic oxide and titanium to 1550°. It dissolves in hydrochloric and sulphuric acid liberating hydrogen.

Titanium dichloride, $TiCl_2$, is made by heating titanous chloride, $TiCl_3$, to redness; disproportionation occurs and the volatile titanic chloride, $TiCl_4$, distils off. Titanium dichloride is a black powder which itself disproportionates at 475° to titanium and titanic chloride. Titanium dichloride is violently oxidised by air, and it dissolves in acids with the evolution of hydrogen. A black **titanium di-iodide** is made by reducing titanic iodide with silver or mercury at a red heat. It is dimorphic and one of the forms has the CdI_2 structure.

SECTION 3. COMPOUNDS CONTAINING A TITANIUM ATOM IN OXIDATION STATE III

The titanium atom in oxidation state III is present in certain compounds in which the bonding probably has ionic character, such as titanous oxide, Ti_2O_3, titanous sulphide,

Ti_2S_3, and titanous chloride, $TiCl_3$, and in certain anionic and cationic octahedral complexes. All the titanous compounds are coloured.

TITANOUS COMPOUNDS WITH IONIC CHARACTER

Titanous oxide, Ti_2O_3, has the corundum lattice. It is made by heating titanium dioxide with carbon to 870°. It is very resistant to chemical attack, but it dissolves in sulphuric acid. The corresponding hydroxide $Ti(OH)_3$, is known.

Titanous chloride, $TiCl_3$, is a violet powder which sublimes at 430°. It is made by reducing anhydrous $TiCl_4$ with hydrogen at 650°, or with silver or mercury. At 600° it disproportionates to $TiCl_2$ and $TiCl_4$. Titanous chloride in aqueous solution reduces perchlorates to chlorides, ferric iron to ferrous, and cupric copper to cuprous. The solution is used in volumetric analysis, but it must be protected from the atmosphere by carbon dioxide or hydrogen. In the presence of platinum, titanous chloride liberates hydrogen from water.

COMPLEX IONS CONTAINING Ti^{III}

Titanous chloride forms a hydrate, $TiCl_3,6H_2O$, which undergoes the same colour changes as $CrCl_3,6H_2O$; the compound $[Ti,6H_2O]Cl_3$ present in aqueous solution is violet, and the compound $[Ti,5H_2O,Cl]Cl_2$ present in alcoholic solution is green. A titanium hexammine chloride is known, $[Ti,6NH_3]Cl_3$, for which the orbital diagram is shown in Fig. 24.10.

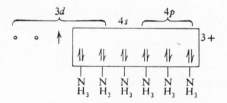

Fig. 24.10.   Orbital diagram for the cation $[Ti,6NH_3]^{3+}$.

and a potassium di-oxalato complex, $K[Tiox_2,2H_2O]$, for which the orbital diagram is shown in Fig. 24.11:

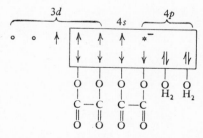

Fig. 24.11.   Orbital diagram for the anion $[Ti(C_2O_4)_2(H_2O)_2]^-$.

$(NH_4)_3[TiF_6]$ is isomorphic with the corresponding fluoro anions formed by Cr^{III} V^{III}, and Fe^{III}.

Table 24.9. *Examples of Types of Compounds*

$$\text{Valency system of atom: } \overbrace{d \quad d \quad d \quad d}^{n-1} \quad d \overbrace{\quad s \quad p \quad p \quad p}^{n}$$

The values of n are: Ti 4, Zr 5, Hf 6, Th 7.†

				Ti
	Interstitial compounds			TiC, TiN
Section	Oxidation state of metal	Nature of unit	Hybridisation	
2	II	Compounds of ionic character		TiO, TiCl$_2$, TiI$_2$, TiSO$_4$
3	III	Compounds of ionic character		Ti$_2$O$_3$, Ti(OH)$_3$ TiX$_3$ [X=F, Cl, Br, I]
		Complex anions	Octahedral	(NH$_4$)$_3$[TiF$_6$], Cs$_2$[TiCl$_5$,H$_2$O] K[Tiox$_2$,2H$_2$O]
		Complex cations	Octahedral	[Ti,6H$_2$O]Cl$_3$ [Ti,6NH$_3$]Cl$_3$ [Ti,5H$_2$O,Cl]Cl$_2$
4	IV	Covalent compounds	Tetrahedral	TiO$_2$, Ti(OC$_2$H$_5$)$_4$ TiX$_4$ [X=F, Cl, Br, I]
		Complex anions	Octahedral	K$_2$[TiF$_6$], K$_2$[TiCl$_6$] (NH$_4$)$_2$[TiBr$_6$],2H$_2$O K$_2$[Ti(SO$_4$)$_3$], (NH$_4$)$_2$[TiO(SO$_4$)$_2$H$_2$O]
		Complex cations	Octahedral	[TiA$_3$][FeCl$_4$]
		Complex anions	Covalent bond number =7	‡(NH$_4$)$_3$[TiF$_7$]
		Neutral complexes	Covalent bond number =8	
		Complex anions	Covalent bond number =8	
		Complex anions	Covalent bond number =10	
		Peroxy compounds		TiO$_3$,2H$_2$O Na$_2$[TiO$_5$,3H$_2$O] ‡(NH$_4$)$_3$[TiO$_2$F$_5$] K$_4$[TiO$_8$,H$_2$O],5H$_2$O K$_2$[TiO$_2$(SO$_4$)$_2$,H$_2$O],2H$_2$O

† Thorium, a member of the actinons (p. 1130), is included for comparison.

formed by the Elements in Sub-Group IV T

Normal prehybridisation electron configuration:

	$n-1$				n		
d	d	d	d	s	p	p	p
		↑	↑	↑	↑		

Zr	Hf	Th†
ZrC, ZrN	HfC, HfN	ThC$_2$, Th$_3$N$_4$
ZrCl$_2$, ZrBr$_2$, ZrI$_2$	HfBr$_2$	
Zr(OH)$_3$ ZrCl$_2$, ZrBr$_3$	HfBr$_3$	
ZrO$_2$, (ZrO)$_4$O(OCOC$_6$H$_5$)$_6$ ZrF$_4$	HfO$_2$ HfF$_4$	ThO$_2$ Th(OC$_2$H$_5$)$_4$ ThF$_4$
K$_2$[ZrF$_6$] [pyrH]$_2$[ZrBr$_6$]	(NH$_4$)$_2$[HfF$_6$]	K$_2$[ThF$_6$], K$_2$[Th(NO$_3$)$_6$] K$_2$[ThCl$_6$], (pyrH)$_2$[ThBr$_6$] Na$_2$[Th(SO$_4$)$_3$] (NH$_4$)$_2$(Th(CO$_3$)$_3$),6H$_2$O
(NH$_4$)$_3$[ZrF$_7$]	(NH$_4$)$_3$[HfF$_7$]	
ZrA$_4$	HfA$_4$,10H$_2$O	ThA$_4$
Zn$_2$[ZrF$_8$] K$_4$[Zrox$_4$],4H$_2$O		K$_4$[Th(SO$_4$)$_4$] K$_4$[Thox$_4$],4H$_2$O
		Na$_6$[Th(CO$_3$)$_5$],12H$_2$O
Na$_4$[Zr$_2$O$_{11}$],9H$_2$O K$_4$[ZrO$_8$,H$_2$O],5H$_2$O	HfO$_3$,2H$_2$O	Th$_2$O$_7$,4H$_2$O

‡ These compounds are isomorphous.

31+A.T.I.C.

SECTION 4. COMPOUNDS CONTAINING A TITANIUM ATOM IN OXIDATION STATE IV

Among the simple compounds in this Section are TiO_2, and the titanic halides $Tihal_4$. Ti^{IV} forms no simple oxalate, nitrate, or sulphate, but it is present in several anionic complexes such as $K_2[TiF_6]$, and cationic complexes such as $[TiA_3][FeCl_4]$. There are also certain peroxy compounds of Ti^{IV}.

COVALENT COMPOUNDS OF Ti^{IV}

Titanic oxide, TiO_2. Addition of alkali to a titanic salt gives a gelatinous precipitate, $TiO_2,2H_2O$. This on heating gives titanic oxide. It is colourless and is isotrimorphic with silica. The three forms are:

$$\text{anatase} \underset{860°}{\rightleftharpoons} \text{brookite} \underset{1040°}{\rightleftharpoons} \text{rutile}$$

The hydrated oxide is easily soluble in acids when first precipitated, but on standing it becomes less soluble. After ignition titanic oxide ceases to be soluble in hydrochloric acid or in dilute sulphuric acid, but it dissolves in hot concentrated sulphuric acid and in dilute hydrofluoric acid.

Among the compounds of titanium in which the atom is tetrahedrally hybridised are titanium tetraethoxide, and the tetrahalides.

The preparations and certain properties of the tetrahalides of titanium and zirconium are summarised in Table 24.10.

Table 24.10. *The Tetrahalides of Titanium and Zirconium*

	TiF_4	$TiCl_4$	$TiBr_4$	TiI_4
Appearance	White deliquescent solid	Colourless liquid	Orange yellow solid	Solid
m.p. °C		-23	39	150
b.p. °C	284	136	230	360
Complexes	$TiF_4,2H_2O$, $TiF_4,4NH_3$	$TiCl_4,C_2H_5OH$, $TiCl_4,2C_2H_5OH$, and complexes with other organic compounds containing oxygen		
Preparation	(i) From the elements, (ii) By excess of HF on $TiCl_4$	(i) From the elements, (ii) Pass Cl_2 over heated TiO_2+C	From the elements	From the elements

	ZrF_4	$ZrCl_4$	$ZrBr_4$	ZrI_4
Appearance	Colourless crystals	White crystals	White crystals	White crystals
Sub.p. (1 atm), °C		331	357	431
m.p. °C		437/25 atm	450/15 atm	499/63 atm
Preparation	(i) By HF on $ZrCl_4$ (ii) Ignite $(NH_4)_2ZrF_6$			HI on ZrC at 340°

COMPLEX IONS CONTAINING Ti^{IV}

Salts of complex anions containing Ti^{IV} include $K_2[Tihal_6]$ (the stability of the anion falls off in the order $F > Cl > Br > I$), $K_2[Ti(SO_4)_3]$ and $(NH_4)_2[(OTi)(SO_4)_2,H_2O]$; an example of a salt of a cationic complex is $[TiA_3]Cl$, where A represents the acetylacetonate radical. All the complexes mentioned are octahedral. The probable orbital diagram for the titanyl sulphate complex is shown in Fig. 24.12.

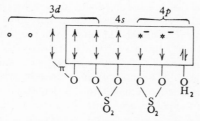

Fig. 24.12. Orbital diagram for the anion $(TiO(SO_4)_2(H_2O))^{2-}$.

Two of the d orbitals in the titanium atom are unused, and one of the bonds exerted by the oxygen atom is a πd bond.

THE PEROXY COMPOUNDS OF TITANIUM

A solution of titanic chloride is coloured orange by the addition of hydrogen peroxide. The hydrated peroxide which can be precipitated from the orange solution has the composition $TiO_3,2H_2O$. Peroxytitanates, for example $(NH_4)_3[TiO_2F_5]$ and $Na_2[TiO_5],3H_2O$, can be prepared by treating titanium salts with hydrogen peroxide. The orange coloured compound $K_2TiO_2(SO_4)_2$ produced by the action of hydrogen peroxide on an alkaline solution of titanyl sulphate liberates iodine in the buffered Riesenfeld test. When hydrogen peroxide is added to a cooled strongly alkaline solution of potassium titanate, a colourless salt is produced. It liberates oxygen in the buffered Riesenfeld test, and hydrogen peroxide can be extracted from its aqueous solution by ether. It is therefore probably $(KO)_4Ti,4H_2O_2,2H_2O$, but it may be $K_4TiO_8,6H_2O$.

Conjectural orbital diagrams for the peroxysalts are shown in Figs. 24.13 and 24.14.

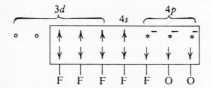

Fig. 24.13. Orbital diagram for the anion $[TiO_2F_5]^{3-}$.

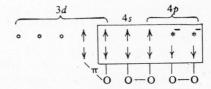

Fig. 24.14. Orbital diagram for the anion $[TiO_5]^{2-}$.

ZIRCONIUM AND HAFNIUM

Zirconium metal shows little chemical activity, but it combines with carbon, nitrogen, oxygen, and the halogens when strongly heated, and it is attacked by hydrofluoric acid and by aqua regia. Little is known about metallic hafnium.

The properties of the compounds of the metals in the sub-Group IV T vary with the atomic number of the element. On passing from titanium to hafnium the electronegativity of the metal diminishes, the ionic character of the compounds increases, and the acidity of the oxides decreases. The solubility of the hydroxides in potassium hydroxide solution diminishes in the order titanium, zirconium, hafnium.

The types of compound formed by titanium, zirconium, and hafnium are closely similar. All three metals form interstitial hydrides, carbides, and nitrides of the types MH_2, MC, and MN; all form oxides of formula MO_2 resembling silica; hydroxides usually written $M(OH)_4$ (although the somewhat slender evidence favours $MO_2,2H_2O$) and salts Na_2MO_3; all form halides $Mhal_4$, dark-coloured easily disproportioned halides $Mhal_2$, and dark-coloured halides $Mhal_3$. Titanium forms the acetylacetonate compound TiA_3Cl, but zirconium and hafnium form the compounds ZrA_4 and HfA_4. Zirconium forms the basic benzoate $(ZrO)_4O(OCOC_6H_5)_6$. An ammoniacal solution of hafnium sulphate when treated with hydrogen peroxide yields a gelatinous precipitate of peroxymonohafnic acid. The similarity of zirconium and hafnium is much closer than that normally found between neighbouring elements in the same Periodic Group because of the effect of the lanthanide contraction (p. 1125).

SUB-GROUP V T. VANADIUM, NIOBIUM, AND TANTALUM

Certain properties of the elements in the sub-Group V T are set out in Table 24.11.

Table 24.11.   *Properties of Metals in sub-Group V T*

	V	Nb	Ta
Atomic number	23	41	73
m.p. °C	1920	2420	3000
b.p. °C	3400	5100	6000
Specific gravity	6·1	8·6	16·6
Ionic radius, M^{5+}	0·59	0·70	—
Atomic radius	1·35	1·47	1·47

Vanadium is a white metal, stable in air. It is attacked by hydrofluoric acid, and by nitric acid, and it readily combines with carbon, nitrogen, or oxygen, if heated.

Niobium is a grey metal. It combines readily with the halogens, and less readily with oxygen. It is soluble in hydrofluoric acid but is rendered passive by nitric acid or by aqua regia. Tantalum is a hard, grey metal. It reacts with fluorine, chlorine, oxygen, nitrogen, and carbon on heating, and it absorbs hydrogen at a red heat. Like niobium it is attacked by hydrofluoric acid, but not by nitric acid or aqua regia.

Examples of the types of compounds formed by these elements are set out in Table 24.12. All the elements form compounds of three main types: (i) interstitial compounds with carbon or nitrogen, (ii) giant molecule compounds with the electronegative elements fluorine, chlorine, and oxygen, (iii) salts with the elements as the central atoms in complex anions. Table 24.12 shows clearly that vanadium forms a very wide range of compounds in which all oxidation states of vanadium are represented. The co-ordination number of the vanadium atom, however, rarely exceeds 6. The lower oxidation states of niobium and tantalum occur less commonly than those of vanadium. The absence of compounds of niobium and tantalum in the oxidation states III and IV is noticeable. Both niobium and tantalum form many complex anions with the metal in the oxidation state V, and in many of them the co-ordination number of the metal is 7; in $K_2[NbOF_7]$ it is 8.

The ligands in the complex anions of all three metals consist either of highly electro-negative fluorine atoms alone, or of one oxygen atom and some other anionic groups such as F, Cl, Br, C_2O_4, or catechol. The stability of the anions containing oxygen as a ligand is connected with the formation of πd bonds between the oxygen atom and the central atom of the anion (for example, see the hybridisation diagram of $K_2[VOF_4]$ (p. 972)). The combination of a p orbital of the oxygen atom with one of the t_{2g} orbitals of the central atom produces a molecular orbital of lower energy than that of the original t_{2g} orbital, and hence the complex is stabilised (Fig. 24.15, p. 972).

VANADIUM

SECTION 2. COMPOUNDS CONTAINING A VANADIUM ATOM IN OXIDATION STATE II

Compounds in this Section resemble the Fe^{II} compounds except that the V^{II} compounds are very much more powerful reducing agents. The Section includes vanadium mon-oxide, VO, vanadium monosulphide, VS, the compounds, Vhal$_2$, the complex anion, $[V(CN)_6]^{4-}$, and the complex cation, $[V,6H_2O]^{2+}$. Compounds of vanadium in oxida-tion state II are known as *vanadous compounds*.

GIANT MOLECULE COMPOUNDS

Vanadium monoxide, VO, is a dense, hard, dark-grey solid with the rocksalt structure.†
It is made by heating a finely divided mixture of vanadium and either vanadium trioxide or pentoxide at 1750° for one hour. Vanadium monoxide disproportionates on heating in vacuo to vanadium trioxide and vanadium. It dissolves in dilute hydrochloric acid, in hydrofluoric acid, and in nitric acid, to give violet solutions.

Vanadium monosulphide, VS, a dark brown solid with the nickel arsenide structure†
is made by passing hydrogen sulphide over vanadium monoxide at a red heat.

Vanadium dichloride, VCl$_2$, exists as pale green, non-volatile, leaflets. It is made:

(i) by passing a stream of dry nitrogen over vanadium trichloride at 800°:

$$2VCl_3 = VCl_4 + VCl_2;$$

   the volatile tetrachloride distils off,

(ii) by heating vanadium tetrachloride at 280°,

(iii) by heating vanadium (but not ferrovanadium which give VCl$_3$) with hydrogen chloride gas.

Vanadium dichloride is a very strong reducing agent, even stronger than chromous chloride, and it converts triphenyl carbinol in hydrochloric acid to triphenylmethyl. At a bright red heat it reduces carbon dioxide:

$$3VCl_2 + 2CO_2 = 2VOCl + VCl_4 + 2CO.$$

In air vanadium dichloride slowly deliquesces and becomes oxidised. It dissolves slowly in water to give a violet solution which turns green and evolves hydrogen. The aqueous solution precipitates Sn, Cu, Ag, as metals from solutions of their salts. Vanadium dichloride reacts with hydrogen fluoride to give vanadium trifluoride.

Light reddish brown crystals of **vanadium dibromide, VBr$_2$,** are obtained by reducing vanadium tribromide, and rose-coloured plates of **vanadium di-iodide** are obtained by reducing vanadium tri-iodide.

† The corresponding Fe^{II} compound has the same structure.

Table 24.12. *Examples of Types of Compounds*

Valency system of atom: $\overbrace{d \quad d \quad d \quad d \quad d}^{n-1} \quad \overbrace{s \quad p \quad p \quad p}^{n}$

The values of n are: V 4, Nb 5, Ta 6.

				V
	Interstitial compounds			VC, V_2C VN
Sec-tion	Oxida-tion state of metal	Nature of unit	Hybridisation	
2	II	Giant molecules		VO, VS VCl_2, VBr_2, VI_2
		Complex anions Complex cation	Octahedral	$K_4[V(CN)_6],3H_2O$ $[V,6H_2O]SO_4,6H_2O$
3	III	Giant molecules		V_2O_3, V_2S_3, $V(OH)_3$, $V(OCOCH_3)_3$ VF_3, VCl_3, VBr_3, VI_3 VOCl, VOBr
		Neutral complexes Complex anions Complex cations	Octahedral	$[V,3H_2O,F_3]$, VA_3 $K_3[VF_6]$, $K_2[VF_5,H_2O]$, $K[VF_4,2H_2O]$ $K_3[V(CN)_6]$ $K_3[V(CNS)_6]$, $Co[VF_5,H_2O]$, $[V,6H_2O]Cl_3$, $[V,6NH_3]Cl_3$, $[V,6H_2O]I_3$
4	IV			VO_2, VF_4, VCl_4 VOF_2, $VOCl_2$, $VOBr_2$, $VO(CN)_2$, $VO(NO_3)_2$, VOA_2
		Complex anions	Trigonal bi-pyramidal	$K_2[VOF_4]$, $(NH_4)_2[VOmal_2]$ See Table 24.14, p. 972
5	V		Tetrahedral	V_2O_5, VOX_3 $[X=F, Cl, Br]$ The vanadic acids
		Covalent compounds Complex anions	Trigonal bi-pyramidal	VF_5 $K[VOF_4]$, $pyrH[VOCl_4]$ $K_2[VO_2F_3]$
		Complex anions	Octahedral	$M[VF_6]$ $[M=K, Na, Ag, NO, \frac{1}{2}Ba]$ $K_2[VOF_5]$, $(NH_4)_2[VOF_5]$ $K_2[VO(C_2O_4)_2,H_2O],H_2O$, $K_2[VO(SO_4)_2,H_2O]$ $K_3[VO_2(C_2O_4)_2]$
			Co-ordination number $=7$	$[pyrH]_4[VOCl_6]$
			Co-ordination number $=8$	

formed by Elements in Sub-Group V T

		$n-1$					n		
Normal prehybridisation electron configuration:	V and Ta	d d d d d ↑ ↑ ↑ ↑ ↑					s p p p ↑ ↑		
	Nb	d d d d d ↑ ↑ ↑ ↑					s p p p		

Nb	Ta
NbC, NbN	TaC, TaN
NbO, NbS	TaCl$_2$, TaBr$_2$
NbCl$_3$, NbBr$_3$	TaCl$_3$, TaBr$_3$
NbO$_2$	TaO$_2$ TaS$_2$
Nb$_2$O$_5$ NbOX$_3$ [X = F, Cl, Br]	Ta$_2$O$_5$
NbX$_5$ [X = F, Cl, Br] NbCl$_2$(OC$_2$H$_5$)$_2$A K[NbOCl$_4$], K[NbOBr$_4$]	TaX$_5$ [X = F, Cl, Br, I] TaCl$_2$(OC$_2$H$_5$)$_2$A
[BrF$_2$][NbF$_6$] K$_2$[NbOX$_5$] [X = F, Cl, Br]	K[TaF$_6$], [BrF$_2$][TaF$_6$]
K$_2$[NbF$_7$] K$_3$[NbOF$_6$], K$_3$[NbO(C$_2$O$_4$)$_3$] K$_3$[NbOcat$_3$]	M$_2$[TaF$_7$] [M = Na, Rb, Cs] K$_3$[TaOF$_6$] K$_3$[TaOcat$_3$]
K$_4$[NbOF$_7$]	Ba$_3$[TaF$_8$]$_2$

COMPLEX ANIONS AND COMPLEX CATIONS

[V,6H$_2$O]SO$_4$,H$_2$O exists as violet crystals. It is made by reducing a solution of vanadium pentoxide in sulphuric acid electrolytically, or with sodium or zinc amalgam. The solution is finally evaporated out of contact with air in the cold over P$_2$O$_5$. VSO$_4$ forms dimorphic solid solutions with chromium sulphate and ferrous sulphate, and takes part in the formation of vitriols, such as VSO$_4$,(NH$_4$)$_2$SO$_4$,6H$_2$O†. It is a strong reducing agent like vanadium dichloride.

Potassium vanadocyanide, K$_4$[V(CN)$_6$],3H$_2$O, consists of brownish-yellow crystals which are very easily oxidised, and must be handled in the absence of air. It is made by adding excess of potassium cyanide solution to the solution obtained by reducing vanadic acetate with potassium amalgam; the crystals are precipitated by the addition of alcohol to the solution.

SECTION 3. COMPOUNDS CONTAINING A VANADIUM ATOM IN OXIDATION STATE III

GIANT MOLECULE COMPOUNDS

Vanadic oxide, V$_2$O$_3$, a black, almost infusible powder with the corundum lattice, is made:

> (i) by reducing vanadium pentoxide with hydrogen or carbon monoxide at a high temperature,
> (ii) by the electrolysis of a weakly alkaline phosphate melt of vanadium pentoxide diluted with sodium chloride; this method is claimed to give a pure product.

Vanadic oxide is slowly oxidised by cold air to the blue dioxide, but when heated in air it inflames and gives the pentoxide. Vanadic oxide dissolves in nitric acid or hydrochloric acid to yield salts. It is wholly basic.

Vanadic sulphide, V$_2$S$_3$, is formed by the action of hydrogen sulphide on vanadic oxide. It is the most stable of the vanadium sulphides. At 400° it combines with sulphur to yield the pentasulphide.

Vanadic hydroxide, V(OH)$_3$, is obtained as a green flocculent precipitate by adding ammonia or alkali to a solution of vanadium trichloride. It rapidly absorbs oxygen from the air. In the absence of air it dissolves in acids to form vanadic salts. It is wholly basic.

Vanadium trihalides. The preparations and certain properties of the vanadium trihalides are given in Table 24.13. Vanadium trifluoride differs from the other compounds in its insolubility in water and in organic solvents. The other vanadium trihalides are coloured, hygroscopic, very soluble solids, all of which form hydrates such as [V,6H$_2$O]Cl$_3$.

Vanadium oxymonohalides. There is no fluorine compound VOF.

VOCl consists of brown crystals which sublime only at high temperatures. It is made by hydrolysing vanadium trichloride with water, by heating VCl$_3$ in a stream of carbon dioxide to 700°, or by heating VOCl$_2$ (p. 971) in hydrogen to red heat. VOCl dissolves with difficulty in water, but readily in nitric acid. Violet octahedral crystals of **VOBr** are made by heating VOBr$_2$ in vacuo at 360°. The crystals decompose at 480° in vacuo to give VBr$_3$ and V$_2$O$_3$. VOBr is slightly soluble in water, and generally less soluble in organic solvents.

† The corresponding Fe^{II} compound has the same structure.

Table 24.13.   *The Preparations and Properties of the Trihalides of Vanadium*

	VF$_3$	VCl$_3$	VBr$_3$	VI$_3$
Appearance	Greenish-yellow solid†	Peach blossom solid	Dark green purple solid	Dark green solid
m.p.	Above 800°			
Volatility	Sublimes at bright red heat	Almost non-volatile	Sublimes at high temperature	
Preparation	(i) Pass HF over VCl$_3$ at 600°	(i) Pass HCl over heated ferro-vanadium	(i) Pass Br$_2$ over vanadium carbide at 600°	Treat vanadium with I$_2$ in vacuo at 150°
	(ii) Heat VF$_4$ in N$_2$ at 600°; the products are VF$_3$ and volatile VF$_5$	(ii) Heat finely divided vana-dium with excess ICl	(ii) Treat powdered vanadium with Br$_2$ at 40°	
	(iii) Treat VCl$_2$ with HF	(iii) Heat VCl$_4$ in N$_2$ to 150°		
Solubility	Almost insoluble in water	Very hygroscopic and very soluble in water which hydrolyses it.	As for VCl$_3$	As for VCl$_3$
	Insoluble in organic solvents	Soluble in organic solvents‡		
Reducing action		At 700° it reduces CO$_2$ to CO		Oxidised by air at 130°. With Cl$_2$ gives VCl$_4$ and ICl$_3$
Dispro-portionation	Stable up to 800°	At dull red heat it dispropor-tionates to VCl$_2$ and VCl$_4$	Does not dispro-portionate	At 280° it de-composes to VI$_2$ and I$_2$
Other reactions	At 500° it is reduced by hydrogen to metal	Liquid NH$_3$ gives [V(NH$_3$)$_6$]Cl$_3$, but gaseous NH$_3$ gives VN + NH$_4$Cl		

† The crystal structure has been examined by X-rays; vanadium is 6 co-ordinate with respect to fluorine.

‡ Soluble in organic solvents containing oxygen atoms which act as donors, but not in benzene, CS$_2$, etc.

NEUTRAL, ANIONIC, AND CATIONIC COMPLEXES

Compounds in this Class furnish examples of complete series of complexes from those such as [V,6H$_2$O]Cl$_3$, in which vanadium is present as a cation with an ionic valency of three, through neutral complexes such as [V,3H$_2$O,F$_3$], to complexes such as K$_3$[VF$_6$] in which the vanadium is present in an anion with a valency of three. The vanadium atom is six co-ordinate. It has been established by X-ray analysis that the anion of K$_2$[V,H$_2$O,F$_5$] is octahedral. There is no evidence for the structures of the other anions, but they are presumed to be octahedral.

Neutral complexes. These include complexes of the type [V,3H$_2$O,F$_3$] and the β-diketone complexes, VA$_3$.

The tri-acetylacetone derivative exists as dark-green prisms, m.p. 185–190°. It is made by treating vanadium trichloride with the diketone in the presence of sodium carbonate. It is insoluble in water, but is easily soluble in chloroform and benzene. It can be distilled without decomposition. In moist air it goes to VOA$_2$ (p. 971).

[V,3H$_2$O,F$_3$]^0 is a green solid. It is made by dissolving V$_2$O$_3$ in aqueous hydrofluoric acid, or by the electrolytic reduction of V$_2$O$_5$ in aqueous hydrofluoric acid. It is slightly soluble in water.

31*

Anionic complexes. *Fluorides.* The alkali metals give fluoride complexes of the three types, $K_3[VF_6]$, $K_2[VF_5,H_2O]$, $K[VF_4,2H_2O]$. X-ray analysis has shown that the anion $[VF_5,H_2O]^{2-}$ is octahedral. Cobalt, nickel, zinc, and cadmium give salts of the type, $Co[VF_5,H_2O]6H_2O$. The ammonium, potassium, rubidium, and caesium salts of the type, $M[VF_4,2H_2O]$ can be crystallised from dilute hydrofluoric acid. The fluoride ion cannot be detected in their aqueous solutions. The salts are green and fairly stable. The solubility increases from potassium to caesium, thus showing that the parent acid is weak.

Cyanides. $K_3[V(CN)_6]$ is made as a precipitate by adding alcohol to a mixture of solutions of vanadium trichloride and potassium cyanide. It is easily soluble in water but insoluble in alcohol. It is the least stable of the complex cyanides of this type from vanadium to cobalt. The aqueous solution deposits $V(CN)_3$; boiling alkalis give $V(OH)_3$. The aqueous solution gives the test for CN.

Cationic complexes. The donor atom is either oxygen or nitrogen; the affinity of vanadium for these atoms is equal (in this, trivalent vanadium resembles aluminium or iron).

The cation $[V,6H_2O]^{3+}$ is obtained when vanadium trichloride or trinitrate crystallises from aqueous solutions. It is presumably present when the simple ion V^{3+} is introduced into aqueous solution.

$[V(NH_3)_6]Cl_3$ and $[V(NH_3)_6]Br_3$ can be made by pouring liquid ammonia on to anhydrous vanadium trichloride or tribromide and allowing the excess to evaporate. The chloride is a red-brown solid. It is oxidised by moist air:

$$[V(NH_3)_6]Cl_3 + O + 2H_2O = NH_4VO_3 + 3NH_4Cl + 2NH_3.$$

It is insoluble in cold water, alcohol, or ether. Dilute HCl converts it to a green solution which turns blue on oxidation.

Vanadium trichloride also forms complexes with alkylamines and with urea.

SECTION 4. COMPOUNDS CONTAINING A VANADIUM ATOM IN OXIDATION STATE IV

Compounds in this Section include vanadium dioxide VO_2, vanadium tetrahalides such as VCl_4, the oxydihalides such as $VOCl_2$, complex anions such as $[VX]^{2-}$ and complex cations such as $[V(H_2O)_6]^{4+}$.

GIANT MOLECULE COMPOUNDS

Vanadium dioxide, VO_2, exists as dark blue crystals. It is made by heating V_2O_5 with V_2O_3 (or with oxalic acid or sulphur dioxide). It dissolves easily in acids to give vanadium monoxy compounds such as $VOCl_2$, and in alkalis to give vanadites derived from the acid $H_2V_4O_9$. Vanadium dioxide is oxidised by heating in air, or with nitric acid, to V_2O_3. With phosphoric acid it gives $VO_2,P_2O_5,3H_2O$ (blue) and $2VO_2,3P_2O_5$, $10H_2O$ (blue). The crystals of vanadium dioxide have the rutile lattice, in which the vanadium atom is six co-ordinate.

Vanadium tetrafluoride, VF_4, a hygroscopic brown powder, is made by the addition of anhydrous hydrogen fluoride to vanadium tetrachloride at a low temperature. At $325°$ in an atmosphere of nitrogen it disproportionates to VF_3 and VF_5. With alkali fluorides in alkaline solution it forms salts $K_2[VOF_4]$.

Vanadium tetrachloride,† VCl_4, is a dark-red dense liquid, m.p. $-28°$, b.p. $154°$. It is made by passing air-free chlorine over ferrovanadium at a red heat. VCl_4 distils over

† VBr_4 and VI_4 are not known.

and the less volatile $FeCl_3$ remains behind. VCl_4 is soluble in water which hydrolyses it to a blue solution of $VOCl_2$:

$$VCl_4 + H_2O = VOCl_2 + 2HCl.$$

It is soluble in carbon disulphide, carbon tetrachloride, and other organic solvents. VCl_4 is stable above 600°. At ordinary temperatures, and more rapidly at 150°, it disproportionates thus:

$$2VCl_4 = 2VCl_3 + Cl_2,$$

but at high temperatures vanadium trichloride disproportionates:

$$2VCl_3 = VCl_4 + VCl_2.$$

The vapour density corresponds to VCl_4, and electron diffraction experiments show that the molecule is tetrahedral. In CCl_4 solution at $-20°$ vanadium tetrachloride is dimeric.

Vanadium monoxy dihalides. VOF_2, is a non-sublimable yellow powder, insoluble in any solvent. It is made by heating $VOBr_2$ to red heat in hydrogen fluoride. $VOCl_2$ exists as green deliquescent crystals decomposed by water. It is made:

(i) by passing a mixture of $VOCl_3$ vapour and hydrogen through a red hot tube,
(ii) by the hydrolysis of VCl_4,
(iii) by the action of concentrated hydrochloric acid on vanadium pentoxide:

$$V_2O_5 + 6HCl = 2VOCl_2 + 3H_2O + Cl_2.$$

$VOBr_2$ is a pale yellow powder which sublimes with decomposition at 330°. $VO(CN)_2$ is known.

NEUTRAL COMPLEX CONTAINING V^{IV}

Vanadyl acetylacetonate, VOA_2,

exists as blue-green crystals. It is made:

(i) by treating $VOSO_4$ with acetylacetone,
(ii) by the atmospheric oxidation of VA_3.

It is insoluble in water, but easily soluble in alcohol, ether, benzene, or chloroform. It crystallises from these organic solvents still retaining its water, which is lost only on melting with complete decomposition. The water is exchanged for ammonia or an amine if the hydrate is treated with a boiling ethereal solution of ammonia or the amine. The four oxygen atoms of the carbonyl groups lie in one plane; the vanadyl group is perpendicular to this plane, with the vanadium atom slightly above it.

COMPLEX ANIONS CONTAINING V^{IV}

The least stable complexes formed by vanadium are those in which the vanadium atom is in the state V^{IV}. Most of the complexes included in Table 24.12, Section 4, and all in Table 24.14, are anions; all include the group VO which appears to exercise a stabilising effect, and only three are obtained in the anhydrous condition. Two of the anhydrous compounds are the fluorovanadate $K_2[VOF_4]$ and the malonatovanadate $(NH_4)_2 [VOmal_2]$. $K_2[VOF_4]$ is made by the action of vanadium tetrafluoride on an aqueous solution of potassium fluoride. $(NH_4)_2[VOmal_2]$ is made by dehydrating the blue tetrahydrate which crystallises on the addition of ammonium carbonate to the solution obtained when malonic acid is heated with a solution of ammonium vanadate. The vanadium atom in the ions $[VOF_4]^{2-}$ and $[VOmal_2]^{2-}$ can be assigned trigonal bipyramidal orbital configuration in accordance with the diagram in Fig. 24.15.

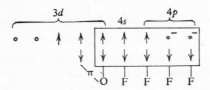

Fig. 24.15.   Orbital diagram for the anion $[VOF_4]^{2-}$.

There are other hydrated salts which can be given the same orbital structure if it is assumed that the water of hydration is not bound to the vanadium atom. A list of some of these compounds is given in Table 24.14, Column 1.

Table 24.14.   *Hydrated Salts Containing the Group VO in the Anion*

Column 1		Column 2	
$Na_2[VOF_4],2H_2O$	Blue		
$(pyrH)_2[VOCl_4],Aq.$	Blue		
$(NH_4)_2[VO(SCN)_4],5H_2O$	Blue		
$K_2[VO(SCN)_4],5H_2O$	Blue	$K_2[V_2O_2(SO_3)_3],Aq.$	Blue
$K_2[VO(SO_3)_2],Aq.$	Green	$K_2[V_2O_2(SO_4)_3]$	Pale blue
$K_2[VO(SO_4)_2]$	Dark blue	$(NH_4)_2[V_2O_2(C_2O_4)_3],8·5H_2O$	Blue
$(NH_4)_2[VO(C_2O_4)_2],2H_2O$	Blue	$K_2[V_2O_2(C_2O_4)_3],4H_2O$	Blue
$(NH_4)_2[VOmal_2],4H_2O$	Blue		
$3H_2O$	Violet		
H_2O	Pink		
anhyd.	Pale violet		
$K_2[VOsal_2],3H_2O$	Pale yellow solid: green solution		
$(NH_4)_2[VOsal_2],3H_2O$	Pale yellow solid: green solution		
$M_2[VOcat_2],cat. Aq.$			

Column 2 of Table 24.14 contains certain salts which are formed as easily as those in Column 1, but too little is known about them to justify an attempt to assign orbital structures to them.

SECTION 5. COMPOUNDS CONTAINING A VANADIUM ATOM IN OXIDATION STATE V

Compounds in this Section include vanadium pentafluoride which is probably polymeric, vanadium pentoxide and the monoxyhalides $VOhal_3$ which probably have tetrahedral configurations, and many complex anions of vanadium of which the configurations are either trigonal bipyramidal or octahedral.

Vanadium pentafluoride, VF_5, is a white solid, m.p. under pressure above 200°, which sublimes at 1 atm at 111°. It is made by heating the tetrafluoride for several hours in nitrogen at 600°, when VF_5 distils over and leaves VF_3 behind. It dissolves easily in water, alcohol, acetone, $CHCl_3$, ligroin, giving yellow solutions. It is insoluble in CS_2. It turns yellow in air from the formation of VOF_3. It attacks glass.

There is no VCl_5 or VBr_5. The absence of these compounds is in accord with the suppression of high covalencies of elements in Period 4.

Vanadium pentoxide, V_2O_5, is a yellow or red amorphous powder, m.p. about 660°. The anhydrous oxide is made by heating ammonium vanadate, NH_4VO_3. If a more active form is required, the crude product should be dissolved in aqueous hydrogen peroxide solution, filtered, and the filtrate heated with nitric acid and alcohol. Brown flakes are precipitated, which should be washed with acetone and preserved under it.

A melt of vanadium pentoxide solidifies to red crystals. It is almost involatile, and can be sublimed only in the electric furnace. It can be heated to 1800° without losing oxygen. It is soluble in water to the extent of 50 mg/litre. It reacts with chlorine at 650° to give $VOCl_3$; with $SOCl_2$ in a sealed tube at 75° it also gives $VOCl_3$. It reacts with concentrated hydrochloric acid to give $VOCl_2$, chlorine, and water. Vanadium pentoxide is amphoteric, giving salts such as VCl_5 or $VOCl_3$ with acids, and vanadates with alkalis. It is readily reduced by heating with hydrogen, carbon monoxide, or tellurium. At a red heat reduction with tellurium gives V_2O_3 and TeO_2; no telluride is produced even in a current of hydrogen. In aqueous solution V_2O_5 is oxidised by hydrogen peroxide to peroxyvanadic acids, but it is reduced by the hydrogen halides, most readily by hydrogen iodide, and by arsenious compounds. Electrolytic reduction may be carried out in phosphate melts. In acid melts V_2O_3 is obtained. In weakly alkaline melts VP is obtained, but V_2O_3 is obtained if the melt is diluted with sodium chloride. In strongly alkaline melts VO is formed. Vanadium pentoxide is used as a catalyst in many oxidation reactions.

Crystalline vanadium pentoxide consists of an infinite array of VO_4 tetrahedra, each of which has three oxygen atoms in common with other VO_4 tetrahedra.

Vanadium monoxytrihalides. Vanadium monoxytrifluoride, VOF_3, is a yellow solid, m.p. 300°, b.p. about 480°. It is made by treating $VOCl_3$ with cold concentrated hydrofluoric acid, or by heating vanadium trifluoride to redness in oxygen. It is very hygroscopic. It dissolves readily in water, and in organic solvents. It attacks glass.

Vanadium monoxytrichloride, $VOCl_3$, is a yellow liquid, m.p. $-79.5°$, b.p. 127°. It is made:

   (i) by heating vanadium pentoxide in chlorine to 650°,
   (ii) by heating vanadium trichloride in oxygen,
   (iii) by heating vanadium pentoxide with thionyl chloride in a sealed tube at 75°.

$VOCl_3$ is very inert to metals, and it can be treated at its boiling point with sodium for 12 hours without action. It is reduced by hydrogen at a red heat to $VOCl_2$ and then to VOCl. It dissolves most non-metals and is miscible with most organic solvents. It is violently hydrolysed by water to vanadium pentoxide.

$VOBr_3$ is a dark red liquid, b.p. 130°/100 mm. It is made by passing bromine vapour at a red heat over V_2O_3, or over a mixture of V_2O_5 and carbon. It readily loses bromine and decomposes suddenly at 180°.

COMPLEX ANIONS CONTAINING V^V

The complexes formed by the vanadium atom in the state V^V are anionic. The orbital configuration is either trigonal bipyramidal as in $K[VOF_4]$, or octahedral as in $K[VF_6]$, see Table 24.12.

$K[VOF_4]$ is made by the action of potassium fluoride on vanadium monoxytrifluoride. The sodium salt is made by the action of bromine trifluoride on sodium vanadite, $NaVO_3$.

$K[VF_6]$ is made by the action of potassium fluoride on vanadium pentafluoride, or, by the interaction of bromine trifluoride and a mixture of potassium fluoride (or potassium chloride) and vanadium trichloride. KVF_6 is stable when heated in vacuo up to 300°, but at 330° it dissociates into potassium fluoride and vanadium pentafluoride. It is soluble in water, but is hydrolysed by it. It fumes in moist air. It is decomposed by 50% sulphuric acid with the precipitation of vanadium pentoxide.

$K_3[VO_2(C_2O_4)_2]$ is made by treating potassium vanadate solution with oxalic acid. It is remarkably stable. Its orbital diagram is shown in Fig. 24.16.

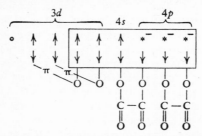

Fig. 24.16. Orbital diagram for the anion $[VO_2(C_2O_4)_2]^{3-}$.

VANADIC ACID AND THE VANADATES

Hydrated forms of vanadium pentoxide may be obtained by the precipitation of vanadates in weakly acid solution, but no vanadic acid of simple constitution has been isolated.

If, say, sodium orthovanadate, Na_3VO_4, is crystallised from a strongly alkaline solution, crystals of $Na_3VO_4,12H_2O$ are obtained. Both the solution and the crystals are colourless. If acid is slowly added to the solution, so that the alkalinity is gradually decreased, the anions present in the solution become more complex, and finally V_2O_5,aq. is precipitated. If further acid is added vanadium is found in the cation. Table 24.15 shows how, with falling pH, changes occur in the nature of the anion in the solution; it also states the colour of the solution at each stage, and the nature of the sodium salt which may be crystallised from it.

Table 24.15. *The Relation between the pH of a Solution of Sodium Vanadate and the Constitution of Vanadic Ions present*

pH	14	12–10·6	8–9	7–6·8	6·8–2·2	2·2–1
Number of vanadium atoms in ion	1	2	4	5		1
Constitution of ion	$[VO_4]^{3-}$	$[V_2O_7]^{4-}$	$[H_2V_4O_{13}]^{4-}$	$[H_4V_5O_{16}]^{3-}$		$[VO]^{3+}$
Sodium salt obtained by crystallisation	Na_3VO_4	$Na_4V_2O_7$	$Na_4[H_2V_4O_{13}]$	$Na_3[H_4V_5O_{16}]$		
Precipitate					$(V_2O_5)n$ aq	
Colour	None	None	None	Brown or red		Pale yellow
Rate of change		reactions fast in both directions ← →		reaction fast → reaction slow ←		

† The table is based on data obtained by Jander and Jahr, *Z.A.C.*, **211**, 1933, 49.

Now crystalline sodium vanadate, $Na_3VO_4,12H_2O$, is isomorphous with sodium ortho-phosphate. This is evidence that the orthovanadates and the orthophosphates have parallel constitutions. It is stated on p. 730 that the constitutions of the polyphosphoric acids which have unbranched chains conform to the general formula $H_{4+n}P_{2+n}O_{7+3n}$. Table 24.16 shows that the constitutions of the sodium vanadates calculated by the same general formula coincide with those given in Table 24.15.

Table 24.16.   *The Sodium Vanadates and the Formula*
$H_{4+n}V_{2+n}O_{7+3n}$

Number of vanadium atoms per anion	n	Formula of the sodium vanadate
1	-1	Na_3VO_4
2	0	$Na_4V_2O_7$
4	2	$Na_4H_2V_4O_{13}$
5	3	$Na_3H_4V_5O_{16}$

It is stated on p. 724 that one OH group on each phosphorus atom in a phosphoric acid has the dissociation properties of a strong acid, and the remaining OH groups on the phosphorus atoms have the dissociation properties of weak acids. The formula of the sodium salt, $Na_4[H_2V_4O_{13}]$, indicates that the vanadic acid from which it is derived has the same property. The formula of the salt, $Na_3[H_4V_5O_{16}]$ suggests that only three of the OH groups have the dissociation properties of a strong acid; considera-tions of symmetry suggest that the four terminal OH groups of the acid, which has the constitution:

have low dissociation constants.

All the statements made so far fit in with the assumption that the vanadic acids detected in solution possess unbranched chain structures. Increase of acidity of the solution lengthens the chain of VO_4 tetrahedra. Some support for this view is found in the rates of conversion of one acid to another. Jander and Jahr found that association or dissociation of two or four tetrahedra was rapid. The addition of a fifth tetrahedron to a chain of four was quick, but the removal of a tetrahedron from a chain of five was very slow, even when excess of alkali was added. The slowness of this change might be connected with the reluctance of the terminal OH groups to ionise.

A sparingly soluble ammonium vanadate is known which is called ammonium metavanadate, and has been assigned the formula NH_4VO_3. Its structure is unknown; it may be either $(NH_4)_4H_2V_4O_{13}$, or, if it is a true metavanadate analogous to the phos-phorus compound, it may be $(NH_4VO_3)_n$, where n is 3 or 4. The corresponding silver salt is made by adding ammonium vanadate solution to silver nitrate solution at the boiling point. Silver "metavanadate" is purified by solution in aqueous ammonia, and reprecipitation with acetic acid, followed by ten minutes' boiling.

If, however, an acid solution of NH_4VO_3 in nitric acid (1:1) is titrated conducti-metrically against silver nitrate solution, two break-points occur, at $Ag_2H_2V_6O_{17}$ and $Ag_4V_6O_{17}$. The second salt is obtained as a brick-red colloidal precipitate by the interaction of theoretical amounts of $AgNO_3$ and $(NH_4)_4V_6O_{17}$ in aqueous solution.

If the parent acid is $H_4V_6O_{17},2H_2O$, or $H_8V_6O_{19}$, it is recognised as the member of the series in Table 24.16, for which the number of vanadium atoms per ion is six, and for which $n = 4$. Here again the number of strongly acid OH groups in the molecule of the acid is two less than the number of vanadium atoms, indicating that the terminal OH groups may be almost non-acidic.

The above arguments furnish strong foundation for the inference that the vanadic acids have constitutions parallel to those of the polyphosphoric acids (p. 724), and hence that the anions are chains of VO_4 tetrahedra with oxygen atoms held in common.

The peroxyvanadic acids. The free acids are not known. Hydrogen peroxide reacts at once on a V_2O_5 solution to give a pale yellow solution. The solution has good electrical conductivity, but it is unstable and rapidly loses oxygen. It is a powerful catalyst in the oxidation of unsaturated hydrocarbons by H_2O_2.

There is little precise evidence for the structures of the peroxyvanadic acids. These are most probably derived by the addition of oxygen atoms to free oxygen atoms in the VO_4 tetrahedra in the normal vanadic acids. The simplest peroxyvanadic acid would be:

$$[H^+]_3 \left[\begin{array}{c} O \\ | \\ O-V-O-O \\ | \\ O \end{array} \right]^{3-}$$

Vanadium (like niobium) is most commonly found in the peroxyacids as the di-acid:

$$\begin{array}{c} H-O-O \qquad\qquad O-O-H \\ \diagdown \qquad\qquad \diagup \\ O-V-O-V-O \\ \diagup \qquad\qquad \diagdown \\ H-O-O \qquad\qquad O-O-H \end{array}$$

It has been stated that polyvanadic acids with long chains do not react with hydrogen peroxide so easily as the polyvanadic acids with short chains.

NIOBIUM

SECTION 2. COMPOUNDS CONTAINING A NIOBIUM ATOM IN OXIDATION STATE II

Niobium forms compounds corresponding to VC and VN which are discussed on pp. 599 and 654. The monoxide and monosulphide of niobium have been made, and their identities have been established by X-ray experiments. The dihalides of niobium have not been reported.

SECTION 3. COMPOUNDS CONTAINING A NIOBIUM ATOM IN OXIDATION STATE III

Compounds of this Section are limited to the trihalides, $NbCl_3$ and $NbBr_3$.

Niobium trichloride, $NbCl_3$, a black, non-volatile solid, is made by passing a mixture of niobium pentachloride vapour and hydrogen through a tube heated to 400–450°. The dark crystals are not affected by water, and are insoluble in other solvents. Niobium trichloride can be oxidised by nitric acid to the pentoxide, and by heating in air or in carbon dioxide, to the oxychloride, $NbOCl_3$. At about 1000° the trichloride disproportionates thus:

$$5NbCl_3 = 3NbCl_5 + 2Nb.$$

Niobium tribromide, $NbBr_3$, is made by a method similar to that used for the preparation of the trichloride. It disproportionates at 925°.

SECTION 4. COMPOUNDS CONTAINING A NIOBIUM ATOM IN OXIDATION STATE IV

Niobium dioxide, NbO_2 is a blue-black powder made by reducing the pentoxide with hydrogen at a high temperature, but below 1300°. It is insoluble in acids (VO_2 is soluble), alkalis, and oxidising agents, but when treated with sodium hydroxide or an oxidising sodium salt it gives sodium niobiate. Up to 1000° it reduces gaseous oxides, but above 1300° it is reduced by hydrogen to Nb_2O.

Neither tetrahalides such as NbF_4 nor the oxyhalides such as $NbOF_2$ are known, and no complexes are formed.

SECTION 5. COMPOUNDS CONTAINING A NIOBIUM ATOM IN OXIDATION STATE V

Niobium forms a pentoxide, pentahalides, oxyhalides, and both trigonal bipyramidal and octahedral complex anions.

Niobium pentoxide, Nb_2O_5, a white infusible powder, is made:

  (i) by dehydrating the colloidal precipitate obtained by the action of a dilute acid on a niobiate solution,

  (ii) by igniting niobium sulphide, nitride, or carbide in air.

It occurs in three forms, one of which is isomorphous with Ta_2O_5. It is insoluble in water, but it dissolves either in fused $KHSO_4$, or in KOH solution.

It reacts with incandescence with BrF_3 to give $[BrF_2{}^+][NbF_6{}^-]$. It is reduced to a lower oxide, perhaps Nb_2O_3, by heating in hydrogen. Its solution can be reduced electrolytically to give a series of solutions differing in colour.

Niobium pentafluoride, NbF_5, a colourless, crystalline solid, m.p. 75·5°, b.p. 217–220°, is made:

  (i) by passing fluorine over niobium pentachloride; the reaction, once started by heat, is exothermic,

  (ii) by treating niobium pentachloride with boiling hydrofluoric acid (aqueous),

  (iii) by heating niobium powder in anhydrous hydrogen fluoride at 250°.

Niobium pentafluoride can be purified by sublimation in vacuo at about 100°. It is hygroscopic, and dissolves in water to give a clear solution. Sodium hydroxide or ammonia precipitates the pentoxide, which dissolves in excess of sodium hydroxide to give sodium niobiate.

Niobium pentachloride, $NbCl_5$, a solid, m.p. 194°, b.p. 241° is made:

  (i) by the action of chlorine on the heated metal,

  (ii) by heating niobium pentoxide in the vapour of CCl_4 at 220°,

  (iii) by passing the vapour of $NbOCl_3$ mixed with chlorine over carbon at 700°,

  (iv) by heating the pentoxide with sulphur chloride.

The solid is pale yellow, the liquid raspberry coloured, and the vapour yellow. It is soluble in organic solvents: alcohol, ether, chloroform, carbon tetrachloride, and in disulphur dichloride, S_2Cl_2. It is hydrolysed by water to Nb_2O_5. It dissolves in concentrated acids, presumably to form complexes, but unlike niobium pentafluoride, it forms no double salts.

$NbCl_5$ vapour is monomeric at 275–300°. Electron diffraction shows that the molecular structure is trigonal bipyramidal, Nb–Cl is 2·29.

Niobium pentabromide, $NbBr_5$, exists as garnet red prisms, m.p. 150°. It is made by passing bromine vapour over metallic niobium. It distils in a stream of CO_2 at 270° without decomposition. It fumes in air and is hygroscopic. Water converts it to $NbOBr_3$ and then to Nb_2O_5.

Electron diffraction shows the molecules in the vapour have the trigonal bipyramidal structure. Nb–Br is 2·46.

Niobium monoxyhalides, NbOhal$_3$. The fluoride, chloride and the bromide are non-volatile solids, not easily decomposed by heat. The fluoride is colourless, the chloride white, and the bromide yellow. The chloride and the bromide are made by passing the gaseous halogen over a heated mixture of niobium pentoxide and carbon; the chloride can also be made by passing carbon tetrachloride vapour over heated niobium pentoxide. The fluoride is made by the action of hydrogen fluoride on a fused mixture of niobium pentoxide and calcium fluoride at a red heat. The chloride and the bromide disproportionate at high temperatures:

$$5NbOCl_3 = Nb_2O_5 + 3NbCl_5,$$

and are oxidised by air at 500° to niobium pentoxide.

The complexes **NbCl$_2$(OC$_2$H$_5$)$_2$A**, where A represents a molecule of acetylacetone or benzoylacetone, contain niobium in the Nb^V state. They are probably neutral. They are made by adding the diketone to niobium pentachloride dissolved in alcohol. They are yellow and crystalline, m.p. 110–130°.

COMPLEX ANIONS CONTAINING Nb^V

Trigonal bipyramidal anions. The salt **K[NbOCl$_4$]** exists as colourless or pale greenish-yellow crystals. It is made by treating niobium pentoxide, oxytrichloride, or pentachloride with potassium chloride in concentrated hydrochloric acid. Water or moist air hydrolyses it to hydrochloric acid and niobium pentoxide. The corresponding bromine compound is similar, but less stable. No fluorine compound has been reported.

Octahedral anions. **K$_2$[NbOF$_5$]** is a salt which contains the commonest type of niobium oxyfluoride complex; **K$_3$[NbOF$_6$]** and **K$_4$[NbOF$_7$]** are both converted to it by crystallisation from water. The potassium salt has one molecule of water of crystallisation; the Rb, Cs, and Tl$^+$ salts are anhydrous. **K$_2$[NbOF$_5$]H$_2$O** is decomposed by alkali. It loses water at 100°, but it can be heated to redness without further decomposition. X-ray analysis shows that the structure of the anion is octahedral. **K$_2$[NbOCl$_5$]** and **K$_2$[NbOBr$_5$]** are both very easily decomposed by water to Nb$_2$O$_5$ and the potassium and hydrogen halides.

Complex anions in which the co-ordination number of the niobium atom is greater than 6. The salt **K$_2$[NbF$_7$]** exists as colourless crystals. It is made (i) by crystallising K$_2$[NbOF$_5$] from hydrofluoric acid, (ii) by fusing KHF$_2$ (but not KF) with niobium pentafluoride. It is stable, if dry, to 100°, but hot water converts it to K$_2$[NbOF$_5$]. The structure of the anion is that of a distorted trigonal biprism.

The oxalato complexes. The salts **M$_3$[NbO(C$_2$O$_4$)$_3$]** exist as colourless crystals. M represents ammonium or an alkali metal. The salts are hydrated: Na, 4H$_2$O; K, 2H$_2$O; Rb, 2H$_2$O; NH$_4$, 1·5 H$_2$O. They are made in solution by treating a niobiate with oxalic acid; the salt is precipitated by the addition of acetone or alcohol. The salts are hydrolysed by water with the precipitation of Nb$_2$O$_5$.

The catechol complexes. The salts **M$_3$[NbO(cat)$_3$]aq.** exist as reddish or yellow crystals. They are made by dissolving freshly precipitated niobium pentoxide in a boiling alkaline solution of catechol. The reaction must be carried out in an atmosphere of nitrogen. The solution is deep yellow. The salts of the different alkali metals differ in the number of hydrogen atoms of the parent acid replaced, in the number of molecules of catechol of crystallisation, and in the number of molecules of water of crystallisation. Examples are: K$_2$H[NbOcat$_3$]2cat,3H$_2$O; (NH$_4$)$_2$H[NbOcat$_3$]$\frac{1}{2}$cat,3H$_2$O; (NH$_4$)$_3$[NbOcat$_3$]9H$_2$O.

TANTALUM

SECTION 2. COMPOUNDS CONTAINING A TANTALUM ATOM IN OXIDATION STATE II

Tantalum forms compounds corresponding to VC and VN (pp. 599 and 654). The compounds TaO and TaS do not exist. $TaCl_2$ and $TaBr_2$ are hard, dark-coloured solids. They are attacked by water with the liberation of hydrogen; tantalum passes into solution as the trihalide. There are no tantalum complexes in this Section.

SECTION 3. COMPOUNDS CONTAINING A TANTALUM ATOM IN OXIDATION STATE III

Tantalum trichloride and tribromide are reported. They are green solids made by the reduction of the pentahalides at high temperatures. They are themselves reducing agents. Tantalum trichloride dissolves in water but it is oxidised on heating thus:

$$TaCl_3 + 5H_2O = Ta(OH)_5 + 3HCl + H_2,$$

and tantalum tribromide also reacts with water yielding hydrogen and $TaO_2,2H_2O$. The tantalum trihalides are much more readily oxidised than the corresponding vanadium compounds.

SECTION 4. COMPOUNDS CONTAINING A TANTALUM ATOM IN OXIDATION STATE IV

Tantalum dioxide, a brown powder, is made by heating Ta_2O_5 in a carbon crucible. When heated in air it is re-oxidised to Ta_2O_5. It does not react with acids, but dissolves in alkalis to give tantalites.

SECTION 5. COMPOUNDS CONTAINING A TANTALUM ATOM IN OXIDATION STATE V

Tantalum forms a pentoxide, pentahalides, but no oxyhalides, and it forms complex anions in which the tantalum atom is in the octahedral valence state.

Tantalum pentoxide, Ta_2O_5, an infusible white powder, is made by heating the metal in oxygen.

It is insoluble in all acids except hydrofluoric, in which it dissolves to give $H[TaF_6],6H_2O$. It is soluble in a mixture of concentrated sulphuric acid and hydrogen peroxide to give a peroxy acid. It is not attacked on ignition by air, chlorine, hydrogen sulphide, or sulphur. It is attacked by carbon tetrachloride vapour, but much less easily than is Nb_2O_5. It can be heated to $1250°$ in hydrogen without change. It reacts with bromine trifluoride to give $[BrF_2][TaF_6]$. It is reduced by ignition with carbon to tantalum dioxide. It is converted to tantalum pentachloride by heating with sulphur chloride, or with chlorine saturated with CCl_4 vapour. A mixture of tantalum pentoxide, and carbon, if heated with bromine, gives tantalum pentabromide; if heated with nitrogen at $1200°$, gives the nitride TaN.

Tantalum pentafluoride, TaF_5, a colourless solid, m.p. $96·8°$, b.p. $229·4°$, is made:

   (i) by the action of boiling anhydrous hydrofluoric acid on tantalum pentachloride,
   (ii) by heating $Ba_3[TaF_8]_2$ to $1000°$ (using platinum vessels).

It is slightly soluble in carbon disulphide, more so in CCl_4 and $CHCl_3$, but not in hydrocarbons. It dissolves in water with a hissing sound (like $AlCl_3$) to give a clear solution, but on boiling all the fluorine is lost as hydrogen fluoride. If it is treated with a boiling alkaline solution, complex tantalifluorides are formed. It reacts quickly with fused potassium hydrogen fluoride to give $K_2[TaF_7]$, but with potassium fluoride the same product is obtained only after long heating at 220–230°. It does not react with potassium chloride.

Tantalum pentachloride, TaCl$_5$, a yellow crystalline solid, m.p. 211°, b.p. 241·6°, is made:

(i) by heating metallic tantalum, or its carbide, nitride, or sulphide in chlorine,
(ii) by heating tantalum pentoxide in chlorine saturated with CCl$_4$ vapour,
(iii) by heating the pentoxide with sulphur chloride.

It is soluble in carbon disulphide; more so in ethyl bromide, CCl$_4$ or CHCl$_3$. It is hydrolysed in dilute hydrochloric acid, but is more stable in the concentrated acid. It burns in air to the pentoxide.

It may be reduced to lower chlorides. If it is heated with aluminium and aluminium chloride, and then further heated under a pressure of 2 or 3 mm so that the aluminium chloride (b.p. 180°) distils off, the residue at 250° has the approximate composition TaCl$_4$, the residue at 350–400° has the composition TaCl$_3$, and at 600°, TaCl$_2$.

Neither by direct oxidation, nor by hydrolysis, is it possible to produce an oxychloride from tantalum pentachloride.

Tantalum pentabromide, TaBr$_5$, a pale yellow crystalline solid, is made:

(i) by igniting a mixture of tantalum pentoxide and carbon in bromine vapour,
(ii) by passing a mixture of bromine and argon over the metal at 300°.

It is decomposed by water.

Tantalum penta-iodide, TaI$_5$, is a brownish-black powder, m.p. 365°. It is made by the action of iodine vapour on the metal. It is hydrolysed by moist air, and is oxidised by oxygen vigorously at 100°. It is insoluble in organic solvents.

COMPLEX ANIONS CONTAINING Ta^V

Octahedral complex anions. Fluorotantalic acid, H[TaF$_6$],6H$_2$O, exists as colourless crystals, m.p. 15°. It is made by dissolving tantalum pentoxide in hydrofluoric acid. Two of its salts are K[TaF$_6$] and [BrF$_2$][TaF$_6$].

Complex anions containing 7-co-ordinate tantalum. K$_2$[TaF$_7$] is made by fusing tantalum pentafluoride with potassium hydrogen fluoride. It is slightly soluble in cold water, more soluble in hot. It melts without decomposition, but at high temperatures it evolves TaF$_5$. It is hydrolysed by water, but it can be recrystallised from dilute hydrofluoric acid. The structure of the anion is similar to that of the anion [NbF$_7$]$^{2-}$.

Attempts to obtain chlorotantalates have failed.

Potassium oxyfluorotantalate, K$_3$[TaOF$_6$], represents the commonest type of fluoro complex formed by tantalum; it is usually made by the action of a neutral fluoride on tantalum pentoxide. Hydrofluoric acid converts it into potassium fluorotantalate. K$_3$[TaOF$_6$] is very unstable, and in warm solution it changes to the fluorotantalate with the liberation of tantalum pentoxide. This change occurs more readily with the highly ionised salts than with the free acid. The ammonium salt is isomorphous with ammonium zirconium heptafluoride, (NH$_4$)$_3$ZrF$_7$.

SUB-GROUP VI T. CHROMIUM, MOLYBDENUM, AND TUNGSTEN

Certain properties of the elements of the sub-Group VI T are set out in Table 24.17.

Chromium is a brilliant white, hard, metal. It is chemically inactive at room temperature, but when heated it combines with the halogens, sulphur, carbon, and nitrogen. It is soluble in dilute hydrochloric acid and nitric acid, but concentrated nitric acid renders it passive.

Table 24.17.   *Properties of the metals in Sub-Group VI T*

	Cr	Mo	W
Atomic number	24	42	74
m.p. °C	1900	2620	3380
b.p. °C	2600	4600	5700
Specific gravity	7·1	10·2	19·3
Ionic radius, M^{6+}	0·52	0·62	—
Atomic radius (12 co-ordination)	1·29	1·40	1·41
Crystal structure	Hexagonal, cubic above 800°		

Molybdenum is a white metal. When heated it reacts with the halogens (except iodine). It is not attacked by dilute acids except nitric acid, but concentrated nitric acid renders it passive. Tungsten is a white metal. It is stable in air at room temperature, but on heating it is oxidised to WO_3. It reacts with fluorine and chlorine, and with nitrogen above 1500°. It is unattacked by acids but it dissolves in fused potassium nitrate. It is made passive by treatment with oxidising agents.

Examples of the types of compounds formed by the elements of sub-Groups VI T are classified in Table 24.18. All the elements can use all their valency electrons for bond formation, but all form many compounds in which several valency electrons are inert. The great majority of the compounds are coloured, infusible, and non-volatile. Of the compounds mentioned in Table 24.19, only the following have observable melting points; they are all compounds of the elements in oxidation states V or VI: MoF_5, $MOCl_5$: WCl_5, WBr_5: CrO_3, MoO_3, WO_3: CrO_2F_2, CrO_2Cl_2, $MoOF_4$, WO_2Cl_2, $WOCl_4$: MoF_6, WF_6, WCl_6.

None of the elements forms any compounds in which it is non-valent,† but chromium forms one complex in which it is in oxidation state 1, and all but one of the valency electrons are inert (Section 1). All three elements form bivalent compounds which are for the most part non-volatile and obviously polymerised. The bivalent chromium and tungsten compounds appear to have simple formulae such as $CrCl_2$, but their structures are unknown. The only molybdenum compound of this type is Mo_6Cl_{12}, which is assigned this formula because of its relation to complexes of known structure, such as $[Mo_6Cl_8(OH)_4(H_2O)_2],12H_2O$. Corresponding complexes are not formed by chromium or tungsten. It is noteworthy that compounds containing chromium and tungsten in oxidation state II are reducing agents, but the corresponding molybdenum compounds are not.

Chromium forms a number of well-characterised trivalent compounds which are neither oxidising nor reducing agents; the corresponding compounds of molybdenum are reducing agents, and those of tungsten are few and ill-characterised. The trivalent condition therefore is most stable for the element of lowest atomic number. The opposite relation holds for the tetravalent state, as it is evident from Table 24.18, Section 4, that the molybdenum and tungsten compounds are better defined than the chromium compounds.

The M^{VI} oxidation state is a stable one for all three elements. The tendency towards higher co-ordination number as the atomic number increases is seen in the halogen

† In such a compound all the valency electrons of the atom are inert, and for bonding use is made of atomic orbitals which in the ground state are unoccupied; the electrons in such orbitals are furnished from other atoms which form ionic or co-ionic bonds with the atom concerned.

Table 24.18. *Examples of Types of Compound*

Valency system of atom: $\overbrace{d\ d\ d\ d}^{n-1}\ \overbrace{s\ p\ p\ p}^{n}$

The values of n are: Cr 4, Mo 5, W 6.

Section	Oxidisation state of metal	Nature of unit	Cr
		Interstitial and unclassified compounds	CrH_3, Cr_3C_2, Cr_7C_3, Cr_4C, CrN, $Cr(NH_2)_3$, Cr_3P, CrP, CrB
1	I	Complex cation	[tri-2:2'dipyridyl Cr] [ClO_4]
2	II	Giant molecules	CrO, $Cr(OH)_2$, CrF_2, $CrCl_2$, $CrBr_2$, CrI_2, $Cr(SO)$, $Cr(OCOCH_3)_2$, $Cr(C_2O_4),H_2O$
		Neutral complexes	
		Complex anions	
3	III	Giant molecules	Cr_2O_3, $Cr(OH)_3$, $CrO\cdot OH$, Cr_2S_3, CrF_3, $CrCl_3$, $CrBr_3$, CrI_3, $Cr_2(SO_4)_3$
		Neutral complexes	[CrA_3], [$Cr_2(C_2O_4)_3$], [$Cr(SCN)_3(H_2O)_3$]
		Complex anions	$K_3[Cr(CN)_6]$, $K_2[Cr(SCN)_5(H_2O)]$
		Complex cations	[$Cr(NH_3)_6$]Cl_3, [$Cr\ en_2\ Cl_2$]Cl
4	IV	Giant molecules	(CrF_4, $CrCl_4$, CrO_2)
		Complex anions	
5	V	Giant molecules	CrF_5
		Complex anions	$K[CrOF_4]$, $Ag[CrOF_4]$, $pyrH[CrOCl_4]$, $K_2[CrOCl_5]$
		Covalent compounds	
		Neutral complexes	
6	VI	Giant molecules	CrO_3
		Covalent compounds	CrO_2F_2, CrO_2Cl_2
		Complex anions	$K[CrO_3Cl]$, $K[CrO_3F]$, K_2CrO_4, $K_2Cr_2O_7$, $K_2Cr_3O_{10}$, $K_2Cr_4O_{13}$
		Polyacids	
		Peroxy compounds	CrO_5, $(NH_3)_3CrO_4$, $K_3[(CN)_3CrO_4]$, K_3CrO_8, $K_2Cr_2O_{12}$
		Compounds containing group XO_2	

† Uranium, a member of the actinons (p. 1135), is included for comparison.

rmed by Elements in sub-Group VI T

ormal prehybridisation electron configuration:

$$\text{Cr and Mo} \quad \overbrace{d\ d\ d\ d\ d}^{n-1}\ \overbrace{s\ p\ p\ p}^{n}$$
$$\qquad\qquad\qquad\quad \uparrow\ \uparrow\ \uparrow\ \uparrow\ \uparrow$$

$$\text{W} \quad \overbrace{d\ d\ d\ d\ d}^{n-1}\ \overbrace{s\ p\ p\ p}^{n}$$
$$\qquad\quad \uparrow\ \uparrow\ \uparrow\ \uparrow\quad \uparrow\ \uparrow$$

Mo	W	U†
MoC, MoN		UH_3, UC, UC_2, UN, UO
Mo_6Cl_{12}	WCl_2, WBr_2, WI_2	
$Mo_6Cl_8,2H_2O,(OH)_4],12H_2O$ $Mo_6Cl_8,2H_2O,Cl_4],6H_2O$ (also Br,I)		
$(H_3O)_2[Mo_6Cl_8,Cl_6],6H_2O$ $K_2[Mo_6Cl_8,Cl_6],4H_2O$	$(H_3O)_2[W_6Cl_8,Cl_6],6H_2O$	
Mo_2O_3, Mo_2S_3, Mo_2Se_3 MoF_3, $MoCl_3$, $MoBr_3$		U_2N_3, U_2S_3, $U(BH_4)_3$ UF_3, UCl_3, UBr_3
$MoCl_3,3H_2O]$, $[MoOCl,3H_2O],H_2O$		
$K_4[Mo(CN)_7],H_2O$, $K_3[MoCl_6]$	$K_3[W_2Cl_9]$	
MoO_2, MoS_2, $MoCl_4$	WO_2, WS_2, WCl_4	UO_2, UOF_2, $UOCl_2$, $U(BH_4)_4$, $Uhal_4$
$K_4[Mo(CN)_8],2H_2O$, $K_3[Mo(OH)_3(CN)_4H_2O]$	$K_4[W(CN)_8]$, $K_2[W(OH)Cl_5]$	$K[UF_5]$, $NH_4[UOF_3]$, $K_2[UCl_6]$, $K_4[Uox_4],5H_2O$
Mo_2S_5, Mo_2Se_5 MoF_5, $MoO(OH)_3$, $MoOCl_3$		U_2O_5, UF_5 UCl_5, UBr_5
$K_2[MoOCl_5]$	$K_2[WOBr_5]$, $pyrH[WOBr_4]$ $K_2[WOCl_5]$, $K[WOCl_4]$, $K_3[W(CN)_8]$	
$MoCl_5$	WF_5, WCl_5	
$MoCl_5,2(C_2H_5)_2O]$		
MoO_3, MoS_3	WO_3, WS_3	US_3
MoF_6, $MoOF_4$, MoO_2F_2, MoO_2Cl_2	WF_6, WCl_6, WBr_6 $WOCl_4$, WO_2Cl_2	UF_6, UCl_6
$K_3[MoO_3F_3]$ K_2MoO_4, $K_2Mo_2O_7$ H_2MoO_4	Na_2WO_4, $Na_2W_2O_7$ H_2WO_4	Na_2UO_4 $Na_2U_2O_7$
$K_6[Te,Mo_6O_{24}]$, $K_3[PMo_{12}O_{40}]$ $K_6[Mo,Mo_6O_{24}]$	$Na_5[HW_6O_{21}],13\frac{1}{2}H_2O$ $K_6[H_2W_{12}O_{40}],18H_2O$	
K_2MoO_8, $K_2Mo_2O_{12}$	$K[HWO_6]$, $K_2[WO_8]$	$K_4[UO_8],10H_2O$
		UO_2F_2, $UO_2(NO_3)_2$, UO_3, U_3O_8, UO_2A_2,H_2O, $K[UO_2F_3]$, $[UO_2(NH_3)_2]Cl_2$

compounds. Chromium forms no compound of the type $Crhal_6$, molybdenum forms a fluoride, but tungsten forms a fluoride, a chloride, and a bromide. Both molybdenum and tungsten form polyacids; the structures of the molybdenum compounds have been most completely elucidated. It has been concluded that the structures are based on the linking together of MoO_6 octahedra, just as the silicates are based on the linking together of SiO_4 tetrahedra. The peroxy compounds of chromium are better characterised than those of molybdenum or tungsten. The peroxychromic acids differ in constitution from the peroxysulphuric acids. All three metals form carbonyls and related compounds which are discussed in Chapter 25.

Complexes are formed by molybdenum and tungsten in oxidation states III, IV, and V, and by chromium in oxidation states III, V, and VI. The complexes of Cr^{III} are remarkably numerous and stable. The complexes of the metals in the higher oxidation states are anions; neutral complexes and complex cations are absent. The orbital diagrams for the complexes formed by the metals are drawn where necessary, and require no general explanation.

Chart 2.41 summarises the chemical relations between compounds of chromium in the oxidation states II, III, IV, V, and VI. Charts 24.2 and 24.3 give similar information for compounds of molybdenum and tungsten.

CHROMIUM

SECTION 1. COMPOUNDS CONTAINING A CHROMIUM ATOM IN OXIDATION STATE I

The chromium atom in the Cr^I state is present in the complex cation in the salt $[tri \cdot 2:2'\text{-dipyridyl Cr}][ClO_4]$. The salt is made by the action of magnesium on $[Cr\ dipyr_3][ClO_4]_2$ in the absence of air. It is dark blue, insoluble in water, but soluble in donating organic solvents. Its magnetic moment is 2·0–2·1 Bohr magnetons, which indicates that four of the $3d$ electrons are paired.

SECTION 2. COMPOUNDS CONTAINING A CHROMIUM ATOM IN OXIDATION STATE II

Chromous oxide, CrO, is formed when chromium amalgam is oxidised by air. It is made by passing a mixture of 2 volumes of nitrogen and 1 volume of hydrogen over fused sodium fluoride containing 1% of chromic oxide in solution. On cooling, brick-red plates separate from the melt. The X-ray powder spectrum is said to be different from that of chromium or chromic oxide.

Chromous oxide burns to chromic oxide when heated in air, and it is reduced to metal when heated in hydrogen. The addition of alkali to chromous chloride solution precipitates a yellow hydroxide, probably $Cr(OH)_2$, which reacts with water liberating hydrogen.

Chromous halides. Chromous fluoride, CrF_2, is made by the action of hydrogen fluoride on red hot chromium, or on chromous chloride in the cold. It is a non-volatile solid, m.p. 1100°, slightly soluble in water and insoluble in alcohol. The colour has been described as green or white. Crystalline CrF_2 has a distorted rutile structure.

Chromous chloride, $CrCl_2$, in the anhydrous condition exists as readily fusible, white, deliquescent crystals. It is made by the action of hydrogen chloride on chromium at a white heat, or by the reduction of chromic chloride with hydrogen at a red heat. Chromous chloride is very soluble and forms the hydrates:

$$\underset{\text{Blue}}{CrCl_2,6H_2O} \overset{I}{\rightleftharpoons} \underset{\text{Blue}}{CrCl_2,4H_2O} \overset{50°}{\underset{II}{\rightleftharpoons}} \underset{\text{Dark green}}{CrCl_2,4H_2O} \rightleftharpoons \underset{\text{Pale blue}}{CrCl_2,3H_2O} \rightleftharpoons \underset{\text{Pale green}}{CrCl_2,2H_2O}$$

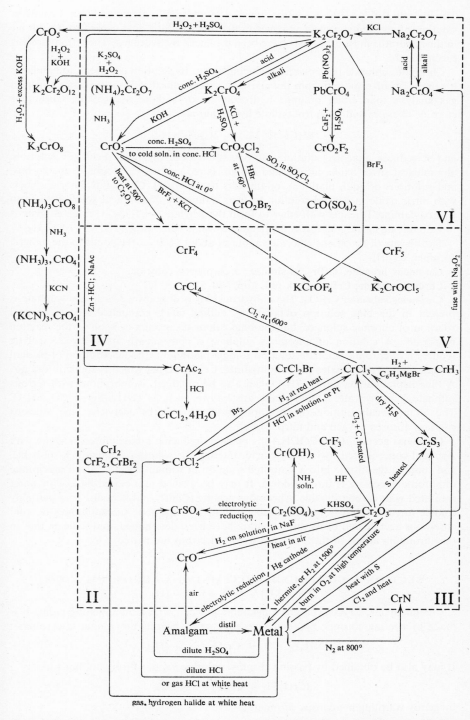

Chart. 24.1. The chemical relations of the compounds of chromium in its different oxidation states.

The hydrate $CrCl_2,4H_2O$ is readily prepared by passing hydrogen chloride through a solution of chromous acetate in concentrated hydrochloric acid cooled to $0°$. All air in the apparatus must previously have been displaced by hydrogen. The tetrahydrate is precipitated.

Chromous chloride is a powerful reducing agent. Its solution is difficult to handle as it rapidly absorbs oxygen from the air; it is a more effective absorbent for oxygen in gas analysis than either quinone hydrosulphite or sodium pyrogallate. Chromous chloride liberates hydrogen from dilute hydrochloric acid:

$$2HCl + 2CrCl_2 = 2CrCl_3 + H_2,$$

and it reduces aqueous solutions of potassium permanganate, Fehling's solution, ammoniacal silver oxide, iodine, and indigo. It reduces mercuric salts to mercurous, and solutions of gold, platinum, or tin salts to the metal. Chromous chloride reacts with nitric oxide in neutral solution to form ammonia, and in acid solution to form hydroxylamine. It reacts with ether to form the ethylate $CrCl_2,OC_2H_5$; the ethylate is not a reducing agent, and forms the neutral chromic complex $[(NH_3)_3CrCl_2OC_2H_5]^0$.

The density of chromous chloride vapour at about $1500°$ corresponds to the dimeric formula, Cr_2Cl_4.

Chromous bromide, $CrBr_2$, is similar to chromous chloride.

Chromous iodide, CrI_2, is dark red, m.p. $790–5°$.

Chromous sulphate, $CrSO_4$. The anhydrous salt is unknown. Chromous sulphate is present in the blue solution obtained by adding much granulated zinc to an acid solution of chromic sulphate, but the blue colour disappears as soon as the reaction moderates. A solution of chromous sulphate is conveniently made by electrolytic reduction of chromic sulphate solution using a platinum cathode. Addition of alcohol to the solution precipitates the pentahydrate, $CrSO_4,5H_2O$, which is stable in dry air. A blue heptahydrate, $CrSO_4,7H_2O$, can also be obtained, isomorphous with ferrous sulphate heptahydrate. Double salts are known such as $(NH_4)_2SO_4,CrSO_4,6H_2O$. The ammoniacal solution of chromous sulphate absorbs acetylene; the aqueous solution absorbs oxygen and nitric oxide.

Chromous acetate, $Cr(OCOCH_3)_2$, is made by reducing potassium dichromate with zinc and concentrated hydrochloric acid, filtering the solution as quickly as possible, and running the filtrate into a saturated solution of sodium acetate. A red precipitate of chromous acetate is thrown down. It may be washed in a closed flask with water saturated with carbon dioxide. Chromous acetate is fairly stable in air. It is sparingly soluble in cold water, but more soluble in hot. The magnetic susceptibilities of solid chromous acetate and of its monohydrate have been determined, and indicate that in the chromium atoms in these crystals all the electrons are paired.

SECTION 3. COMPOUNDS CONTAINING A CHROMIUM ATOM IN OXIDATION STATE III

Chromic oxide, Cr_2O_3, is a green insoluble powder, with a high melting point. It is made by heating chromic hydroxide (p. 987), or by heating ammonium dichromate:

$$(NH_4)_2Cr_2O_7 = Cr_2O_3 + N_2 + 4H_2O.$$

It may also be obtained by passing chromyl chloride vapour through a hot tube:

$$2CrO_2Cl_2 = Cr_2O_3 + O + 2Cl_2,$$

by gently warming mercurous chromate:

$$2Hg_2(CrO_4) = 4Hg + Cr_2O_3 + 5O,$$

or by reducing sodium dichromate by fusion with sulphur:

$$Na_2Cr_2O_7 + S = Na_2SO_4 + Cr_2O_3.$$

Chromic oxide is insoluble in water or in acids. It reacts with fused potassium hydrogen sulphate:

$$6KHSO_4 + Cr_2O_3 = Cr_2(SO_4)_3 + 3K_2SO_4 + 3H_2O,$$

or with fused sodium peroxide:

$$3Na_2O_2 + Cr_2O_3 = 2Na_2CrO_4 + Na_2O,$$

or with an alkaline solution of potassium permanganate:

$$2KOH + 2KMnO_4 + Cr_2O_3 = 2MnO_2 + 2K_2CrO_4 + H_2O.$$

Chromic oxide is oxidised by 70% perchloric acid to chromium trioxide, CrO_3. It is reduced by aluminium in the thermite process to metallic chromium, and by hydrogen under certain conditions to chromous oxide (p. 984).

Chromic oxide has the corundum structure (p. 349), in which there are no discrete Cr_2O_3 molecules.

Chromic hydroxide, $Cr(OH)_3$, is thrown down as a green-grey flocculent precipitate when ammonia solution is added to a boiling solution of a chromic salt. If precipitation is carried out in the cold, or by use of potassium or sodium hydroxide, the ammonium ion or alkali is present in the precipitate. Chromic hydroxide is amphoteric; it dissolves in acids to give chromic salts and in fused or aqueous alkalis to give chromites.

Chromic sulphide, Cr_2S_3, is a paramagnetic green or black solid. It is made by heating chromium (or chromic oxide or chromic chloride) with sulphur, or by heating chromic hydroxide or chloride with hydrogen sulphide. It cannot be made by precipitating a chromic salt with a sulphide in aqueous solution, because it is so readily hydrolysed that in such conditions only the hydroxide is obtained, according to the equation:

$$2CrCl_3 + 6H_2O + 3(NH_4)_2S = 2Cr(OH)_3 + 6NH_4Cl + 3H_2S.$$

Chromic sulphide burns in air to chromic oxide, or to a basic sulphate. It is not decomposed by water, or by acids except nitric acid or aqua regia.

The chromic halides, $Crhal_3$. The chromic halides are solids with high sublimation points; they appear to be giant molecule compounds rather than simple covalent compounds.

Chromic fluoride, CrF_3, is a green crystalline compound with a high melting point. It sublimes at 1200°. It is made by the action of hydrofluoric acid on chromic oxide, or by the action at a red heat of hydrogen chloride on a mixture of calcium fluoride and chromic oxide. It forms several hydrates. The structure is isomorphous with that of AlF_3 (p. 537).

Chromic chloride, $CrCl_3$, in the anhydrous state exists as peach-blossom coloured crystals. It is made by passing chlorine at a high temperature over metallic chromium, or over a mixture of chromic oxide and carbon. If heated alone it partly dissociates, but it may be sublimed at a red heat in an atmosphere of chlorine. If quite pure it is unaffected by cold water, acetone, alcohol, or ether, but if contaminated with a trace of chromous salt it dissolves readily in these solvents. Crystalline chromic chloride has a layer structure. The chromium atoms are in one third of the octahedral holes between planes of close-packed chlorine atoms. Chromic bromide and chromic iodide are known.

Chromic sulphate, $Cr_2(SO_4)_3$. The anhydrous salt is made by allowing a mixture of equal parts of dry chromic hydroxide and concentrated sulphuric acid to stand for several weeks. It is a bluish-violet (peach-blossom colour) crystalline mass, which dissolves in water only in the presence of a trace of a chromous salt. Several hydrates are known: $Cr_2(SO_4)_3,18H_2O$ violet; $9H_2O$ and $3H_2O$ violet; $6H_2O$ green.

CHROMIC COMPLEXES

Chromium in the Cr^{III} state forms a greater range of complexes than any other metal. A complex may be neutral, or an anion, or a cation. An example of a neutral complex is chromium acetylacetonate, $[CrA_3]$, a reddish-violet solid, m.p. 214°, b.p. 340°. The vapour is green. The complex is made by heating chromic hydroxide with acetylacetone. It is both thermally and chemically stable. Two anionic complexes are the oxalato complex in the salt $K_3[Cr(C_2O_4)_3]$, and the catechol complex in the salt $K_3[Cr\,cat_3]$.

Many series of the anion, neutral, and cation complexes of chromium in the Cr^{III} state can be obtained by varying the stoichiometric proportions of two ligands (one an anion, and the other neutral) in the complex. For example, thiocyanate ions and water molecules give the series:

$$K_3[Cr(SCN)_6], \quad K_2[Cr(SCN)_5(H_2O)], \quad K[Cr(SCN)_4(H_2O)_2],$$
$$[Cr(SCN)_3(H_2O)_3]^0, \quad [Cr(SCN)_2(H_2O)_4]Cl, \quad [Cr(SCN)(H_2O)_5]Cl_2,$$
$$[Cr(H_2O)_6]Cl_3.$$

Each of these complex salts is made by treating a chromic salt in aqueous solution for several days at 50° with the correct concentration of potassium thiocyanate solution. The neutral complexes and the salts of the cation complexes (not the salts of the anions) can be extracted with ether from the aqueous solution. The salts are red and do not give the reactions for chromic or thiocyanate ions until they have been standing in aqueous solution for some days. Among the other complexes in which the ligands are anions are the chromicyanide complex in the salt $K_3[Cr(CN)_6]$ a yellow solid less stable than potassium ferricyanide, and halide complexes such as that in the salt $K_3[CrF_6]$, and, more commonly, in $K_2[CrX_3,H_2O]$.

Amines and ammonia may play the part of water in the above mentioned aquo complexes (except that complexes of the type, $K_2[Cr(NH_3)X_5]$ are unknown). The replacement of the hydrogen atoms in ammonia by alkyl or aryl groups weakens the ligand bonds. The effect of the aryl group is less than that of the alkyl group. Ring formation by diamines or triamines has a stabilising effect on the complex. The strongly alkaline base $[Cr(NH_3)_6](OH)_3$ is made by treating an aqueous solution of hexammino chromic chloride with silver oxide; it separates as a yellow precipitate when alcohol or ether is added to the solution.

In a chromic complex two or more different kinds of ligand molecules may be attached to one chromium atom. Such an arrangement may give rise to isomerism. Complexes such as the cation in $[Cr(NH_3)_4Cl_2]Cl$ show geometrical isomerism, and those such as the cation in $[Cr\,en_2Cl_2]Cl$ show optical isomerism.†

SECTION 4. COMPOUNDS CONTAINING A CHROMIUM ATOM IN OXIDATION STATE IV

This appears to be an unstable oxidation state of chromium and it is represented by few compounds.

---

† Limitations of space forbid an adequate treatment of the complexes of chromium and also those of the other transition elements. The complexes possess an extensive chemistry, and those of appropriate structure display many types of isomerism. Detailed accounts, given in compact and generalised forms, are to be found in *Chemical Elements and Their Compounds*, by N. V. Sidgwick, and in *Modern Aspects of Inorganic Chemistry*, by H. J. Emeleus and J. S. Anderson (Routledge and Kegan Paul Ltd.).

Chromium tetrafluoride, CrF_4, is a brown amorphous solid which gives a blue vapour. It is hydrolysed by water to give Cr^{III} and Cr^{VI}.

Chromium tetrachloride, $CrCl_4$, is a gas made by heating a mixture of chromium trichloride and chlorine to 600–700°. It is condensed by rapid cooling with solid CO_2, but it begins to lose chlorine at $-80°$.

Chromium dioxide, CrO_2, a black powder, is obtained by heating $Cr(OH)_3$ in oxygen at 350°, but its constitution is not certain.

SECTION 5. COMPOUNDS CONTAINING A CHROMIUM ATOM IN OXIDATION STATE V

There are few representatives of chromium compounds in which the chromium atom is in the Cr^V oxidation state, and none of them is well characterised.

Chromium pentafluoride, CrF_5, is a red, fairly volatile solid. It is at once hydrolysed by water to Cr^{III} and Cr^{VI}.

$KCrOF_4$ is a light purple powder. It is obtained by the action of bromine trifluoride on potassium dichromate. The purple $KCrOF_4, \frac{1}{2}BrF_3$ is first formed, which on heating to 130–150° loses BrF_3. An equimolecular mixture of CrO_3 and KCl gives the same product when treated with BrF_3.

$AgCrOF_4$ is made by the action of BrF_3 on silver dichromate. It is a purple powder which reacts with moist air to give silver chromate:

$$AgCrOF_4 + 2H_2O + O = AgCrO_4 + 4HF.$$

The orbital diagram of the anion $[CrOF_4]^-$ is:

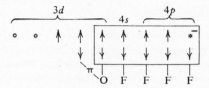

Fig. 24.17. Orbital diagram for the anion $[CrOF_4]^-$.

The yellow pyridine and quinoline salts of the ion $[CrOCl_4]^-$ are known. Garnet red salts of the formula $M_2(CrOCl_5)$ where M is K, Rb, Cs, or NH_4, are made by reducing chromium trioxide at 0° with very concentrated hydrochloric acid. The orbital diagram for the complex anion is shown in Fig. 24.18:

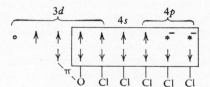

Fig. 24.18. Orbital diagram for the anion $[CrOCl_5]^{2-}$.

SECTION 6. COMPOUNDS CONTAINING A CHROMIUM ATOM IN OXIDATION STATE VI

Chromium trioxide, CrO_3, exists as red crystals, m.p. 197°. It is made by adding concentrated sulphuric acid to a concentrated solution of potassium dichromate. The precipitated red crystals are washed with concentrated nitric acid free from oxides of nitrogen, and the nitric acid is removed by warming to 70°.

Chromium trioxide volatilises to give a red vapour just above its melting point. It is extremely soluble in water to give a red solution. There is a eutectic point at $-155°$; the composition is 60.5% of CrO_3.

Chromium trioxide when heated begins to lose oxygen at about $300°$. It is a powerful oxidising agent. It inflames alcohol. The concentrated solution is reduced by most organic substances.

The crystal structure of chromium trioxide is that of AlF_3; each chromium atom is surrounded by six oxygen atoms.

Chromic acid. The aqueous solution of chromium trioxide contains the acids H_2CrO_4, $H_2Cr_2O_7$, $H_2Cr_3O_{10}$, and $H_2Cr_4O_{13}$, derived by the association of one or more molecules of chromic oxide with a molecule of water. None of the acids has been isolated, but there are many stable and well-known salts of the ions $[CrO_4{}^{2-}]$ and $[Cr_2O_7{}^{2-}]$. The salts $K_2Cr_3O_{10}$ and $K_2Cr_4O_{13}$ have been prepared as red crystals by boiling potassium dichromate with nitric acid. Acid salts such as $KHCrO_4$ are not known.

Chromic acid is a useful oxidising agent. It oxidises sulphur dioxide, hydrogen sulphide, stannous chloride, arsenious oxide, ferrous sulphate, and hydrogen iodide, to the usual oxidation products. In these reactions chromic acid is reduced to the Cr^{III} oxidation state. Chromic acid is not reduced by hydrochloric acid unless the hydrochloric acid is extremely concentrated.

The chromates are coloured. **Sodium chromate, Na_2CrO_4,** exists as yellow deliquescent crystals. Its solubility in water is 76.6 gm/100 gm at $20°$. Its hydrates and their transition points are:

$$10H_2O \overset{20°}{\rightleftharpoons} 6H_2O \overset{26°}{\rightleftharpoons} 4H_2O \overset{63°}{\rightleftharpoons} \text{anhydrous salt.}$$

The anhydrous salt separates from the supersaturated solution if concentrated over 80% sulphuric acid. The anhydrous salt, and the deca- and hexa-hydrates form solid solutions with the corresponding compounds of sodium sulphate. **Potassium chromate** is made by evaporating a solution obtained by mixing potassium hydroxide and chromium trioxide in the correct proportions. It forms non-deliquescent crystals without water of crystallisation, m.p. $968°$. It is less soluble than the sodium salt. Barium chromate (yellow), silver chromate (red), and lead chromate (chrome yellow) are insoluble in water, but are soluble in alkaline or acid solutions.

The dichromates are salts of the condensed acid, $H_2Cr_2O_7$, the structure of which is analogous to that of disulphuric acid (p. 846). Sodium dichromate dihydrate exists as red crystals. It is very soluble in water; at $20°$ 180 gm dissolve in 100 gm of water. Garnet red crystals of anhydrous potassium dichromate are made by adding the calculated quantity of sulphuric acid to a solution of the normal chromate and crystallising. The crystals are non-deliquescent; 12.7 gm dissolve in 100 gm of water at $20°$, but the solubility in hot water is greater. Ammonium dichromate is made by mixing the calculated quantities of chromium trioxide and ammonia in solution and crystallising. It is a useful laboratory source of chromic oxide (p. 986).

Chromyl fluoride, CrO_2F_2, exists as violet-red crystals which sublime at $29.6°$, m.p. $31.6°$. The liquid is orange-red. It is prepared by the action of chromium trioxide and anhydrous hydrogen fluoride at room temperature in a copper flask. It is extremely reactive, especially with oxidisable organic compounds.

Chromyl chloride, CrO_2Cl_2, is a deep red liquid, m.p. $-95.5°$, b.p. $116.7°$. It is made either by heating a mixture of a chromate and a chloride with concentrated sulphuric acid, or by adding concentrated sulphuric acid to a cold solution of chromium trioxide in concentrated hydrochloric acid:

$$CrO_3 + 2HCl = CrO_2Cl_2 + H_2O.$$

Chromyl chloride is miscible with CCl_4, CS_2, and $CHCl_3$. It is a strong oxidising agent and inflames phosphorus, sulphur, ammonia, and alcohol. Its oxidising reaction takes place smoothly if moderated by the use of a solvent. For example, a solution of chromyl chloride in carbon disulphide oxidises toluene to benzaldehyde.† If chromyl chloride is added to a saturated solution of potassium chloride, red crystals of potassium chloro-chromate (Peligot's salt) are formed:

$$CrO_2Cl_2 + KCl + H_2O = KCrO_3Cl + 2HCl.$$

If chromyl chloride is treated with sulphur trioxide in sulphuryl chloride solution, chromyl sulphate $CrO(SO_4)_2$ is formed. This compound is colourless and very sensitive to water. It is decomposed by heating to 100–200°. Chromyl bromide has been obtained in an impure condition.

THE PERCHROMIC COMPOUNDS

No generally accepted structures have been assigned to the perchromic compounds. It is possible, however, to write consistent orbital structures for all of them on the assumption that each peroxy group is bound to a chromium atom to form a ring structure. The following orbital diagrams are conjectural, but they fit the experimental evidence so far as it goes:

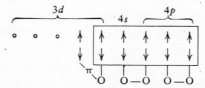

Fig. 24.19. Orbital diagram for CrO_5. CrO_5 is diamagnetic and has two peroxy groups per chromium atom.

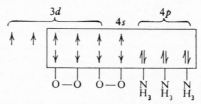

Fig. 24.20. Orbital diagram for $(NH_3)_3CrO_4$. The paramagnetic moment is equivalent to two unpaired electrons. The diagram for $K_3[(CN_3)_3CrO_4]$ would be similar.

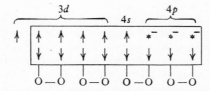

Fig. 24.21. Orbital diagram for the anion $[CrO_8]^{3-}$. The paramagnetic moment is equivalent to one unpaired electron. The four O_2 groups are situated at the apices of a tetrahedron surrounding the chromium atom.

† This is Etard's reaction. It is remarkable that the reaction goes no further, although benzaldehyde is a reducing agent.

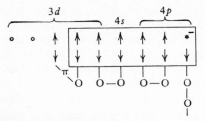

Fig. 24.22. Orbital diagram for the anion $[Cr_2O_{12}]^{2-}$. The anion is diamagnetic.

Chromium peroxide, CrO_5, has not been isolated. It is present in the blue solution obtained by adding hydrogen peroxide to an acidified solution of potassium dichromate. The peroxide is unstable in aqueous solution, in which it decomposes in a few minutes, but it dissolves in ether to give a blue solution which retains its colour for some time.

By adding 97% hydrogen peroxide to chromium trioxide dissolved in methyl ether at $-80°$ a dark blue solution is obtained. If this is separated from the excess of chromium trioxide and evaporated at $-30°$, very explosive dark blue crystals are formed with the composition $(CH_3)_2O,CrO_5$.

Chromium peroxide reacts with acids in aqueous solution to form chromic salts:

$$3H_2SO_4 + 2CrO_5 = Cr_2(SO_4)_3 + 3H_2O + 7O.$$

With alkalis it yields chromates:

$$K_2O + CrO_5 = K_2CrO_4 + O_2,$$

and with silver nitrate it also yields chromates. It reduces potassium permanganate solution quantitatively in the presence of a trace of molybdate:

$$4KMnO_4 + 5CrO_5 + 6H_2SO_4 = 2K_2SO_4 + 4MnSO_4 + 10O_2 + 5H_2CrO_4 + H_2O.$$

This relation shows that the CrO_5 molecule contains two peroxide oxygen groups.

Chromium peroxide in ethereal solution combines with pyridine to give a co-ordination compound pyr,CrO_5, insoluble in pyridine, but soluble in organic solvents, and monomeric in benzene, nitrobenzene, and bromoform. It is explosive. Chromium peroxide in ethereal solution reacts with alkaline hydrogen peroxide in alcohol to give $K_2Cr_2O_{12},2H_2O$ (blue), and in more strongly alkaline solution to give K_3CrO_8 (red).

Chromium peroxide is diamagnetic. Its structure has been suggested on p. 991.

$CrO_4,3NH_3$, is formed (i) by treating an ammoniacal solution of a chromate with hydrogen peroxide at $0°$, or (ii) by treating the red ammonium perchromate, $(NH_4)_3CrO_8$, with 10% ammonia solution at $40°$. Brown $CrO_4,3NH_3$ separates out. The ammonia compound has a paramagnetic moment equivalent to two unpaired electrons; an orbital structure for the compound is suggested on p. 991.

If potassium cyanide is added to the brown solution of the above ammonia compound the derivative $CrO_4,(KCN)_3$ is obtained. A structure for this derivative which corresponds to that of the ammonia compound is also suggested on p. 991.

The red peroxychromates. Red potassium peroxychromate, K_3CrO_8, is made by reaction between hydrogen peroxide and potassium dichromate in strongly alkaline solution below $0°$. It contains 3·5 peroxy groups per chromium atom, and has a paramagnetic moment equivalent to one unpaired electron. The potassium salt is the most stable of the red peroxychromates. It can be obtained dry; the sodium and ammonium salts cannot be obtained dry. The salts explode at the following temperatures: K $178°$, Na $115°$, NH_4 $50°$. The red peroxychromates are isomorphous with the peroxyvanadates, and have the same crystal structure as the peroxyniobiates and peroxytantalates.

The blue peroxychromates. Blue potassium peroxychromate, $K_2Cr_2O_{12}$, is made (i) by treating the ethereal solution of CrO_5 with a mixture of hydrogen peroxide and potassium hydroxide in alcoholic solution, or (ii) by adding 30% hydrogen peroxide to an ice-cold solution of potassium sulphate and ammonium dichromate. The potassium, sodium, and ammonium salts, crystallise with two molecules of water of crystallisation. The corresponding very explosive thallous salt $Tl_2Cr_2O_{12}$ is anhydrous, which establishes the fact that there is no hydrogen peroxide of crystallisation in the potassium compound. The potassium salt contains 2·5 peroxy groups per chromium atom, and it is diamagnetic.

A structure for the blue peroxychromate ion is suggested on p. 992.

MOLYBDENUM

The principal types of compound formed by molybdenum are included in Table 24.18, and a synopsis of the chief chemical changes undergone by these compounds is shown by Chart 24.2.

Molybdenum forms the interstitial compounds MoC and MoN, but no compound in which its oxidation state is 1. The molybdenum compounds in Section 2 are different from the chromium and tungsten compounds in the same Section. There are no simple compounds of the type MoX_2, but instead a series of complexes formed from the compound Mo_6Cl_{12} without reduction or oxidation.

SECTION 2. COMPOUNDS CONTAINING A MOLYBDENUM ATOM IN OXIDATION STATE II

Molybdenum forms a number of complex compounds with the halogens in which the groups Mo_6Cl_8 and Mo_6Br_8 play important parts. The structures of the following four compounds have been determined by X-ray experiments:

$$[Mo_6Cl_8,2H_2O,(OH)_4],12H_2O$$

$$[Mo_6Cl_8,2H_2O,Cl_4],6H_2O$$

$$(NH_4)_2[Mo_6Cl_8,Cl_6]$$

$$(H_3O)_2[Mo_6Cl_8,Cl_6],6H_2O.$$

The eight chlorine atoms of the group Mo_6Cl_8 are at the corners of a cube, and the six molybdenum atoms are at the centres of the cube faces; the six ligands are at the apices of an octahedron superscribing the Mo_6Cl_8 unit. Other compounds containing the group Mo_6Cl_8 are:

$[Mo_6Cl_8,2H_2O,Br_4],4H_2O$	$K_2[Mo_6Cl_8,Cl_6],4H_2O$
$[Mo_6Cl_8,2H_2O,Br_4],10H_2O$	$K_2[Mo_6Cl_8,Br_6],6H_2O$
$[Mo_6Cl_8,2H_2O,I_4],10H_2O$	$K_2[Mo_6Cl_8,I_6],6H_2O.$

The anhydrous compound, Mo_6Cl_{12}, is made (i) by the action of chlorine on heated molybdenum, (ii) by the action of carbonyl chloride on molybdenum at 630°, (iii) by heating $MoCl_3$ in a stream of carbon dioxide; the trichloride disproportionates into $MoCl_4$ and Mo_6Cl_{12}; the volatile $MoCl_4$ is removed by the carbon dioxide stream, leaving Mo_6Cl_{12} as a residue.

Mo_6Cl_{12} is a yellow infusible non-volatile powder. It is insoluble in water, toluene, ligroin, or acetic acid, but it dissolves in alcohol and ether, and in concentrated HCl, HBr, and HI, and in alkalis. It is unattacked by dilute acids. In solution it has no reducing power. It reacts with silver nitrate by double decomposition, but the silver salt is not reduced:

$$Mo_6Cl_{12}+4AgNO_3+2H_2O = [Mo_6Cl_8,(NO_3)_4,2H_2O]+4AgCl.$$

32+A.T.I.C.

994

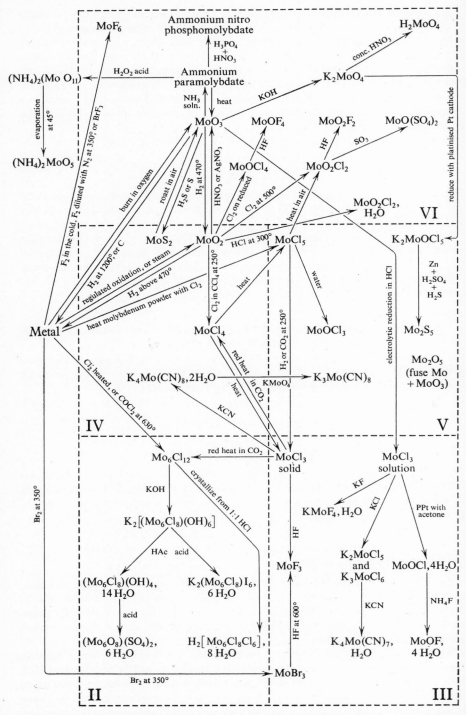

Chart 24.2. The chemical relations of the compounds of molybdenum in its different oxidation states.

The reaction which takes place when Mo_6Cl_{12} dissolves in potassium hydroxide may be written:

$$Mo_6Cl_{12} + 6KOH = K_2[Mo_6Cl_8,(OH)_6] + 4KCl.$$

The addition of acetic acid or ammonium chloride to the solution causes the precipitation of a hydrated hydroxide:

$$K_2[Mo_6Cl_8,(OH)_6] + 2HAc + Aq. = 2KAc + [Mo_6Cl_8,2H_2O,(OH)_4],12H_2O,$$

which dissolves in acids to form salts.

SECTION 3. COMPOUNDS CONTAINING A MOLYBDENUM ATOM IN OXIDATION STATE III

The compounds in this Section correspond to the chromium compounds in the Section, and include the oxide Mo_2O_3, the sulphide Mo_2S_3, and the trihalides, all of which are giant molecules, the oxyfluorides such as $MoOF,4H_2O$, and salts containing a molybdenum atom in a complex anion, such as $K_3[MoCl_6]$. There is also the cyanide $K_4[Mo(CN)_7],H_2O$ which is interesting because the anion contains a lone electron pair in one of the $5d$ orbitals. All the compounds of Mo^{III} are reducing agents. Little is known about Mo_2O_3 and Mo_2S_3.

Molybdenum trihalides. The preparations and certain properties of these compounds are summarised in Table 24.19. They are all coloured infusible solids, stable to fairly high temperatures.

Table 24.19. *Preparations and Properties of the Molybdenum Trihalides*

	MoF_3	$MoCl_3$	$MoBr_3$
Appearance	Dark pink solid	Dark red crystals	Dark green needles
Preparation	Pass HF over $MoBr_3$ at 600°	Pass HCl over $MoBr_3$ at a dull red heat	Pass Br_2 over molybdenum at 350–400°
Effect of heat	Unchanged	Decomposes at a red heat to $MoCl_4$ and Mo_6Cl_{12}	
Effect of heat in air	Oxidised to Mo_2O_3 and HF	Oxidised	
Reduction	Reduced by H_2 to metal		Reduced by NH_3 gas to metal
Structure	AlF_3		
Solubility in water		Insoluble	Insoluble

By the electrolytic reduction of MoO_3 in hydrochloric acid a red solution is obtained which contains the very soluble complex $MoCl_3,3H_2O$. The complex reduces cupric, silver, and mercuric salts, and unites with potassium chloride in alcoholic solution to yield K_2MoCl_5,H_2O, which is deposited on warming.

Molybdenum oxyhalides, $MoOHal,4H_2O$. The fluoride, the chloride, and the bromide are known. The fluoride, $MoOF,4H_2O$, is an insoluble buff-coloured precipitate made by the action of ammonium fluoride on $MoOCl,4H_2O$ in air-free aqueous solution. The chloride, $MoOCl,4H_2O$, is made by reducing MoO_3 electrolytically, and is precipitated from the resultant solution by acetone in the complete absence of air. The precipitate is usually buff-coloured, but by varying the conditions it can be obtained in a brown or green form. It is readily soluble in water in which it dissolves as a non-electrolyte which subsequently hydrolyses. Lead acetate gives no precipitate with the freshly prepared solution. Molybdenum oxychloride is easily oxidised by air and is a reducing agent. Its solution reduces cupric and ferric salts, and reduces mercuric chloride and silver nitrate to the metals. The bromine derivative is similar to the chlorine compound.

SECTION 4. COMPOUNDS CONTAINING A MOLYBDENUM ATOM IN OXIDATION STATE IV

The compounds in this Section include the oxide MoO_2, the sulphide MoS_2, the tetrahalides, and many salts containing molybdenum in the anion. The molybdenum atom in the anions often contains a lone electron pair in one of the d orbitals.

Molybdenum dioxide, MoO_2, a reddish-brown powder, is made:

(i) by the regulated oxidation of molybdenum,
(ii) by the action of steam on molybdenum,
(iii) by the reduction of MoO_3 with hydrogen at 470°.

Molybdenum dioxide is insoluble in alkaline or acid solutions. It unites with chlorine at 600° to give MoO_2Cl_2, and it is oxidised by silver nitrate (which is reduced to silver) to molybdenum trioxide. At 500° it is reduced by hydrogen to the metal. Molybdenum dioxide has the rutile crystal structure. It is a fairly good conductor of electricity.

Molybdenum disulphide, molybdenite, MoS_2, can be made by the action of hydrogen sulphide on molybdenum trioxide, or by fusing molybdenum trioxide with sulphur and potassium carbonate. It has a layer lattice; each molybdenum atom is at the centre of a trigonal prism, and six sulphur atoms are at the apices. It is diamagnetic. At about 200° the crystals have metallic conductivity. On strong heating molybdenum sulphide is decomposed into its elements.

The only member of the **molybdenum tetrahalides** which is well-known is the chloride $MoCl_4$, which is made:

(i) by heating molybdenum dioxide with a solution of chlorine in carbon tetrachloride at 250°,
(ii) by heating molybdenum trichloride to a red heat in a stream of carbon dioxide, when it disproportionates giving Mo_6Cl_{12} (non-volatile) and volatile $MoCl_4$.

Molybdenum tetrachloride is an easily volatile brown powder. It is soluble in alcohol without decomposition, but it reacts with water to give the hydrolysis products of $MoCl_3$ and $MoCl_5$. When heated it disproportionates to $MoCl_3$ and $MoCl_5$.

Complex anions of Mo^{IV}. The salt $K_4[Mo(CN)_8],2H_2O$ is made by the action of a large excess of potassium cyanide on $MoCl_3,3H_2O$, or on $MoOCl_3$. The salt is yellow. It is diamagnetic. The anion is dodecahedral with the eight CN groups at the apices and the molybdenum atom at the centre. The orbital diagram is shown in Fig. 24.23:

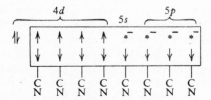

Fig. 24.23. Orbital diagram for the anion $[Mo(CN)_8]^{4-}$.

Other salts are $K_4[MoO_2(CN)_6]$,xAq. violet, and $K_3[Mo(OH)_3(CN)_4,H_2O]$,xAq. blue. The orbital diagram of the anion of the blue salt is shown in Fig. 24.24:

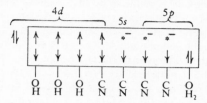

Fig. 24.24.   Orbital diagram for the anion $[Mo(OH)_3(CN)_4(H_2O)]^{3-}$.

SECTION 5. COMPOUNDS CONTAINING A MOLYBDENUM ATOM IN OXIDATION STATE V

The existence of the oxide Mo_2O_5 is doubtful, and the dark violet powder which is assigned this formula is probably a mixture of MoO_2 and MoO_3. Molybdenum penta-sulphide, Mo_2S_5 is made by reducing a solution of ammonium molybdate in 20% sulphuric acid with zinc until wine red. The solution is saturated with hydrogen sulphide, and a dark brown precipitate of $Mo_2S_5,3H_2O$ is obtained. The precipitate is insoluble in water, but soluble in strongly acid or alkaline solutions. Nearly complete dehydration can be effected by warming the precipitate in a stream of carbon dioxide.

Molybdenum pentahalides. Molybdenum pentafluoride, MoF_5, an olive green solid, is obtained by the action of fluorine on molybdenum hexacarbonyl at $-75°$. If the solid is heated to $+170°$ in vacuo a light yellow liquid is obtained which solidifies at $+64°$ and has the composition MoF_5.

Molybdenum pentachloride, $MoCl_5$, exists as dark green hygroscopic crystals, m.p. 194°, b.p. 268°. It is made by heating molybdenum powder in chlorine. The vapour is dark red. When heated in air it is oxidised to the white oxychloride, MoO_2Cl_2. It reacts violently with water to give the green oxychloride, $MoOCl_3$, and with alcohol to liberate hydrogen chloride. It forms the complex $MoCl_5,2(C_2H_5)_2O$ with ether, but it is reduced by pyridine to a complex $MoCl_4,(pyr)_x$. The density of $MoCl_5$ vapour is normal, and electron diffraction experiments show that the molecule is a trigonal bipyramid.

Complexes. The neutral complex $MoCl_5,2(C_2H_5)_2O$ has been mentioned. A complex anion is present in the salt $K_2[MoOCl_5]$ which is made by the reduction of potassium molybdate at a platinised platinum cathode. The salt is soluble in water to give a reddish-brown solution; the colour fades as insoluble $MoO(OH)_3$ is precipitated by hydrolysis. The magnetic moment of the anion corresponds to the presence of one unpaired electron.

SECTION 6. COMPOUNDS CONTAINING A MOLYBDENUM ATOM IN OXIDATION STATE VI

Molybdenum trioxide, MoO_3, is made:

  (i) by heating molybdenite, MoS_2, in air,
 (ii) by heating molybdic acid or ammonium molybdate,
(iii) by burning metallic molybdenum in oxygen,
 (iv) by oxidising molybdenum dioxide with nitric acid or silver nitrate.

Molybdenum trioxide is a white solid which on heating turns yellow and sublimes; it melts at 795° to a yellow liquid, b.p. 1155°. It is sparingly soluble in cold (0·107 gm/100 gm at 18°), more soluble in hot water (2·06 gm/100 gm), but it does not give molybdic acid. Molybdenum trioxide is reduced by hydrogen at 500° to give reddish-brown MoO_2; at 1200° it gives a grey powder of metallic molybdenum. It is also reduced to metal by carbon at a good heat. It reacts with dry gaseous hydrogen chloride at 150–200° to give the crystalline compound $MoO_3,2HCl$. It dissolves in excess of ammonia solution to give ammonium molybdate, $(NH_4)_2MoO_4$, but on evaporation the solution deposits crystals of the paramolybdate $(NH_4)_6Mo_7O_{24},4H_2O$. Molybdenum trioxide dissolves in alkaline hydroxide and carbonate to give X_2MoO_4, but if fused with calcium carbonate at 1000° it gives Ca_3MoO_3. If a solution of molybdenum trioxide in hydrochloric acid is electrolysed an aqueous solution of molybdenum trichloride is obtained.

In the crystal of molybdenum trioxide the atoms are arranged in MoO_6 octahedra. Each octahedron shares two corners and two edges with other octahedra, thus giving rise to a layer structure. The structure of MoO_3 differs from those of CrO_3 and WO_3. The MoO_3 structure is common in sulphides but rare in oxides.

Molybdenum hexafluoride, MoF_6, a white crystalline compound, m.p. 17·5°, b.p. 35°, is the only hexahalide of molybdenum. It is made:

   (i) by the action of fluorine diluted with nitrogen on molybdenum at 350°,
   (ii) by the action of hydrogen fluoride on Mo_6Br_{12} at 800–860°,
   (iii) by the action of bromine trifluoride on molybdenum or on Mo_6Br_{12},
   (iv) by the action of fluorine on molybdenum hexacarbonyl above 50°.

Molybdenum hexafluoride is quite stable, and it is not attacked by dry air, chlorine, or sulphur dioxide. It is immediately hydrolysed by water. The results of experiments on the Raman and infrared spectra indicate that the molecule is a regular octahedron.

Molybdenum oxyhalides. $MoOF_4$, a colourless deliquescent crystalline compound, m.p. 97°, b.p. 180°, is obtained by the action of hydrogen fluoride on the product (perhaps $MoOCl_4$) resulting from the action of chlorine on partially reduced molybdenum dioxide. $MoOF_4$ dissolves in water to form a colourless solution which on evaporation leaves molybdenum trioxide.

MoO_2F_2, a colourless solid, is made by the action of hydrogen fluoride on MoO_2Cl_2.

MoO_2Cl_2, a white or pale yellow crystalline compound, is made:

   (i) by passing dry chlorine over MoO_2 heated to 700°,
   (ii) by heating MoO_3 to 150–300° in dry gaseous hydrogen chloride.

It sublimes easily, and melts only under pressure. It is easily soluble in water, alcohol, ether, and acetone; in the last two solvents its molecular weight is normal. It is the starting point for the preparation of other molybdenum compounds.

Complexes. The anion in $K_3[MoO_3F_3]$ has an octahedral structure; a probable orbital diagram is shown in Fig. 24.25:

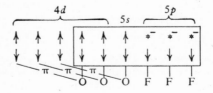

Fig. 24.25. Orbital diagram for the anion $[MoO_3F_3]^{3-}$.

Molybdic acid, H_2MoO_4, exists as fine white needles. It is made by treating a solution of a molybdate with concentrated nitric acid. Yellow crystals of the hydrate H_2MoO_4,H_2O separate from the solution, and on gentle warming the anhydrous acid is obtained. Molybdic acid is sparingly soluble in water (0·1 gm in 100 gm at 18°) and the solution is acid to litmus. The acid may be reduced to molybdenum compounds in which the valency of molybdenum is less than six. The crystal of H_2MoO_4 consists of anionic layers built up of MoO_6 octahedra which share corners in two directions. Some of the simple molybdates are: Li_2MoO_4, m.p. 705°, Na_2MoO_4, m.p. 687°, K_2MoO_4, m.p. 926°, and Ag_2MoO_4. The silver salt and the sodium salt are isomorphous and have a spinel structure (p. 349); the molybdenum atoms are in tetrahedral holes, and the silver atoms in octahedral holes.

The dimolybdates such as $Na_2Mo_2O_7$ cannot be made in solution, but can be obtained by fusing the constituent oxides together.

THE HETEROPOLY MOLYBDIC ACIDS

Many salts are known having complex anions which contain molybdenum atoms, oxygen atoms, and a much smaller proportion of atoms of another acid-forming element. There are two main classes of such salts:

6-heteropoly acid salts, for example, $K_6(Te,Mo_6O_{24})$,
12-heteropoly acid salts, for example, $K_3(P,Mo_{12}O_{40})$.

The anions are built up by the use of oxygen bridges. The unit is the octahedral group MoO_6. In the anion of the 6-heteropoly acids a ring structure of six octahedra is arranged so that each octahedron shares two edges (that is four oxygen atoms) with its neighbours. The composition of the ring of six octahedra is Mo_6O_{24}.† Such a ring contains a central space which has exactly the size and configuration of one of the six octahedra. An atom of co-ordination number 6 is now placed in the central space, and shares six oxygen atoms from the octahedra forming the ring. The composition of the anion Te,Mo_6O_{24} is thus accounted for. There are, however, several ways in which six octahedra conforming to the above conditions can be arranged in a ring with a seventh octahedron at the centre. Two of these are shown in Fig. 24.26(a) and (b). The first has been shown experimentally to be the structure of the telluromolybdate ion.

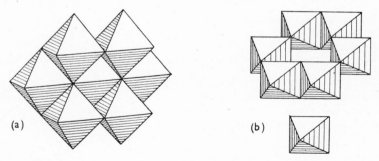

(a)   (b)

Fig. 24.26. Two ways of arranging six octahedra in a ring. In Fig. (a) a seventh octahedron is drawn to indicate how it fits into the central space. In Fig. (b) the seventh octahedron which exactly fits the central space is drawn separately.

† Each molybdenum atom in the ring is associated with 4 oxygen atoms each shared with another molybdenum atom, and with two oxygen atoms which are not shared. Hence the number of oxygen atoms in the unit ring is $6(4 \times \frac{1}{2} + 2) = 24$.

The structure of the twelve heteropoly acids may be described as follows. If three MoO_6 octahedra are taken and arranged so that one oxygen atom is held in common, and also that each octahedron shares two oxygen atoms with each of two neighbours, the arrangement shown in Fig. 24.27(b) is obtained.

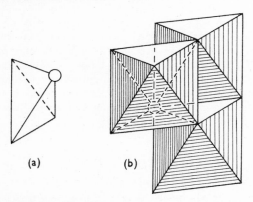

(a)   (b)

Fig. 24.27. Diagrammatic sketch to illustrate the structure of the ion $[PMo_{12}O_{40}]^{3-}$. Fig. (b) shows three MoO_6 octahedra viewed from above. (Lines indicating the edges of the four lower faces of the two octahedra on the right have been omitted for the sake of clarity.) The oxygen atom at O is common to the lowest apex of the octahedron on the left, and to one equatorial apex of each of the other two octahedra. Other oxygen atoms are shared by the octahedra where their apices are coincident. The point O on the PO_4 tetrahedron (Fig. (a)) corresponds to the point O common to the three octahedra. If three other units of three octahedra linked as in Fig. (b) are given the appropriate orientations and placed so that the oxygen atoms held in common by three octahedra are at the other apices of the PO_4 tetrahedron, a model of the group $Mo_{12}O_{40}$ is obtained. The P atom is at the centre of the tetrahedron.

If four of the groups are taken and arranged as a basket, a tetrahedral hole is obtained at the centre. This hole accommodates an atom which forms an ion XO_4. The four oxygen atoms co-ordinated with X are the four each of which is held in common by three octahedral groups. The composition of the anion is arrived at thus:

Oxygen atoms common to 3 octahedra $= 12 \times \frac{1}{3} = 4$,
Oxygen atoms common to 2 octahedra $= 12 \times 4 \times \frac{1}{2} = 24$,
Oxygen atoms free $= 12$
        Total $= 40$.

Hence the anion of potassium phosphomolybdate is $PMo_{12}O_{40}$. The canary-coloured precipitate obtained in the cold by adding a solution of a phosphate to a solution of ammonium molybdate containing nitric acid is $(NH_4)_3[PMo_{12}O_{40}],2HNO_3,H_2O$. If heated to 150–180° it leaves a residue $(NH_4)_3[PMo_{12}O_{40}]$.

THE ISOPOLYMOLYBDIC ACIDS

Potassium paramolybdate has the formula $K_6[MoMo_6O_{24}]$. The structure of the anion is closely related to that of the telluromolybdate anion, but the arrangement of the seven MoO_6 octahedra (Fig. 24.26(b)), differs from that of the octahedra in the telluromolybdate ion (Fig. 24.26(a)).

The structures described above are found in crystalline polymolybdates. It is not known whether the anions exist in solution. Acidification of the simple molybdate anion MoO_4^{2-} yields condensed anions. Two examples of such reactions are:

$$7MoO_4^{2-} + 8H^+ = [Mo_7O_{24}]^{6-} + 4H_2O,$$
$$8MoO_4^{2-} + 12H^+ = [Mo_8O_{26}]^{4-} + 6H_2O,$$

and it is not possible to decide which of these or other similar reactions actually occurs.

Peroxymolybdic acids. Addition of hydrogen peroxide to acid solutions of molybdates produces a red or yellow colour. Explosive salts, assigned the compositions K_2MoO_6, K_2MoO_8, and $(NH_4)_2Mo_2O_{11},2H_2O$, have been obtained from the solutions, but there is no clear account of their chemistry.

Molybdenum blue. It has long been known that a blue solution is obtained if an acid solution of Mo^{VI} is gently reduced, or an acid solution of Mo^V is gently oxidised. If the solution is alkaline or too strongly acid the colour fails to appear. If the molybdenum compound to be oxidised or reduced is sparingly soluble the reactions may be carried out in aqueous suspension. The substance responsible for the blue colour is an oxide of molybdenum: its composition is variable and is usually 67·11% to 68·17% molybdenum. The balance of opinion regards the condition of the oxide as colloidal. The blue oxide can be prepared free from other substances by the reduction of a suspension of MoO_3 with molybdenum. The colloidal solution so obtained can be evaporated in an inert atmosphere.

TUNGSTEN

The principal types of compounds formed by tungsten are included in Table 24.18, and a synopsis of the chief chemical changes undergone by these compounds is shown by Chart 24.3.

SECTION 2. COMPOUNDS CONTAINING A TUNGSTEN ATOM IN OXIDATION STATE II

WCl_2, WBr_2, and WI_2 are infusible, non-volatile, coloured powders made by reducing higher halides. The chloride attacks water liberating hydrogen, and in this and in other reactions it shows itself to be a powerful reducing agent. In this it differs from Mo_6Cl_{12}. WBr_2 and WI_2 are insoluble in water. The tungsten dihalides are certainly polymerised but their structures are unknown.

The acid $(H_3O)_2[W_6Cl_8,Cl_6],6H_2O$ exists as yellow needles.

SECTION 3. COMPOUNDS CONTAINING A TUNGSTEN ATOM IN OXIDATION STATE III

In contrast to the chemistry of chromium, tungsten forms no simple compounds in the state W^{III}, and few complexes. A complex anion is present in the salt $M_3[W_2Cl_9]$, where M represents NH_4, K, Rb, Cs, or Tl, or a complex cation such as $[Co(NH_3)_6^{3+}]$ or $[Ag(NH_3)_2^+]$. The alkali metal salts are anhydrous and greenish yellow, and they may be crystallised from water. The salts of complex cations are almost insoluble. It has been shown by X-ray analysis that the alkali metal salts are isomorphous, and that the anion consists of two octahedra with one face in common (compare $Fe_2(CO)_9$). The anion is diamagnetic.

SECTION 4. COMPOUNDS CONTAINING A TUNGSTEN ATOM IN OXIDATION STATE IV

Tungsten (again in contrast to chromium) forms a number of stable compounds in which it is present in the W^{IV} state, including an oxide, a sulphide, and complex anions.

32*

1002

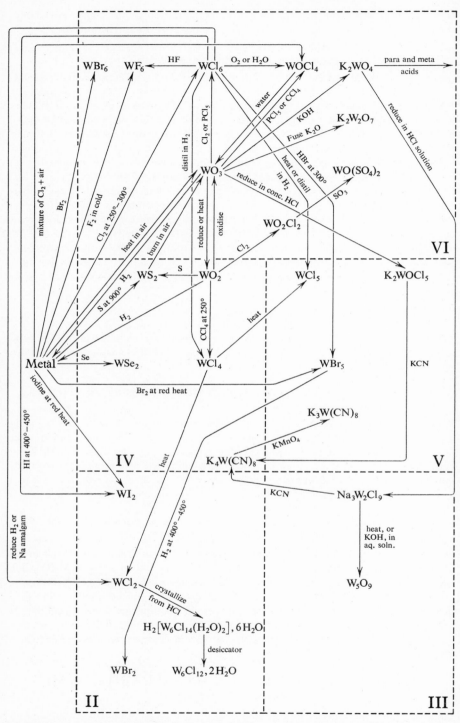

Chart 24.3. The chemical relations of the compounds of tungsten in its different oxidation states.

Tungsten dioxide, a brown powder with the rutile crystal structure, m.p. about 1600° in nitrogen, is made by the reduction of WO_3. It is easily oxidised to WO_3, and reduced by hydrogen to the metal. Chlorine oxidises it to WO_2Cl_2. Tungsten disulphide WS_2 has much the same properties and the same crystal structure as MoS_2.

The only definite tetrahalide of tungsten is the chloride, WCl_4, made by the reduction of WCl_6 with hydrogen at a high temperature, or by the action of CCl_4 on WO_2 at 250°. It is an infusible, non-volatile, hygroscopic grey substance.

The potassium hydroxychlorotungstate, $K_2[W(OH)Cl_5]$ is a dark green solid which dissolves in water to a red solution not changed by exposure to air. The complex cyanide, $K_4[W(CN)_8]$ is yellow, stable to air, and is not hydrolysed in solution.

SECTION 5. COMPOUNDS CONTAINING A TUNGSTEN ATOM IN OXIDATION STATE V

The only simple compounds of W^V are the chloride and bromide, but several complex anions are known. Tungsten pentachloride, WCl_5, and tungsten pentabromide are described in Table 24.20.

Table 24.20.   *Tungsten Pentachloride and Pentabromide*

	WCl_5	WBr_5
Appearance	Dark green needles, greenish yellow vapour	Brown or black needles, dark brown vapour
m.p. °C	248	271
b.p. °C	276	333
Preparation	Heat WCl_6, or distil it in hydrogen	Treat tungsten with Br_2 at a red heat, or pass HBr over WCl_6 at 275°
Properties	Hydrolysed by water to a green solution which becomes colourless on oxidation of tungsten to WO_3 Burns in air to $WOCl_4$	Hydrolysed by water

Three salts containing complex anions with W^V present are $K_2[WOCl_5]$, $K[WOCl_4]$, and $K_3[W(CN)_8]$. The complex cyanide is made by the oxidation of $K_4[W^{IV}(CN)_8]$ with potassium permanganate; it is remarkable that the oxidation proceeds no further.

SECTION 6. COMPOUNDS CONTAINING A TUNGSTEN ATOM IN OXIDATION STATE VI

The compounds of tungsten in this state are some of the most familiar and best-characterised.

Tungstic oxide, WO_3, is a lemon yellow powder, orange when hot, melting at 1473° to a green liquid, b.p. above 1750°. It is made by heating tungsten in air.

Tungstic oxide is completely volatile in chlorine at 500°, perhaps as a result of conversion to the oxychloride. It is reduced by hydrogen to blue W_4O_{11}, or to WO_2, or to the metal. It is converted by CCl_4 in a sealed tube at 200° to $WOCl_4$, and at 280° to WCl_6. It is reduced by carbon monoxide at 800° to WO_2. When heated with silver in vacuo a mixture of Ag_2WO_4 and the oxide W_3O_8 is produced. When heated with calcium carbonate at 1000° Ca_3WO_3 is formed. Tungstic oxide is insoluble in water or acids, but it dissolves in alkaline solutions to give tungstates. The crystal structure of tungstic oxide is the same as that of CrO_3 (p. 990).

The tungsten hexahalides. The preparations and properties of the tungsten hexahalides are summarised in Table 24.21. It should be noted that tungsten forms a hexachloride and a hexabromide. No other element forms a hexabromide, and only one other element, uranium, forms a hexachloride. Many other elements besides tungsten form hexafluorides, including: S, Se, Te, Mo, U, Re, Os, Ir, Pt, Np, Pu.

Table 24.21. *The Hexahalides of Tungsten*

	WF_6	WCl_6	WBr_6
Appearance	Fuming volatile liquid	Violet or steel blue crystals	Blue-black needles
m.p. °C	2·5	275	(Decomposes on
b.p. °C	19·5	347	gentle heating)
Preparation	(i) Action of fluorine on metal (ii) Action of HF on WCl_6 in the cold	(i) Action of dry chlorine on reduced W at low red heat (ii) Action of Cl_2, SCl_2, or PCl_5, on WO_3, or WS_3	Pass Br_2 vapour diluted with N_2 over warmed tungsten
Properties	Hydrolysed by water Gives coloured solutions with organic solvents Attacks all metals except Au and Pt	Hydrolysed by water to $WOCl_4$ Is reduced by H_2 to WCl_5 and WCl_2, by HI at 400° to WI_2, by HBr at 275° to WBr_5	Hydrolysed by water Gives violet-red solutions with organic solvents
Structure	Vapour density is normal. Raman and infrared spectra show octahedral configuration	Vapour density is normal.† Electron diffraction shows octahedral configuration	

† There is slight dissociation at the b.p.

The **tungsten oxychlorides**, $WOCl_4$ and WO_2Cl_2, are well-characterised crystalline compounds. $WOCl_4$, m.p. 209°, b.p. 233°, is formed by passing moist chlorine over tungsten, by the action of oxygen or moisture on WCl_6, or by treating WO_3 with PCl_5, CCl_4, or WCl_6 vapour. It reacts violently with water to give WO_3. Its vapour density is normal up to 440°. WO_2Cl_2 consists of yellow crystals, m.p. 265°. It is made by passing a stream of chlorine diluted with nitrogen over WO_2 at 540°. It is volatile, but less volatile than $WOCl_4$. On heating strongly it disproportionates, thus:

$$2WO_2Cl_2 = WO_3 + WOCl_4.$$

It is stable in moist air, and is only slowly hydrolysed by water.

THE TUNGSTIC ACIDS

The tungstates are even more complicated than the molybdates, and the existence of solid solutions of one salt in another, and the stability of imperfect crystal lattices, makes the elucidation of the principal types very difficult. It does not seem that there is exact correspondence between the tungstates and the molybdates. The following classes of acids and salts are definitely characterised.

Normal tungstic acid, H_2WO_4. A white or bright yellow hydrate, H_2WO_4,H_2O, is precipitated when a solution of sodium tungstate is treated with cold dilute hydrochloric acid. The precipitate changes to the dark yellow anhydrous acid, H_2WO_4, which is insoluble in water, and in acids other than hydrofluoric acid and alcoholic hydrochloric acid. The dark yellow acid is precipitated at once if the reacting solutions are hot.

Sodium tungstate, Na_2WO_4, is obtained by dissolving tungsten trioxide in sodium hydroxide solution, and crystallising the solution. Other metal tungstates may be obtained from it by double decomposition. All tungstates other than those of the alkali metals and magnesium are insoluble. Sodium tungstate has the spinel crystal structure; the tungsten atoms are in tetrahedral holes, and sodium atoms in octahedral holes.

$Na_2W_2O_7$ is made by fusing the oxides in the correct proportions. In the crystal the anion is an infinite complex structure of WO_4 tetrahedra and WO_6 octahedra which hold certain oxygen atoms in common. The ion $[W_2O_7]^{2-}$ does not exist in solution.

There are two types of polytungstates: paratungstates, for example, $Na_5[HW_6O_{21}]$, $13\frac{1}{2}H_2O$, and metatungstates, for example, $K_6[H_2W_{12}O_{40}],18H_2O$.

Sodium paratungstate is made by adding hydrochloric acid to a boiling solution of Na_2WO_4 until a precipitate of H_2WO_4 just becomes permanent. Sodium paratungstate separates on cooling. The paratungstates (including ammonium paratungstate) are insoluble, except those of the alkali metals and magnesium.

The alkali metatungstates are made by boiling a solution of the normal tungstate with tungstic acid. They are more soluble than the normal tungstates or the paratungstates. The structure of the anion $[H_2W_{12}O_{40}]$ is similar to that of the anion $[PMo_{12}O_{40}]$ but the tetrahedral holes are empty, as there is no atom playing the part of the phosphorus atom. The metatungstates are isomorphous with the phosphotungstates and the silicotungstates.

Sodium tungstate bronzes are coloured substances made by the slight reduction of sodium tungstate with hydrogen or tin. The structure may be regarded as a perovskite lattice (which, if perfect, would have the composition $NaWO_3$), from which up to two-thirds of the sodium atoms are missing. For every sodium atom missing the electron concentration in the oxygen complex anion is maintained by the oxidation of a tungsten atom from W^V to W^{VI}.

SUB-GROUP VII T. MANGANESE, TECHNETIUM, AND RHENIUM

Certain properties of the elements of the sub-Group VII T are set out in Table 24.22. Those of technetium are omitted as little is known about this element.

Manganese is a brittle, hard, grey metal. It is highly reactive. It reacts with dilute acids, and slowly decomposes water. It reacts with the halogens, and with nitrogen and carbon. Rhenium reacts with oxygen if heated, and with chlorine, bromine, and with sulphur, but not with nitrogen. It is not attacked by dilute acids.

The metals in sub-Group VII T exhibit a range of seven oxidation states, one more than the number exhibited by the metals in sub-Group VI T. In general, manganese tends to form compounds in which it is in a low oxidation state, and rhenium to form compounds in which it is in higher oxidation states. Manganese in the Mn^{II} state forms a variety of types of compounds (Table 24.23) which are the well-known manganous compounds, but rhenium forms no corresponding compounds. Manganese in the Mn^{III} state forms many compounds to which there are corresponding rhenium compounds, but some types, notably among the complex anions, are found only for manganese. State IV is a very stable state for rhenium. State V is not represented by any manganese compounds, and state VI only by the manganates. State VII is the most stable state for rhenium. There is a sharp contrast between the thermal stability of

Table 24.22. *Properties of the Metals in sub-Group VII T*

	Mn	Re
Atomic number	25	75
m.p. °C	1250	3170
b.p. °C	2100	—
Specific gravity	7·4	21·0
Ionic radius, M^{2+}	0·80	—
Ionic radius, M^{3+}	0·62	—
Atomic radius (12 co-ordination)	1·37	1·37

Re_2O_7, which can be distilled at 355°, and Mn_2O_7, which decomposes at 0° and explodes at 10°. The perrhenates are much less powerful oxidising agents than the permanganates; hydrogen sulphide reduces potassium permanganate to manganous sulphate, but it reacts with potassium perrhenate to give potassium thioperrhenate, $KReO_3S$.

MANGANESE

SECTION 1. COMPOUNDS CONTAINING A MANGANESE ATOM IN OXIDATION STATE I

The only compounds in which a manganese atom is present in oxidation state I are the sodium and potassium salts of the anion $[Mn(CN)_6]^{5-}$. Solutions of these salts can be prepared by the reduction of an alkaline solution of the manganocyanides $Na_4[Mn(CN)_6]$ or $K_4[Mn(CN)_6]$ by aluminium powder. The salts $M_5[Mn(CN)_6]$ are colourless. The solutions are strong reducing agents, they liberate hydrogen on boiling and they react with atmospheric oxygen.

SECTION 2. COMPOUNDS CONTAINING A MANGANESE ATOM IN OXIDATION STATE II

MANGANESE COMPOUNDS CONTAINING THE ION Mn^{2+}

The electronic configuration of the ground state of the manganese atom suggests that the manganous ion, Mn^{2+}, should be fairly stable. The following soluble manganous salts can be obtained in the anhydrous condition: $MnCl_2$, $Mn(NO_3)_2$, $MnSO_4$, and it is probable that the manganous ion is present in these salts. Other salts which perhaps also contain the manganous ion are stated in Table 24.23. Although the Mn^{II} state is more stable than the Cr^{II} state the manganous salts are easily oxidised by moist air to $MnOOH$.

Manganous carbonate, $MnCO_3$, is made by adding sodium bicarbonate to manganous chloride solution through which carbon dioxide is passing. (A more alkaline solution would yield some manganous oxide.) A precipitate is obtained which is white, but the pure crystalline compound is pink. Manganous carbonate is insoluble in water unless carbon dioxide is present, when it dissolves slightly as the bicarbonate. Manganous carbonate is decomposed by heat below 100° to give manganous oxide and carbon dioxide. Above 300° the manganous oxide and the carbon dioxide may react, thus:

$$3MnO + CO_2 = Mn_3O_4 + CO.$$

Manganous nitrate, $Mn(NO_3)_2$, is obtained as the hexahydrate by dissolving manganous carbonate in dilute nitric acid, or by boiling manganese dioxide with dilute nitric acid containing oxalic acid or sugar. Pink deliquescent crystals are formed on evaporation. The crystals are soluble in alcohol. The tetra-, tri- and mono-hydrates are also known. If heated alone the hexahydrate decomposes to steam, nitrogen dioxide, and manganese dioxide. If heated with concentrated nitric acid it loses water to yield the monohydrate. If the monohydrate is warmed with concentrated nitric acid containing nitrogen pentoxide in solution it yields the anhydrous salt. The anhydrous salt reacts with acetic anhydride to give manganic acetate; the liberated nitric acid oxidises the manganous acetate.

Manganous sulphate, $MnSO_4$, is obtained in solution by dissolving manganous carbonate in dilute sulphuric acid. If the solution is crystallised between 9° and 27° the pentahydrate is obtained. Other hydrates are known containing 7, 4, 2, and 1 molecules of water of crystallisation. $MnSO_4,7H_2O$ is isomorphous with $FeSO_4,7H_2O$, and $MnSO_4,5H_2O$ is isomorphous with $CuSO_4,5H_2O$. $(NH_4)_2SO_4,MnSO_4,6H_2O$ is isomorphous with ferrous ammonium sulphate. Other double sulphates of general formulae $M_2Mn(SO_4)_2,xH_2O$ are known, in which if:

M is Na, K, Rb, Tl	then x may be 0
Na, K, Rb	x may be 2
Na, K	x may be 4
Rb, Cs, NH₄	x may be 6.

The double salt $MnAl_2(SO_4)_4,22H_2O$ is a pseudo alum.

If any hydrate of manganous sulphate is heated to 280° the anhydrous salt is formed, m.p. 700°, which may be heated to 800° without decomposition. Anhydrous manganous sulphate may also be obtained by heating manganese dioxide with sulphuric acid.

Manganous fluoride, MnF_2. If excess of ammonium fluoride is added to manganous chloride solution a white precipitate of $(NH_4)_2MnF_4$ is obtained. If this is heated to 300° in an atmosphere of carbon monoxide manganous fluoride is obtained as a white powder. Single crystals have been prepared, m.p. 930°. Manganous fluoride can also be made by dissolving manganous oxide or metallic manganese in hydrofluoric acid, or by fusing manganous chloride with sodium fluoride. Manganous fluoride is slightly soluble in water (1·06 gm in 100 gm at 20°) in which it is hydrolysed. It is oxidised by fluorine to manganic fluoride, MnF_3.

Manganous chloride, $MnCl_2$, is obtained in solution by dissolving manganese dioxide in hydrochloric acid. On evaporation the hexahydrate is deposited, which changes to the tetrahydrate in accordance with the equilibria:

$$MnCl_2,6H_2O \xrightarrow{-2°} MnCl_2,4H_2O \begin{smallmatrix} \nearrow \alpha,\ stable \\ \\ \searrow \beta,\ labile \end{smallmatrix} \quad MnCl_2,4H_2O$$

$$MnCl_2,2H_2O \xrightarrow{190°} MnCl_2.$$

Table 24.23.   *Examples of Types of Compounds formed by Elements in Sub-Group VII T*

$$\overbrace{}^{n-1}\qquad\overbrace{}^{n}$$

Valency system of atom: $d\ \ d\ \ d\ \ d\ \ d\ \ s\ \ p\ \ p\ \ p$

The values of n are: Mn 4, Tc 5, Re 6.

$$\overbrace{}^{n-1}\qquad\overbrace{}^{n}$$

Normal prehybridisation electron configuration: $\overset{\uparrow}{d}\ \overset{\uparrow}{d}\ \overset{\uparrow}{d}\ \overset{\uparrow}{d}\ \overset{\uparrow}{d}\ \overset{\uparrow}{s}\ \overset{\uparrow}{p}\ p\ p$

				Mn	Re
Section	Oxidation state of metal	Nature of unit	Hybridisation		
1	I	Complex anions	Octahedral	$Na_5[Mn(CN)_6]$, $K_5[Mn(CN)_6]$	
2	II	Simple cation		$MnCO_3$, $Mn(NO_3)_2$, $MnSO_4$, $MnCl_2$, MnC_2O_4	
		Giant molecules		MnO, $Mn(OH)_2$, MnS, MnS_2, MnF_2	
		Neutral complexes	Tetrahedral	MnA_2	
			Octahedral	$MnA_2,2H_2O$, $MnA_2,2NH_3$	
		Complex anions	Tetrahedral	$Na_2[Mn(OH)_4]$, $(NH_4)_2[MnF_4]$	
			Octahedral	$Ba_2[Mn(OH)_6]$, $K_4[Mn(CN)_6]$	
3	III	Giant molecules		Mn_2O_3, $MnOOH$, $Mn_2(SO_4)_3$, MnF_3, $MnCl_3$, $Mn(CH_3COO)_3,2H_2O$	Re_2O_3, $ReCl_3$, $ReBr_3$
		Neutral complexes	Octahedral	MnA_3	
		Complex anions	Tetrahedral		$K[ReCl_4]$, $K[ReBr_4]$
				$Na_2[MnF_5]$, $(NH_4)_2[MnF_5]$	
			Octahedral	K, Rb, $Cs[MnCl_5]$ $Na_2[MnF_5,H_2O]$, $K_2[MnF_5,H_2O]$ $Ag_2[MnF_5,H_2O],3H_2O$ $K_3[Mn(CN)_6]$, $K_3[Mn(C_2O_4)_3],3H_2O$ $K[Mn(C_2O_4)_2,2H_2O]$	
4	IV	Giant molecules		MnO_2	ReO_2, ReS_2, $ReSe_2$, ReF_4
		Complex anions		$K_2[MnO_3]$ $K[MnF_5]$ $K_2[MnX_6]$ $X = F$, Cl, or CN	$K_2[ReO_3]$ $K_2[ReX_6]$ $X = F$, Cl, Br, or I
5	V				$ReCl_5$ $Na[ReO_3]$, $K_2[ReOCl_5]$
6	VI			K_2MnO_4	ReO_3, ReF_6 $ReOCl_4$
7	VII			Mn_2O_7 $KMnO_4$	Re_2O_7, Re_2S_7 $HReO_4$, $KReO_4$ $Ba_3[ReO_5]_2$ $K[ReO_3S]$ $ReOF_5$, ReO_2F_3 ReO_3Cl, ReO_3Br

Anhydrous manganous chloride exists as pink crystals, m.p. 650°, isomorphous with calcium chloride. It is volatile above the melting point. Manganous chloride is oxidised by air at 500–900° to Mn_2O_3. Manganous chloride dissolves freely in water (73·6 gm in 100 gm of water at 20°). In aqueous solution containing ammonium chloride it is hydrolysed and oxidised to $MnOOH$.

Manganous chloride acts as an acceptor molecule. Besides the hydrates mentioned above, it forms ammines with 1, 2, and 6 molecules of ammonia, alcoholates with 2 and

3 molecules of alcohol, and it forms green solutions in ether. It reacts with a large excess of ammonium fluoride in aqueous solution to precipitate $(NH_4)_2MnF_4$. It combines with pyridine to yield $MnCl_2,pyr_2$, which is said to have a tetragonal planar structure, and to be isomorphous with $CoCl_2,pyr_2$. If a mixture of manganous chloride and hexamethylene tetrammine in acetic anhydride and ethyl alcohol is crystallised, the compound $MnCl_2,2(CH_2)_6N_4,2H_2O$ is obtained.

Manganous chloride reacts with sodium phosphate (Na_2HPO_4) in excess to precipitate $Mn_3(PO_4)_2,7H_2O$. In the presence of ammonium chloride and ammonia, however, a pink glittering crystalline precipitate of $MnHPO_4,H_2O$ is obtained, which on heating yields the anhydrous salt, and at a red heat $Mn_2P_2O_7$. Manganous chloride crystallises with the $CdCl_2$ lattice.

MANGANOUS COMPOUNDS CONSISTING OF GIANT MOLECULES IN WHICH THE BONDS HAVE SOME IONIC CHARACTER

Manganous oxide, MnO, is made by heating manganous carbonate, or any higher oxide of manganese, in hydrogen or carbon monoxide; or by heating manganous carbonate alone at 100°, or manganous oxalate at 300°. Manganous oxide is usually obtained as a greyish-green powder, but if a higher oxide is reduced by hydrogen containing a trace of hydrogen chloride the product is emerald green and crystalline. Manganous oxide is almost insoluble in water. It is readily oxidised even by air in the cold, to Mn_3O_4 or Mn_2O_3. It is not reduced by hydrogen below 1200°. Manganous oxide has a sodium chloride lattice. The distance Mn–O is 2·21.

Manganous hydroxide, Mn(OH)$_2$. If a solution of potassium hydroxide containing hydroxylamine chloride is added to an aqueous solution of a manganous salt, manganous hydroxide is precipitated as a flocculent precipitate which is converted into a microcrystalline form by heating. The hydroxylamine hydrochloride is added to minimise atmospheric oxidation. Ammonia in the presence of ammonium chloride does not precipitate manganous hydroxide.

The solubility product of manganous hydroxide is $2·2 \times 10^{-13}$ at 25°. In the presence of acids manganous hydroxide acts as a strong base:

$$Mn(OH)_2 = Mn^{2+} + 2OH^-,$$

but it is soluble in alkalis to produce salts such as $Na_2[Mn(OH)_4]$ and $Ba_2[Mn(OH)_6]$. Manganous hydroxide is rapidly oxidised in air to the brown manganic hydroxide $MnOOH$; a method for determining the oxygen dissolved in water is based on this reaction.

The crystal structure of manganous hydroxide is similar to that of $Mg(OH)_2$; each manganese atom is surrounded by six OH groups to form a CdI_2 lattice. The structure contains no hydroxyl bonds.

Manganous sulphide, MnS. If a mixture of ammonia and ammonium sulphide is added to an aqueous solution of a manganous salt, a flesh-coloured precipitate is formed. The precipitate is a mixture of manganous sulphide and manganous hydrosulphide, which on standing changes to a greenish-blue powder of manganous sulphide. Manganous sulphide is also formed by heating manganous carbonate with sulphur, or by heating manganous oxide, carbonate, or sulphate in hydrogen sulphide. Manganous sulphide dissolves readily in dilute acids, even in acetic acid.

Manganous disulphide, MnS$_2$ (hauerite), crystallises with the pyrites structure, and hence contains Mn^{II}. In hauerite the distance S–S is normal, but Mn–S is unusually large (similar relations hold for $MnSe_2$ and $MnTe_2$). Hauerite is paramagnetic; the magnetic moment is 6·1 Bohr magnetons.

Mn^{II} COMPLEXES

Neutral complexes. Manganous acetylacetonate. If manganous oxide or carbonate is treated with acetylacetone in an atmosphere of nitrogen, manganous acetylacetonate is obtained as a yellow powder:

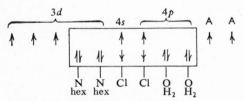

The acetylacetonate gives a dihydrate and a diammine. It is insoluble in water, but is soluble in benzene. The dihydrate is also soluble in benzene. Similar complexes are made with benzoyl acetone, acetoacetic ester, acetone dicarboxylic ester, and salicyl aldehyde.

The complex $[MnCl_2,2(CH_2)_6N_4,2H_2O]^0$ is mentioned on p. 1009. It has been shown that the manganese atom lies on the common three-fold axis of the two hexamethylene tetrammine groups. The Mn—Cl bonds are at right-angles to these, and the Mn—O bonds are at right-angles to both. The magnetic susceptibility is equivalent to five unpaired electrons in the molecule, which indicates that the molecule is a high spin complex (Table 24.5, p. 953). In terms of the valence bond interpretation of the ligand-field theory (p. 954), the orbital diagram is shown in Fig. 24.28:

Fig. 24.28. Orbital diagram of the neutral complex $[MnCl_2((CH_2)_6N_4)_2(H_2O)_2]^0$.

Complex anions. The complex salts $Na_2[Mn(OH)_4]$, $Ba_2[Mn(OH)_6]$, and $(NH_4)_2[MnF_4]$ have already been mentioned. $K_4[Mn(CN)_6]$ is made by dissolving manganous carbonate in aqueous potassium cyanide solution; a yellow solution is formed from which blue potassium manganocyanide crystallises out. Zinc or cadmium salts give violet precipitates with the solution, aluminium salts give a blue precipitate; the precipitates soon decompose. The manganocyanides are oxidised by air to the manganicyanides, $K_3[Mn(CN)_6]$. Manganocyanic acid may be obtained by treating the lead salt with dilute sulphuric acid. It forms colourless crystals, soluble in water, which quickly decomposes it.

SECTION 3. COMPOUNDS CONTAINING A MANGANESE ATOM IN OXIDATION STATE III

MANGANIC COMPOUNDS CONSISTING OF GIANT MOLECULES IN WHICH THE BONDS HAVE SOME IONIC CHARACTER

It is doubtful whether the ion Mn^{3+} exists; manganic salts are unstable and in solution either disproportionate or readily undergo hydrolysis.

Manganic oxide, Mn₂O₃, a black powder, is made by igniting manganese dioxide or a manganous salt in air at 500–900°. If heated in air above 950°, or in hydrogen above 230°, it loses oxygen to yield Mn_3O_4. It dissolves in dilute hydrofluoric acid or in hydrocyanic acid. Manganic oxide reacts with sulphur dioxide to yield manganous sulphite, manganous dithionate, and some manganous sulphate. Manganic oxide is the typical example of the $C–M_2O_3$ crystal structure. The lattice may be regarded as a fluorite lattice from which a quarter of the anions have been removed, and the positions of the cations have been slightly adjusted.

Manganic hydroxide, MnOOH, is the product of the combined oxidation and hydrolysis of a manganous salt. It is made by passing chlorine into a suspension of manganous carbonate in water:

$$3MnCO_3 + Cl_2 + H_2O = 2MnOOH + MnCl_2 + 3CO_2.$$

When treated with nitric acid it disproportionates thus:

$$2MnOOH + 2HNO_3 = Mn(NO_3)_2 + MnO_2 + 2H_2O.$$

Manganic fluoride, MnF₃, a red crystalline solid, is made by the action of fluorine on manganous iodide. On heating it dissociates into fluorine and manganous fluoride. Fluorine diluted with nitrogen reacts at 100–150° with potassium permanganate, or with any oxide of manganese stable at that temperature, to give mainly manganic fluoride with a little manganous fluoride. An aqueous solution of manganic fluoride is made by dissolving manganic oxide in hydrofluoric acid. The red dihydrate, $MnF_3,2H_2O$, may be crystallised from the solution. Manganic fluoride is hydrolysed if the solution is diluted.

Manganic chloride, MnCl₃, is obtained in ethereal solution by saturating a suspension of manganese dioxide in ether with gaseous hydrogen chloride at − 70°. The solution in ether is green. The solid is precipitated as a brown crystalline mass on the addition of carbon tetrachloride. At − 40° manganic chloride decomposes to manganous chloride and chlorine.

Manganic sulphate, Mn₂(SO₄)₃, a dark green powder, stable to 300°, is made by heating precipitated manganese dioxide with concentrated sulphuric acid at 138°. The solid product is drained on a porous plate, washed with concentrated nitric acid, and heated to 130° to expel the nitric acid:

$$4MnO_2 + 6H_2SO_4 = 2Mn_2(SO_4)_3 + 6H_2O + O_2.$$

Manganic sulphate dissolves in water to give a violet solution from which a precipitate of MnOOH separates by hydrolysis.

The manganic ion plays the part of the trivalent cation in alums. Coral red crystals of $CsMn(SO_4)_2,12H_2O$ can be obtained, but they are hydrolysed by water, and manganic alums containing other alkali metals are even more easily decomposed. The manganic alums when heated yield anhydrous compounds which are probably salts of a sulphato complex. The anhydrous caesium compound is perhaps $Cs[Mn(SO_4)_2]$.

Manganic acetate. Cinnamon-brown crystals of the dihydrate, $Mn(CH_3COO)_3,2H_2O$ are made by the action of acetic anhydride on hydrated manganous nitrate; the nitric acid liberated during the reaction oxidises the manganese from the Mn^{II} to the Mn^{III} state. Manganic acetate is also obtained by oxidising manganous acetate with chlorine or potassium permanganate. It is hydrolysed by water, but can be crystallised from acetic acid, alcohol, or pyridine. Manganic acetate dissolves in potassium cyanide solution to give potassium manganicyanide.

NEUTRAL Mn^{III} COMPLEXES

Manganic acetylacetonate, MnA₃, exists as brilliant black crystals, greenish when powdered, m.p. 172°. It is readily soluble in benzene, chloroform, and ethyl acetate. The complex is monomeric, both in solution and in the vapour.

COMPLEX ANIONS CONTAINING Mn^{III}

Halogeno-anionic complexes are of two types, M_2Mnhal_5 and M_2Mnhal_5,H_2O. It is probable that the water molecule is constitutional and is co-ordinated to the manganese atom. Among the fluorine complexes are the red salts Na_2MnF_5, $(NH_4)_2MnF_5$, and K_2MnF_5,H_2O, and the almost black silver salt $Ag_2MnF_5,4H_2O$. The chlorine derivatives are made by reducing potassium permanganate with concentrated hydrochloric acid and adding potassium chloride to the resulting solution. The K, Rb, and Cs salts are anhydrous; the NH_4 salt has one molecule of water per manganese atom.

Potassium manganicyanide, $K_3[Mn(CN)_6]$, forms dark red crystals isomorphous with potassium ferricyanide. The K, Na, Li, and NH_4 salts are known, and can be crystallised from water, although they are slowly hydrolysed to manganic oxide. A solution of potassium manganicyanide is obtained by blowing air through a solution of potassium cyanide to which manganous carbonate has been added. Crystals are precipitated by the addition of alcohol to this solution.

Oxalato complexes. Potassium trioxalato manganate trihydrate $K_3[Mn(C_2O_4)_3],3H_2O$ exists as deep red-violet crystals which, if dry, are stable in diffused daylight. It is prepared by the action of oxalic acid on potassium permanganate in alkaline solution:

$$5H_2C_2O_4 + KMnO_4 + K_2CO_3 = K_3[Mn(C_2O_4)_3] + 5H_2O + 5CO_2.$$

It is very soluble in water; on dilution it forms the diaquo complex. The Na, NH_4, Tl^I, and $[Co(NH_3)_6]$ salts have been made; they are very soluble and difficult to purify.

The observed magnetic moment of $K_3[Mn(C_2O_4)_3],3H_2O$ is 4·88 Bohr magnetons, which corresponds to the presence of four unpaired electrons in the manganese atom. The anion must therefore be a high spin complex, and its hybridisation diagram is probably:

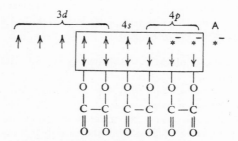

Fig. 24.29. Orbital diagram for the anion $[Mn(C_2O_4)_3]^{3-}$.

Potassium diaquo dioxalato manganate, $K[Mn(C_2O_4)_2,2H_2O]$, is obtained in solution by the action of oxalic acid on potassium permanganate in the correct proportions. The solution is dark red, but alcohol precipitates from it pale green crystals of the salt. It has been observed that the ions $[Mn(C_2O_4)_2,2H_2O]^-$ and $[Mn(C_2O_4),4H_2O]^+$ are present in solution during the reduction of potassium permanganate by oxalic acid.

Malonato manganate ions are known. They are similar to the oxalato anions, but are easier to make because the acid group is not liable to oxidation by Mn^{III}. The acid

$H_3O[Mn\ mal_2,2H_2O]$ is a dark green powder, fairly stable to air and light but decomposed by water.

Phosphato complexes. The acid $H_3O[Mn(PO_4H)_2(H_2O)_2]$ is made by dissolving manganic acetate in very concentrated phosphoric acid. The acid is violet, and it has been shown by transport experiments that the acid is monobasic and that the manganese is in the anion.

SECTION 4. COMPOUNDS CONTAINING A MANGANESE ATOM IN OXIDATION STATE IV

The compounds of manganese in the Mn^{IV} oxidation state include the giant molecule compound manganese dioxide, the manganites such as K_2MnO_3, and the anionic complexes present in the salts $KMnF_5$, and K_2MnCl_6. The ion Mn^{4+} is present in manganese dioxide, but the ion is unstable in water. There are no simple covalent compounds of Mn^{IV}.

Manganese dioxide, MnO_2, is a black solid. It is made by heating manganous nitrate; different detailed procedures are recommended by different authors. At about 500° manganese dioxide loses oxygen to give Mn_2O_3 and Mn_3O_4. Manganese dioxide is insoluble in water. It is a fairly good conductor of electricity; the specific conductance at 0° is $0.16\ ohm^{-1}\ cm^{-1}$.

Manganese dioxide dissolves in hydrochloric acid liberating chlorine:

$$MnO_2 + 4HCl = Mn^{4+} + 4Cl^- + 2H_2O,$$
$$Mn^{4+} + 2Cl^- = Mn^{2+} + Cl_2,$$

and in sulphuric acid liberating oxygen; the violet colour which appears in the reaction with sulphuric acid is due to the manganous ion Mn^{2+}. Manganese dioxide reacts with hydrogen fluoride at 450–500° to yield manganous fluoride:

$$2MnO_2 + 4HF = 2MnF_2 + O_2 + 2H_2O.$$

An aqueous suspension of manganese dioxide reacts with sulphur dioxide in two ways according to the equations:

(a) $MnO_2 + SO_2 = MnSO_4$ (BaO_2 and PbO_2 undergo corresponding reactions),
(b) $2MnO_2 + SO_2 = Mn_2O_3 + SO_3$,
   $Mn_2O_3 + 3SO_2 = Mn_2(SO_3)_3$,
   $Mn_2(SO_3)_3 = MnSO_3 + MnS_2O_6$.

The precipitate obtained by reducing potassium permanganate in alkaline solution has the composition H_2MnO_3. This hydrated manganese dioxide reddens blue litmus, and dissolves in concentrated alkalis to give manganites.

Manganese dioxide has the rutile lattice.

The pink salt **$KMnF_5$,** is made by the action of bromine trifluoride on potassium permanganate; excess of bromine trifluoride is removed by evaporation in vacuo at 20°. There are several salts of the general formula $K_2[MnX_6]$, where X represents F, Cl, or CN.

Potassium hexafluoromanganite, $K_2[MnF_6]$, exists as golden yellow crystals which at high temperatures have the cubic lattice of $K_2[PtCl_6]$. It is made by treating potassium manganate, K_2MnO_4, with concentrated hydrofluoric acid, or by treating a mixture of equal molecular proportions of potassium permanganate and potassium chloride with bromine trifluoride. It is hydrolysed by water to manganese dioxide. $K_2[MnCl_6]$ is obtained by the action of gaseous hydrogen chloride on potassium permanganate dissolved in glacial acetic acid, and $K_2[Mn(CN)_6]$ by the action of potassium cyanide on potassium permanganate in saturated aqueous solution. Both salts are red and are decomposed by water.

SECTION 6. COMPOUNDS CONTAINING A MANGANESE ATOM IN OXIDATION STATE VI

The only compounds in which manganese is present in the oxidation state Mn^{VI} are the manganates.

Potassium manganate, K_2MnO_4, is prepared by heating manganese dioxide with potassium hydroxide and potassium nitrate (air is used as the oxidant in industrial processes). The product is a green mass which is extracted with water containing a little alkali. A solution of potassium manganate can be obtained by boiling a strong solution of potassium permanganate with potassium hydroxide:

$$4KMnO_4 + 4KOH = 4K_2MnO_4 + 2H_2O + O_2.$$

Potassium manganate can be isolated as dark green crystals, soluble in alkaline aqueous solution, but hydrolysed by water:

$$3K_2MnO_4 + 2H_2O = 2KMnO_4 + MnO_2 + 4KOH.$$

If heated to 500° the crystals lose oxygen and yield K_2MnO_3. Potassium manganate is isomorphous with potassium sulphate, and $Na_2MnO_4,10H_2O$ is isomorphous with $Na_2SO_4,10H_2O$.

SECTION 7. COMPOUNDS CONTAINING A MANGANESE ATOM IN OXIDATION STATE VII

There are two compounds in which manganese is present in the oxidation state Mn^{VII}, potassium permanganate and manganese heptoxide.

Potassium permanganate, $KMnO_4$, is made by treating the solidified green melt of potassium manganate with dilute sulphuric acid:

$$3K_2MnO_4 + 2H_2SO_4 = 2KMnO_4 + MnO_2 + 2K_2SO_4 + 2H_2O.$$

It is also produced in solution by the treatment of manganous compounds with numerous oxidising agents, including sodium periodate, potassium peroxydisulphate, potassium peroxydiphosphate, sodium bismuthate and nitric acid, and lead dioxide and nitric acid. Potassium permanganate crystallises in small purple rhombic crystals with a green iridescence. It is not very soluble in water (6·34 gm in 100 gm at 20°). It is isomorphous with potassium perchlorate, and forms solid solutions with barium sulphate. When heated alone it gives off oxygen at 200°:

$$2KMnO_4 = K_2MnO_4 + MnO_2 + O_2;$$

at a red heat the manganate also decomposes:

$$2K_2MnO_4 = 2K_2MnO_3 + O_2.$$

In alkaline or neutral solution potassium permanganate is reduced to manganese dioxide, and in dilute sulphuric acid solution to manganous sulphate. It is reduced by hydrochloric acid.

Manganese heptoxide, Mn_2O_7, exists as dark green, explosive, crystals. It is made by adding powdered potassium permanganate to cooled concentrated sulphuric acid. A dark green solution is formed which is explosive. If ice-cold water is added to the solution manganese heptoxide separates as a dark oil, which can be crystallised by freezing in liquid air. Manganese heptoxide is stable at $-5°$, but it begins to give off oxygen at 0°, and at about 10° it explodes yielding manganese dioxide.

Manganese heptoxide, if added slowly to excess of cold water produces a violet solution of permanganic acid, $HMnO_4$, which may be concentrated to 20%. The acid decomposes to manganese dioxide if attempts are made to concentrate it further.

RHENIUM

Rhenium forms stable compounds in which it is present in all oxidation states from Re^{III} to Re^{VII}. The most stable states are Re^{IV} and Re^{VII}. There are, however, no Re^{II} compounds corresponding to the manganous compounds and no Re^{I} compounds corresponding to $M_5[Mn(CN)_6]$.

SECTION 3. COMPOUNDS CONTAINING A RHENIUM ATOM IN OXIDATION STATE III

The most familiar compounds of rhenium in the Re^{III} state are the oxide Re_2O_3, the chloride $ReCl_3$, the bromide $ReBr_3$, and the complex chlorides and bromides such as $KReBr_4$, in which rhenium is present in the anion. The fluoride ReF_3 does not exist; rhenium trichloride reacts with hydrogen fluoride at 350° to give metallic rhenium, thus:

$$2ReCl_3 + 6HF = 6HCl + 3F_2 + 2Re.$$

Rhenium trichloride, however, is very much more stable than manganic chloride (p. 1007).

GIANT MOLECULE COMPOUNDS

Rhenium oxide, Re_2O_3, is obtained as a black precipitate by the action of potassium hydroxide on rhenium trichloride. It has no acid properties. If boiled in alkaline solution it disproportionates to ReO, ReO_2, and Re_2O_7. It is said by some authors to liberate hydrogen from water.

Rhenium trichloride, $ReCl_3$, is obtained in the form of dark red crystals by distilling rhenium pentachloride in a stream of nitrogen:

$$ReCl_5 = ReCl_3 + Cl_2,$$

or by heating silver hexachlororhenite, Ag_2ReCl_6. It dissolves in acetone, water, and hydrochloric acid to give deep red solutions. It is reduced by hydrogen at 250–300° to hydrogen chloride and metallic rhenium. An alkaline aqueous solution is very readily oxidised by air (mainly to Re^{IV}); oxidation takes place less easily in neutral solution, and not at all in acid solution, probably because of the formation of the complex $H[ReCl_4]$. If rhenium trichloride is heated in air or oxygen it burns to a dark green vapour which contains $Re^{VII}O_3Cl$ and $Re^{VI}OCl_4$.

Rhenium trichloride is not a simple ionic compound. The freshly made aqueous solution gives no precipitate with silver nitrate. The molecular weight in glacial acetic acid corresponds to the formula Re_2Cl_6, which suggests a structure like that of Al_2Cl_6 or Fe_2Cl_6:

Rhenium tribromide, $ReBr_3$, a greenish-black solid, can be made:

  (i) by treating hydrated rhenic oxide with hydrobromic acid,
  (ii) by heating silver hexabromorhenite in a high vacuum to a moderate temperature:

$$2Ag_2[ReBr_6] = 4AgBr + 2ReBr_3 + Br_2,$$

  (iii) by heating metallic rhenium in a stream of bromine and nitrogen at 450°.

Rhenium tribromide sublimes at 500°, either in nitrogen or in a vacuum, to a dark green-yellow vapour.

Rhenium tri-iodide is not known.

COMPLEX ANIONS CONTAINING Re^{III}

The addition of an alkali metal chloride to a solution of rhenic chloride in concentrated hydrochloric acid precipitates the complex salt $M[ReCl_4]$ as a red solid; the pyridine salt $pyrH[ReCl_4]$ is also dark red, and is only slightly soluble in water. The rubidium and caesium salts in the presence of excess alkali metal chloride are only slightly soluble in water and can be used for the detection of rhenic chloride. The complex salts disproportionate on heating at 550–600°, thus:

$$6K[ReCl_4] = 3K_2[ReCl_6] + 2ReCl_3 + Re.$$

The complexes derived from rhenic bromide, for example $K[ReBr_4]$, are similar to the chloride complexes.

SECTION 4. COMPOUNDS CONTAINING A RHENIUM ATOM IN THE OXIDATION STATE IV

With the exception of oxidation state Re^{VII} the oxidation state Re^{IV} is the most stable adopted by rhenium. The compounds of rhenium in the state Re^{IV} include the oxide ReO_2, the rhenites such as K_2ReO_3, rhenium tetrafluoride, ReF_4, and the complex salts such as $K_2[ReF_6]$.

Rhenium dioxide, ReO$_2$, a non-volatile black powder, is made by burning the metal in a limited supply of oxygen, or by reducing higher oxides with hydrogen. If heated in vacuo it disproportionates into Re_2O_7 and the metal; it combines with oxygen on warming to give Re_2O_7. It dissolves in concentrated hydrochloric acid and in solutions of alkali metal chlorides, to give hexachloro complexes $M_2[ReCl_6]$. Rhenium dioxide reacts with fused sodium hydroxide in the absence of air to yield brown insoluble sodium rhenite, Na_2ReO_3. If air is present the rhenite is oxidised first to the hyporhenate $NaReO_3$ (yellow), then to the rhenate Na_2ReO_4 (green), and ultimately to the mesoperrhenate Na_3ReO_5. Oxidising agents such as nitric acid, hydrogen peroxide, and chlorine, convert rhenium dioxide to perrhenic acid. A mixture of fluorine and nitrogen at 100–150° reacts with rhenium dioxide to yield $ReOF_5$ and ReO_2F_3. Rhenium dioxide is more acidic than basic.

A hydrated form of rhenium dioxide is obtained by the electrolytic reduction of acid or alkaline perrhenate solutions.

Rhenium disulphide, ReS$_2$, a soft black substance, volatile with some decomposition at 1000°, is made:

(i) by fusing together rhenium and sulphur,
(ii) by heating Re_2S_7 to 250°,
(iii) by the action of hydrogen sulphide on a solution of $K_2[ReCl_6]$.

Rhenium disulphide is insoluble in solutions of sodium hydroxide, sodium sulphide, and in hydrochloric acid or sulphuric acid. Rhenium disulphide has the CdI_2 layer lattice.

Rhenium tetrafluoride, ReF$_4$, a dark green solid, which melts at 124·5° to a dark green liquid, is made by passing the vapour of rhenium hexafluoride mixed with hydrogen or sulphur dioxide through a heated platinum tube. It is not very volatile, but it can be sublimed in an atmosphere of sulphur dioxide at 500°. It attacks silica above 80°.

The existence of $ReCl_4$, $ReBr_4$, and ReI_4 is doubtful.

COMPLEX ANIONS CONTAINING Re^{IV}

The following salts of the general formula $X_2[Rehal_6]$ are known:

$K_2[ReF_6]$ (green) giving a green aqueous solution,
$M_2[ReCl_6]$, where M represents K, Rb, Cs, NH_4, $N(CH_3)_4$, Ag, Tl^+, or $2Hg^{2+}$;
  the alkali metal salts are green, the silver salt is orange, and the thallous salt is
  yellow,
$K_2[ReBr_6]$ (brick red),
$K_2[ReI_6]$ (black).

The potassium salts of the derivatives of each of the four halogens can be obtained by the reduction of potassium perrhenate with hydrogen iodide in the presence of the halogen hydride, as expressed for example by the equation:

$$2KReO_4 + 6KI + 16HF = 2K_2[ReF_6] + 4KF + 3I_2 + 8H_2O.$$

$K_2[ReF_6]$ has the $K_2[PtCl_6]$ antifluorite structure (p. 1055).

$K_2[ReCl_6]$ can be made by the reaction just described, or by dissolving rhenium dioxide in concentrated hydrogen chloride and adding potassium chloride to the solution. It is produced when potassium chloride reacts with rhenium pentachloride (chlorine is evolved), and when potassium chloride reacts with rhenium trichloride (metallic rhenium separates). It can be purified by recrystallisation from dilute hydrochloric acid.

In neutral solution $K_2[ReCl_6]$ is hydrolysed after a long time to rhenium dioxide; in alkaline solution it undergoes a complex series of disproportionations. If treated with excess of potassium cyanide and hydrogen peroxide it yields the orange crystalline salt $K_3[ReO_2(CN)_4]$ containing rhenium in the Re^V state.

The hexaiodo salt, $K_2[ReI_6]$, is the only one of the four halogen compounds to be attacked by sulphuric acid with which it reacts thus:

$$K_2[ReI_6] + H_2SO_4 = K_2SO_4 + HI + HReI_5.$$

SECTION 5. COMPOUNDS CONTAINING A RHENIUM ATOM IN OXIDATION STATE V

Neither the oxide Re_2O_5 nor the hydroxide $Re(OH)_5$ has been prepared. This is not surprising as both these compounds would be expected to disproportionate to ReO_2 and Re_2O_7. The compounds discussed in this Section are rhenium pentachloride, $ReCl_5$ (of which the structure is unknown), and salts of complex anions in which the rhenium atom is combined with oxygen. All the compounds are coloured. The orbital diagrams of the complex anions can be simply conjectured if the $5d$ electrons of the rhenium atom are assumed to be linked to the oxygen atoms by πd bonds, thus:

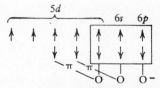

Fig. 24.30. Orbital diagram for the anion $[ReO_3]^-$.

[ReOCl$_5$]$^{2-}$

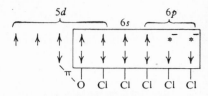

Fig. 24.31. Orbital diagram for the anion [ReOCl$_5$]$^{2-}$.

Sodium hyporhenate, NaReO$_3$, exists as pale yellow crystals. It is made by fusing NaReO$_4$, ReO$_2$, and NaOH in the absence of air. In the dry state, if free from alkali, it disproportionates into sodium rhenite Na$_2$ReO$_3$ and sodium perrhenate, NaReO$_4$, but in the presence of water or acids ReO$_2$ is obtained instead of sodium rhenite. Sodium hyporhenate is oxidised by air to sodium perrhenate.

Rhenium pentachloride, ReCl$_5$, is a dark brown solid which can be volatilised in vacuo to a brown vapour. It is obtained by the action of chlorine on metallic rhenium. ReOCl$_4$ and ReCl$_3$ are formed at the same time. If the mixture is heated the ReOCl$_4$ distils off, and if the heating is continued under vacuum, the ReCl$_5$ sublimes, leaving a residue of ReCl$_3$. Rhenium pentachloride shows a strong tendency to disproportionate so that rhenium adopts the oxidation states Re^{IV} and Re^{VII}. When distilled in nitrogen it yields rhenium trichloride (p. 1015). When heated in oxygen it burns yielding ReOCl$_4$ and ReO$_3$Cl. When heated with potassium chloride it yields potassium hexachlororhenite, K$_2$[ReCl$_6$].

COMPLEX ANIONS CONTAINING Re^V

Among the anionic complexes of Re^V are oxalato- and tartrato-complexes, the anion [ReO$_2$(CN)$_4$]$^{3-}$ mentioned on p. 1017, and the anion in the salt described below.

K$_2$[ReOCl$_5$],H$_2$O, is a yellowish-green compound precipitated by the addition of potassium chloride to the green solution obtained by the electrolytic reduction of a solution of potassium perrhenate in hydrochloric acid. The salt is readily hydrolysed by water to rhenium dioxide, and by dilute hydrochloric acid to a mixture of potassium chlororhenite and potassium perrhenate. It is readily oxidised by air (unlike K$_2$[ReCl$_6$]) to potassium perrhenate. The yellow ammonium salt (NH$_4$)$_2$[ReOCl$_5$] is known.

SECTION 6. COMPOUNDS CONTAINING A RHENIUM ATOM IN OXIDATION STATE VI

Three compounds containing rhenium in the Re^{VI} state are well-characterised, ReO$_3$, ReF$_6$, and ReOCl$_4$.

Rhenium trioxide, ReO$_3$, is a brick-red solid which appears green when observed in thin layers. It is best made by heating the compound of rhenium heptoxide and dioxan (p. 1019), to 145°. The yield is 98·6%.

Rhenium trioxide is not attacked by water, hydrochloric acid, or dilute sodium hydroxide solution. If fused with sodium hydroxide in the absence of air, the melt turns green, but sodium rhenate, Na$_2$ReO$_4$, cannot be isolated, probably because it disproportionates. If rhenium trioxide is boiled with concentrated alkali, or heated alone in vacuo, it decomposes thus:

$$3Re^{VI}O_3 = Re^{IV}O_2 + Re_2^{VII}O_7.$$

The crystal structure of rhenium trioxide is similar to that of CrO$_3$ and WO$_3$; it is the typical example of an important crystal structure (p. 349).

Rhenium hexafluoride, ReF$_6$, is a pale yellow crystalline solid, m.p. 18·8°. The liquid is also yellow, b.p. 47·6°. It is made by the action of pure fluorine on rhenium at

125° in a fluorite tube. Rhenium hexafluoride is extremely reactive. It attacks silica below 30°:

$$3ReF_6 + 3SiO_2 = ReF_4 + 2ReO_3F + 3SiF_4.$$

It reacts with water:

$$3ReF_6 + 10H_2O = 2HReO_4 + ReO_2 + 18HF,$$

and it also reacts with glass, fats, and ligroin. It is reduced to rhenium tetrafluoride by hydrogen at 200°, by carbon monoxide at 300°, by sulphur dioxide at 400°, and by metallic rhenium at 500°; at higher temperatures it is reduced to the metal. The vapour density of rhenium hexafluoride corresponds to the formula ReF_6.

$ReOCl_4$, a dark brown solid, m.p. 28°, is made by heating a mixture of rhenium pentachloride and rhenium trichloride with oxygen to 150°. With concentrated hydrochloric acid it gives a brown solution containing the acid H_2ReOCl_6, but this almost at once decomposes, and the overall reaction can be written:

$$3ReOCl_4 + 6HCl = 3H_2ReOCl_6$$
$$3H_2ReOCl_6 + 5H_2O = H_2ReCl_6 + 2HReO_4 + 12HCl.$$

The brown salt K_2ReOCl_6 has been isolated, but it is also readily hydrolysed.

The oxyfluorides $ReOF_4$ and ReO_2F_2 have been reported, but their existence is disputed.

SECTION 7. COMPOUNDS CONTAINING A RHENIUM ATOM IN OXIDATION STATE VII

The compounds in this Section include rhenium heptoxide and the perrhenates which are the most stable compounds of rhenium.

Rhenium heptoxide, Re_2O_7, is a yellow solid, m.p. 304°, made by heating rhenium in air above 150°, or by evaporating a solution of perrhenic acid, $HReO_4$, to dryness. If cold oxygen impinges on hot rhenium, white rhenic heptoxide is formed, but it becomes yellow if heated to 150°. At $-80°$ rhenium heptoxide is colourless. It boils at about 355°, and begins to sublime to a colourless vapour at 220°.

Rhenium heptoxide dissolves freely in water to form perrhenic acid. It is also soluble in alcohol (which it does not oxidise), acetic acid, and slightly in ether and chloroform. It unites with dioxan to give the compound $Re_2O_7,3C_4H_8O_2$ a grey hygroscopic powder, m.p. 90–100°. Rhenium heptoxide is reduced to lower oxides by carbon monoxide and by sulphur dioxide, slowly in the cold and more rapidly if heated. It is reduced by hydrogen at 300° to ReO_2, and at 500° to the metal.

The vapour density of rhenium heptoxide is normal up to 520°.

Perrhenic acid, $HReO_4$, is known only in aqueous solution. The solution is obtained by dissolving rhenium heptoxide in water, and also by treating a lower oxide, or metallic rhenium, with hydrogen peroxide. The solution is colourless. It yields rhenium heptoxide on evaporation. Perrhenic acid is a much less powerful oxidising agent than permanganic acid. Reducing agents such as $SnCl_2$, $TiCl_3$, VCl_2, and $CrCl_2$ reduce it to $ReCl_4$; in very acid conditions $CrCl_2$ continues the reduction to $ReCl_3$. When $SnCl_2$ is the reducing agent the intermediate stage $ReCl_5$ can be detected.

Many salts of perrhenic acid are known. The perrhenic ion is colourless, roughly spherical, and only slightly deformable. Other anions possessing these properties are MnO_4, ClO_4, IO_4, BF_4, and SO_3F. The salts of these ions are similar in crystalline form and in solubility, but not necessarily in thermal stability. $KReO_4$ melts at 518° and distils unchanged at 1 atm at 1370°. The potassium salts of the other ions begin to decompose at the following lower temperatures:

KBF_4	$KClO_4$	KIO_4	$KMnO_4$
500°	400°	600°	200°

The solubilities of salts containing these ions are low if the cation is that of an organic base, or is a complex metal ion such as $[Co(NH_3)_6]^{2+}$ or is a univalent metal ion of high atomic number (K, Rb, Cs, Tl, Ag). The solubilities when the cation is Li, Na, Ca, Sr, Cu, Mg, Zn, Cd, Co, Ni, are much greater.

The reaction of potassium perrhenate with fluorine are mentioned in Table 24.24. The crystalline form of potassium perrhenate is tetragonal; the structure of the perrhenate ion is tetrahedral.

Barium mesoperrhenate, $Ba_3(ReO_5)_2$, is made by adding barium hydroxide or sodium hydroxide to a solution of barium perrhenate. The salt is yellow when cold and red when hot. It dissolves to a colourless solution in water because the mesoperrhenate is hydrolysed to the normal salt. Barium mesoperrhenate is decomposed by carbon dioxide to barium carbonate and barium perrhenate, thus indicating that the second and third dissociation constants of mesoperrhenic acid are small.

Potassium thioperrhenate, $KReO_3S$, is formed when potassium perrhenate in neutral solution is reduced by hydrogen sulphide:

$$KReO_4 + H_2S = KReO_3S + H_2O;$$

the prolonged action of hydrogen sulphide causes further replacement of oxygen atoms by sulphur. The solution is greenish yellow. Addition of thallous nitrate precipitates $TlReO_3S$, which can be crystallised from water and alcohol. If a solution of potassium thioperrhenate is acidified, rhenium heptasulphide is formed:

$$7HReO_3S = Re_2S_7 + 5HReO_4 + H_2O.$$

Oxidising agents convert potassium thioperrhenate to the perrhenate, sulphuric acid, and free sulphur.

Rhenium heptasulphide, Re_2S_7, is obtained as the monohydrate by the action of hydrogen sulphide or sodium thiosulphate on an acidified solution of potassium perrhenate. Precipitation occurs quantitatively if the reagent is sodium thiosulphate in a 2–7 N solution of sulphuric acid. Rhenium heptasulphide is obtained in the anhydrous condition as a fine black powder by the action of hydrogen sulphide on dry rhenium heptoxide.

Rhenium heptasulphide readily decomposes with the evolution of heat to rhenium disulphide and sulphur. It is oxidised to perrhenic acid by air, and by nitric acid, bromine water, or hydrogen peroxide. The heptaselenide of rhenium is similar to the heptasulphide.

Rhenium (Re^{VII}) oxyhalides. The preparations and properties of certain oxyhalides of Re^{VII} are given in Table 24.24.

Table 24.24. *The Re^{VII} Oxyhalides*

Formula	Appear-ance	m.p. °C	b.p. °C	Preparation	Properties
$ReOF_5$	Cream coloured solid	34·5	55	Treat ReO_2 or $KReO_4$ with a mixture of F_2 and N_2 at 150°	Fumes in moist air, and dissolves in water forming $HReO_4$ and HF. When dry does not attack glass
ReO_2F_3	Pale yellow solid	95	200	Formed during the preparation of $ReOF_5$	As for $ReOF_5$
ReO_3Cl	Colourless liquid	4·5	131	Heat Re_2O_7 with excess of a mixture of $ReCl_3$ and $ReCl_5$	With moist air gives $HReO_4$ and HCl
ReO_3Br	White solid	39·5	163	Heat rhenium in a mixture of O_2 and Br_2 vapour, and distil over Re_2O_7	

Observations have been made on the microwave spectrum of ReO_3Cl from which it has been calculated that the distance Re–Cl is 2·23, Re–O is 1·76, and the angle ClReO is 108°. Hence the molecule is approximately tetrahedral. Hybridisation diagrams of all four compounds can be drawn if it be assumed that πd bonds link the oxygen atoms to the rhenium atom. The orbital diagram of ReO_3Cl for example, is:

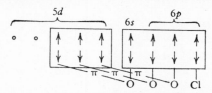

Fig. 24.32. Orbital diagram for ReO_3Cl. The $5d$ orbitals are hybridised (p. 159).

GROUP VIII. IRON, RUTHENIUM, AND OSMIUM

Certain properties of the elements of the Group VIII are set out in Table 24.25.

Table 24.25. *Properties of the Metals in Group VIII*

	Fe	Ru	Os
Atomic number	26	44	76
m.p. °C	1539	2400	2700
b.p. °C	2900	3900	4600
Specific gravity	7·9	12·2	22·4
Ionic radius			
M^{2+}	0·75	—	—
M^{3+}	0·60	—	—
Atomic radius (12 co-ordination)	1·26	1·34	1·35

Iron exists in three allotropic forms: α-ferrite (cubic body-centred) which changes at 906° to γ-ferrite† (cubic face-centred), which changes to δ-ferrite (cubic body-centred) at 1401°. It is ferromagnetic below the Curie point (p. 943), at 770°.

Iron is a soft, malleable, and ductile metal, not hardened by quenching. Iron combines directly with boron, carbon, silicon, phosphorus, oxygen, sulphur, and chlorine. It is permeable to hydrogen above 350°. It reacts with steam at a red heat. It dissolves in dilute hydrochloric or sulphuric acid to yield hydrogen and a ferrous salt; with dilute nitric acid it forms ferrous nitrate and ammonium nitrate. Concentrated nitric acid renders it passive.

Ruthenium is a hard white metal. It exists in four allotropic forms. It reacts with oxygen when heated yielding RuO_2; it reacts with chlorine. It is insoluble in pure mineral acids and in aqua regia. It dissolves in aqua regia to which potassium chlorate has been added, and in fused potassium hydroxide.

Osmium is a bluish white, very hard metal. It is slowly oxidised by air at room temperature to the volatile OsO_4, and more quickly if heated. The massive metal is unattacked by acids (including aqua regia). If fused with a mixture of sodium peroxide and sodium hydroxide it yields sodium osmiate.

The compounds formed by the three elements in Group VIII follow much the same pattern as those formed by elements in sub-Group VII T, with the difference that the

† α-ferrite above the Curie point used to be known as β-ferrite.

Table 24.26. Examples of Types of Compounds formed by Elements in Group VIII

Valency system of atom: $\overbrace{d\ d\ d\ d\ d}^{n-1}\ \overbrace{s\ p\ p\ p}^{n}$
The values of n are: Fe 4, Ru 5, Os 6.

Normal prehybridisation electron configuration: $\overbrace{d\ d\ d\ d\ d}^{n-1}\ \overbrace{s\ p\ p\ p}^{n}$

Section	Oxidation state	Nature of unit	Fe	Ru	Os
		Interstitial compounds	Fe_3C, Fe_2N, Fe_4N		
2	II	Simple cation	$Fe(NO_3)_2,6H_2O$, $FeSO_4$	$RuCl_2$, $RuBr_2$	
		Giant molecules	FeO, Fe_3O_4, FeS, FeS_2	RuS_2, $RuSe_2$, $RuTe_2$	OsS_2, $OsSe_2$, $OsTe_2$
		Neutral complexes	$FeA_2,2pyr$		
		Complex anions	$K_4[Fe(CN)_6]$, $K_2[Fe(CN)_5NO]$, $KFeIII[Fe(CN)_6]$	$K_4[Ru(CN)_6]$, $KFe[Ru(CN)_6]$	$K_4[Os(CN)_6]$
		Complex cations	$[Fe6NH_3]Cl_2$	$[Ru\ dipyr_3]Cl_2$, $[Ru(NH_3)_4(SO_2)Cl]Cl$	
3	III	Simple cation	$Fe_2(SO_4)_3$, $Fe(NO_3)_3,6H_2O$	$RuCl_3$, $RuBr_3$, RuI_3, $Ru(OH)_3$	$Os(NO_3)_3$
		Giant molecules	Fe_2O_3, Fe_3O_4, FeF_3, $FeCl_3$, $FeBr_3$		
		Neutral complexes	FeA_3, $Fesal_3$, $Fecat_3$	RuA_3	
		Complex anions	$K_3[Feox_3]$, $K_3[Fe(CN)_6]$, $K_2[Fe(CN)_5NO]$	$M[Ruhal_4],xH_2O$, $K_2[RuCl_5]$, $K_2[RuCl_5,H_2O]$, $K_3[RuCl_6]$, $K_3[Ruox_3]$	$K_3[OsCl_6]$, $K_2[Os(NO_2)_5]$
		Complex cations	$[Fe(NH_3)_6]Cl_3$, $[FeCNS]Cl_2$	$[Ru(NH_3)_6]Cl_3$, $[Ru(NH_3)_5Cl]Cl$, $[Ru(NH_3)_4(H_2O)_2]Br_3$	
4	IV		—	RuO_2, $Ru(OH)_4$, $RuCl_4,5H_2O$, $Ru(SO_4)_2$, $K_2[RuX_6]$, $K_2[RuX_5OH]$ [X=Cl or Br] $K_2[Ruox_3]$	OsO_2, OsF_4, $OsCl_4$, $OsBr_4$, OsI_4, $K_2[OsX_6]$ [X=F, Cl, Br, I]
5	V		—	RuF_5	—
6	VI		K_2FeO_4	K_2RuO_4, $Rb_2[RuO_2Cl_4]$	OsF_6, K_2OsO_4, $K_2[OsO_2Cl_4]$, $K_2[OsO_3Cl_2]$, $K[OsNCl_4]$, $K_2[OsNCl_5]$
7	VII		—	$KRuO_4$	
8	VIII		—	RuO_4	OsO_4

lightest element, iron, is present (except in K_2FeO_4) in oxidation states II and III only. The oxidation states IV, V, VI, VII, and VIII are attained by ruthenium, and states IV, VI, and VIII by osmium. Cationic complexes are not found among the compounds of the metals in the higher oxidation states.

IRON

Iron forms the well-known ferrous Fe^{II} and ferric Fe^{III} salts; in the ferrous salts two electrons of the iron atom are used in forming bonds, and in the ferric state three electrons are so used. There are no oxides or halides of iron in an oxidation state higher than Fe^{III}, although the oxidation state of Fe^V is attained in the nitroprusside ion $[Fe(CN)_5NO]^{2-}$, and Fe^{VI} is attained in the ferrates and in iron pentacarbonyl (p. 1083).

Iron forms interstitial compounds with carbon (p. 599) and nitrogen (p. 654). The compound cementite, Fe_3C, is formed when carbon dissolves in molten iron. The cementite separates when the melt crystallises, and it is an important constituent of steel. In the crystal of cementite the carbon atoms are at the centres of distorted trigonal prisms, and the iron atoms are at the apices. There are two nitrides of iron, Fe_2N and Fe_4N. Fe_2N is made by passing ammonia at 400–$500°$ over iron. Fe_4N is made by heating Fe_2N to $600°$ in vacuo.

The oxides and sulphides of iron are giant molecule compounds in which either the ferrous or the ferric ion is present; in Fe_3O_4 both ions are present. It is convenient to treat these compounds in a single Section as they are related to one another. The ferrous salts and complexes are then discussed, and afterwards the ferric salts and complexes. Another giant molecule in which both ferrous and ferric ions are present is Prussian blue (p. 1030).

THE OXIDES, HYDROXIDES, AND SULPHIDES OF IRON

THE OXIDES OF IRON

It is usually assumed that the three oxides FeO, Fe_3O_4, and Fe_2O_3 are chemical compounds. They are in fact giant molecule structures in which a cubic close-packed array of negative oxygen ions is electrically neutralised by the appropriate proportions of Fe^{2+} and Fe^{3+} ions.

Fe_3O_4 has the spinel structure. The unit cell consists of 32 oxygen ions; it contains 8 tetrahedral holes and 16 octahedral holes. The 8 tetrahedral holes are occupied by Fe^{3+} ions; one half the octahedral holes are occupied by Fe^{2+} ions and the other half by Fe^{3+} ions.

Fe_2O_3 exists in two forms, γ-Fe_2O_3 (ferromagnetic) and α-Fe_2O_3 (paramagnetic); the α form is found naturally as haematite. The structure of γ-Fe_2O_3 is derived from the spinel structure. There are $21\frac{1}{3}$ Fe^{3+} ions per unit cell and these are distributed at random among the tetrahedral and octahedral holes. In α-Fe_2O_3 the Fe^{3+} ions are present in octahedral holes only. In the ideal structure of FeO all the octahedral holes would be occupied by Fe^{2+} ions. It is found, however, that the proportion of iron atoms to oxygen atoms in ferrous oxide is always slightly less than $1:1$, and hence a small number of Fe^{3+} ions are present. It is seen from the above considerations that γ-Fe_2O_3 is closely related to Fe_3O_4, and that α-Fe_2O_3 is related to FeO.

Ferrous oxide is metastable below $570°$; if iron is heated above this temperature in an atmosphere of oxygen at very low pressure pure ferrous oxide is obtained. It is black, melts at about $1360°$, and is diamagnetic. Below $570°$ it disproportionates to Fe_3O_4 and iron. γ-Fe_2O_3 is made by the oxidation of Fe_3O_4. α-Fe_2O_3 is made by heating the α form of the hydrated oxide, or by heating ferric nitrate. It melts at about $1550°$.

Fe_3O_4 is a ferromagnetic black substance m.p. 1538°. It is insoluble in water and in acids. It conducts electricity, probably by the transfer of electrons between the Fe^{2+} and Fe^{3+} ions in the octahedral holes in the crystal lattice. It is made by the partial oxidation of ferrous compounds, or of iron.

There are many double oxides of iron and other elements which are sometimes referred to as ferrites. They are best regarded as close-packed assemblies of oxygen ions with metal ions in the tetrahedral and octahedral holes. Examples of these oxides are given below, and in brackets is added the crystal structure which indicates the arrangement of the metal ions:

$LiFeO_2$ (rocksalt), $AgFeO_2$, $ZnFe_2O_4$ (spinel),

$MgFe_2O_4$ (spinel), $K_2Fe_2O_4$ (cristobalite).

The compound $K_2O,11Fe_2O_3$ is analogous to β-alumina (p. 534).

HYDROXIDES OF IRON

Ferrous hydroxide is obtained as a white precipitate when alkali is added to a solution of a ferrous salt in air-free water. It is not precipitated by the addition of ammonia and ammonium chloride, partly because the solubility product (3×10^{-14}) is fairly high, and partly because of the formation of ammines of the ferrous ion. In the presence of air the precipitate rapidly turns green. Ferrous hydroxide is unstable and it decomposes on standing to Fe_3O_4, water and hydrogen. It is a strong reducing agent. It has the $CdCl_2$ layer structure; hydroxyl bonds are not present.

Ferric hydroxide is often written for convenience as $Fe(OH)_3$, but no compound of this composition has been isolated. Ferric hydroxide can be obtained in colloidal solution.

$FeO \cdot OH$ occurs as goethite corresponding to diaspore (p. 535), and as lepidosite, corresponding to boehmite. The structures of the iron and aluminium compounds are similar; hydroxyl bonds play important parts in both structures.

Ferric ethylate, $Fe(OC_2H_5)_3$, exists as dark brown crystals. It is made by the action of sodium ethylate on ferric chloride dissolved in absolute alcohol, from which it can be recrystallised. It is hydrolysed by water, giving an electrolyte-free colloidal solution of ferric hydroxide.

SULPHIDES OF IRON

There are two sulphides of iron, ferrous sulphide FeS, and iron pyrites FeS_2, which also contains iron in the ferrous state.

Pure ferrous sulphide is made by passing a mixture of hydrogen sulphide and excess hydrogen over ferric oxide at 1000°. It forms colourless crystals, m.p. 1193°, almost insoluble in water. When formed by precipitation by the action of ammonium sulphide on a ferrous solution it is black. At high temperatures it dissociates. It is easily oxidised by moist air, and it reacts with boiling water to give hydrogen and sulphuric acid. With mineral acids it yields hydrogen sulphide.

Ferrous sulphide has the nickel arsenide structure. In the naturally occurring form, pyrrhotite, the ratio of iron atoms to sulphur atoms is slightly less than 1:1.

Iron pyrites is found naturally. It is chemically inert at room temperature, but if heated it burns in air to ferric oxide and sulphur dioxide. Its crystal structure can be described in terms of the rocksalt structure; the S_2^{2-} ions are discrete and occupy the positions of the Cl^- ions in rock salt, and the Fe^{2+} ions occupy the positions of the Na^+ ions. Another form of FeS_2 is marcasite in which the same structural units are arranged less symmetrically.

There is no compound Fe_2S_3.

SECTION 2. COMPOUNDS CONTAINING AN IRON ATOM IN OXIDATION STATE II

COMPOUNDS IN WHICH THE IRON ATOM IS PRESENT AS THE SIMPLE CATION Fe^{2+}

Ferrous sulphate. Green crystals of the hydrate $FeSO_4,7H_2O$ are obtained by crystallising a solution of iron in dilute sulphuric acid. When pure the crystals are said to be bluish-white and quite stable in air. The anhydrous salt is made by heating the heptahydrate. If the temperature is too high SO_2 and SO_3 are evolved and ferric oxide is left. Other hydrates formed by ferrous sulphate are 1 and 4.

Ferrous sulphate heptahydrate is known as green vitriol, and is isomorphous with the heptahydrates of certain other divalent metals including Mg, Mn, Co, Ni, Cu. The double sulphate $FeSO_4,(NH_4)_2SO_4,6H_2O$ is well known; the ammonium radical may be replaced by K, Rb, Cs, Tl^+. An aqueous solution of ferrous sulphate is very slowly oxidised by air; the oxidation is more rapid if the solution is alkaline.

Ferrous nitrate is known only in the form of the hydrates $Fe(NO_3)_2,6H_2O$ and $Fe(NO_3)_2,9H_2O$. It can be made by dissolving iron in cold dilute nitric acid. On warming with a dilute acid, nitric oxide is evolved and a ferric salt is formed.

GIANT MOLECULE COMPOUNDS CONTAINING Fe^{II}

The oxides and sulphides of iron are discussed on p. 1023. Among the other giant molecule compounds of ferrous iron are the four ferrous halides. The preparations and properties of these compounds are set out in Table 24.27.

Table 24.27. *The Ferrous Halides*

	FeF_2	$FeCl_2$	$FeBr_2$	FeI_2
Appearance	White tetragonal crystals	Colourless rhombohedral crystals	Yellow hexagonal crystals	Dark red hexagonal crystals
Lattice	Rutile	$CdCl_2$	CdI_2	CdI_2
m.p. °C	1075	672		177
b.p. °C	1100	1030		
Solubility in water	Slight	High	High	Soluble
Hydrates	0, 4, 8	0, 1, 2, 4, 6	0, 2, 4, 6, 9	0, 4, 6
Preparation	(i) Reduce FeF_3 with hydrogen (ii) Treat anhydrous $FeCl_2$ with F_2 in the cold	(i) Reduce $FeCl_3$ with hydrogen (ii) Treat iron with hydrogen chloride below 500°	Treat iron with bromine	Treat iron with iodine
Reactions	It is resistant to hydrogen up to 400° but at higher temperatures it is reduced to iron	It is very easily oxidised	It is oxidised by air above 300° to Fe_2O_3 and Br_2	
Complexes	$K[FeF_3]$ $K_2[FeF_4]$	$Li[FeCl_3],3H_2O$ $K,Rb,Cs[FeCl_3],2H_2O$ $Rb_2,Cs_2[FeCl_4],2H_2O$ $K_3Na[FeCl_6]$	None	None

33+A.T.I.C.

Each of the four ferrous halides can be obtained in solution by dissolving iron in the appropriate aqueous acid. Ferrous iodide can be made in solution by treating iron with an aqueous suspension of iodine. The vapour density of ferrous chloride is normal between 1300° and 1500°.

FERROUS COMPLEXES

Iron in the Fe^{II} state forms neutral, anionic, and cationic complexes.

Neutral complexes. Chelate derivatives of diketones, salicylaldehyde, and similar compounds are obtained by the action of the diketone on ferrous chloride in the presence of pyridine added to neutralise the liberated acid. The complexes normally contain two chelate rings and two co-ordinated molecules of the base, as for example in ferrous dipyridine diacetylacetonate:

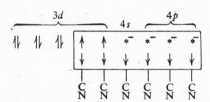

Complex anions are fairly numerous, the most important being those which contain nitrogen such as the anions present in the salts $KCa[Fe(NO_2)_6]$, potassium ferrocyanide $K_4[Fe(CN)_6]$, and potassium nitroprusside $K_2[Fe(CN)_5NO]$.

The ferrocyanides. The formula of the ferrocyanide ion is $[Fe(CN)_6]^{4-}$. Like all the ferrocyanide complexes it is diamagnetic. The orbital diagram is:

  3d   4s   4p

Fig. 24.33. Orbital diagram for the anion $[Fe^{II}(CN)_6]^{4-}$.

Salts of the ion are known with all the alkali metal ions, with all the alkaline earth metal ions except that of beryllium, and also with the ions NH_4^+ and Tl^+. All these salts are hydrated. They are pale yellow, and readily soluble in water. Other salts are known and are for the most part insoluble. More than one kind of cation may be present in a salt, as for example in $Ag_3K[Fe(CN)_6]$ and $CaK_2[Fe(CN)_6]$. Cupric ferro-cyanide, $Cu_2[Fe(CN)_6]$ is used as a semipermeable membrane in experiments in osmosis.

The alkali metal ferrocyanides are stable up to a red heat at which they decompose into the metal cyanide and numerous other products. With dilute sulphuric acid they liberate hydrogen cyanide, and with concentrated sulphuric acid carbon monoxide. In aqueous solution the ferrocyanide ion gives no reactions for ferrous ions or cyanide ions, and at pH 10 exchange with radioactive cyanide ion is negligible. In alkaline solution ferrocyanides are not oxidised by air. Oxidation to ferricyanide is slow in neutral solution and rapid in acid solution.

If dry potassium ferrocyanide is treated with methyl sulphate, or if silver ferrocyanide is treated with methyl iodide, compounds of composition $[(CH_3)_6Fe(CN)_6]SO_4$ and $[(CH_3)_6Fe(CN)_6]I_2$ are obtained. The structure of the iodide has been shown to be $[(CH_3NC)_6Fe]I_2$ to which the orbital diagram in Fig. 24.34 may be assigned.

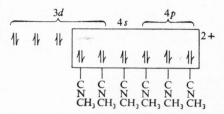

Fig. 24.34. Orbital diagram for the cation $[(CH_3NC)_6Fe]^{2+}$.

Other compounds of this type have been prepared and examined.

Another important series of complexes of ferrous iron has the general formula $M_x[Fe(CN)_5X]$. X may represent H_2O, NH_3, $(CH_3)_3N$, SO_3^-, NO_2, CO, or NO; the value of x depends on the number of electrons contributed by the group X to the valency orbitals of the iron atom. The carbonyl compound $K_3[Fe(CN)_5CO]$ is formed by the action of carbon monoxide on a hot solution of potassium ferrocyanide. The orbital diagram of the anion is shown in Fig. 24.35.

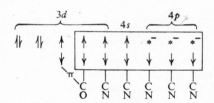

Fig. 24.35. Orbital diagram for the anion $[Fe(CN)_5CO]^{3-}$.

The carbonyl derivative is less easily oxidised than the ferrocyanide ion; its diminished activity may perhaps be accounted for by the presence of the πd bond. The corresponding free acid $H_3[Fe(CN)_5CO],H_2O$ has been isolated.

Potassium nitroprusside, $K_2[Fe(CN)_5NO]$, which exists as red hygroscopic crystals, is made by the action of 30% nitric acid on a ferrocyanide or ferricyanide, or by the action of sodium nitrite on an acid solution of potassium ferrocyanide:

$$K_4[Fe(CN)_6] + NaNO_2 = K_4[Fe(CN)_5NO_2] + NaCN,$$

$$K_4[Fe(CN)_5NO_2] + H_2O = K_2[Fe(CN)_5NO] + 2KOH.$$

In acid conditions the alkali is neutralised, and hydrogen cyanide is liberated. The first reaction is promoted if the hydrogen cyanide is swept out of solution by a stream of nitrogen.

Potassium nitroprusside is not oxidised in acid or neutral solution, but in alkaline solution it is oxidised by potassium permanganate. It reacts with the sulphide ion (but not with hydrogen sulphide) to give a reddish violet colouration which is used as a test for the sulphide ion:

$$K_2S + K_2[Fe(CN)_5NO] = K_4[Fe(CN)_5NOS].$$

The sodium and potassium salts of the thionitroferrocyanide have been isolated.

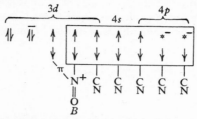

Fig. 24.36.   Orbital diagram for the nitroprusside ion $[Fe(CN)_5NO]^{2-}$. For the explanation of the bonding of the NO group see p. 1113.

The **complex cations** formed by ferrous iron include ferrous chloride hexammine $[Fe(NH_3)_6]Cl_2$ which has a dissociation pressure of only 6 mm at 20°, the tetrapyridine compound $[Fepyr_4]Cl_2$, and chelate complexes such as $[Fe(en)_3]Cl_2$.

SECTION 3. COMPOUNDS CONTAINING AN IRON ATOM IN OXIDATION STATE III

IONIC COMPOUNDS AND COMPOUNDS IN WHICH THE IRON ATOM (Fe^{III}) HAS IONIC CHARACTER

The existence of the cation Fe^{3+} in simple salts of ferric iron is not certain. **Ferric sulphate** forms the hydrates $Fe_2(SO_4)_3,xH_2O$ where x may be 3, 6, 7, 9, 10, or 12. The anhydrous salt can be obtained by carefully heating any of the hydrates, or by heating ferrous sulphate with concentrated sulphuric acid for about one hour. The crystals of ferric sulphate which form on cooling may be washed with alcohol and ether, and dried. The anhydrous sulphate is a dimorphic white powder which dissolves slowly in water if pure, but quickly if a trace of ferrous sulphate is present. When heated it decomposes to ferric oxide and sulphur trioxide. Ferric sulphate forms an alum.

Ferric nitrate exists only as the hydrates $Fe(NO_3)_3,6H_2O$ and $Fe(NO_3)_3,9H_2O$. It does not form complexes. **Ferric fluoride, ferric chloride,** and **ferric bromide** are well-characterised compounds. Neither ferric iodide nor any complex which might be derived from it have been prepared. The three ferric halides have polymeric structures in aqueous solution, and in the vapours just above the boiling points. The preparations and properties of the ferric halides are summarised in Table 24.28.

Table 24.28.   *The Ferric Halides*

	FeF_3	$FeCl_3$	$FeBr_3$
Appearance	Pale green solid	Dark red crystals with a green iridescence	Dark red-brown crystals
Lattice	ReO_3	BiF_3	
m.p. °C		306	
b.p. °C	(It can be sublimed in HF above 1000°)	316	
Solubility in water	Slight	Very soluble, hygroscopic	Very soluble
Hydrates expressed as $(Fe_2hal_6)xH_2O$	0, 6, 9	0, 4, 5, 7, 12	0, 12
Preparation	(i) Treat metallic iron, or $FeCl_2$, or $FeCl_3$ with F_2 (ii) Heat Fe_2O_3 in HF	(i) Heat iron in dry Cl_2 (ii) Heat a mixture of Fe_2O_3 and C in Cl_2	Heat iron or $FeBr_2$ with Br_2 at 190°

Table 24.28—*continued*

	FeF_3	$FeCl_3$	$FeBr_3$
Reactions	Heated in H_2 gives FeF_2 and then metal. Heated in air or steam gives Fe_2O_3. It is only slightly hydrolysed by water	Dissociates above 500° to $FeCl_2 + Cl_2$. It is highly hydrolysed in water to colloidal $Fe(OH)_3$	It loses halogen easily. In boiling aqueous solution it gives $FeBr_2 + Br_2$
Constitution	The solution gives no reactions for Fe^{3+} or F^- ions. The solution may contain the unionised complex	The vapour density at 400° corresponds to Fe_2Cl_6, and at 750° (in presence of excess Cl_2) to $FeCl_3$. The absorption spectrum eliminates $Fe[FeCl_6]$, and the structure of the vapour is in accord with electron diffraction results	
Complexes	$[FeF_4]^-$ $[FeF_5]^{2-}$ $[FeF_5,H_2O]^{2-}$ $[FeF_6]^{3-}$	$[FeCl_4]^-$ $[FeCl_5]^{2-}$ $[FeCl_5,H_2O]^{2-}$ $[FeCl_6]^{3-}$ $FeCl_3,2C_2H_5OH$ $FeCl_3,(C_2H_5)_2O$ Forms complexes with donor solvents such as $POCl_3$, acetone and methyl alcohol, in which it is very soluble	$[FeBr_4]^-$ $[FeBr_5]^{2-}$ Highly soluble in ether, alcohol, and acetic acid

The oxides and sulphides of ferric iron are discussed on p. 1023.

FERRIC COMPLEXES

Iron in the Fe^{III} state forms neutral, anionic, and cationic complexes.

Neutral complexes. Ferric acetylacetonate, which exists as garnet red prisms, m.p. 179°, is made by the action of acetylacetone on an aqueous solution of ferric chloride containing sodium acetate. The structure is trichelate.

It is soluble in organic solvents. It is stable to acids but is decomposed to colloidal ferric hydroxide on boiling with alkalis. Ferric trichelate neutral complexes are also formed with salicylic acid and with catechol. The highly coloured ferric iron derivatives of phenols and aromatic amines are non-chelate complexes.

Complex anions. Ferric iron forms complex anions with monobasic and dibasic organic acids. The structure of the ferric acetate complex has been shown to be $[Fe_3(CH_3COO)_6](CH_3COO)_3$. There are many salts of the trioxalato anion:

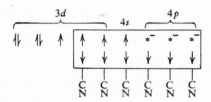

Those of the alkali metals are emerald green and are hydrated. If exposed to light the anion is destroyed because the ferric iron is reduced by the oxalate group. The trioxalato ion is asymmetric; it has been resolved, but is found to racemise rapidly. In aqueous solution the anion is decomposed just sufficiently to give the tests for the ferric ion and the oxalate ion.

Potassium ferricyanide, $K_3[Fe(CN)_6]$, exists as dark red crystals isomorphous with those of the corresponding manganese and chromium compounds. It has been shown by X-ray analysis that in potassium ferricyanide the six cyanide groups are octahedrally arranged about the iron atom. The orbital diagram is shown in Fig. 24.37:

Fig. 24.37.   Orbital diagram for the ferricyanide anion $[Fe^{III}(CN)_6]^{3-}$.

Salts of the ferricyanide ion are formed with all the alkali metal ions, with all the alkaline earth metals ions except that of beryllium, and also with the ions NH_4^+, Zn^{2+}, Cd^{2+}, Mn^{2+}, Co^{2+}, Cu^{2+}, Ni^{2+}, Fe^{2+}. Some, but not all, of the ferricyanides are hydrated; the ferricyanides of the bivalent metals zinc, cadmium, and the transition metals just mentioned all have 8 molecules of water of crystallisation. The ferricyanides of silver and the heavy metals are insoluble. The ferricyanides are less stable than the ferrocyanides. In alkaline solution they are oxidising agents.

Prussian blue is an interesting example of a giant molecule containing iron atoms and cyanogen groups. A brilliant blue colouration, Prussian blue, appears if (a) a solution of a ferrous salt is brought into contact with potassium ferricyanide, or (b) if a solution of a ferric salt is brought into contact with potassium ferrocyanide. The composition of the blue substance is the same in both cases and is $KFe[Fe(CN)_6], H_2O$.

X-ray analysis has shown that the iron atoms in this substance are arranged on two interpenetrating face-centred cubic lattices (another way of describing the structure is to say that iron atoms occupy the positions both of the sodium ions and of the chlorine ions in rock salt). Each pair of iron atoms is considered to be linked by a $—C\equiv N$: group thus, $Fe—\overset{+}{C}\equiv\overset{-}{N}—Fe$, so that CN groups are situated along all the cube edges in the structure. The number of iron atoms in unit cell is 8/8, and the number of CN groups is 12/4; these numbers correspond to the composition $Fe_2(CN)_6$. The potassium ions are situated at the centres of alternate cubes. The structural relation of ferric ferricyanide (Berlin green), Prussian blue, and potassium ferrous ferrocyanide (white and insoluble) are shown in Fig. 24.38.

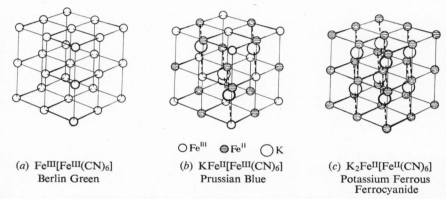

$\bigcirc Fe^{III}$ $\ominus Fe^{II}$ $\bigcirc K$

(a) $Fe^{III}[Fe^{III}(CN)_6]$
Berlin Green

(b) $KFe^{II}[Fe^{III}(CN)_6]$
Prussian Blue

(c) $K_2Fe^{II}[Fe^{II}(CN)_6]$
Potassium Ferrous
Ferrocyanide

Fig. 24.38. The relationship between (a) Berlin green, (b) Prussian blue, and (c) potassium ferrous ferrocyanide. (Reproduced by permission from *Structural Inorganic Chemistry* by A. F. Wells, 2nd Edition, Oxford University Press.)

Ferric iron also forms complexes of the general formula $M_x[Fe(CN)_5X]$, where X may be H_2O, NH_3, NO_2, or NO. The compound $K_3[Fe(CN)_5NO]$, dark yellow in neutral solution, and violet in the presence of acid, is made by the action of nitric oxide on $K_2[Fe(CN)_5H_2O]$ which is itself made by the hydrolysis of potassium ferri-cyanide solution exposed to light. The orbital diagram:

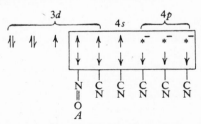

Fig. 24.39. Orbital diagram for the anion $[Fe(CN)_5NO]^{3-}$.

should be compared with that of $K_2[Fe(CN)_5NO]$, p. 1028. The different modes of linking adopted by the NO group in these two compounds could account for their difference in colour.

Complex cations containing ferric iron are known, but they are not very stable. The ammines $[Fe(NH_3)_6]Cl_3$ and $[Fe(NH_3)_6]Br_3$ can be formed from the dry halides and ammonia gas. They are decomposed by water. The blood-red colour produced when a thiocyanate is added to a solution of a ferric salt is considered to be largely due to the complex cation $[FeCNS]^{2+}$.

SECTION 6. COMPOUNDS CONTAINING AN IRON ATOM IN OXIDATION STATE VI

The only representatives of compounds containing iron in the state Fe^{VI} are the ferrates. **Potassium ferrate K_2FeO_4** is made by treating a suspension of freshly prepared ferric hydroxide in concentrated potassium hydroxide solution with chlorine. Potassium ferrate is deep red. It is isomorphous with K_2XO_4, where X represents S, Se, Cr, or Mo. It is fairly stable. The aqueous solution is a strong oxidising agent. If it is acidified oxygen is evolved:

$$4[FeO_4]^{2-} + 20H^+ = 4Fe^{3+} + 3O_2 + 10H_2O.$$

It will oxidise ammonia to nitrogen in the cold. By analogy with the structure proposed for the sulphate ion (p. 779), the orbital diagram would be:

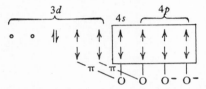

Fig. 24.40.   Orbital diagram for the ferrate ion $[FeO_4]^{2-}$.

RUTHENIUM AND OSMIUM

These elements are rare. Their chemistries are extensive, but introduce no new principles, and they are therefore discussed only in brief and general terms. Both ruthenium and osmium form compounds in which the metal is in the oxidation states II, III, IV, VI, and VIII. Ruthenium is the only element in the Group to attain oxidation states V and VII. Ru^V is present in the compound RuF_5, a dark green solid, m.p. 101° which is very reactive and attacks glass, and Ru^{VII} is present in $KRuO_4$. The most frequently attained oxidation state for ruthenium is III, and for osmium IV.

SECTION 1. COMPOUNDS CONTAINING A RUTHENIUM ATOM OR AN OSMIUM ATOM IN OXIDATION STATE II

It is doubtful whether ruthenium or osmium form the simple cations Ru^{2+} and Os^{2+}, but reduction of $RuCl_3$ gives a blue solution which probably contains Ru^{2+}, from which a blue chloride of the correct composition has been obtained; the corresponding bromide has also been made. Both are intensely strong reducing agents. A dark-brown osmium dichloride has been reported but it is not a reducing agent and may have been incorrectly described. Ruthenium and osmium are bivalent in the giant molecule compounds RuS_2 and OsS_2 which have the pyrites structure. Complex cations such as those in $[Ru\ dipyr_2]Cl_2$ and $[Ru\ dipyr_3]Cl_2$ are made by the direct action of dipyridyl (α, α'-(2,2'-)) on ruthenium trichloride. Reduction of Ru^{III} occurs, and the complex of bivalent ruthenium is obtained. The tridipyridyl complex is stable up to 300° and resists attack by acids and bases. The corresponding hydroxide is a strong base. Ammines of bivalent ruthenium are numerous, but the cation never contains more than five NH_3 groups. The complex $[Ru^{II}(NH_3)_4(SO_2)Cl]Cl$ is remarkable because the group SO_2 appears to be playing the same part as the group CO in a carbonyl; the orbital diagram in Fig. 24.41 may be conjectured:

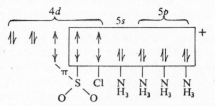

Fig. 24.41. Orbital diagram for the cation
$[Ru^{II}(NH_3)_4(SO_2)Cl]^+$.

Complex cations of bivalent osmium appear to be rare, but complex anions of ruthenium and osmium are known corresponding to the iron compounds.

SECTION 3. COMPOUNDS CONTAINING A RUTHENIUM ATOM OR AN OSMIUM ATOM IN OXIDATION STATE III

Ruthenium trichloride $RuCl_3$ is the most important compound of ruthenium. It is made (i) by the action of chlorine on the metal at 450°, (ii) by evaporating a solution of ruthenium tetroxide in hydrochloric acid in a current of hydrogen chloride. It crystallises in black leaflets with a layer lattice. It is soluble in water, by which it is readily hydrolysed to $Ru(OH)_3$. The tribromide and tri-iodide are also known. Osmium trichloride can be prepared; there is evidence that it is polymerised. Ruthenium forms complex cations of the types mentioned in Table 24.26. $[Ru(NH_3)_6]X_3$ is extremely stable. It is paramagnetic (2·0 Bohr magnetons). The neutral complex RuA_3 is a blood-red powder insoluble in water but soluble in organic solvents. Ruthenium forms many complex anions (see Table 24.26). The trivalent state is not very important for osmium, but the trichloride and certain complex anions are well-characterised.

SECTION 4. COMPOUNDS CONTAINING A RUTHENIUM ATOM OR AN OSMIUM ATOM IN OXIDATION STATE IV

The oxide RuO_2 is obtained by heating ruthenium in oxygen; osmium dioxide, however, has to be made by reducing OsO_4 or by hydrolysing $K_2[OsCl_6]$. RuO_2 forms stable blue crystals; it is not very reactive, but is reduced by hydrogen. OsO_2 is reduced by hydrogen and oxidised by air. The only binary halide of tetravalent ruthenium is the chloride $RuCl_4,5H_2O$ which is known only as the hydrate. The halides of osmium, OsF_4, $OsCl_4$, and OsI_4 are reported, but they are not well characterised. Complex anions of both metals in the tetravalent state are known; complex cations are uncommon.

SECTION 6. COMPOUNDS CONTAINING A RUTHENIUM ATOM OR AN OSMIUM ATOM IN OXIDATION STATE VI

All three elements in the Group, iron, ruthenium, and osmium, are present in the oxidation state VI in the ferrates, the ruthenates, and the osmiates; the general formula s K_2MO_4. The ammonium ruthenate with the empirical formula $(NH_4)_2RuO_4$ has the constitution $[RuO_2(NH_3)_2(OH)_2]^0$. Ruthenium and osmium are present in the oxidation state VI in the complex anions $[RuO_2Cl_4]^{2-}$ and $[OsO_2Cl_4]^{2-}$. Osmium alone forms a hexafluoride OsF_6, a yellow, crystalline solid, m.p. 34·5°, b.p. 47·5°, which is

33*

obtained, together with OsF_4, by the action of fluorine on metallic osmium. The vapour is colourless and poisonous. OsF_6 attacks glass, most non-metals, and most metals except the noble ones. It is hydrolysed by water to OsO_2, OsO_4, and HF. The complexes formed by osmium in the state VI, both anionic and cationic, are numerous.

SECTION 8. COMPOUNDS CONTAINING A RUTHENIUM ATOM OR AN OSMIUM ATOM IN OXIDATION STATE VIII†

Both ruthenium and osmium form oxides RuO_4 and OsO_4 in which the metals are octavalent. Ruthenium tetroxide is dimorphic, one form is yellow, m.p. 25·5° and the other orange, m.p. 27°. The tetroxide is made by passing chlorine into a solution of potassium ruthenate; the volatile tetroxide distils over. Ruthenium tetroxide is volatile but it explodes if heated above 100°. It is decomposed by sunlight. In all its reactions it is reduced. It has a strong smell and is poisonous.

Osmium tetroxide is easily made by heating osmium in air. It is a yellow solid, m.p. 40°, b.p. 131°. It is poisonous. It is soluble in water and the solution behaves as a very weak acid. It is a fairly strong oxidising agent which oxidises concentrated hydrochloric acid and organic substances. Much work has been done on osmium tetroxide with a view to determining its constitution. The molecular weight of osmium tetroxide is normal when it is vaporised at 250°, and when it is dissolved in phosphorus oxychloride. Electron diffraction experiments, the absorption spectrum and the Raman spectrum all indicate that the four oxygen atoms are tetrahedrally arranged round the osmium atom. The distance Os–O is short, 1·66. The molecule is diamagnetic. The orbital diagram in Fig. 24.42 is in accord with the experimental evidence, but it requires four hybrid d orbitals to form πd bonds with the oxygen atoms. The greatest

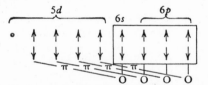

Fig. 24.42.   Conjectural orbital diagram for OsO_4.

number which it has been possible to construct is three (p. 160); there is a fourth hybrid orbital, but it is not orthogonal to the other three.

GROUP IX. COBALT, RHODIUM, AND IRIDIUM

Certain properties of the elements of Group IX are set out in Table 24.29.

Table 24.29.   *Properties of the Metals in Group IX*

	Co	Rh	Ir
Atomic number	27	45	77
m.p. °C	1492	1960	2443
b.p. °C	2900	3900	—
Specific gravity	8·8	12·4	22·4
Ionic radius, M^{2+}	0·72	—	—
Atomic radius (12 co-ordination)	1·25	1·34	1·36

† The compound formed by the action of fluorine on metallic osmium was at one time thought to be OsF_8. It has been shown experimentally by X-ray diffraction, and by infrared and Raman spectra that the compound so formed is OsF_6. B. Weinstock and J. G. Malm, *J. Amer. Chem. Soc.*, 1958, **80**, 4466.

Cobalt is a lustrous hard white metal. The crystal structure is hexagonal close-packed below 492°, and cubic close-packed above this temperature. Cobalt is ferromagnetic below the Curie point 1000°. Cobalt when heated is oxidised by air. It dissolves slowly in dilute hydrochloric acid or dilute sulphuric acid, and more rapidly in dilute nitric acid. It is dissolved by fused potassium hydroxide at 550°.

Rhodium is a hard white metal. It reacts with oxygen slowly at 100°. Chlorine at a red heat converts it to $RhCl_3$. It is insoluble in all acids and in aqua regia unless finely divided. It dissolves in fused $KHSO_4$, and in fused potassium hydroxide in the presence of an oxidising agent.

Iridium is a brittle white metal which is oxidised only very slowly when heated in air. It is insoluble in acids including aqua regia. It is insoluble in fused alkalis. It is attacked by chlorine at a red heat, by fused potassium sulphate, and by a fused mixture of potassium hydroxide and nitrate.

Table 24.30. *Examples of the Types of Compounds formed by Cobalt, Rhodium, and Iridium*

$$\text{Valency system of atom:} \overbrace{d \quad d \quad d \quad d}^{n-1} \quad \overbrace{s \quad p \quad p \quad p}^{n}$$

The values of n are: Co 4, Rh 5, Ir 6

Normal prehybridisation electron configuration of the atom:

$$\overbrace{\underset{\uparrow\downarrow\ \uparrow\downarrow\ \uparrow\ \uparrow\ \uparrow}{d \quad d \quad d \quad d \quad d}}^{n-1} \quad \overbrace{\underset{\uparrow\ \uparrow}{s \quad p \quad p \quad p}}^{n}$$

Oxidation state	Nature of unit	Co	Rh	Ir
	Oxides and sulphides	CoO, Co_2O_3, Co_3O_4 $Co(OH)_2$, $CO_2O_3,2H_2O$ CoS, CoS_2, Co_3S_4, Co_2S_3 Co_9S_8	(RhO), Rh_2O_3, RhO_2, $Rh(OH)_3$ Rh_2S_3, Rh_3S_4, Rh_2S_5 Rh_9S_8	Ir_2O_3, IrO_2, IrO_3 $Ir(OH)_3$, $Ir(OH)_4$ IrS, Ir_2S_3, IrS_2 IrS_3
II	Cation M^{2+}	$Co(NO_3)_2,3H_2O$, and 6 and 9 H_2O $Co(SO_4)$ and hydrates $CoX_2[X=F, Cl, Br, I]$	$RhCl_2$	$IrX_2[X=F, Cl, Br, I]$
	Neutral complexes	CoA_2, $[Co(NH_3)_2Cl_2]^0$		
	Complex anions	$Na[CoA_3]$ $K_2[Co(CNS)_4]$, $K_2[Co(NO_2)_4]$ $K_4[Co(CN)_6]$, $K_4[CoCl_6]$		$K_4[Ir(CN)_6]$
	Complex cations	$[Co(NH_3)_6]Cl_2$	$[Rh\ pyr_6]Cl_2$ $[Rh(As(C_2H_5)_3)_4]Cl_2$	
III	Cation M^{3+}	$Co_2(SO_4)_3,18H_2O$ CoF_3	RhX_3 [X = F, Cl, Br, I]	IrX_3 [X = Cl, Br, I]
	Neutral complexes	CoA_3	$[Rh(NH_3)_3Br_3]^0$	$[Ir(NH_3)_3Br_3]^0$
	Complex anions	$K_3[Co(CN)_6]$, $K_3[Co(NO_3)_6]$	$K_3[Rh(CN)_6]$	$K_3[IrX_6]$ [X = Cl, Br, I, NO_2, CN, $\frac{1}{2}SO_3$, $\frac{1}{2}SO_4$] $K_3[Irox_3]$
	Complex cations	$[CO(H_2O)_6]Cl_3$ $[Co(NH_3)_6]Cl_3$	$[Rh(NH_3)_6]Cl_3$ $[Rh(NH_3)_5H_2O]Cl_3$ ‡$[Rh(NH_3)_5Cl]Cl_2$	$[Ir(NH_3)_6]Cl_3$ $[Ir(NH_3)_5H_2O]Cl_3$
IV		$[(NH_3)_5Co—O_2—Co(NH_3)_5]Cl_5$	RhF_4	IrF_4, $IrCl_4$ $K_2[IrX_6]$ [X = F, Cl, Br] $[Ir(NH_3)_4Cl_2]Cl_2$
V		—	—	—
VI		—	—	IrF_6, $IrOF_4$

‡ A complete X-ray study of this compound has been made.

Examples of the types of compounds formed by the three metals are set out in Table 24.30. Cobalt and rhodium form compounds in which the oxidation states of the metals are II, III, or IV. Iridium in addition forms compounds in which it attains the oxidation state VI. There are no compounds, however, in which any higher oxidation state is reached.

COBALT

THE OXIDES, HYDROXIDES, AND SULPHIDES OF COBALT

THE OXIDES OF COBALT

The oxides of cobalt, like the oxides of iron, are solids, and their compositions depend on the presence of Co^{2+} and Co^{3+} ions in the holes between the close-packed oxygen ions. It is therefore convenient to discuss them together.

Cobaltous oxide, CoO, is a pale green solid, m.p. 1935°. It has the sodium chloride lattice; the oxygen ions are close-packed and cobaltous ions are in all the octahedral holes. It is made by heating cobaltous nitrate or carbonate in vacuo to 1000°, or by heating cobaltous hydroxide. It is predominantly a basic oxide but it dissolves in concentrated sodium hydroxide solution to give a deep blue solution. This solution is readily oxidised by air to give a black precipitate of hydrated cobaltic oxide. Cobaltous oxide absorbs oxygen, and the product on heating yields the oxide Co_3O_4 with the spinel structure.

Co_3O_4 is a black solid which is made by the ignition of cobaltous nitrate below 1000°, by heating Co_2O_3,H_2O, or by heating cobaltous oxide in air. It is isomorphous with Fe_3O_4, and it must therefore have a corresponding distribution of Co^{3+} and Co^{2+} ions in the tetrahedral and octahedral holes in the lattice (see p. 1023). At 900° Co_3O_4 loses oxygen and yields cobaltous oxide. It absorbs oxygen up to the composition Co_2O_3 without change in the spinel lattice. The cobaltic oxide thus produced must therefore correspond to γ-Fe_2O_3 (p. 1023).

Cobaltic oxide, Co_2O_3. Many authors declare that the existence of this oxide is doubtful, but the crystallographic evidence mentioned in the previous paragraph indicates that the γ-form can be obtained. The dehydration of the hydrate Co_2O_3,H_2O cannot be carried out without loss of oxygen.

THE HYDROXIDES OF COBALT

Cobaltous hydroxide, $Co(OH)_2$, exists in a blue form and in a pink form. The blue form is precipitated by adding an alkali to a solution of a cobaltous salt at 0°; the pink by adding a solution of a cobaltous salt to an alkali. The blue form changes to the pink form on warming. The colours are not explained; they may be due to differences in particle size. Cobaltous hydroxide has the CdI_2 layer lattice. It is fairly readily oxidised by air to hydrated cobaltic oxide.

Cobaltic hydroxide. The composition of cobaltic hydroxide is $Co_2O_3, 2H_2O$. It can be made by precipitating a cobaltic salt with alkali, or by oxidising cobaltous oxide or Co_3O_4 in the presence of moisture.

SULPHIDES OF COBALT

Cobaltous sulphide, CoS, is a red solid, m.p. above 1100°. If hydrogen sulphide is passed into a solution of cobaltous chloride containing acetic acid a black crystalline precipitate of cobaltous sulphide is obtained which is soluble in cold dilute hydrochloric acid only with difficulty. If sodium sulphide or ammonium sulphide is used as the precipitant (air being excluded) the precipitate is amorphous and is easily soluble in cold dilute hydrochloric acid with the evolution of hydrogen sulphide. If air is present the precipitate contains oxygen. Cobaltous sulphide has the NiAs structure.

There are other sulphides of cobalt, CoS_2, Co_3S_4, Co_9S_8, and Co_2S_3. The first three are obtained together when cobalt is heated with sulphur. CoS_2 has the pyrites structure, and hence contains the ion Co^{2+}. The structures of Co_3S_4 and Co_9S_8 are in some respects similar to the spinels; the sulphur atoms are close-packed and the cobalt atoms are in the lattice holes.

Co_2S_3 is precipitated if hydrogen sulphide is passed into a solution of a cobaltic ammine, but it is not stable, and on warming it changes to a mixture of the cobaltous sulphides CoS and CoS_2.

SECTION 2. COMPOUNDS CONTAINING A COBALT ATOM IN OXIDATION STATE II

COMPOUNDS IN WHICH THE COBALT ATOM MAY BE PRESENT AS THE SIMPLE CATION Co^{2+}

There are no compounds in which it can be definitely stated that the simple ion Co^{2+} is present. The nitrate and the sulphate are probably complexes, and the halides giant molecule structures. Cobaltous nitrate is known only in the form of hydrates which dissolve in water to give pink solutions. The hexahydrate $Co(NO_3)_2,6H_2O$, which exists as red hygroscopic crystals, is normally obtained by crystallisation of an aqueous solution of cobaltous nitrate. Below $21°$ it changes to $Co(NO_3)_2,9H_2O$ and above $55·5°$ to $Co(NO_3)_2,3H_2O$. The hexahydrate is easily soluble in organic solvents. Cobaltous sulphate, $CoSO_4$, can be obtained in the anhydrous condition. It is hygroscopic, soluble in water (39·5 gm in 100 gm at $25°$), and it forms hydrates with 7, 6, and 1 molecules of water of crystallisation, isomorphous with the corresponding nickel salts.

Cobaltous halides. The preparations and properties of the cobaltous halides are summarised in Table 24.31.

COBALTOUS COMPLEXES

Cobalt in the Co^{II} state forms neutral, anionic, and cationic complexes, but the number of cobaltous complexes which has been reported is only about one-tenth of the number of cobaltic complexes.

Neutral complexes. Cobaltous acetylacetonate, CoA_2, exists as red crystals which sublime without melting to a red vapour. It is made by the action of acetylacetone on cobaltous hydroxide. It is soluble in water and in alcohol. The cobaltous atom in the compound is 4 co-ordinate, and it becomes 6 co-ordinate when the compound forms diammines with ammonia or pyridine. (See also under "ammine complexes.")

Complex anions. Complex anions containing the Co^{II} atom are present in the following potassium salts: the easily oxidised cobaltocyanide $K_4[Co(CN)_6]$ and cobaltonitrite $K_2[Co(NO_2)_4]$, the cobaltothiocyanate $K_2[Co(CNS)_4],4H_2O$, the oxalato compound $K_2[CoOx_2]$, the chloro derivative $K_2[CoCl_4]$. The salt $K[CoA_3]$ contains the unusual anion $[CoA_3]^-$ in which the cobalt atom has accepted an electron from a cation which enables it to form a trichelate complex with acetylacetone.

Potassium cobaltocyanide, $K_4[Co(CN)_6]$, exists as violet crystals which dissolve in water to give a deep red solution. The salt is very readily oxidised by air to the cobalticyanide; in the absence of air it decomposes water forming the cobalticyanide and liberating hydrogen.

Table 24.31.   *The Cobaltous Halides*

	CoF$_2$	CoCl$_2$	CoBr$_2$	CoI$_2$
Appearance	Pink crystalline solid	Pale blue solid	Green solid	α: stable, black solid giving red solutions β: unstable, yellow solid, giving colourless solutions
Lattice	Rutile	CdI$_2$		
m.p. °C		735	678	α, 520 in vacuo
b.p. °C		1049		α, 570 with decomposition
Solubility in water	Moderate, 1·4% at room temperature	High, 34·4% at room temperature†	High‡	
Hydrates	0, 4	0, 1, 1½, 2 (blue) 4, 6 (pink)	0, 2 (blue) 6 (red)	0, 2, 4 (green) 6, 9 (red)
Reactions	Stable to water and to ammonia at room temperature. With water at a red heat gives CoO and HF	Very hygroscopic	Very hygroscopic forming a red liquid	α very hygroscopic
Preparation	Treat anhydrous COCl$_2$ with HF at room temperature, or dehydrate CoF$_2$,4H$_2$O	Heat cobalt in chlorine, or by the thermal decomposition: 6[Co(NH$_3$)$_5$Cl]Cl$_2$ = 6CoCl$_2$ + 6NH$_4$Cl + 22NH$_3$ + N$_2$	Heat cobalt in bromine, or heat cobaltous oxide in hydrogen bromide	α. Heat finely divided cobalt in HI at 400–450°

† CoCl$_2$ is also freely soluble in alcohol and acetone, and sparingly soluble in methyl cyanide, methyl acetate, and pyridine.

‡ CoBr$_2$ is also freely soluble in alcohol, acetone, and methyl acetate. The molecular weight is normal in solution in pyridine.

Potassium cobaltothiocyanate, K$_2$[Co(CNS)$_4$],4H$_2$O, is a blue solid. Its concentrated aqueous solution is blue but turns pink on dilution. The sodium salt has 8 molecules of water of crystallisation. The mercury salt Hg[Co(CNS)$_4$] is insoluble.

Na[CoA$_3$] exists as pale pink needles insoluble in water and in alcohol. It is made by treating sodium cobaltinitrite Na$_3$[Co(NO)$_6$] with sodium acetylacetonate in excess. No compound corresponding to Na[CoA$_3$] can be made from any metal in Group II.

Complex halides. Many complex cobalto halides and their hydrates are known of the types § (i) M[CoX$_3$], (ii) M$_2$[CoX$_4$] and (iii) M$_4$[CoX$_6$].

When X represents F   the types are (i), (ii)

                                 Cl   (i), (ii), (iii)

                                 Br   (ii), (iii)

                                 I   (ii), (iii).

All the types and their hydrates are highly coloured.

Ammine complexes. Hexammine and tetrammine cobaltous cations are known, and also diammine complexes with zero ionic valency. The hexammine complexes such as [Co(NH$_3$)$_6$]Cl$_2$ have been shown by X-ray analysis to be octahedral, and the diammine complexes such as [Co(NH$_3$)$_2$Cl$_2$]^0 are thought to be square planar. The ammonia molecules may be replaced by those of amines, pyridine, and quinoline, and by ethylene diamine. The diammines exhibit *cis-trans* isomerism, and the isomers differ in colour, one blue the other pink. The two isomers of the nonvalent compound [CoCl$_2$pyr$_2$]^0 have different magnetic moments, at 20° the violet 5·34 and the pink 4·60 Bohr magnetons. The hexammine cations are paramagnetic.

§ The compound of the composition Cs$_3$CoCl$_5$ has been shown to have the constitution Cs$_3$[CoCl$_4$]Cl.

THE COLOURS OF COBALTOUS COMPOUNDS

Cobaltous compounds and their solutions are coloured pink or blue. The absorption band of the pink compounds is at Å 5100. There is no precise band for the blue state. The blue colour is more intense than the pink and conceals it, so that a mere visual examination of a solid or solution gives no indication of the proportions of blue and pink compounds present. A complete explanation of the colour relations is still awaited. There is a lot of evidence indicating that a complex cobaltous cation, whether 2, 4, or 6 co-ordinate, is pink, and that the complex anion (again irrespective of the co-ordination) is green or blue. A pink solution of cobaltous chloride turns blue on concentration, or on the addition of potassium or calcium chloride:

$$2[Co,6H_2O]^{2+} + 4Cl^- = [Co,4Cl]^{2-} + [Co,6H_2O]^{2+} + 6H_2O.$$

pink   blue

Mercury and zinc expel cobalt from an anionic complex, and hence turn a blue cobaltous solution red:

$$[Co,4Cl]^{2-} + 2HgCl_2 + 6H_2O = 2[Hg,4Cl]^{2-} + [Co,6H_2O]^{2+}.$$

blue   pink

There is also evidence that the tetrahedrally co-ordinated cobaltous ion is blue, and the octahedrally co-ordinated cobaltous ion is pink.

SECTION 2. COMPOUNDS CONTAINING A COBALT ATOM IN OXIDATION STATE III

COMPOUNDS IN WHICH THE COBALT ATOM Co^{III} HAS IONIC CHARACTER

Cobaltic salts can often be prepared by electrolysing a solution of a cobaltous salt dissolved in a solution of the parent acid of the salt. Cobaltic fluoride hydrate, cobaltic acetate, cobaltic carbonate, cobaltic oxalate, and cobaltic sulphate can all be made by this process, or by slight modifications of it. All cobaltic salts are strong oxidising agents, as they tend to revert to the corresponding cobaltous salts.

Cobaltic sulphate exists as blue crystals of the hydrate $Co_2(SO_4)_3,18H_2O$. It is stable if dry, but if moist it changes to cobaltous sulphate with the liberation of oxygen. The cobaltic ion plays the part of a trivalent ion in the alums. Potassium cobaltic alum is diamagnetic.

Cobaltic fluoride, CoF_3. The only cobaltic halide which has certain existence is cobaltic fluoride, which is known in the anhydrous state, and as the hydrate $CoF_3,3\frac{1}{2}H_2O$. Anhydrous cobaltic fluoride is a pale brown crystalline solid. When heated it begins to decompose at about 250°; if heated in a stream of carbon dioxide at 350° it is completely decomposed to cobaltous fluoride. It liberates oxygen from water and chlorine from hydrochloric acid, and it fluorinates many elements such as silicon, phosphorus, bromine, iodine, and sulphur. It is insoluble in alcohol, ether, and benzene. Its crystals possess the ReO_3 structure, in which they resemble FeF_3 and AlF_3.

The hydrate $CoF_3,3\frac{1}{2}H_2O$ can be made by electrolysing a saturated solution of cobaltous fluoride in hydrofluoric acid; it is precipitated as a green powder. By analogy with $CrF_3,3\frac{1}{2}H_2O$, which Werner formulated $[Cr(H_2O)_6][CrF_6]H_2O$ the hydrate of cobaltic fluoride might be written $[Co(H_2O)_6][CoF_6]H_2O$. It is difficult to believe, however, that such a structure would be stable since the anhydrous cobaltic fluoride liberates oxygen so readily from water.

COBALTIC COMPLEXES

Although the co-ordination number of the cobalt atom in the cobaltic complexes is always six the range of complexes, neutral, anionic, and cationic formed by cobalt in the cobaltic state is one of the widest formed by any element. The range includes numerous cationic complexes many of which contain two, three, or four cobalt atoms in the cation, as for example in the sulphate:

$$\left[(NH_3)_4Co \underset{\underset{\underset{H_2}{N}}{\nwarrow \nearrow}}{\overset{\overset{\overset{H}{O}}{\swarrow \searrow}}{}} Co(NH_3)_4 \right] (SO_4)_2,2H_2O$$

Complexes which contain more than one atom of the acceptor metal are known as polynuclear complexes. Cobalt does not appear to form polynuclear anionic complexes.

The addition of ligands to the cobaltic ion results in the formation of complex ions which are very stable. The simple cobaltic ion in cobaltic sulphate, in cobaltic alums, and in cobaltic fluoride is an oxidising agent, as it tends to change to the cobaltous ion, but the complex cobaltous ion $[Co^{II}(NH_3)_6]^{2+}$ is so easily oxidised to the complex cobaltic ion $[Co^{III}(NH_3)_6]^{3+}$ that it is attacked by atmospheric oxygen at room temperature. If the ligands to the cobalt atom are negatively charged so that the simple cobaltous or cobaltic cations are converted to anions, the same relative stability is observed; the cobaltic anionic complexes are more stable than the cobaltous complexes. This is seen in the cyanogen complexes; potassium cobaltocyanide is a strong reducing agent.

Neutral complexes. Cobaltic acetylacetonate, CoA_3, exists as dark green crystals, m.p. 241°. It is made by treating an oxidised solution of a cobaltous salt with acetylacetone. It is soluble in organic solvents, and its molecular weight in benzene is normal.

Anionic complexes. Potassium cobalticyanide, $K_3[Co(CN)_6]$, is very easily obtained by the oxidation of the strong reducing agent potassium cobaltocyanide (p. 1037). It is almost colourless, and is isomorphous with potassium ferricyanide. The cobalticyanides of the alkali metals are soluble in water; the cobalticyanides of lithium and sodium are hydrated, but those of the other alkali metals are anhydrous. The anion $[Co(CN)_6]^{3-}$ is so stable that free cobalticyanic acid can be isolated. The acid combines with alcohol to form salts of the type $(C_2H_5OH_2)_3[Co(CN)_6]$ which if warmed in vacuo yield the anhydrous acid. If the acid is heated with alcohol in a sealed tube the cyanide groups are attacked and compounds of the type $H_2[Co(CN)_5(NCC_2H_5)]$ are obtained.†

The pentacyano compounds of cobaltic cobalt appear to be less numerous and less stable than those of ferric iron. The carbonyl compound $K_2[Co(CN)_5CO]$ is known; its orbital diagram is similar to that of $K_3[Fe(CN)_5CO]$ (p. 1027).

Sodium cobaltinitrite, $Na_3[Co(NO_2)_6]$, is formed by adding a concentrated solution of cobaltous nitrate in 50% acetic acid to a concentrated solution of sodium nitrite at 50° while a stream of air is passed through the solution. It is easily soluble in water, but the solution decomposes with the evolution of oxygen. Potassium cobaltinitrite is stable to light and air, and as it is sparingly soluble it can be made by precipitating a solution of the sodium salt with potassium chloride.

Complex cations. The cationic cobaltic complexes are extremely numerous, and in a book of this general character it is not possible even to mention examples of all the important types. The simplest type of complex cation is the ammine $[Co(NH_3)_6]^{3+}$.

† Compare the behaviour of potassium ferricyanide (p. 1031).

The ammonia molecules may be exchanged, in part at least, for those of other amines including diamines, for H_2O, and (with consequent alteration of the valency of the cation as a whole) for anions such as NO_2^-, NO_3^-, Cl^-, and OH^-. Chelate complexes are frequent and if the ligands are appropriate they exhibit optical isomerism.†

SECTION 4. COMPOUNDS CONTAINING A COBALT ATOM IN OXIDATION STATE IV

A peroxide binuclear cationic complex salt of cobalt is known with the constitution: $[(NH_3)_5Co—O—O—Co(NH_3)_5]Cl_4$. Each cobalt atom in the complex salt is in the state Co^{III}, and the orbital diagram for the cation is explained in Fig. 24.43.

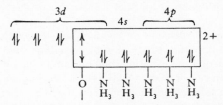

Fig. 24.43. Orbital diagram for the group $[CoO(NH_3)_5]^{2+}$.
The cation $[(NH_3)_5CoO_2Co(NH_3)_5]^{4+}$ is derived by the linking of two groups at the oxygen atom.

This peroxy complex, however, can be oxidised to the complex:

$$[(NH_3)_5Co—O—O—Co(NH_3)_5]Cl_5.$$

An electron has been removed from one of the cobalt atoms which is thus converted to the Co^{IV} state. The orbital diagram of this cobalt atom is shown in Fig. 24.44.

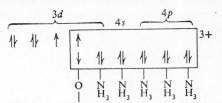

Fig. 24.44. Orbital diagram for the group $[CoO(NH_3)_5]^{3+}$.
The cation $[(NH_3)_5CoO_2Co(NH_3)_5]^{5+}$ is derived by the union of the group in Fig. 24.43 with the group in Fig. 24.44 at the oxygen atoms.

The magnetic moment of the complex is 1·6 Bohr magnetons.
Another example of a complex containing Co^{IV} is the octammine:

$$\left[(NH_3)_4\overset{IV}{Co} \overset{\overset{H_2}{N}}{\diagup \diagdown} \overset{III}{Co}(NH_3)_4 \right] Cl_4$$

This complex also has a magnetic moment of 1·6 Bohr magnetons.
Several other examples of binuclear peroxy complexes of cobalt containing one of the two cobalt atoms in the state Co^{IV} can be given, but a cobalt atom in this state is not known in any other circumstances.

† See footnote on p. 988.

RHODIUM AND IRIDIUM

The compounds of rhodium and iridium (Table 24.30) like those of cobalt are stabilised by complex formation. There are no simple ionic or covalent binary compounds of rhodium or iridium with any electronegative element such as oxygen, sulphur, fluorine, or chlorine. The binary compounds are either autocomplexes or giant molecule structures. If there are any simple binary compounds at all they are to be found among compounds in which the iridium atom is tetravalent or hexavalent.

The oxides, hydroxides, and sulphides of rhodium and iridium are difficult to classify because it is not possible to decide whether they are molecular compounds or whether they consist of close-packed oxygen or sulphur ions with metal ions in the lattice holes. They are therefore discussed together irrespective of the apparent valencies of the metals.

The reported oxides and hydroxides of rhodium are RhO, Rh_2O_3, and $Rh(OH)_3$. The existence of RhO is doubtful. Rh_2O_3, a grey crystalline solid with the corundum structure, is made by heating the metal or rhodium nitrate in air to about 800°; it is decomposed to the elements at 1200°. $Rh(OH)_3$ is precipitated by adding sodium hydroxide or baryta to a solution of $Na_3[RhCl_6]$ or of $RhCl_3$. There is some indication of the existence of RhO_2, for if the yellow solution of $Rh(OH)_3$ in excess of alkali is submitted to electrolytic oxidation the solution turns blue, and an olive green powder separates, which is richer in oxygen than $Rh(OH)_3$. Attempts to dehydrate the powder bring about its decomposition.

The oxides and hydroxides of iridium are Ir_2O_3, IrO_2, IrO_3, and $Ir(OH)_3$, and $Ir(OH)_4$. Ir_2O_3 can be obtained by heating $K_2[IrCl_6]$ with sodium carbonate. It decomposes into its elements at about 1150°. IrO_2 is a black powder made by heating powdered iridium in air or oxygen or by igniting the hydrate $IrO_2,2H_2O$ in dry nitrogen at 300°. It has a rutile lattice. It is thermally stable up to 650°. The hydrate is made as a blue precipitate by carefully adding alkali to boiling $IrCl_4$ solution; it may be dried in vacuo. It is soluble in hydrochloric acid to give $H_2[IrCl_6]$. Iridium trioxide is made by igniting iridium in strongly oxidising conditions; it always contains less than the theoretical quantity of oxygen and is a strong oxidising agent.

The sulphides of rhodium, indicated by phase-rule evidence supported by X-ray experiments, are Rh_2S_3, and Rh_9S_8. The sulphides of iridium are Ir_3S_4, Ir_2S_5, IrS, Ir_2S_3, IrS_2, and IrS_3. IrS, a solid with metallic glance, is formed when iridium burns in sulphur. Ir_2S_3, a brown solid, is precipitated by hydrogen sulphide from a solution of Ir_2O_3 in hydrochloric acid. It decomposes to its elements at 1000°. IrS_3, a dark grey powder insoluble in acids, is formed by heating iridium trichloride with excess sulphur in vacuo at 600°, and afterwards extracting the uncombined sulphur with carbon disulphide and sodium sulphide.

Rh^{II} **and** Ir^{II}. The only binary compounds which may contain rhodium in the state Rh^{II} are RhO and $RhCl_2$. The existence of these two compounds is doubtful, but there are several compounds containing complex cations having rhodium in this oxidation state. Two examples are $[Rh(pyr)_6]Cl_2$ and $[Rh(As(C_2H_5)_3)_4]Cl_2$. The only compounds of Ir^{II} are IrS, the dihalides, and a few complex salts, for example $K_4[Ir(CN)_6]$.

Rh^{III} **and** Ir^{III}. All the trihalides of rhodium and iridium except IrF_3 are known, but it is improbable that metal atoms are present in these compounds as simple cations. No acetylacetonates or similar neutral complexes have been reported, but anionic and cationic complexes of both metals are numerous. Complexes containing rhodium and iridium in oxidation state III are the most stable compounds of these metals.

Rh^{IV} **and** Ir^{IV}. There is evidence that when rhodium is treated with fluorine at 50° a volatile rhodium fluoride is produced which is probably RhF_4. IrF_4 is a not very volatile yellow oil. It decomposes in air, and reacts with water. There is some evidence for the existence of $IrCl_4$, but none for that of $IrBr_4$ or IrI_4. Iridium forms anionic and cationic complexes containing Ir^{IV}, but in this it is not imitated by rhodium.

Rh^{VI} and Ir^{VI}. There are no hexavalent compounds of rhodium, but IrF_6 is well-characterised. It is a pale yellow solid which melts at 44° to a brown liquid which boils at 53° to a yellow vapour. It is very reactive. With water it yields $Ir(OH)_4$, HF, O_2, and O_3. Chlorine converts it to IrF_4 with the formation of ClF. It attacks silica above 200°, and therefore its preparation by reaction between the elements at 260° has to be carried out in fluorspar vessels. $IrOF_4$ is formed when IrF_6 comes into contact with damp glass.

GROUP X. NICKEL, PALLADIUM, AND PLATINUM

Certain properties of the elements of Group X are set out in Table 24.32.

Table 24.32. *Properties of the Metals of Group X*

	Ni	Pd	Pt
Atomic number	28	46	78
m.p. °C	1453	1552	1769
b.p. °C	2820	3200	3800
Specific gravity	8·9	12·0	21·45
Atomic radius (12 co-ordination)	1·25	1·37	1·39
Ionic radius, M^{2+}	0·69	—	—
Solubility of hydrogen in metal at 25°; vols. per vol. of metal	4·15	753·3	4·05

Nickel is a silver-grey metal which is hard, malleable, and ductile. It is ferromagnetic; the Curie point is 340°. Nickel is resistant to oxygen at room temperature, but when heated it reacts slowly to give nickel oxide. It decomposes steam slowly at a red heat. Nickel is not attacked by hydrochloric acid, but it dissolves in dilute nitric acid; concentrated nitric acid renders it passive. Nickel is not attacked by fused alkalis. At 60° it reacts with carbon monoxide to yield $Ni(CO)_4$.

Palladium is a white metal, which is malleable and ductile. It is unattacked by air at room temperature, but at a red heat it yields PdO. It is attacked by fluorine and by chlorine. It is dissolved by nitric acid, and by hydrochloric acid in the presence of oxygen. It is attacked by fused alkalis at a red heat. Palladium is able to absorb large quantities of hydrogen; it absorbs up to 900 times its own volume of hydrogen (measured at atmospheric pressure) at room temperature. The hydrogen enters the palladium by first forming a monatomic layer on the surface which travels into cracks in the crystal, and finally penetrates into the body of the lattice to form an interstitial hydride. During the absorption of hydrogen the crystal structure of palladium remains face-centred cubic, but the lattice expands. Two stages of expansion can be detected: in the first the lattice parameter increases steadily from 3·883 to 3·984, and in the second the lattice parameter increases suddenly from 3·984 to 4·018, and thereafter more slowly. The whole of the hydrogen can be removed from palladium by warming the metal in vacuo to 100°.

It has been shown experimentally that the paramagnetism of palladium containing dissolved hydrogen falls as the amount of hydrogen increases, and reaches a minimum when the composition of the interstitial hydride is $PdH_{0.6}$. The relation between this result and the structure of the hydride has been considered by Pauling. The prehybridisation electron configuration of the palladium atom is $4d^8 5s^1 5p^1$. The distribution of

Table 24.33. *Examples of Types of Compounds Formed by Nickel, Palladium, and Platinum*

Valency systems of atoms: $\overbrace{d\ d\ d\ d}^{n-1}$ $\overbrace{s\ p\ p\ 6}^{n}$
The values of n are: Ni 4, Pd 5, Pt 6

Normal prehybridisation electron configuration of the atom: $\overbrace{d\ d\ d\ d}^{n-1}\ \overbrace{s\ p\ p\ p}^{n}$

Section	Oxidation state	Nature of unit	Ni	Pd	Pt
		Oxides and sulphides	NiO, Ni$_2$O$_3$, Ni(OH)$_2$, NiS, NiS$_2$, Ni$_3$S$_2$		
1A	0		K$_4$[Ni(CN)$_4$]		
1B	I		K$_2$[Ni(CN)$_3$], NiCN		
2	II	Cation M^{2+}	Ni(NO$_3$)$_2$, NiSO$_4$, Ni(ClO$_4$)$_2$ NiX$_2$ [X=F, Cl, Br, I]	PdO, PdS, Pd(OH)$_2$ PdX$_2$	PtO, PtS, Pt(OH)$_2$ PtX$_2$
		Neutral complexes	Ni dimethylglyoxime Ni salicylaldoxime [Ni en$_2$ Br$_2$]^0	PdA$_2$ Pd dimethylglyoxime [Pd(NH$_3$)$_2$Cl$_2$]^0 [(PdXR$_2$)$_2$]^0 X=Cl, I, NO$_2$, CNS, SC$_2$H$_5$ R=a phosphine, an arsine, CO, or C$_2$H$_4$	PtA$_2$ Pt dimethylglyoxime [Pt(NH$_3$)$_2$Cl$_2$]^0 [(PtXR$_2$)$_2$]^0 [PtCl$_2$NH$_3$C$_2$H$_4$]^0
		Complex anions	K$_2$[Ni(CN)$_4$] K$_2$[Ni ox$_2$], 6H$_2$O K$_4$[Ni(NO$_2$)$_6$]	K$_2$[Pd(CN)$_4$], K$_2$[PdX$_4$] X=Cl, Br, I	K[PtCl$_3$C$_2$H$_4$] K$_2$[PtCl$_4$], K$_2$[Pt(NO$_2$)$_4$] K$_2$[Pt(CN)$_4$]
		Complex cations	[Ni(NH$_3$)$_6$]Cl$_2$	[Pd(NH$_3$)$_4$]X$_2$, X=Cl, OH	[Pt(NH$_3$)$_4$][PtCl$_4$]
3	III			Pd$_2$O$_3$, PdF$_3$, Cs$_2$[PdCl$_5$]	Pt$_2$O$_3$, PtX$_3$, X=F, Cl, Br, I, CN [Pt(N(C$_2$H$_5$)$_3$)$_4$Cl]Cl$_2$ [Pt(N(C$_2$H$_5$)$_3$)$_2$Cl$_3$]^0
4	IV			PdO$_2$, PdS$_2$ K$_2$[PdX$_6$] X=Cl, Br [Pd pyr$_2$Cl$_2$]Cl$_2$	PtO$_2$, PtX$_4$ X=F, Cl, Br, I [Pt(NH$_3$)$_2$(NO$_3$)$_4$]^0 K$_2$[PtCl$_6$], [K$_2$Pt(SCN)$_6$] [Pt(NH$_3$)$_6$]Cl$_4$
5	VI				PtF$_6$

electrons in the $4d$ orbitals is that shown at the head of Table 24.33. In order to render the palladium atom diamagnetic, the two d orbitals occupied by unpaired electrons would have to receive two additional electrons, either by transfer of the 5-shell electrons of the same atom, or by donation from an atom of some other element. The composition of palladium hydride, $PdH_{0.6}$, at the point of minimum paramagnetic susceptibility was explained by Pauling on the assumption that there is on an average 0·6 vacancy in the d orbitals of each palladium atom which has to be filled with electrons from atoms of some other element before every palladium atom has 10 electrons in the $4d$ orbitals. These electrons are provided by the absorbed hydrogen atoms; the protons thus set free are distributed in holes in the palladium crystal lattice. The fractional number of vacancies is assumed to result from resonance between the three possible electron configurations of the valency system of the palladium atom: $4d^8 5s^2$, $4d^9 5s^1$, and $4d^{10}$.

Platinum is a soft white metal which is malleable and ductile. It is not attacked by oxygen, but it reacts with fluorine at 500° and with chlorine at 1500°. It is scarcely attacked by acids other than aqua regia. It is rapidly attacked by fused alkalis, and it combines with silicon, phosphorus, arsenic, and lead and certain other elements. Platinum vessels therefore should be used with discretion as containers for chemical reagents.

Examples of types of compounds formed by the three metals are set out in Table 24.33. The penultimate d shells in the atoms contain three electron pairs. These three pairs remain undisturbed when the atom enters into chemical combination, and hence the numbers of oxidation states exercised by the metals in Group X are less than those exercised by the metals in the previous Groups.

All the compounds of palladium and platinum are diamagnetic†. This means that either (i) the two unpaired d electrons are used for σ bond formation as in $K_2[PtCl_6]$, (ii) that the two unpaired electrons are paired off in one of the d orbitals, leaving the unoccupied d orbital free to enter the planar hybridised system dsp^2, as in $K_2[Pd(CN)_4]$, (iii) the two unpaired d electrons form πd bonds as in $K_4[Pd(CN)_4]$, or (iv) that one of the two unpaired d electrons is promoted to a p orbital as in PdO.

NICKEL

SECTION 1A. COMPOUNDS CONTAINING A NICKEL ATOM IN OXIDATION STATE 0

$K_4[Ni(CN)_4]$ is one of the compounds which contain a nickel atom in the zero oxidation state.‡ It is a yellow solid made by reducing the salt $K_2[Ni^I(CN)_3]$ with potassium or calcium in liquid ammonia. It turns black in air, and decomposes water with the evolution of hydrogen. The orbital diagram would be:

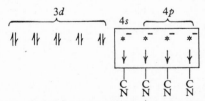

Fig. 24.45. Orbital diagram of the anion $[Ni(CN)_4]^{4-}$.

† An exception is the paramagnetic PdF_3.

‡ On the assumption that πd bonds are present in nickel carbonyl $Ni(CO)_4$, the nickel atom in this compound is in the oxidation state Ni^{IV}. If two CN groups in $K_4[Ni(CN)_4]$ have the electron configuration $:C≡\overset{\circ\circ}{\underset{\circ}{N}}$ (where ° represents an electron contributed by a potassium atom) an orbital diagram similar to that in Fig. 25.16 (p. 1101) may be drawn for the anion $[Ni(CN)_4]^{4-}$.

SECTION 1ᴮ. COMPOUNDS CONTAINING A NICKEL ATOM IN OXIDATION STATE I

NiCN and $K_2[Ni(CN)_3]$ are two compounds in which the nickel atom is present in oxidation state I. $K_2[Ni(CN)_3]$ is a dark oily liquid. It is made by reducing a cold saturated solution of $K_2[Ni(CN)_4]$ with sodium amalgam or some other powerful reducing agent. The product is precipitated with alcohol. It rapidly decomposes in air. It dissolves in water to give an intensely red coloured solution which rapidly decomposes in the cold to give metallic nickel and $K_2[Ni(CN)_4]$; if the solution is boiled hydrogen is evolved and $K_2[Ni(CN)_4]$ is formed. The solution is more stable in alkaline conditions. The solution is oxidised by air, $AgNO_3$, $PbCl_2$, and $HgCl_2$ to divalent nickel. The solution absorbs carbon monoxide and nitric oxide.

$K_2[Ni(CN)_3]$ is diamagnetic. It is probably dimeric with metal to metal bonds.

NiCN is made by acidifying the red aqueous solution of $K_2[Ni(CN)_3]$; the insoluble orange NiCN is precipitated. The precipitate dissolves in potassium cyanide solution to form the red solution again. NiCN is oxidised in air to $Ni(CN)_2$ and NiO. It absorbs carbon monoxide to give $Ni(CN)CO$.

THE OXIDES, HYDROXIDES, AND SULPHIDES OF NICKEL

The oxides of nickel are NiO, Ni_2O_3; there is also the hydroxide $Ni(OH)_2$. There are three sulphides NiS, NiS_2, Ni_3S_2.

Nickel oxide, NiO, is a green solid. It is made by igniting the hydroxide of the carbonate in the absence of air at 600°, or by heating the nitrate to 1000°. The product obtained by heating nickel in air is nickel oxide contaminated with the metal and with Ni_2O_3. Nickel oxide has the sodium chloride lattice.

Nickel trioxide, Ni_2O_3, has not been isolated, but it is assumed to be formed on charging an Edison accumulator, when the two reversible reactions proceed to the right:

$$Fe^{2+} + 2e \rightleftharpoons Fe; \quad 2Ni^{2+} \rightleftharpoons 2Ni^{3+} + 2e.$$

If a nickel salt is treated with bromine and sodium hydroxide a black precipitate is obtained, which if dried and gently warmed at 138° has the composition Ni_2O_3,H_2O. It decomposes if the removal of the water is attempted.

Nickel hydroxide, $Ni(OH)_2$, is obtained as a green precipitate when sodium hydroxide is added to a solution of a nickel salt. It cannot be made by the hydration of nickel oxide. It is almost insoluble in water but it dissolves in aqueous ammonia, probably to form $[Ni(NH_3)_4](OH)_2$. Nickel hydroxide has the CdI_2 structure in which there are no hydroxyl bonds; it is isomorphous with cobaltous hydroxide.

The sulphides of nickel are NiS, NiS_2 (with the pyrites structure) and Ni_3S_2. **Nickel sulphide, NiS,** is formed as a black precipitate when ammonium sulphide is added to a neutral or slightly acid solution of a nickel salt. It is not precipitated in acid solution, but once precipitated it will not redissolve in any acid except aqua regia. It has the nickel arsenide crystal structure.

SECTION 2. COMPOUNDS CONTAINING A NICKEL ATOM IN OXIDATION STATE II

COMPOUNDS CONTAINING A NICKEL ATOM WHICH DISPLAYS IONIC CHARACTER

Among the compounds in which a nickel atom displays ionic character are nickel carbonate, $NiCO_3$, nickel acetate $Ni(OCOCH_3)_2$, nickel nitrate $Ni(NO_3)_2$, nickel sulphate $NiSO_4$, nickel perchlorate $Ni(ClO_4)_2$, and the nickel halides (Table 24.34).

Nickel nitrate, $Ni(NO_3)_2$, is made in solution by dissolving nickel hydroxide or carbonate in nitric acid. It crystallises as a hydrate which may have 9, 6, 4, or 2 molecules of water of crystallisation. The emerald green hexahydrate is isomorphous with the corresponding cobaltous compound. Nickel nitrate is said to be obtainable in the anhydrous state if the dihydrate is heated with a mixture of 100% nitric acid and nitrogen pentoxide.

Nickel sulphate forms hydrates with 7, 6, 5, 4, 3, 2, and 1 molecules of water of crystallisation. The heptahydrate is a vitriol, isomorphous with those formed by Mg, Mn, Fe, Co, Zn. The hexahydrate is dimorphic. The Ni^{2+} ion plays the part of a bivalent ion in the double sulphates $M_2^+M^{2+}(SO_4)_2,6H_2O$. Anhydrous nickel sulphate is greenish-yellow. It is insoluble in cold water by which it is only very slowly hydrated.

NICKELOUS, Ni^{II}, COMPLEXES

Complexes in which the ligands are bonded to the nickel atom by nitrogen atoms are much more stable than those in which the bonding is through oxygen atoms.

Neutral complexes. A diacetylacetonate of nickel, NiA_2, is reported which has a square planar configuration.[†] Nickel in the state Ni^{II} forms neutral complexes with diamines, with the dioximes of α-diketones, and with tertiary phosphines.

$[Ni\ en_2Br_2]^0$ is an example of a neutral complex with a diamine as ligand. Its stability is low, and it changes to a complex cation $[Ni\ en_3]^{2+}$ and nickel bromide.

The general structure of dioxime nickel complexes is:

$$
\begin{array}{ccc}
\text{R—C} & \text{———} & \text{C—R} \\
\| & & \| \\
\text{HO—N} & \searrow \quad \swarrow & \text{N}\rightarrow\text{O} \\
& \text{Ni} & \\
\text{O}\leftarrow\text{N} & \nearrow \quad \nwarrow & \text{N—OH} \\
\| & & \| \\
\text{R—C} & \text{———} & \text{C—R}
\end{array}
$$

Table 24.34. *Nickel Dihalides*

	NiF_2	$NiCl_2$	$NiBr_2$	NiI_2
Appearance	Greenish-brown solid	Yellow solid	Yellow solid	Black solid
Lattice	Rutile	$CdCl_2$	$CdCl_2$	$CdCl_2$
Behaviour on heating	It can be sublimed in HF above 1000°	Sublimes at 993° Melts at 1000° in sealed tube	Sublimes at a high temperature	
Solubility in water, gm/ 100 gm	Sparingly[‡]	Easily, 67·8/26°	33/25°	144/25°
Hydrates	0, 4 (green, easily soluble)	0, 2, 4, 6, 7 (all green and deliquescent)	0, 3, 6, 9	0, 6
Reactions	It is stable. It is not attacked by concentrated acids, nor by electro-negative elements. It reacts with sodium			
Preparation	Heat anhydrous $NiCl_2$ with NH_4F To make $NiF_2,4H_2O$ dissolve $NiOH_2$ in HFaq.	Burn nickel in chlorine, or heat the hydrate or ammine	Treat nickel with bromine at a red heat, or heat the hydrate	Treat nickel with iodine
Anionic complexes	K_2NiF_4	$KNiCl_3$	$CsNiBr_3$	

[†] S, Shibata, *Bull Chem. Soc. Japan*, 30, 1957, 753.
[‡] Anhydrous NiF_2 is very slow to hydrate, in which it resembles CdF_2 and MnF_2.

The complex has a planar configuration, the orbital diagram being:

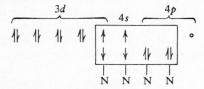

Fig. 24.46. Orbital diagram for the dioxime nickel complexes.

It has been shown that nickel benzyl-methyl glyoxime is diamagnetic and that it exists in two forms α, m.p. 168°, and β m.p. 76° which must be the geometrical isomers:

$$C_6H_5CH_2\!-\!C\!-\!\!-\!\!-\!C\!-\!CH_3$$
$$HO\!-\!N \qquad N\!\rightarrow\!O$$
$$Ni$$
$$O\!\leftarrow\!N \qquad N\!-\!OH$$
$$C_6H_5CH_2\!-\!C\!-\!\!-\!\!-\!C\!-\!CH_3$$

$$C_6H_5CH_2\!-\!C\!-\!\!-\!\!-\!C\!-\!CH_3$$
$$HO\!-\!N \qquad N\!\rightarrow\!O$$
$$Ni$$
$$O\!\leftarrow\!N \qquad N\!-\!OH$$
$$CH_3\!-\!C\!-\!\!-\!\!-\!C\!-\!CH_2C_6H_5$$

Many other nickel complexes of the glyoxime type have been shown to exhibit geometrical isomerism, and to be diamagnetic. Oximes may also be linked to nickel by oxygen and by nitrogen as in nickel salicylaldoxime:

which has a planar structure and is diamagnetic.†

Complex anions. Among the important anionic complexes of nickel are the nickelo-cyanides, $K_2[Ni(CN)_4]$, the nitro complexes $K_4[Ni(NO_2)_6]$, the oxalato nickel complex $K_2[Ni\ ox_2]6H_2O$ which becomes anhydrous at 200°, and the thio-oxalato complex $K_2[Ni(O_2C_2S_2)_2]$. In the majority of the anionic complexes of bivalent nickel the co-ordination number of the nickel atom is 4.

Potassium nickelocyanide, $K_2[Ni(CN)_4]$, is made in solution by adding excess of potassium cyanide to a solution of a nickel salt. The solution of potassium nickelo-cyanide gives none of the reactions of the ion Ni^{2+}, but the anion is broken up by

† The benzoin-oxime nickel compound

$$C_6H_5\!-\!C\!-\!O \qquad N\!=\!C\!-\!C_6H_5$$
$$Ni$$
$$C_6H_5\!-\!C\!=\!N \qquad O\!-\!C\!-\!C_6H_5$$

is paramagnetic. Others of these complexes are paramagnetic to about the extent of Ni^{2+}, but it has not been shown that they are tetrahedral.

strong mineral acids. The salt and its solution are diamagnetic, and hence the complex must be planar. The anhydrous salt is pale yellow, and the monohydrate is orange.

Potassium nickelonitrite, $K_4[Ni(NO_2)_6]$, can be obtained in the anhydrous state. It is brownish red and stable in air to about 100°. It dissolves in water to give a green solution. The complex in solution is decomposed by boiling or by sodium hydroxide, or by hydrogen sulphide.

Nickelonitrites are formed by Li, Na, K, and Tl^+, and by Sr, Ba, Cd, Hg, Pb. Those of the bivalent metals have the K_2PtCl_6 structure. There is a series of yellow or brown complexes of the general formula $M^+_2M^{2+}[Ni(NO_2)_6]$, where M^+ may represent K, Rb, Cs, NH_4, Tl, and M^{2+} may represent Mg, Ca, Sr, Ba, Zn, or Hg. They are anhydrous, isomorphous with one another, with the corresponding mixed cuprinitrites and cobaltonitrites, and with potassium cobaltinitrite $K_3[Co(NO_2)_6]$.

The potassium dithio-oxalato nickel salt $K_4[Ni(O_2C_2S_2)_2]$, is made by adding potassium dithio-oxalate to a solution of a nickel salt. An intense purple colour is produced, and the solution on crystallisation yields purple crystals of the complex. The anion:

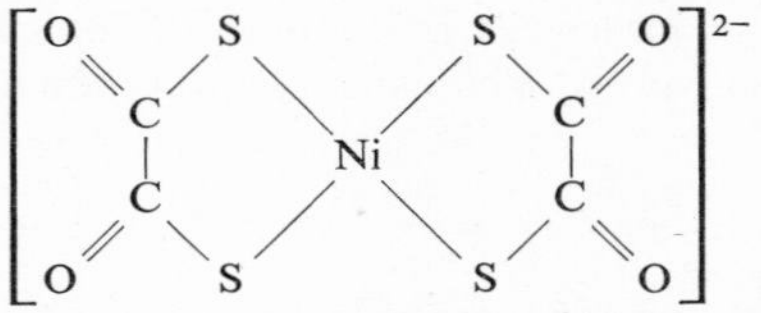

is planar. On the addition of sodium hydroxide or hydrogen sulphide to its solution nickel is slowly precipitated as the hydroxide or the sulphide.

Complex cations. The simplest type of complex cation containing nickel is found in $[Ni(NH_3)_6]Cl_2$. The stability of a bivalent hexammino complex of this form is greater for nickel than for any other bivalent metal. The ammonia molecules may be replaced by those of amines, but the stability falls with increase in size and number of the alkyl groups in the amine. Diamines such as ethylene diamine, produce very stable complexes which are usually trichelate; they are not decomposed by water or by potassium cyanide.

The salts $[Ni(NH_3)_6]Cl_2$ and $[Ni(NH_3)_6](NO_3)_2$ have been shown to have the $K_2[PtCl_6]$ structure.

PALLADIUM

Palladium forms compounds in which it is present in the oxidation states II, III, and IV. The palladous (Pd^{II}) compounds include the oxide PdO (which differs in crystal structure from FeO, CoO, and NiO), the hydroxide $Pd(OH)_2$, the halides (of which all except the fluoride have continuous bridge structures), the nitrate and the sulphate. By far the most interesting compounds of Pd^{II} are the complexes, particularly the neutral complexes, some of which have unusual constitutions. Compounds containing a palladium atom in the state Pd^{IV} include $K_4[Pd(CN)_4]$ in which two of the penultimate d electrons of the palladium atom are used in forming πd bonds.

SECTION 2. COMPOUNDS CONTAINING A PALLADIUM ATOM IN OXIDATION STATE II

PALLADIUM COMPOUNDS WITH IONIC CHARACTER

Palladous oxide, PdO, is a black powder which is made by heating palladium in oxygen, or by fusing palladous chloride with sodium nitrate at 600°. It decomposes at 875°. It is a very strong oxidising agent which converts hydrogen to water and carbon monoxide to carbon dioxide. It is insoluble in acids. In the crystal of palladous oxide each palladium atom is surrounded by four oxygen atoms at the corners of a square, the palladium atom being at the centre; each oxygen atom is the centre of a tetrahedral group of palladium atoms. This structure, which differs from the sodium chloride structure of nickel oxide, indicates the strong tendency of the palladium atom to adopt the dsp^2 hybridisation. The sulphide PdS has a crystal structure which is similar to that of PdO.

Palladous hydroxide, Pd(OH)$_2$, is made by the hydrolysis of palladous nitrate. It is soluble in acids. It cannot be dehydrated to palladous oxide without decomposition.

Palladous fluoride, PdF$_2$, is a brown powder best made by heating palladium trifluoride with the calculated quantity of palladium powder. It is soluble in hydrochloric acid. It has the rutile structure.

Palladous chloride, PdCl$_2$, exists as hygroscopic red crystals, m.p. about 940°, sublimation point (1 atm) 738°. It begins to decompose at about 600°. It is soluble in water from which it can be crystallised as the dihydrate. In solution it is very easily reduced to the metal by hydrogen, carbon monoxide, or ethylene. The anhydrous crystals have been shown to consist of coplanar chains of the form:

$$\cdots \text{Pd} \overset{\text{Cl}}{\underset{\text{Cl}}{<>}} \text{Pd} \overset{\text{Cl}}{\underset{\text{Cl}}{<>}} \text{Pd} \overset{\text{Cl}}{\underset{\text{Cl}}{<>}} \cdots$$

Palladous iodide, PdI$_2$, is obtained as a dark red precipitate by adding potassium iodide to an aqueous solution of palladous chloride. It is very insoluble in water, and can be used for the estimation of palladium. At 360° it is completely decomposed to the metal.

PALLADOUS, Pd^{II}, COMPLEXES

Neutral complexes of palladium are of the types: palladium acetylacetonate PdA$_2$, oxime complexes, [Pd(NH$_3$)$_2$Cl$_2$]^0, and [PdP(CH$_3$)$_3$Cl$_2$]$_2$^{0}. The range of complexes is greater than that of the corresponding nickel compounds, and the compounds are more stable.

Palladium acetylacetonate, PdA$_2$, exists as yellow crystals. In solution in benzene it is monomeric.

The dioximine derivatives of α-diketones form compounds of palladium corresponding to those of nickel:

$$\begin{array}{c} R_1\!-\!C\!\!-\!\!-\!\!-\!\!-\!C\!-\!R_2 \\ \| \qquad \| \\ N \qquad N \\ HO \searrow \qquad \swarrow O \\ Pd \\ O \nwarrow \qquad \nearrow OH \\ N \qquad N \\ \| \qquad \| \\ R_1\!-\!C\!\!-\!\!-\!\!-\!\!-\!C\!-\!R_2 \end{array}$$

They are made by the action of the dioxime on a solution of palladous chloride in hydrochloric acid solution. The palladium derivative of the oxime in which R$_1$ is C$_6$H$_5$CO and R$_2$ is CH$_3$ is highly insoluble, and may be used for the determination of palladium (distinction from platinum). It exists in two forms, α yellow, m.p. 175°, β dark yellow, m.p. 207°. They are probably *cis* and *trans* isomers of the planar complex.

[Pd(NH$_3$)$_2$Cl$_2$]°. There is a wide range of complexes with analogous formulae. The ammonia molecules can be replaced by those of amines, hydrazine, diamines, and PR$_3$ (where R is an alkyl group), arsines AsR$_3$, thioethers SR$_2$, and selenoethers

SeR_2. The chlorine atoms can be replaced by other radicals, univalent including Br and I but not F, or bivalent including the oxalato group.

The complex $[Pd(NH_3)_2Cl_2]^0$ is obtained by treating $K_2[PdCl_4]$ with ammonia, or $[Pd(NH_3)_4]Cl_2$ with hydrochloric acid. The neutral diammines have a square planar configuration, and hence show geometrical isomerism, but often only one form can be obtained, which is normally the *trans* form.

The tertiary phosphines and tertiary arsines and the thioethers and selenoethers are made by heating the phosphine or other alkyl derivative with $(NH_4)_2[PdCl_4]$ in water. Again although there is no doubt that these have planar configurations, only one form, the *trans*, is known.

There are many neutral complexes of palladium of the general formula $[(PdXR_2)_2]^0$. X may represent a tertiary phosphine, a tertiary arsine, carbon monoxide, or ethylene, but not an amine. R may represent Cl, I, NO_2, CNS, or SC_2H_5.

The phosphine and arsine derivatives are made by treating the complex $[PdX_2Cl_2]^0$ with boiling alcohol, which eliminates one molecule of phosphine or arsine. In solution the complexes are shown by molecular weight determinations to be dimeric, and X-ray analysis of the tertiary methyl arsine chloride and bromide indicate the structure:

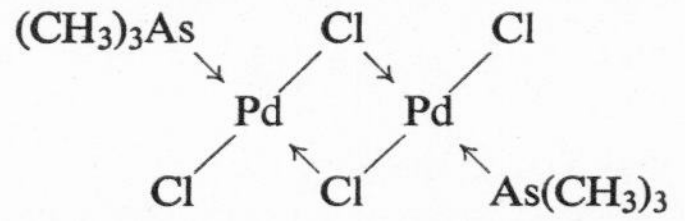

The possible isomeric formulae are the *cis* derivative and the derivative in which both arsine groups are attached to the same palladium atom. The chemical reactions of the compounds indicate that in solution all the isomers are present in tautomeric equilibrium. The chlorine atoms in the bridges may be replaced by Br, NO_2, CNS, C_2H_5S, and $(OCO)_2$.

Complex anions are present in the salts $K_2[Pd(CN)_4]$ and $K_2[Pd\ hal_4]$ (where hal represents Cl, Br, and I, but not F). X-ray analysis of $Ba[Pd(CN)_4],4H_2O$ shows that the structure of the anion is square planar, and that the water molecules are attached to the barium ion.

Complex cations. The simplest type of complex cation is found in $[Pd(NH_3)_4]Cl_2$, which is made by direct combination of palladous chloride and ammonia. The base $[Pd(NH_3)_4](OH)_2$ exists as colourless crystals. It is strongly alkaline and precipitates the hydroxides of Cu and Fe from their salts. The ammonia molecules may be replaced by other amines or diamines. There is a large body of evidence that these cations have square planar configurations.

SECTION 3. COMPOUNDS CONTAINING A PALLADIUM ATOM IN THE OXIDATION STATE III

There are only a few compounds of Pd^{III}, the hydrated oxide Pd_2O_3, the fluoride PdF_3, and the complexes $Cs_2[PdCl_5]$ and $Rb_2[PdCl_5]$ of which the structures are not certain.

Pd_2O_3 can be made in a hydrated form by the careful oxidation of palladous nitrate solution with ozone. It is a chocolate brown powder which reverts to PdO slowly in the cold, and explosively on heating. It is insoluble in nitric acid or sulphuric acid, but it dissolves in hydrochloric acid with the evolution of chlorine.

Palladium trifluoride, PdF_3, a black crystalline powder, is obtained by the action of fluorine on the metal or on palladous fluoride. It is isomorphous with FeF_3, CoF_3, and RhF_3. It is very hygroscopic. It is a strong oxidising agent; it is reduced by hydrogen with incandescence, with hydrochloric acid it evolves chlorine, and with water it evolves oxygen. It is paramagnetic.

SECTION 4. COMPOUNDS CONTAINING A PALLADIUM ATOM IN OXIDATION STATE IV

The compounds of Pd^{IV} are more stable than those of Pd^{III}, but nevertheless they are oxidising agents with a strong tendency to revert to the Pd^{II} state. The compounds include PdO_2, PdS_2, $K_2[PdCl_6]$, $K_2[PdBr_6]$, $[Pdpyr_2Cl_2]Cl_2$; there are no binary compounds of Pd^{IV} with the halogens.

PdO_2 is obtained as a dark red precipitate by adding alkali to $K_2[PdCl_6]$. At $200°$ it loses oxygen to yield PdO, and it is a strong oxidising agent.

$K_2[PdCl_6]$ is made by adding potassium chloride solution to the solution obtained by the oxidation of a solution of palladous chloride with chlorine. The hexachloride separates as red crystals. The rubidium and caesium salts are almost insoluble in cold water. The hexachlorides yield chlorine when treated with boiling water, and nitrogen when treated with concentrated ammonia solution.

$[Pdpyr_2Cl_2]Cl_2$, an orange powder, is made by treating a suspension of $[Pdpyr_2Cl_2]$ in chloroform with chlorine.

PLATINUM

SECTION 2. COMPOUNDS CONTAINING A PLATINUM ATOM IN THE OXIDATION STATE II

The platinous compounds include the hydroxide $Pt(OH)_2$, the oxide PtO, the sulphide PtS, and the dark-coloured insoluble dihalides, $Pthal_2$, which are briefly described in Table 24.35.

Platinous hydroxide, $Pt(OH)_2$, a black powder, is an unstable substance made by the action of hot potassium hydroxide solution on platinous chloride or $K_2[PtCl_4]$ in an inert atmosphere. It is reduced by hydrogen peroxide to metal, and is oxidised by ozone or potassium permanganate to the dioxide, PtO_2.

Platinous oxide, PtO, is a grey powder. It is made by heating the hydrate, but it cannot be obtained in pure condition because the hydrate cannot be completely dehydrated without loss of oxygen. It is soluble in acids but not in alkalis.

Platinous sulphide, PtS, is a green powder, which is made either by fusing sulphur and platinum, or by fusing platinous chloride with sulphur and sodium carbonate. Its crystal structure is similar to that of palladous oxide and palladous sulphide.

PLATINOUS, Pt^{II}, COMPLEXES

Neutral Complexes

Platinous acetylacetonate, PtA_2 forms yellow crystals. It is made by treating platinum chloroplatinite, $K_2[PtCl_4]$, with acetylacetone in the presence of an alkali. Other compounds in which only two or three of the chlorine atoms in $K_2[PtCl_4]$ are replaced by A are formed at the same time.

Platinous dioxime derivatives. The platinous derivatives of the α-dioximes are dichelate. They can be volatilised in a vacuum without decomposition. The structures are similar to those of the corresponding palladium derivatives.

Neutral ammine derivatives. There are many neutral complexes of the type $[PtAm_2X_2]^0$. Am here represents NH_3, C_6H_5NC, C_4H_9NC (tertiary butyl isocyanide), C_2H_4, R_3P, R_3As, R_2S, where R is an alkyl group; X represents Cl, Br, I, CNS, NO_2, $\frac{1}{2}O_2C_2O_2$.

Table 24.35. *The Halides of Platinum*

Platinum dihalides			
	PtF₂	PtCl₂	PtBr₂	PtI₂

	PtF_2	$PtCl_2$	$PtBr_2$	PtI_2
Appearance Solubility in water	Yellow green solid	Brown green solid Insoluble Dissolves in hydro-chloric acid to give $H_2[PtCl_4]$	Brown solid Insoluble	Black solid Insoluble
Preparation	From the elements	From the elements	Heat $H_2[PtBr_4]$ or $H_2[PtBr_6]$	Treat $PtCl_2$ with Kl

Platinum trihalides			

	PtF_3	$PtCl_3$	$PtBr_3$	PtI_3
Appearance Range of thermal sta-bility† Solubility in water	Very hygroscopic and easily soluble	Very dark green solid 364–374° Dissolves but $PtCl_3$ cannot be recover-ed from the solu-tion. When warmed with hydrochloric acid it reacts: $2PtCl_3+4HCl=$ $H_2[PtCl_4]+$ $H_2[PtCl_6]$	Dark green solid 368–405° Insoluble	Black solid, like graphite 242–264° Insoluble

Platinum tetrahalides‡			

	PtF_4	$PtCl_4$	$PtBr_4$	PtI_4
Appearance Solubility in water Hydrates Preparation	Yellow or red crystals Water hydrolyses it violently Pass fluorine over red hot platinum	Reddish brown crystals Hygroscopic and readily soluble§ 0, 1, 4, 5, 7 Heat $H_2[PtCl_6]$ to 300°	Dark brown powder Slightly soluble§ Dissolve platinum in hydrobromic acid containing free bromine	Brown-black powder Treat concentrated $H_2[PtCl_6]$ solution with a hot solution of KI

† Determined by tensiometric studies on the behaviour of Pt hal₂ and Pt hal₄ in the presence of halogen vapour at 1 atm pressure.
‡ PtF_6 is known (p. 1059).
§ The solutions contain the complex acid $H_2[Pt\ hal_4(OH)_2]$.

The complexes $[(PtAmCl_2)_2]^0$ have the dimeric structure:

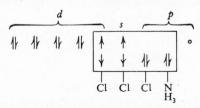

for which the hybridisation diagram of one platinum atom would be:

Fig. 24.47. Orbital diagram for one platinum atom in the complex $[Pt_2Cl_4Am_2]^0$.

Other neutral complexes are found among the ethylene complexes which are described later.

Complex Anions

The red salt $K_2[PtCl_4]$ is obtained by boiling a solution of $K_2[PtCl_6]$ with potassium oxalate. Potassium nitrite reacts with potassium chloroplatinite to give colourless $K_2[Pt(NO_2)_4]$, and potassium cyanide reacts to give the dichroic (yellow or blue) platinocyanide, $K_2[Pt(CN)_4],3H_2O$.

Complexes of Pt^{II} containing ethylene and other unsaturated carbon compounds. $K_2[PtCl_4]$ combines with ethylene to give the complex $K[PtCl_3C_2H_4]$. Other unsaturated substances which give corresponding complexes are alkyl and aryl ethylenes, allyl alcohol and allyl acetate. When $K[PtCl_3C_2H_4]$ is treated with ammonia a neutral complex $[PtCl_2(NH_3)C_2H_4]^0$ is obtained. Another type of neutral complex $[(PtCl_2C_2H_4)_2]^0$ is made by treating a solution of, say, dimethyl ethylene in boiling benzene with $PtCl_4$. There is no ethylene complex with more than one ethylene molecule per atom of platinum.

The dimeric complex $[(PtCl_2C_2H_4)_2]^0$ exists as orange crystals soluble in chloroform and benzene. Its molecular weight in benzene shows it to have the dimeric formula. It decomposes at $125-130°$. It reacts with excess of pyridine to give $[PtCl_2pyr_2]^0$, and with excess of quinoline to give $[PtCl_2quin.C_2H_4]^0$.

The molecules of the monomeric complex $[PtCl_2(NH_3)(C_2H_4)]^0$ and of the complex anion $[PtCl_3C_2H_4]^-$ may perhaps contain an ethylene radical bound to a platinum atom by the overlapping of p orbitals of the carbon atoms with the d_{xz} and the d_{yz} orbitals of the platinum atom. If this is so the orbital diagrams would be:

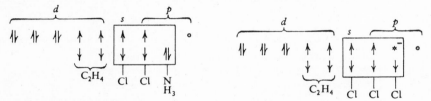

Fig. 24.48. Orbital diagrams for the complexes $[PtCl_2(NH_3)C_2H_4]^0$ and $[PtCl_3C_2H_4]^-$.

It has been concluded, however, that the bonding is somewhat more complicated than this, and an alternative view may be explained as follows. The platinum atom is tetragonally hybridised and is linked to the ethylene molecule and to the three other units by σ bonds. The σ bond to the ethylene molecule (which retains its normal orbital structure) is made by the overlapping of the region of the π bond having $+$ symmetry with the hybridised platinum orbital (which also has $+$ symmetry). One d orbital and one p orbital (shown as ₒ in the diagrams) of the platinum atom are hybridised to form a three-centred π bond with the two carbon atoms of the ethylene molecule.†
An orbital diagram for the dimeric complex $[(PtCl_2C_2H_4)_2]^0$ can be drawn on similar principles, if the structure is assumed to be:

$$
\begin{array}{ccc}
Cl & Cl & Cl \\
\diagdown \;\; \diagup & \searrow & \diagup \;\; \diagdown \\
Pt & & Pt \\
\diagup \;\; \diagdown & \nwarrow & \diagdown \\
C_2H_4 & Cl & C_2H_4
\end{array}
$$

Complex Cations

An interesting example of a complex cation is $Pt(NH_3)_4$ in the compound $Pt(NH_3)_4PtCl_4$. Both cation and anion are square planar.

† J. Chatt and L. A. Duncanson, *J. Chem. Soc.*, 1953, 2939.

SECTION 3. COMPOUNDS CONTAINING A PLATINUM ATOM IN OXIDATION STATE III

Examples of compounds containing a platinum atom in the state Pt^{III} are mentioned in Table 24.33. The compounds are either simple, such as Pt_2O_3aq., Pt hal$_3$, $Pt(CN)_3$, or complex, such as $[Pt(N(C_2H_5)_3)_4Cl]Cl_2$, $[Pt(N(C_2H_5)_3)_2Cl_3]^0$, $K_2[PtCl_5]$. The molecular weight of none of these compounds is known, and there is no confirmation of the monomeric formulae written above. It is not possible to conclude definitely whether Pt^{III} is a stable state of the platinum atom, or whether compounds written as PtX_3 are not in fact $PtX_2 \cdot PtX_4$.

The hydrated oxide Pt_2O_3,aq. can be made as a dark brown precipitate by treating platinum trichloride with potassium hydroxide. It cannot be dehydrated. It is not oxidised by air. It dissolves in concentrated alkali but not in acids.

Brief accounts of the platinum trihalides are included in Table 24.35.

Complexes which may contain Pt^{III} are made by gently oxidising the complexes of Pt^{II}. The salt $[Pt(N(C_2H_5)_3)_4Cl]Cl_2$ is brilliant red. It is made by oxidising the colourless $[Pt^{II}(N(C_2H_5)_3)_4]Cl_2,2H_2O$ with hydrogen peroxide. The red salt, however, dissolves in hot water to a pale yellow solution which behaves as though it contains Pt^{II} and Pt^{IV}; if solutions of Pt^{II} and Pt^{IV} are mixed the red salt is precipitated.

SECTION 4. COMPOUNDS CONTAINING A PLATINUM ATOM IN OXIDATION STATE IV

Among the compounds of Pt^{IV} are the hydrated oxide, PtO_2, the platinum tetrahalides (Table 24.35), and numerous complexes. Pt^{IV} forms as many complexes as Pt^{II}, the most stable being those in which nitrogen atoms are linked to the platinum atom. The ammine complexes include all possible compounds from $[Pt(NH_3)_6]Cl_4$ to $K_2[PtCl_6]$, and the chlorine atoms can be replaced in turn by OH until $K_2[Pt(OH)_6]$ is reached.

PtO_2,aq. If an aqueous solution of platinum tetrachloride is boiled with sodium hydroxide, and acetic acid is added, a white precipitate is obtained which turns yellow on boiling. It has the composition $PtO_2,3H_2O$. It is amphoteric and dissolves in alkalis to give $Na_2[Pt(OH)_6]$. The trihydrate undergoes dehydration in the stages:

$$PtO_2,3H_2O \xrightarrow{\text{over conc. } H_2SO_4} PtO_2,2H_2O \xrightarrow{100°} PtO_2,H_2O.$$

pale yellow soluble   brown   black
in HCl or NaOH   insoluble

Platinum dioxide cannot be obtained free from water, as the monohydrate cannot be dehydrated without loss of some oxygen. The dissociation pressure of PtO_2, however (1 atm at 400°), is lower than that of PtO or Pt_2O_3.

No acetylacetonates of Pt^{IV} are known, but there are examples of non-ionic complexes, such as $[Pt(NH_3)_2Cl_4]^0$. $[Pt(en)NH_2(NO_2)_2Cl]^0$ is a strong base like ammonia; it reacts with hydrochloric acid to form the salt $[Pt(en)NH_3(NO_2)_2Cl]Cl$ which may be compared to NH_4Cl.

Chloroplatinic acid, $H_2[PtCl_6]$, and its derivatives are important compounds of platinum. The free acid is made by dissolving platinum in aqua regia. Brownish red deliquescent crystals of $H_2[PtCl_6],6H_2O$ separate on evaporation. The crystals are easily soluble in water, alcohol, or ether. The alkali metals salts are anhydrous except those of lithium and sodium which have six molecules of water of crystallisation. The amine salts of chloroplatinic acid have been used for the characterisation of amines. Potassium fluoroplatinate has been reported. The free acids and many salts of bromoplatinic acid and of iodoplatinic acid are known. $K_2[Pt(SCN)_6]$ is made by boiling a solution of $K_2[PtCl_6]$ with potassium thiocyanate; the red crystals separate on cooling.[†]

† $K_2[PtCl_6]$ is an example of a type of crystal structure. The octahedral anions $[PtCl_6]^{2-}$ occupy the positions of the O^{2-} ions in an antifluorite lattice (p. 348), and the cations K^+ occupy the positions of the Na^+ ions.

THE PLATINUM ALKYLS

Platinum forms a number of compounds in which it is directly linked to methyl group
Certain of these compounds are discussed below.

Trimethyl platinum iodide, $(CH_3)_3PtI$,† is an orange crystalline compound whic
decomposes without melting at 250°. It is insoluble in water,‡ but soluble in benzen
in which it has an association factor of about 5. It is made by treating platinic chloric
with magnesium methyl iodide:

$$PtCl_4 + 3Mg(CH_3)I = (CH_3)_3PtI + 2MgCl_2 + MgI_2.$$

It is not attacked in the cold by acids or alkalis, but it reacts with moist silver oxide t
yield a hydroxyl derivative $(CH_3)_3PtOH$, which is insoluble in water and is not attacke
by cold mineral acids. $(CH_3)_3PtI$ in benzene solution takes up ammonia to gi
$(CH_3)_3Pt(NH_3)_2I$, and it reacts with thallous acetylacetonate (p. 562) to give:

$$
\begin{array}{c}
\text{CH}_3 \\
\text{O=C} \\
(CH_3)_3Pt \qquad\qquad \text{C—H} \\
\text{O—C} \\
\text{CH}_3
\end{array}
$$

$(CH_3)_3PtA$ forms colourless crystals which decompose without melting at 200°. I
association factor in benzene is only 3%; the association factors for the correspondin
derivatives of other diketones are lower.

Tetramethyl platinum, $(CH_3)_4Pt$, is a solid which decomposes at high temperature
without melting and is soluble in cold benzene. It is made by treating $(CH_3)_3PtI$ wit
sodium methyl.

Hexamethyl platinum, $(CH_3)_3Pt$—$Pt(CH_3)_3$, is a solid very soluble in benzene i
which it is monomeric. It reacts with iodine to form $(CH_3)_3PtI$.

The structures of all these compounds have been examined, and the results a
surprising. The electron configuration of the platinum atom:

d	d	d	d	d	s	p	p	p
↑↓	↑↓	↑↓	↑	↑	↑	↑	·	·

indicates that the atom could exert four covalencies and one or two co-ionic valence

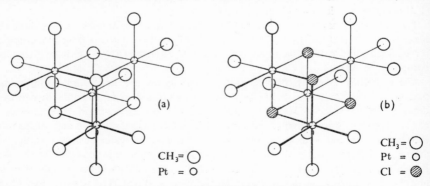

Fig. 24.49. Structures of (a) $(CH_3)_4Pt$, and (b) $(CH_3)_3PtCl$.

† The iodine atom can be replaced by Cl, CN, NO_3, OH, $\frac{1}{2}SO_4$.
‡ The alkyl halides of platinum, mercury, and thallium are almost the only compounds of th
type not attacked by air and water.

All the formulae mentioned (if the substances are assumed to be monomeric) are in accordance with the available valencies. From X-ray experiments,† however, it has been deduced that $(CH_3)_4Pt$ and $(CH_3)_3PtCl$ are tetrameric. The platinum atoms are situated at alternate corners of a cube, and the other groups, CH_3 or Cl, surround the platinum atoms octahedrally as in Fig. 24.49.

It does not appear possible to reconcile this structure with any processes of bonding so far discussed.

SECTION 5. COMPOUNDS CONTAINING A PLATINUM ATOM IN OXIDATION STATE VI

Platinum hexafluoride, PtF_6, is obtained when fluorine vapour interacts with a platinum filament near a liquid nitrogen cold finger. It exists as dark red crystals, m.p. $56.7°$. The vapour resembles bromine vapour.

GROUP XI. COPPER, SILVER, AND GOLD

Certain properties of the elements of Group XI are set out in Table 24.36.

Table 24.36. *Properties of the Metals in Group XI*

	Cu	Ag	Au
Atomic number	29	47	79
m.p. °C	1083	961	1063
b.p. °C	2580	2180	2660
Specific gravity	8·96	10·5	19·3
Atomic radius (12 co-ordination)	1·28	1·44	1·44
Ionic radius, M^+	0·96	1·26	1·37

Copper is a red, malleable, and ductile metal. It is attacked by oxygen; at a red heat CuO is formed; at $1100°$, Cu_2O. Copper is not attacked by steam, or by non-oxidising acids. Copper is attacked by sulphur, selenium, and the halogens. It is attacked by dilute sulphuric acid in the presence of air, by hot concentrated sulphuric acid, and by nitric acid, dilute or concentrated. Aqueous ammonia in the presence of air dissolves copper to form a blue solution containing $[Cu,4NH_3](NO_2)_2$. A concentrated aqueous solution of potassium cyanide dissolves copper with the liberation of hydrogen. Copper is converted to cupric oxide by fused potassium hydroxide. Above $450°$ hydrogen diffuses through copper.

Silver is a white, malleable, and ductile metal. Silver is not attacked by oxygen, but liquid silver dissolves oxygen; about twenty times the volume of the metal is dissolved at the melting point. All the oxygen is rejected on solidification. Silver is attacked by the halogens at a low red heat, by ozone, and by sulphur. Silver is less liable to attack by non-oxidising acids than is copper; silver dissolves in hot concentrated sulphuric acid, and in moderately concentrated nitric acid. Silver is not attacked by ammonia, by alkaline solutions, or by fused alkalis in the presence of air, or by potassium cyanide.

Gold is a yellow, malleable, and ductile metal. It is unaffected by air. It is attacked by the halogens, but not by any single acid. Gold dissolves in aqua regia, and in fused alkalis and nitrates, and in potassium cyanide solution in the presence of oxygen.

† R. E. Rundle and J. H. Sturdivant, *J.A.C.S.*, **69**, 1947, 1561.

Table 24.37. Examples of Types of Compounds formed by Copper, Silver, and Gold

Valency system of atom: $\overbrace{d\ d\ d\ d\ d}^{n-1}\overbrace{s\ p\ p\ p}^{n}$ Normal prehybridisation electron configuration of the atom: $\overbrace{d\ d\ d\ d\ d}^{n-1}\overbrace{\uparrow\downarrow\ \uparrow\ \uparrow\ \uparrow}^{n}$

The values of n are: Cu 4, Ag 5, Au 6.

Section	Oxidation state of metal	Nature of unit	Hybridisation	Cu	Ag	Au
		Interstitial compounds		CuH, Cu$_3$N		
		Simple ionic compounds			AgNO$_3$, AgNO$_2$, AgClO$_4$	
		Covalent compounds		CuC$_2$H$_5$, CuC$_6$H$_5$	AgC$_6$H$_5$	
1	I	Giant molecule compounds	Tetrahedral when 4 co-ordinate	Cu$_2$C$_2$, CuCN, CuCNS, Cu$_2$O, Cu$_2$S, Cu$_2$SO$_4$, CuX [X=F, Cl, Br, I]	Ag$_2$C$_2$, AgCN, Ag$_2$O, Ag$_2$S, AgX [X=F, Cl, Br, I]	AuCN, Au$_2$O, Au$_2$S AuX (X=Cl, Br, I)
		Neutral complexes		CuCl·CO·H$_2$O, CuCl·C$_2$H$_4$ [(C$_2$H$_5$)$_3$AsCuI]$_4$	[(C$_2$H$_5$)$_3$AsAgI]$_4$	AuCl·CO (C$_2$H$_5$)$_3$AsAuI
		Complex anions		K[Cu(CN)$_2$], K$_2$[Cu(CN)$_3$] K$_3$[Cu(CN)$_4$], K[CuCl$_2$] K$_2$[CuCl$_3$], K$_3$[CuCl$_4$]	K[Ag(CN)$_2$], K$_2$[Ag(CN)$_3$] K$_3$[Ag(CN)$_4$] H[AgCl$_2$], K[Ag(S$_2$O$_3$)]	K[Au(CN)$_2$] K[AuCl$_2$], K$_3$[Au(S$_2$O$_3$)$_2$]
		Complex cations		[Cu(NH$_3$)$_2$]$_2$SO$_4$,2H$_2$O [Cu(CH$_3$CN)$_4$]NO$_3$ [CuCO]$_2$SO$_4$,H$_2$O	[Ag(NH$_3$)$_2$]Cl [Ag(NH$_3$)$_3$]Cl	[AuNH$_3$]Cl [AuS:C(NH$_2$)$_2$]Cl

			Category	Geometry			
2	II	Non-chelate	Giant molecule compounds	Square planar when 4 co-ordinate	CuO, Cu(OH)$_2$, CuS / CuX$_2$ [X=F, Cl, Br]	AgF$_2$	
			Neutral complexes		[Cupyr$_2$Cl$_2$]^0, [Cu(H$_2$O)$_2$Cl$_2$]^0		
			Complex anions		M$_2$[CuX$_4$] [X=F, Cl, Br, I, CN] / M[CuX$_3$] [X=F, Cl]		
			Complex cations		[Cu(NH$_3$)$_4$]X$_2$ [X=OH, Cl, NO$_3$, $\frac{1}{2}$SO$_4$]	[Ag pyr$_4$]S$_2$O$_8$ / [Ag pyr$_4$](NO$_3$)$_2$	
		Chelate	Neutral complexes		Cu(NH$_2$CH$_2$OCO)$_2$, CuA$_2$		
			Complex anions		Na$_2$[Cu(C$_2$O$_4$)$_2$],2H$_2$O		
			Complex cations		[Cu en$_2$]SO$_4$	[Ag phen$_2$]S$_2$O$_8$	
3	III		Giant molecule compounds	Square Planar			AuO·OH, Au$_2$O$_3$
			Neutral complexes				(C$_2$H$_5$)$_3$PAuCl$_3$, pyrAuBr$_3$, Au$_2$X$_6$ [X=Cl, Br, I] auric alkyls, Au$_2$(C$_2$H$_5$)$_4$C$_2$O$_4$
			Complex anions				M[AuX$_4$] [X=Cl, Br, I, OH, CN]
			Complex cations				[Au(NH$_3$)$_4$]Cl$_3$

The electron configurations of the atoms of copper, silver, and gold (Table 24.37) indicate that the penultimate d shell is complete, and that the outermost shell is occupied by one unpaired electron. All the metals form univalent compounds, and complexes which would be expected if none of the d orbitals were used for bond formation. For example, $[Ag(NH_3)_2]Cl$ is linear, and the anion in $K_3[Cu(CN)_4]$ is tetrahedral. The univalent compounds of copper and gold, however, are not stable, and in the presence of water the ions Cu^+ and Au^+ disproportionate to the metal and the ions Cu^{2+} and Au^{3+}. The Cu^I and Au^I states are stable only in complexes in which the atoms of copper and gold are the central atoms.

In order to attain higher oxidation states the atoms of copper, silver, and gold must release electrons from the penultimate d shells to take part in bond formation. From consideration of the electron configurations of the atoms, it would appear that the inclusion of one penultimate d orbital in a set of hybridised orbitals would render the atom trivalent, as the unpaired electron from the outermost shell and the two electrons from the d orbital would be available for bond formation. This conclusion applies to gold, since the highest oxidation state attained by gold is Au^{III}. Hence the pre-hybridisation configuration for gold is:

$$
\begin{array}{c}
\overbrace{\qquad\qquad\qquad 5d \qquad\qquad\qquad}\quad 6s \quad \overbrace{\quad 6p \quad} \\
\uparrow\downarrow \quad \uparrow\downarrow \quad \uparrow\downarrow \quad \uparrow\downarrow \quad \uparrow \qquad \uparrow \qquad \uparrow \quad \cdot \quad \cdot
\end{array}
$$

The atom in state Au^{III} uses all the unpaired electrons for bond formation, and in addition gains an electron pair by forming an anion such as $[Au(CN)_4]^-$, or by accepting an electron pair as in $(AuCl_3)_2$. The compounds containing 4 co-ordinate gold atoms have planar structures, and thus show that the hybridisation of the atom is dsp^2.

The highest oxidation states for copper and silver, however, are Cu^{II} and Ag^{II}, and hence only two of the three electrons which might seem to be available are used for bonding. A discussion of the orbital structures for copper in the Cu^I and Cu^{II} states will serve the case for both metals.

The prehybridisation configuration of the Cu^I atom is:

$$
\begin{array}{c}
\overbrace{\qquad\qquad\qquad 3d \qquad\qquad\qquad}\quad 4s \quad \overbrace{\quad 4p \quad} \\
\uparrow\downarrow \quad \uparrow\downarrow \quad \uparrow\downarrow \quad \uparrow\downarrow \quad \uparrow\downarrow \qquad \uparrow \qquad \cdot \quad \cdot \quad \cdot
\end{array}
$$

In the cuprous compounds the $4s$ and $4p$ orbitals of the copper atom are tetrahedrally hybridised, and form four σ bonds, all occupied by electron pairs. The tetrahedral structure is found in the crystalline cuprous halides with the zinc blende structure, in complex cations in salts such as $[Cu(SC \cdot NH_2 \cdot CH_3)_4]Cl$, and in complex anions such as that in the salt $K_3[Cu(CN)_4]$. The anions in the salt $K_2[CuCl_3]$ consist of chains of tetrahedra, two corners of each tetrahedron being shared.

The prehybridisation configuration of the Cu^{II} atom indicates the promotion of a $3d$ electron to a $4p$ orbital, thus:

$$
\begin{array}{c}
\overbrace{\qquad\qquad\qquad 3d \qquad\qquad\qquad}\quad 4s \quad \overbrace{\quad 4p \quad} \\
\uparrow\downarrow \quad \uparrow\downarrow \quad \uparrow\downarrow \quad \uparrow\downarrow \quad \uparrow \qquad \uparrow \qquad \uparrow \quad \cdot \quad \cdot
\end{array}
$$

The simple Cu^{2+} ion would result if the $4s$ and $4p$ electrons were expelled from the atom; the ion would be paramagnetic and coloured owing to the presence of one unpaired electron in the d shell. The structures of many cupric compounds are planar, indicating that the copper atom has adopted dsp^2 hybridisation. Since the Cu^{II} atom forms only two covalent bonds, it must be assumed that one unpaired electron is promoted to an anti-bonding orbital (p. 135), and that the planar cupric compounds have an excited prehybridisation configuration for the Cu^{II} atom, thus:

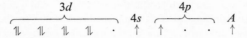

Such an assumption would account for the orbital structures of the cupric phthalo-cyanines, and the neutral complexes $[Cu^{II}pyr_2Cl_2]^0$ and $[Cu^{II}(H_2O)_2Cl_2]^0$.

The interatomic distances in many crystalline cupric compounds such as $CuCl_2$ and $CuBr_2$ indicate that the copper atom is 6 co-ordinate, and that the 4 planar arrangement is better regarded as the equatorial plane of a distorted octahedron. It would appear, however, that an orbital structure could be assigned to such an arrangement only if the electron pair in one occupied d orbital were promoted to an anti-bonding orbital.

Silver, like copper, attains the oxidation states I and II, but although Cu^{II} and Ag^{II} correspond in structure there is a big difference in the stability of their compounds. In aqueous solution, in contact with metallic copper, the cupric ion is stable with regard to the cuprous ion (p. 1062), and cuprous compounds are made by reducing cupric compounds. For silver, however, the argentous ion is stable, and the few argentic compounds that have been prepared are obtained by the severe oxidation of argentous compounds.

All three metals in both their oxidation states form many complexes. The cuprous atom in cuprous complexes has a variable co-ordination number, but it is frequently 4; the argentous atom has co-ordination numbers 2 or 3, and rarely 4; the aurous atom normally has co-ordination number 2, and only in a very few complexes is it 3 or 4.

COPPER

The properties of metallic copper are mentioned on p. 1057. Examples of the types of compounds formed by copper are set out in Table 24.37. Copper forms two compounds which are probably interstitial, the hydride CuH and the nitride Cu_3N, but the majority of copper compounds are divided into the cuprous compounds with copper in the oxidation state Cu^I, and the cupric compounds with copper in the oxidation state Cu^{II}.

INTERSTITIAL COPPER COMPOUNDS

Copper hydride, CuH. A brown precipitate is obtained if cupric sulphate is reduced with hypophosphorous acid. It always contains copper and copper oxide. It is slowly oxidised by air in the cold. On heating it gives off hydrogen, explosively at 110°. The crystal lattice is identical with that of metallic copper, but the distance Cu—Cu is 3·06 instead of 2·70.

Cuprous nitride, Cu_3N, is made by passing ammonia over red hot copper, or over cupric fluoride at 280°. It is a dark green powder with considerable thermal stability. When treated with acids it shows the normal behaviour of a cuprous compound, yielding the cupric salt and metallic copper. The crystal structure is reported† to be anti-rhenium trioxide; such a structure is very near to that of a cubic close-packed system of copper atoms with nitrogen atoms in the octahedral holes. The atomic radius of copper, 1·23 for the 6 co-ordinate atom, would permit such a structure (see p. 343).

† R. Juza and H. Hahn, *Z. anorg. Chem.*, **239**, 1938, 282.

SECTION 1. COMPOUNDS CONTAINING A COPPER ATOM IN OXIDATION STATE I

The cuprous state is stable at high temperatures. Cupric oxide, cupric chloride, cupric bromide, and cupric sulphide all dissociate at about 1000° to the cuprous salt, and cuprous fluoride exists only above this temperature. In solution, however, the cuprous ion disproportionates:

$$2Cu^+ = Cu^{2+} + Cu.$$

Assuming that the solubility of metallic copper in water is constant, the equilibrium constant, $K = [Cu^{2+}]/[Cu^+]^2 = 10^{+6}$, and the reaction normally proceeds from left to right. If the conditions are such that the concentration of cuprous ions is very low, either through the insolubility of the cuprous salt used, or through the formation of a stable cuprous complex such as $[Cu(NH_3)_2]_2SO_4$ or $K_3[Cu(CN)_4]$, then the reaction proceeds from right to left.

COVALENT COMPOUNDS AND GIANT MOLECULE COMPOUNDS

Cuprous ethyl and cuprous phenyl. Cuprous iodide dissolves in an ethereal solution of magnesium ethyl bromide at $-18°$ to give a green solution which may contain CuC_2H_5, but decomposition occurs rapidly. If, however, phenyl magnesium iodide is used and the reagents are protected from oxidation by nitrogen, a grey precipitate of CuC_6H_5 separates from the green solution. It decomposes at 80° to copper and diphenyl. It is insoluble in benzene and is slowly hydrolysed by water to benzene and cuprous oxide.

Cuprous acetylide. A brown precipitate with the composition Cu_2C_2,H_2O is produced when acetylene is passed into an ammoniacal solution of a cuprous salt. On drying at 80–100° over calcium chloride the anhydrous substance Cu_2C_2 remains. It is insoluble in solvents. It explodes if heated to 120°, or in contact with oxidising agents. It regenerates acetylene when dissolved in potassium cyanide solution or in dilute hydrochloric acid.

Cuprous cyanide, CuCN, is formed as a colourless precipitate, m.p. (with decomposition) 473°, when potassium cyanide (not in excess) is added to a solution of a cupric salt. It is insoluble in water and in dilute acids. It is soluble in excess potassium cyanide solution to give $K[Cu(CN)_2]$, in concentrated hydrochloric acid, and in aqueous solutions of ammonium salts. It does not absorb carbon monoxide.

Cuprous thiocyanate, CuCNS, is precipitated when potassium thiocyanate solution is added to a solution of a cupric salt containing sulphurous acid. The precipitate is anhydrous, highly insoluble, and can be heated to 180° without decomposition. It is used for the gravimetric determination of copper.

Cuprous oxide (cuprite), Cu$_2$O, is a red powder obtained when an alkaline solution of cupric sulphate is reduced with glucose, or when cupric oxide is maintained at a temperature above 1000°. Cuprous oxide is insoluble in water. It is attacked by sulphuric acid or nitric acid to yield the cupric salt and metallic copper; the nitric acid dissolves the copper with the evolution of nitric oxide. Concentrated hydrochloric acid dissolves cuprous oxide to form the complex acid $H_3[CuCl_4]$. Cuprous oxide is soluble in concentrated ammonia solution. Cuprous oxide is soluble in molten copper and lowers the melting point of the metal.

The crystal of cuprous oxide consists of two independent interpenetrating cubic structures. Each of the two structures is built up in the following way. A face-centred cubic lattice of oxygen ions contains additional oxygen ions in one half of the tetrahedral holes; the cuprous ions are situated in each tetrahedral group between the oxygen ions as in Fig. 24.50. The only other substance with a similar crystal structure is silver oxide, Ag_2O.

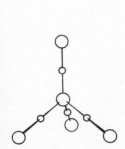

Fig. 24.50.   One tetrahedral group in the Cu_2O crystal structure.

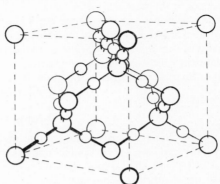

Fig. 24.51.   One of the two inter-penetrating structures in the Cu_2O lattice. (Reproduced with permission from *Structural Inorganic Chemistry* by A. F. Wells, 2nd. edition, Oxford University Press.)

Cuprous sulphate, Cu_2SO_4. The anhydrous salt is made by treating cuprous oxide with dimethyl sulphate. It disproportionates on contact with water. The cationic complexes, $[CuCO]_2SO_4,H_2O$ and $[Cu(NH_3)_2]_2SO_4$ are stable.

Cuprous sulphide, Cu_2S, is formed by the direct union of the elements. It is dimorphic. The crystal structure of the low temperature form is unknown. That of the high temperature form consists of a zinc blende lattice in which are situated all the sulphur atoms and one half of the copper atoms. The remaining copper atoms are distributed in the interstices. Cuprous sulphide has a defect structure of composition Cu_9S_5.

The cuprous halides. The preparations and properties are set out in Table 24.38.

Table 24.38.   *The Cuprous Halides*

	CuF†	CuCl	CuBr	CuI
Appearance		Colourless solid	Pale yellow solid	Colourless or white solid
m.p. °C		430	483	588
b.p. °C		1367	1345	1293
Lattice		Zinc blende	Zinc blende	Zinc blende
Constitution in vapour		Dimeric at 1600–1700°	Dimeric at 1000°	Monomeric at 1000°
Properties		Insoluble in water. Easily soluble in NH_3 or in HCl solution; both solutions absorb carbon monoxide A good conductor of electricity	Insoluble	Insoluble
Preparation		Treat cupric chloride with concentrated hydrochloric acid and copper		Add potassium iodide solution to a solution of a cupric salt

† CuF is present in fused CuF_2, but on cooling, however rapidly, only CuF_2 and copper are obtained.

CUPROUS COMPLEXES

Copper in the state Cu^I forms neutral, anionic, and cationic complexes. The strength of the bond between the copper atom and the ligand diminishes in the order Cu—N, Cu—S, Cu—O. The highest co-ordination number attained by copper in the complexes is 4, but this value is not necessarily reached. In the isonitrile complexes and in complexes in which the ligands are bonded to copper by oxygen atoms only, the highest co-ordination number is 2, and in the ammines the value is usually 2 but it may be 3.

Neutral Complexes

Cuprous copper forms neutral complexes with carbon monoxide, with ethylene, and with the tertiary alkyl phosphines and arsines.

$CuCl,CO,H_2O$. Cuprous chloride suspended in water, or dissolved in hydrochloric acid or in aqueous ammonia, absorbs carbon monoxide up to the proportion one molecule of carbon monoxide to one atom of copper. The carbon monoxide is expelled if the solution is warmed; it is oxidised to carbon dioxide by oxygen or by a cupric salt.

From a cold solution of the complex, colourless crystals may be obtained of the composition $CuCl,CO,H_2O$. Water or some other electron donor is an essential constituent; the complex $CuCl,CO$ does not exist. The dimeric formula in which the copper atom is 4 co-ordinate has been suggested:

$$\begin{array}{ccccc}
OC & & Cl & & CO \\
\searrow & & \searrow & & \swarrow \\
& Cu & & Cu & \\
\nearrow & & \nwarrow & & \nwarrow \\
H_2O & & Cl & & OH_2
\end{array}$$

$CuCl,C_2H_4$. This complex is formed if ethylene is passed over cuprous chloride in the dry state. If ethylene is passed through a suspension of cuprous chloride in water a clear solution is obtained. The dissociation pressure of ethylene is 1 atm at $-8°$ for the dry complex, and at $0°$ for the solution.

Cuprous halide complexes with phosphines and arsines. Addition compounds have been made of cuprous chloride, bromide, and iodide with the tertiary alkyl phosphines and arsines. They lose the phosphine or arsine easily. The structure of the compound $(C_2H_5)_3As,CuI$ is of interest. It is made by the action of the arsine on a solution of cuprous iodide in concentrated potassium iodide solution. In solution in acetone or benzene it is tetrameric. X-ray analysis shows it to have a structure in which each copper atom and each arsenic atom is 4 co-ordinate:

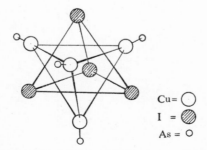

$$Cu = \bigcirc$$
$$I = \oslash$$
$$As = \circ$$

Fig. 24.52.   Arrangement of Cu, I, and As atoms in the molecule of $(C_2H_5)_3As,CuI$.

Complex Anions

Cyanide complexes. The three salts $K[Cu(CN)_2]$, $K_2[Cu(CN)_3]$, and $K_3[Cu(CN)_4]$ have been prepared. $K_3[Cu(CN)_4]$ is the most stable and it is present in all but the most dilute aqueous solutions of cuprous cyanide in potassium cyanide; the dissociation constant:

$$K = \frac{[Cu^+][CN^-]^4}{[Cu(CN)_4{}^{3-}]} = 2 \times 10^{-27}.$$

Chloride complexes are present in the salts $K[CuCl_2]$, $K_2[CuCl_3]$, $K_3[CuCl_4]$. In solution the anions chiefly present are $[CuCl_2]^-$ and $[CuCl_3]^{2-}$. Corresponding complexes are formed by all the halogens except fluorine.

Complex Cations

Cuprous ammines. $[Cu(NH_3)_2]_2SO_4,2H_2O$ separates as colourless crystals when cupric sulphate in concentrated ammonia solution is reduced by copper in the cold.

Cuprous nitriles. $[Cu(CH_3CN)_4]NO_3$ is made by dissolving copper in silver nitrate dissolved in methyl cyanide. On removal of the solvent by evaporation the salt remains as a colourless crystalline powder. It is stable so long as no methyl cyanide is removed.

An example of co-ordination through a sulphur atom is given by the thioacetamide complex:

$$\left[Cu \left(S{=}C \underset{CH_3}{\overset{NH_2}{<}} \right)_4 \right] Cl$$

SECTION 2. COMPOUNDS CONTAINING A COPPER ATOM IN OXIDATION STATE II

There is no evidence at all for the existence of the simple cupric ion Cu^{2+}. The cupric compounds are either giant molecule compounds or complexes.

GIANT MOLECULE COMPOUNDS

Cupric oxide, CuO, a black solid, m.p. 1026° is made by heating cupric nitrate, cupric hydroxide, or basic cupric carbonate. Above 1000° it loses oxygen to form cuprous oxide. It is easily reduced to the metal. It is insoluble in water, but dissolves in acids to give cupric salts.

The crystal lattice of cupric oxide is similar in certain respects to those of PdO and PtO. Four oxygen atoms occupy square planar positions round each copper atom, but copper atoms are disposed tetrahedrally round each oxygen atom. The tetrahedra, however, are not regular.

Cupric sulphide, CuS, is precipitated in an impure form by the action of hydrogen sulphide on cupric sulphate solution. It can be obtained pure by heating copper powder with a carbon disulphide solution of sulphur in a sealed tube at 100° for some hours. The crystals have a complicated layer structure.

Cupric hydroxide, $Cu(OH)_2$, a pale blue solid, is made by adding ammonia to a boiling solution of cupric sulphate until the green precipitate turns blue. The precipitate is washed and digested with sodium hydroxide solution at 30°. The direct addition of sodium hydroxide solution to a cupric salt precipitates a basic salt.

Cupric hydroxide is insoluble in water and in dilute alkali; it is very slightly soluble in concentrated alkali probably to form a cuprite, $K_2[CuO_2]$. It is soluble in acids, and in aqueous ammonia solution, in which the complex hydroxide $[Cu(NH_3)_4](OH)_2$ is formed.

34*

Table 24.39. *The Cupric Halides*

	CuF$_2$	CuCl$_2$	CuBr$_2$	CuI$_2$
Appearance	White crystalline salt; red liquid	Dark brown solid	Black crystals	[Breaks up as soon as formed into CuI + I, the cation oxidising the anion]
Lattice	Fluorite	Flat chains	Flat chains	
m.p. °C	950	498		
Solubility in water, gm/ 100 gm	Slight: 0·075	75·5†		
Hydrates	0, 1, 2	0, 1, 2,‡ 3, 4	0, 4	
	Hydrolysed by warm water			
Behaviour on heating	At 1000° gives CuF + F	At a red heat gives CuCl + Cl	At a red heat gives CuBr + Br	

† Also soluble in organic solvents containing oxygen.

‡ The dihydrate is light blue; its configuration is planar $H_2O-\underset{\underset{Cl}{|}}{\overset{\overset{Cl}{|}}{Cu}}-OH_2$.

CUPRIC COMPLEXES

Cupric copper forms neutral, anionic, and cationic complexes both non-chelate and chelate. The cupric atom has a much stronger affinity for oxygen, and a weaker affinity for nitrogen, than the cuprous atom.

NON-CHELATE COMPLEXES

Neutral complexes. Cupric copper forms no complexes with carbon monoxide. Nitric oxide is absorbed in solutions of cupric anionic complexes (not by solutions of cationic complexes) up to the proportion NO:Cu = 3·6:1. It is interesting to note that the ion Cu^{2+} has one electron less than the ion Cu^+, while the molecule NO has one electron more than the molecule CO.

Complex anions. The principal non-chelate anions containing cupric copper are formed from cupric cyanide, and from the cupric halides. $K_2[Cu(CN)_4]$ is a white very soluble, compound. Some of the halogen complexes are mentioned below:

$(NH_4)_2[CuF_4],2H_2O$		Pale blue, almost insoluble
$M[CuF_3]$	M = K, Rb	White
$Li[CuCl_3],2H_2O$		Garnet red
$(NH_4)[CuCl_3],2H_2O$		Blue
$M[CuCl_3]$	M = NH$_4$, K, Cs	Red
$M_2[CuCl_4],2H_2O$	M = NH$_4$, K, Cs	Green or blue
$Cs_2[CuCl_4]$		Yellow.

The crystal structures of certain of these complexes have been examined, and are a reminder that the plausibility of a chemical formula is no guide to the way in which atoms are related to one another in a solid compound. The anions in $Cs[CuCl_3]$ consist of flat chains of $CuCl_3$ groups thus:

in which each copper atom is 4 co-ordinate. The crystal structure of $K_2[CuCl_4],2H_2O$ has been shown to be an aggregate of $[CuCl_2\text{—}(OH_2)_2]$ molecules and of Cl^- and K^+ ions. Here again the copper atoms are 4 co-ordinate, but not in the manner suggested by the formula $K_2[CuCl_4]$ ordinarily assigned to the complex.† The complexes containing bromine are analogous to those of chlorine. $K_2[CuI_4]$ is known, but the iodide derivatives are difficult to make on account of the instability of CuI_2.

The non-chelate **complex cations** of cupric copper include cupric salts with water of hydration, and the ammines. The number of molecules of water of hydration co-ordinated to the cupric ion is normally 4. In the ammines $[Cu(NH_3)_n]X_2$, n is normally 4, but it may be 6 as in $[Cu(NH_3)_6]Br_2$ and $[Cu(NH_3)_6]I_2$, or 2 as in pale blue $[Cu(NH_3)_2](NO_2)_2$, made by warming violet blue $[Cu(NH_3)_4](NO_2)_2$.

In the ammines the nitrogen atoms are strongly bonded to the copper. The freezing point of a cupric sulphate solution is not changed by the addition of four equivalents of ammonia. The dissociation pressure of ammonia over $[Cu(NH_3)_4]SO_4$ does not reach 1 atm until 90°. $[Cu(NH_3)_4](OH)_2$ is a strong base.

Substituted ammonias in complex cations are less firmly bound to copper than is ammonia itself; the complexes are less stable, and the co-ordination number of copper is often reduced from 4 to 2. The following salts are for most purposes regarded as containing Cu^{2+} ions, but more strictly the copper atom is present in a complex cation.

Cupric nitrate is normally known only in solution, or as one of the hydrates $Cu(NO_3)_2,3H_2O$, $Cu(NO_3)_2,6H_2O$, $Cu(NO_3)_2,9H_2O$. The trihydrate on heating yields the basic nitrate $Cu_4(OH)_6(NO_3)_2$ which at higher temperatures decomposes to cupric oxide.

Anhydrous cupric nitrate has been prepared.‡ It consists of blue green crystals which are volatile at 200°. It is suggested that the molecules in the vapour have a ferrocene structure.

Cupric sulphate is made by the action of sulphuric acid on cupric oxide or on the basic carbonate. It is soluble in water, but insoluble in alcohol. It crystallises from water as the pentahydrate which in air effloresces to the trihydrate. On warming the changes occur:

$$CuSO_4,3H_2O \xrightarrow{100°} CuSO_4,H_2O \xrightarrow{250°} \underset{\text{colourless}}{CuSO_4} \xrightarrow{750°} CuO.$$

The crystal structure of cupric sulphate pentahydrate is discussed on p. 390. Cupric sulphate forms isodimorphous solid solutions with ferrous sulphate, $(Cu,Fe)SO_4,5H_2O$ and $(Cu,Fe)SO_4,7H_2O$. The double salt with ammonium sulphate has the composition $CuSO_4,(NH_4)_2SO_4,6H_2O$. Hydrogen chloride reacts with cupric sulphate to give chlorocupric acid:

$$CuSO_4 + 4HCl = H_2[CuCl_4] + H_2SO_4,$$

which indicates the stability of the anion $[CuCl_4]^{2-}$.

Cupric perchlorate, $Cu(ClO_4)_2,6H_2O$, m.p. 60°, loses two molecules of water of crystallisation when dried over sulphuric acid in the cold, but it loses no more water in any circumstances without decomposition. Hence the constitution of the partially dehydrated salt is $[Cu(H_2O)_4](ClO_4)$.

CHELATE COMPLEXES

Cupric copper forms many chelate complexes. In a few of them the copper is bound to the ligands by nitrogen atoms as in the very stable $[Cu\ en_2]SO_4$, and in some by sulphur

† It may be recalled that in crystalline $CuSO_4$, $5H_2O$, which is frequently written as $[Cu(H_2O)_4]SO_4,H_2O$ the copper atoms are 6-co-ordinate (p. 390).
‡ C. C. Addison and B. J. Hathaway, *Proc. Chem. Soc.*, 1957, 19.

atoms, but in the majority the copper is bound to the ligands by oxygen atoms, or by oxygen atoms and nitrogen atoms.

Neutral complexes. Copper forms many dichelate neutral complexes with β-diketones and similar compounds. They are insoluble in water, but soluble in organic solvents including hydrocarbons. Cupric acetylacetone is a dark blue solid, m.p. above 230°; it sublimes below the m.p. It is made by adding cupric acetate to a solution of acetylacetone.

Copper forms dichelate compounds with aminoacids. The derivative of glycine (H_2NCH_2COOH) is a deep violet blue, and is slightly soluble in water. The dichelate complex has the structure:

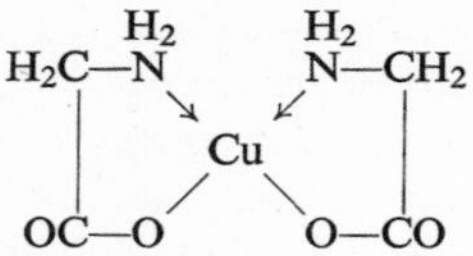

Cupric disalicyldioxime has the structure:

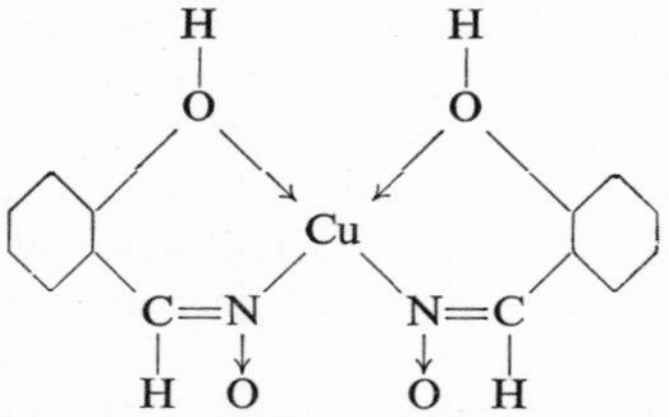

This complex is so insoluble that it is precipitated from a cupric solution containing acetic acid in the presence of any other metal. The cupric dimethylglyoxime compound has a structure which is non-planar; the two rings are inclined to one another at 28°.†

Complex anions include the carbonato and oxalato complexes of which the sodium salt $Na_2[Cu(C_2O_4)_2],2H_2O$ is an example. The complex cations include the dichelate and trichelate ethylene diamine derivative.

SILVER

The properties of metallic silver are mentioned on p. 1057. Examples of the types of compounds formed by silver are set out in Table 24.37. Silver does not form interstitial compounds. The large majority of silver compounds contain the silver atom in oxidation state I. They include the very unstable alkyls and aryls, a number of giant molecule compounds, and neutral, anionic, and cationic complexes. The ionic character of the compounds is much greater than that of the corresponding compounds of copper. The simple ion Ag^+ is probably present in argentous nitrate and in argentous perchlorate. The argentic, Ag^{II}, compounds are described on p. 1070. There is an interesting solid compound Ag_2F which has a layer structure. The succession of layers is silver, silver, fluorine. It is made by treating silver with aqueous silver fluoride solution at 50° for some time. It is decomposed by water to silver and silver fluoride; it is also decomposed by heating to 200°.

SECTION 1. COMPOUNDS CONTAINING A SILVER ATOM IN OXIDATION STATE I

Argentous alkyls and aryls. Silver ethyl and silver phenyl are far less stable than the corresponding copper compounds. AgC_2H_5 has been made by the action of lead tetraethyl on silver nitrate at $-70°$, but it decomposes above $-50°$. AgC_6H_5 is made by the

† E. Frasson et al., *J. Inorg. Nuclear Chem.*, **8**, 1958, 452.

action of magnesium phenyl iodide on silver chloride suspended in ether, but it decomposes violently if it is freed from ether.

Argentous acetylide, Ag_2C_2, is similar to the cuprous compound, but more explosive. It reacts with nitric acid and sulphuric acid to regenerate acetylene.

Argentous cyanide, AgCN, is a colourless solid, m.p. 320–350°. It is very slightly soluble in water and in dilute acids, but is soluble in concentrated acids, in ammonia solution, and in potassium cyanide solution. In the cold the crystals absorb one molecule of ammonia per atom of silver. It has been shown that the atoms in the crystal of argentous cyanide are arranged in chains Ag—C—N—Ag—C—N—Ag. The distance Ag—Ag is 5·26.

Argentous oxide, Ag_2O, is an almost black powder made by adding alkali to argentous nitrate solution. It is easily soluble in ammonia, from which it separates as violet crystals. It is almost insoluble in water, but the solution is alkaline, and readily absorbs carbon dioxide from the air. Argentous oxide effects, by double decomposition, the replacement of hydrogen atoms by OH groups in organic compounds. When heated it begins to dissociate about 200°. It reacts with ozone and with hydrogen peroxide to yield oxygen and silver. It has the cuprite crystal structure (p. 1063).

Argentous sulphide, Ag_2S, is precipitated when hydrogen sulphide is passed into silver nitrate solution. It is insoluble in ammonia, and in sodium thiosulphate solution.

Argentous salts of oxyacids. Argentous nitrate, $AgNO_3$, a colourless solid, m.p. 209°, is made by dissolving silver in nitric acid. The nitrite, $AgNO_2$, is obtained as a pale yellow precipitate by adding sodium nitrite to argentous nitrate solution. It decomposes at 100° to silver, argentous nitrate, and nitric oxide. Argentous perchlorate, $AgClO_4$, is deliquescent and very soluble in water, from which it crystallises as the monohydrate. It is also soluble in toluene, and it forms the crystalline solid, $AgClO_4,(CH_3C_6H_5)$. Argentous sulphate is made by dissolving silver in hot concentrated sulphuric acid.

The argentous halides. The preparations and properties are set out in Table 24.40.

Table 24.40.   *The Argentous Halides*

	AgF	AgCl	AgBr	AgI
Appearance	Colourless deliquescent cubic crystals	Colourless cubic crystals, orange liquid	Pale yellow cubic crystals	γ-form: pale yellow cubic crystals
m.p. °C	435	455	434	555 (decomp.)
b.p. °C		1550		
Lattice	Rocksalt	Rocksalt	Rocksalt	γ zinc blende; at 137° changes to β hexagonal; at 146° changes to α wurtzite
Solubility in water, gm/ 100 gm	182 Forms hydrates $4H_2O$ and $2H_2O$	8.9×10^{-5}	8.4×10^{-6}	3×10^{-7}
Other solvents	Slightly soluble in aqueous ammonia	Soluble in solutions of NH_4OH, KCN, $Na_2S_2O_3$	Soluble in solutions of KCN, $Na_2S_2O_3$	Soluble in solutions of KCN, $Na_2S_2O_3$

Argentous iodide is trimorphic. The α-form is an example of a crystalline condition in which the anions are present in a rigid lattice, while the cations are in the liquid state and free to move about the crystal.†

† Wells, *Structural Inorganic Chemistry*, p. 134.

ARGENTOUS COMPLEXES

Neutral complexes. There is evidence that argentous silver forms neutral complexes with carbon monoxide and with ethylene, but the compounds obtained are less well-characterised than the corresponding cuprous compounds. Argentous iodide forms addition compounds with $(C_2H_5)_3P$ and with $(C_2H_5)_3As$. The compounds have sharp melting points and resemble in preparation and properties the corresponding compounds of cuprous copper. They are tetrameric.

Argentous complex anions. Cyanide complexes. The complex salts $K_3[Ag(CN)_4]$, $K_2[Ag(CN)_3]$, and $K[Ag(CN)_2]$ are known. The anion $[Ag(CN)_2]^-$ with the dissociation constant 4×10^{-17} is the most stable of the three. The anion has a linear structure which indicates that the hybridisation of the silver atom is digonal.

Halide complexes. Argentous chloride is 100 times more soluble in normal hydrochloric acid solution than in water, owing to the formation of the complex acid $H[AgCl_2]$.

Thiosulphate complexes. The ready solubility of argentous halides in sodium hiosulphate solution has long been known because of its importance in photography. There are three types of complex anion:

$$M[Ag(S_2O_3)] \qquad M = Li(\tfrac{1}{2}H_2O), Na, K, NH_4$$
$$M_3[Ag(S_2O_3)_2] \qquad M = K$$
$$M_5[Ag(S_2O_3)_4] \qquad M = Na, K, NH_4.$$

The salts have a sweet taste.

Argentous complex cations. With ammonia and amines the silver atom forms cations of the constitution $[Ag2NH_3]^+$ and $[Ag3NH_3]^+$; in its ammine cationic complexes the silver atom is not 4 co-ordinate. In $[Ag2NH_3]^+$ the silver atom is digonally hybridised. The solution of argentous cyanide in ammonia solution is explained by the formation of a salt of two complex ions, $[Ag2NH_3][Ag(CN)_2]$, which is soluble in water.

SECTION 2. COMPOUNDS CONTAINING A SILVER ATOM IN OXIDATION STATE II

The argentic, Ag^{II}, compounds are so much less stable than the cupric compounds that only the fluoride, AgF_2, and certain complex cations are known. They are prepared by submitting argentous salts to powerful oxidation processes.

Argentic oxide, AgO. If an aqueous solution of argentous nitrate is electrolysed, a black deposit is obtained at the anode. A black deposit is also obtained by the action of potassium peroxydisulphate on argentous nitrate solution. The black deposit yields argentous oxide and oxygen when gently heated. Its composition and constitution are uncertain.

The ion Ag^{2+}. Ozone reacts with a solution of argentous nitrate in concentrated nitric acid at $0°$ to produce a black paramagnetic solution. The solution has oxidising properties but it does not contain hydrogen peroxide. With water it yields oxygen and the argentous ion. It is inferred that the solution contains the ion Ag^{2+}.

Argentic fluoride, AgF_2, a black or brown solid, m.p. $690°$, is made by the action of fluorine on silver at $300°$. It is paramagnetic, and has strong oxidising properties; with water or dilute acids it liberates ozone. It is thermally stable, and it may be heated to $700°$ under fluorine at $\tfrac{1}{10}$ atm pressure without being decomposed.

Argentic complex cations. Argentic silver forms complex cations with ligands containing nitrogen, such as pyridine, α,α-dipyridyl, or phenanthroline. Potassium peroxydisulphate acting on argentous nitrate dissolved in pyridine yields orange crystals of [Agpyr$_4$]S$_2$O$_8$; the same oxidising agent acting on argentous nitrate dissolved in phenanthroline or dipyridyl yields [Agphen$_2$]S$_2$O$_8$ or [Agdipyr$_2$]S$_2$O$_8$. When dipyridyl is used it is also possible to prepare the octahedral complex cation [Agdipyr$_3$]$^{2+}$. The electrolytic oxidation of argentous nitrate dissolved in pyridine yields [Agpyr$_4$](NO$_3$)$_2$. From these salts, by double decomposition, it is possible to prepare the hydrogen sulphates, the perchlorates, and the chlorates of the cations. All the cations are oxidising agents, and have paramagnetic susceptibilities equivalent to a range of magnetic moment from 0·9 to 1·6 Bohr magnetons.

GOLD

The properties of metallic gold are mentioned on p. 1057, and the principal types of compounds which it forms are set out in Table 24.37. Gold forms the aurous, Au^I, compounds which are easily decomposed, and the much more stable auric, Au^{III}, compounds in which the co-ordination number of the gold atom is invariably 4.

SECTION 1. COMPOUNDS CONTAINING A GOLD ATOM
IN OXIDATION STATE I

Aurous alkyls and aryls. Gold aryls can be made in ethereal solution by the action of the appropriate aryl magnesium bromide on gold carbonyl chloride, AuClCO, but they are very unstable. Aurous alkyls are not known.

Aurous oxide, Au$_2$O, is precipitated as a violet powder when dilute potassium hydroxide solution is added to aurous chloride, or to K[AuBr$_2$]. If aurous oxide is heated to 225° it yields a mixture of gold and auric oxide. It reacts with ammonia to form NAu$_3$(NH$_3$).

Aurous sulphide, Au$_2$S, an insoluble dark brown solid, is made by passing hydrogen sulphide through a solution of K[AuBr$_2$]. It is unaffected by water or dilute acids, but it dissolves in aqua regia and in potassium cyanide solution.

Aurous cyanide, AuCN, exists as yellow, very insoluble, crystals. It is formed when auric cyanide decomposes, or by heating K[Au(CN)$_2$] with hydrochloric acid to 50°. The arrangement of atoms in crystalline aurous cyanide is similar to that in argentous cyanide. Aurous cyanide is more stable than either cuprous cyanide or argentous cyanide, but if heated to a red heat it decomposes leaving a deposit of gold. It has a strong tendency to complex formation.

The aurous halides. Aurous fluoride does not exist; it would tend to be ionic, and the aurous ion is itself unstable.

Aurous chloride, AuCl, an insoluble yellow solid, is made by heating auric chloride to 175°. At higher temperatures aurous chloride decomposes to gold and chlorine. With water it disproportionates yielding gold and auric chloride. There is some evidence that aurous chloride is dimeric.

Aurous bromide, AuBr, is made by warming auric bromide at 115°. When heated or moistened it behaves like aurous chloride.

Aurous iodide, AuI, is less soluble than either the chloride or the bromide, and hence is easier to prepare, and more stable when made. It is formed when auric iodide decomposes at room temperature, when hydrogen iodide reacts with auric oxide, when iodine reacts with gold, and when potassium iodide reacts with auric chloride.

Neutral complexes. When carbon monoxide is passed into a solution of auric chloride in tetrachloroethylene at 120°, colourless crystals of $AuCl \cdot CO$ are obtained. The crystals are soluble in benzene and ether, but are decomposed by water to carbon monoxide and gold. The composition of $AuCl \cdot CO$ differs from that of the carbon monoxide complex of cuprous chloride, $CuCl \cdot CO \cdot H_2O$ (p. 1064).

Aurous iodide forms complexes with tertiary phosphines and tertiary arsines. The complexes are made by adding phosphine or arsine to an aqueous-alcoholic solution of $H[AuCl_4]$ containing potassium iodide. Unlike the phosphine and arsine complexes of cuprous iodide the aurous iodide complexes are monomeric.

Complex anions. Cyanide complexes. Potassium aurocyanide $K[Au(CN)_2]$, is made by dissolving fulminating gold (below), in potassium cyanide solution, or by the action of dilute potassium cyanide solution on metallic gold in the presence of oxygen or hydrogen peroxide:

$$2Au + 4KCN + H_2O + O = 2K[Au(CN)_2] + 2KOH.$$

Halide complexes. The complex salt $K[AuCl_2]$ is unstable, and if moistened, quickly decomposes giving metallic gold. $K[AuBr_2]$ is made by reducing $K[AuBr_4]$.

Thiosulphate complexes. The complex salt $K_3[Au(S_2O_3)_2]$ is the only example of a complex anion in which a gold atom in state Au^I is 4-co-ordinate.

Complex cations. Aurous halides, if heated with aqueous ammonia, yield colourless complexes of the type $[Au(NH_3)]Cl$, which are insoluble in water, but soluble in aqueous ammonia. Thiourea forms the cation complex $[AuS:C(NH_2)_2]Cl$.

SECTION 3. COMPOUNDS CONTAINING A GOLD ATOM IN OXIDATION STATE III

There is no evidence that gold is ever divalent; the assumption that a d electron is promoted to an anti-bonding orbital which was made to explain the formation of cupric and argentic compounds is not necessary to explain the formation of auric compounds.

The auric compounds are more stable than the aurous compounds. The simple ion Au^{3+} does not exist; auric compounds are covalent. In the auric compounds the co-ordination number of the gold atom is always four, and the arrangement of other atoms round the gold atom is planar. Many auric compounds contain a gold atom with the valencies:

$$\overset{\displaystyle |}{\underset{\displaystyle |}{-Au\leftarrow}}$$

Because of the strong tendency of the auric gold atom to become 4-co-ordinate, the auric compounds fall into two classes, the giant molecule compounds and complexes.

GIANT MOLECULE COMPOUNDS

Auric hydroxide, AuOOH, is obtained by treating with nitric acid the precipitate $Mg[AuO_2]$ formed by the action of magnesia on an aqueous solution of auric chloride. If the hydroxide is gently heated at 140°, auric oxide is obtained.

Auric oxide, Au_2O_3, is a brown solid. It decomposes at 155° to aurous oxide and oxygen. Auric oxide is soluble in potassium hydroxide to yield potassium aurate, $K[Au(OH)_4],H_2O$, and in aqueous ammonia to give fulminating gold, a dark powder of uncertain composition and constitution.

AURIC COMPLEXES

Neutral Complexes

Among the non-chelate neutral complexes are:

$$(C_6H_5CH_2)_2SAuBr_3, \quad (C_2H_5)_3PAuCl_3 \quad \text{and} \quad pyrAuBr_3.$$

Most of the neutral auric complexes, however, are chelate. Some interesting examples are discussed below.

The auric halides. Auric fluoride has not been reported. The other auric halides have dimeric planar structures:

$$
\begin{array}{ccccc}
\text{Cl} & & \text{Cl} & & \text{Cl} \\
\diagdown & \swarrow & & \diagdown & \\
& \text{Au} & & \text{Au} & \\
\diagup & & \nearrow & & \diagdown \\
\text{Cl} & & \text{Cl} & & \text{Cl}
\end{array}
$$

Auric chloride, $(AuCl_3)_2$, a brown solid, is made by heating at 120° crystals of aurichloric acid $H[AuCl_4],4H_2O$. It can also be obtained by the action of chlorine water on gold. It decomposes to aurous chloride and chlorine at 175°. It is soluble in water, alcohol, and ether. Molecular weight determinations have shown that the vapour is dimeric.

Auric bromide, $AuBr_3$, is a dark brown substance which very easily loses bromine to give aurous bromide. It is made by heating finely divided gold with bromine, or by gently warming $H[AuBr_4]$. It is dimeric in solution in bromine.

Auric iodide, AuI_3, is a dark green nearly insoluble solid which decomposes very easily. It is made by the action of auric chloride on potassium iodide solution:

$$AuCl_3 + 4KI = K[AuI_4] + 3KCl$$

$$3K[AuI_4] + AuCl_3 = 4AuI_3 + 3KCl.$$

Auric alkyls. These compounds furnish a good example of the tendency of Au^{III} to become tetravalent. There are three types of auric alkyls, but instead of the simple constitutions:

$$AuR_3 \qquad AuR_2Cl \qquad AuRCl_2$$

they possess the complex constitutions:

$$
\begin{array}{ccc}
\begin{array}{ccc}
\text{R} & & \text{R} \\
\diagdown & & \diagup \\
& \text{Au} & \\
\diagup & & \nwarrow \\
\text{R} & & \text{X}
\end{array}
&
\begin{array}{ccc}
\text{R} & & \text{R} \\
\diagdown & & \diagup \\
& \text{Au} & \\
\nearrow & & \diagdown \\
\text{Y} & & \text{Y} \\
\diagdown & & \swarrow \\
& \text{Au} & \\
\diagup & & \diagdown \\
\text{R} & & \text{R}
\end{array}
&
\begin{array}{ccc}
\text{R} & & \text{R} \\
\diagdown & & \diagup \\
& \text{Au} & \\
\diagup & & \diagdown \\
\text{Y} & & \text{Y} \\
\diagdown & & \swarrow \\
& \text{Au} & \\
\diagup & & \diagdown \\
\text{Y} & & \text{Y}
\end{array}
\end{array}
$$

where R is a alkyl radical, X represents pyridine, or tolylamine $N(CH_2C_6H_5)H_2$, and Y represents Cl, Br, or CN.

The etherates and ammines of the auric trialkyls are very unstable; the diethyl etherate of the trimethyl derivative decomposes at $-35°$.

The dialkyl compounds are liquids or low-melting solids. They are made by treating the acid $H[AuCl_3(OH)]$ dissolved in ether or pyridine, with the appropriate Grignard reagent. The cyanides are formed by treating the halide with silver cyanide. The dialkyl compounds are colourless, and are soluble in organic solvents but not in water. The molecular weights of the dialkyl compounds dissolved in benzene or bromoform show that they are dimeric. The constitution:

$$\diagdown \diagup \diagdown \diagup$$
$$Au \qquad Au$$
$$\diagup \diagdown \diagup \diagdown$$

has been confirmed by X-ray analysis. The dialkyl cyanides are tetrameric, and have a square structure which arises naturally from the axial valencies of the group —C≡N—, and the square hybridisation of the auric atom:

$$
\begin{array}{ccc}
R & & R \\
| & & | \\
R\!-\!Au\!-\!N\!\equiv\!C\!-\!Au\!-\!R \\
| & & | \\
C & & N \\
\parallel & & \parallel \\
N & & C \\
| & & | \\
R\!-\!Au\!-\!C\!\equiv\!N\!-\!Au\!-\!R \\
| & & | \\
R & & R
\end{array}
$$

This structure for auric dipropyl cyanide has been established by X-ray analysis. The compound $((C_2H_5)_2Au)_2SO_4$ is also dimeric. The oxalate:

$$
\begin{array}{ccccc}
C_2H_5 & & O\!=\!C\!-\!O & & C_2H_5 \\
\diagdown & \swarrow & & & \diagup \\
& Au & | & & Au \\
\diagup & & O\!-\!C\!=\!O & \nearrow & \diagdown \\
C_2H_5 & & & & C_2H_5
\end{array}
$$

however, is monomeric.

The monoalkyl compounds (made by the action of the halogen on the auric dialkyl) are deep red. Their dimeric constitutions with two alkyl groups on one gold atom:

$$
\begin{array}{ccccc}
R & & Cl & & Cl \\
\diagdown & \swarrow & \diagdown & & \diagup \\
& Au & & Au \\
\diagup & & \diagdown & \nearrow & \diagdown \\
R & & Cl & & Cl
\end{array}
$$

are established by their high dipole moments, and by their reaction with potassium bromide which gives $K[AuBr_4]$ and $(C_2H_5)_2AuBr_2$. The aryl auric complexes appear to be less stable than the alkyl compounds. The only type of aryl compound known is the diaryl R_2AuY, with properties similar to those of the alkyl compounds.

Anionic Complexes

There are many acids and salts of the general formula $M[AuX_4]$, where M represents H, or the cations of many metals, and X represents OH, a halogen, or CN. Mixed complex anions of this type are common; salts of the series of five anions $[Au(OH)_4]$ to $[AuCl_4]$ are known. The aqueous solution of auric chloride contains the acid $H[AuCl_3OH]$. The anion in $K[AuBr_4]$ has been shown by X-ray analysis to be planar. The red bromoauric acid $H[AuBr_4]$ is made by heating auric bromide with hydrogen bromide.

Complex Cations

The salt $[Au(NH_3)_4]Cl_3$ is made by the action of ammonia on chloroauric acid. It is colourless. The chloride ion may be replaced by ions of other halogens and by the ions of oxyacids. The oxyacid salts are very stable.

CHAPTER TWENTY-FIVE

THE CARBONYLS, CARBONYL HYDRIDES, CARBONYL HALIDES, NITROSYLS, AND π-COMPLEXES OF THE TRANSITION METALS

The transition metals form compounds with the carbonyl group, with the nitrosyl group, and with certain unsaturated hydrocarbons. These compounds present certain common problems in structural chemistry, and they are therefore grouped together for discussion in the present chapter. The solutions to these structural problems are to be found in the parts played in bond formation by the d orbitals of the penultimate shells of the metal atoms.

THE CARBONYLS OF THE TRANSITION METALS

A carbonyl of a transition metal contains an atom of the metal directly linked to a number of carbonyl groups and to no other elements or groups. The carbonyls may be divided into three classes (see Table 25.1): (i) the *monomeric carbonyls* of general formula $M(CO)_x$, which contain one metal atom per molecule, (ii) the *bridged carbonyls* of general formula $M_2(CO)_y$, which contain two metal atoms per molecule, and (iii) the *polynuclear carbonyls* which contain three or four metal atoms per molecule. For many metal carbonyls the molecular weights, and also the geometrical distributions of the atoms in the molecule, are known. It is generally accepted that the metal atom in a carbonyl is directly linked to the carbon atom of the carbonyl group. All the monomeric carbonyls, except iron pentacarbonyl, are colourless, and all the bridged and polynuclear carbonyls, except dirhenium decacarbonyl, are coloured. The monomeric carbonyls are more volatile than the others. The thermal stability of all classes of carbonyls (judged by the temperature at which thermal dissociation begins) is roughly the same.

During the past few years a great deal of successful work has been done in interpreting the structures of the metal carbonyls and their derivatives in terms of modern theories of valency. The application of molecular orbital theory and of the ligand-field theory has been of great value. In this chapter the structures are explained in terms of the valence bond theory, by means of which a self-consistent pattern of structures is developed. Two assumptions are made:

(i) that the directions of the valencies exerted by the metal atoms in the carbonyls are determined by hybridisation, and that once σ bonds have been established the metal may also exert π bonds which are formed by using either pure or hybrid d orbitals (p. 156),

(ii) that the formation of a carbonyl enables all the d orbitals in the valence shell of the metal atom to be fully occupied by electrons.

The electronic configurations of the valence shells in the prehybridisation states of the atoms of the transition metals are given in Table 25.2.

Table 25.1. *The Carbonyls of the Transition Metals*

Group VI T	Group VII T	Group VIII	Group IX	Group X
Monomeric carbonyls				
$Cr(CO)_6$ Colourless crystals Sublimes, m.p. 149° Decomp. *ca.* 100°		$Fe(CO)_5$ Yellow liquid m.p. $-20°$; b.p. 103° Decomp. 130°		$Ni(CO)_4$ Colourless liquid m.p. $-25°$; b.p. 43° Decomp. 100°
$Mo(CO)_6$ Colourless crystals Sublimes Decomp. 150°		$Ru(CO)_5$ Colourless liquid m.p. $-22°$ Sublimes Decomp. 50°		
$W(CO)_6$ Colourless crystals Sublimes		$Os(CO)_5$ Colourless liquid m.p. $-15°$		
Bridged carbonyls				
	$Mn_2(CO)_{10}$ Golden yellow crystals m.p. 155°	$Fe_2(CO)_9$ Yellow crystals Decomp. 100°	$Co_2(CO)_8$ Orange red crystals m.p. 51° Non-volatile	
		$Ru_2(CO)_9$ Orange crystals Decomp. 150°	$Rh_2(CO)_8$ Orange crystals m.p. 76° Decomp. 76°	
	$Re_2(CO)_{10}$ Colourless crystals m.p. 177° Sublimes Decomp. 177°	$Os_2(CO)_9$ Yellow crystals m.p. 224° Sublimes	$Ir_2(CO)_8$ Yellow-green crystals Sublimes in CO at 160°	
Polynuclear carbonyls				
		$Fe_3(CO)_{12}$ Green crystals Decomp. 140°	$Co_4(CO)_{12}$ Black solid Decomp. 60°	
		$Ru_3(CO)_{12}$ Green crystals	$[Rh(CO)_3]n$ Red solid Decomp. 150°	
			$Rh_4(CO)_{11}$ Black solid	
			$[Ir(CO)_3]n$ Yellow solid Sublimes in CO at 210° Decomp. 210°	

It is possible to devise a consistent method of formulating the orbital structures of the carbonyls by choosing the correct number of *ns*, *np*, and $(n-1)d$ metallic orbitals for hybridisation, and then arranging bonds so that all the unpaired electrons in the unhybridised $(n-1)d$ orbitals are paired. This is possible because the molecule of carbon monoxide can adopt at least three different electron configurations, and hence may be bonded to the metal atom in more than one way. The canonical forms of the carbon monoxide molecule, and its possible modes of combination are shown in Table 25.3.

Table 25.2. *Electron Configurations of the Valence Shells of Atoms of the Transition Metals in the Prehybridisation State.*

n is the Principal Quantum Number

$n=4$	$n=5$	$n=6$	$(n-1)d$					ns	np
Cr	Mo	W	↑	↑	↑	↑	↑	↑	· · ·
Mn	Tc	Re	↑	↑	↑	↑	↑	↑	↑ · ·
Fe	Ru	Os	↑↓	↑	↑	↑	↑	↑	↑ · ·
Co	Rh	Ir	↑↓	↑↓	↑	↑	↑	↑	↑ · ·
Ni	Pd	Pt	↑↓	↑↓	↑↓	↑	↑	↑	↑ · ·

The formulae in the second row of Table 25.3 show how for each canonical form it is possible to make links in different ways between the atom of a transition metal, M, and the carbon atom of the carbonyl group without disturbing the mode of linkage of carbon to oxygen. There is no need of the three hypothetical formulae, IV, V, or VI, to account for the structure of any carbonyl so far reported; this suggests that the oxygen atoms in a carbonyl do not carry a formal negative charge. For the purpose of this Chapter, it is assumed that the carbonyl group in a metallic carbonyl is in one of the combination states I, II, or III.

GROUP VI. THE CARBONYLS OF THE METALS CHROMIUM, MOLYBDENUM, AND TUNGSTEN

The transition metals in Group VI form carbonyls of one type only, $M(CO)_6$.

Chromium hexacarbonyl, $Cr(CO)_6$. Chromium hexacarbonyl exists as colourless rhombic crystals. It can be obtained by the following methods. †

(1) Carbon monoxide at 50 atm pressure and at room temperature is passed into a suspension of chromic chloride in ether, which has been treated with phenyl magnesium bromide at $-70°$ (Job's reaction).

(2) A chromium acetylacetonate complex salt, or a chromic or chromous salt of an organic acid in pyridine solution, is exposed to carbon monoxide at 100–300 atm pressure at 80–170° in the presence of powdered zinc or magnesium. The yield is about 85%.‡

(3) A solution of a chromic salt dissolved in ether is treated with $Al(C_2H_5)_3$ and carbon monoxide at a high temperature and pressure.§

Crystals of chromium hexacarbonyl sublime without decomposition. They are soluble in ether, chloroform, carbon tetrachloride, and benzene. Chromium hexa-carbonyl is resistant to chemical attack. It does not react with air, bromine, cold aqueous alkalis, dilute acids, or with concentrated sulphuric acid or concentrated hydrochloric acid. It is, however, decomposed by chlorine or by concentrated nitric acid. It does not react with thiols, or with nitric oxide. With an alkali metal in liquid ammonia the reaction occurs $Cr(CO)_6 + 2Na = Na_2[Cr(CO)_5] + CO$.

† Attempts to prepare $Cr(CO)_6$ by methods (2) and (3) on p. 1079 used for the preparation of $Mo(CO)_6$ and $W(CO)_6$, have been unsuccessful.

‡ *Ann. Reports*, 1957, 124.

§ *Ann. Reports*, 1958, 146.

Table 25.3. *The Canonical Forms and Modes of Bonding of the Molecule CO*

	I	II	III	IV	V	VI
Canonical forms of the molecule CO	$:\overset{-}{C} \overset{\pi}{-} \overset{+}{O}:$		$:C \overset{\pi}{-} \overset{..}{O}:$		$:\overset{+}{C} - \overset{-}{\underset{..}{O}}:$	
Possible modes of combination of the canonical forms with atoms of a metal, M, M', or M"	$\overset{-}{M} - \overset{\pi}{C} \overset{\pi}{-} \overset{+}{O}:$	$M \overset{\pi d}{-} C \overset{\pi}{-} \overset{..}{O}:$	$\underset{M \quad M'}{C} \overset{\pi}{-} \overset{..}{O}:$	$M^+ \overset{\pi d}{-} \overset{\pi d}{C} - \overset{-}{\underset{..}{O}}:$	$\underset{M^+ \quad M'}{\overset{\pi d}{C}} - \overset{-}{\underset{..}{O}}:$	$\underset{M^+ \quad M' \quad M''}{C} - \overset{-}{\underset{..}{O}}:$

Although remarkably stable towards ordinary chemical reagents, $Cr(CO)_6$ reacts with amines such as pyridine

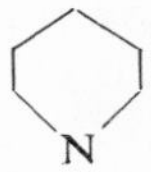

o-phenanthroline

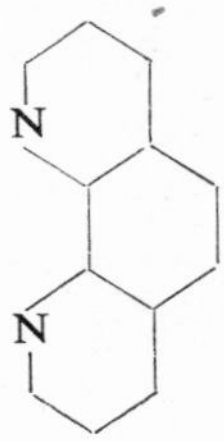

and ethylene diamine

$$H_2C—NH_2$$
$$H_2C—NH_2$$

to yield products in which CO groups in the molecule of $Cr(CO)_6$ are replaced by molecules of the amine. In these substitution compounds one nitrogen atom of the amine appears to play the same part in saturating the valency of the chromium atom as one CO group. For example, above 140°, pyridine reacts with $Cr(CO)_6$ to yield the succession of compounds:

$$Cr(CO)_6 \rightarrow \underset{\text{yellow brown}}{Cr(CO)_4pyr_2} \rightarrow \underset{\text{yellow red}}{Cr_2(CO)_7pyr_5} \rightarrow \underset{\text{bright red}}{Cr(CO)_3pyr_3}$$

All these compounds are coloured solids. $Cr(CO)_3pyr_3$ is stable in air. It is decomposed by acids according to the equation:

$$Cr(CO)_3pyr_3 + 6HCl = (pyrH)_3CrCl_6 + 3CO + 1\tfrac{1}{2}H_2.$$

$Cr(CO)_3pyr_3$, if heated in vacuo, loses pyridine to yield $Cr_2(CO)_6pyr_3$, which is pyrophoric. If chromium hexacarbonyl is treated with potassium hydroxide in methyl alcohol solution in a sealed tube at 100° the reaction occurs:

$$Cr(CO)_6 + KOH + 5H_2O = K[Cr(CO)_3(H_2O)_2OH] + 3HCOOH$$

The product gives a red aqueous solution but is hydrolysed thus:

$$H_2O + K[Cr(CO)_3(H_2O)_2OH] = KOH + Cr(CO)_3(H_2O)_3.$$

With few exceptions the reactions of chromium carbonyl (other than those which lead to complete decomposition) yield products in which the co-ordination number of chromium remains as 6.

Molybdenum hexacarbonyl, $Mo(CO)_6$, and tungsten hexacarbonyl, $W(CO)_6$. Both these compounds exist as colourless crystals. They can be made:

(i) By Job's Grignard reaction, in which either $MoCl_5$ or WCl_6 is treated with carbon monoxide in the presence of phenyl magnesium bromide.

(ii) By the action of carbon monoxide at 225° and 200 atm pressure on metallic molybdenum or tungsten reduced in the presence of iron or copper.

(iii) By the action of carbon monoxide on the metal in the presence of a sulphide and copper or iron to act as the ultimate acceptor of the sulphur.

(iv) By the action of carbon monoxide under pressure on the compounds K_3MoCl_6 or $K_3W_2Cl_9$ in the presence of another metal.

Crystals of $Mo(CO)_6$ and $W(CO)_6$ sublime at 40° and 50° respectively, and exert a vapour pressure of 1 atm at 156° and 175°, respectively. Molybdenum and tungsten hexacarbonyls are not attacked by air, cold aqueous alkalis, acids (except concentrated nitric acid) or by thiols or nitric oxide. They are decomposed by bromine or chlorine. With pyridine, phenanthroline, and ethylene diamine, they form derivatives similar in colour and parallel in composition to the corresponding derivatives of chromium. Their reactions with sodium in liquid ammonia correspond to that of chromium hexacarbonyl; the derivatives $Na_2[Mo(CO)_5]$ and $Na_2[W(CO)_5]$ are formed.

STRUCTURES OF THE HEXACARBONYLS

The molecular formula $M(CO)_6$ suggests an octahedral configuration which is confirmed by the results of electron diffraction experiments. The internuclear bond lengths (to within ± 0.05) are:

	M—C	M—O	C—O
Cr	1·92	3·08	1·16
Mo	2·08	3·23	1·15
W	2·06	3·19	1·13

The orbital diagram of $Cr(CO)_6$ is drawn below (Fig. 25.1). The bond structure shown in perspective is drawn in Fig. 25.2, which shows two kinds of bonds between Cr and C: I simple covalent bonds Cr—C≡O, and II double bonds Cr—^{π}C=O. The structure shown is one of a number of canonical forms, and in the resultant resonance structure all Cr—C bonds are identical.

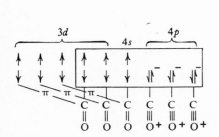

Fig. 25.1.   Orbital diagram of $Cr(CO)_6$.

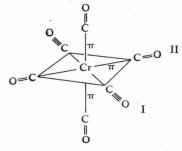

Fig. 25.2.   Bond structure of $Cr(CO)_6$.

Each of the six CO groups is linked to the metal atom by a σ bond. Three of the CO groups are linked also by π bonds to the metal atom. The π bonds are constructed from the d orbitals of the metal atom in the manner described on p. 156.

There is chemical evidence that the carbonyl groups are of two kinds labelled I and II (Fig. 25.2), distinguished by their bonding to the metal atom. Carbonyl groups I are bound to the metal atoms by simple co-ionic bonds. These carbonyl groups should be replaceable by any other molecules capable of donating lone electron pairs to the metal atom, as for example $N(CH_3)_3$ or H_2O. Such a molecule as $N(CH_3)_3$ or H_2O, however, is incapable of using the lone electron pair to form one σ bond and one π bond, and therefore it could not replace any of the carbonyl groups labelled II. It is therefore predictable that all derivatives of $Cr(CO)_6$ in which the maximum replacement of carbonyl groups by ligands of the types NR_3 or OR_2 has been made, will have the form $Cr(CO)_3(NR_3)_3$ or $Cr(CO)_3(OR_2)_3$. Similar considerations apply to the hexacarbonyls of molybdenum and tungsten.

The list of derivatives of the hexacarbonyls in Table 25.4 shows that this prediction is fulfilled. Only those derivatives with formulae printed in italics contain fewer than three carbonyl groups per metal atom. The existence of the isocyanide and the diarsine derivatives does not invalidate the structure assigned to the hexacarbonyls (Fig. 25.2), because the ligands RNC and $C_6H_4(As(CH_3)_2)_2$ can be represented by canonical forms corresponding to those of carbon monoxide thus:

$$\overset{+}{O}\equiv\overset{-}{C}: \qquad R-\overset{+}{N}\equiv\overset{-}{C}: \qquad \begin{array}{c} C_6H_4 \\ \diagdown \\ CH_3-As: \\ \diagup \\ CH_3 \end{array}$$

$$O=C\diagup \qquad R-N=C\diagup \qquad \begin{array}{c} C_6H_4 \\ \diagdown \diagup \\ CH_3-As \\ \diagup \diagdown \\ CH_3 \end{array}$$

Table 25.4.   *Derivatives of the Hexacarbonyls*

R represents an alkyl or aryl group. L represents NX_3, PX_3, AsX_3, or SbX_3, where X is CH_3, Cl, or C_6H_5. Formulae in italics describe compounds which contain fewer than three carbonyl groups per metal atom.

Chromium	Molybdenum	Tungsten
Neutral complexes		
$Cr(CO)_5NH_3$		
$Cr(CO)_5C_5H_5N$		
$Cr(CO)_4$ pyr$_2$		$W(CO)_4$ pyr$_2$
$Cr(CO)_4$ phen	$Mo(CO)_4$ phen	$W(CO)_4$ phen
†$Cr(CO)_4$ diarsine	$Mo(CO)_4$ diarsine	$W(CO)_4$ diarsine
$Cr_2(CO)_7$ pyr$_5$		
$Cr_2(CO)_6$ pyr$_3$		
$Cr_2(CO)_6$ en$_3$	$Mo_2(CO)_6$ en$_3$	
$Cr(CO)_3(NH_3)_3$		
$Cr(CO)_3L_3$	$Mo(CO)_3L_3$	$W(CO)_3L_3$‡
$Cr(CO)_3(RNC)_3$		
$Cr(CO)_3(H_2O)_3$		
$Cr(CO)_3$ pyr$_3$	$Mo(CO)_3$ pyr$_3$	$W(CO)_3$ pyr$_3$
$Cr(CO)_3$ phen pyr	$Mo(CO)_3$ phen pyr	$W(CO)_3$ phen pyr
	$Mo(CO)_2$ pyr SC_6H_5	
†$Cr(CO)_2$ *(diarsine)*$_2$	$Mo(CO)_2$ *(diarsine)*$_2$	$W(CO)_2$ *(diarsine)*$_2$
§$Cr(RNC)_6$	$Mo(RNC)_6$	$W(RNC)_6$
Salts containing complex anions		
$K[Cr(CO)_3(H_2O)_2OH]$		
$K_3[Cr(CO)_3(CN)_3],2NH_3$		
π-complexes		
$C_4H_4SCr(CO)_3$	$C_7H_8Mo(CO)_3$	
‖$ArCr(CO)_3$	$(C_7H_7)_2(Mo(CO)_3)_2$	
	$[(C_7H_7{}^+)Mo(CO)_3][BF^-]$	

† H. L. Nigran and R. S. Nyholm, *Proc. Chem. Soc.*, 1957, 321. Diarsine has the formula

‡ E. W. Abel, M. A. Bennett, and G. Wilkinson, *J. Chem. Soc.*, 1959, 2323.
§ *Ann. Reports*, 1954, 141.
‖ Ar may be an aromatic hydrocarbon, a primary, secondary, or tertiary aromatic amine, or an ester of benzoic acid.

It is therefore not surprising that the diarsine ligand replaces four CO groups and that the RNC ligand replaces all six. The only compound in Table 25·4 which appears to be anomalous is $Mo(CO)_2pyrSC_6H_5$.

By contrast with the hexacarbonyls and their derivatives the properties of the compound $K_3[Cr(C_2H)_6]$ (derived from acetylene) may be considered. Each acetylene residue must be linked to the chromium atom by one σ bond only, and there can be no double bonds. The unhybridised $3d$ orbitals take no part in bonding, and the anion $[Cr(C_2H)_6]^{3-}$ must contain at least one unpaired electron. The compound is coloured orange, it is paramagnetic, and it is very sensitive to air, water, and shock. In these properties it differs from the hexacarbonyls and their derivatives.

GROUP VII. THE CARBONYLS OF THE METALS MANGANESE, TECHNETIUM, AND RHENIUM

Manganese carbonyl $Mn_2(CO)_{10}$, and rhenium carbonyl $Re_2(CO)_{10}$ are crystalline substances. No technetium carbonyl has been reported, but the chemistry of technetium is so little known that this does not necessarily mean that no technetium carbonyl exists.

Manganese carbonyl, $Mn_2(CO)_{10}$. Manganese carbonyl forms volatile golden yellow crystals, m.p. 155° in a sealed tube. It is made by treating manganese iodide and magnesium with carbon monoxide in ether under high pressure. It is soluble in organic solvents. With iodine it forms $Mn(CO)_5I$. Its structure corresponds to that of rhenium carbonyl (below). With substituted phosphines, arsines, and stibines, manganese carbonyl gives monomeric, paramagnetic compounds of the type $Mn(CO)_4(PR_3)$.† In the presence of o-phenanthroline and a nickel salt it yields $[Ni(C_{12}H_8N_2)_3]$ $[Mn(CO)_5]$, and with sodium in liquid ammonia, $Na^+[Mn(CO)_5]^-$. Treatment with diazomethane yields $Mn(CO)_5CH_3$, a colourless, stable, diamagnetic compound, m.p. 95°; derivatives of other monovalent organic radicals can be obtained.

Rhenium carbonyl, $Re_2(CO)_{10}$. The most satisfactory method of preparation of rhenium carbonyl is the reduction of rhenium heptoxide by carbon monoxide at 250° and 200 atm:

$$Re_2O_7 + 17CO = Re_2(CO)_{10} + 7CO_2.$$

The reaction is quantitative. Potassium perrhenate, $KReO_4$, and rhenium hepta-sulphide, Re_2S_7, also react with carbon monoxide under pressure to yield the carbonyl, but less easily. Metallic rhenium does not react with carbon monoxide under any conditions to produce rhenium carbonyl.

Rhenium carbonyl forms colourless, monoclinic crystals. It sublimes at 140°, but has no smell. It decomposes above the m.p. 177°. It is chemically stable, and is unattacked by alkalis or by cold, concentrated mineral acids. It is decomposed by hot concentrated nitric acid or sulphuric acid. It reacts with the halogens to produce stable rhenium carbonyl halides, $Re(CO)_5X$ (p. 1110). It reacts with amines to form the amine derivatives $Re(CO)_3pyr_2$ and $Re(CO)_3phen$.

The molecular weight of rhenium carbonyl in solution indicates the dimeric formula $Re_2(CO)_{10}$. The infrared absorption spectrum shows that there are no bands in the neighbourhood of 1800 cm^{-1}; this is taken to indicate that there are no bridging carbonyl groups in the molecule (see p. 1089). X-ray diffraction analysis‡ shows that the molecule of rhenium carbonyl contains two directly linked metal atoms. The distance Re–Re is 3·02; the covalent bond length would be 2·56. Each rhenium atom has octahedral co-ordination; of the six bonds, five go to carbonyl groups, and

† *Ann. Reports*, 1957, 135.
‡ L. F. Dahl, E. Ishishi, and R. E. Rundle, *J. Chem. Phys.*, **26**(2), 1957, 1750.

one to the other metal atom. The two octahedral groups in the molecule are turned through 45° with respect to one another (Fig. 25.3). An orbital diagram consistent with the experimental evidence outlined above is drawn in Fig. 25.4.

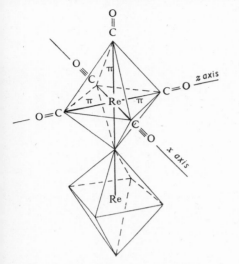

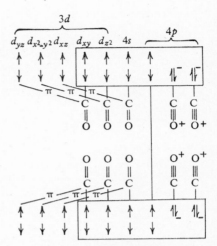

Fig. 25.3. Structure of the molecule $Re_2(CO)_{10}$. For clarity, bonds and CO groups are shown in one octahedron only.

Fig. 25.4. Orbital diagram of $Re_2(CO)_{10}$.

The results of molecular weight determinations, infrared spectrum observations, and X-ray diffraction experiments show that the structure of $Mn_2(CO)_{10}$ is similar to that of $Re_2(CO)_{10}$.

GROUP VIII. THE CARBONYLS OF THE METALS IRON, RUTHENIUM, AND OSMIUM

Iron pentacarbonyl, $Fe(CO)_5$. Iron pentacarbonyl is a liquid, stable to air. It is prepared (i) by the action of carbon monoxide at 200 atm pressure on iron heated to 200°, and (ii) by the action of carbon monoxide at 200 atm pressure and 200° on ferrous iodide in the presence of copper, which is present to act as an acceptor for the iodine. It is thought that the volatile iron carbonyl iodide is first formed

$$FeI_2 + 4CO = Fe(CO)_4I_2,$$

and that this reacts with copper thus:

$$CO + Fe(CO)_4I_2 + 2Cu = Fe(CO)_5 + Cu_2I_2.$$

Ferrous sulphide may be substituted for ferrous iodide, but ferrous chloride and bromide give very small yields.

The physical properties of iron pentacarbonyl are included in Table 25.5, and a summary of its chemical reactions is given in Chart 25.1. Iron pentacarbonyl is soluble in methyl alcohol, ether, acetone, and benzene. It is 1% dissociated at 130°, and dissociation is complete at 216°. If it is heated by radiation to 200–250° it yields finely divided iron, which is pure except for traces of carbon and oxygen. When it is irradiated with near ultraviolet light the reversible equilibrium

$$2Fe(CO)_5 \rightleftharpoons Fe_2(CO)_9 + CO$$

is moved to the right, and iron enneacarbonyl is formed.

1084

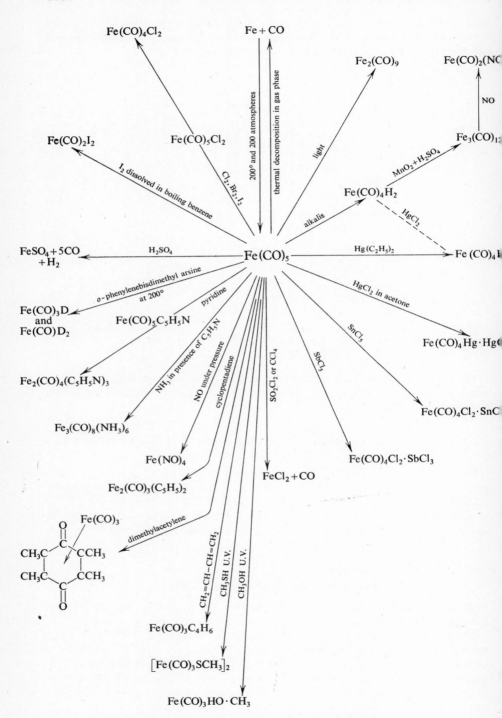

Chart 25.1. Summary of reactions of iron pentacarbonyl.

Some of the principal reactions of iron pentacarbonyl are briefly discussed in the following paragraphs.

Hydrolysis. $Fe(CO)_5$ is hydrolysed by water and acids, giving ferrous sulphate:

$$Fe(CO)_5 + H_2SO_4 = FeSO_4 + 5CO + H_2,$$

by strong bases, giving iron carbonyl hydride and the carbonate ion almost quantitatively:

$$Fe(CO)_5 + 2OH^- = Fe(CO)_4H_2 + CO_3^{2-},$$

and by ammonia, giving iron carbonyl hydride and carbamic acid:

$$Fe(CO)_5 + H_2O + NH_3 = Fe(CO)_4H_2 + NH_2COOH.$$

Reaction with halogens. $Fe(CO)_5$ reacts with the halogens in non-aqueous solvents to form unstable addition compounds of the type $Fe(CO)_5X_2$, which spontaneously lose CO to form the stable tetracarbonyl halides, $Fe(CO)_4X_2$. The velocities of these reactions follow the sequence $Cl < Br < I$; CN does not react.

Reactions with amines. $Fe(CO)_5$ reacts with ammonia and ethylene diamine, under ordinary conditions, to yield addition products such as $Fe(CO)_5NH_3$ and $Fe(CO)_5en$. In the presence of pyridine at $65°$, however, it reacts with ammonia to yield $Fe_3(CO)_8(NH_3)_6$, which is formulated $(Fe(NH_3)_6)(Fe_2(CO)_8)$. Pyridine reacts slowly with $Fe(CO)_5$ to give the pyrophoric compound $Fe_2(CO)_4pyr_3$.

Reaction with nitric oxide. Nitric oxide, under pressure below $45°$, reacts with $Fe(CO)_5$ to yield $Fe(NO)_4$, a black crystalline compound with a high dissociation pressure of NO. If NO is passed into $Fe(CO)_5$ dissolved in methyl alcohol a compound is obtained which is thought to have the composition $Fe(NO)(OH)OMe \cdot MeOH$.

Reactions with metallic and non-metallic halides. In its reactions with halides, $Fe(CO)_5$ behaves as a reducing agent; the iron atom becomes divalent and either CO or CO_2 is liberated. Chlorine is withdrawn from carbon tetrachloride and sulphonyl chloride, thus:

$$Fe(CO)_5 + 2CCl_4 = C_2Cl_6 + FeCl_2 + 5CO,$$
$$Fe(CO)_5 + SO_2Cl_2 = SO_2 + FeCl_2 + 5CO.$$

Stannic chloride and antimony pentachloride are reduced to stannous chloride and antimonious chloride:

$$Fe(CO)_5 + SnCl_4 = SnCl_2 + Fe(CO)_4Cl_2 + CO,$$
$$Fe(CO)_5 + SbCl_5 = SbCl_3 + Fe(CO)_4Cl_2 + CO,$$

and additive compounds are then formed between the iron carbonyl chloride and the tin or antimony chloride:

$$(CO)_4Fe \underset{\displaystyle Cl}{\overset{\displaystyle Cl}{\diagdown\!\!\diagup}} Sn \underset{\displaystyle Cl}{\overset{\displaystyle Cl}{\diagup\!\!\diagdown}} \qquad\qquad (CO)_4Fe \underset{\displaystyle Cl}{\overset{\displaystyle Cl}{\diagdown\!\!\diagup}} Sb\!\!-\!\!Cl \underset{\displaystyle Cl}{\overset{\displaystyle Cl}{\diagup\!\!\diagdown}}$$

Mercuric chloride reacts with $Fe(CO)_5$ in acetone to yield the mercury derivative of iron carbonyl hydride:

$$Fe(CO)_5 + 2HgCl_2 + H_2O = Fe(CO)_4Hg_2Cl_2 + 2HCl + CO_2.$$

Reaction with unsaturated hydrocarbons. Iron pentacarbonyl reacts with cyclopentadiene at $300°$ to yield the π-complex ferrocene (p. 1118). Iron pentacarbonyl reacts with dimethyl acetylene in sunlight to give another π-complex which is a derivative of quinone:

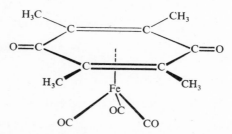

In this reaction a chain molecule (acetylene) has been converted to a ring; the process might be employed as a new method of organic synthesis.

Structure of iron pentacarbonyl. The vapour density and the freezing points of benzene solutions of iron pentacarbonyl show that the molecular formula is $Fe(CO)_5$. Electron diffraction and X-ray analysis show that the molecule has the form of a regular trigonal bipyramid.† The dipole moment, though finite, is small.‡ The molecule is diamagnetic. The infrared spectrum of $Fe(CO)_5$ in the gaseous and liquid states has been observed by Sheline and Pitzer, Table 25.6.

The distance Fe—C is 1·84.

On the assumption that the iron atom in $Fe(CO)_5$ is in the trigonal bipyramidal valence state, the orbital diagram constructed according to the procedure described on p. 163 is shown in Fig. 25.5:

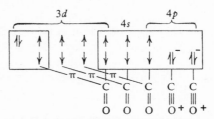

Fig. 25.5.   Orbital diagram of $Fe(CO)_5$.

The bond structure shown in perspective is drawn in Fig. 25.6.

The structure of iron pentacarbonyl represented in Fig. 25.6, suggests, by analogy with the structure of chromium hexacarbonyl, that two molecules of pyridine, or one molecule of *o*-phenanthroline, might replace the two co-ionically linked carbonyl groups in the molecule to yield derivatives of the type $Fe(CO)_3pyr_2$. Ammonia in the presence of pyridine, however, reacts with iron pentacarbonyl to yield $Fe_3(CO)_8(NH_3)_6$, a complex reaction which is typical; as Chart 25.1 shows, the co-ordination number of iron normally alters when iron pentacarbonyl reacts with other substances. This distinction implies that whereas the octahedral configuration is the only one possible for derivatives of the carbonyls of chromium, molybdenum, and

† Ewens and Lister, *Trans. Faraday Soc.*, 35(2), 1939, 681. Powell and Ewens, *J. Chem. Soc.*, 286, 1939.

‡ This does not necessarily indicate that the molecule has an asymmetrical configuration. Sutton and Coop, *J. Chem. Soc.*, 1938, 1269, have shown that the d.p.m. of a number of symmetrical complex compounds (for example, benzoquinone, 0·67, beryllium acetylacetonate, 1·8) may be explained by atom polarisation, set up by vibrations of opposed links, each of which possesses a large link moment, and whose vector sum in the equilibrium position is zero.

tungsten, the trigonal bipyramidal configuration of iron pentacarbonyl is unstable, and is liable to change either to a tetrahedral configuration as in iron carbonyl hydride or iron tetranitrosyl, or to an octahedral configuration as in compounds of the type $Fe(CO)_4Cl_2$.

Ruthenium pentacarbonyl, $Ru(CO)_5$, and osmium pentacarbonyl, $Os(CO)_5$. The chemistry of the pentacarbonyls of ruthenium and osmium is less well-known than

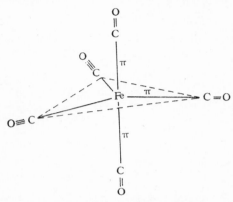

Fig. 25.6.   Bond structure of $Fe(CO)_5$.

that of the pentacarbonyl of iron. Table 25.5 includes the information available on the carbonyls of ruthenium and osmium. Ruthenium pentacarbonyl is made by the action of carbon monoxide on reduced ruthenium or on ruthenium tri-iodide in the presence of silver (for conditions, see Table 25.5). Metallic osmium, unlike iron and ruthenium, does not react with carbon monoxide, but osmium pentacarbonyl can be made by the action of carbon monoxide on osmium tri-iodide,† or on osmium tetroxide:

$$OsO_4 + 9CO = Os(CO)_5 + 4CO_2.$$

Ruthenium and osmium pentacarbonyls are volatile liquids at room temperature. They are photosensitive, like the corresponding iron compound, and yield enneacarbonyls under the influence of light. Ruthenium pentacarbonyl decomposes at 50° to yield the enneacarbonyl and another compound which is presumably the tetracarbonyl, $Ru_3(CO)_{12}$.

Iron enneacarbonyl, $Fe_2(CO)_9$. Iron enneacarbonyl, a crystalline substance, is made by the irradiation of iron pentacarbonyl with near ultraviolet light. Iron pentacarbonyl is dissolved in its own volume of glacial acetic acid, and the solution, cooled with water, is irradiated for six hours. Golden crystals of the enneacarbonyl are precipitated, and are filtered off.

Iron enneacarbonyl crystallises in the triclinic system. The crystals are described as yellow, orange red, or resembling flakes of gold. They are diamagnetic. Iron enneacarbonyl is slightly soluble in alcohol and acetone, more soluble in toluene and pyridine, and almost insoluble in water, ether, benzene, and many other organic compounds. It is non-volatile. When warmed to 50° it yields $Fe_3(CO)_{12}$. At 100° it decomposes to give iron, carbon monoxide, and some $Fe(CO)_5$ and some $Fe_3(CO)_{12}$. When pure it is unattacked by air. It reacts with nitric oxide at 75–100°. The reaction is complex. $Fe(CO)_2(NO)_2$ is formed, together with $Fe(CO)_5$ and $Fe_3(CO)_{12}$. After a time decomposition sets in with violence. In acetone or benzene solution at 80° iron

† The ease of formation of the carbonyl from the halides is $Cl < Br < I$.

Table 25.5. *The Preparations and Comparable Properties and Reactions of the Pentacarbonyls of Iron, Ruthenium, Osmium*

	Iron	Ruthenium	Osmium
Preparation			
(i) Direct synthesis	(i) Reduced iron reacts with CO at 200° and 200 atm	(i) Reduced ruthenium reacts with CO at 200° and 200 atm	(i) No reaction
(ii) CO on the metallic halide	(ii) FeI_2 (but not $FeBr_2$ or $FeCl_2$) reacts in the presence of Cu	(ii) RuI_3 mixed with finely divided silver, reacts, best at 170° and 450 atm	(ii) OsI_3 reacts at 120° and 200 atm in presence of Cu (iii) OsO_4 reacts with CO at 100° and 50 atm
Properties			
(i) State	(i) Amber-coloured viscid liquid	(i) Colourless liquid	(i) Colourless liquid
(ii) m.p.	(ii) $-20°$	(ii) $-21°$, white crystals	(ii) $-15°$
(iii) b.p.	(iii) 103°		
(iv) v.p. at 18°	(iv) 28·2 mm	(iv) 50 mm	
(v) Decomposition temperature	(v) Decomposition begins at 130°	(v) Decomposes at 50° to give $Ru_2(CO)_9$ and $Ru_3(CO)_{12}$	
(vi) Solubility in water	(vi) (Reacts)	(vi) Insoluble	
(vii) Solubility in organic solvents	(vii) Dissolves in alcohol and in acetic acid	(vii) Dissolves readily in alcohol, chloroform and benzene	
Reactions			
(i) Light	(i) Near ultraviolet radiation yields $Fe_2(CO)_9$	(i) Near ultraviolet radiation yields $Ru_2(CO)_9$	
(ii) Heat	(ii) Heated in vapour phase to 200° yields iron and CO	(ii) Heated to 50° yields a mixture of $Ru_2(CO)_9$ and $Ru_3(CO)_{12}$	
(iii) Hydrolysis	(iii) Strong or weak bases yield $Fe(CO)_4H_2$ by different routes	(iii) Dissolves in KOH to form a strongly reducing solution which presumably contains $Ru(CO)_4H_2$	
(iv) Halogens	(iv) First gives $Fe(CO)_5X_2$, and then spontaneously $Fe(CO)_4X_2$	(iv) Evolves CO, and gives such compounds as $Ru(CO)Br$	

enneacarbonyl reacts with *o*-phenanthroline to give [Fe phen₃][Fe(CO)₈]; in pyridine at higher temperatures the product is [Fe phen₃][Fe₄(CO)₁₃]. Iron enneacarbonyl reacts with acetylene derivatives.†

The molecular formula of iron enneacarbonyl, $Fe_2(CO)_9$, is inferred from the X-ray diffraction‡ and electron diffraction§ experiments which have shown that it possesses the symmetrical structure shown in Fig. 25.7(a).

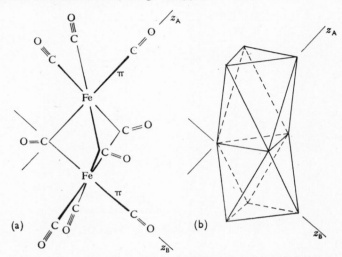

Fig. 25.7. (a) Bond structure of $Fe_2(CO)_9$. (b) Geometrical configuration of $Fe_2(CO)_9$.

Infrared absorption spectra have been recorded for iron enneacarbonyl and for cobalt octacarbonyl. The positions of the bands are given in Table 25.6.

Table 25.6. *Absorption Bands in the Infrared Spectra of Carbonyls, cm⁻¹*

Fe₂(CO)₉‖	Co₂(CO)₈	Fe(CO)₅	Co(CO)₄H	C₂(C₆H₅)₂Co₂(CO)₆
597		472		
662		620		
		639		
1828	1858			
2034	2025	1994		
	2043	2025		2025
		2028		
		2045		2050
2080	2070	2070		
				2090
				3096

It is assumed that the bands near 1800 are characteristic of a carbonyl group joined

† Powell and Ewens, *J. Chem. Soc.*, 1939, 286.
‡ Ewens and Lister, *Trans. Faraday Soc.*, **35**, 1939, 681.
§ W. Hübel et al., *J. Inorg. Nucl. Chem.*, 9, 1959, 204.
‖ R. K. Sheline and K. S. Pitzer, *J. Amer. Chem. Soc.*, **72**, 1950, 1107.

to two different atoms† (1700 is a band characteristic of the carbonyl group in a ketone), and that those near 2050 are characteristic of a carbonyl group linked to one metal atom only. The orbital diagram, Fig. 25.8, is drawn on the assumption that the iron atoms are in the octahedral valence state.

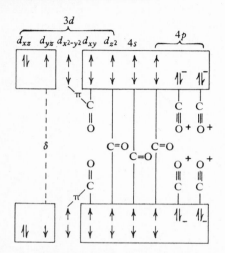

Fig. 25.8. Orbital diagram for $Fe_2(CO)_9$.

Such a diagram accounts for the three bridging carbonyl groups, and for six other carbonyl groups, each of which is attached only to one or other of the two iron atoms. Two of these six carbonyl groups (one on each iron atom) are linked to the iron atom by πd bonds. Since iron enneacarbonyl is diamagnetic, all electrons in the molecule must be paired. Of the five $3d$ orbitals in each iron atom, three are assigned (Fig. 25.8) to bonds with carbonyl groups, and one is occupied by a lone pair. The fifth is represented as forming a δ bond (p. 1091) with the corresponding d orbital of the other iron atom. This procedure is justified by the existence of at least four compounds other than iron enneacarbonyl (Table 25.7) for which paramagnetic properties would be deduced from their bond structures, but which are either diamagnetic, or have smaller molecular paramagnetic moments than would be expected. In all these cases the shape of the molecule or ion is such that two metallic atoms, each possessing one unpaired electron, are brought so close together that the metal-to-metal distance is of the order of twice the covalent radius of the metal.

The octahedral hybridisation which accounts for the bond structure is described on p. 154, and the direction of the four σ bonds in the equatorial plane (XY plane) are shown in Fig. 5.9 (p. 155). The $d_{x^2-y^2}$ orbital forms a πd bond directed along any one of these σ bonds (Fig. 5.12). The δ bond between the two iron atoms is formed by a hybrid orbital which results from a linear combination of the d_{xz} and d_{yz} orbitals (p. 161). The wave functions of the two possible hybrid orbitals are:

$$\psi_1 = \frac{1}{\sqrt{2}}\psi_{d_{xz}} + \frac{1}{\sqrt{2}}\psi_{d_{yz}}$$

$$\psi_2 = \frac{1}{\sqrt{2}}\psi_{d_{xz}} - \frac{1}{\sqrt{2}}\psi_{d_{yz}};$$

† Bands near 1800, however, are found in the compounds $Cr(CO)_3L_3$ (Table 25.4) in which there are no bridging carbonyl groups (see the paper by E. W. Abel and others, footnote p. 1081).

Table 25.7.   *Compounds in which δ Bonds may be present*†

Compound	Metal-to-metal distance	2 × covalent radius of the metal atom	Notes
$Cu_4I_4(As(C_2H_5)_3)_4$	2·6	2·70	
![Fe2 phen complex structure]	2·7	2·46	Calculated moment 1·73, observed 1·4
$(Tl_2Cl_9)^{3-}$	3·6	3·4	
$(W_2Cl_9)^{3-}$	2·46	2·74	Diamagnetic
$Fe_2(CO)_9$	2·46	2·46	

The structure in the second row is:

$$\left[\begin{array}{ccc} & H & \\ & | & \\ & O & \\ phen & \diagup \ \diagdown & phen \\ \ \ \ \ \ \diagup Fe \ \ \ Fe \diagdown \ \ \ \ \ \\ phen & \diagdown \ \diagup & phen \\ & O & \\ & | & \\ & H & \end{array} \right] Cl_4$$

† A δ bond is formed by the *lateral overlap* of two *d* orbitals originally in parallel planes.

each hybrid contains half the charge cloud from each of the atomic orbitals of which it is composed. ψ_1 is formed by the combination of half the positive symmetry region of one atomic wave function with one half the positive symmetry region of the other, to make one lobe of positive symmetry for the hybrid; similarly for the negative symmetry.‡ ψ_2 is formed by combining the whole region of positive symmetry of one atomic orbital with the whole region of negative symmetry of the other atomic orbital. ψ_1 forms a *d* orbital in a vertical plane designated by $\theta = 0°$ and $\phi = 45°$; ψ_2 forms a *d* orbital in a plane designated by $\theta = 45°$ and $\phi = 45°$.

The hybrid orbital used for the *d-d* bond between the iron atoms is ψ_2. This orbital lies parallel to the plane of one of the faces of the octahedron. This face is common to both octahedra (Fig. 25.7). ψ_2 thus overlaps laterally with a similar orbital from the other iron atom, and a δ bond is formed with its axis at right angles to the common face. ψ_1 is occupied by a lone pair (Fig. 25.8).

The orbital diagram of iron enneacarbonyl leads to a bond structure (Fig. 25.7(a)) based on a configuration of two octahedra with one face in common (Fig. 25.7(b)). The axis of the δ bond between the two iron atoms passes through the centre of the common face. The distance C—O in the bridge carbonyl groups is 1·3.

Ruthenium enneacarbonyl, $Ru_2(CO)_9$, and osmium enneacarbonyl, $Os_2(CO)_9$. Ruthenium enneacarbonyl is made by the irradiation of ruthenium pentacarbonyl. It can also be made by heating a solution of ruthenium pentacarbonyl in benzene to 50°. Neither of these methods is available for making osmium enneacarbonyl, which is obtained by the action of carbon monoxide on osmium tri-iodide in the presence of copper.

The two enneacarbonyls are yellow crystalline substances. The volatility, solubility in inert solvents, and stability towards heat, increase with increasing molecular weight. Ruthenium enneacarbonyl reacts with iodine to yield $Ru(CO)_2I_2$, and with nitric oxide to give the pentanitrosyl compound $Ru(NO)_5$.

‡ The reader is recommended to make a three-dimensional model of the d_{xy} and d_{yz} atomic orbitals. The positive symmetry region of each atomic orbital is imagined to be divided into two halves by a plane which contains the atomic nucleus and the axis of the *whole* of the positive symmetry region; similarly for the region of negative symmetry.

Iron dodecacarbonyl, $Fe_3(CO)_{12}$. Iron dodecacarbonyl is produced:

(i) By the disproportionation of $Fe_2(CO)_9$. A toluene solution is heated at 70°. On cooling, green crystals of $Fe_3(CO)_{12}$ separate from the solution:

$$3Fe_2(CO)_9 = 3Fe(CO)_5 + Fe_3(CO)_{12}.$$

(ii) By the oxidation of iron carbonyl hydride with hydrogen peroxide or manganese dioxide:

$$3Fe(CO)_4H_2 + 3H_2O_2 = Fe_3(CO)_{12} + 6H_2O.$$
$$3Fe(CO)_4H_2 + 3MnO_2 + 3H_2SO_4 = Fe_3(CO)_{12} + 3MnSO_4 + 6H_2O.$$

(iii) By the action of acids on iron carbonyl hydride.

Iron dodecacarbonyl forms green monoclinic crystals, soluble in organic solvents such as toluene, ligroin, alcohol, ether, and pyridine, and also in iron pentacarbonyl. It is volatile in steam without decomposition, but if heated alone above 100° it breaks down into metallic iron and carbon monoxide. At 85° it reacts with nitric oxide to yield $Fe(CO)_2(NO)_2$.

With pyridine, iron dodecacarbonyl undergoes the reaction:

$$2Fe_3(CO)_{12} + 3C_5H_5N = Fe_3(CO)_9pyr_3\dagger + 3Fe(CO)_5,$$

and with alcohol:

$$2Fe_3(CO)_{12} + 3CH_3OH = Fe_3(CO)_9(CH_3OH)_3\dagger + 3Fe(CO)_5.$$

Thioethers react with it on heating to give the dimeric complexes $[Fe(CO)_3SR_2]_2$; they do not react with iron pentacarbonyl. Iron dodecacarbonyl reacts with acetylene derivatives.‡

The molecular weight of iron dodecacarbonyl in solution in iron pentacarbonyl accords with the formula $Fe_3(CO)_{12}$. The crystals are diamagnetic; magnetic susceptibility at 15° is -0.07×10^{-6} cgs units.

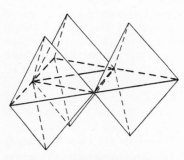

Fig. 25.9. Three trigonal bipyramids arranged as in the molecule $Fe_3(CO)_{12}$. An iron atom is at the centre of each pyramid and a CO group at each apex.

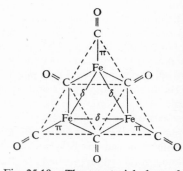

Fig. 25.10. The equatorial plane of the molecule $Fe_3(CO)_{12}$.

The configuration of the $Fe_3(CO)_{12}$ molecule has been determined by X-ray analysis.§ The three iron atoms are situated at the apices of a triangle. Each iron atom is bonded to three non-bridging carbonyl groups and to two bridging carbonyl groups. The distance Fe—Fe is 2·80, and indicates that there are metal to metal links.

† Hieber formulates these compounds as complex ferrous salts of iron carbonyl hydride, e.g. $[Fe(CH_3OH)_n][Fe_3(CO)_n]$, *Ann. Reports*, 1957, 125.
‡ W. Hübel et al., *J. Inorg. Nucl. Chem.*, **9**, 1959, 204.
§ Dahl and Rundle, *J. Chem. Phys.*, **26**(2), 1957, 1752.

The structure has been explained in terms of the molecular orbital theory.† It may be explained in terms of the valence bond theory as follows. Each iron atom is hybridised trigonal-bipyramidally ($d_{z^2}sp^3$). The three trigonal bipyramids (Fig. 25.9) are arranged so that the carbonyl groups (the bridging carbonyl groups) at two of the equatorial apices of each bipyramid are held in common by two bipyramids (Fig. 25.10). The orbital configuration of each iron atom is shown in Fig. 25.11, from which it is seen that the d_{yz} and d_{xz} orbitals are available to form Fe—Fe bonds.

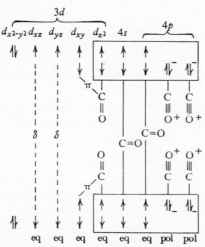

Fig. 25.11.   Orbital diagram for $Fe_3(CO)_{12}$. The equatorial bonds are indicated as "eq" and the polar bonds as "pol." The diagram is drawn as if only two iron atoms are concerned; the modification necessary for it to refer to a ring of three iron atoms is easily imagined.

The evidence for the existence of $Ru_3(CO)_{12}$ is not strong; no compound $Os_3(CO)_{12}$ has been reported.

GROUP IX. THE CARBONYLS OF THE METALS COBALT, RHODIUM, AND IRIDIUM

Cobalt octacarbonyl, $Co_2(CO)_8$. Cobalt octacarbonyl (sometimes called "cobalt tetracarbonyl") exists as orange transparent crystals, m.p. 51°. They are almost non-volatile; the vapour pressure at 15° is 0·072 mm. Cobalt octacarbonyl is made by four methods.

(1) *By the direct action of carbon monoxide on metallic cobalt.* Reaction between carbon monoxide and reduced metallic cobalt occurs most rapidly at 220° and 250 atm; no reaction at all takes place if the carbon monoxide is at 1 atm pressure.

(2) *By the action of carbon monoxide on certain compounds of cobalt in the presence of metallic copper.* Dry carbon monoxide‡ at 200° and 200 atm in the presence of metallic copper§ reacts with certain binary compounds of cobalt to yield the carbonyl.

---

† D. A. Brown, *J. Inorg. Nucl. Chem.*, **5**, 1958, 289.
‡ If moisture is present, $Co(CO)_4H$ is formed.
§ If cadmium or zinc are used as halogen acceptors, quantitative yields of $Co_2(CO)_8Cd$ and $Co_2(CO)_8Zn$ are obtained.

Table 25.8.   *Relation between the Yield of $Co_2(CO)_8$ and the Properties of the Cobalt Compound used in its Synthesis*

Compound	CoS	CoI_2	$CoBr_2$	$CoCl_2$	CoF_2	CoO
Heat of formation of compound in kcal	20	about 25	55	77	about 150	58
Lattice of compound	NiAs	CdI_2	CdI_2	$CdCl_2$	Rutile	Rocksalt
Relative amounts of $Co_2(CO)_8$ formed in 15 hours under the same conditions	100	100	9	3·5	0	0

Table 25.8 shows that cobalt compounds of low thermal stability, forming non-ionic lattices, are the most efficient. After the reaction the sulphur or halogen is present in combination with cuprous copper for example:

$$2CoS + 8CO + 4Cu = Co_2(CO)_8 + 2Cu_2S.$$

The reaction continues even if a screen is interposed between the cobalt compounds and the copper, thus showing that the transference of the sulphur or halogen from the cobalt to the copper must be due to the formation of a volatile intermediate, such as $Co(CO)I_2$. The variation in the efficiency of the reactions for the compounds mentioned in Table 25.8 may be due to the variation in the stabilities of the volatile intermediates which may be formed from them.

(3) *By the action of an acid on a solution of cobalt carbonyl hydride.* Hydrogen is evolved and $Co_2(CO)_8$ remains.

(4) *By the thermal decomposition of cobalt carbonyl hydride.* Cobalt carbonyl hydride is cooled to $-79°$ in a closed vessel. It is allowed to warm up to about $-30°$. Some of it decomposes. The vessel is recooled, and the hydrogen which has been liberated is pumped off. This process is repeated until all the cobalt carbonyl hydride is decomposed.

Cobalt octacarbonyl is insoluble in water, but is soluble to some extent in alcohol, ether, carbon disulphide, $Ni(CO)_4$, and in naphtha. $Co_2(CO)_8$, either pure or in solution, decomposes on standing or at temperatures above $51°$ to yield black crystals of the tricarbonyl $[Co(CO)_3]_n$. At $60°$, these crystals themselves decompose to give CO and metallic cobalt. The chemical reactions of cobalt octacarbonyl are summarised in Chart 25.2.

Hydrolysis and reactions with acids and bases. By exposure to air $Co_2(CO)_8$ is converted to a deep violet basic carbonate of cobalt. It is only very slowly attacked by non-oxidising acids, such as hydrochloric or sulphuric. It is hydrolysed by bases in two ways.

Strong bases, such as baryta, convert it to a mixture of cobalt carbonyl hydride and cobalt tricarbonyl:

$$3Co_2(CO)_8 + 4OH^- = 4Co(CO)_4H + 2CO_3^{2-} + 2Co(CO)_3.$$

Weak bases, such as ammonia, convert it to a mixture of cobalt carbonyl hydride and cobaltous hydroxide:

$$3Co_2(CO)_8 + 4H_2O = 4Co(CO)_4H + 2Co(OH)_2 + 8CO.$$

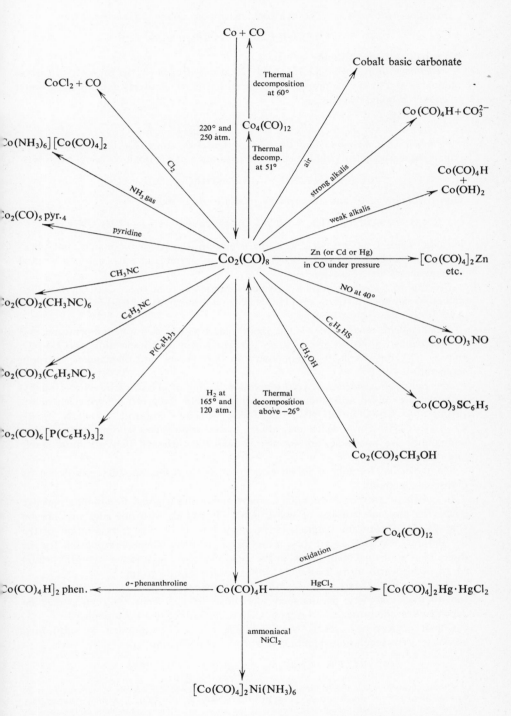

Chart 25.2. Summary of reactions of cobalt octacarbonyl and cobalt carbonyl hydride.

Reaction with halogens. The halogens decompose cobalt octacarbonyl thus:

$$Co_2(CO)_8 + 2Br_2 = 2CoBr_2 + 8CO.$$

No cobalt carbonyl bromide is formed.

Reaction with hydrogen. At 165° and 120 atm hydrogen (in the presence of carbon monoxide at 150 atm to prevent decomposition) partly converts cobalt octacarbonyl to cobalt carbonyl hydride:

$$Co_2(CO)_8 + H_2 = 2Co(CO)_4H.$$

Reaction with ammonia and the amines. Gaseous ammonia reacts directly with cobalt octacarbonyl to yield the cobalt hexammine salt of cobalt carbonyl hydride:

$$3Co_2(CO)_8 + 12NH_3 = 2[Co6NH_3][Co(CO)_4]_2 + 8CO.$$

Dimethylamine at 0° and atmospheric pressure reacts thus:

$$3Co_2(CO)_8 + 20NH(CH_3)_2 = 2[Co(CO)_4]_2[Co(NH(CH_3)_2)_6] + 8HCON(CH_3)_2.$$

Pyridine yields $Co_2(CO)_5pyr_4$, with the evolution of carbon monoxide, and phenanthroline yields [Co phen$_3$] [Co(CO)$_4$]$_2$ which is insoluble in water and can be used for gravimetric determination.

Reaction with alcohols, acetone, and thiols. Methyl alcohol yields $Co(CO)_5 \cdot CH_3OH$, and ethyl alcohol $Co_2(CO)_5 \cdot 1\frac{1}{2}C_2H_5OH$. Phenyl thiol yields $Co(CO)_3SC_6H_5$. Acetone gives $[Co(COMe_2)_6][Co(CO)_4]_2$.

Reaction with nitric oxide. Nitric oxide reacts slowly at room temperature, and instantaneously at 40° to give a cherry red liquid with the composition $Co(CO)_3NO$, m.p. $-1 \cdot 1°$, b.p. $78 \cdot 6°$. It is monomeric in the vapour, and diamagnetic at room temperature.

Reaction with isonitriles. If cold ethereal solutions of cobalt carbonyl and methyl isonitrile are mixed and allowed to warm to room temperature, brownish-yellow prisms of $Co_2(CO)_2(CH_3NC)_6$ crystallise. Phenyl isonitrile similarly yields $Co_2(CO)_3(C_6H_5NC)_5$,† which crystallises as brownish-yellow rhombohedra. These compounds are non-ionic, and compared with the carbonyl, they are more stable and deeper in colour.

The molecular formula of cobalt octacarbonyl, $Co_2(CO)_8$ has been established by cryoscopic methods.

In cobalt octacarbonyl the cobalt atoms are in the trigonal bipyramidal valence state. The molecule consists of two trigonal bipyramids with one edge in common (Fig. 25.12). The orbital diagram is shown in Fig. 25.13. The hybridisation of the d_{xz} and d_{yz} orbitals gives a hybrid d orbital (ψ_2, p. 1090) which is responsible for the direct linking of the cobalt atoms in the molecule, and also another hybrid d orbital (ψ_1, p. 1090) which forms a πd bond with a polar carbonyl group.

The action of $P(C_6H_5)_3$ in giving a dimeric diamagnetic derivative (in contradistinction to the monomeric paramagnetic derivative formed from $Mn_2(Co)_{10}$) may be dependent on the presence of bridging CO groups in the cobalt compound.

Cobalt octacarbonyl reacts with acetylene and with a number of substituted acetylenes. The reaction is quantitative at room temperature:

$$RC\!:\!CR + Co_2(CO)_8 = C_2RRCo_2(CO)_6 + 2CO.$$

† Some authorities give this compound the composition $Co_2(CO)_4(C_6H_5NC)_5$, and regard it as an ionic derivative of cobalt carbonyl hydride, $[(C_6H_5NC)_5Co^+][Co(CO)_4^-]$. A similar uncertainty applies to the diamagnetic compound formed by the action of triphenyl phosphine on cobalt octacarbonyl. Some authors formulate it as $Co_2(CO)_6(P(C_6H_5)_3)_2$, and others as $[(P(C_6H_5)_3)_2Co(CO)_3^+]$ $[Co(CO)_4^-]$, *Ann. Reports*, 1957, 125 *et seq.*

The derivative formed from diphenyl acetylene forms deep purple crystals, m.p. 110°, which sublime at 90° under 1 mm pressure. It is diamagnetic, and monomeric in cyclohexane. The infrared spectra of three of these acetylene derivatives have been

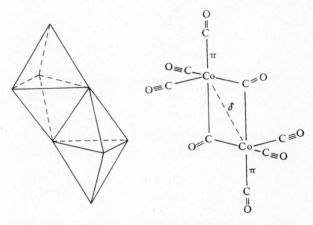

Fig. 25.12. Configuration and bond structure of the molecule $Co_2(CO)_8$.

examined† (Table 25.6, p. 1089). There is no band at 1858 cm⁻¹, corresponding to the bridge carbonyl groups in cobalt carbonyl. The band at 3096 cm⁻¹ is present only

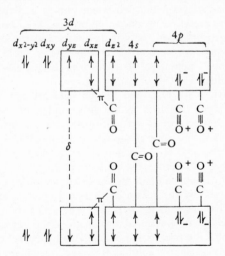

Fig. 25.13. Orbital diagram of $Co_2(CO)_8$.

in derivatives formed from acetylene itself, and it is said to be characteristic of a C—H bond in an ethylenic or aromatic molecule.

All the above observations can be correlated with an orbital structure derived by

† R. A. Friedel, Greenfeld, Markby, H. W. Steinberg, I. Wender, Wotiz, *J. Amer. Chem. Soc.*, **76**, 1954, 1457.

the replacement of the two bridge carbonyl groups in cobalt octacarbonyl by an acetylene residue,† thus:

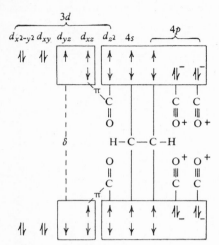

Fig. 25.14.   Orbital diagram for $C_2H_2Co_2(CO)_6$.

The orbital structure shown in Fig. 25.14 does not account for the absorption band at 3096 cm^{-1} which is ascribed to the presence of an ethylenic bond. In a few cases an orbital structure given in this chapter represents only one of a number of canonical forms. In the case of the structure in Fig. 25.14 another canonical form is obtained by supposing the δ bond between the two cobalt atoms and the bond between the two carbon atoms in the acetylene residue to be broken. If πd bonds are now formed between the released d orbitals on the cobalt atoms and the carbon atoms in the acetylene residue, an ethylenic structure is obtained (Fig. 25.15). Comparison with Fig. 25.13 shows that the orientation of the d orbitals concerned is correct for the formation of the πd bonds.

Rhodium octacarbonyl, Rh$_2$(CO)$_8$, and iridium octacarbonyl, Ir$_2$(CO)$_8$. Rhodium octacarbonyl is most readily prepared by the direct union of metallic rhodium and carbon monoxide at high pressures. It is also formed (along with the tricarbonyl) when rhodium tri-iodide reacts with carbon monoxide at a temperature below 100°, and at high pressures, in the presence of a halogen acceptor, such as metallic copper.‡ It exists as orange crystals which decompose at the m.p. 76°.

Iridium octacarbonyl cannot be made by the direct action of carbon monoxide on the metal. It may be made by the action of carbon monoxide at 200° and 200 atm on one of the complex halides K_2IrBr_6 or K_2IrI_6. The octacarbonyl may be separated from the tricarbonyl, either by fractional sublimation (the octacarbonyl sublimes in carbon monoxide at 160°, the tricarbonyl at 210°) or by extraction with chloroform, in which the octacarbonyl is slightly soluble. It is a yellow-green crystalline substance. It is readily converted into the tricarbonyl by the action of heat, alkalis, or acids.

The dodecacarbonyls of cobalt, rhodium, and iridium. The dodecacarbonyls of these metals have the general formula $M_4(CO)_{12}$. Cobalt dodecacarbonyl is made by warming

† The orbital structure in Fig. 25.14 was privately proposed by one of the authors (P.J.D.) in 1955. A very careful X-ray analysis of the compound published by W. G. Sly in 1959 (*J. Amer. Chem. Soc.*, 1959, **81**, 18) indicates a configuration of the molecule which corresponds to this orbital structure.

‡ Zinc and cadmium may also be used as acceptor metals since, unlike cobalt, rhodium does not form mixed carbonyls.

cobalt octacarbonyl to 60°, or by oxidising cobalt carbonyl hydride below −26°. Rhodium dodecacarbonyl is made by treating rhodium trichloride with carbon monoxide under pressure below 100° in the presence of copper. Iridium dodeca-carbonyl is made similarly from iridium tri-iodide. The three dodecacarbonyls are highly coloured crystalline substances; the cobalt compound is black, the rhodium compound red, and the iridium compound orange-yellow. They all decompose on

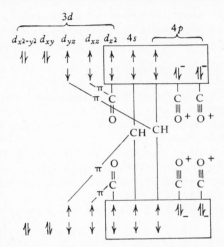

Fig. 25.15. Ethylenic structure of $C_2H_2Co_2(CO)_6$. Note that the d_{yz} and d_{xz} orbitals are no longer hybridised.

slight heating, the cobalt compound at 60°, the rhodium compound at 150°, and the iridium compound at 210°. They are chemically inert. Cobalt dodecacarbonyl does not react with nitric oxide (compare the behaviour of $Fe_3(CO)_{12}$, p.1092). The molecular weight of $Co_4(CO)_{12}$ has been determined by freezing point observations on its solution in iron pentacarbonyl.

GROUP X.† NICKEL TETRACARBONYL, Ni(CO)₄

Nickel carbonyl is a colourless, volatile liquid. It can be made by four principal methods.

By direct synthesis. Nickel carbonyl is formed when carbon monoxide at atmospheric pressure is passed over reduced nickel at 30–50°. The action is accelerated by raising the pressure to 100–200 atm and the temperature to 250°. The reduced nickel is best made by the reduction of the oxalate or hydroxide by carbon monoxide below 300°. Its reactivity is much diminished if it is made by reduction of the oxide with hydrogen, or if it is subsequently heated to 350°.

By the action of carbon monoxide on nickel iodide. If nickel iodide is heated with carbon monoxide under pressure in the presence of, but not in direct contact with, a halogen accepting metal, quantitative conversion to the carbonyl occurs. It is conjectured that a volatile nickel carbonyl halide is responsible for conveying the halogen from the nickel to the halogen accepting metal.

By the action of carbon monoxide on the salt of iron carbonyl hydride and the nickel hexammine cation. This reaction is described under the preparation of iron carbonyl hydride (p. 1102).

† No carbonyls of palladium or platinum are known.

By the disproportionation of univalent nickel. When potassium nickel cyanide, $K_2[Ni(CN)_4]$, is reduced with potassium amalgam a red solution is obtained (Belucci and Corelli, 1913). The compound $K_2[Ni(CN)_3]$ may be isolated from this solution.† It absorbs carbon monoxide at $-9°$, probably forming $K_2[Ni(CN)_3CO]$. When the solution of this compound is treated with acid, the reaction occurs:

$$4K_2[Ni(CN)_3CO] + 2HCl = Ni(CO)_4 + 3K_2[Ni(CN)_4] + 2KCl + H_2.$$

Nickel carbonyl is formed when carbon monoxide is passed into an alkaline suspension of nickel cyanide or of nickel sulphide. The reaction for the sulphide is:

$$NiS + 4CO = Ni(CO)_4 + S; \quad S + CO + 4OH^- = S^{2-} + CO_3^{2-} + 2H_2O.$$

Nickel carbonyl is a colourless liquid, m.p. $-23°$, b.p. $43°$. It is strongly diamagnetic; the magnetic susceptibility is $-3 \cdot 131 \times 10^{10}$ cgs units. Nickel carbonyl is insoluble in water, but is soluble in organic solvents. It is extremely lethal. Its chemistry is outlined in the following paragraphs.

Thermal decomposition. Nickel carbonyl is 6% dissociated at $100°$, but is more or less thermally stable up to 180–$200°$.

Action with halogens. Gaseous chlorine reacts with nickel carbonyl to yield nickel chloride and nickel carbonyl chloride. Bromine reacts in a corresponding manner. In organic solvents all three halogens yield the nickel halide and carbon monoxide.

Action with acids. Gaseous hydrogen chloride reacts readily with nickel carbonyl; gaseous hydrogen bromide and iodide have no action. Aqueous sulphuric acid reacts thus:

$$Ni(CO)_4 + H_2SO_4 = NiSO_4 + H_2 + 4CO.$$

Concentrated sulphuric acid reacts with detonation. Aqueous halogen acids have no action.

Action with amines. o-Phenanthroline reacts with an alcoholic solution of $Ni(CO)_4$ to give the very stable ruby-red compound $Ni(CO)_2 \cdot phen$. The action of pyridine is somewhat dubiously described; the principal product reported is $Ni_2(CO)_3pyr_2$.

Action with nitric oxide. Slightly moist NO attacks nickel carbonyl in the gaseous state or in solution in chloroform to give a compound of intense blue colour, $Ni(NO)OH$. In alcoholic solution the compounds $Ni(NO)OH \cdot EtOH$ or $Ni(NO)OH \cdot 2MeOH$ are produced, also blue. All dissolve in water or alcohol, giving alkaline solutions, reduce $AgNO_3$ to metallic silver, and on acidification show by their reducing power the presence of univalent nickel:

$$2Ni(NO)OH + 4HCl = 2NiCl_2 + 3H_2O + N_2O.$$

Nickel carbonyl reacts with sulphur and with hydrogen sulphide, but thiols are said not to attack it. It does not react with mercuric chloride.

Structure of nickel carbonyl. The vapour density of nickel carbonyl, and the freezing point of its solution in benzene, indicate the molecular formula $Ni(CO)_4$. Electron diffraction experiments show that the configuration is tetrahedral. The Ni—C—O group is linear. The distance Ni—C is $1 \cdot 82$, and C—O is $1 \cdot 15$. The dipole moment is $0 \cdot 3 \times 10^{-18}$. Work has been done on the Raman spectrum, which is said to show that the oxygen atom is triply bound to the carbon atom in the CO groups.

The nickel atom in the carbonyl must be tetrahedrally hybridised, and the orbital structure is shown in Fig. 25.16. The bond structure is shown in Fig. 25.17.

The chemistry of nickel carbonyl supports such a structure. o-Phenanthroline reacts with an alcoholic solution of the carbonyl to give a very stable ruby-red compound, $Ni(CO)_2phen$, and o-phenylene bisdimethylarsine replaces two carbonyl

† Treatment of this compound with acid precipitates the orange NiCN.

groups only to give Ni(CO)$_2$(*diarsine*). These reactions are readily explained as the replacement of the two C≡O groups by one molecule of phenanthroline or diarsine.

P(CF$_3$)$_3$ reacts with nickel carbonyl at room temperature to yield (CF$_3$)$_3$PNi(CO)$_3$ and [(CF$_3$)$_3$P]$_2$Ni(CO)$_2$, but the reaction proceeds no further.† Attempts to replace three carbonyl groups by treating nickel carbonyl with excess of P(CF$_3$)$_3$ at 100° have failed. Methyl isonitrile and phenyl isonitrile react with nickel carbonyl in ethereal solution to yield yellow crystals of Ni(CO)(CH$_3$NC)$_3$ and Ni(C$_6$H$_5$NC)$_4$. These compounds are non-ionic and more stable than nickel carbonyl. Their existence does not

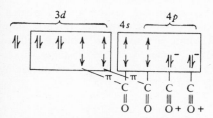

Fig. 25.16. Orbital diagram for Ni(CO)$_4$.

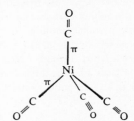

Fig. 25.17. Bond structure of Ni(CO)$_4$.

help to elucidate the structure of nickel carbonyl, because the isocyanide group is a resonance structure of canonical forms which correspond to both the forms I and II of the carbonyl group (p. 1081), and hence, so far as the combination of orbitals is concerned, there is no reason why the group X—N—C should not partially or completely replace all the carbonyl groups in any metallic carbonyl.

THE CARBONYL HYDRIDES

Elements in Groups VI T, VII T, VIII, IX, and X form carbonyl hydrides. Table 25.9 gives the formulae and certain properties of these compounds.

Table 25.9. *The Carbonyl Hydrides*

Group	Formula	Properties
VI T	Cr(CO)$_5$H$_2$	White crystalline, volatile, unstable
VII T	Mn(CO)$_5$H	m.p. −20°. Sublimes in vacuo below m.p.
	Re(CO)$_5$H	
VIII	Fe(CO)$_4$H$_2$	m.p. −70°. Pale yellow liquid, stable only below −10° Tetrahedral molecular configuration
XI	Co(CO)$_4$H	m.p. about −30°. Yellow liquid. b.p. (extr.) 10° Tetrahedral molecular configuration
	Rh(CO)$_4$H	m.p. −10°. Yellow liquid
	Ir(CO)$_4$H	
X	[Ni(CO)$_3$H]$_2$	

The hydrogen atoms in the carbonyl hydrides are weakly acidic. The carbonyl hydrides give rise to salts of the alkali metals, and to more stable salts with bulky cations, such as the hexammines of the transition metals. The hydrogen atoms can be replaced by methyl groups or by halogen atoms. Nevertheless, the bonds to the hydrogen atoms are unlikely to be ionic because of the high volatility of the carbonyl hydrides. There is evidence that in iron carbonyl hydride (p. 1102) and in cobalt carbonyl

† A. B. Burg and W. Mahler, *J. Amer. Chem. Soc.*, **80**, 1958, 2334.

hydride (p. 1106) the hydrogen atoms lie within the atomic orbital systems of the metal atoms. The orbital diagrams in Figs. 25.18, 25.20, and 25.21 are in accord with the structural and chemical properties of the carbonyl hydrides. In these orbital diagrams the hydrogen atoms are shown bonded directly to the metal atoms by unique *s-d* bonds, the nature of which is unknown. When a hydrogen atom is replaced by a methyl group or a halogen atom it is suggested that a change occurs in the valence state of the metal, so that a normal hybrid σ bond is made available for bonding the methyl group or the halogen atom to the metal. The nature of the rearrangement is seen by comparing orbital diagrams (a) and (b) in Fig. 25.20.

Chromium carbonyl hydride, $Cr(CO)_5H_2$. When chromium hexacarbonyl is treated with metallic sodium in liquid ammonia, $Na_2Cr(CO)_5$ is obtained. If chromium hexacarbonyl is treated with alcoholic potassium hydroxide a brilliant yellow derivative is formed, which on acidification gives a white crystalline substance which is volatile and unstable. This substance is probably $Cr(CO)_5H_2$. The orbital diagram for this compound would be that drawn in Fig. 25.18.

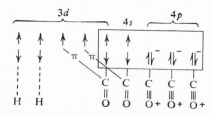

Fig. 25.18.　Orbital diagram for $Cr(CO)_5H_2$.

Iron carbonyl hydride, $Fe(CO)_4H_2$. Iron carbonyl hydride is best prepared† by the hydrolysis of iron pentacarbonyl with baryta:

$$Fe(CO)_5 + 2OH^- = Fe(CO)_4H_2 + CO_3^{2-};$$

the reaction is almost quantitative. It is also formed by the decomposition of salts of iron carbonyl hydride, either by means of acids (the reaction also proceeds quantitatively):

$$[Fe\ en_3][Fe(CO)_4] + 2H^+ = Fe^{2+} + Fe(CO)_4H_2 + 3en,$$

or by carbon monoxide:

$$[Ni(NH_3)_6][Fe(CO)_4H]_2 + 4CO = [Fe(CO)_4H]_2[Ni(CO)_4] + 6NH_3,$$
$$3[Fe(CO)_4H]_2[Ni(CO)_4] = 3Fe(CO)_4H_2 + Fe_3(CO)_{12} + 3Ni(CO)_4.$$

Iron carbonyl hydride is a volatile, malodorous, pale yellow liquid, stable only below $-10°$. It dissolves in water to give a yellow solution. It is easily soluble in pyridine and in liquid ammonia; the solutions are good conductors.

Iron carbonyl hydride decomposes above $-10°$, liberating hydrogen, iron pentacarbonyl, and polynuclear carbonyls. The decomposition is accompanied by the appearance of a deep red colour, which is unexplained. Iron carbonyl hydride is a strong reducing agent. It is attacked by atmospheric oxygen to give the dodecacarbonyl.

† Iron carbonyl hydride is *not* obtained by the following methods applicable to the preparation of $Co(CO)_4H$:

  (i) the action of CO on FeS in the presence of moisture and metallic copper,
  (ii) the action of hydrogen on $Fe(CO)_5$,
  (iii) the action of $CO + H_2$ on iron,
  (iv) the action of $CO + H_2 + Cu$ on FeS.

No $Fe(CO)_4H_2$ is formed when $Fe_3(CO)_{12}$ or $Fe(CO)_4I_2$ is heated with $H_2 + CO$. The product of all these six reactions is iron pentacarbonyl.

In concentrated solution, with mild oxidising agents such as a mixture of manganese dioxide and sulphuric acid, the same product is obtained almost quantitatively (equation on p. 1092).

Iron carbonyl hydride may be estimated by its reduction, and consequent decolorisation, of methylene blue. Powerful oxidising agents in concentrated solution, e.g. H_2O_2, bring about its complete decomposition into $Fe(OH)_3$, CO, and CO_2 (Chart 25.3).

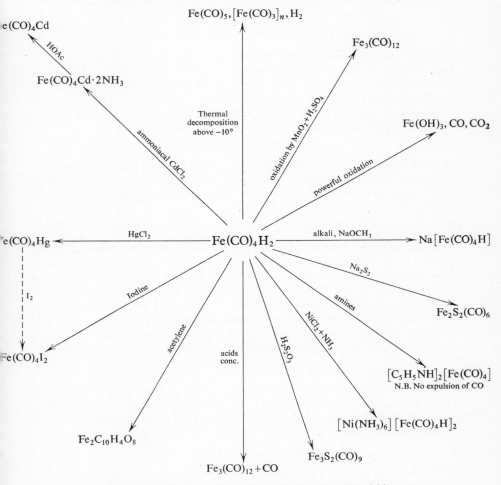

Chart 25.3. Summary of reactions of iron carbonyl hydride.

Reaction with acids. Iron carbonyl hydride reacts with fairly strong hydrochloric or sulphuric acid; it gives a green precipitate of $Fe_3(CO)_{12}$ with liberation of CO.

Reaction with halogens. Iron carbonyl hydride reacts with iodine to give $Fe(CO)_4I_2$.

Reactions with bases to form true salts. Iron carbonyl hydride behaves as a weak acid. It forms both acid and normal salts with the alkali and alkaline earth metals. The compound $Na[Fe(CO)_4H]MeOH$ is obtained by the hydrolysis of iron carbonyl hydride solution with sodium methoxide. The acid salts of calcium and magnesium, e.g. $[Fe(CO)_4H]_2Mg$, are obtained by treating the aqueous solution of iron carbonyl hydride with a suspension of calcium hydroxide or magnesium hydroxide.

The normal salts of the alkaline earth metals are sparingly soluble in ammonia solution, and are precipitated when the alkaline earth iodide is added to the carbonyl hydride in ammonia solution:

$$Fe(CO)_4H_2 + BaI_2 + 2NH_3 = BaFe(CO)_4 + 2NH_4I.$$

The normal salts of the alkali and alkaline earth metals may also be prepared by treating a solution of iron carbonyl hydride in liquid ammonia with a solution of the metal, or the metallic amide, in liquid ammonia:

$$Fe(CO)_4H_2 + 2KNH_2 = Fe(CO)_4K_2 + 2NH_3.$$

The salts of the alkali and alkaline earth metals are unstable and pyrophoric.

Iron carbonyl hydride forms more stable salts with bulky cations. Pyridine and *o*-phenanthroline react with it to yield the very stable salts, $[C_5H_5NH]_2[Fe(CO)_4]$, and $[phen.H_2][Fe(CO)_4]$. It is noteworthy that the amines do not expel CO from $Fe(CO)_4H_2$.

Iron carbonyl hydride forms a large number of sparingly soluble salts with hex-ammino cations. With ammonia the salts have the general formula:

$$[M^{II}(NH_3)_6][Fe(CO)_4H]_2,$$

where M^{II} is Mn, Fe, Co, Ni. These salts are readily obtained by dissolving $Fe(CO)_5$ in concentrated ammonia solution, and adding a solution of, say, nickel hexammino chloride. They are stable in the absence of air. The cobalt salt is decomposed by carbon monoxide thus:

$$2[Co(NH_3)_6][Fe(CO)_4H]_2 + 8CO = 2Co(CO)_4H + 12NH_3 + Fe(CO)_4H_2 + Fe_3(CO)_{12}.$$

The salts $[M^{II}phen_3][Fe(CO)_4H]_2$ may also be prepared by the action of $Fe(CO)_5$ containing dissolved ammonia on the trisphenanthroline M^{II} cation. M^{II} may be Fe, Co, Ni. The salts are stable in air, and are less reactive than the ammonia compounds, and are very sparingly soluble. The iron salt can be used for gravimetric determination of $Fe(CO)_5$. Solutions of the complex cation salts in acetone or methyl alcohol have conductivities typical of the solutions of strong electrolytes.

Reactions with compounds of mercury, cadmium, and zinc. Mercuric chloride reacts with $Fe(CO)_4H_2$ solution to precipitate the very stable yellow compound $Fe(CO)_4Hg$,

$$Fe(CO)_4H_2 + HgCl_2 = 2HCl + Fe(CO)_4Hg.$$

This compound is also obtained when mercuric chloride acts on $Na[Fe(CO)_4H]MeOH$, or on $Fe(CO)_5$. It is non-volatile and insoluble in all solvents. It is unaffected by air, or by boiling pyridine. If heated to 150° it breaks down into metallic mercury, iron, and CO. It reacts with iodine at room temperature, thus:

$$Fe(CO)_4Hg + 2I_2 = Fe(CO)_4I_2 + HgI_2,$$

and with excess of mercuric chloride to give the compound $Fe(CO)_4Hg_2Cl_2$.

Ammoniacal solutions of cadmium or zinc salts with $Fe(CO)_4H_2$ yield the insoluble compounds $Fe(CO)_4Cd \cdot 2NH_3$ and $Fe(CO)_4Zn \cdot 3NH_3$. The pyridine compound $Fe(CO)_4Cd \cdot 2pyr$ is also known. These compounds are decomposed by acids with increasing difficulty in the order:

$$Fe(CO)_4 \cdot Zn \cdot 3NH_3 \xrightarrow{\text{HOAc}} Fe(CO)_4H_2,$$

$$Fe(CO)_4 \cdot Cd \cdot 2NH_3 \xrightarrow{\text{HOAc}} Fe(CO)_4Cd \xrightarrow{\text{HCl}} Fe(CO)_4H_2$$

$Fe(CO)_4Hg$ unaffected by acids.

Table 25.10 contains the metallic derivatives mentioned above, and other examples of compounds of this type.

Table 25.10. *Metallic Derivatives of Iron Carbonyl Hydride*

$Fe(CO)_4Hg$	$Fe(CO)_4Cu_2 \cdot 2NH_3$
$Fe(CO)_4Hg_2Cl_2$	$Fe(CO)_4Ag_2 \cdot phen$
$Fe(CO)_4Cd \cdot 2NH_3$	$Fe(CO)_4(HgCH_3)_2$
$Fe(CO)_4Zn \cdot 3NH_3$	$Fe(CO)_4Pb(C_2H_5)_2.$

In these compounds iron carbonyl hydride is formally dibasic, the compounds which contain amines are not derived from stable ammine cations, and the properties of the compounds are not those of typical salts.

Reaction with sulphurous acid. Iron carbonyl hydride reacts with sulphurous, selenous, or tellurous acids to produce compounds of the type $Fe_3X_2(CO)_9$, where X represents S, Se, Te. The compounds are diamagnetic, hydrophobic, and relatively stable. Infrared spectra observations support the structure:

$$\begin{array}{c} X \\ | \\ (CO)_3Fe \diagdown \quad Fe(CO)_3 \; Fe(CO)_3 \\ | \\ X \end{array}$$

Reaction with acetylene. Iron carbonyl hydride in alkaline solution reacts with acetylene to yield a complex $Fe_2C_{10}O_8H_4$. X-ray examination shows that the corresponding complex formed from dimethylacetylene has the atomic arrangement:†

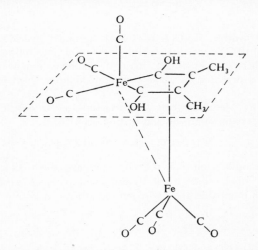

Fig. 25.19. Diagrammatic sketch of the atomic arrangement in $Fe_2C_{10}O_8H_2(CH_3)_2$. The groups in the rectangle lie in the plane of the rectangle which is at right angles to the plane of the paper. The bonds drawn vertically are parallel to the plane of the paper.

It is presumed that in the acetylene compound the methyl groups are replaced by hydrogen atoms. It is suggested that the bond between the lower iron atom and the FeC_4 ring has the same character as the bond between the metal atoms and an aromatic ring in a π-complex (p. 1116).

Structure of iron carbonyl hydride. Electron diffraction has shown that the configuration of iron carbonyl hydride is tetrahedral.‡ Two of the distances Fe—C are

† A. A. Hock and O. S. Mills, *Proc. Chem. Soc.*, 1958, 233.
‡ Ewens and Lister, *Trans. Faraday Soc.*, **35**, 1939, 681.

1·84, and two are 1·79. It has been established by observations on the broad line resonance spectrum of iron carbonyl hydride† that the hydrogen atoms are directly bonded to the iron atom, and that the distance Fe—H is about 1·1. The hydrogen atom therefore lies within the atomic orbital system of the iron atom.

The orbital structure diagram in Fig. 25.20(a) can be assigned to the molecule. The reaction of iron carbonyl hydride with iodine to yield the monomeric $Fe(CO)_4I_2$ could be explained by a change in the valence state of the iron atom from tetrahedral to octahedral, so that the $Fe(CO)_4I_2$ has a structure corresponding to the orbital diagram in Fig. 25.20 (b).

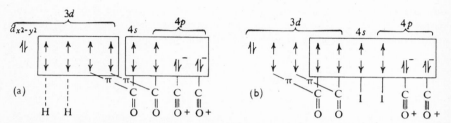

Fig. 25.20.   (a) Orbital diagram for tetrahedral configuration of $Fe(CO)_4H_2$. (b) Orbital diagram for octahedral configuration of derivatives of $Fe(CO)_4H_2$; that for $Fe(CO)_4I_2$ is drawn as an example.

Cobalt carbonyl hydride, $Co(CO)_4H$. Cobalt carbonyl hydride is a liquid, m.p. −26·2°, b.p. (extr.) 10°. The crystals, liquid, and vapour, are yellow. It is malodorous and poisonous. There is no antidote, injury from inhalation is permanent. Cobalt carbonyl hydride is prepared by three principal methods, each of which is briefly described below.

1. *Direct synthesis.* Metallic cobalt is partly converted to cobalt carbonyl hydride when heated with carbon monoxide and hydrogen (50 atm):

$$2Co + 8CO + H_2 = 2Co(CO)_4H.$$

This method is a modification of that used to prepare cobalt octacarbonyl (p. 1093). Cobalt sulphide or cobalt iodide are partly converted to cobalt carbonyl hydride when heated with carbon monoxide and hydrogen (50 atm) or moisture in the presence of copper:

$$2CoS + 8CO + H_2 + 4Cu = 2Co(CO)_4H + 2Cu_2S,$$

$$2CoS + 9CO + H_2O + 4Cu = 2Co(CO)_4H + CO_2 + 2Cu_2S.$$

2. *Hydrolysis of cobalt octacarbonyl.* Cobalt octacarbonyl when hydrolysed by a base yields the carbonyl hydride, together with other compounds of cobalt. The details and equations of the reactions are given on p. 1094.

3. *Action of carbon monoxide on cobaltous complexes.* All these reactions appear to follow a common route. In the first place cobalt octacarbonyl is formed by disproportionation:

$$6K_2[CoX_4] + 8CO = 4K_3[CoX_6] + Co_2(CO)_8.$$

The octacarbonyl is then hydrolysed according to the equation:

$$3Co_2(CO)_8 + 4H_2O = 4Co(CO)_4H + 2Co(OH)_2 + 8CO.$$

† E. D. Bishop, J. C. Down, P. R. Entage, R. E. Richards, and G. Wilkinson, *J. Chem. Soc.,* 1959, 2484.

The cobaltous complexes that may be used are potassium cobaltous cyanide, $K_2[Co(CN)_4]$, potassium cobaltous tartrate, $K_2[Co\{C_2H_2(OH)_2(CO_2)_2\}_2]$ and potassium cobaltous cysteinate:

$$K_2\left[Co\left(\begin{array}{c} S-CH_2 \\ | \\ N-C-COO \\ H_2 \; | \\ H \end{array}\right)_2\right]$$

In practice cobalt carbonyl hydride is conveniently made by this method by passing carbon monoxide into an aqueous solution of cobaltous nitrate containing potassium hydroxide and potassium cyanide. The solution is subsequently acidified, and the carbonyl hydride is swept out of the solution by a stream of carbon monoxide, and after drying, is collected in a tube cooled to $-79°$.

The equation for the action of carbon monoxide on potassium cobaltous cysteinate is:

$$9K_2[Co(S\cdot CH_2C\cdot CO_2\cdot H\cdot NH_2)_2] + 8CO + 2H_2O = 2Co(CO)_4H + Co(OH)_2$$
$$+ 6K_3[Co(S\cdot CH_2\cdot C\cdot CO_2\cdot H\cdot NH_2)_3].$$

Further absorption of carbon monoxide then leads to the formation of more carbonyl hydride, and the liberation of potassium cysteinate:

$$K_3[Co(S\cdot CH_2\cdot C\cdot CO_2\cdot H\cdot NH_2)_3] + 6CO + 7KOH = Co(CO)_4H + 2K_2CO_3$$
$$+ 3H_2O + 3KS\cdot CH_2\cdot CHNH_2\cdot COOK.$$

The potassium cysteinate reacts with the cobalt hydroxide to form the cobaltous complex again, and so cobalt carbonyl hydride can be made by passing carbon monoxide into an alkaline solution of a cobalt salt containing a little cysteine.

Cobalt carbonyl hydride is thermally unstable and decomposes rapidly at $-18°$ into the octacarbonyl and hydrogen. Nevertheless its tendency to be formed is so great that it is obtained from cobaltous compounds by reactions which for iron give $Fe(CO)_5$ and for nickel give $Ni(CO)_4$. It is a strong reducing agent, and reduces methylene blue. Atmospheric oxygen, or manganese dioxide, converts it to $Co_4(CO)_{12}$. It is an acid. Its solution in water reacts with ammoniacal solutions of cobalt or nickel salts to give:

$$[Co(CO)_4]_2[Co(NH_3)_6] \quad \text{or} \quad [Co(CO)_4]_2[Ni(NH_3)_6],$$

or in the presence of o-phenanthroline, the corresponding compounds with o-phenanthroline as ligand. Simple metallic salts have not been isolated, but they are assumed to be present in aqueous solution after the hydrolysis of cobalt octacarbonyl (p. 1094). For a summary of the reactions of cobalt carbonyl hydride see chart 25.2 (p. 1095).

Cobalt carbonyl hydride gives rise to a number of metallic derivatives analogous to those formed from iron carbonyl hydride. They are:

$Co(CO)_4Tl.$

$(Co(CO)_4)_2M$ where M is Zn, Cd, Hg, Sn, Pb,

$(Co(CO)_4)_3M$ where M is Ga, In, Tl.

These compounds are soluble in organic solvents, in which they are monomeric. They are insoluble in water. They may be sublimed, and they melt with some decomposition at about $70°$. They are thus more stable than the carbonyl hydride itself.

Electron diffraction analysis shows that the molecular configuration of cobalt carbonyl hydride is tetrahedral. Three of the distances C–O are 1·83, the fourth is 1·75. Molecular orbital treatment of the bond Co—H indicates that the hydrogen nucleus is within the orbital system of the cobalt atom.† By analogy with iron carbonyl hydride, the orbital diagram in Fig. 25.21 (a) may be assigned to the carbonyl hydride,‡ which on chemical reaction may change to the trigonal bipyramidal configuration shown in Fig. 25.21 (b) and so account for the covalent metallic derivatives mentioned on p. 1107.

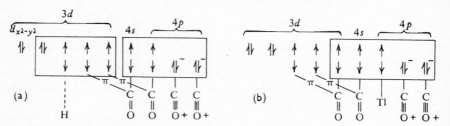

Fig. 25.21.   (a) Orbital diagram for the tetrahedral configuration of Co(CO)₄H.   (b) Orbital diagram for the trigonal bipyramidal configuration of derivatives of Co(CO)₄H; that for Co(CO)₄Tl is drawn as an example.

THE CARBONYL HYDRIDES OF RHODIUM AND IRIDIUM

Little is known about the carbonyl hydrides of rhodium and iridium. Both are formed by the action of moist carbon monoxide under pressure on the metallic sulphide in the presence of copper:

$$2IrS + H_2O + 9CO + 4Cu = 2Ir(CO)_3(COH) + CO_2 + 2Cu_2S.$$

Rhodium carbonyl hydride is also formed by the action of a mixture of carbon monoxide and hydrogen under pressure on the metal. The rhodium compound is a pale yellow volatile liquid, f.p. −10°, and its composition is Rh(CO)₄H. The iridium compound is assumed to have the same composition. It yields a colourless precipitate when added to a solution of mercuric chloride.

NICKEL CARBONYL HYDRIDE

Nickel carbonyl hydride, Ni(CO)₃H₂, is formed by the action of nickel carbonyl on metallic sodium in liquid ammonia:

$$Ni(CO)_4 + 3Na + 2NH_3 = Ni(CO)_3H_2 + NaCO + 2NaNH_2.$$

The NaCO and NaNH₂ are precipitated, leaving nickel carbonyl hydride in solution. The hydrogen atoms in nickel carbonyl hydride are non-acidic.

THE CARBONYL HALIDES OF THE TRANSITION METALS

The formulae of the carbonyl halides of the transition metals are set out in Table 25.11. Both the range and the stability of the carbonyl halides are greatest for the metals of Groups VII, VIII, and IX.

† F. A. Cotton, *J. Amer. Chem. Soc.*, **80**, 1958, 4425.
‡ Infrared spectrum shows no O—H stretching vibration, *Ann. Reports*, 1956, 106.

Table 25.11.   *The Transition Metal Carbonyl Halides, and certain of their Derivatives*†

Periodic Group

VI	VII	VIII	IX	X	XI
Cr	$Mn(CO)_5X$	$Fe(CO)_5X_2$ $Fe(CO)_4X_2$ $Fe(CO)_2pyr_2X_2$ $Fe(CO)_2phenX_2$ $Fe(CO)_2X_2$ $Fe(CO)_2I$ $Fe(CO)pyr_2I_2$ $[Fe(CO)_3Br_2]_3$ $Fe(CO)_4en_2I_2$ $Fe(CO)_3Hg \cdot HgI_2$	$Co(CO)I_2$	Ni	$Cu(CO)X$
Mo	Tc	$Ru(CO)_2X_2$ $Ru(CO)Br$	$[Rh(CO)_2X]_2$	Pd	$(Ag_2SO_4)CO$
W	$Re(CO)_5X$ $Re(CO)_3pyr_2Cl$ $Re(CO)_3phenCl$	$Os(CO)_4X_2$ $Os(CO)_3X_2$ $[Os(CO)_4X]_2$	$Ir(CO)_3X$ $Ir(CO)_2X_2$	Pt	$Au(CO)Cl$

† X represents Cl, Br, or I.

The compounds in Table 25.11 present a range of metal valencies which cannot at first sight be reconciled with those present in more familiar compounds. Some regularity may be introduced, at least for metals in Groups VII and VIII, in terms of the orbital diagrams in Figs. 25.22 and 25.23:

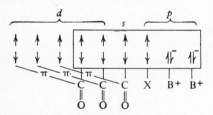

Fig. 25.22.   Orbital diagram for carbonyl halides of metals in Group VII.

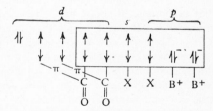

Fig. 25.23.   Orbital diagram for carbonyl halides of metals in Group VIII.

In these orbital diagrams the metal atoms are octahedrally hybridised. X represents a halogen atom linked to the metal by a covalent bond. B represents a ligand (normally a carbonyl group) linked to the metal by a co-ionic bond. Such a bond can be formed not only by carbon monoxide molecules, but also by other molecules which have electron pairs available for donation. Figs. 25.22 and 25.23 explain the constitutions of the rhenium carbonyl halides and of the iron compounds $Fe(CO)_4X_2$ and $Fe(CO)_2X_2pyr_2$. The compound $Fe(CO)_5X_2$ could be represented as ionic if it is assumed that one of the halogen atoms X accepts an electron from the iron atom and becomes an anion. Room is thus made for the linkage of an additional carbonyl group to the iron atom by a co-ionic bond, and the compound thus represented has the formula $[Fe(CO)_5Cl^+]Cl^-$.

The structures of all the compounds in the column headed VII in Table 25.11 are described by the orbital diagram in Fig. 25.22, and the structures of about one half of the compounds in the column headed VIII are described by the orbital diagram in Fig. 25.23. The proportion of ligands to metal atoms in the remaining compounds in column VIII is small, and unoccupied orbitals must be present in the molecules of these compounds unless they are polymerised. Some of the best characterised of the metal carbonyl halides with only a small number of ligands per metal atom are the ruthenium compounds, $Ru(CO)_2I_2$ and $RuCOBr$. These compounds are no doubt polymerised, but the constitutions of possible low polymers bear no obvious relationship to the orbital structures of the carbonyls, $Fe_2(CO)_9$ or $Fe_3(CO)_{12}$.†

The carbonyl halides of the metals of Group IX also contain only a small number of ligands per metal atom. There is insufficient evidence to decide whether a modified orbital diagram of the type shown in Fig. 25.23 could be used to explain their constitutions.

MANGANESE CARBONYL HALIDES, AND RHENIUM CARBONYL HALIDES

Both manganese and rhenium form carbonyl halides of the type $M(CO)_5X$, where X represents Cl, Br, or I. The compounds may be obtained by the action of the halogen on the metal decacarbonyl at about $100°$. The order of the activity of the halogens is $I > Br > Cl$. The rhenium compounds may also be made by the action of carbon monoxide (i) on potassium chloro- or bromo-rhenate in the presence of copper powder, (ii) on metallic rhenium in the presence of the appropriate cupric halide, (iii) on potassium rhenate in the presence of carbon tetrachloride. The rhenium carbonyl halides, and no other carbonyl compounds, are formed when carbon monoxide reacts with a halide or a complex halide of rhenium;‡ there is no reaction by which any rhenium carbonyl halide can be converted to rhenium carbonyl.

The rhenium carbonyl halides are stable, odourless, colourless (Cl and Br), or yellow (I) crystalline compounds. They are insoluble in water, but soluble in organic solvents. They sublime readily in an atmosphere of carbon monoxide at about $100°$. They decompose at about $400°$. The thermal decomposition of $Re(CO)_5X$ (where X represents Cl, Br, or I) yields the dimeric $[Re(CO)_4X]_2$; the reaction is reversible. $[Re(CO)_4I]_2$ reacts with pyridine to give the monomeric compound $Re(CO)_3pyrI$.

Rhenium carbonyl chloride reacts with boiling pyridine to give $Re(CO)_3pyr_2Cl$, and with phenanthroline in benzene solution to give the yellow crystalline compound $Re(CO)_3phenCl$. These two derivatives are stable to hot hydrochloric acid, and to cold nitric acid and sulphuric acid. Other donating compounds, such as ammonia, methyl-isonitrile, and triphenyl phosphine react with rhenium carbonyl chloride to give ionic compounds of the type $[Re(CO)_4(NH_3)_2]Cl$; potassium cyanide yields the complex $K[Re(CO)_4(CN)_2]$.

---

† If it be admitted that unoccupied orbitals may be included in a hybridisation system, then a metal carbonyl halide such as $Fe(CO)_2I_2$ may be assigned the orbital diagram

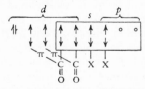

which is identical with that in Fig. 25.23 except that the co-ionically bound carbonyl groups B are absent. If this treatment is acceptable the number of compounds in Table 25.11 to which orbital diagrams cannot be assigned is reduced to four: $Ru(CO)Br$, $Fe(CO)pyr_2I_2$, $Fe(CO)_4en_2I_2$, and $[Fe(CO)_3Br_2]_3$.

‡ The corresponding reaction with potassium chloromolybdate yields molybdenum hexacarbonyl (p. 1079).

The molecular weights and the constitutions of the rhenium carbonyl halides have not been determined, but the conjectural orbital diagram, Fig. 25.22 is consistent with the properties of the compounds and with the formulae of their derivatives mentioned above.

IRON TETRACARBONYL DIHALIDES

Certain properties of the iron tetracarbonyl dihalides indicating their relative stability are set out in Table 25.12.

Table 25.12.   *The Iron Tetracarbonyl Dihalides*

	$Fe(CO)_4Cl_2$	$Fe(CO)_4Br_2$	$Fe(CO)_4I_2$
Decomposition temperature	10°	55°	75°
Heat of reaction (kcal): $FeX_2 + 4CO = Fe(CO)_4X_2$; ΔH	$-17\cdot9$	$-28\cdot3$	$-38\cdot9$
Heat of reaction (kcal): $Fe(CO)_5 + X_2(g) = Fe(CO)_4X_2$ $+ CO$; ΔH	$-45\cdot8$	$-43\cdot4$	$-23\cdot1$
Stability of $Fe(CO)_2pyr_2X_2$	Non-existent	Decomposes at 0°	Stable but photosensitive
Stability of $Fe(CO)_2phenX_2$	Decomposes at $-10°$	Stable but photosensitive	Stable not photosensitive

Iron tetracarbonyl di-iodide, $Fe(CO)_4I_2$, is made:

  (i) by the action of iodine on $Fe(CO)_5$ above 0°,
 (ii) by the action of carbon monoxide at 110 atm on an ethereal solution of ferrous iodide:

$$FeI_2 + 4CO = Fe(CO)_4I_2,$$

(iii) by the action of iodine on $Fe(CO)_4Hg$, or on $Fe(CO)_4H_2$.

Iron tetracarbonyl di-iodide is a brown powder which sublimes in a vacuum. It dissolves in organic solvents in which it is a non-electrolyte. In solution in ethylene dibromide and in nitrobenzene it is monomeric. On treatment with water, or with pyridine in excess at room temperature, it decomposes to carbon monoxide and ferrous iodide. The course of thermal decomposition of iron tetracarbonyl di-iodide varies with the nature of the atmosphere in which it is heated; in hydrogen $Fe(CO)_2I_2$ is formed, but in carbon dioxide FeI_3 and $Fe(CO)_2I$ are formed.

Iron tetracarbonyl di-iodide reacts with amines such as pyridine and phenanthroline to give the substitution products $Fe(CO)_2pyr_2I_2$ and $Fe(CO)_2phenI_2$. The compound $Fe(CO)_2pyr_2I_2$ is sensitive to light, which promotes its further reaction with pyridine to give $Fe(CO)pyr_3I_2$. Iron tetracarbonyl di-iodide reacts with thionyl chloride to yield a reactive, brown crystalline solid, $Fe(CO)_2Cl_2$:

$$Fe(CO)_4I_2 + 2SOCl_2 = Fe(CO)_2Cl_2 + I_2 + 2CO + SO_2 + SCl_2.$$

Iron dicarbonyl di-iodide, $Fe(CO)_2I_2$, is a red solid. Its alcoholic solution reacts with phenanthroline to yield dark-red $Fe(CO)_2phenI_2$, and with pyridine to yield the green solid $Fe(CO)_2pyrI_2$. $Fe(CO)_2I$ has been reported, and it is said to give bright red unstable FeI on decomposition.

RUTHENIUM CARBONYL HALIDES

Three ruthenium carbonyl halides have been reported, $Ru(CO)_2I_2$, $Ru(CO)_2Br_2$, and $Ru(CO)Br$. Ruthenium iodide reacts with carbon monoxide at ordinary pressure, thus:

$$RuI_3 + 2CO = Ru(CO)_2I_2 + I.$$

Ruthenium enneacarbonyl reacts with iodine to yield the same compound. $Ru(CO)_2I_2$ is polymeric, diamagnetic, highly stable, and has a low vapour pressure. With pyridine it gives $Ru(CO)_2pyr_2I_2$, and with triphenyl phosphine it gives the corresponding phosphine compound; these two derivatives appear to correspond to $Fe(CO)_4I_2$. With potassium cyanide $Ru(CO)_2I_2$ gives $K_2[Ru(CO)_2(CN)_2I_2]$.

Ruthenium carbonyl bromide, $Ru(CO)Br$, is made by the action of carbon monoxide on $RuBr_3$ at 183° and 350 atm pressure. It is colourless, crystalline, and is slowly decomposed by water. It reduces ammoniacal silver nitrate solution. At 200° it decomposes thus:

$$2Ru(CO)Br = Ru(CO)_2Br_2 + Ru.$$

OSMIUM CARBONYL HALIDES

The osmium carbonyl halides $Os(CO)_4X_2$ are made from the halides ($OsCl_3$, Os_2Br_9, or osmium oxyiodide) by the action of carbon monoxide at 120° and 200 atm pressure. (If the autoclave lining is a halogen acceptor, the carbonyls are formed.)

$Os(CO)_3Cl_2$ is a colourless solid, m.p. about 270°, decomposition temperature 280°. It is insoluble in water and in most acids. If heated with oxygen it yields osmium tetroxide.

COBALT CARBONYL HALIDES

The only cobalt carbonyl halide is $Co(CO)I_2$, an intermediate product in the reaction of CoI_2 with carbon monoxide under pressure. It is formed at room temperature under 100 atm of carbon monoxide. It is a dark brown crystalline solid with a high dissociation pressure of carbon monoxide. It is perceptibly volatile at room temperature.

RHODIUM CARBONYL HALIDES

$Rh_2(CO)_4Cl_2$	$Rh_2(CO)_4Br_2$	$Rh_2(CO)_4I_2$
orange yellow	red-brown	ruby-red
m.p. 123°	m.p. 118°	m.p. 114°

The three compounds have been made by heating the metallic halide with carbon monoxide under pressure in the absence of a halogen acceptor. All are covalent, sublime easily, and are soluble in organic solvents. The chloride has been shown by the cryoscopic method to be dimeric. The chloride reacts with triphenyl phosphine, triphenyl arsine, and triphenyl stibine to give compounds of the type $Rh((C_6H_5)_3P)_2(CO)Cl$. These compounds are monomeric, diamagnetic, and they are non-electrolytes. They are stable to heat, acids, and alkalis.

IRIDIUM CARBONYL HALIDES

There are two types of iridium carbonyl halides:

	$Ir(CO)_2X_2$	$Ir(CO)_3X$
Sublimation temperature	*ca* 150°	*ca* 115°
Colour:		
Cl	Colourless	Pale brown
Br	Pale yellow	Chocolate
I	Pale yellow	Dark brown.

Both types of compound are formed by heating the iridium trihalide monohydrate, IrX_3,H_2O, to 150° in carbon monoxide at 1 atm pressure. The displaced halogen separates as $COCl_2$, $COBr_2$, or I_2. The ease of preparation is in the order $Cl > Br > I$. $Ir(CO)_3X$ is more stable than $Ir(CO)_2X_2$ which loses carbon monoxide on standing in air. $Ir(CO)_3X$ is decomposed by water to give the metal and carbon monoxide.

THE METALLIC NITROSYLS

Some of the data concerning the principal nitrosyl compounds of the transition metals (excluding those compounds in which the NO group is part of a complex ion) are collected in Table 25.13. Little is known about these compounds, and only in a few cases are the degrees of polymerisation, or the magnetic properties known. It is possible, however, to suggest orbital structures based on principles which have been found serviceable for the carbonyls.

The molecule of nitric oxide is regarded as a resonance structure of the canonical forms:

$$\cdot\ddot{N}\overset{\pi}{-}\ddot{O}\colon \qquad \overset{+}{N}\overset{-}{-}\ddot{O}\colon \qquad \colon\ddot{N}\overset{\pi}{-}\overset{+}{O}\cdot$$

The electronic configuration of the group NO is so flexible that to lay down a hard and fast electronic configuration in terms of any particular forms for a molecule such as $Fe(NO)_4$ is probably unjustified. Nevertheless, the metallic nitrosyls may be consistently formulated by making use of the four configurations for the NO group:

$$\underset{A}{R\overset{}{-}\ddot{N}\overset{\pi}{-}\ddot{O}\colon} \qquad \underset{B}{R\overset{\pi}{-}\overset{+}{N}\overset{\pi}{-}\ddot{O}\colon} \qquad \underset{C}{\overset{-}{R}\overset{}{-}\overset{+}{N}\overset{\pi}{-}\ddot{O}\colon} \qquad \underset{D}{\overset{-}{R}\overset{\pi}{-}\overset{+}{N}\overset{\pi}{-}\ddot{O}\colon}$$

R is one atom of the metal. It should be noted (i) that configuration B requires the transfer of one electron from the nitrogen atom to some orbital of the metal other than the two orbitals engaged in bonding the nitrogen atom to the metal, (ii) that in configuration C the nitrogen atom has donated an electron pair to the metal, and has thus established a co-ionic bond, (iii) that configuration C is paramagnetic, (iv) that in configuration D the unpaired electron on the nitrogen atom in C is used for making a πd bond with the metal atom. Certain structures are drawn below.

$Fe(NO)_4$

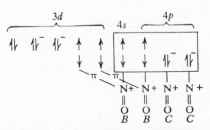

Fig. 25.24(a).   Orbital diagram of $Fe(NO)_4$.

Fe(NO)$_2$(CO)$_2$

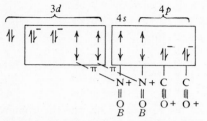

Fig. 25.24(b).　Orbital diagram of Fe(NO)$_2$(CO)$_2$.

Fe$_2$(NO)$_4$I$_2$

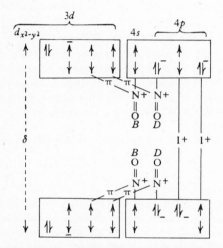

Fig. 25.24(c).　Orbital diagram of Fe$_2$(NO)$_4$I$_2$.

The above orbital diagram is drawn on the assumption that the geometrical configuration is analogous to that of Roussin's red salt:

$$
\begin{array}{ccccc}
 & & R & & \\
 & & | & & \\
ON & & S & & NO \\
 & \searrow & \downarrow & & \\
 & Fe & \cdots\cdots & Fe & \\
 & \nearrow & \uparrow & & \\
ON & & S & & NO \\
 & & | & & \\
 & & R & &
\end{array}
$$

Fe(NO)$_3$Cl

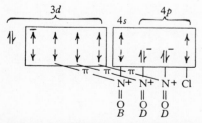

Fig. 25.24(d).　Orbital diagram of Fe(NO)$_3$Cl.

Table 23.15. *Metallic Nitrosyl Compounds*

Name of compound	Formula	Degree of polymerisation	Preparation	Physical state	m.p.	b.p.	Magnetic properties	Notes
Iron tetranitrosyl	$Fe(NO)_4$		NO under pressure on $Fe(CO)_5$ below 45°	Black crystals				No vapour pressure at 0°. Decomposes above 0° to $Fe(NO)$ and $Fe(NO)_2$
Iron dinitrosyl dicarbonyl	$Fe(NO)_2(CO)_2$	Monomeric (Electron diffraction shows that the molecular configuration is tetrahedral)	NO on $Fe_2(CO)_9$ or $Fe_3(CO)_{12}$ at 85°	Deep red crystals	18·4°	110°		It decomposes in a vacuum. Quickly oxidised by air. Soluble in organic solvents, but not in water. o-Phenanthroline, and methyl, phenyl and p-tolyl isocyanide replace the CO groups. Iodine yields $Fe_2(NO)_4I_2$
	$Fe_2(NO)_4I_2$							
	$Fe_2(NO)_4Cl_2$	Dimeric						
	$Fe_2(NO)_4(SC_2H_5)_2$	Dimeric						
	$Fe_2(NO)_4(SC_6H_5)_2$	Dimeric						
	$Fe_2(NO)_4(S \cdot SO_3K)_2$						Diamagnetic	
Roussin's red salt	$Fe_2(NO)_4(SK)_2$						Diamagnetic	
Roussin's black salt	$Fe_4(NO)_7S_3K$							
	$Fe(NO)_3Cl$		NO on $FeCl_2$, in presence of iron powder at 70°	Dark red needles				Sublimes at 110°. Readily loses NO
	$Fe(NO)Cl$							
	$Co_2(NO)_4Cl_2$							
	$Co(NO)Cl$							
	$Ni(NO)Cl$	"Considered tetrameric"						o-Phenanthroline yields $Ni(NO)Cl$, 2-phen

The following geometrical configurations have been suggested:

Roussin's black salt   **[Ni(NO)I]$_4$**

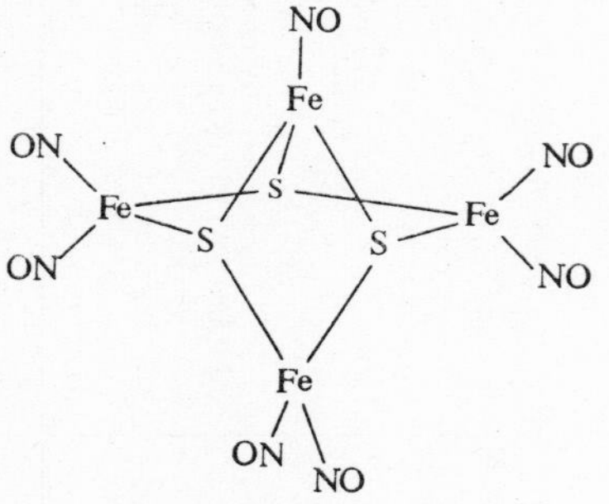

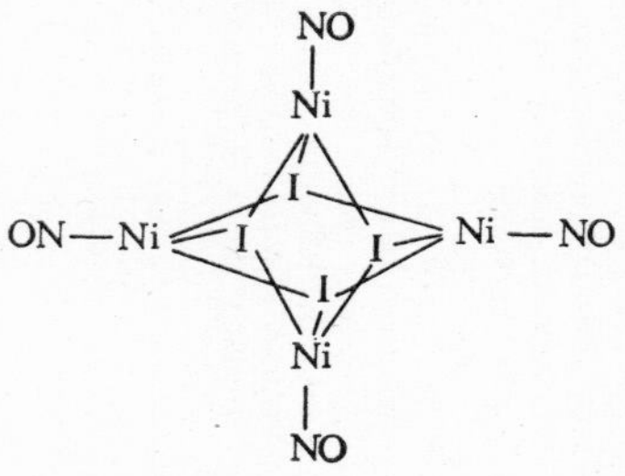

Fig. 25.25.   Fe$_4$S$_3$(NO)$_7$.   Fig. 25.26.   Ni$_4$(NO)$_4$I$_4$.

The nitrosyl halides of empirical formula, M(CO)$_n$hal. Among the metal nitrosyl halides described by this formula are:

Fe(NO)Cl   Co(NO)Cl   Ni(NO)Cl

Fe$_2$(NO)$_4$Cl$_2$ Co$_2$(NO)$_4$Cl$_2$

Fe(NO)$_3$Cl

No fluorides are known; this may be due either to the absence of *d* orbitals in the fluorine atom, or to the high electronegativity of fluorine. The stability of the compounds is in the order:

Fe > Co > Ni

I > Br > Cl.

The compounds may be prepared by the action of nitric oxide on the metal^{II} halide in the presence of a halogen acceptor such as iron, cobalt, nickel, or zinc; the halogen acceptor may be omitted in the preparation of the more stable compounds. The reaction temperature is about 100°. All the compounds are non-polar, slightly soluble in organic solvents, and readily sublimed.

π-COMPLEXES

The name *π-complex* has been given to compounds in which an unsaturated organic molecule is bonded to a metal atom by interaction of atomic orbitals of the metal with the generalised π orbitals of the unsaturated molecule. The unsaturated organic molecule is usually cyclic as in ferrocene described below, but open chain compounds also form π-complexes as for example, butadiene reacts with iron pentacarbonyl to yield the complex:

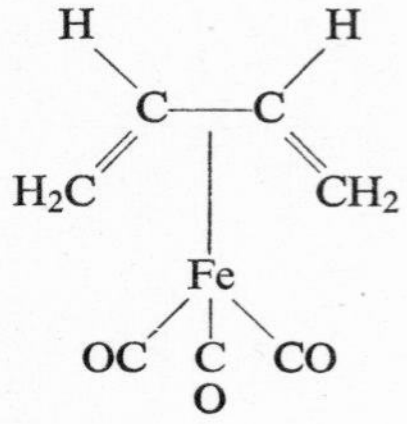

THE CYCLOPENTADIENYLS[†]

Cyclopentadiene:

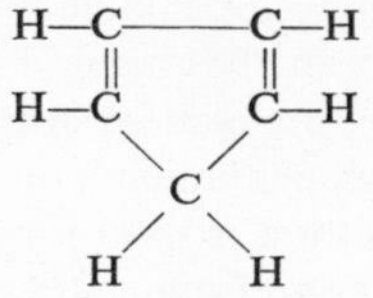

forms with sodium and magnesium the ionic compounds $Na(C_5H_5)$ and $Mg(C_5H_5)_2$. In various ways it is possible to prepare cyclopentadienyl compounds of the transition metals from vanadium to nickel, all of which have the formula $M(C_5H_5)_2$, where M is one atom of the metal; similar compounds are formed by transition metals of the higher periods. X-ray analysis shows that the dicyclopentadienyl compounds (including that of magnesium) have a sandwich structure:

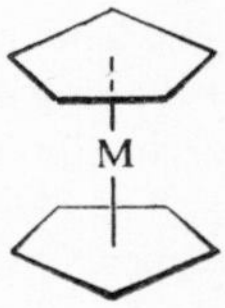

in which the metal atom appears to be related to each ring as a whole, and not to any particular carbon atoms. When the substance is present as vapour or in solution, the rings are free to rotate about a common axis passing through the metal atom. When the substance is crystalline the freedom of rotation is lost, and the rings are fixed in positions in which they are mutually staggered.[‡]

From these simple compounds, carbonyls, carbonyl hydrides, and carbonyl halides can be derived, and in some cases the carbonyl groups can be replaced by nitrosyl groups.

All the dicyclopentadienyl compounds of the transition metals have closely similar properties. The m.p. are within a few degrees of 173° for metals in period 4; the m.p. for the ruthenium compound is 196°, and for the osmium compound 219°. The compounds sublime and are thermally stable. They are soluble in common organic solvents. The dicyclopentadienyls of magnesium, vanadium, chromium, iron, cobalt, and nickel are isomorphous, crystallising in the monoclinic system. The infrared and Raman spectra of all the compounds are similar, and are characterised by five maxima.

The dicyclopentadienyls of the transition metals are made by four general methods.

(1) By the action of cyclopentadiene diluted with nitrogen on the reduced metal at about 300°. This method is used for making iron dicyclopentadienyl.

(2) By the action of cyclopentadiene on a metallic carbonyl at about 300°. This

---

† P. L. Pauson, *Quart. Rev. IX*, 1955, 391.

‡ The dicyclopentadienyl compounds of tin and lead have angular configurations:

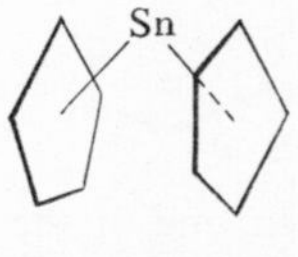

L. D. Dave, T. F. Evans, and G. Wilkinson, *J. Chem. Soc.*, 1959, 3684.

method is used for the preparation of chromium, iron, cobalt, and nickel dicyclopenta-dienyls, but except in the case of chromium the yield is poor. Molybdenum and tungsten hexacarbonyls yield cyclopentadienyl carbonyls.

(3) By the action of magnesium cyclopentadienyl bromide on the metallic chloride, or on the acetylacetonate complex of the metal. This method is used for making the dicyclopentadienyls of magnesium, manganese, iron, ruthenium, cobalt, and nickel.

(4) By the action of sodium cyclopentadienyl on the anhydrous metallic chloride in tetrahydrofuran solution. This method is used for making the dicyclopentadienyls of chromium, molybdenum, tungsten, and manganese. The yield is 70%.

(5) By the action of potassium cyclopentadienyl in liquid ammonia on a compound such as $Ni(NH_3)_6(SCN)_2$. The compound $Ni(NH_3)_6(C_5H_5)_2$ is obtained, which loses ammonia on heating. This method is also used for cobalt, chromium, and molybdenum.

Iron dicyclopentadienyl, or ferrocene, $Fe(C_5H_5)_2$, is an orange solid, m.p. 173°, volatile above 100°, b.p. 249°. The vapour is monomeric, and is not pyrolysed at 470°. It is insoluble in water. It is chemically stable, and is not affected by boiling water (it may be distilled in steam), or by boiling concentrated solutions of sodium hydroxide or hydrochloric acid. It is easily oxidised to the cation $[Fe(C_5H_5)_2]^+$. The cyclopenta-dienyl rings have aromatic rather than ethylenic properties, but NO_2^+ and Br convert ferrocene to the cation, and do not enter the ring as substituents.

Ferrocene is diamagnetic and has zero dipole moment. The infrared spectrum indicates C—H bonds of one type only. The sandwich structure has been confirmed by X-ray analysis, from which the distance C–C is 1·4, and Fe–C is 2·04, and by electron diffraction analysis from which the distance C–C is 1·44, and Fe–C is 2·05. The delocalisation energy of the π bonds in the ring is 113 kcal per mole.

Manganese dicyclopentadienyl, $Mn(C_5H_5)_2$, crystallises in the rhombic system at room temperature, but above 158° the brown rhombic crystals change into a colourless form which melts at 172°. This physical change is correlated with changes in magnetic properties. Manganese dicyclopentadienyl is paramagnetic, and its paramagnetism increases with temperature. At −253° its magnetic moment is 1 Bohr magneton, at 159° it is 4·8, and at the m.p. 172° it is 5·8. These effects are explained by a change from antiferromagnetism (p. 946) to ferromagnetism as the temperature rises. The changes are reversible. Manganese dicyclopentadienyl has a reactivity similar to that of magnesium dicyclopentadienyl, which is evidence for an ionic structure.

Nickel dicyclopentadienyl, $Ni(C_5H_5)_2$, is more reactive than the iron compound. Carbon monoxide or nitric oxide displace one or both of the rings from combination with the metal. By electron diffraction the distance Ni–C is 2·18. $Ni(C_5H_5)_2$ is para-magnetic to the value indicated by two unpaired electrons.

The orbital structure of the dicyclopentadienyl compounds. The structure of iron dicyclopentadienyl has been interpreted in terms of molecular orbital theory. For convenience of discussion it is assumed that the molecule of iron dicyclopentadienyl is orientated so that its axis is along the z axis, and the planes of the rings are in the xy plane:

It is deduced that the bond between one of the cyclopentadienyl rings and the iron atom is furnished by a molecular orbital compounded of a generalised π orbital which concerns all five carbon atoms of the ring, and the $3d_{xz}$ orbital of the iron atom. One of the generalised π orbitals of the ring has symmetry suitable for overlapping with the $3d_{xz}$ orbital of the iron atom. For this orbital, $m = \pm 1$, and consequently the angular momentum of the generalised π orbital is also described by $m = \pm 1$. The energy of this generalised π orbital is approximately equal to that of the $3d_{xz}$ orbital, and the two orbitals are able to overlap with the formation of a strong bond.

The second cyclopentadienyl ring is attached to the iron atom by the same mechanism, except that the $3d_{yz}$ orbital is used. The orbital diagram for the iron atom in the structure so far developed for iron dicyclopentadienyl is:

It has been pointed out, however, that the charge clouds of the bonding orbitals along the z axis must repel the charge in the d_{z^2} orbital. It is suggested that this repulsion is relieved by the hybridisation of the d_{z^2} and the $4s$ orbitals, to give a hybrid orbital, A, with energy less than that of either of the component orbitals, and another hybrid orbital, B, with energy greater than that of either of the component orbitals. The orbital diagram for the configuration of least energy then becomes:

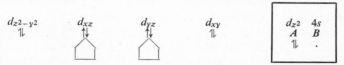

This configuration is in accord with the experimental observation that iron dicyclopentadienyl is diamagnetic. The electron configuration of manganese dicyclopentadienyl from a diagram constructed on the same principles, indicates that one of the orbitals $3d_{x^2-y^2}$ or $3d_{xy}$ contains only one electron, and predicts that the compound would be paramagnetic by one Bohr unit. The chromium compound would be paramagnetic by two Bohr units, and so on. The electrons in the dicyclopentadienyls of cobalt and nickel additional to those in the iron compound must be placed in one or two of the $4p$ orbitals, and so these compounds also would be paramagnetic. These predictions are in accord with observations.

THE METAL DICYCLOPENTADIENYL HALIDES

The transition metal dicyclopentadienyl halides fall into two classes, the covalent compounds of titanium and niobium, and the ionic halides of the cations such as $[(C_5H_5)_2Fe]^+$.

The covalent halides. Titanium forms the compounds $(C_5H_5)_2Tihal_2$, where hal may be F, Cl, or Br. The bromide is volatile and is soluble in many organic solvents, but is sparingly soluble in water; the fluoride is more soluble in water. The bromide reacts with alkalis to yield $(C_5H_5)_2TiBrOH$. It reacts with lithium aryls to form compounds of the type $(C_5H_5)_2Ti(C_6H_5)_2$. Although the bromide has the properties of a covalent compound it is possible to obtain ionic derivatives of titanium dicyclopentadienyl, such as the perchlorate, $[(C_5H_5)_2Ti](ClO_4)_2$. Niobium dicyclopentadienyl bromide, $(C_5H_5)_2NbBr_3$ is converted by alkalis to $(C_5H_5)_2NbBr_2OH$. The structures of the covalent dicyclopentadienyl metallic halides are conjectured to be those given in Figs. 25.27 and 25.28.

The ionic halides. Although the halides of titanium and niobium are covalent, the ion $[(C_5H_5)_2Ti]^{2+}$ must be present in the perchlorate. Other ions are $[(C_5H_5)_2M]^+$, where M may be V, Cr, Mo, W, Fe, Ru, Co, Rh, Ni. The oxidation-reduction potentials of the reaction $(C_5H_5)_2M \rightleftharpoons [(C_5H_5)_2M]^+$, where M is Fe, Ru, Ni, and of the reaction $[(C_5H_5)_2Ti]^+ \rightleftharpoons [(C_5H_5)_2Ti]^{2+}$, have been measured polarographically.

A typical ionic dicyclopentadienyl chloride is ferricinium chloride, $[(C_5H_5)_2Fe]Cl$. It is exceedingly soluble in water, but completely insoluble in ether. The aqueous

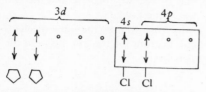

Fig. 25.27. Suggested orbital diagram for $(C_5H_5)_2TiCl_2$.

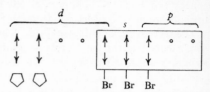

Fig. 25.28. Suggested orbital diagram for $(C_5H_5)_2NbBr_3$.

solution yields precipitates with ions such as I_3^-, the tetraphenyl borate ion, and the picrate ion†. The Ni, Co, and Rh dicyclopentadienyl ions also give insoluble salts with the same reagents. $(C_5H_5)_2Cr$ is a strong reducing agent which dissolves in dilute acid to give a blue solution. This solution contains the ion $[(C_5H_5)_2Cr]^+$ but it does not give the above precipitation reactions.

THE METAL CYCLOPENTADIENYL CARBONYLS

A list of metal cyclopentadienyl carbonyls is given in Table 25.15. It is to be noted that (except in the case of $(C_5H_5)_2Fe(CO)_2$) in each molecule or ion one atom of metal is associated with one pentadienyl ring. The following two methods are available for the preparation of these compounds.

(1) *By the action of the carbonyl of the metal on cyclopentadiene.* $(C_5H_5)_2Cr(CO)_6$ may be made this way, but only if the conditions are mild (p. 1117). The corresponding compounds of molybdenum and tungsten are made when the reaction takes place at 250–300°, and the iron compound, $(C_5H_5)_2Fe_2(CO)_4$, is made similarly using $Fe(CO)_5$. Cobalt octacarbonyl reacts exothermally with cyclopentadiene at room temperature.

(2) *By the action of the metal dicyclopentadienyl on carbon monoxide.* $(C_5H_5)_2Cr(CO)_6$ is made by this method using carbon monoxide at 100 atm and 160°. (At 110° the violet-brown salt is obtained $[(C_5H_5)_2Cr^+][(C_5H_5Cr(CO)_3^-]$. The compounds of vanadium, manganese, and cobalt can be made without the isolation of the metal dicyclopentadienyl; carbon monoxide is passed over the product resulting from the treatment of sodium cyclopentadienyl with the metallic halide.

The properties of the metal cyclopentadienyl carbonyls are summarised briefly in Table 25.14.

The structure of $(C_5H_5)_2Fe_2(CO)_4$ has been determined‡ by X-ray analysis (Fig. 25.29). The distance Fe–Fe is the same as that in iron enneacarbonyl.

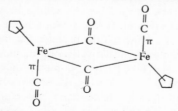

Fig. 25.29. The structure of $(C_5H_5)_2Fe_2(CO)_4$.

†Ferricinium picrate may be made by the oxidation of ferrocene in benzene with benzoquinone in the presence of picric acid.
‡ O. S. Mills, *Acta. Cryst.*, **11**, 620, 1958.

Table 25.14. *The Metal Cyclopentadienyl Carbonyls*

Formula	Physical state	m.p.	Magnetism	Notes
$(C_5H_5)V(CO)_4$	Pale orange solid	138°	Diamagnetic	Loses CO above 110° in vacuo
$(C_5H_5)_2Cr_2(CO)_6$	Blue green solid		Diamagnetic	Reacts with CO at 100 atm and 250° to give $Cr(CO)_6$
$(C_5H_5)_2Mo_2(CO)_6$			Diamagnetic	
$(C_5H_5)_2W_2(CO)_6$			Diamagnetic	
$(C_5H_5)_3Cr_2(CO)_3$				A salt: $[(C_5H_5)_2Cr]^+[C_5H_5Cr(CO)_3]^-$
$(C_5H_5)Mn(CO)_3$	Pale yellow solid	77°	Diamagnetic	Sublimes unchanged in air above 60°. Reacts with NO to give $[(C_5H_5)Mn(CO)_2NO]^+$, isolated as the chloroplatinate
$(C_5H_5)_2Fe_2(CO)_4$				Oxidised by air in acid conditions in the presence of a chloride to $[(C_5H_5)Fe(CO)_2^+][Cl^-]$
$(C_5H_5)_2Fe(CO)_2$				Made by treating $(C_5H_5)Fe(CO)_2Cl$ with $Na(C_5H_5)$. Decomposes rapidly at 80° to ferrocene and $(C_5H_5)_2Fe_2(CO)_4$
$(C_5H_5)Co(CO)_2$	Dark red liquid	b.p. 75° at 22 mm	Diamagnetic	Loses CO in vacuo. CO can be replaced by PCl_3

The absorption spectrum shows a maximum at 1760 cm^{-1} which is associated with a bridging CO group (p. 1089), and also at 1936 and 1982 cm^{-1} which show the presence of a —C=O group. By making use of the principles applied in assigning a structure to cobalt octacarbonyl (p. 1097), the orbital diagram shown in Fig. 25.30 may be drawn for $(C_5H_5)_2Fe_2(CO)_4$.

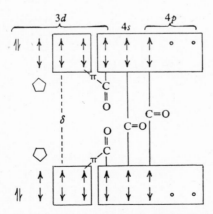

Fig. 25.30. Orbital diagram for $(C_5H_5)_2Fe_2(CO)_4$.

In the molecule of $(C_5H_5)_2Fe_2(CO)_4$ (Fig. 25.29) each iron atom is at the centre of a trigonal bipyramid. The Fe—C_5H_5 bond passes through the centre of one of the edges of the bipyramid. CO groups are situated at one polar and at two equatorial apices of

36+a.t.i.c.

the bipyramid. The two apices joined by the edge through which passes the Fe—C$_5$H$_5$ bond are not occupied by any ligands. This fact is expressed in the orbital diagram (Fig. 25.30) by the absence of electrons in two of the five hybrid σ orbitals of each iron atom.

Orbital diagrams may be assigned to the other metal cyclopentadienyl carbonyls and their derivatives as in Table 25.15. These structures make use of the canonical forms of CO and NO, as explained on pp. 1078 and 1113. Table 25.15 shows that two hybrid orbitals in every one of the structures formulated in this way are regularly unoccupied by electrons. The orbital structure of ferrocene (p. 1119) (the molecule of which contains two cyclopentadienyl rings), has four unoccupied orbitals if the three 4p orbitals are taken into account. It is difficult not to conclude that these unoccupied orbitals are in some way associated with the cyclopentadienyl ring.

THE METAL CYCLOPENTADIENYL CARBONYL HYDRIDES

These appear to be limited to the Cr, Mo, W compounds, of the type (C$_5$H$_5$)Cr(CO)$_3$H. The chromium compound is made by treating chromium dicyclopentadienyl with a mixture of carbon monoxide and hydrogen (cf. method 2, p. 1120). The compounds can also be prepared by treatment of the metal hexacarbonyls with lithium cyclopentadienyl, followed by acidification. The chromium compound is a yellow crystalline solid, m.p. 58°, at which temperature it decomposes to yield (C$_5$H$_5$)$_2$Cr$_2$(CO)$_6$. It dissolves in alkalis to yield salts. The solution of the sodium salt with mercuric cyanide gives Hg((C$_5$H$_5$)Cr(CO)$_3$)$_2$, which is soluble in organic solvents. The mercury compound with the ion [(C$_5$H$_5$)$_2$Cr$^+$] gives the salt [(C$_5$H$_5$)$_2$Cr$^+$][(C$_5$H$_5$)Cr(CO)$_3$$^-$]. This is soluble in water, but is nevertheless volatile.

Table 25.15. *Cyclopentadienyl Carbonyls, Cyclopentadienyl Carbonyl Hydrides, Cyclopentadienyl Carbonyl Halides, and Cyclopentadienyl Carbonyl Nitrosyl derivatives of the Transition Metals*

Group	Compound	Orbital diagram†	Assumed valence state of the metal atom
V	(C$_5$H$_5$)V(CO)$_4$		Octahedral
VI	(C$_5$H$_5$)$_2$Cr$_2$(CO)$_6$		Octahedral
VII	(C$_5$H$_5$)Mn(CO)$_3$		Trigonal bipyramidal
VIII	(C$_5$H$_5$)$_2$Fe$_2$(CO)$_4$		Trigonal bipyramidal

† The orbital diagrams are in an abbreviated form; comparison of Fig. 25.30 with the orbital diagram for (C$_5$H$_5$)$_2$Fe$_2$(CO)$_4$ in the table should make the symbolism clear.

Table 25.15 (*continued*).

Group	Compound	Orbital diagram	Assumed valence state of the metal atom
	$(C_5H_5)_2Fe(CO)_2$	⇅ ○ ○ ⇅ ⇅ ⇅ ⇅ ∘ ∘ CO CO	Tetrahedral
IX	$(C_5H_5)Co(CO)_2$	⇅ ⇅ ○ ⇅ ⇅ ⇅ ⇅ ∘ ∘ CO CO	Tetrahedral
VI	$(C_5H_5)Cr(CO)_3H$	⬠ ⇅ ⇅ ⇅ ⇅ ⇅ ⇅ ∘ ∘ H CO CO CO	Trigonal bipyramidal
VIII	$(C_5H_5)Fe(CO)_2Cl$	⇅ ⬠ ⇅ ⇅ ⇅ ⇅ ⇅ ∘ ∘ CO CO Cl	Trigonal bipyramidal
	$[(C_5H_5)Fe(CO)_2OH_2]^+$	⇅ ⬠ ⇅ ⇅ ⇅ ⇅ ⇅ ∘ ∘ $^+$ CO CO OH₂	Trigonal bipyramidal
VI	$(C_5H_5)Cr(CO)_2NO$, also Mo and W	⬠ ⇅ ⇅ ⇅ ⇅ ⇅ ⇅ ∘ ∘ NO CO CO B	Trigonal bipyramidal
X	$(C_5H_5)NiNO$	⇅ ⇅ ⇅ ○ ⇅ ⇅ ⇅ ∘ ∘ NO B	Trigonal
VI	$(C_5H_5)Cr(NO)_2Cl$ chlorine may be replaced by CH_3 or CH_2Cl	⬠ ⇅ ⇅ ⇅ ⇅ ⇅ ⇅ ∘ ∘ NO NO Cl D B	Trigonal bipyramidal
VI	$[(C_5H_5)Mo(CO)_2NO^+]$	⬠ ⇅ ⇅ ⇅ ⇅ ⇅ ⇅ ∘ ∘ $^+$ CO CO NO	Trigonal bipyramidal

THE METAL CYCLOPENTADIENYL CARBONYL HALIDES

Iron cyclopentadienyl dicarbonyl chloride, $(C_5H_5)Fe(CO)_2Cl$, is made by the atmospheric oxidation of $(C_5H_5)_2Fe_2(CO)_4$ in acid conditions in the presence of a chloride. It is a red diamagnetic solid. It decomposes at 87° to yield some ferrocene. It is somewhat soluble in water, but it can be completely extracted from the solution with chloroform, and so must be largely covalent. It reacts slowly with silver nitrate. Prolonged heating with KCN gives $(C_5H_5)Fe(CO)_2CN$. The corresponding bromide is also known. The compound $[(C_5H_5)Fe(CO)_2H_2O^+]Cl^-$ is ionic.

THE METAL CYCLOPENTADIENYL NITROSYL DERIVATIVES

$(C_5H_5)Cr(CO)_2NO$ exists as orange crystals. The corresponding compounds of Mo and W are known. $(C_5H_5)NiNO$ is a fairly stable, diamagnetic, dark red, volatile liquid. It is made by the direct action of nitric oxide on nickel dicyclopentadienyl.

36*

CHAPTER TWENTY-SIX

THE LANTHANONS AND ACTINONS

THE LANTHANONS

The lanthanons are the metals in Period 6 with atomic numbers 57–71. The electron configurations of these elements are shown in Table 26.1.

Table 26.1. *Electron Configurations of the Outer Shells of the Lanthanon Atoms in the Ground State*

Element	Atomic number Z	Quantum shell $n=4$				Quantum shell $n=5$			$n=6$
		s	p	d	f	s	p	d	s
La	57	2	6	10		2	6	1	2
Ce	58	2	6	10	2	2	6		2
Pr	59	2	6	10	3	2	6		2
Nd	60	2	6	10	4	2	6		2
Pm	61	2	6	10	5	2	6		2
Sm	62	2	6	10	6	2	6		2
Eu	63	2	6	10	7	2	6		2
Gd	64	2	6	10	7	2	6	1	2
Tb	65	2	6	10	9	2	6		2
Dy	66	2	6	10	10	2	6		2
Ho	67	2	6	10	11	2	6		2
Er	68	2	6	10	12	2	6		2
Tm	69	2	6	10	13	2	6		2
Yb	70	2	6	10	14	2	6		2
Lu	71	2	6	10	14	2	6	1	2

The electronic structure of the lanthanon atoms is characterised by the presence of occupied f orbitals in the quantum shell $n=4$. It has been shown† that the $4f$ orbitals for elements of atomic number 47–56 have a large spatial extension which brings them

† M. Goeppert Mayer, *Phys. Rev.*, **60**, 1941, 184.

to the periphery of the atom, but a high energy level which precludes their occupation by electrons. With increase of atomic number the spatial extension contracts, and the energy level falls. The change at cerium ($Z = 58$) is sudden. The energy of the $4f$ orbitals falls greatly, and occupation of the orbitals by electrons is favoured, but the marked contraction opposes the use of $4f$ electrons for bond formation. Since all the lanthanons attain the oxidation state III, and three of them, cerium, praseodymium, and terbium, attain oxidation state IV, it appears that electrons are so firmly held in the $4f$ orbitals that only one (or at most two) can be ionised or used for forming σ bonds.

In the ground state the outermost shell ($n = 6$) of each lanthanon atom is occupied by two s electrons. The electron configuration of the penultimate shell ($n = 5$) is s^2p^6, except for the three elements lanthanum, gadolinium, and lutecium, for which the configuration is $s^2p^6d^1$. In the lanthanum atom the $4f$ orbitals are unoccupied, in gadolinium the $4f$ orbitals are half-occupied, and in lutecium the $4f$ orbitals are completely occupied. The number of electrons occupying the $4f$ orbitals increases with atomic number as shown in Table 26.1.

The lanthanons are remarkable for their similarity in chemical properties, which is explained by the nearly identical configurations of the electrons available for bond formation. For each atom the valency electrons consist of two electrons in the $6s$ orbital, and an additional lightly held electron in either a $5d$ or a $4f$ orbital.† The chemical properties of the lanthanons, however, are not identical, (i) because the successive addition of electrons to the $4f$ (or $5d$) orbitals of the atoms on the aufbau principle while maintaining the electrical neutrality of the atom, causes variations in the distribution of the negative charge, and (ii) because the effective nuclear charge $(Z_{eff})_{ion}$ (p. 955) of the ions M^{3+} increases steadily with increasing atomic number (see below), and hence the electronegativities of the ions increase, and the radii of the ions decrease. The basic strengths of the hydroxides formed by the lanthanons therefore fall with increasing atomic number.

Ionic radii; the lanthanon (or lanthanide) contraction. The observed values of the ionic radii of the trivalent lanthanon ions are set out in Table 26.2. Like the ions of the transition elements (p. 955), the ionic radii show a progressive diminution with increasing atomic number. This diminution is known as the *lanthanon contraction*. The evaluation of the eigenfunctions of the $4f$ orbitals of the *atoms* of the lanthanons shows that the orbitals lie within the $5d$ and $6s$ orbitals, and hence the screening power of a $4f$ electron is unity (p. 136). Therefore the addition of an electron to the $4f$ orbitals on the aufbau principle exactly balances the additional unit of nuclear charge, and there is no change in $(Z_{eff})_{mol}$. On the simple central field theory $(Z_{eff})_{mol}$ for all *atoms* of the lanthanons is 2·65 and hence it would be predicted that the atomic radii should also remain constant. Experiment shows that there is a slight variation in the value of the atomic radius along the series (Table 26.2), and that the atomic radii of europium and ytterbium are anomalous. These two metals crystallise with cubic lattices and attain oxidation state II.

When the atom is triply *ionised*, the screening power of a $4f$ electron is no longer equal to unity, as the shell ($n = 4$) then becomes the penultimate shell, and each time an electron is added to the $4f$ orbitals the effective nuclear charge $(Z_{eff})_{ion}$ is increased by 0·15. On the central field model it would be expected that $(Z_{eff})_{ion}$ would be inversely proportional to r_{ion} (p. 955). Fig. 26.1 shows that this relation holds‡ accurately for the lanthanon M^{3+} ions.

---

† The energies of the $5d$ and the $4f$ orbitals are very nearly equal for the lanthanons of low atomic number.

‡Although the screening constants given on p. 136 must be applied with caution to atoms of high atomic number, Figs. 26.1 and 26.3 show that progressive changes of properties of closely related sets of elements of high atomic number can be interpreted by the use of these constants.

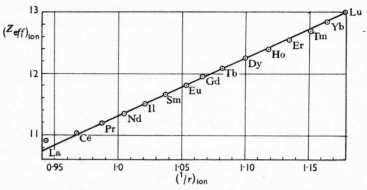

Fig. 26.1.   Relation of ionic radius to $(Z_{eff})_{ion}$ for M^{3+} ions of the lanthanons. (Values of r_{ion} are taken from D. H. Templeton and C. H. Dauben, *J. Amer. Chem. Soc.*, **76**, 5237 (1954).)

Table 26.2.   *Radii of the Atoms†and the Ions M^{3+}‡ of the Lanthanons*

Metal	At. No.	Crystal Structure§	Atomic radius	Ionic radius	Metal	At. No.	Crystal Structure§	Atomic radius	Ionic radius
La	57	h.c.p.	1·87	1·061	Tb	65	h.c.p.	1·77	0·923
Ce	58	f.c.c.	1·81	1·034	Dy	66	h.c.p.	1·77	0·908
Pr	59	h.c.p.	1·82	1·013	Ho	67	h.c.p.	1·76	0·894
Nd	60	h.c.p.	1·82	0·995	Er	68	h.c.p.	1·75	0·881
Pm	61	—	—	(0·979)	Tm	69	h.c.p.	1·74	0·869
Sm	62	rhom.	—	0·964	Yb	70	f.c.c.	1·93	0·858
Eu	63	b.c.c.	2·04	0·950	Lu	71	h.c.p.	1·74	0·848
Gd	64	h.c.p.	1·79	0·938					

† Values from Bommer, *Z. anorg. Chem.*, **242**, 1939, 277.
‡ Values from D. H. Templeton and C. H. Dauben, see Fig. 26.1.
§ Data from F. H. Spedding and A. H. Daone, *Progress in Nuclear Energy, Series V. Metallurgy and Fuels*, p. 413 (Pergamon Press, 1956).

The magnetic properties of the lanthanon M^{3+} ions. Cabrera‖ has measured the magnetic susceptibilities of the trivalent ions of the lanthanons in aqueous solution. The results (which are in close accord with those of other workers), expressed as the magnetic moments of the ions, are set out in Table 26.3, column 2.

The magnetic moments of ions of the transition metals are assumed to be due to electron spin only; as the orbitals occupied by unpaired electrons are near the peripheries of the ions, it is generally supposed that the orbital angular momenta are quenched by external fields. From the very high values of the magnetic moments for Tb^{3+}, Dy^{3+}, Ho^{3+}, and Er^{3+}, it is clear that at least for these ions the orbital contributions must be taken into account. Since the $4f$ orbitals are well shielded from outside fields by the electrons of the $n=5$ and $n=6$ quantum shells, this is a reasonable con-

‖ B. Cabrera, *Comp. rend.*, 1925, **180**, 668.

Table 26.3.   *The Magnetic Moments of the M³⁺ Lanthanon Ions*

1	2	3			4							5	6
Ion M^{3+}	Observed magnetic moment Bohr magnetons	Calculated magnetic moment			Electron distribution in 4f orbitals (The orbitals are designated by the magnetic quantum number, m)							$\sum m$	Colour of ion
		Hund	Van Vleck	Assuming a breakdown in the Russell-Saunders coupling	$+3$	-3	$+2$	-2	$+1$	-1	0		
	Cabrera												
La	0·0	0·0	0·0	0·0									Colourless
Ce	2·39	2·54	2·56	2·73					↑			+1	Colourless
Pr	3·60	3·58	3·62	3·83					↑		↑	+1	Green
Nd	3·62	3·62	3·68	3·87					↑	↑	↑	0	Red
Pm	—	2·68	2·83	2·83					↑	↑	↑↓	0	Pink
Sm	1·54	0·84	1·60	1·73					↑↓	↑↓	↑	0	Yellow
Eu	3·61	0·0	3·45	3·83		↑	↑↓		↑	↑	↑	+1	Pink
Gd	8·2	7·94	7·94	7·9	↑	↑	↑	↑	↑	↑	↑	0	(Ultraviolet)
Tb	9·6	9·7	9·7	9·93	↑↓	↑	↑	↑	↑	↑	↑	+3	Pink
Dy	10·5	10·6	10·6	10·9	↑↓	↑	↑↓	↑	↑	↑	↑	+5	Yellow
Ho	10·5	10·6	10·6	10·9	↑↓	↑	↑↓	↑	↑↓	↑	↑	+6	Yellow
Er	9·5	9·6	9·6	9·87	↑↓	↑	↑↓	↑	↑↓	↑	↑↓	+6	Red
Tm	7·2	7·6	7·6	7·83	↑↓	↑	↑↓	↑	↑↓	↑↓	↑↓	+5	Green
Yb	4·4	4·5	4·5	4·73	↑↓	↑	↑↓	↑↓	↑↓	↑↓	↑↓	+3	Colourless
Lu	—	0·0	0·0	0·0	↑↓	↑↓	↑↓	↑↓	↑↓	↑↓	↑↓	0	Colourless

clusion. It is also clear that there is a minimum value for the magnetic moment of lanthanon trivalent ions at Pm^{3+}, Sm^{3+}, and Eu^{3+}; any acceptable general expression for the magnetic moment of the lanthanon ions must indicate this minimum. Values for the magnetic moments calculated by Hund are set out in column 3 of Table 26.3. Agreement between observed and calculated values is good except for Sm^{3+} and Eu^{3+}. In making his calculations, Hund assumed that the Russell-Saunders LS coupling applies throughout. Van Vleck and Frank† applied to Hund's theory a second order correction allowing for the separation of the multiplet states. The results were in better agreement with experiment than were Hund's results (Table 26.3).‡

It is interesting to compare Hund's values with those derived from a simple calculation which assumes a breakdown of the Russell-Saunders coupling due to the applied magnetic field, and consequently a resultant magnetic moment formed by the addition of the separate spin and orbital magnetic moments. The resultant magnetic moments of the ions obtained by this method are shown in Table 26.3, column 3; column 4 in the Table shows the electron configurations on which the calculations are based. The 4f orbitals are designated by the magnetic quantum numbers m. The magnetic moment of a given ion can be deduced from the electron configuration in the following manner.

The angular momentum of orbital motion in the direction of the field for one electron is given by $mh/2\pi$. The magnetic moment arising from this orbital motion is:

$$\frac{\epsilon}{2m_0 c} \times \text{angular momentum} = \frac{m\epsilon h}{4\pi m_0 c}$$
$$= m \text{ Bohr magnetons.}$$

If the total magnetic moment of the atom due to orbital motion of all the electrons in occupied f orbitals is taken to be $\sum m$ Bohr magnetons, and the total spin magnetic

† J. H. Van Vleck and A. Frank. *Phys. Rev.*, 1929, **34**, 1494 and 1625.
‡ A similar correction applied to calculations concerning the ions of the iron group, however, gave no agreement with experiment, and it was assumed that the orbital moments of these ions must be quenched in the strong crystalline field.

moment as $\sqrt{(n(n+2))}$ Bohr magnetons (p. 948), then total magnetic moment of ion = $[\sum m + \sqrt{(n(n+2))}]$ Bohr magnetons.

It will be seen that this calculation produces values for the magnetic moments of the ions which are in good agreement throughout with the experimental values. The agreement is not so precise as that shown by Hund's values for most of the ions, but the observed values for Sm^{3+} and Eu^{3+} no longer appear anomalous. The magnetic evidence suggests that from Gd^{3+} to Lu^{3+}, the electron configurations of the $4f$ orbitals follow a regular pattern in accordance with Hund's rule, but for ions of lanthanons of atomic number less than 64, the pattern of electron configurations is irregular and appears to override Hund's rule. It may be conjectured that the introduction of one to five electrons into $4f$ orbitals would produce asymmetrical fields which would cause the pairing up of otherwise unpaired electrons. This general concept is analagous to

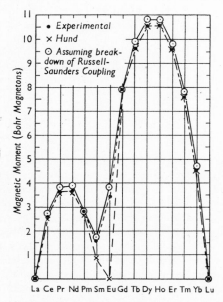

Fig. 26.2. Relation between observed and calculated magnetic moments of the lanthanon M^{3+} ions.

that used by the ligand-field theory in the prediction of high-spin and low-spin complexes (p. 950).

The relations between the observed and calculated values of the magnetic moments are set out graphically in Fig. 26.2.

Colour of ions. The absorption spectra of the compounds of trivalent lanthanons consist of a few well-defined and highly characteristic bands. In this they differ from the spectra of coloured salts of other elements. The colours of the M^{3+} ions are stated in Table 26.3. It will be noted that if gadolinium ($Z = 64$) is taken as the starting point, the sequence of colours is the same for decrease or increase of atomic number. This relation is known as the Main Smith colour sequence.

The lanthanon metals. The crystal structures of the lanthanon metals are set out in Table 26.2. The melting points of the metals rise fairly regularly from about 800° for cerium to about 1500° for lutecium. The metals are electropositive and tarnish easily in moist air; they burn to oxide at about 300°. They liberate hydrogen from water and are attacked by acids but not by alkalis. The metals absorb hydrogen to form interstitial hydrides. By direct action with the appropriate elements they form acetylides MC_2, nitrides MN, and oxides, sulphides, and tellurides, M_2X_3. They also combine directly with the halogens to give trihalides, $Mhal_3$.

Chemical properties of the lanthanons. All the lanthanons attain oxidation state III in the trivalent cations M^{3+}. With the exception of samarium, europium, and ytterbium, which attain state II, and of cerium and praseodymium which attain state IV, no member of the series attains any other oxidation state.

Oxidation state III is the most stable state for all the lanthanons (except for cerium combined with oxygen). In this state the chemical properties and the physical properties of compounds of the lanthanons are so closely similar that the isolation of a pure compound of any given lanthanon is a matter of extreme difficulty. Much skill and patience have been expended in successfully isolating compounds of each of the lanthanons, but descriptions of these experiments must be sought elsewhere.

Lanthanons in oxidation state III. The chemistry of the lanthanons in oxidation state III is in general what would be predicted for trivalent electropositive metals. The oxides M_2O_3 are basic and soluble in acids, and are easily prepared by the ignition of oxyacid salts. Hydroxides are known of composition $M(OH)_3$ and $MO \cdot OH$. The trifluorides are insoluble. The other trihalides are coloured and soluble, and crystallise with 6 or 7 molecules of water of crystallisation. The oxalates, nitrates, nitrites, and sulphates all crystallise with water of crystallisation, thus indicating a considerable tendency to complex formation.

Lanthanons in oxidation state IV. Cerium and praseodymium attain oxidation state IV by the loss of one electron from the $4f$ orbital in addition to the loss of the $5d$ and $6s$ electrons. Cerium forms the ion Ce^{4+} which is stable in aqueous solution. The ion Ce^{4+} is present in $Ce(ClO_4)_4$ which appears to be a normal salt. Cerium also forms ceric oxide CeO_2 and ceric hydroxide $Ce(OH)_4$. Ceric oxide is a pale yellow solid, m.p. about 2600°, which has the fluorite structure. It is more stable than the trioxide Ce_2O_3. When Ce_2O_3, or $Ce(NO_3)_3$, or $Ce(OH)_3$, is heated in oxygen the residue is CeO_2. If $Ce(OH)_4$ is dissolved in hydrochloric acid, however, chlorine is evolved and $CeCl_3$ is formed. It is possible to obtain $pyr_2[CeCl_6]$ from the solution of $Ce(OH)_4$ in concentrated hydrochloric acid, and hence the chloride $CeCl_4$ must be present at least temporarily in the solution. The ceric ion forms other complexes. The sulphate in solution answers to no tests for Ce^{4+} ions, and hence must be a complex. The acetylacetone complexes of Ce^{III} and Ce^{IV} are known. Both are associated with water molecules, $CeA_3,3H_2O$ and $CeA_4,10H_2O$, but their constitutions are unknown.

Praseodymium forms the ion Pr^{4+}, but this is so easily reduced that it oxidises the ion Ce^{3+}. Praseodymium also gives rise to the oxide PrO_2, and to praseodymates such as Na_2PrO_3. Praseodymic oxide, PrO_2, is black and has the fluorite lattice; it liberates chlorine from hydrochloric acid.

TbO_2 is recognised, but otherwise evidence on the quadrivalency of neodymium and terbium although carefully considered by many authors, does not appear to be convincing. Consideration of the magnetic properties of LaS_2 and of CeS_2 suggests that these compounds should be formulated $La_2S_3 \cdot S$ and $Ce_2S_3 \cdot S$.

Lanthanons in oxidation state II. Samarium, europium, and ytterbium form compounds in which they are present in oxidation state II. In this state samarium and europium have unpaired electrons in the f shell; the compounds are coloured and paramagnetic. Ytterbium in this state, however, by transferring the $5d$ electron to a $4f$ orbital completes the $4f$ shell. Many of its compounds are coloured; anhydrous $YbCl_2$ is diamagnetic.

The samarium, Sm^{II}, compounds are made either by reducing the trivalent compounds with a metallic amalgam, or by heating the trihalide to 500–900° alone, or with hydrogen. Samarium dichloride is made by reducing samarium trichloride with sodium amalgam in solution in absolute alcohol. The dichloride is insoluble in alcohol and is precipitated. The sparingly soluble sulphate, chromate, and phosphate can be precipitated from a freshly prepared solution of samarium di-iodide. Samarium di-iodide, a dark green solid, m.p. 840° is made by reducing SmI_3 with hydrogen at 350°. It dissolves in water to give a green solution, but on standing hydrogen is evolved and $SmI_2(OH)$ is precipitated. The oxide and sulphide of divalent samarium are not known.

The dihalides of europium, $Euhal_2$ (including the fluoride), are made by reducing the trihalides with hydrogen at about 600°. The difluoride has the fluorite lattice. The dichloride forms a dihydrate, $EuCl_2,2H_2O$, which resembles $BaCl_2,2H_2O$. Europium dihalides and the sulphide are extremely readily oxidised by air.

EuS, $EuSe$, $EuTe$ are black solids made by heating $EuCl_2$ with S, Se, Te, in hydrogen. They all have the sodium chloride lattice. The magnetic moments are 7·4 to 7·9 Bohr magnetons. $EuSO_4$ has the same lattice as $BeSO_4$. From this brief account it is seen that there is a similarity between europous compounds and the corresponding compounds of the alkaline earth metals.

The divalency of ytterbium can be explained by the tendency of a large shell to hasten to completion, which results in the absorption of the $5d$ electron into the $4f$ shell. This tendency might also explain the divalency of samarium, but it is not certain whether the electron configuration of europium can be explained in this way.

THE ACTINONS

The actinons are the elements following actinium in the seventh Period of the periodic table. They are radioactive, and therefore of the greatest importance in the study of nuclear chemistry and of the principles which underlie the conversion of mass into energy. For this reason, actinon compounds have been the subject of intensive research, and although many of them have been isolated only in milligram quantities or less, a large body of accurate data concerning their properties has been accumulated. Experimental work on properties of the actinons and their compounds is somewhat different from normal work in chemistry and physics because only thorium and uranium occur naturally in quantities which permit work on a macrochemical scale; the other elements are made artificially by nuclear bombardment, and the quantities obtainable are such that microchemical methods must be used, or are so very small that tracer techniques must be employed. Since the radioactivity of the actinons renders them injurious to health, experiments must normally be conducted by remote control. Even when larger quantities of material are available much of the experimental work is done using microchemical methods, because the small quantity of the elements used minimises the danger to health and the interference of the radioactivity with the course of the experiments.

The object of work on the actinons has been largely concerned with the preparation and isolation of pure substances to facilitate experiments on nuclear physics. The orbital structures of the actinon atoms are not easy to determine because the energy differences between the orbitals near the periphery are not large, and hence the correlation between the properties of the actinon compounds and their orbital structures cannot be made with certainty. In this chapter no attempt is made to give a complete account of all the actinons. A general account is given first followed by a more detailed treatment of thorium and uranium.

The electron configuration of the atoms of the actinons in the ground state is set out in Table 26.4.

Table 26.4. *Electron Configuration of the Three Outer Shells of the Atoms of the Actinons in the Ground State*

Symbol of element	Name of element	Atomic number Z	Quantum shell $n=5$				Quantum shell $n=6$				$n=7$	Oxidation state
			s	p	d	f	s	p	d	f	s	
Ac	Actinium	89	2	6	10		2	6	1		2	III
Th	Thorium	90	2	6	10		2	6	2		2	IV
Pa	Protactinium	91	2	6	10	2	2	6	1		2	IV, V
U	Uranium	92	2	6	10	3	2	6	1		2	III, IV, V, VI
Np	Neptunium	93	2	6	10	4	2	6	1		2	III, IV, V, VI
Pu	Plutonium	94	2	6	10	6	2	6			2	III, IV, V, VI
Am	Americium	95	2	6	10	7	2	6			2	III, (IV), V, VI
Cm	Curium	96	2	6	10	7	2	6	1		2	III, (IV)
Bk	Berkelium	97	2	6	10	8	2	6	1		2	III, IV
Cf	Californium	98	2	6	10	10	2	6			2	III
E	Einsteinium	99	2	6	10	11	2	6			2	
Fm	Fermium	100	2	6	10	12	2	6			2	
Mv	Mendelinium	101	2	6	10	13	2	6			2	
No	Nobelium	102	2	6	10	14	2	6			2	
		(103)	2	6	10	14	2	6	1		2	

There is agreement that for all the actinons the quantum shells $n=1$, 2, 3, and 4, and the orbitals 5s, 5p, 5d, 6s, 6p, and 7s are completely occupied. There has been much discussion of the distribution of electrons between the 5f and the 6d orbitals. The electron configuration in Table 26.4 is that recommended by Katz and Seaborg,† and is in accord with the view that actinium in Period 7 corresponds to lanthanum in Period 6, and that the actinons form a set of 14 elements which are to be placed below the lanthanons in the periodic table. According to this view the two sets of inner transition elements correspond as shown in Table 26.5.

Table 26.5. *Relation of Actinons to Lanthanons*

Lanthanons	57 La	58 Ce	59 Pr	60 Nd	61 Pm	62 Sm	63 Eu	64 Gd	65 Tb	66 Dy	67 Ho	68 Er	69 Tm	70 Yb	71 Lu
Actinons	89 Ac	90 Th	91 Pa	92 U	93 Np	94 Pu	95 Am	96 Cm	97 Bk	98 Cf	99 E	100 Fm	101 Mv	102 No	(103)

Table 26.5 indicates that only one member of the actinons ($Z=103$) remains to be identified. If it is possible to bring about nuclear changes which produce elements of atomic number higher than 103 it is predicted that the elements will be transition elements which will take their places in the periodic table under hafnium, tantalum, and tungsten.‡ Classification by chemical experiment will be difficult, however, as the half life periods of the new elements will be short.

† *The Chemistry of the Actinide Elements*, London (Methuen and Co., Ltd.), 1957.
‡ A different electron configuration is accepted by some authors who regard thorium, protactinium, and uranium as analogous to hafnium, tantalum, and tungsten, so that the next three electrons added to the actinium atom on the aufbau principle take their places in the 6d orbitals. On this view neptunium is the first member of the inner transition series, with the electron configuration $5f^1 6d^4 7s^2$. The configurations of the remaining electrons are obtained by the aufbau addition of electrons to the 5f orbitals. If these configurations are accepted, four elements have yet to be identified to complete the second inner transition series, and einsteinium (and not curium) is the element in which the 5f orbitals are half-filled.

The allocation of electrons to the 5f or 6d orbitals in the actinon atoms is more uncertain than the allocation to the 4f or 5d orbitals in the lanthanum atoms, because the external shielding of the 5f electrons from crystal and other fields is less than that of the 4f electrons. The 5f electrons also have lower binding energies than the 4f electrons. The binding energies of the 5f and 6d orbitals are approximately equal for thorium, protactinium, and uranium, and for these elements in particular a precise determination of electron configuration is difficult. The difference in energy between the 5f and 6d orbitals may be so small that it is within the range of chemical binding energy. If this is so the configuration may vary with the oxidation state of the metal and with the nature of the compounds it forms.

Use of the 5f orbitals in bonding. It is mentioned on p. 1125 that a change in the spatial extension and energy of the 4f orbitals with atomic number becomes sudden at cerium. For elements of lower atomic number than cerium the 4f orbitals have a large extension and high energy, and for elements of higher atomic number the 4f orbitals have a contracted extension and lower energy. Hence for the lanthanons the 4f orbitals become occupied at the very point when the spatial extension is too small to enable them to form molecular orbitals with orbitals of other atoms. In Period 7 the contraction of the 5f orbitals occurs but it is less sudden than in Period 6. Hence the actinons may use the 5f orbitals for bonding. The complete valency system of the actinons consists of the orbitals 5f, 6d, 7s, and 7p.

The actinon metals melt at about 1000° and boil at about 3000°. Their specific gravities range from 11 to 20 as shown in Table 26.6.

Table 26.6.   *Certain Properties of the Actinon Metals*

	Ac	Th	Pa	U	Np	Pu	Am
Lattice or crystal form at room temperature	F.c.c.	F.c.c.	Tetragonal	Orthorhombic	Orthorhombic	Monoclinic	Hexagonal
Number of other solid forms	—	1	—	2	2	5	—
m.p. °C	1050	1750	< 1875	1132	640	640	About 800
b.p. °C	←			about 3000			→
Specific gravity at 25°		11·7	15·4	19·0	20·5	19·7	11·9
Action with air	Oxidises rapidly	Tarnishes	Tarnishes	Reacts	No reaction		

Oxidation states of the actinons. All the elements from uranium to berkelium attain oxidation state III, and all the elements from thorium to berkelium attain oxidation state IV, but this state for americium and curium is not stable (Table 26.4). U, Np, Pu, and Cm attain oxidation states V and VI, but for americium and curium states above III are increasingly unstable; for curium no state above III is known in aqueous solution (Cm^{IV} is found in solid CmO_2 and CmF_4). These generalisations are illustrated by the formulae of the actinon halides given in Table 26.7. The sudden outbreak of the range of four oxidation states at uranium is one of the reasons advanced for regarding uranium as the first member of the second inner transition series.

The actinons attain higher oxidation states than the lanthanons (compare Table 26.4 with p. 1129). This is correlated with the fact that the $5f$ orbitals are more spatially extended and of greater energy than the $4f$.

Table 26.7. *Formulae of the Actinon Halides*

Element	Fluorides				Chlorides				Bromides		Iodides
Ac 89				AcF_3				$AcCl_3$		$AcBr_3$	(AcI_3)
Th 90			ThF_4				$ThCl_4$		$ThBr_4$		ThI_4 ThI_3
Pa 91		(PaF_5)	PaF_4			$(PaCl_5)$	$PaCl_4$		$(PaBr_5)$		(PaI_5)
U 92	UF_6	UF_5	UF_4	UF_3	UCl_6 UCl_5	UCl_4	UCl_3		UBr_4	UBr_3	UI_4 UI_3
Np 93	NpF_6		NpF_4	NpF_3			$NpCl_4$	$NpCl_3$	$NpBr_4$	$NpBr_3$	NpI_3
Pu 94	PuF_6		PuF_4	PuF_3				$PuCl_3$		$PuBr_3$	PuI_3
Am 95			AmF_4	AmF_3				$AmCl_3$		$AmBr_3$	AmI_3
Cm 96			CmF_4	CmF_3							

Types of cation formed by the actinons. The characteristic cations formed by the actinons are M^{3+}, M^{4+}, MO_2^+, MO_2^{2+}. These ions are stable in acid aqueous solution. The ability of the different actinons to form these ions is shown in Table 26.8.

Table 26.8. *The Actinon Cations and their Colours*

	M^{4+}	MO_2^{2+}	M^{3+}	MO_2^+
Ac	—†	—	Colourless	—
Th	Colourless	—	—	—
Pa	Colourless	—	—	(Colourless)
U	Green	Yellow	Red	(Colour unknown)
Np	Yellow green	Pink to red	Blue to purple	Green
Pu	Orange brown	Yellow to orange	Blue to violet	(Reddish purple)
Am	—	Brown	Pink	Yellow
Cm	—	—	Colourless	

† The symbol — shows that a particular metal forms no ion of the type indicated.

The stabilities of the above ions in aqueous solution may be summarised as follows:

U^{3+} in aqueous solution evolves hydrogen on standing; aqueous solutions of Np^{3+} and Pu^{3+} are stable, but are easily oxidised to Np^{4+} and Pu^{4+}. All the remaining trivalent ions up to No^{3+} are stable.

U^{4+} and Np^{4+} are stable to water, but are slowly oxidised by air to UO_2^{2+} and NpO_2^{2+}. Pu^{4+} disproportionates to Pu^{3+} and PuO_2^{2+} when the solution is strongly acid. Little is known about the other quadrivalent ions.

UO_2^+ disproportionates to U^{4+} and UO_2^{2+}. The ions PuO_2^+ and AmO_2^+ behave similarly, but NpO_2^+ is more stable.

UO_2^{2+} is stable and difficult to reduce. NpO_2^{2+}, PuO_2^{2+} and AmO_2^{2+} are stable, but are fairly easy to reduce.

Ionic radii of the actinons. The radii of the trivalent and quadrivalent ions of the actinons are set out in Table 26.9. It is seen that for the ions M^{3+} and M^{4+} the ionic radii contract slightly with increasing atomic number. There is thus an actinon contraction corresponding to the lanthanon contraction.

Table 26.9.   *Ionic Radii of the Actinons*

Element	Radius of ion M³⁺	Radius of ion M⁴⁺
Ac 89	1·11	
Th 90	(1·08)	0·99
Pa 91	(1·05)	0·96
U 92	1·03	0·93
Np 93	1·01	9·92
Pu 94	1·00	0·90
Am 95	0·99	0·89

The relations between the ionic radii and $(Z_{eff})_{ion}$ for the ions M⁴⁺ is shown in Fig. 26.3. The linear relation which is observed for the lanthanon M³⁺ ions is approximately retained; this shows that even among the heavy elements the screening

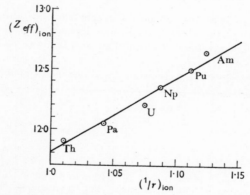

Fig. 26.3. Relation between ionic radius and $(Z_{eff})_{ion}$ for the actinon M⁴⁺ ions. (Values of r_{ion} are taken from W. H. Zachariesen, *Phys. Rev.*, 1948, **73**, 1104.)

constants can be used to correlate properties of closely related elements. If the corresponding relation is plotted for the ions Np³⁺, Pu³⁺, and Am³⁺ it is found that the three points lie on a straight line.

THORIUM

Thorium metal can be made by reducing thorium dioxide with calcium at 1000°. The metal is electropositive and reactive; its reactivity is similar to that of magnesium. It tarnishes in air, and is attacked by water and acids. Thorium compounds have ionic character. Thorium hydroxide, Th(OH)₄, is not acidic, and is insoluble in potassium hydroxide. All the four valency electrons of the thorium atom are normally used together in bond formation; thorium is rarely bivalent or tervalent. Thorium metal does not absorb nitrogen or oxygen at high temperatures, and it does not form an interstitial carbide or nitride corresponding to TiC or TiN, but it combines with hydrogen. An acetylide ThC_2 is known (p. 580). The large ionic radius of thorium enables carbon atoms to be accommodated in the metal lattice as acetylide ions. Thorium nitride has the composition Th_3N_4.

Table 26.10. *Thorium Halides*

	ThF_4	$ThCl_4$	$ThBr_4$	ThI_4
Appearance	White crystals	Colourless deliquescent needles	Colourless crystals	
m.p. °C	1111	770	769	566
b.p. °C		922	857	839
Preparation	(i) From elements at 500° (ii) HF on $ThCl_4$ at 400°	(i) From elements at red heat (ii) Heat ThO_2 in $Cl_2 + S_2Cl_2$	From elements at low red heat	From elements at low red heat
Solubility in water	Very insoluble	Soluble but slightly hydrolysed	Soluble but hydrolysed	Soluble but hydrolysed
Hydrates	$ThF_4,3H_2O$	$ThCl_4, 9, 8, 7, H_2O$		$ThI_4,10H_2O$

The properties and preparations of the thorium halides are set out in Table 26.10. Thorium tetrachloride is largely ionic. It is little hydrolysed in aqueous solution, and when fused it conducts electricity. (Liquid titanium tetrachloride is not a conductor.) Thorium tetrachloride forms additive compounds with organic compounds containing oxygen. Thorium forms a simple oxalate, $Thox_2,6H_2O$, and a simple nitrate, sulphate, and chlorate. It forms complex anions with the ions of weak acids, such as carbonic acid in $Na_6[Th(CO_3)_5],12H_2O$ and $(NH_4)_2[Th(CO_3)_3],6H_2O$. One of the $5f$ orbitals in the thorium atom in the pentacarbonato ion appears to be used for bond formation. Thorium salt solutions with hydrogen peroxide give a precipitate of $Th_2O_7,4H_2O$, of which the constitution is unknown.

URANIUM

Although uranium is regarded as the third member of the actinons (p. 1131), in many of its properties it closely resembles molybdenum and tungsten. A comparison of the types of compounds formed by uranium with those formed by the elements in sub-Group VI T can be made by reference to Table 24.17. The chief differences are (i) the absence of divalent compounds of uranium, (ii) the absence of complexes of trivalent and pentavalent uranium, and (iii) the existence of the ion UO_2^{2+}, a type of ion which is peculiar to the actinons. The metal and different types of uranium compounds in the order given in Table 24.17, are briefly considered below.

Uranium metal is highly reactive. At slightly elevated temperatures it reacts with all the common non-metals, including hydrogen and nitrogen, but it reacts with carbon only at about 2000°. With steam it gives a mixture of UO_2 and UH_3. It reacts with acids but not with alkalis.

Uranium hydride, UH_3, a brittle solid which conducts electricity, and inflames spontaneously in air, is made by heating uranium in hydrogen at 250–300°. If the hydride is heated above 300° hydrogen is released, leaving pure very finely divided uranium. The nature of uranium hydride is obscure. It is not ionic. Each uranium atom is surrounded by six other uranium atoms at a distance of 3·32, and so it is not inter-stitial.

Interstitial compounds. UC, UN, and UO all have the sodium chloride structure. UC is made from the elements at 2100°. At 2400°, with excess carbon, UC_2 is formed with a crystal structure similar to that of calcium carbide. UC_2 ignites in air at 400°, and decomposes cold water with the formation of hydrocarbons. U_2C_3 is also known. A second nitride, UN_2, with the fluorite structure, is stable under nitrogen at 100 atm pressure.

U^{III}. All the compounds of uranium in oxidation state III appear to be giant mole-cules. They include $U(BH_4)_3$, U_2S_3, and the three halides UF_3, UCl_3, and UBr_3. $U(BH_4)_3$, a brown-red non-volatile solid, which detonates violently, is made by heating $U(BH_4)_4$ at 100°. Grey crystals of U_2S_3 are obtained when UBr_3 is heated in hydrogen sulphide for 10 hours. The uranium trihalides are made by reducing the tetrahalides with hydrogen. All are red-brown solids. The fluoride is insoluble in water, and is resistant to acids except nitric acid, but the chloride and the bromide are hygroscopic and dissolve in water easily. The aqueous solution of the chloride evolves hydrogen and precipitates $U(OH)_4$.

Evidence of the inclusion of the $5f$ orbitals of uranium in the valence system of the atom is furnished by paramagnetic resonance experiments.† These experiments show that if Nd^{3+} and U^{3+} are dissolved in single crystals of CaF_2, and SrF_2 both ions have the f^3 configuration, but a hyperfine structure due to interaction with the fluorine nuclei is present in the case of U^{3+} only. It is concluded that the 5f electrons in U^{3+} have a small overlap with orbitals of the fluorine atoms, but there is no corresponding overlap between the $4f$ electrons in Nd^{3+} and the fluorine atoms.

U^{IV}. The compounds of uranium in oxidation state IV include the oxide UO_2, the sulphide US_2, the borohydride $U(BH_4)_4$, the halides $Uhal_4$, a few salts of oxyacids, and a number of anionic complexes.

U(BH₄)₄, a dark green solid, is made by treating UF_4 with aluminium borohydride. It is stable in the cold, but it reacts with air, water, alcohol, and hydrochloric acid. It can be methylated with boron trimethyl, giving ultimately $U(BH_3CH_3)_4$. If heated to 100° it yields diborane and uranium triborohydride:

$$2U(BH_4)_4 = 2U(BH_4)_3 + B_2H_6 + H_2.$$

UO₂, a brown or black powder, m.p. 2176°, is made by reducing UO_3 or U_3O_8 with hydrogen. It dissolves in nitric acid to give uranyl nitrate, but it is insoluble in other acids. It has the fluorite structure.

US₂, a grey crystalline powder, is made from the elements. It is slowly attacked by water, and rapidly by acids.

Uranium tetrahalides. All the tetrahalides are known: UF_4, a green solid, m.p. about 1000°; UCl_4, hygroscopic dark green crystals, m.p. 567°, b.p. 618°; UBr_4, hygroscopic dark brown crystals; UI_4, deliquescent black crystals, m.p. about 500°. All except the bromide are made by direct combination of the elements; UBr_4 is made by the action of hydrogen bromide on UCl_4, or by the action of bromine on a mixture of U_3O_8 and carbon. All the tetrahalides are reduced by hydrogen to the trihalides. UF_4 is scarcely soluble in water or in acids, but it is hydrolysed by boiling alkalis to $U(OH)_4$. The other halides are soluble in water and are hydrolysed in solution.

Salts. Uranium in oxidation state IV forms a chlorate, a perchlorate, and a sulphate which crystallises as the hydrates $U(SO_4)_2,4H_2O$ and $U(SO_4)_2,8H_2O$. The only nitrate is the basic salt $UO(NO_3)_2$. The salts are green, soluble in water, and easily hydrolysed. There is little evidence for the existence of the simple ion U^{4+}.

† Bleaney, Llewellyn Jones, *Proc. Phys. Soc. London*, **69B**, 1956, 858.

Complexes. The complexes of U^{IV} include $K[UF_5]$, $NH_4[UOF_3]$, $M_2[UCl_6]$ where M is any alkali metal, $M_2[UBr_6]$ where $M = Na$ or K, and sulphato complexes such as $(NH_4)_4[U(SO_4)_4]$ and oxalato complexes such as $K_4[Uox_4], 5H_2O$.

U^V. Uranium in the oxidation state V is present in UF_5, UCl_5, and probably in the oxide U_2O_5, and in the ion UO_2^+.

U^{VI}. Uranium in oxidation state VI forms two simple covalent compounds UF_6 and UCl_6, and a large number of stable compounds based on the group UO_2.

Uranium hexafluoride, UF_6, exists as very hygroscopic pale yellow crystals which sublime at 56·5°. It melts under pressure at 64°. It is made by the action of fluorine on uranium in the presence of a little chlorine, or by the action of fluorine on UCl_5. Uranium hexafluoride is not attacked by air, oxygen, chlorine, or iodine, but it is reduced by hydrogen to UF_4. It is rapidly hydrolysed by water to UO_2F_2 or UO_3. It reacts with aromatic hydrocarbons forming HF and liberating carbon. The molecule is octahedral.

Uranium hexachloride, UCl_6, is one of the only two hexachlorides known, the other being WCl_6. It is made by disproportionation of UCl_5. It decomposes very easily.

THE GROUP UO₂

The group UO_2 is so firmly knit that it has the properties of an electropositive metal. The classification that has been applied in preceding chapters of this book to the derivatives of metals (ionic compounds, giant molecule compounds, simple covalent compounds, neutral, anionic, and cationic complexes) can be applied to the derivatives of the group UO_2. UO_2 forms no simple covalent compounds. The crystal structures of certain giant molecule compounds of UO_2 have been ascertained, and these contain the linear group O—U—O. Whether the UO_2 group in all its compounds retains this arrangement is not known. The UO_2 derivatives are described below in the same order as if the group were a metal.

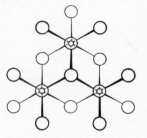

Fig. 26.4. Part of one layer of the UO_2 structure. The three uranium atoms shown (small circles) lie in the plane of the paper.

It has been suggested that $5f$ bonding is present in the ions MO_2^{2+} and MO_2^+ which are characteristic of certain actinons, but are not formed by any lanthanons. The oxygen compounds UO_3, U_3O_8, and UO_2F_2 have closely related crystal structures. The unit common to all these structures consists of a modified cadmium iodide structure with uranium atoms in the positions of the cadmium atoms (Fig. 26.4). The layers, however, are not close-packed on one another, but are linked through additional oxygen atoms, A, placed between the uranium atoms on axes at right angles to the planes of the layers. The arrangement in UO_3 is shown in Fig. 26.5. In UO_2F_2 the oxygen atoms in the layers are replaced by fluorine atoms, and each oxygen atom A is bound to one uranium atom only (Fig. 26.6). Two A oxygen atoms are interposed between each pair of layers, but there appears to be no chemical bond between them. The same arrangement is found in M_2UO_4, where M is Li, Na, K, ½Ca, ½Sr. In these compounds the co-ordination number of the uranium atom is 8, but its oxidation number remains VI, as 2 electrons are transferred to each uranium atom from the six oxygen atoms which surround it in the layer.

Ionic compounds. *Uranyl nitrate, $UO_2(NO_3)_2$,* a yellow powder, is made by dissolving UO_3 in nitric acid. It forms hydrates with 2, 3, or 6 molecules of water. It is very soluble in water and is slightly hydrolysed in solution. It dissolves in ether and acetone.

The hexahydrate is insoluble in ether. Among the other uranyl salts are the perchlorate, the sulphate, and the oxalate.

Uranyl chloride, bromide, and iodide are hygroscopic solids, soluble in water from which they crystallise as hydrates. Uranyl fluoride is probably a giant molecule compound (see below).

Giant molecule compounds. The crystal structures of UO_3, U_3O_8, and UO_2F_2 have been determined and have already been described.

UO_3, a hygroscopic powder, is made by heating uranyl nitrate, or ammonium uranate, or $UO_2(OH)_2$. On heating it loses oxygen and forms U_3O_8. It forms uranyl salts with acids, and uranates with metallic oxides.

U_3O_8, a green solid, is made by igniting UO_2, UO_3, or $(NH_4)_2U_2O_7$ in air. It is slightly volatile and can be sublimed at about $1300°$; at higher temperatures some

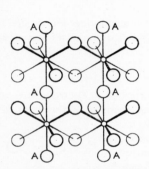

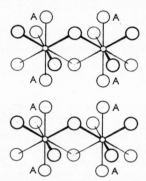

Fig. 26.5. Diagrammatic perspective of four uranium atoms showing UO_2 structure in UO_3. The planes of the layers are at right angles to the plane of the paper.

Fig. 26.6. Diagrammatic perspective of four uranium atoms in the UO_4 ion and in UO_2F_2. The orientation is the same as that in Fig. 26.5.

UO_2 is formed. It is scarcely attacked by hydrochloric acid, or by dilute sulphuric acid, but it is converted by nitric acid to $UO_2(NO_3)_2$, by hydrofluoric acid to UO_2F_2 and UF_4, and by concentrated sulphuric acid to $UO_2(SO_4)$ and $U(SO_4)_2$.

The uranates may be derived from the simple acid H_2UO_4, or they may be derived from condensed acids such as $H_2U_2O_7$. Salts of condensed acids up to $H_2U_6O_{19}$ are known. Uranium, however, does not form heteropoly acids; this is a clear mark of distinction between tungsten and uranium. Ammonia added to a solution of uranyl nitrate precipitates $(NH_4)_2U_2O_7$, a yellow powder, which like all uranates (even those of the alkali metals) is insoluble in water; sodium hydroxide added to a solution of uranyl acetate precipitates $Na_2U_2O_7$. The insolubility of the diuranates is in contrast to the solubility of the ditungstates.

UO_2F_2 is a hygroscopic solid made by dissolving UO_3 in hydrofluoric acid and evaporating the solution. It is soluble in water and alcohol, but insoluble in ether. It is non-volatile, and if heated in air it yields UO_3.

Neutral complexes. Uranyl acetylacetonate is an orange-yellow solid with the composition UO_2A_2,H_2O. If formed in the presence of quinoline or pyridine the composition is UO_2A_2B, but if formed in the presence of NH_3, $N(CH_3)H_2$, or aniline, the composition is UO_2A_2,HA,B, where B represents a molecule of the base.

Complex anions are numerous and of many types. Examples are present in the salts $K[UO_2F_3]$, $K_3[UO_2F_5]$, $K_4[UO_2F_6]$, $K_2[UO_2Cl_4]$, $K[UO_2(NO_3)_3]$, $K_2[UO_2(CN)_4]$ the only uranium cyanide derivative, and $K_2[UO_2(SO_4)_2(H_2O)_2]$. Many of these complex salts crystallise as hydrates.

Complex cations of the type present in the salt $[UO_2(NH_3)_2]Cl_2$ are known. The ammonia molecules may be replaced by molecules of ether, aniline, pyridine, or quinoline, and the chloride ion by the bromide or the nitrate ion.

Peroxyuranates. The compound $K_4[UO_8],10H_2O$, is made by treating uranyl nitrate with potassium peroxide solution. If uranyl nitrate solution is treated with hydrogen peroxide a compound of composition $UO_4,2H_2O$ is precipitated, which is stable up to 100°. This substance, however, does not react with bases and is not the parent acid of the peroxyuranates.

APPENDIX

Change of the independent variable.

Transformation from cartesian to polar form (see Fig. 1.7).

Let

$$x = r\cos\theta, \qquad\qquad r = \sqrt{(x^2+y^2)},$$

$$y = r\sin\theta, \qquad\qquad \theta = \tan^{-1}\frac{y}{x},$$

$$\frac{\partial x}{\partial r} = \cos\theta = \frac{x}{r}, \qquad\qquad \frac{\partial r}{\partial x} = \frac{x}{\sqrt{(x^2+y^2)}} = \cos\theta,$$

$$\frac{\partial y}{\partial r} = \sin\theta = \frac{y}{r}, \qquad\qquad \frac{\partial r}{\partial y} = \frac{y}{\sqrt{(x^2+y^2)}} = \sin\theta,$$

$$\frac{\partial x}{\partial \theta} = -r\sin\theta = -y, \qquad\qquad \frac{\partial \theta}{\partial x} = -\frac{y}{x^2+y^2} = -\frac{\sin\theta}{r},\dagger$$

$$\frac{\partial y}{\partial \theta} = r\cos\theta = x, \qquad\qquad \frac{\partial \theta}{\partial y} = \frac{x}{x^2+y^2} = \frac{\cos\theta}{r}.$$

If $V = f(x, y)$, $x = f'(r, \theta)$, and $y = f''(r, \theta)$,

$$\frac{\partial V}{\partial x} = \frac{\partial V}{\partial r}\frac{\partial r}{\partial x} + \frac{\partial V}{\partial \theta}\frac{\partial \theta}{\partial x} = \cos\theta\frac{\partial V}{\partial r} - \frac{\sin\theta}{r}\frac{\partial V}{\partial \theta},$$

$$\frac{\partial V}{\partial y} = \frac{\partial V}{\partial r}\frac{\partial r}{\partial y} + \frac{\partial V}{\partial \theta}\frac{\partial \theta}{\partial y} = \sin\theta\frac{\partial V}{\partial r} + \frac{\cos\theta}{r}\frac{\partial V}{\partial \theta}.$$

$$\frac{\partial V}{\partial r} = \frac{\partial V}{\partial x}\frac{\partial x}{\partial r} + \frac{\partial V}{\partial y}\frac{\partial y}{\partial r} = \frac{x}{r}\frac{\partial V}{\partial x} + \frac{y}{r}\frac{\partial V}{\partial y},$$

$$\frac{\partial V}{\partial \theta} = \frac{\partial V}{\partial x}\frac{\partial x}{\partial \theta} + \frac{\partial V}{\partial y}\frac{\partial y}{\partial \theta} = -y\frac{\partial V}{\partial x} + x\frac{\partial V}{\partial y}.$$

It is therefore possible to substitute polar operations for the equivalent cartesian operations as follows:

$$\frac{\partial}{\partial x} \equiv \cos\theta\frac{\partial}{\partial r} - \frac{\sin\theta}{r}\frac{\partial}{\partial \theta},$$

$$\frac{\partial}{\partial y} \equiv \sin\theta\frac{\partial}{\partial r} + \frac{\cos\theta}{r}\frac{\partial}{\partial \theta}.$$

It is sometimes convenient to use the following equivalences:

$$r\frac{\partial}{\partial r} \equiv x\frac{\partial}{\partial x} + y\frac{\partial}{\partial y},$$

$$\frac{\partial}{\partial \theta} \equiv x\frac{\partial}{\partial y} - y\frac{\partial}{\partial x}.$$

$\dagger$ If $u = \tan^{-1}a$, $\dfrac{da}{du} = \sec^2 u$, $\dfrac{du}{da} = \dfrac{1}{\sec^2 u}$, $= \dfrac{1}{1+\tan^2 u}$, $= \dfrac{1}{1+a^2}$.

Transformation of $\dfrac{\partial^2 V}{\partial x^2}$ and $\dfrac{\partial^2 V}{\partial y^2}$ to polar co-ordinates.

$$\frac{\partial^2 V}{\partial x^2} = \left(\frac{\partial}{\partial x}\right)^2 V$$

$$= \left(\cos\theta\,\frac{\partial}{\partial r} - \frac{\sin\theta}{r}\,\frac{\partial}{\partial\theta}\right)^2 V$$

$$= \cos\theta\,\frac{\partial}{\partial r}\left[\cos\theta\,\frac{\partial V}{\partial r} - \frac{\sin\theta}{r}\,\frac{\partial V}{\partial\theta}\right] - \frac{\sin\theta}{r}\,\frac{\partial}{\partial\theta}\left[\cos\theta\,\frac{\partial V}{\partial r} - \frac{\sin\theta}{r}\,\frac{\partial V}{\partial\theta}\right]$$

$$= \cos^2\theta\,\frac{\partial^2 V}{\partial r^2} - \frac{2\sin\theta\cos\theta}{r}\,\frac{\partial^2 V}{\partial r\,\partial\theta} + \frac{\sin^2\theta}{r^2}\,\frac{\partial^2 V}{\partial\theta^2}$$

$$+ \frac{\sin^2\theta}{r}\,\frac{\partial V}{\partial r} + \frac{2\sin\theta\cos\theta}{r^2}\,\frac{\partial V}{\partial\theta}. \tag{A.1}$$

Also,

$$\frac{\partial^2 V}{\partial y^2} = \left(\frac{\partial}{\partial y}\right)^2 V$$

$$= \left(\sin\theta\,\frac{\partial}{\partial r} + \frac{\cos\theta}{r}\,\frac{\partial}{\partial\theta}\right)^2 V$$

$$= \sin\theta\,\frac{\partial}{\partial r}\left[\sin\theta\,\frac{\partial V}{\partial r} + \frac{\cos\theta}{r}\,\frac{\partial V}{\partial\theta}\right] + \frac{\cos\theta}{r}\,\frac{\partial}{\partial\theta}\left[\sin\theta\,\frac{\partial V}{\partial r} + \frac{\cos\theta}{r}\,\frac{\partial V}{\partial\theta}\right].$$

$$= \sin^2\theta\,\frac{\partial^2 V}{\partial r^2} + \frac{2\sin\theta\cos\theta}{r}\,\frac{\partial^2 V}{\partial r\,\partial\theta} + \frac{\cos^2\theta}{r^2}\,\frac{\partial^2 V}{\partial\theta^2}$$

$$+ \frac{\cos^2\theta}{r}\,\frac{\partial V}{\partial r} - \frac{2\sin\theta\cos\theta}{r^2}\,\frac{\partial V}{\partial\theta}. \tag{A.2}$$

Adding equations (A.1) and (A.2),

$$\frac{\partial^2 V}{\partial x^2} + \frac{\partial^2 V}{\partial y^2} = \frac{\partial^2 V}{\partial r^2} + \frac{1}{r}\,\frac{\partial V}{\partial r} + \frac{1}{r^2}\,\frac{\partial^2 V}{\partial\theta^2}. \tag{A.3}$$

Transformation of $\nabla^2 V$.

$$\nabla^2 V \equiv \frac{\partial^2 V}{\partial x^2} + \frac{\partial^2 V}{\partial y^2} + \frac{\partial^2 V}{\partial z^2},$$

and the operator

$$\nabla^2 \equiv \frac{\partial^2}{\partial x^2} + \frac{\partial^2}{\partial y^2} + \frac{\partial^2}{\partial z^2}.$$

Let

$$x = r\sin\theta\cos\phi,$$
$$y = r\sin\theta\sin\phi,$$
$$z = r\cos\theta.$$

If

$$u = r\sin\theta,$$
$$x = u\cos\phi,$$

and

$$y = u\sin\phi,\dagger$$

therefore,

$$\nabla^2 V = \frac{\partial^2 V}{\partial u^2} + \frac{1}{u}\,\frac{\partial V}{\partial u} + \frac{1}{u^2}\,\frac{\partial^2 V}{\partial\phi^2} + \frac{\partial^2 V}{\partial z^2}.$$

$\dagger$ u, ϕ, and z are known as *cylindric* or *cylindrical* co-ordinates.

37+A.T.I.C.

Also,

$$\frac{\partial^2 V}{\partial u^2}+\frac{\partial^2 V}{\partial z^2}=\frac{\partial^2 V}{\partial r^2}+\frac{1}{r}\frac{\partial V}{\partial r}+\frac{1}{r^2}\frac{\partial^2 V}{\partial \theta^2} \qquad \text{(cf. A.3)}$$

and

$$\frac{\partial V}{\partial u}=\sin\theta\,\frac{\partial V}{\partial r}+\frac{\cos\theta}{r}\frac{\partial V}{\partial \theta}\quad\text{(p. 1140),}$$

therefore

$$\nabla^2 V=\frac{\partial^2 V}{\partial r^2}+\frac{2}{r}\frac{\partial V}{\partial r}+\frac{1}{r^2}\frac{\partial^2 V}{\partial \theta^2}+\frac{\cot\theta}{r^2}\frac{\partial V}{\partial \theta}+\frac{1}{r^2\sin^2\phi}\frac{\partial^2 V}{\partial \phi^2}. \qquad \text{(A.4)}$$

Equation (A.4) is sometimes written as:

$$\nabla^2 V=\frac{\partial^2 V}{\partial r^2}+\frac{2}{r}\frac{\partial V}{\partial r}+\frac{1}{r^2}\left[\frac{1}{\sin\theta}\frac{\partial}{\partial \theta}\left(\sin\theta\,\frac{\partial V}{\partial \theta}\right)+\frac{1}{\sin^2\theta}\frac{\partial^2 V}{\partial \phi^2}\right],$$

or

$$\nabla^2 V=\frac{1}{r^2}\frac{\partial}{\partial r}\left[r^2\frac{\partial V}{\partial r}\right]+\frac{1}{r^2}\left[\frac{1}{\sin\theta}\frac{\partial}{\partial \theta}\left(\sin\theta\,\frac{\partial V}{\partial \theta}\right)+\frac{1}{\sin^2\theta}\frac{\partial^2 V}{\partial \phi^2}\right].$$

Particle in a ring.

The transformation from cartesian to polar co-ordinates may be carried out as follows.

Let

$$x=r\phi,$$

then, since

$$\frac{\partial\psi}{\partial\phi}=\frac{\partial\psi}{\partial x}\frac{\partial x}{\partial\phi},$$

$$\frac{\partial\psi}{\partial x}=\frac{1}{r}\frac{\partial\psi}{\partial\phi},$$

$$\frac{\partial^2\psi}{\partial x^2}=\frac{\partial}{\partial\phi}\left(\frac{\partial\psi}{\partial x}\right)\frac{\partial\phi}{\partial x},$$

$$=\frac{1}{r^2}\frac{\partial^2\psi}{\partial\phi^2}.$$

Solution of a partial differential equation by separation of the variables.

There may be many solutions of the equation, some unattainable by ordinary methods. It is assumed that one or more of the possible solutions are products of factors, each of which is a function of one variable only. The original equation is separated into a number of equations equal to the number of variables. These subsidiary equations are solved, and those solutions are chosen which satisfy necessary conditions of the particular problem described by the original equation.

For example, if

$$\frac{\partial^2 V}{\partial x^2}+\frac{\partial^2 V}{\partial y^2}=0,$$

assume that

$$V=X(x)\,Y(y),$$

where X and Y are functions of one independent variable only.†

† This method may be extended for more than two variables.

Then,

$$\frac{\partial V}{\partial x} = Y\frac{\mathrm{d}X}{\mathrm{d}x},$$

$$\frac{\partial V}{\partial y} = X\frac{\mathrm{d}Y}{\mathrm{d}y},$$

$$\frac{\partial^2 V}{\partial x^2} = Y\frac{\mathrm{d}^2 X}{\mathrm{d}x^2}, \qquad \frac{\partial^2 V}{\partial y^2} = X\frac{\mathrm{d}^2 Y}{\mathrm{d}y^2},$$

and therefore

$$Y\frac{\mathrm{d}^2 X}{\mathrm{d}x^2} + X\frac{\mathrm{d}^2 Y}{\mathrm{d}y^2} = 0.$$

Dividing by V,

$$\frac{1}{X}\frac{\mathrm{d}^2 X}{\mathrm{d}x^2} + \frac{1}{Y}\frac{\mathrm{d}^2 Y}{\mathrm{d}y^2} = 0.$$

If the equations can be solved, each term must be separately equal to a constant. Let

$$\frac{1}{X}\frac{\mathrm{d}^2 X}{\mathrm{d}x^2} = -m^2,$$

then

$$\frac{1}{Y}\frac{\mathrm{d}^2 Y}{\mathrm{d}y^2} = m^2,$$

and therefore the solutions of the two subsidiary equations are

$$X = C_1 e^{\pm imx},$$

$$Y = C_2 e^{\pm my},$$

where C_1 and C_2 are constants. m^2 is known as a *separation constant*. The solution for V is the product of the solutions for X and Y.

Polynomials.

A polynomial in x is a sum of multiple powers of x. The degree of the polynomial is given by the highest power.

For instance, if

$$X(x) = a_0 + a_1 x + a_2 x^2 + \cdots a_n x^n, \tag{A.5}$$

the function is a polynomial of the nth degree.

Power series.

The expression given in equation (A.5) is also said to be a *power series*. If, as more and more terms are taken in the series, X approaches closer and closer to a definite value, say s, the series is said to be *convergent*. The series may consist of both positive and negative terms. It is said to be *absolutely convergent* when the series of positive terms is convergent. If s_n is the sum of n terms of the series, the error, E_n, in summing the series to the nth term only is given by

$$E_n = s - s_n.$$

For some series the limit of convergence is infinity. Any function which can be differentiated $(n+1)$ times can be expressed as a power series up to terms of the nth degree, but the sum will generally have an error E_n. It is often helpful, in solving differential equations, to express a function as a power series, and to choose n so that the error is as small as possible. An approximate solution may sometimes be obtained by this method.

Singular points. If an equation in x and y contains such terms that $f(x, y)$ becomes indeterminate for one or more points, these points are known as *singular points*. For instance, if the function contains a term $(x-a)$, the point $x=a$ is a singular point unless the function remains finite when $x=a$.

Regular points. If the function containing $(x-a)$ remains finite when $x=a$, the point is said to be a *regular point*.

Regular integrals. If the solution of an equation can be expressed in the form of a power series such as

$$y = x^s(a_0 + a_1x + a_2x^2 + a_3x^3 + \cdots \infty)$$

the solution is known as a *regular integral*.

Regular singular points. A singular point (in whose neighbourhood the coefficients of the equation are uniform) where all the integrals are regular is said to be a *regular singular point*.

Indicial equation.

For solution by a power series, the function (say y) is expressed as

$$y = x^s(a_0 + a_1x + a_2x^2 + \cdots \infty).$$

Values are found from this equation for $\dfrac{dy}{dx}$, $\dfrac{d^2y}{dx^2}$, etc., and the results are substituted in the original differential equation. Coefficients of each power of x are equated to zero, and the resulting equation, which is in s only, is known as the *indicial equation*. For instance, in the solution of Schrodinger's equation for the hydrogen atom, the following equation occurs (p. 35),

$$\frac{d}{dx}\left[x(2-x)\frac{dR}{dx}\right] + \left(\beta - \frac{m^2}{x(2-x)}\right)R = 0$$

$$(2x - x^2)\frac{d^2R}{dx^2} + (2 - 2x)\frac{dR}{dx} + \left(\beta - \frac{m^2}{x(2-x)}\right)R = 0. \qquad (A.6)$$

Let

$$R = x^s(a_0 + a_1x + a_2x^2 + \cdots),$$

$$\frac{dR}{dx} = sa_0x^{(s-1)} + (s+1)a_1x^s + \cdots,$$

$$\frac{d^2R}{dx^2} = s(s-1)a_0x^{(s-2)} + s(s+1)a_1x^{(s-1)} + \cdots.$$

Substituting in (A.6) and writing only the lower terms,

$$2s(s-1)a_0x^{s-1} - s(s-1)a_0x^s + \cdots + 2sa_0x^{s-1} - 2sa_0x^s + \cdots$$

$$+ \left(\beta - \frac{m^2}{x(2-x)}\right)(a_0x^s + \cdots) = 0.$$

Multiplying by $x(2-x)$ and taking terms only of lowest power of x, and equating to zero,

$$4s(s-1)a_0x^s + \cdots + 4sa_0x^s + \cdots - m^2a_0x^s = 0,$$

therefore

$$4s(s-1) + 4s = m^2,$$

$$4s^2 = m^2,$$

and

$$s = \frac{m}{2}.$$

Legendre polynomials.

The Legendre equation may be written as

$$(1-\mu^2)\frac{d^2y}{d\mu^2} - 2\mu\frac{dy}{d\mu} + l(l+1)y = 0.$$

l is a constant (but is not necessarily an integer at this stage).

Expressing y as a power series,

$$y = a_0 + a_1\mu + a_2\mu^2 + a_3\mu^3 + a_4\mu^4 + \cdots + a_n\mu^n,$$

$$\frac{dy}{d\mu} = a_1 + 2a_2\mu + 3a_3\mu^2 + 4a_4\mu^3 + \cdots + na_n\mu^{n-1},$$

$$\frac{d^2y}{d\mu^2} = 2a_2 + 6a_3\mu + 12a_4\mu^2 + \cdots + n(n-1)a_n\mu^{n-2}.$$

Substituting in the Legendre equation, and equating to zero the coefficients of μ^n,

$$-n(n-1)a_n - 2an_n + l(l+1)a_n = 0,$$
$$a_n(n(n+1) - l(l+1)) = 0.$$

Since a_n is not zero, polynomial solutions of the type chosen are only possible if l is an integer.

The Legendre equation is of great importance to physicists; it occurs in the solution of certain problems involving eigenfunctions in which l plays the part of a quantum number. Another very important equation is the *associated Legendre equation* which takes the form

$$\frac{d}{dz}\left[(1-z^2)\frac{dP}{dz}\right] + \left(\beta - \frac{m^2}{1-z^2}\right)P = 0 \qquad \text{(see 2.8, p. 35)}$$

When expressed in polar coordinates, and using (2.11), it becomes

$$\frac{1}{\sin\theta}\frac{d}{d\theta}\left(\sin\theta\frac{d\Theta}{d\theta}\right) - \frac{m^2\Theta}{\sin^2\theta} + l(l+1)\Theta = 0.$$

This form may be recognised as the θ dependent part of the Schrödinger equation for the hydrogen atom. When $m=0$, it reduces to the Legendre equation. The solution by a power series of the associated Legendre equation is possible only if both l and m are integers; thus l and m appear as quantum numbers.

Fourier series.

A Fourier series is the sum of the displacements of a simple harmonic wave and its harmonic components. If all the components are included in the sum, the series is an infinite one; if a finite number of components are present, the series is finite. The sum of the series gives the resultant displacement when the fundamental and components are superposed. This is shown by the well-known example of the complex wave which may be recorded from the sound produced by a single note played on a musical instrument. The complex wave may be analysed into the fundamental and overtones (harmonic components).

A Fourier series may be written in the form

$$s(\theta) = a_0 + a_1\cos\theta + a_2\cos 2\theta + a_3\cos 3\theta + \cdots + a_n\cos n\theta + \cdots$$
$$+ b_1\sin\theta + b_2\sin 2\theta + b_3\sin 3\theta + \cdots + b_n\sin n\theta.$$

The coefficients $a_0, a_1, a_2\ldots$ represent the amplitudes of the component waves. In the case of the note recorded by the musical instrument they may be of widely differing values and some of them may be zero; the relative values of the coefficients determine the quality or timbre of the note heard.

For the mathematical properties of Fourier series the student is recommended to consult textbooks such as *Mathematics for the Chemist*, by G. J. Kynch (Butterworth 1954), and *Mathematics and Wave Mechanics*, by R. H. Atkin (Heinemann 1956).

Reduced mass.

The rotational energy of a molecule depends on the moment of inertia. The diatomic molecule is assumed to be in the form of a simple dumb-bell (Fig. A.1).

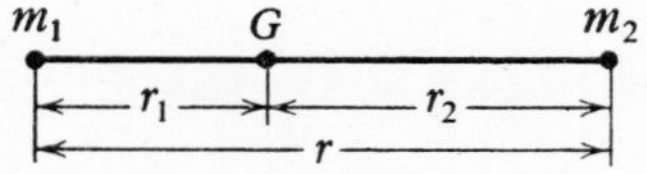

Fig. A.1.

If m_1 and m_2 are the masses of the two nuclei, r_1 and r_2 their respective distances from the centre of gravity G, and if I is the moment of inertia of the whole about G_3 and r the total length,

$$I = m_1 r_1{}^2 + m_2 r_2{}^2. \tag{A.7}$$

Taking moments about m_1,

$$m_2 r = (m_1 + m_2)r_1, \quad \text{and} \quad r_1 = \frac{m_2}{m_1 + m_2} r.$$

Similarly,

$$r_2 = \frac{m_1}{m_1 + m_2} r.$$

Substituting for r_1 and r_2 in equation (A.6),

$$I = \frac{m_1 m_2}{m_1 + m_2} r^2.$$

Hence the moment of inertia is the same as that of a mass $\dfrac{m_1 m_2}{m_1 + m_2}$ at a point distant r from the centre of gravity.

If $\mu = \dfrac{m_1 m_2}{m_1 + m_2}$, μ is said to be the *reduced mass*.

Coulomb forces in model used for the determination of bond lengths.

(i) *Single bond* (Fig. A.2(a)).
Repulsion between electrons gives potential energy term

$$E' = \frac{\epsilon^2}{2r_M}.$$

Therefore

$$\frac{r_M}{2} \frac{dE'}{dr_M} = -\frac{\epsilon^2}{4r_M}.$$

(See equation 11.16. All signs are changed in this equation.)

(ii) *Double bond* (Fig. A.2(b)).
Repulsion between electrons gives potential energy term

$$E' = \frac{2\epsilon^2}{2r_M} + \frac{4\epsilon^2}{\sqrt{2}r_M},$$

therefore

$$\frac{r_M}{2} \frac{dE'}{dr_M} = -\frac{\epsilon^2}{2r_M} - \sqrt{2}\frac{\epsilon^2}{r_M} = -1\cdot915\,\frac{\epsilon^2}{r_M}.$$

(iii) *Triple bond* (Fig. A.2(c)).

Repulsion between electrons gives potential energy term

$$E' = \frac{3\epsilon^2}{2r_M} + \frac{6\epsilon^2}{r_M} = \frac{15}{2}\frac{\epsilon^2}{r_M},$$

therefore

$$\frac{r_M}{2}\frac{dE'}{dr_M} = -\frac{15}{4}\frac{\epsilon^2}{r_M}.$$

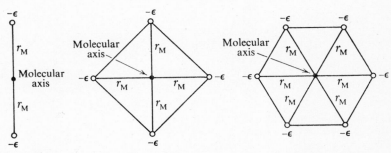

(a) Single bond   (b) Double bond   (c) Triple bond

Fig. A.2.

Energy of a charged particle travelling with constant velocity round a circular path under the influence of a Coulomb attraction.

If E is the total energy of the particle, T its kinetic energy, and V its potential energy, and if ϵ and m are the charge and mass of the particle, v its linear velocity, and r the radius of the circular path,

$$T = \tfrac{1}{2}mv^2,$$

$$V = -\frac{\epsilon^2}{r},$$

and

$$E = T + V.$$

Since

$$\frac{mv^2}{r} = \frac{\epsilon^2}{r^2},$$

$$2T = -V,$$

and

$$E = -T.$$

AUTHOR INDEX

SUBJECT INDEX

When a description or discussion extends over several pages only the first page is given in the index. Where there are several references the page on which an entry is defined or discussed is indicated by bold type. Certain entries refer to tables which contain information not repeated in the text.

Where the index concerns chemical compounds it is constructed as generally as possible. For example, "sodium sulphate" should be sought for under "alkali metal sulphates" and under "sulphates". Readers are reminded that the names of many compounds begin with numerical prefixes, e.g. disulphur dichloride.